HANDBOOK OF PHYSIOLOGY

SECTION 7: Endocrinology, VOLUME II, PART 2

HANDBOOK OF PHYSIOLOGY

A critical, comprehensive presentation

of physiological knowledge and concepts

SECTION 7: # Endocrinology

VOLUME II.
Female Reproductive System, Part 2

Section Editors: ROY O. GREEP
EDWIN B. ASTWOOD

Volume Editor: ROY O. GREEP

Executive Editor: STEPHEN R. GEIGER

American Physiological Society, WASHINGTON, D.C., 1973

Contents

CHAPTER 30

Functional microanatomy of the primate uterine cervix

CHARLES E. GRAHAM | *Yerkes Regional Primate Research Center, Emory University, Atlanta, Georgia*

CHAPTER CONTENTS

THE UTERINE CERVIX has been studied from two major points of view. The object of one body of research has been to define the functional significance of the uterine cervix in reproductive processes and to understand the mechanisms by which this role is executed; this approach has been undertaken chiefly with a view to developing methods of combating obstetric problems and infertility resulting from cervical factors and also with the hope of discovering improved methods for preventing unwanted conceptions.

A second major avenue of investigation has been concerned with the histogenesis of squamous carcinoma of the uterine cervix, a disease that is, except for mammary cancer, the most frequently occurring form of cancer in women. This latter subject has, directly or indirectly, evoked many studies on the histology of the cervix that attempted to define the borderline between normality and pathology. Success is not yet complete, largely per-

Preparation of this chapter assisted by NIH Grant RR-00165.

haps because insufficient attention has been paid to the range of normal response to the steroid hormones and also because of a lack of perspective resulting from inattention to the comparative approach. These considerations accordingly receive special emphasis in this chapter.

The uterine cervix, like other secondary sex organs, is a target of the ovarian hormones; this means that every level of organization depends on the hormonal milieu. It is thus appropriate to examine the microanatomy of the cervix in terms of any changes in morphology brought about by the sex steroids and, wherever possible, to give due attention to the relationship of such changes in morphology to changes in function.

FUNCTIONS OF THE CERVIX

The ability of the uterine cervix to perform apparently conflicting functions that center around the regulation of access to, and egress from, the uterine cavity is remarkable. Essentially the cervix functions to facilitate entry of spermatozoa into the uterine cavity, to allow the escape of menstrual debris, and to permit passage of the fetus at delivery, but to prevent entry of infectious organisms and other foreign matter. Resolution of these conflicting demands is achieved in part by histological and biochemical changes that result in appropriately altered properties. These changes are controlled and coordinated chiefly by the ovarian hormones, the estrogens and progesterone. These hormones bring about major changes in many of the secondary sex organs, especially the uterus, in preparation for the various phases of female reproductive function—copulation, fertilization, implantation, maintenance of the embryo, delivery, and lactation. The uterine cervix participates in this succession of events.

Retention and Delivery of the Fetus

The properties of the cervix depend chiefly on the mechanical characteristics of the cervical wall and on the quantity and physical characteristics of the mucus secreted by the cervical epithelium. For instance, changes in the consistency, and probably the contractility, of the cervical wall, which are mediated in part by the sex steroids, prepare the organ for its function of retention of the embryo during pregnancy. Before delivery, other mechanisms bring about the softening and dilation of the cervix, which permit passage of the fetus; the hormone, relaxin, which is known to be secreted by the placenta and the corpus luteum, is thought to participate in these changes (97). If labor commences before cervical relaxation and dilation have occurred, the powerful uterine contractions can bring about rupture of the uterus.

Considerable hypertrophy of the cervical glands and abundant secretion of mucus take place during pregnancy. At this time, in contrast to its characteristic properties in a nonpregnant condition, the mucus becomes viscid and thick, forms a plug in the cervical canal, and forms a mechanical and physiological barrier against the entry of pathogenic organisms. This protection is vital to the well-being of the embryo, which lacks the immunologic defenses of the adult organism.

Sperm Migration and Transport

The character of the cervical mucus changes dramatically at about the time of ovulation, and only at this most appropriate time does it favor the migration of spermatozoa toward the mature ovum (101). The cervical mucus is thought to assist the migration of spermatozoa in a selective fashion, as it appears to retard the migration of defective spermatozoa (106). In some mammals, such as the ewe, the cervix functions as a reservoir for the spermatozoa, which are liberated over several days (47); thus the probability that a single mating will lead to fertilization is increased. Motile spermatozoa have been recovered from the human genital tract as long as 7 days after coitus (106), although it is doubtful that they are capable of fertilization after so long an interval. A more average period of retained motility is 48 hr (8). At present, whether the primate cervix performs a reservoir function is undetermined, but, according to Bishop (8), sperm longevity in the cervical mucus of the estrous macaque is only 24 hr.

The rapidity with which spermatozoa appear at the ovarian end of the genital tract in a number of species suggests that some mechanism other than flagellation accounts for their transport (105). In the cow and bitch, spermatozoa traverse the cervix within minutes after insemination (40, 129). Uterine contractions function in the transport of spermatozoa in these species. In the cow, for example, copulation apparently brings about a reflex stimulation of the posterior pituitary through a hypothalamic route; release of oxytocin, which increases the motility of the estrous bovine uterus but is without effect during the luteal phase, results (68, 69, 127–129).

Evidence that the human cervix possesses contractile properties, subject to modification by various hormones, is described later in this chapter. However, it has not so far been possible to demonstrate by direct means that cervical contractions play a physiological role in sperm transport, nor has it been possible to show that a neuroendocrine reflex similar to that described in the cow or one involving the sympathetic nervous system (24) influences the contractility of the human cervix. Indirect evidence based on observed migration rates of spermatozoa in the human genital tract is inconclusive. In one experiment in which semen was placed on the cervix of human subjects and the cervix was subsequently removed, spermatozoa traversed the uterus in 30 min (113). In a similar study in which semen was applied after removal of the uterus, 67 min were required for the appearance of spermatozoa in the oviduct (15). The velocity of sperm in midcycle mucus has been measured at 2.9 mm/min (16), a speed sufficient to account for the migration times observed in these experiments, if it is assumed that spermatozoa travel continuously in the same direction. This assumption at first sight seems unlikely, as spermatozoa exhibit highly erratic movements in vitro, but it has been proposed that one of the functions of cervical mucus is to orient the direction of migration of spermatozoa (125). As the rate of sperm transport in the intact human uterus might be considerably less than that established by the experiments described above in which it was unfortunately necessary to remove the uterus, it remains quite possible that contractions of the cervix function in sperm transport in human beings.

Menstruation

Menstrual fluid passes through the cervix; as far as is known, the cervix plays a passive role. The importance of this route of drainage is seen when the cervix is occluded; retrograde menstruation may then occur through the Fallopian tubes into the abdominal cavity and may sometimes lead to implantation of endometrial fragments and consequent endometriosis (98).

Malfunction

Malfunction of the cervix can lead to infertility in two main ways: because conception becomes impossible or because the organ fails in its role in the maintenance of pregnancy. Barriers to conception can be due to physiological reasons, such as the production of mucus hostile to sperm penetration, or can result from congenital or mechanical factors, such as stricture of the endocervical canal. Pregnancy cannot proceed to term if the cervix is incompetent to retain the conceptus within the uterine corpus; with such incompetence of the internal os, the fetus passes prematurely into the cervical canal, usually during the second trimester, with rupture of the membranes and abortion.

GENERAL ANATOMY

The only primate species in which the microanatomy of the cervix has been extensively studied is man, and even in man the available information is very incomplete as far as hormonal influences are concerned. Comparative data on other primates are rare. Therefore it is necessary to base the following general description of the primate cervix on the human organ; attention is drawn to similarities or differences between man and other primates whenever opportunity allows. The anatomy of the uterus of some representative primates is illustrated in Figure 1.

Anatomically the cervix is the cylindrical, elongated, caudal part of the uterus, but histologically it is constructed rather differently from the uterine corpus, in keeping with its specialized functions. The dome-shaped portion projecting into the vaginal vault is known as the ectocervix or portio vaginalis, and the remainder is the endocervix. The endocervical canal, which is an extension of the lumen of the uterine corpus, pierces the endocervix and opens into the vagina in the center of the ectocervix at the external os. The region where the endocervical canal dilates to become the lumen of the corpus is called the *internal os*. In most species the external os appears as a transverse slit, but in some smaller

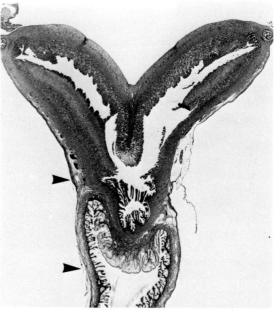

FIG. 2. Horizontal section of uterus of *Tupaia glis* in which the bicornuate condition is shown. Slight torsion of the cervix (*arrows*) prevents the endocervical canal from being seen in its entirety. Mallory's azan. × 10.

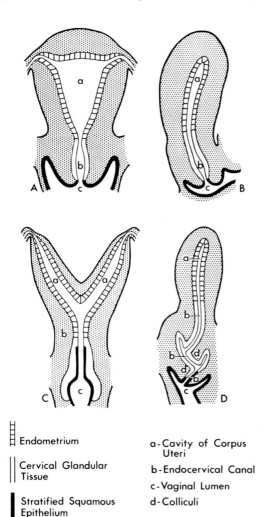

Endometrium

Cervical Glandular Tissue

Stratified Squamous Epithelium

a-Cavity of Corpus Uteri

b-Endocervical Canal

c-Vaginal Lumen

d-Colliculi

FIG. 1. Schematic anatomy of the primate uterus. *A*: man, horizontal section. *B*: man, sagittal section. *C*: *Galago crassicaudatus*, horizontal section. *D*: rhesus monkey, sagittal section.

species and in some immature animals it is more circular.

The stratified squamous epithelium of the vagina is continuous with similar epithelium covering the ectocervix. In the region of the external os, the ectocervical epithelium forms a junction (the squamocolumnar junction) with the tall columnar secretory epithelium of the endocervix. The endocervical epithelium merges cranially with the endometrial epithelium in the vicinity of the internal os. In all primates there is a junction between the stratified epithelium of the lower genital tract and the columnar epithelium of the upper part. The location of this junction is variable. In man the junction is in the region of the external os, but in some other forms it is well inside the os.

In the region of the human internal os, there is a junction between the predominantly muscular tissue of the corpus uteri and the predominantly fibrous tissue of the cervix. In some individuals this junction is abrupt; in others it is gradual. There is no constant relationship between the position of the internal os, the endocervical-endometrial junction, and the fibromuscular junction, and attempts to define an anatomically distinct region of the uterus, the isthmus uteri, on the basis of a supposed constant relationship between these junctions have therefore run into difficulties (2, 25, 26, 28). Aschoff (2) considered that the isthmus was a definite region bounded cranially by the point where the endocervical canal opens into the lumen of the corpus uteri (the anatomic internal os) and caudally by the point where the endocervical epithelium commences. Danforth and Chapman (25, 26, 28) have drawn attention to the fact that the isthmus uteri is essentially similar to the endometrium, except that it is not capable of complete secretory response in the second half of the menstrual cycle, and it therefore should not be regarded as a separate entity. Danforth emphasized the importance of the fibro-muscular junction as defining the junction of the cervix and uterus.

The general anatomic organization, as represented by man, may be regarded as typical of the order, Primates. But the primitive forms, namely the strepsirhines (the prosimians) and *Tarsius* (a New World primate with many primitive features), differ from the typical pattern inasmuch as the genital tract is constructed on a plan reflecting the origin of the primates from the insectivores. This primitive condition is chiefly exemplified by the possession of a bicornuate uterus (see Fig. 1C). The tree shrews (Tupaidae) occupy an intermediate position between the primates and the insectivores and are excluded from the order, Primates, by some authorities (72). In the tree shrew (*Tupaia glis*), the uterus is bicornuate, and there is a short undivided sector caudal to the point of fusion of the cornua, which is usually referred to as the corpus (Fig. 2). The uterus is well differentiated anatomically from the vagina into which it projects and has a definite ectocervix demarcated by a dorsal and a ventral fornix. No distinction between the so-called corpus and a separate endocervical component appears possible.

The strepsirhines (prosimians) show varying degrees of reduction of the primitive bicornuate condition. All animals of this group and also the haplorhine primate, *Tarsius*, have partially divided uteri. The uterine horns are relatively large in some forms, such as the lorisoids, and small in others, such as the Indriidae. The caudal, fused portion of the uterus contains a single canal that opens into the vagina. In some genera of prosimians, such as *Lemur* and *Hapalemur*, vaginal fornices demarcate a well-developed ectocervix. In the lorisoids, *Nycticebus coucang* and *Perodicticus potto*, however, the ectocervix is poorly developed and is represented only by an annular thickening at the junction of uterus and vagina; there is thus a common uterovaginal cavity [(72); C. E. Graham, unpublished observations]. In the greater bush baby (*Galago crassicaudatus*) there is no clear demarcation between the uterus and the vagina (see Fig. 1C).

Although the undivided portion of the uterus has been referred to as the corpus uteri, at least part of this portion of the uterus, by virtue of its location and microscopic anatomy, would appear to correspond with the endocervix of higher primates.

In *Tupaia*, for example, the cranial portion of the undivided canal that passes through the so-called corpus is lined by ciliated cells and interspersed with a few mucin-secreting cells. The lowermost portion of the canal is lined by a tall, columnar, mucin-secreting epithelium, which extends into the vagina; this epithelium resembles the endocervical epithelium of higher primates (see Fig. 2). In *P. potto*, the undivided portion of the uterus contains glands that resemble the endometrial glands of the cornua, but it lacks the characteristic endometrial stroma; instead, the epithelium lies directly on a col-

lagenous connective tissue, as in higher primates. In *G. crassicaudatus*, the undivided portion of the uterus is mainly lined by numerous mucous glands embedded in a collagenous matrix. The prosimians show various stages of specialization of the caudal portion of the uterus (i.e., the cervix), but it is never as well demarcated anatomically and histologically, as it is in higher primates. The prosimian endocervix should thus be regarded as an indefinite region of the lower uterus usually characterized by glands of the familiar endocervical type and set in a matrix of collagenous connective tissue.

Among the Cebidae, some forms show a variability in the degree of development of the cervix, which is probably related to the maturity of the individual or to the breeding season. A grossly visible cervix was recognizable in only one of six owl monkeys (*Aotes trivarigatus*); it was demarcated in this specimen by small vaginal fornices (C. E. Graham, unpublished observations; Fig. 3). A similar variability was noted by Hill (73) in the hairy saki (*Pithecia monarchus*). The wall of the cervix in *Aotes trivarigatus* is demarcated microscopically from the vagina; it has fewer collagen fibers, which are relatively diffusely arranged. In the vagina, wide, dense, longitudinal bands of collagen and muscle alternate with bands of smooth muscle; in the cervix the collagen and muscle are more intermingled. The junction between corpus uteri and endocervix is marked by a further decrease in the amount of collagen in the wall of the uterus and by a great increase in the mass of the muscular tissue. The epithelium of the cervical canal is poorly differentiated from that of the uterine corpus, but the glands in the two parts of the uterus differ structurally, as is the case with the more primitive species of primates previously described.

In *Lagothrix*, the cervix does not protrude into the vagina but imperceptibly merges with it (36).

Marmosets have a well-developed ectocervix. Because of the small size of the animals and consequently of the organ, the glands penetrate relatively deeply into the connective tissue of the organ, indeed to its deepest parts; the organ is thus much less fibrous than in larger species.

The cervices of many New and Old World monkeys are somewhat specialized. Instead of following a straight or curved course, the cervical canal is thrown into a series of sagittal folds, and the glandular epithelium is highly developed. The cervix of macaques, such as the rhesus

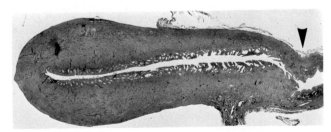

FIG. 3. Sagittal section of uterus of *Aotes trivarigatus*; the poorly differentiated cervix is shown. *Arrow* indicates the ectocervix. Mallory's azan. × 6.

FIG. 4. Sagittal section of rhesus monkey uterus; detours of the endocervical canal around the colliculi are shown. Mallory's azan. × 2.

monkey (*Macaca mulatta*), is large, and the canal is bent into two almost right-angled bends, as described by Clark & Corner (20) in 1935 (Figs. 1*D* and 4). These folds in the canal wall, which are defined by the sharp bends in the canal, are called *colliculi*. The main colliculus is the most caudal, and it is located on the dorsal wall of the cervix. At the base of the colliculi are deep transverse clefts, which, like the rest of the canal wall and colliculi, are richly provided with secretory endocervical glands. In some individuals a third colliculus may be recognized. A similar arrangement exists in the Celebese black ape (*Cynopithecus niger*). The cervix of the bonnet and toque macaques (*M. radiata* and *M. sinica*) is larger and even more complexly folded than that of the rhesus monkey (71). Colliculi also occur in the African monkey, *Cercopithecus mona*.

Similar systems of colliculi have been described in the squirrel monkey (21), and they occur in some other New World monkeys, such as the cebus monkey (*Cebus albifrons*). In the squirrel monkey (*Saimiri sciurea*) the colliculi are variable in number and size. The most inferior and largest, the primary colliculus, is sometimes sufficiently large to project through the external os. The colliculi are large and conspicuous in ovariectomized, estrogen-treated animals but much smaller in untreated, ovariectomized individuals (C. E. Graham, unpublished observations).

The function of the colliculi is unknown. They obviously increase the length and surface area of the endocervical canal, and this permits an increase in the amount of glandular tissue the cervix can accommodate. That the increased length of the cervical canal is a significant selective factor preventing abnormal spermatozoa with deficient motile properties from reaching and fertilizing the mature ovum appears possible but unlikely.

Baboons, drills, mandrills, and the anthropoid apes have an unfolded cervical canal similar to that of man. The cervix of gibbons is notable for the very small ectocervical segment; the portio vaginalis hardly protrudes into the vagina.

MICROANATOMY OF THE SUBMUCOSA

Connective and Contractile Tissue

In the adult human being, the epithelium rests directly on the fibrous substance of the cervix, but in neonates there is a cellular layer, which is somewhat similar to that of the endometrium, immediately beneath the endocervical epithelium (61, 123). During postnatal development, this tissue becomes increasingly replaced by fibrous elements and is unrecognizable from the deeper connective tissue by the time of the first menstruation.

The major component of the human cervix is fibrous connective tissue (25, 28). The quantity of muscular tissue is variable from individual to individual; typically about 10–15 % of the cervical wall is composed of randomly scattered muscle fibers, but occasionally the fibers appear as small bundles toward the central portion of the tissue. In some individuals, virtually no smooth muscle can be found. In others, 45 % of the cervix may be composed of smooth muscle. These strands of cervical muscle are continuous with the muscle of the corpus uteri and are reflected caudally onto the vaginal vault. Despite the continuity between the cervical musculature and the corpus musculature, Danforth (25, 26) emphasized the dissimilarity between the scattered muscle strands of the cervix, which are widely separated from one another by a collagenous matrix, and the closely packed, collagen-sparse muscle of the corpus and isthmus. Muscle fibers are virtually absent from the portio vaginalis.

A number of studies reviewed by Bell (6) have shown that the human cervix possesses the property of contractility. It has been demonstrated that strips of tissue from the isthmic region are capable of contraction but that, under similar conditions, strips from the corpus are not (114). Evidence exists that a number of hormones influence cervical contractility. Danforth (26) has noted that the pregnant human cervix is capable of contraction after stimulation with pitocin in vitro. Bell (6) has noted an insensitivity of the nonpregnant cervix of lower mammals to oxytocin in vitro but an ability to respond for a period at the time of parturition. Recently it has been shown that strips of cervical tissue from nonpregnant women contract spontaneously in vitro and that addition of prostaglandin E_2 brings about a relaxation of the tissue (96). This observation is of great interest, since prostaglandins are hormones produced by the seminal vesicles of the male and are secreted in the semen: there is thus a possibility that insemination may result in a change in the muscular tone of the cervix.

It has been claimed that the cervix exercises a sphincter action (83). There is radiological evidence that the lumen of the isthmus widens during the proliferative phase of the menstrual cycle and during the administration of estrogen to amenorrheic women and that it narrows during the secretory phase and during the administration of progesterone (3, 10).

The role of a fully developed sphincter mechanism can easily be understood in terms of the function of the cervix in regulating access to the cavity of the corpus. However, convincing histological evidence of such a sphincter is lacking, as Danforth (26) has been at pains to point out. Nevertheless some authors still insist on its existence; a sphincter is formed by a spiral arrangement of muscle fibers, according to Krantz & Phillips (83). The contractile properties of the isthmus uteri have already been noted. On the basis of all the available evidence, the view of Bengtsson (7), that the region of the internal os acts functionally as a sphincter at least under some conditions, even though no anatomic specialization is detectable, must be accepted.

The condensation of muscle fibers usually observed around uterine vessels suggested to Danforth (26) that the function of the cervical musculature is to protect the vessels during pregnancy and parturition and that the muscle fibers may be concerned in the prompt return of the cervix to its normal contours after labor.

The ratio of muscle to connective tissue components is quite variable among the nonhuman primates. Old World species, such as the macaques, many New World monkeys, and the orangutan (*Pongo pygmaeus*) show a pattern similar to that of man, with a great preponderance of fibrous tissue. The cervix of the chimpanzee is somewhat more muscular. In the prosimians that have been studied by the present author (*Galago crassicaudatus*, *Nycticebus coucang*, and *Perodicticus potto*), the wall of the uterovaginal tract has a conspicuous muscular component, a wide band of circular muscle originating in the myometrium, which is continuous with similar muscle in the vagina. This band of muscle lies beneath a wide layer of collagen in the cervical region. The muscular tissue is well developed in the cervix of *Microcebus murinus*.

Among the New World monkeys, *Aotes* shows a somewhat similar structure, except that the circular muscle layer is thinner in the cervical region than elsewhere, and close to the position of the squamocolumnar junction, the circular muscle layer completely disappears and is replaced by dense, longitudinally oriented collagen fibers.

A band of longitudinal muscle in the outer wall of the genital tract extends from vagina to corpus in the prosimians. This deep layer of longitudinal muscle is continuous in some species and intermittent in others. Its reduction in higher primates appears to be associated with the increasing specialization of the cervix.

Vascularity, edema, and collagen content of the human cervix increase during pregnancy. The ability of the cervical stroma to undergo a fundamental transformation at the time of delivery is a crucial property of the organ enabling it to stretch and allow passage of the fetus. The endocervical canal becomes dilated to about 10 cm (27, 65). This degree of deformation of the organ is possible because the collagen fibrils appear to become less closely bound together at the time of delivery (27, 124). The collagen fibers are normally composed of tightly interwoven bundles of fibrils bound together by a cementing substance (90). In late pregnancy, however, when edema is pronounced, there are clear spaces between neighboring fibers; the fiber diameters are slightly increased and appear less dense. Immediately postpartum the collagen fibers appear to dissociate into their fibrillar components, since they are of lesser diameter and more highly branched than in the nonpregnant cervix. A reduction in the hydroxyproline concentration of the cervix was found in postpartum cervices when compared with normal cervices; this suggests that the actual amount of collagen becomes reduced in the cervix sometime before delivery. This apparent decrease in the hydroxyproline content might also be accounted for by an increase in the proportion of the ground substance (27). The extent to which changes in the collagen fibers themselves and in the ground substance that binds them together are responsible for the loosening of the cervical connective tissue remains to be determined. Likewise the precise role of relaxin and other hormones in controlling these changes has yet to be elucidated, but there is some evidence from experiments with human subjects that estrogens play a dominant role (108).

Decidual reactions of the endocervical stroma and even of the stroma in the region of the everted endocervical mucosa at the external os are not uncommon, and decidual polyps are frequent in this region during pregnancy (110). No satisfactory explanation is available as to why the cervical stroma sometimes participates in this characteristically endometrial transformation.

Mesonephric Remnants

Persistent remains of the mesonephric system can be found in the middle portion of the cervical wall or near the external os in about 1 % of human cervices (77, 99). These groups of tubules are composed of cuboidal cells with translucent, pale cytoplasm and large, ovoid or round nuclei.

Innervation

The sympathetic and parasympathetic nerve supply of the human cervix enters with the blood vessels from the intersacral folds and may follow the blood vessels for the greater part of their length. These nerves originate in the lateral sympathetic chains of the paravertebral ganglia, the lowermost lumbar and sacral elements of this chain, and from the first four sacral nerves (31, 81, 82).

Histologically, nerve fibers are found most abundantly in the region of the isthmus uteri, and fibers are also plentiful in the endocervix. Fibers that end on, and between, the muscle cells of the endocervix have been described (81). A rich plexus of nonmyelinated fibers with many free nerve endings lies just below the cervical epithelium and surrounds the capillaries (31, 82), and free endings can be demonstrated in the papillae of connective tissue that project into the stratified epithelium of the portio vaginalis (31, 85), as well as in occasional Doigel-Krause corpuscles near the external os (82).

With classic histological methods, investigators have not been able to distinguish between adrenergic and other types of nerve fibers. A specific histochemical fluorescence method that permits the identification of nerve fibers and cell bodies containing the adrenergic transmitter, norepinephrine, has been devised, however. The method depends on a reaction between formaldehyde and norepinephrine that produces a substance, which, when activated by ultraviolet radiation, emits a green fluorescence (23, 41). It has been shown by means of this technique that the number of adrenergic fibers is considerably larger in the cervix than in the rest of the uterus (104). Some of the adrenergic fibers end on smooth muscle fibers and some in the wall of blood vessels.

Studies with the fluorescent method revealed the interesting fact that a significant proportion of the adrenergic fibers originate in adrenergic ganglionic formations located at the cervicovaginal junction. This arrangement of "short" adrenergic neurones originating in ganglia local to the effector organ is unique to the reproductive system (104). It has been demonstrated at the cellular level that the amount of norepinephrine in the uterus and cervix can significantly change during pregnancy and under the influence of the sex steroids (120). These unique features of the sympathetic system of the genital tract suggest a physiological role related to reproductive function. Among other possibilities, an adrenergic motor control of the cervix, which may be of special importance during pregnancy and immediately postpartum, has been proposed (104).

Vascular System

The human cervix is supplied by one or two branches from each uterine artery, and these give off smaller branches to the substance of the cervix. The main (descending) cervical branches surround the cervix and anastomose with vessels of contralateral origin and with branches of the vaginal artery. Corresponding branches of the uterine veins provide the venous drainage of the cervix. The branches of these vessels also anastomose extensively. A well-developed capillary network lies below the cervical epithelium (1).

Lymphatic System

The organization of the complicated lymphatic system of the cervix is of great importance because of the role of lymphatics in the dissemination of cervical carcinoma. Two sets of lymphatics drain the cervix, a superficial group located beneath the peritoneum and mucosa and a second group serving the deeper parts of the organ. These lymph channels converge to form a network in the region of the isthmus known as the paracervical plexus. This plexus is drained by three main pairs of channels that follow the course of the uterine blood vessels outward toward the various lymph nodes of the pelvic region. A more detailed review of the anatomy of the lymphatic system may be found in Fluhmann's work on the cervix uteri (46).

Lymph follicles have been described directly beneath the cervical epithelium or deeper in the stroma of the cervix in about half of adult human cervices (83). The follicles contain primitive reticular and reticuloendothelial cells and all sizes of lymphocytes and lymphoblasts. The follicles are supplied with blood and lymph vessels. An accumulation of inflammatory cells not organized into follicles is almost always evident in the immediate region of the squamocolumnar junction, even in the absence of clinical evidence of inflammation. Lymphocytes are the predominant cell type.

Hamilton noted that leukocytes are an important component of the cervical secretion in the rhesus monkey and that they are most numerous near the external os where they are present in the cervical wall (63). Leukocytes were found to be abundant during the menstrual cycle, especially on days 1–3 and at about the time of ovulation.

MICROANATOMY OF THE EPITHELIA

The Stratified Epithelium

The epithelium of the ectocervix is a stratified squamous epithelium, a type typically found in areas of the body, such as the cheek, esophagus, anal canal, and vagina, where protection against friction must be afforded. The stratified epithelium of the mammalian genital tract differs from other stratified squamous epithelia in that it is peculiarly responsive to the ovarian hormones, especially the estrogens, and it undergoes histological changes during the reproductive cycle.

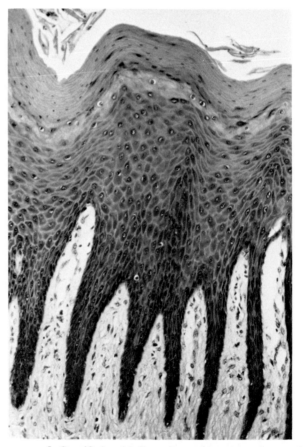

FIG. 5. Stratified epithelium from the cervix of a squirrel monkey; marked stratification and cornification are shown with desquamation of cornified cells into the lumen. Papillae of connective tissue project into the base of the epithelium, which results in a greatly increased complement of basal cells. Hematoxylin and eosin. × 200.

The epithelium is not a simple flat sheet of tissue. Numerous fingerlike papillae of connective tissue containing blood vessels and nerve fibers project into the base of the epithelium; consequently in a vertical section the base of the epithelium follows an irregular course, which misleadingly suggests a corrugated configuration (Fig. 5). A section that is slightly oblique to the vertical results in an impression of apparently isolated islands of connective tissue within the thickness of the epithelium.

Dierks recognized five layers in the stratified epithelium, although often not all these layers are necessarily recognizable simultaneously in a single specimen (32, 62). In fact, full development of the epithelium occurs only in the presence of adequate estrogenic stimulation. The deepest zone is the single layer of cells in contact with the basement membrane. This layer, the stratum cylindricum, is also known as the basal cell layer or germinative layer. Mitoses occur in this layer.

The second layer, the stratum spinosum profundum, contains several layers of polyhedral cells (parabasal cells) characterized by prominent cytoplasmic intercellular bridges. Some cells undergoing mitosis appear to be located in the stratum spinosum profundum and the next layer, the stratum spinosum superficiale. On the basis of autoradiographic data, it appeared that mitoses were actually more frequent in the stratum spinosum

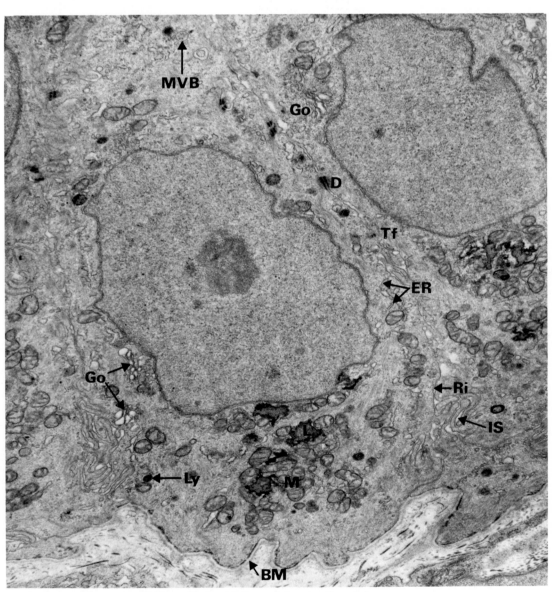

FIG. 6. Stratum germinativum of human cervical stratified epithelium. A basal cell contains numerous mitochondria (M), lipid granules (L), lysosome-like bodies (Ly), a well-developed Golgi complex (Go), multivesicular bodies (MVB), and a small amount of endoplasmic reticulum (ER). Free ribosomes (Ri) are seen. Tonofilaments (Tf) are inconspicuous. Intercellular spaces (IS) are narrow. The cells are separated from the underlying stroma by a continuous basement membrane (BM). Dark plaques on upper surface of basement membrane are half-desmosomes. OsO₄. Lead citrate. × 8,500. [From Hackemann et al. (62).]

than in the basal layer, because more cells in the stratum spinosum incorporated tritiated thymidine and therefore were synthesizing DNA in preparation for cell division (116). However, some caution should be exercised in assigning dividing cells to the stratum spinosum. Dividing cells in the stratum spinosum profundum may in fact be basal cells by virtue of having retained a narrow connection with the basement membrane, which is not visible in the plane of section. Rothman (112) points out that close examination of serial sections often reveals that the mitotic figures that appear to be situated in the stratum spinosum in one section actually belong to the basal layer of a papilla appearing in the next section. There is some evidence from studies in mice that the location of mitoses may be partially dependent on the levels of sex steroids: cells undergoing mitosis are restricted to the basal layer during estrogenic stimulation but occur in other layers after administration of progesterone (5). The question of the location of cells under-

going mitosis is not only important for an understanding of the cell population dynamics of the epithelium, but also because, in squamous cervical carcinoma and in preneoplastic conditions, cell divisions definitely do occur in various levels of the epithelium.

In the third zone, the stratum spinosum superficiale, the cells (intermediate cells) begin to show some flattening, are often vacuolated, and contain abundant glycogen.

Above the stratum spinosum superficiale is the stratum granulosum comprising a few layers of closely packed, flattened cells containing keratohyalin granules.

The outermost zone is the stratum corneum or superficial layer, which is composed of extremely flattened cells with pyknotic nuclei. Although the nuclei are persistent in this layer in man, they may not be in all primates; for example, vaginal smears of the chimpanzee contain variable numbers of anucleate cells, some of which may originate from the cervix (58).

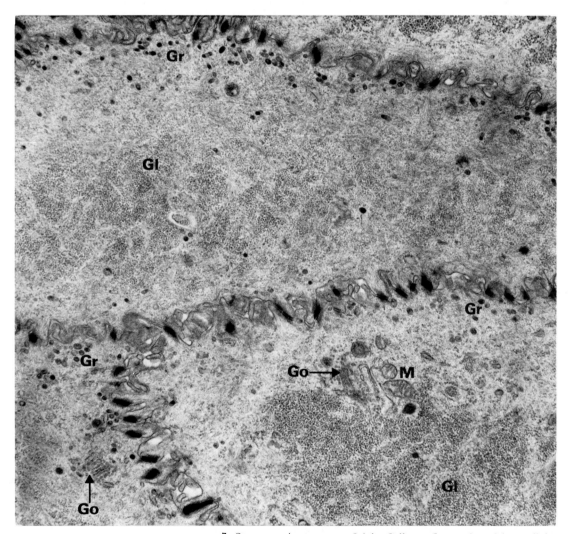

FIG. 7. Stratum spinosum superficiale. Cells are flattened, and intercellular spaces have diminished. Numerous small granules (*Gr*) line the distal border of each cell; a few are scattered throughout the cytoplasm. The Golgi complex (*Go*) is still prominent in this stratum. Glycogen (*Gl*) is abundant. A few mitochondria (*M*) are present. OsO$_4$. Lead citrate. $\times$ 8,500. [From Hackemann et al. (62).]

Study of the cornified stratified epithelium with the electron microscope reveals the details of differentiation of the cells as they pass from the basal layer to the surface; evidence of active synthetic ability is shown at first, and later a diminishing complement of organelles associated with normal cellular processes is demonstrated. This transition in the epithelium, which shows successive stages in the differentiation and aging of the cells, is so gradual that boundaries of the five zones described under the light microscope cannot be defined (62). For most purposes it is sufficient to recognize three main layers: the basal layer; the stratum spinosum (or intermediate layer); and the stratum functionalis. The fine structure of these layers is illustrated in Figures 6–8.

Mitochondria, the Golgi complex, endoplasmic reticulum, ribosomes, lysosome-like bodies, and lipidlike granules are recognizable in the deeper cells of the epithelium, but they disappear or become degenerate in the stratum functionalis. Glycogen is absent from the basal layer, appears in the deeper parts of the stratum spinosum, and is most abundant in the upper layers of this zone. It is reduced in quantity in the stratum functionalis.

In normal squamous epithelium the surface of the epithelial cells is provided with interdigitating microvilli. Numerous points of attachment exist between adjacent cells. These points of attachment are of two types, desmosomes and nexuses; the latter are most abundant in the intermediate layer. Desmosomes are complex structures, in the region of which the cell membranes are 250–300 A apart and are attached to one another by dense proteinaceous material within the extracellular space. At nexuses the adjacent cell membranes are separated by a space of only 20 A, which is spanned by small subunits. Nexuses form sites of low-resistance electrical coupling between cells, which indicates that small ions, such as potassium, and perhaps larger molecules can pass from cell to cell. Nexuses are infrequent or absent in cervical carcinomas (92).

Fine structural details characteristic of cornification are prominent in the cervical stratified epithelium. Tono-

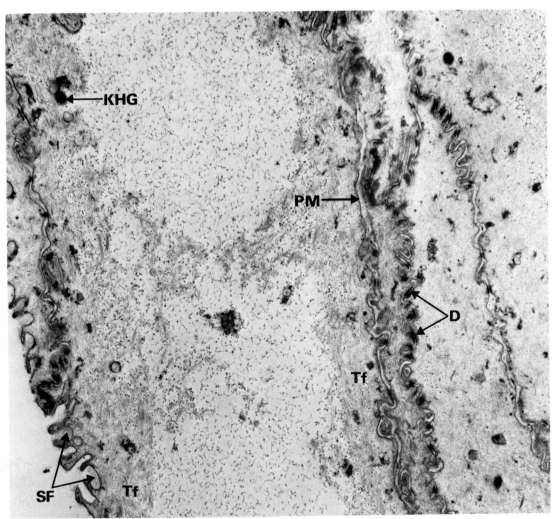

FIG. 8. Stratum functionalis. Cells are markedly flattened and deficient in organelles. The plasma membrane (*PM*) is thickened, and keratohyalin granules (*KHG*) are present in small numbers. Glycogen is relatively sparse. Tonofilaments (*Tf*) are aggregated near the cell periphery. OsO₄. Lead citrate. × 8,500. [From Hackemann et al. (62).]

filaments are present in the basal and adjacent cells. Toward the surface they become concentrated near to, and parallel with, the cell surface, but they do not become aggregated into tonofibrils to the extent that they do in epidermis. Keratohyalin granules and possible precursor granules (60) appear in the outer cells of the stratum spinosum, which correspond with the stratum granulosum of the light microscope. Keratohyalin granules are not nearly so numerous in the cervical stratified epithelium as in epidermis and are not invariably associated with tonofilaments. In general the fine structure of the cervical stratified epithelium is remarkably similar to that of epidermis, and the differences noted above are related to the fact that cornification of the cervical mucosa is normally less extreme than in epidermis. However, some more marked differences between cervical epithelium and epidermis do exist; these include the absence of melanin in the former and the presence of quantities of glycogen, especially in the estrogen-stimulated animal. Further differences are that cervical epithelium normally cornifies only during suitable stimulation by steroid hormones and that the cervical stratified epithelium in some primates has the ability to secrete mucin (see subsection METAPLASIA AND MODULATION).

Occasionally cervical stratified epithelium demonstrates a latent competence to reach more advanced stages of cornification than normal, as in leukoplakia or hyperkeratosis, pathological conditions in which areas of heavily cornified epithelium appear on the portio vaginalis (Fig. 9).

The thickness of the zones of the squamous epithelium depends on the hormonal status of the individual, since the rate of proliferation and type of maturation of the cells are determined by the sex steroids, among other factors. Estrogenic secretion or administration evokes increased proliferation with a concomitant increase in the thickness of the epithelium and increased cornification. In the absence of adequate stimulation by the ovarian steroids, the stratum corneum and perhaps other layers of the epithelium are absent, and the epithelium is composed of relatively immature cells.

The cervical epithelium is typically thin and atrophic in immature and postmenopausal individuals. In the newborn and in postpartum human infants, it is hypertrophied and hyperplastic because of the persistent influence of the large amount of estrogens synthesized by the maternofetal unit (51) in contrast to the corpus, which remains small (78). The cervix atrophies after birth and usually shows no evidence of estrogenic response by 4 or 6 weeks postpartum.

Increased amounts of glycogen and increased activity of the associated enzymes concerned with its synthesis and breakdown have been demonstrated in the cervical stratified epithelium of ovariectomized squirrel monkeys (*Saimiri sciurea*) during estrogenic stimulation (54). A further increase in the amount of glycogen is noted if progesterone treatment follows estrogen administration (21).

The ability of the stratified epithelium to proliferate

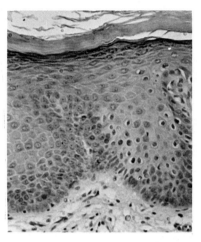

FIG. 9. Leukoplakia in human cervical epithelium characterized by thick surface layer of cornified cells in which no traces of nuclei remain. Hematoxylin and eosin. × 1,300.

rapidly in response to estrogenic stimulation is partly dependent on a large component of germinative cells. The numerous peglike papillae of connective tissue that penetrate into the base of the epithelium have the effect of greatly increasing the number of germinative cells over the number that would be present if the epithelial-stromal boundary was flat. The stromal papillae also probably have an important role in bringing the vascular supply close to a greater number of the epithelial cells than would otherwise be possible (see Fig. 9). Since blood vessels do not penetrate the basement membrane, the basal cells are the closest to the vascular supply and it seems that the more distant these cells are from the vascular system, the more difficulty they must have in obtaining substrates and in disposing of toxic metabolites. Probably cell-to-cell exchange of substrates and metabolites is of great importance in the economy of stratified epithelia, as the well-developed intercellular processes of the stratum spinosum would suggest. Pinocytotic vesicles, sometimes prominent in basal cells (62), and nexuses in the intermediate layer (92) may also be important in exchange of materials. The lack of an extracellular source of nutrients at higher levels in the epithelium is clleary suggested by the intracellular storage of glycogen in lower levels of the epithelium and its subsequent disappearance in the outer layers; it presumably provides an energy source for synthetic processes associated with cornification. This concept has been discussed by Bradfield (13) with respect to the epidermis.

The Columnar Epithelium

The mucosa of the endocervix is thrown into a number of irregularly arranged folds or rugae called the *plicae palmitae*, which are large enough to be seen with the naked eye. The cervical glands are a system of clefts that run in all directions over the surface of the endocervical canal; these clefts may intersect but never cross one another. The larger clefts are the grooves between the plicae palmitae; there are also numerous smaller clefts.

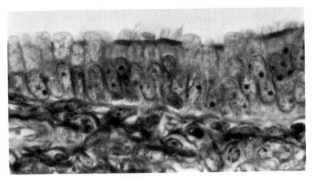

FIG. 10. Ciliated and secretory cells in the endocervix of a squirrel monkey. Hematoxylin and eosin. × 1,500.

The clefts, which are lined by a columnar mucus-secreting epithelium, branch as they penetrate into the connective tissue of the cervix. The clefts also frequently send off blind diverticula, which run horizontally beneath the surface of the mucosa and in histological sections falsely suggest that the cervical glands are of a racemose type (46).

In women the entire endocervical canal, or all except the lowermost portion, is lined with a cuboid-to-columnar mucin-secreting epithelium. A variable amount of the lower part of the endocervical canal may be lined by stratified epithelium. Among the columnar mucin-secreting cells of the primate cervix are scattered ciliated cells, singly or in small groups (Fig. 10). The ciliated cells tend to be concentrated at the crest of the ridges between adjacent cervical glands, but they also occur within the glands. The nucleus of the columnar cells is usually oval and basally placed when the cells are full of mucin, although there is a good deal of variability in individual cell morphology (34). The mucin is easily demonstrated with the periodic acid-Schiff stain after diastase digestion, which indicates that it contains a neutral polysaccharide. It has been proposed that ciliated cells and secretory cells are different phases of a single cell type (117), although definite proof is lacking at the present time.

With the electron microscope, the secretory cells are found to be filled with abundant secretory granules (Fig. 11), some of which appear to be surrounded by a limiting membrane (18), although the existence of such a membrane has been disputed (30). The distal border of the secretory cells is provided with abundant microvilli. According to Davies & Woolf (30), the mucus droplets form in the infranuclear region of the secretory cells, where they frequently lie within complex whorls of membranes. The formation of droplets is closely associated with the rough endoplasmic reticulum and the Golgi area (18, 30) in accordance with modern concepts of the mechanics of cellular secretion (42, 84).

There has been some disagreement as to whether secretion of mucus is apocrine (63) or merocrine (18, 30, 46, 67, 86). Blebs of apical cytoplasm may be observed protruding into the lumen in carefully prepared histological material (see Fig. 10). The application of mucin staining methods suggests that these blebs are principally composed of mucus about to be released into the lumen. Care

must be taken to distinguish true secretory cells from ciliated cells, since the latter present a similar appearance if the cilia are masked by the presence of heavily stained mucus with which they are usually heavily clogged. Electron-microscopic studies show the accumulation of secretion droplets or granules in the distal cytoplasm of the cell. These droplets are separated from one another and from the lumen by fragile cytoplasmic envelopes, and they tend to bulge into the lumen (see Fig. 11). Fragmentation of the cytoplasmic envelope and secretion would probably entail loss of only minimal amounts of cytoplasm (30, 67).

The ciliated cells also contain granules, but they are relatively few in number. Whether the content of these granules is similar to that of the secretory cells is unknown. The endoplasmic reticulum and the Golgi membranes are sometimes well developed (49, 122). The cilia are of the motile kind with nine peripheral and two central tubular fibers, a basal granule, and striated rootlets (86).

In man it has been difficult to demonstrate a well-marked series of changes in the columnar epithelium during the menstrual cycle at the histological level. This is due in part to the difficulty of obtaining suitable material, the need for careful fixation of this very delicate epithelium, and the almost invariable presence of mucin in the cells and in the lumen, which makes variations in the rate of secretion of mucus difficult to detect (4). An additional complication is that, during periods of active secretion, the secretory cycle of adjacent cells is not synchronous (122). The literature on histological changes in the endocervical epithelium has been reviewed by Hartman (66). A number of workers failed to find any consistent changes in the human endocervical epithelium during the menstrual cycle (12, 35, 126). In three studies it was noted that the columnar cells reach their peak height at midcycle (67, 121, 132); this coincides with an obvious increase in production of mucus at this time. Wollner (135) has considered that there is extensive exfoliation and regeneration of the endocervical columnar epithelium during menstruation, but this observation has not been confirmed. Study with the electron microscope reveals that the mitochondria are small and few in number and endoplasmic reticulum is scanty during the follicular phase of the cycle and that these elements are larger and more frequent during the luteal phase (67). The length of the microvilli increases from 0.2μ to 1.0μ (11). The ciliated cells do not appear to undergo a series of changes related to the menstrual cycle (67).

Cyclic changes in the endocervical epithelium are evidently subtle; they are quantitative rather than qualitative in nature. This conclusion is supported by Hamilton (63) who, in a careful study with well-preserved tissue, showed that there is a discernible cycle of changes in the rhesus monkey (*Macaca mulatta*) cervical epithelium. Peaks in cell height occur on days 3, 14, and 22 in the usual 28-day menstrual cycle. Each of these three peaks of development of the secretory cells is followed by active secretion of cervical mucus, which is produced

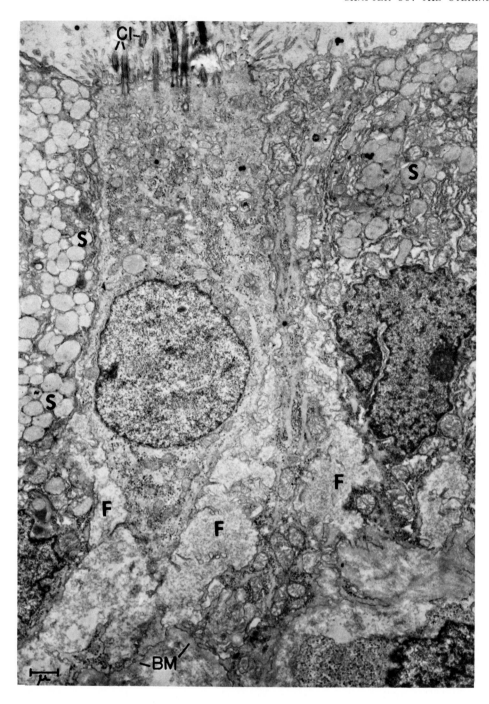

FIG. 11. First trimester human columnar epithelium as seen with the electron microscope; a ciliated cell in the center and secretory cells on either side are shown. Cilia, *Cl*; secretory granule, *S*; extracellular areas, *F*; basement membrane, *BM*. × 5,760. [From Chapman et al. (18).]

sparsely or not at all at other times in the cycle. Sloughing of the epithelial lining does not take place during menstruation.

Although it was claimed that the three peaks of cellular development and secretory activity in the rhesus monkey correspond with fluctuations in the secretion of estrogens (63, 66), there is in fact no good evidence for the existence of more than two peaks of estrogenic secretion in this species. Recently published data on estrogen excretion in the rhesus monkey suggest that these two verified peaks do, however, correspond approximately with the second two peaks of cellular activity in the cervix (19,

75). Gonadectomy and hormone replacement experiments have shown that cell elongation and development similar to that occurring in intact rhesus monkeys can be induced by the administration of estrogens (Figs. 12 and 13). When the estrogen level is reduced, the cells discharge their contents. Similar studies in man have confirmed that enlargement of cervical glands and secretion of mucin by the endocervical epithelium depend on estrogen (136, 137, 139). Estrogen treatment of the rhesus monkey followed by simultaneous estrogen-progesterone administration produced a typical progestational response characterized by the maximal proliferation and

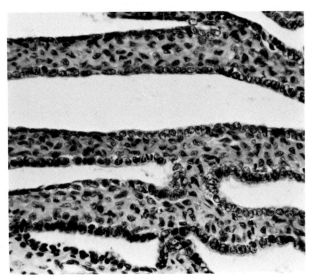

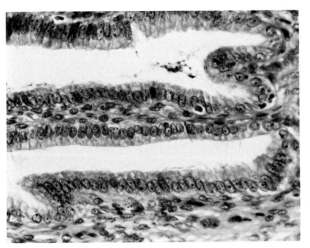

FIG. 13. Well-developed cervical columnar epithelium from an ovariectomized squirrel monkey after estrogen administration. Hematoxylin and eosin. × 400.

FIG. 12. Cervical epithelium from an ovariectomized squirrel monkey; an atrophic cuboidal epithelium is shown. Compare Fig. 13. Hematoxylin and eosin. × 400.

ramification of cervical glands (63). A similar development of the glands characterized the luteal phase of the menstrual cycle. Progesterone alone has little or no effect on the cervix.

The increase in mucous secretion at about the time of ovulation is accompanied by marked biochemical changes in the mucus that facilitate sperm migration through the cervix. These changes are exemplified by an alteration in the consistency of the mucus such that it can be drawn out into long threads (up to 15 cm at midcycle in the human female), a property called *spinnbarkeit*. This property and another feature of human and rhesus monkey mucus, the ability to form complex, fernlike crystallization patterns at midcycle, have been used to determine the optimum period for conception (29). The function and biophysics of cervical mucus are described in detail in another chapter.

During pregnancy the cervix of the rhesus monkey becomes a highly labyrinthine structure because of the great hypertrophy of the glands, and so produces a great quantity of mucus. This development of the cervix reaches its maximum just before parturition (26). Considerable glandular development of the human cervix also takes place during pregnancy. Study with the electron microscope has failed to demonstrate any glycogen in the columnar cells during pregnancy or indeed in any other physiological state. Expanded cisternae of the endoplasmic reticulum are notable in the third trimester (18, 86).

The Basement Membrane

The epithelial cells of the cervix rest on a thin layer of material that is stainable with periodic acid-Schiff, which indicates the presence of a neutral mucopolysaccharide component, and with aniline blue, which stains collagen. A condensation of reticular fibers may also be demonstrated in this area with suitable techniques. The exact

nature of the basement membrane has evoked much discussion, especially because it has been difficult to reconcile light-microscopic findings with the membrane described by investigators using the electron microscope. Interest also has centered around the basement membrane, because the main criterion of the invasiveness of cervical carcinoma is that the epithelial cells have breached the basement membrane and begun to infiltrate the stroma. However, this criterion may in some instances be misleading; new basement membrane may be laid down at the boundary of invasive tumor in areas where active epithelial invasions are no longer taking place. Further confusion derives from the fact that some authors have considered the basement membrane seen with the light microscope to be continuous, and others have considered it to be discontinuous or have even disputed its existence (130). These discrepancies are resolved by the demonstration that Schiff reagents made up in different ways vary considerably in their staining properties (87, 109). Schiff reagent is used by most workers to demonstrate the basement membrane. Dougherty & Low (33) confirmed the continuity of the basement membrane in the normal cervix by means of the electron microscope.

With the electron microscope the basement membrane is found to consist of a superficial electron-transmitting layer, the lamina lucida, and a deeper electron-opaque layer, the lamina densa, which is sandwiched between the plasma membrane of the basal cells and a layer of collagen fibers [(18, 138); see Fig. 6]. The collagen fibers apparently correspond to the aniline blue-positive basement membrane discernible with the light microscope. The stromal surface of the lamina densa is connected to the underlying collagen by fine fibrils; similar fibrils traversing the lamina lucida pass from the lamina densa to the basal cells. Desmosome-like structures are deployed along the plasma membrane of the basal cells opposite the lamina lucida (see Fig. 6); however, the lack of a contiguous cell membrane in this area means that the desmosome-like structures are not matched by a similar opposing organelle, as is the case where cell membranes are adjacent to one another. Consequently these basally located organelles are termed *half-desmosomes*.

The Squamocolumnar Junction

The squamocolumnar junction region is an area of great interest, first because cervical squamous carcinomas usually appear in this region of the cervix and second because the junction shifts in position as a result of various factors, which gives the appearance of a dynamic interplay between the stratified and columnar epithelia.

TYPES OF JUNCTION. The human squamocolumnar junction appears as an abrupt juxtaposition of typical stratified squamous epithelium and columnar epithelium in some histological sections, but in other specimens, even from the same individual, there may be a continuous area of intergradation, usually referred to as a transition zone. There is sometimes a mixture of patches of squamous and columnar cells in the region of transition, so that the squamocolumnar junction appears several times in a single longitudinal section. In the presence of an abrupt junction, the adjacent stratified area may nevertheless show some of the features of the epithelium of the transition zone. Semantic problems concerning the concept of a junction are liable to arise because to some the concept of a junction necessarily implies a discontinuity, whereas an intergradation is often present. It is quite convenient in fact to recognize two basic types of junction—an abrupt junction, if there is an immediate change from a unilayered to a multilayered epithelium, and a transitional junction, if there is a gradual intergrade between the two types, such that no point of discontinuity is present.

POSITION IN RELATION TO AGE. Although the squamocolumnar junction usually lies close to the external cervical os in man, in the squirrel monkey and some other species, the junction lies within the endocervical canal at the base of, or even on, the colliculi. In the rhesus monkey the junction may be situated at the base of the inferior colliculus or on the ectocervix. It has been suggested that the level of the junction in rhesus monkeys may depend on the age of the animal—it may rise in the endocervical canal with advancing age (20)—but a more comprehensive study did not provide confirmation (115). In a sagittal section of the rhesus monkey or squirrel monkey cervix, the squamocolumnar junction is seen twice—it appears more cranially located on one surface of the canal than on the other (see Fig. 1)—but in species without colliculi, the squamocolumnar junction usually appears at the same level on opposite sides of the endocervical canal.

In the human female the exact position of the squamocolumnar junction is partly dependent on the age of the individual and ultimately, it seems, on her hormonal

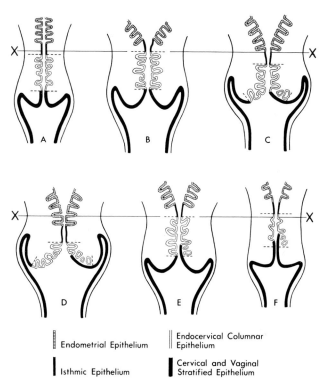

FIG. 14. Distribution of the human cervical epithelia at different ages. *A*, child; *B–D*, sexually mature woman. Different degrees of eversion of the mucosa on the left side of each diagram are shown; growth of the stratified epithelium back to the external os is shown on the *right*. *E* and *F*, the cervix after the menopause and in senility, respectively; withdrawal of the mucosa and stratified epithelium into the canal are shown. *X–X* indicates the level of the anatomic internal os; note the changes in position of the isthmic epithelium relative to this point and also the constancy of the length of the endocervical columnar epithelium demarcated by *broken lines*. [Adapted from Ober et al. (100).]

status (Fig. 14). In the newborn the junction most often lies within the endocervical canal, but in about one-third of the cases, the junction is situated on the ectocervix, so that the endocervical glands are exposed; in such cases the junction almost invariably recedes into the canal within a few weeks of birth (93).

In immature females the junction is normally within the canal. In young, sexually mature women, the junction is most often found outside the external os, so that columnar epithelium appears on the vaginal surface of the ectocervix. With advancing years of sexual maturity, however, the junction returns to the vicinity of the external os, and in the climacteric the junction is usually found within the endocervical canal. In the senile individual the junction is quite high in the endocervical canal, so that stratified squamous epithelium occupies much of the lower part of the canal (64, 100, 118). Although there is a tendency for the surface columnar epithelium to disappear from the portio vaginalis with advancing years of sexual maturity, glands lined with columnar epithelium may still be found beneath the squamous epithelium, which replaces it. These glands either open to the surface through an aperture in the stratified epithelium or they lack an opening to the surface, in which case they become distended with secretion and thus form retention cysts known as Nabothian follicles.

These age-related changes can best be explained primarily in terms of changes in conformation of the cervix, which result in eversion or inversion of the mucosa. In an important series of papers, Hamperl, Kaufmann, Ober, and Schneppenheim (64, 100, 118) demonstrated that the actual length of the endocervical epithelium is somewhat constant—it is unrelated to the age of the individual. In individuals in which the columnar epithelium is exposed on the portio vaginalis, the junction of the endocervical and endometrial epithelia is correspondingly lower in the uterine canal compared with those individuals in which the squamocolumnar junction is at the external os or within the endocervical canal. The appearance of columnar epithelium on the portio vaginalis in young women is therefore not due to a proliferation of columnar cells at the expense of stratified epithelium. Rather, it appears that the increase in the total volume of the cervix accompanying the attainment of sexual maturity leads to a change in the overall conformation of the cervix, which results in a tendency toward eversion of the endocervical mucosa at the external os. A similar explanation may be applied to the ectropion (eversion) frequently seen in the newborn cervix, since a considerable hypertrophy of the organ is manifest at this time. The involution of the cervical tissues after birth associated with the cessation of estrogen production by the maternofetal unit and after the menopause with cessation of ovarian function is accompanied by withdrawal of the endocervical mucosa back into the endocervical canal. When the endocervical mucosa is everted and exposed to the vaginal environment, there is a tendency toward replacement of the surface columnar cells by stratified squamous epithelium, so that during the years of sexual maturity the position of the junction gradually shifts toward the external os. Thus the exposed endocervical glands become covered by a surface layer of new stratified epithelium, and, when these glands are drawn back into the cervical canal after the menopause, the newly formed stratified epithelium is drawn back into the canal with them.

Eversions of the mucosa are also frequently associated with pregnancy, but they usually disappear a few months after parturition. This rate of resolution is not obviously correlated with endocrinological factors, because it i unrelated to cessation of lactation and recommencement of menstruation (91). Permanent eversions sometimes result if the cervical lips become lacerated during delivery.

The reddish appearance of exposed endocervical mucosa on the ectocervix was formerly thought to signify inflammation, and it was widely believed that the surface epithelium had a tendency to slough off, an impression perhaps sustained by careless handling of pathological specimens during histological processing, which led to loss of the delicate epithelium. Consequently eversions were, and indeed still are, frequently termed erosions. Many eversions do have some associated inflammation, and in extreme cases tissue destruction and ulceration do indeed take place, but these are the exceptions rather than the rule. The squamocolumnar junction area in adults normally has some inflammatory cells in its vicinity (lymphocytes and polymorphonuclear leukocytes). No definite function has been ascribed to the presence of these leukocytes, but it is conceivable that the abrupt type of junction represents a discontinuity in the protective epithelial lining that provides a potential port of entry into the tissues for pathogens, and a concentration of the cellular defenses at this point is thus understandable. Cervical erosions were formerly implicated in cervical carcinogenesis, but this view is no longer held.

As described above, a change in the position of the squamocolumnar junction relative to the external os can result from a change in the overall conformation of the organ; in this situation the position of the squamocolumnar junction remains unchanged relative to a fixed point in the underlying connective tissue because the epithelium and stroma together are displaced relative to the external os. Apart from this type of alteration, the position of the squamocolumnar junction may also change relative to a fixed point in the connective tissue: that is, there is a change in the actual histological distribution of the stratified and columnar epithelia. The tendency for everted columnar epithelium to be replaced by newly formed stratified epithelium has already been mentioned (64, 100, 118). The occasional presence of stratified epithelium in the cervical glands has suggested to some workers that it has displaced columnar cells. The formation of new stratified epithelium is termed *epidermization*. The subject of epidermization is considered more fully later in this chapter.

HORMONAL RELATIONSHIPS. The squamocolumnar junction shows a considerable amount of variability of histological structure. Transitional junctions are characterized by a progressive reduction in cell layers from the ectocervical epithelium toward the endocervical epithelium. This type of transition is especially seen in some prosimians. In the mouse similar appearances also exist, and it has been possible to relate a well-defined series of changes in the squamocolumnar junction to the estrous cycle [(50); Fig. 15]. These changes are most instructive when we reconsider the primate cervix. In the mouse during diestrus (i.e., during the interval between successive estrous cycles) or in ovariectomized animals, there is a gradual transition in number of cell layers between the stratified and columnar epithelium. During the follicular stage of the estrous cycle (proestrus) or soon after the injection of ovariectomized animals with an appropriate dose of estrogen, the surface layer of the vaginal epithelium differentiates into large, distended cells containing huge quantities of mucin. This layer of

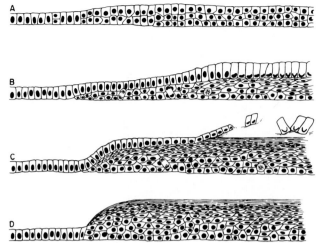

FIG. 15. Changes in the mouse cervix during the estrous cycle; uterus at *left*, vagina at *right*. *A*: diestrus—epithelium atrophic, junction transitional. *B*: proestrus—hypertrophy of epithelium begins, junction of epithelium transitional. The surface layer of mucified cells produced by the vaginal epithelium is continuous with the uterine epithelium. *C*: early estrus—proliferation of stratified epithelium has led to the formation of an abrupt junction, and keratinization of the surface layers is resulting in the desquamation of the mucified cells. *D*: metestrus—keratinization and loss of the mucified cells are complete. *A* and *B* are two types of transitional junction; *C* and *D* are abrupt junctions. [Adapted from Graham (51).]

cells may be traced cranially into the transition zone where the cells decrease in size, contain less mucin, and eventually merge with the cuboid-to-columnar cells of the uterine lumen. Thus there is a transition between the stratified and columnar epithelia, both in terms of the number of cell layers and in terms of differentiation of the surface layer of cells. The mucoid differentiation of the vaginal and cervical stratified epithelium is a transitory response to estrogenic stimulation; it is rapidly followed by a wave of proliferation and keratinization, which begins at the caudal end of the vagina and proceeds cranially with two different effects. First, all the vaginal and cervical stratified epithelium proliferates and thickens up to the point where the epithelium becomes unilayered; consequently an abrupt junction appears in place of the transition. Second, as the wave of keratinization travels cranially up the vagina and cervix, the mucified cells are desquamated, almost or entirely up to the now abrupt squamocolumnar junction, so that the continuity between the surface layer of the vaginal epithelium and the uterine columnar epithelium is lost. These changes demonstrate that the transition sometimes present between the columnar and stratified epithelia of mice actually conceals a latent discontinuity that is revealed by the response to estrogenic stimulation (50). It also becomes clear that, in the area of transition, all epithelium composed of more than one cell layer should be considered stratified epithelium.

There is some limited evidence that similar changes can occur in the squamocolumnar junction of higher primates, although these changes are by no means so clear-cut or dramatic as in the mouse. Although abrupt

junctions were infrequent in ovariectomized squirrel monkeys (*Saimiri sciurea*), almost all junctions were abrupt in animals treated with estradiol benzoate sufficient to cause increased stratification of the vaginal and cervical stratified epithelium (55). In a comparison of cervices from human fetuses and neonates (which normally show evidence of stimulation by estrogens produced by the maternofetal unit) with cervices of nonstimulated immature females, it was noted that most of the former had abrupt junctions, whereas most of the latter did not; this suggests that in man, too, the character of the squamocolumnar junction is at least partially determined by the estrogenic status of the individual (51). Both abrupt and transitional junctions do occur in human adults. Transitions in human cervices are sometimes orderly and even but are sometimes somewhat irregular. The area of transition varies in extent from 1 mm to as much as 13 mm (43, 45, 46).

METAPLASIA AND MODULATION. The most striking aspect of the estrogenic response of the cervicovaginal stratified epithelium of the mouse is the ability of the proliferating population of cells to produce progeny capable of differentiating into two types of mature cells. Mucin-secreting cells are formed with subcornifying doses of estrogen, and larger doses cause cornification (95). This "transformation of an adult or fully differentiated tissue of one kind into a differentiated tissue of another kind . . ." is termed *metaplasia* (131, 134). This unusual ability of the mouse cervicovaginal epithelium to exhibit two distinct routes of differentiation under hormonal control distinguishes it from most other target tissues of the sex steroids. The more typical response to hormonal stimulation is merely the activation of an already established form of differentiation; transformations of this order are termed *modulations* (131). An example of modulation is the transformation of the seminal vesicle epithelium of the rat by androgenic stimulation from an inactive cuboidal epithelium to an active columnar secretory epithelium (131). The epithelium of the upper vagina and that of the lower cervix of some prosimians closely resemble the cervical stratified epithelium of the mouse. In intact, anestrous galagos (*Galago crassicaudatus*) and in the lorises (*Perodicticus potto* and *Nycticebus coucang*) the upper part of the cervicovaginal stratified epithelium is two cells thick, and the superficial layer of cells contains mucin and is similar to, and continuous with, the columnar epithelium of the endocervix. After three to five daily injections of 23.0 μg estradiol benzoate in oil, the stratified epithelium in galagos becomes hypertrophied and shows a well-developed columnar, mucin-containing superficial layer above several layers of cornifying cells (C. E. Graham, unpublished observation; Fig. 16). The columnar layer is subsequently shed, and a cornified epithelium remains. It would be of great interest to determine if the cervicovaginal epithelium of other primitive primates can undergo a similar transformation.

The cervicovaginal epithelium of higher primates is

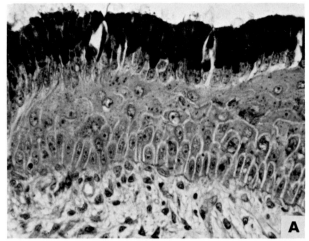

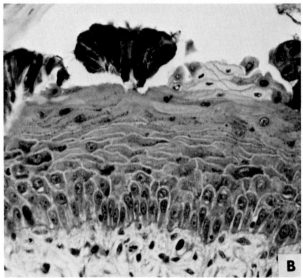

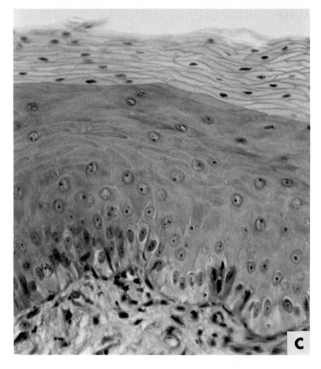

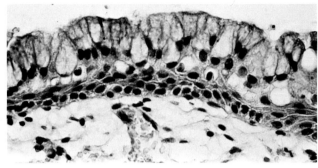

FIG. 17. Adult human cervical epithelium composed of several layers of cells, the outermost having the morphology of endocervical columnar cells. Hematoxylin and eosin. × 310.

not capable of a generalized mucification response. Attempts to produce such a change in the squirrel monkey with estrogenic stimulation of varying intensity and duration, with and without interaction with progesterone, have been unsuccessful (C. E. Graham, unpublished observations). However, the stratified epithelium of the transition zone of intact nonhuman primates occasionally does show a tendency to produce a mucified surface layer.

In man localized areas of stratified epithelium that have a tendency toward mucification and are situated in the transition zone of the cervix have been the subject of many reports. In such areas the epithelium is variable in thickness; it may be composed of only two layers: a layer of cuboidal cells situated on the basement membrane (reserve cells, basal cells) and above it a layer of cuboidal-to-columnar cells containing mucin. The epithelium is often composed of a number of cell layers, which may be rather undifferentiated or may possess definite squamous characteristics. Mucin may be demonstrable in several layers of cells or may be restricted to the outermost layer. In the most striking cases the surface layer of cells is tall and columnar, contains mucin, and bears a striking resemblance to the cells of the endocervical columnar epithelium (Figs. 17–19) with which it is sometimes continuous. Areas of epithelium with some of these characteristics have been recorded in as many as 95% of human cervices examined (17).

On comparative grounds the occasional presence of mucified cells in the transition zone of man is probably evidence of a dual ability of this area of epithelium to mucify and to cornify. However, perhaps because of

FIG. 16. Cervical epithelium of *Galago crassicaudatus* after 5 daily injections with 23.0 μg estradiol benzoate in oil. Response to estrogen treatment begins at the base of the vagina and advances cranially. Consequently *A, B,* and *C,* which are progressively more caudal areas of the cervical stratified epithelium, show successive stages of estrogenic response. *A:* development of a layer of tall, darkly stained, columnar, mucin-containing cells at the surface of the uncornified stratified epithelium. Dark granules in the deeper layers are glycogen. Periodic acid-Schiff. *B:* formation of additional cell layers in the epithelium and commencement of cornification and desquamation of mucified cells. Periodic acid-Schiff. *C:* complete cornification of the epithelium and loss of mucified layer. Periodic acid-Schiff after diastase digestion. × 400.

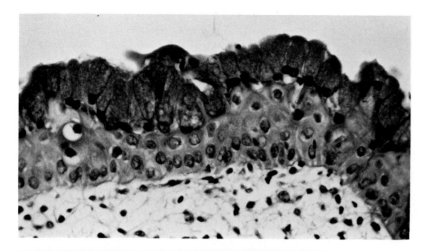

FIG. 18. An example of cervical stratified epithelium from an adult woman; stratified epithelium is shown with a surface layer of columnar cells darkly stained for mucin. Periodic acid-Schiff after diastase digestion. × 310.

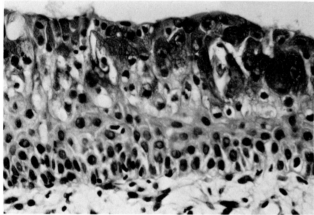

FIG. 19. Cervical stratified epithelium from an adult human female. Mucification is not restricted to the surface layer of cells, and the mucified cells are not of the tall columnar type. Periodic acid-Schiff after diastase digestion. × 310.

lack of access to comparative data, students of the human cervix have been led to conclude from the frequent similarities between the mucified cells of the transition zone and the endocervical cells that the two cell types are identical; consequently it has been necessary to explain how endocervical columnar cells come to be situated on the surface of a stratified epithelium. Two hypotheses that might account for this peculiar relationship and have met with wide acceptance must be considered.

It has been suggested that the proliferation of stratified epithelium and its lateral migration along the basement membrane to a subcolumnar position could result in the appearance of mucified endocervical cells on the surface of a stratified epithelium. Only the basal cells of the stratified epithelium might so migrate and thus form a subcolumnar layer of "reserve cells." Under suitable hormonal conditions the reserve cells could undergo hyperplasia, which would lead to the formation of a multilayered epithelium (37, 93, 94, 98). The newly formed stratified epithelium is thus postulated to originate directly from previously existing stratified epithelium, and the presence of mucin in the surface cells is held to be a consequence of a different (columnar epithelium) origin of these cells. However, the facts that

reserve cells also often contain traces of mucin (17) or that in some cases more than a single layer of cells at the surface of the epithelium contain mucin (see Fig. 19) are inconsistent with this hypothesis.

An alternative and more widely accepted origin for stratified epithelium with a columnar surface layer is the proliferation of columnar cells, which are postulated to be capable of dedifferentiating and dividing mitotically to form a layer of reserve cells representing the germinal layer of the forming stratified epithelium. The reserve cells undergo a series of divisions (reserve cell hyperplasia) which lead to stratification. The original columnar cells remain at the surface of the newly formed layers of cells and so give rise to the characteristic surface layer. This process, illustrated in Figure 20, is called *squamous metaplasia*, or *prosoplasia* (43).

The new stratified epithelium eventually matures and develops squamous characteristics, and the columnar cells are shed. Areas of epithelium corresponding with each of these stages of squamous metaplasia can be found in the transition zone of human cervices (e.g., Figs. 17 and 18); however, that these types of epithelium represent different stages of a temporal process is an assumption for which there is no direct evidence.

It is necessary to draw attention to the distinction between squamous metaplasia and the type of metaplasia that occurs in the vaginal epithelium of mice and prosimians. Squamous metaplasia, the hypothetical transformation of a columnar, mucin-producing epithelium into a stratified, cornifying epithelium, involves a radical change in the organization and in the cellular relationships of the epithelium, as well as a change in the biochemical products of differentiation. This is clearly a change of a different order from that described in the vagina of mice and prosimians, where the basic organization of the stratified epithelium remains unchanged, but the route of differentiation is altered.

EPIDERMIZATION. The replacement of columnar cells by stratified epithelium said to occur in everted cervical mucosa in man (see subsection POSITION IN RELATION TO AGE) is termed *epidermization*. The hypotheses of squamous metaplasia and of lateral migration of stratified epithelium not only seem to explain the origin of the mucified

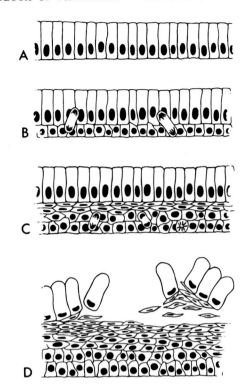

FIG. 20. Schematic diagram illustrating the stages of metaplasia. Columnar epithelium (*A*) commences to undergo cell divisions and forms a subjacent layer of cells, reserve cells (*B*). The reserve cells undergo further divisions and form a stratified epithelium (*C*). The original columnar cells are finally desquamated (*D*). [Adapted from Graham (51).]

cells of the human transition zone but also conveniently provide a possible mechanism by which epidermization might take place, since both hypotheses require that columnar epithelium be replaced by stratified epithelium. It is probably this coincidence that has led to the general acceptance of one or the other of these hypotheses. It is unfortunate that the lack of substantive proof for either hypothesis has been widely ignored; as a result, the presence of a surface layer of mucified cells in the transition zone is itself frequently interpreted as evidence that epidermization is occurring. This line of thought is obviously somewhat circular and may have led to the impression that epidermization is more frequent than there is actually good reason to believe. It is in fact difficult, if not impossible, on the basis of present knowledge, to determine from histological material if epidermization is taking place (except in carefully arranged experiments); attempts to do so require unacceptable assumptions concerning the nature of the process—for example, that it occurs by squamous metaplasia.

The idea that new stratified epithelium is formed in the cervix by squamous metaplasia has gained particularly wide credence without great justification, partly because this hypothesis simultaneously seems to explain some of the bizarre histological appearances found in the human cervix and also because it fits in well with

the concept of plasticity of the cervical epithelium, as expressed by its tendency to undergo neoplastic changes. Overready acceptance of the metaplasia hypothesis has led to frequent use of the term *metaplasia* in an almost descriptive sense when reference is to stratified epithelium in locations considered to be abnormal, such as within endocervical glands or within the endocervical canal; it is often not clear if reference to a particular theory of origin of the stratified epithelium is either intended or justified. The term *reserve cell hyperplasia* is similarly used or, rather, misused.

The concept of squamous metaplasia as applied to the human cervix has gained support from studies that seemed to show that metaplastic changes can be induced in the cervix of experimental animals. Treatment of female rats, mice, and rhesus monkeys with very high doses of estrogenic compounds for extended periods of time results in the replacement of much or all the cervical epithelium by stratified epithelium (9, 38, 39, 44, 48, 74, 88, 103, 107, 119, 140). In a detailed reexamination of this work, it was found that such estrogen-induced epidermization in the cervix of mice and epidermization induced by the implantation of threads into the cervical canal is almost entirely the result of proliferation and extension of existing stratified squamous epithelium (52, 53, 56). In the rhesus monkey the extent of replacement of endocervical columnar cells by stratified squamous epithelium is quite striking after several months of chronic estrogenic stimulation. However, small areas of stratification could be identified at the base of many of the cervical glands in intact animals, and, after prolonged estrogen treatment, the new stratified epithelium formed probably arose from these previously existing areas and not by metaplasia of columnar cells. No histological appearances suggesting that metaplasia was taking place occurred (57). In the squirrel monkey, during prolonged treatment with the estrogenic compound, diethylstilbestrol, small foci of stratified squamous epithelium appeared near the squamocolumnar junction. The apparent isolation of these foci from the main area of stratified squamous epithelium at first suggested that they had arisen in situ by metaplasia of columnar cells. However, serial sections showed that the apparently isolated foci of stratified epithelium were confluent with one another and with the main body of stratified epithelium and formed a reticular arrangement. It was therefore concluded that the newly formed reticular network of stratified epithelium represented areas of outgrowth from existing stratified epithelium (59).

The cervicovaginal stratified epithelium of mammals is characteristically a cornifying epithelium. However, an ability of this stratified epithelium to differentiate toward mucification, as well as cornification, has been noted in a number of widely scattered mammalian species. Such mucification occurs either during the estrous cycle or in pregnancy in the cow, the ewe, the rat, the mouse, the guinea pig, the bank vole (*Evotomys glareolus*), the golden hamster (*Mesocricetus auratus*), and several species of bat, as well as in the prosimians already mentioned (14, 22, 50, 80, 89, 95, 111). Only a few other species have been studied in sufficient detail to exclude the possibility that mucification of the cervical or vaginal stratified epithelium might occur in certain circumstances. The scattered distribution of the species that possess the ability to mucify suggests that mucification is a widely distributed property of the cervicovaginal epithelium in Mammalia. If so, the absence of a generalized mucification response in the higher primates may be interpreted as the loss of a primitive feature associated with the specialization of the cervix. During estrus, the vaginal epithelium of most mammals forms a cornified membrane thought to provide protection against possible mechanical trauma during copulation, and, in some species at least, the same epithelium produces mucin in other physiological states. In higher primates the cervix has become specialized, as exemplified by the more complex organ of macaques and by the restricted distribution of muscle fibers in most haplorrhine primates. The functions of protection and mucin secretion no longer reside in the same epithelial component but are segregated to the cervical stratified epithelium and the endocervical columnar epithelium, respectively.

The occurrence of mucin-secreting cells in association with the stratified epithelium of the transition zone of women and some other higher primates may represent a vestigial remnant of a generalized ability of the mammalian cervicovaginal epithelium to differentiate in this way. In other words, the stratified epithelium of the transition zone of man may possess the inherent capability to differentiate into mucin-secreting cells; such cells need not derive from the endocervical columnar epithelium, as has been so widely believed. The frequent morphological similarity between the mucified cells of the stratified epithelium and the adjacent columnar epithelium may be regarded merely as one characteristic of the morphological transition between the two types of epithelium.

Whether the route of differentiation actually taken by the epithelium of the transition zone is determined by the sex steroids in man, as is the case in rodents, remains to be established (5, 80, 95), but some evidence does exist that this is indeed the case. It has been noted that stratified epithelium with columnar cells at its surface is particularly frequent in women during pregnancy, during the perinatal period, in postmenopausal patients with endometrial hyperplasia (a condition that indicates excessive endogenous estrogen levels), in menopausal and postmenopausal women treated with high doses of estrogen, and in patients with feminizing tumors of the ovary (70).

Final clarification of this issue of the histogenesis of stratified epithelium with mucoid differentiation in the transition zone of higher primates is obviously basic to any further advances in the understanding of the hormonal responses of this area. It will also affect the un-

derstanding of the histogenesis of squamous carcinoma, since this lesion has been proposed to arise from areas of metaplasia (76, 79, 102, 133).

CONCLUSION

In this chapter the microanatomy of the cervix has been examined in terms of the various functions the organ performs. It has been seen that the ovarian hormones, especially the estrogens, modify the anatomy to a considerable extent concomitantly with changes of function. A number of outstanding problems remain to be solved, however, before it can be said that our understanding of the cervix as a target organ of ovarian steroids and other hormones nears completion.

Our knowledge of the cervical function of most primates is based on comparisons with man. This situation is unsatisfactory, as the human cervix and that of other primates shows various specializations, such as the reduction of smooth muscle in higher primates and the labyrinthine structure of the macaque cervix.

The greater proportion of muscular tissue in the cervix of lower primates suggests that contractility has a relatively important role in the cervical function of these animals.

The extent to which the contractile properties of the human cervical wall have functional significance has yet to be determined. Little is known of the mechanisms that initiate and control muscle fiber contraction in this organ. In the reproductive system the endocrine regulation of contractility is more evident and has hitherto received more attention than neural control. The discovery of a well-developed adrenergic innervation admits the possibility that nervous control may be of some importance. The integration of endocrine and neural control of the cervix and other reproductive organs is a challenging field of investigation likely to lead to the development of some new concepts of neuroendocrine relationships, foreshadowed, indeed, by discovery of a new type of neurone in the cervix and other reproductive organs, the "short" adrenergic fiber.

The extent to which the cervicovaginal epithelium of the higher primates and man retains the primitive ability to differentiate in two ways remains to be elucidated. The cervicovaginal epithelium of prosimians, which possesses this capability of switching from mucification to cornification under hormonal control, offers a fascinating model for the study of the mechanisms for controlling cell determination and differentiation.

Much remains to be learned of the basic microanatomy of the primate cervix. Comparative study is difficult because many species of primates are rare and not easy to obtain. It is essential to examine the microanatomy in various physiological states and under various conditions of hormonal stimulation, because, as has been seen, some characteristics of the cervix are only revealed under specific hormonal conditions.

REFERENCES

1. ABLAING, G., D', III, AND R. MIHATA. Capillary pattern of the human cervix. *Obstet. Gynecol.* 25: 593–596, 1965.
2. ASCHOFF, L. Zur Cervixfrage. *Monatsschr. Geburtsch. Gynaekol.* 22: 611–615, 1905.
3. ASPLUND, J. The uterine cervix and isthmus under normal and pathological conditions: a clinical and roentgenological study. *Acta Radiol. Suppl.* 91: 1–76, 1952.
4. ATKINSON, W. B., L. B. SHETTLES, AND E. T. ENGLE. Histochemical studies on the secretion of mucus by the human endocervix. *Am. J. Obstet. Gynecol.* 56: 712–716, 1948.
5. BARKER, T. E., AND B. E. WALKER. Initiation of irreversible differentiation in vaginal epithelium. *Anat. Record* 154: 149–160, 1966.
6. BELL, G. H. Abnormal uterine action in labour. *J. Obstet. Gynaecol. Brit. Empire* 59: 617–623, 1952.
7. BENGTSSON, L. P. Cervical insufficiency. *Acta Obstet. Gynecol. Scand.* 97, Suppl. 1: 7–36, 1968.
8. BISHOP, D. W. Biology of spermatozoa. In: *Sex and Internal Secretions*, edited by W. C. Young. Baltimore: Williams & Wilkins, 1961, vol. II, p. 707–796.
9. BO, W. J. The origin and development of estrogen-induced uterine metaplasia. *Arch. Pathol.* 64: 595–600, 1957.
10. BORELL, U., AND I. FERNSTRÖM. The sphincter mechanism of the isthmus uteri. *Acta Obstet. Gynecol. Scand.* 32: 7–12, 1953.
11. BORELL, U., O. NILSSON, AND A. WESTMAN. The cyclical changes occurring in the epithelium lining the endometrial glands. *Acta Obstet. Gynecol. Scand.* 38: 364–369, 1959.
12. BRADBURN, G. B., AND C. F. WEBB. Cyclic variations in the endocervix. *Am. J. Obstet. Gynecol.* 62: 997–1008, 1951.
13. BRADFIELD, J. R. G. Glycogen of vertebrate epidermis. *Nature* 167: 40–41, 1951.
14. BRAMBELL, F. W. R., AND I. W. ROWLANDS. Reproduction of the bank vole (*Evotomys glareolus*, Schreber). I. The oestrous cycle of the female. *Phil. Trans. Roy. Soc. London, Ser. B* 226: 71–97, 1936.
15. BROWN, R. L. Rate of transport of spermia in human uterus and tubes. *Am. J. Obstet. Gynecol.* 47: 407–411, 1944.
16. CARLBORG, L., E. D. B. JOHANSSON, AND C. GEMZELL. Sialic acid content and sperm penetration of cervical mucus in relation to total urinary oestrogen excretion and plasma progesterone levels in ovulatory women. *Acta Endocrinol.* 62: 721–731, 1969.
17. CARMICHAEL, R., AND B. L. JEAFFRESON. Basal cells in the epithelium of the human cervical canal. *J. Pathol. Bacteriol.* 49: 63–68, 1939.
18. CHAPMAN, G. B., E. C. MANN, R. WEGRYN, AND C. HULL. The ultrastructure of human cervical epithelial cells during pregnancy. *Am. J. Obstet. Gynecol.* 88: 3–16, 1964.
19. CHATTERJEE, S., AND B. K. ANAND. Estimations of oestrogens from female monkey's urine. *Indian J. Med. Res.* 55: 973–980, 1967.
20. CLARK, O. H., AND G. W. CORNER. The cervix uteri of the rhesus monkey. *Anat. Record* 63: 247–252, 1935.
21. COLBORN, G. L., W. J. BO, AND C. M. LANG. Observations on the cervix uteri of the squirrel monkey. *J. Morphol.* 122: 81–88, 1967.
22. COLE, H. H. A study of the mucosa of the genital tract of the cow, with special reference to the cyclic changes. *Am. J. Anat.* 46: 261–301, 1930.
23. CORRODI, H., AND N. Å. HILLARP. Fluoreszenzmethoden zur histochemischen Sichtbarmachung von Monoaminen. 2. (1) Indentifizierung des fluoreszierenden Produktes aus Dopamin und Formaldehyd. *Helv. Chim. Acta* 47: 911–918, 1964.
24. CROSS, B. A. Hypothalamic influences on sperm transport in the male and female genital tract. In: *Recent Progress in Endocrinology of Reproduction*, edited by C. W. Lloyd. New York: Acad. Press, 1959, p. 167–177.
25. DANFORTH, D. N. The fibrous nature of the human cervix,

and its relation to the isthmic segment in gravid and nongravid uteri. *Am. J. Obstet. Gynecol.* 53: 541–560, 1947.
26. DANFORTH, D. N. The distribution and functional activity of the cervical musculature. *Am. J. Obstet. Gynecol.* 68: 1261–1271, 1954.
27. DANFORTH, D. N., J. C. BUCKINGHAM, AND J. W. RODDIC, JR. Connective tissue changes incident to cervical effacement. *Am. J. Obstet. Gynecol.* 80: 939–945, 1960.
28. DANFORTH, D. N., AND J. C. F. CHAPMAN. The incorporation of the isthmus uteri. *Am. J. Obstet. Gynecol.* 59: 979–988, 1950.
29. DAVID, A., AND L. MASTROIANNI, JR. Cervical mucus arborization in the rhesus monkey. *J. Reprod. Fertility* 17: 495–499, 1968.
30. DAVIES, J., AND R. B. WOOLF. Histology and fine structure of the adult human cervix uteri. *Clin. Obstet. Gynecol.* 6: 265–304, 1963.
31. DAVIES, A. A. The innervation of the uterus. *J. Obstet. Gynaecol. Brit. Empire* 40: 481–497, 1933.
32. DIERKS, K. Der normale mensuelle Cyclus der menschlichen Vaginalschleimhaut. *Arch. Gynaekol.* 130: 46–69, 1927.
33. DOUGHERTY, C. M., AND F. M. LOW. The fine structure of the basement membrane of the uterine cervical epithelia: observations with the electron microscope. *Am. J. Obstet. Gynecol.* 76: 839–850, 1958.
34. DUARTE, E. A study of the endocervical columnar cells. I. Morphology and frequency. *Mem. Inst. Oswaldo Cruz* 64: 43–77, 1966.
35. DUPERROY, G. Morphological study of the endocervical mucosa in relation to the menstrual cycle and to leucorrhea. *Gynaecologia* 131: 73–86, 1951.
36. ECKSTEIN, P. The reproductive tract of sub-human primates. In: *Primatologia*, edited by H. Hofer, A. H. Schultz, and D. Starck. New York: Karger, 1958, vol. III, pt. I, p. 542–629.
37. EICHHOLZ, P. *Experimentelle Untersuchungen über Epithelmetaplasie (Dissertation)*. Berlin: Königsberg, 1902.
38. ENGLE, E. T., C. KRAKOWER, AND C. D. HAAGENSEN. Estrogen administration to aged female monkeys with no resultant tumors. *Cancer Res.* 3: 858–866, 1943.
39. ENGLE, E. T., AND P. E. SMITH. Some uterine effects obtained in female monkeys during continued oestrin administration, with especial reference to the cervix uteri. *Anat. Record* 61: 471–483, 1935.
40. EVANS, E. I. The transport of spermatozoa in the dog. *Am. J. Physiol.* 105: 287–293, 1933.
41. FALCK, B. Observations on the possibilities of the cellular localization of monoamines by a fluorescence method. *Acta Physiol. Scand. Suppl.* 197: 1–25, 1962.
42. FAWCETT, D. W. Structural and functional variations in the membranes of the cytoplasm. In: *Intracellular Membraneous Structure*, edited by S. Seno and E. V. Cowdry. Okayama: Japan Soc. Cell Biol., 1969, p. 15–40.
43. FLUHMANN, C. F. The histogenesis of squamous cell metaplasia of the cervix and endometrium. *Surg. Obstet. Gynecol.* 97: 45–58, 1953.
44. FLUHMANN, C. F. Squamous metaplasia in the rat uterus. *Arch. Pathol.* 59: 238–246, 1955.
45. FLUHMANN, C. F. The squamocolumnar transitional zone of the cervix uteri. *Obstet. Gynecol.* 14: 133–148, 1959.
46. FLUHMANN, C. F. *The Cervix Uteri and Its Diseases*. Philadelphia: Saunders, 1961.
47. GIBBONS, R. A. The function of the cervix. *J. Reprod. Med.* 3: 126–128, 1969.
48. GITLIN, G. On the mode of development of stratified squamous epithelium in the rat's uterus following prolonged estrogen stimulation. *Anat. Record* 120: 637–661, 1954.
49. GOMPEL, C. The ultrastructure of the human endometrial cell studied by electron microscopy. *Am. J. Obstet. Gynecol.* 84: 1000–1009, 1962.
50. GRAHAM, C. E. Cyclic changes in the squamo-columnar

junction of the mouse cervix uteri. *Anat. Record* 155: 251–260, 1966.

51. GRAHAM, C. E. Uterine cervical epithelium of fetal and immature human females in relation to estrogenic stimulation. *Am. J. Obstet. Gynecol.* 97: 1033–1040, 1967.

52. GRAHAM, C. E. Mechanism of induced epidermization in in the mouse uterine cervix. *Am. J. Obstet. Gynecol.* 99: 470–478, 1967.

53. GRAHAM, C. E. Mechanism of induced epidermization in the uterine cervix: age effects. *Am. J. Obstet. Gynecol.* 100: 745–751, 1968.

54. GRAHAM, C. E. Glycogen and glycogen-metabolizing enzymes in the squirrel monkey uterine cervix. *Am. J. Obstet. Gynecol.* 102: 989–996, 1968.

55. GRAHAM, C. E. Estrogen-induced changes at the cervical squamocolumnar junction of the squirrel monkey. *Am. J. Obstet. Gynecol.* 104: 839–845, 1969.

56. GRAHAM, C. E. Thread-induced epidermization in the uterine horn of mice, and the influence of 20-methylcholanthrene. *Oncology* 25: 83–93, 1971.

57. GRAHAM, C. E. Response of the rhesus monkey uterine cervix to chronic estrogenic stimulation. *Am. J. Obstet. Gynecol.* 108: 1192–1196, 1970.

58. GRAHAM, C. E., N. GUILLOUD, AND J. W. MCARTHUR. Reproductive endocrinology of the chimpanzee: a preliminary report. *Proc. Intern. Congr. Primatol., 2nd* 2: 66–72, 1969.

59. GRAHAM, C. E., AND S. L. MANOCHA. The effect of chronic estrogenic stimulation on the squirrel monkey cervical epithelium. *Virchows Arch. B* 7: 147–156, 1971.

60. GRUBB, C., M. HACKEMANN, AND K. R. HILL. Small granules and plasma membrane thickening in human cervical squamous epithelium. *J. Ultrastruct. Res.* 22: 458–468, 1968.

61. GRUENAGEL, H. H. Die Plattenepithel-Cylinderepithel-Grenze an der Portio vaginalis uteri bei unreifen und reifen Neugeborenen, Säuglingen und Kindern bis zu 9 Jahren. *Frankfurter Z. Pathol.* 68: 465–496, 1957.

62. HACKEMANN, M., C. GRUBB, AND K. R. HILL. The ultrastructure of normal squamous epithelium of the human cervix uteri. *J. Ultrastruct. Res.* 22: 443–457, 1968.

63. HAMILTON, C. E. Observations on the cervical mucosa of the rhesus monkey. *Carnegie Inst. Wash. Contrib. Embryol.* 33: 82–101, 1949.

64. HAMPERL, H., AND C. KAUFMANN. The cervix uteri at different ages. *Obstet. Gynecol.* 14: 621–631, 1959.

65. HARKNESS, M. L. R., AND R. D. HARKNESS. Changes in the physical properties of the uterine cervix of the rat during pregnancy. *J. Physiol., London* 148: 524–547, 1959.

66. HARTMAN, C. G. Cyclic changes in the endocervix of the monkey and the origin of the cervical mucus. *Ann. NY Acad. Sci.* 97: 564–570, 1962.

67. HASHIMOTO, M., Y. MORI, A. KOMORI, T. SHIMOYAMA, AND K. AKASHI. Electron microscopic studies on the fine structure of the human uterine cervix. *J. Japan. Obstet. Gynecol. Soc.* 6: 99–107, 1959.

68. HAYS, R. L., AND N. L. VANDEMARK. Stimulatory action of breeding on the release of oxytocin as measured by intramammary pressure. *J. Dairy Sci.* 34: 496–497, 1951.

69. HAYS, R. L., AND N. L. VANDEMARK. Effects of oxytocin and epinephrine on uterine motility in the bovine. *Am. J. Physiol.* 172: 557–560, 1953.

70. HELLMAN, L. M., A. H. ROSENTHAL, R. W. KISTNER, AND R. GORDEN. Some factors influencing the proliferation of the reserve cells in the human cervix. *Am. J. Obstet. Gynecol.* 67: 899–915, 1954.

71. HILL, W. C. O. The menstrual cycle of the toque macaque (*Macaca sinica* Linn.), with observations on its uterine structure, compared with that of other macaques. *Ceylon J. Sci.* 5: 21–36, 1939.

72. HILL, W. C. O. *Primates, Comparative Anatomy and Taxonomy.* I. *Strepsirhini.* Edinburgh: Edinburgh Univ. Press, 1953.

73. HILL, W. C. O. *Primates, Comparative Anatomy and Taxonomy.*

IV. *Cebidae.* Edinburgh: Edinburgh Univ. Press, 1960, pt. A.

74. HISAW, F. L., AND F. C. LENDRUM. Squamous metaplasia in the cervical glands of the monkey following oestrin administration. *Endocrinology* 20: 228–229, 1936.

75. HOPPER, B., AND W. W. TULLNER. Urinary estrone and plasma progesterone levels during the menstrual cycle of the rhesus monkey. *Endocrinology* 86: 1225–1230, 1970.

76. HOWARD, L., C. C. ERICKSON, AND L. D. STODDARD. A study of the incidence and histogenesis of endocervical metaplasia and intra-epithelial carcinoma. *Cancer* 4: 1210–1223, 1951.

77. HUFFMAN, J. W. Mesonephric remnants in the cervix. *Am. J. Obstet. Gynecol.* 56: 23–40, 1948.

78. HUNTER, R. H. Observations on the development of the human female genital tract. *Carnegie Inst. Wash. Contrib. Embryol.* 22: 91–108, 1930.

79. JOHNSON, L. D., C. L. EASTERDAY, H. GORE, AND A. T. HERTIG. The histogenesis of carcinoma in situ of the uterine cervix: a preliminary report of the origin of carcinoma in situ in subcylindrical cell anaplasia. *Cancer* 17: 213–229, 1964.

80. KLEIN, M. The mucification of the vaginal epithelium in rodents. *Proc. Roy. Soc. London, Ser. B* 124: 23–29, 1937.

81. KRANTZ, K. E. Innervation of the human uterus. *Ann. NY Acad. Sci.* 75: 770–784, 1959.

82. KRANTZ, K. E. The gross and microscopic anatomy of the human vagina. *Ann. NY Acad. Sci.* 83: 89–104, 1959.

83. KRANTZ, K. E., AND W. P. PHILLIPS. Anatomy of the human uterine cervix, gross and microscopic. *Ann. NY Acad. Sci.* 97: 551–563, 1962.

84. KUROSUMI, K. Golgi apparatus and its derivatives, with special reference to secretory granules. In: *Intracellular Membraneous Structure*, edited by S. Seno and E. V. Cowdry. Okayama: Japan Soc. Cell Biol., 1969, p. 259–276.

85. LABATE, J. S. The surgical anatomy of the superior hypogastric plexus—"presacral nerve." *Surg. Gynecol. Obstet.* 67: 199–211, 1938.

86. LAGUENS, R. P., J. LAGRUTTA, O. R. KOCH, AND F. QUIJANO. Fine structure of human endocervical epithelium. *Am. J. Obstet. Gynecol.* 98: 773–780, 1967.

87. LODIN, Z., J. FALTIN, AND K. SHARMA. Attempts at standardization of a highly sensitive Schiff reagent. *Acta Histochem.* 26: 244–254, 1967.

88. LOEB, L., V. SUNTZEFF, AND E. L. BURNS. Growth processes induced by estrogenic hormones in the uterus of the mouse. *Am. J. Cancer* 34: 413–427, 1938.

89. MATTHEWS, L. H. Notes on the genitalia and reproduction of some African bats. *Proc. Zool. Soc. London, Ser. B* 111: 289–346, 1941.

90. MAXIMOW, A. A., AND W. BLOOM. *A Textbook of Histology* (7th ed.). Philadelphia: Saunders, 1957, p. 63.

91. McLAREN, H. C. The involution of the cervix. *Brit. Med. J.* 1: 347–352, 1952.

92. McNUTT, N. S., AND R. S. WEINSTEIN. Carcinoma of the cervix: deficiency of nexus intercellular junctions. *Science* 165: 597–599, 1969.

93. MEYER, R. Die Epithelentwicklung der Cervix und Portio vaginalis uteri und die Pseudoerosio congenita (congenitales histologisches ektropium). *Arch. Gynaekol.* 91: 579–598, 1910.

94. MEYER, R. Die Erosion und Pseudoerosion der Erwachsenen. *Arch. Gynaekol.* 91: 658–691, 1910.

95. MEYER, R. K., AND W. M. ALLEN. The production of mucified cells in the vaginal epithelium of certain rodents by oestrin and by corpus luteum extracts. *Anat. Record* 56: 321–343, 1933.

96. NAJAK, Z., K. HILLIER, AND S. M. M. KARIM. The action of prostaglandins on the human isolated non-pregnant cervix. *J. Obstet. Gynaecol. Brit. Commonwealth* 77: 701–709, 1970.

97. NALBANDOV, A. V. *Reproductive Physiology* (2nd ed.). San Francisco: Freeman, 1964.

98. NOVAK, E. R., AND J. D. WOODRUFF. *Gynecologic and Obstetric Pathology* (5th ed.). Philadelphia: Saunders, 1962, p. 483.

99. NOVAK, E., J. D. WOODRUFF, AND E. R. NOVAK. Probable mesonephric origin of certain female genital tumors. *Am. J. Obstet. Gynecol.* 68: 1222–1242, 1954.

100. OBER, K. G., P. SCHNEPPENHEIM, H. HAMPERL, AND C. KAUFMANN. Die Epithelgrenzen im Bereiche des Isthmus uteri. *Arch. Gynaekol.* 190: 346–383, 1958.

101. ODEBLAD, E. The functional structure of human cervical mucus. *Acta Obstet. Gynecol. Scand.* 47, Suppl. 1: 57–79, 1968.

102. OLD, J. W., G. WIELENGA, AND E. VON HAAM. Squamous carcinoma in situ of the uterine cervix. I. Classification and histogenesis. *Cancer* 18: 1598–1611, 1965.

103. OVERHOLSER, M.D., AND E. ALLEN. Atypical growth induced in cervical epithelium of the monkey by prolonged injections of ovarian hormone combined with chronic trauma. *Surg. Gynecol. Obstet.* 60: 129–136, 1935.

104. OWMAN, C., E. ROSENGREN, AND N-O. SJÖBERG. Adrenergic innervation of the human female reproductive organs: a histochemical and chemical investigation. *Obstet. Gynecol.* 30: 763–773, 1967.

105. PARKES, A. S. The biology of spermatozoa and artificial insemination. In: *Marshall's Physiology of Reproduction*, edited by A. S. Parkes. London: Longmans, 1960, vol. I, pt. II, p. 161–263.

106. PERLOFF, W. H., AND E. STEINBERGER. In vivo survival of spermatozoa in cervical mucus. *Am. J. Obstet. Gynecol.* 88: 439–442, 1964.

107. PFEIFFER, C. A., AND E. ALLEN. Attempts to produce cancer in rhesus monkeys with carcinogenic hydrocarbons and estrogens. *Cancer Res.* 8: 97–127, 1948.

108. PINTO, R. M., W. RABOW, AND R. A. VOTTA. Uterine cervix ripening in term pregnancy due to the action of estradiol-17β. *Am. J. Obstet. Gynecol.* 92: 319–324, 1965.

109. PUNDEL, J. P. The so-called diastase-resistant PAS-positive material in the human vaginal epithelium: a cyto- and histochemical study. *Acta Cytol.* 10: 428–439, 1966.

110. REID, D. E. *A Textbook of Obstetrics.* Philadelphia: Saunders, 1962.

111. RESTALL, B. J. Histological observations on the reproductive tract of the ewe. *Australian J. Biol. Sci.* 19: 673–686, 1966.

112. ROTHMAN, S. *Physiology and Biochemistry of the Skin.* Chicago: Univ. of Chicago Press, 1954.

113. RUBENSTEIN, B. B., H. STRAUSS, M. L. LAZARUS, AND H. HANKIN. Sperm survival in women. Motile sperm in the fundus and tubes of surgical cases. *Fertility Sterility* 2: 15–19, 1951.

114. SANDBERG, F., A. INGLEMAN-SUNDBERG, L. LINDGREN, AND G. RYDÉN. *In vitro* studies of the motility of the human uterus. Part V. The effects of L-sparteine, D-sparteine and retamine (7-hydroxy-sparteine) on the spontaneous motility in different parts of the pregnant and non-pregnant uterus. *J. Obstet. Gynaecol. Brit. Empire* 66: 939–945, 1959.

115. SANDYS, O. C., AND S. ZUCKERMAN. Observations on the cervix uteri and the urethra of monkeys. *J. Anat.* 72: 352–357, 1938.

116. SCHELLHAS, H. F. Cell renewal in the human cervix uteri: a radio-autographic study of DNA, RNA, and protein synthesis. *Am. J. Obstet. Gynecol.* 104: 617–632, 1969.

117. SCHILLER, E. The epithelium of the uterine endocervix. *Acta Cytol.* 3: 333–337, 1959.

118. SCHNEPPENHEIM, P., H. HAMPERL, C. KAUFMANN, AND K. G. OBER. Die Beziehungen des Schleimepithels zum Plattenepithel an der Cervix uteri im Lebenslauf der Frau. *Arch. Gynaekol.* 190: 303–345, 1958.

119. SCOTT, R. B., AND L. R. WHARTON, JR. The effects of ex-

cessive amounts of diethylstilbestrol on experimental endometriosis in monkeys. *Am. J. Obstet. Gynecol.* 69: 573–591, 1955.

120. SJÖBERG, N-O. New considerations on the adrenergic innervation of the cervix and uterus. *Acta Obstet. Gynecol. Scand.* 43, Suppl. 3: 28–32, 1969.

121. SJÖVALL, A. Untersuchungen über die Schleimhaut der Cervix uteri; die verschiedenen Schleimhautbilder der Frau während des mensuellen Cyklus, im Kindesalter, im Senium und bei einigen hormonellen Störungen. *Acta Obstet. Gynecol. Scand.* 18, Suppl. 4: 13–253, 1938.

122. STEGNER, H.-E., AND R. BELTERMANN. Die Elektronenmikroskopie des Cervixdrüsenepithels und der sog. Reservezellen. *Arch. Gynaekol.* 207: 480–504, 1969.

123. STERNBERG, W. H., W. H. CLARK, AND R. C. SMITH. Malignant mixed Müllerian tumor (mixed mesodermal tumor of the uterus). *Cancer* 7: 704–724, 1954.

124. STIEVE, H. Der Halsteil der menschlichen Gebärmutter, seine Veränderungen während der Schwangerschaft, der Geburt und des Wochenbettes und ihre Beschreibung. *Z. Mikroskop. Anat. Forsch.* 11: 291–441, 1927.

125. TAMPION, D., AND R. A. GIBBONS. Orientation of spermatozoa in mucus of the cervix uteri. *Nature* 194: 381, 1962.

126. TOPKINS, P. The histologic appearance of the endocervix during the menstrual cycle. *Am. J. Obstet. Gynecol.* 58: 654–663, 1949.

127. VANDEMARK, N. L., AND R. L. HAYS. Rapid sperm transport in the cow. *Fertility Sterility* 5: 131–137, 1954.

128. VANDEMARK, N. L., AND R. L. HAYS. Sperm transport in the perfused genital tract of the cow. *Am. J. Physiol.* 183: 510–512, 1955.

129. VANDEMARK, N. L., AND A. N. MOELLER. Speed of spermatozoan transport in reproductive tract of estrous cow. *Am. J. Physiol.* 165: 674–679, 1951.

130. WARREN, J. W., M. B. DOCKERTY, R. B. WILSON, AND J. S. WELCH. Basement membrane in the uterine cervix. *Am. J. Obstet. Gynecol.* 95: 23–28, 1966.

131. WEISS, P. *Principles of Development; a Text in Experimental Embryology.* New York: Holt, 1939.

132. WHEELER, J. D., AND S. DANZIGER. A histochemical study of the cervix uteri. *Obstet. Gynecol.* 5: 739–754, 1955.

133. WHEELER, J. D., AND A. T. HERTIG. The pathologic anatomy of carcinoma of the uterus. I. Squamous carcinoma of the cervix. *Am. J. Clin. Pathol.* 25: 345–375, 1955.

134. WILLIS, R. A. Metaplasia. In: *The Borderland of Embryology and Pathology* (2nd ed.). Washington: Butterworths, 1962, p. 519–583.

135. WOLLNER, A. The histologic correlationship of endometrial and cervical biopsies, with comments on the etiology of endocervicitis. *Am. J. Obstet. Gynecol.* 36: 10–21, 1938.

136. WOLLNER, A. The etiology and treatment of endocervicitis and cervical erosions. *Am. J. Obstet. Gynecol.* 37: 947–963, 1939.

137. WOLLNER, A. Menstrual cycle in human cervical mucosa and the clinical significance. *Am. J. Surg.* 57: 331–335, 1942.

138. YOUNES, M. S., H. D. STEELE, E. M. ROBERTSON, AND S. A. BENCOSME. Correlative light and electron microscope study of the basement membrane of the human ectocervix. *Am. J. Obstet. Gynecol.* 92: 163–171, 1965.

139. ZONDEK, B. The effect of prolonged administration of estrogen on the uterus and the anterior pituitary of human beings. *J. Am. Med. Assoc.* 114: 1850–1854, 1940.

140. ZUCKERMAN, S. Effects of prolonged oestrin-stimulation on the cervix uteri. *Lancet* 1: 435–437, 1937.

CHAPTER 31

Composition and function of cervical secretion

K. S. MOGHISSI | *Department of Gynecology and Obstetrics, Wayne State University, School of Medicine, Detroit, Michigan*

CHAPTER CONTENTS

IN MOST MAMMALIAN SPECIES the deposition of semen in the female genital tract is followed by a rapid transport of spermatozoa to the site of fertilization (96, 108, 138, 150, 151). In some mammals (mouse, rat, hamster, ferret, dog, pig, mare), ejaculation takes place in the uterus; the cervix is almost completely bypassed. In such species as rabbit and cat and in primates, including man, the uterine cervix plays a distinct role in the process of sperm migration.

The purpose of this review is to examine the current knowledge of the biochemical and biophysical properties of cervical secretion and its function with respect to sperm transport and survival. Related human and animal studies are considered.

ANATOMY

In mammals the cervix represents the terminal portion of the uterus and separates the vagina from the uterine cavity (Fig. 1). It is a thick-walled, cylindrical structure that tapers at its inferior extremity. In woman the canal of the cervix measures 2.5–3 cm in length, is fusiform in shape, and is flattened in its posterior; its middle third is slightly dilated. The average transverse diameter at its widest point is 7 mm. The external os is the opening in the portiovaginalis that connects the cervical canal with the vagina. Histologically the cervix differs from the corpus uteri. The pars vaginalis of the cervix is lined with stratified squamous epithelium similar to that of the vagina, and it normally shows no hornification. The epithelial cells of the endocervix are tall, columnar, and picket cell-like, rest on a thin basement membrane, and form a single layer; their nuclei are oval and are located basally. The upper portion of the cytoplasm of these cells contains clear droplets of mucus. Some ciliated cells have been observed with the electron microscope in man and with light microscopy in the rabbit (30). The cervical glands are of a racemose type and are lined with epithelium resembling that of endocervix. Studies by Fluhmann (39) strongly suggest that, instead of racemose glands, the basic epithelial structure of the cervical mucosa is an intricate system of clefts or grooves, which, grouped together, give an illusory impression of glands. These clefts may run in an oblique, transverse, or longitudinal direction but never cross one another, although they may bifurcate or extend downward. Cyclic changes in the shape and diameter of the cervix have been described. In the immediate premenstrual period and during the menstruation, the isthmus of the cervix (the narrow part of the canal between the endocervix and endometrial cavity) is short, wide, and atonic. Isthmic tone gradually increases during the proliferative phase, which affects, particularly, the lower segment of the isthmus. In the luteal phase, progressive lengthening and narrowing of the isthmus occur and result in a hypertonic, tubular appearance that persists until the immediate premenstrual phase (84). There is considerable species variation in the anatomic characteristics and histological makeup of the uterine cervix (Table 1). Similarly, histological differ-

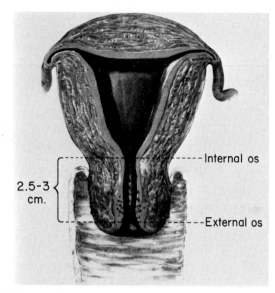

FIG. 1. Human uterus.

ences and varying cyclic changes in the cervical mucosa of a number of mammals have been observed and are described in the chapter by C. Graham in this volume.

BLOOD SUPPLY OF THE CERVIX

The blood supply of the cervix is derived primarily from the uterine artery; the azygous arteries of the vagina and ascending branches of the vaginal arteries also contribute. The venous drainage parallels arterial vessels and communicates with the vascular network of bladder neck. Veins from the cervix join the uterine and ovarian venous plexuses and empty finally into the hypogastric veins. Zinser (160) has demonstrated that the major source of blood supply to mucous-producing endocervical epithelia is from the first branches of the uterine arteries as they descend along the body of the cervix. From these arterial networks are derived radial arterioles that course toward the endocervix. The entire endocervical canal is thus crossed by a terminal vascular plexus of narrower caliber than the plexuses supplying the portio vaginalis. As they enter the cervix, these vessels are spiral in appearance and become straight as they reach the periphery. Vaginal branches of the uterine arteries and those of the vaginal artery supply the squamous epithelium. These vessels are highly ramified and convoluted, are of large caliber, and terminate in parallel, palisadelike capillaries.

NERVE SUPPLY OF THE CERVIX

In man the nerve supply of the cervix is derived from three plexuses of the pelvic autonomic system: the superior, middle, and inferior hypogastric plexuses. The superior and middle hypogastric plexuses, the presacral nerve, and the uterinus magnus all contribute to the inferior hypogastric plexus, which consists of several parallel nerves on each side of the pelvis that descend at a point posterior to the common iliac artery and terminate in the uterosacral ligaments. From the medial section of the primary division of sacral nerves, fibers (nervi erigentes) emanate to reach the pelvic plexus in the uterosacral ligaments.

The pelvic plexus therefore contains sympathetic (inferior hypogastric fibers) and parasympathetic (nervi erigentes) components. The sensory components, which are visceral for the most part, are found in the nervi erigentes. There are apparently a fair number of sensory fibers in the sympathetic component as well.

On either side of the cervix, in the base of the broad ligament, is the so-called Lee-Frankenhäuser or hypogastric ganglion the location of which is reputed to be superficial to the internal iliac and its branches and parallel to the lateral pelvic wall. This is actually a plexus, the major part of which terminates in large branches that enter the uterus primarily through the uterosacral ligaments in the region of the internal os (67).

Giro (48) has studied the terminal nerve supply to the endocervical glands in rodents and women. He observed a rich system of nerve endings at the base of the cylindrical epithelium of the cervical canal in rabbits, rats, and guinea pigs. Similarly he found numerous nerve fibers following the vascular network in the submucosa and, independent of the vascular system, in the endocervix of women. Collateral branches of these terminal nerves were observed in contact with endocervical crypts. Other nerve fibers were found to traverse the submucosa of the cervical crypts and form a dense network around the epithelial invagination. These fibers were in contact intimately with glandular epithelium and actually appeared to enter into these columnar cells. Nerve endings bordering the epithelial covering of the cervical canal were perpendicular to the base of the epithelial cells but did not make contact with them.

Adham & Schenk (1) have used specific histochemical methods for norepinephrine and for acetylcholinesterase to delineate the pattern of autonomic innervation of the rat cervix. Cholinergic nerve trunks and bundles derived from the adventitial nerves entered the muscle bundles and divided to form muscular and vascular branches. According to these investigators, the neuroterminals in the cervix were more developed and more cellular than those in the vagina. The richness of innervation decreased near the uterus. They noted also that the adrenergic innervation of the cervical muscularis was less developed than the cholinergic innervation. The density of the adrenergic and cholinergic innervation appeared most prominent during estrus and least prominent during diestrus.

Giro (48) believes that the nerve endings in the cervix may transmit impulses through the sympathetic nerve system to the pituitary gland to influence its secretory activity.

TABLE 1. *Anatomic Characteristics of the Cervix in Various Mammalian Species*

Species	Anatomic Characteristics	Mucosal Folds	Transition to Vaginal Epithelium	Ref.
Cat (*Felis catus*)	Remarkably short (2 mm in length); lacks a true external os; continuous with dorsal wall of vagina; external os is V-shaped and surrounded by vaginal fornices anteriorly and on both sides but not dorsally	Inconspicuous	Gradual and distinct; lying near external os	28
Cattle (*Bos taurus*)	Firm, thick-walled, 5–10 cm in length, 3–4 cm in thickness, heavy muscular layers; mucosa forms numerous thick overlapping folds forming a spiral canal, ("plica palmata"); main folds increase in height in a craniocaudal direction, and the lowest ones project into vagina; lamellated mucosa lined by a single layer of columnar nonciliated, mucus-producing epithelium	Four longitudinal annular folds or rings of mucous membrane arranged spirally; throughout the length of these folds the mucosa thrown up in secondary, tertiary, and often quaternary folds	Continuous; epithelia in the os and in the vaginal portion adjacent to it are similar	25, 53, 59
Dog (*Canis familiaris*)	Short and thick-walled segment, 0.3–1 cm in length; continuation of myometrial fibers and fibroelastic and fibromuscular tissues form body of cervix; external os opens in short, cone-shaped vaginal portio and is sharply defined; internal os not well defined; tunica propria not well defined; glandular uterine epithelium present in proximal part of cervical canal	Small vaginal folds surround external os; numerous mucosal folds at proestrus	Irregular or indistinct; folds of vaginal epithelium alternate with endometrial epithelium above level of external os	28
Guinea pig (*Cavia porcellus*)	Two internal ora and one common external os protrude into vagina	Simple during diestrus; increase in number and complexity during proestrus		64
Horse (*Equus caballus*)	Internal os is indefinite; external os opens on summit of a definite portio, which projects into vaginal fornices; tubular glands absent; epithelial mucous cells secrete abundant mucus during estrus; 7.5 cm in length	Conspicuous folds in mucosa		54
Man (*Homo sapiens*)	Uterine lumen tapers from fundus toward isthmus but in the cervix expands into a spindle-shaped canal; lower part of cervix (portio vaginalis) projects into vagina forming anterior and posterior fornix; mucosa contains numerous extensively branched crypts lined with mucus-secreting columnar epithelium, some of which are ciliated; outer surface of portio vaginalis is smooth, covered with a mucous membrane similar to that of vagina, with a lamina propria and well-separated papillae	Branching folds on surface; longitudinal ridge or raphe on the anterior and posterior surface of canal; from these ridges mucosal folds extend at angles toward each side	Abrupt; borderline is just inside the external os; in some cases patches of columnar epithelium may extend for short distances on outer surface of portio vaginalis; in others vaginal end of cervical canal has stratified epithelium	9, 28

TABLE 1.—*Continued*

Species	Anatomic Characteristics	Mucosal Folds	Transition to Vaginal Epithelium	Ref.
Mink (*Mustela vison*)	Cervical canal straight and simple; external orifice is a transverse slit; little difference between length of dorsal and ventral lips of cervix—ventral fornix is far deeper than the dorsal; transverse fold of vaginal wall covers much of dorsal lip			32
Monkey, baboon (*Papio porcarius*) and (*Papio hamadryas*)	Transition from uterus to cervix marked by abrupt lateral expansion of central lumen, which becomes increasingly wide toward lower part of cervix; external os is a coronal slit between a thicker anterior and a thinner posterior lip	Folds that form an arbor vitae very similar to that in women	Clearly demarcated, distinguishable microscopically about 4 mm within lips of of cervix	163
Monkey, bonnet (*Macaca radiata*)	Large and complex compared to rhesus monkey; mucosal lining composed of large epithelial cells, which also line the crypts that dip in all directions; copious vaginal discharge	Complex folds that render passage tortuous	Clearly demarcated, but position varies in different animals	162
Monkey, rhesus (*Macaca mulatta*)	Cervical canal not straight but thrown into several sharp turns; external os is slitlike and lies nearer anterior cervix; dorsal lip is thicker than ventral one; dorsal fornix is deeper than the anterior	Colliculi (2–3) project into cervical canal; main colliculus forms projection of ventral cervical wall, 2nd colliculus is small, opposite junction of cranial and dorsal surfaces of the 1st colliculus; these 2 formations are constant; 3rd and most cranial colliculus (present in 40% of cases) is small and cut off from ventral wall	Line of transition of cylindrical cervical and vaginal squamous epithelium varies in position independently of age; it may be situated between vaginal surface of cervix and apex of cul de sac below main colliculus	125
Monkey, squirrel (*Saimiri sciureus*)	A dilatation of the distal portion of the endocervical canal to form a vestibule-like chamber; 9 mm in diameter, 10 mm in length	Vestibule occupied in varying degree by fibromuscular projections or colliculi; vary in size, number, and degree to which they occupy vestibule	Variable	24
Pig (*Sus domesticus*)	Narrow diameter, 10 cm in length, densely fibrous, nonglandular mucous membrane; its lower end gradually becomes wider and passes into the vagina without forming a proper external os or vaginal fornices; rounded prominences are present on its internal surface	Tough projections arranged in corkscrew fashion similar to spiral twisting of tip of boar's penis; ridges best developed in middle of cervical canal and are distally continuous with 2 longitudinal vaginal folds	No clear demarcation	28, 133
Rabbit (*Oryctolagus cuniculus*)	Two fully separated cervical canals possessing internal and external ora; high columnar epithelium without any glands continue beyond external os into uppermost vagina; vaginal portions of cervical segments surrounded by complete ring of fornices	Extensively folded mucous membrane	Continuous	28, 31

TABLE 1.—*Continued*

Species	Anatomic Characteristics	Mucosal Folds	Transition to Vaginal Epithelium	Ref.
Rat (*Rattus norvegicus*)	Two separate cervical canals, 3–5 mm in length; cervical segment projects only slightly into vagina; unlike that of mouse, fornix is very shallow		Two segments—lower one similar to the vagina and upper one transitional between lower cervix and uterus	52
Sheep (*Ovis aries*)	Cervix much narrower than uterus and vagina; mucous membrane lined by single-layered, high columnar and frequently ciliated epithelium	Mucous membrane is less folded than in cow and mare; conical ridges fit accurately into each other and close off cervix		28

From El-Banna (30).

CERVICAL SECRETION

Cervical mucus is a complex secretion produced constantly by the secretory cells of the endocervix. A small amount of endometrial, tubal, and possibly follicular fluids may also contribute to the cervical mucous pool. In addition to these, cellular debris from uterine and cervical epithelia and leukocytes is also present. About 100 mucous-secreting glandular units in the cervical canal (110) produce mucus at the rate of 20–60 mg/day in normal women of reproductive age. During midcycle the amount increases tenfold and may reach up to 700 mg/day (118). Cyclic variation in the amount, physical properties, and chemical content of the cervical mucus in other species has also been described and is discussed in more detail below (Fig. 2).

Physical Properties of Cervical Mucus

Cervical mucus is a heterogeneous secretion with a number of rheological properties, including viscosity, flow elasticity, spinnbarkeit, thixotropy, and tack or stickiness (7, 20).

VISCOSITY. Since cervical mucus is not a true fluid or a homogeneous substance, its viscosity cannot be measured with any degree of accuracy. Anomalous viscous behavior is the general term applied to secretions such as cervical mucus.

FLOW ELASTICITY. The property of cervical mucus whereby it resumes its original shape after deformation caused by external pressure or stress is referred to as flow elasticity or retraction. When a material showing flow elasticity is caused to flow along a tube and the pressure is suddenly released, the material recoils to regain its original position.

SPINNBARKEIT. The capacity of liquids to be drawn into threads is known as spinnbarkeit (fibrosity). A sample of mucus is stretched between a glass slide and a cover slip. An estimate of spinnbarkeit is made by measuring the length (in centimeters) of the thread before it breaks (Fig. 3).

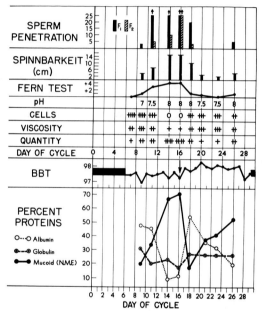

FIG. 2. Correlation of basal body temperature (*BBT*) with changes of cervical mucous properties. F_1 and F_2, number of spermatozoa in the first and second microscopic fields ($\times$ 200), respectively, from interface 15 min after the start of in vitro sperm-cervical mucous penetration test. *Arrow*, probable time of ovulation. Note that maximal sperm penetration coincides with increase in spinnbarkeit, ferning, pH, and mucin content and decrease in viscosity, cellularity, and albumin concentration of the mucus. *N.M.F.*, nonmigrating fraction. [From Moghissi & Neuhaus (101).]

PLASTICITY. Plasticity allows a material to be deformed continuously and permanently without rupture. It is observed predominantly in pregnancy.

TACK. Tack refers to the stickiness of the mucus and is measured by quickly drawing away a cover slip from a sample of mucus on a slide. The mucus does not form long threads but adheres to the cover slip and can be drawn only 1–2 cm away from the glass slide (Fig. 4). All samples of cervical mucus exhibit such stickiness, but only during pregnancy does mucus show this property to a marked degree.

FIG. 3. Technique for determining spinnbarkeit (fibrosity) of cervical mucus.

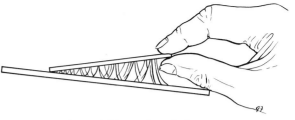

FIG. 4. Tack or stickiness of cervical mucus.

Rheological properties of cervical mucus are known to change during the menstrual or estrous cycle. From the termination of menstruation to the time of ovulation, viscosity and flow elasticity progressively decrease and spinnbarkeit increases. After ovulation and during the luteal phase, spinnbarkeit decreases and flow elasticity and viscosity markedly increase (see Fig. 2). In cattle the decrease in viscosity and increase in flow elasticity are encountered during estrus and are reversed in diestrus (7, 20, 30, 95).

The specific density of cervical mucus is probably close to that of an 0.8 % saline solution of the same temperature (109). The osmotic pressure of cervical mucus remains unchanged during the menstrual cycle. The optical transparency of cervical mucus is high at ovulation and low premenstrually and postmenstrually, when diffuse light scattering is considerably increased. The index of refraction is about 1.336 at midcycle and 1.338–1.346 at other phases of the menstrual cycle (109). Static samples of cervical mucus do not exhibit birefringence.

Such physical properties of cervical mucus as spinnbarkeit, viscosity, and flow elasticity are of clinical value in *a*) determining the time of ovulation; *b*) determining the optimal time for induction of ovulation; *c*) determining the optimal time for artificial insemination; *d*) recognizing anovulation; *e*) diagnosing pregnancy; or *f*) diagnosing ovarian dysfunction (22, 57, 95, 99).

FERNING. Papanicolaou (113) was first to discover that cervical mucus, when spread on a slide and allowed to dry, exhibits an intriguing pattern of arborization with crystallization (Fig. 5). He also observed the relationship between crystallization and estrogen activity and between changes in other properties of the mucus. This phenomenon, also termed *ferning* or *fern test*, occurs particularly at the time of ovulation and has been used extensively for detecting ovulation and as an index of circulating estrogen level in clinical medicine. Crystallization of cervical mucus has also been observed in cattle, sheep, goat, pig, horse, dog, and rabbit and in the primates (26, 30). Ferning results when true crystals of

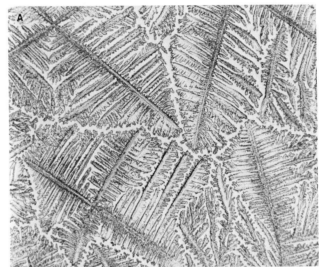

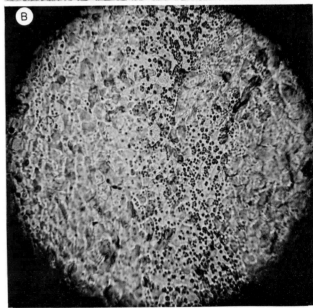

FIG. 5. Ferning (crystallization) of cervical mucus. *A*: marked ferning; × 60 *B*: absence of ferning; × 80.

sodium and potassium chloride form around a small and optimal amount (1–1.5 %) of organic matter (77, 161). Arborization with crystal formation is not specific for cervical mucus and may occur in any protein or colloid solution that contains electrolytes. If the protein content is too high (4–6 %), as seen in mucus during pregnancy, ferning does not occur. Other epithelial secretions and

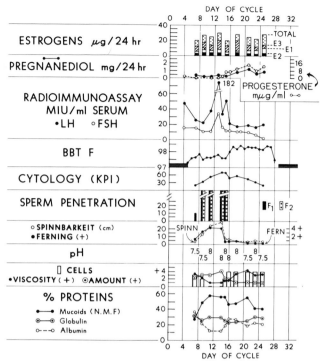

FIG. 6. Correlation of urinary estrogen excretion, urinary pregnanediol, serum gonadotrophins (*FSH* and *LH*), serum progesterone, basal body temperature (*BBT*), karyopiknotic index (*KPI*) of vaginal cytology with cervical mucous properties during a menstrual cycle in a normal woman. F_1 and F_2, number of spermatozoa in the first and second microscopic fields ($\times$ 200), respectively, from interface 5 min after the start of in vitro sperm-cervical mucous penetration test. Note optimal changes of the mucus described in Fig. 2 immediately after the surge of LH and the rise of estrogens.

biological fluids—nasal mucus, amniotic fluid, follicular fluid, and cerebrospinal fluid—exhibit the same phenomenon (161).

Ferning appears between days 8 and 10 of a typical cycle in women and reaches its peak at the time of ovulation. Immediately after ovulation it decreases or disappears completely (95, 161). Serial evaluations of ferning correlated with basal body temperature, vaginal cytology, estrogen and progesterone excretion, midcycle rise of luteinizing hormone (LH) and follicle-stimulating hormone (FSH), and other properties of cervical mucus indicate a high degree of accuracy by the crystallization pattern in predicting the peak of estrogenic activity and the onset of ovulation (Fig. 6).

Postovulatory mucus and mucus during pregnancy do not crystallize (13, 95). In cattle (3) and sheep the peak of arborization occurs at the onset of estrus. In the pig this phenomenon is observed most frequently 2 days before estrus (30). In the primate maximal ferning coincides with ovulation time and disappears during the luteal phase (26).

Biochemical Properties of Cervical Mucus

Because of relative ease of collection and the larger amounts available, human and bovine cervical mucus

have been studied extensively and is used as a model in this discussion. Knowledge of the chemical content of mucus of other species is scanty. Human cervical mucus contains usually about 92–94 % water. At ovulation, when the mucus is most abundant, the water content rises to 98 % (117). Bovine mucus contains 98.6 % water during estrus, and at other times the water content varies between 92 and 96 % (29). Human and bovine estrous cervical secretions contain 1 % inorganic salts of which the principal constituent is NaCl (0.7 %). Traces of K, Mg, Ca, Cu, phosphates, sulfates, and bicarbonate are also present (45, 46, 156). The mucus is isotonic with saline throughout the cycle. The salt content of dry mucus, however, shows an increase coinciding with the time of ovulation. Since the concentration of salt remains constant while the gross amount changes cyclically, the water content of the mucus must change in the same proportion as the salt to maintain a constant concentration. In other words, there is relative increase in the secretion of water and salt and a decrease in the amount of organic material in the dry weight of the midcycle mucus, which incidentally favors the occurrence of the ferning phenomenon. In bovine cervical mucus, calcium concentration is high near estrus; the potassium content increases during the luteal phase (112). The osmotic pressure of cervical mucus remains the same throughout the cycle. Ascorbic acid has been detected in cervical mucus and is lowest in concentration at midcycle (66).

LOW-MOLECULAR-WEIGHT ORGANIC COMPOUNDS. Human cervical mucus contains the free simple sugars (glucose, maltose, mannose) and other reducing substances (11, 118). The free sugars decrease during the ovulatory period. Glucose, however, increases in the mucus at midcycle, and its detection at this time forms the basis of a test for predicting ovulation (14). The possible role of reducing substances in sperm nutrition is considered later. Glucose has not been detected in any appreciable amount in the cervical secretion of cows and sheep during the ovulatory period.

The lipid content of human cervical mucus has been investigated, as shown in Table 2. Serial determination of lipids has revealed a decrease in the amount of total lipids, cholesterol, and lipid phosphorous at midcycle, whereas the ratio of cholesterol to lipids remains the same. It is believed that cyclic changes in the concentration of these lipids is not the result of an active process under hormonal control but simply a passive one depending in part perhaps on cell content of the mucus (12).

The biological function of the lipids in human cervical

TABLE 2. *Lipids of Human Cervical Mucus*

Constituent	Dry Weight	Wet Weight
Total lipids, mg/100 g	2,900	82
Cholesterol, mg/100 g	470	13
Lipid phosphorus, mg/100 g	33	0.91
Cholesterol:lipid phosphorus	14:1	14:1

From Breckenridge & Pommerenke (12).

mucus has not been determined. A lipid fraction isolated from egg yolk, however, has been shown to have a protective function for bull spermatozoa subjected to temperature shock.

Free α-amino acids have been detected in human and bovine cervical secretions. These include glutamic acid, taurine, alanine, glycine, valine, leucine, glutamine, serine, methionine, lysine, arginine, and aspartic acid. Asparagine, histidine, cysteine, threonine, and tyrosine have been found in occasional samples. A decrease in the concentration of the various amino acids is noted during the midcycle phase. This may be a reflection of aqueous dilution of the mucus at this period (115). Urea has been found also in bovine cervical mucus (46).

HIGH-MOLECULAR-WEIGHT COMPONENTS. Ultracentrifugation of the mucus results in two fractions: the supernatant, which contains the soluble macromolecules (polysaccharides, enzymes, and serum-type proteins), and the sediment (gel), which consists mainly of high-molecular-weight glycoproteins (mucins).

Glycogen is the principle polysaccharide of cervical secretion. Amylase, an enzyme capable of reducing glycogen to utilizable glucose, has been found in the mucus.

Enzymes. In Table 3 the enzymes found in human cervical secretion are listed. Alkaline phosphatase [K. Moghissi and F. Syner, unpublished data; (135)], esterase, and amino peptidase (K. Moghissi and F. Syner, unpublished data) show a marked postovulatory rise and seem to reflect a luteal effect. Amylase (134) and muramidase (lysozyme) activity (128) decrease at midcycle and increase after ovulation. Among the fibrinolytic enzyme systems, only stabile tissue activator has been shown to undergo cyclic changes. Plasminogen is present in minute amount (1/5,000 of the amount found in normal plasma), and plasmin is found only in occasional samples (5). Alkaline phosphatase is the only enzyme thus far detected in uncontaminated bovine mucus. This enzyme appears in bovine cervical mucus 48 hr before ovulation, increases to a peak at the time of ovulation, and then decreases (44, 45).

Proteins. Pooled human cervical mucus contains about 1–3 % (102, 131, 136) and bovine mucus 0.5–4.6 % (30)

TABLE 3. *Enzymes of Human Cervical Mucus*

Enzyme	Cyclic Variation
Alkaline phosphatase	Increased after ovulation
Esterase	Increased after ovulation
Amino peptidase	Increased after ovulation
Amylase	Activity lowest at midcycle
Muramidase (lysozyme)	Activity lowest at midcycle
Fibrinolytic enzyme system	
Stabile tissue activator	Activity lowest at midcycle
Proactivator	
Plasminogen	
Plasmin*	

* Seen only occasionally.

TABLE 4. *Proteins of Human Cervical Mucus*

Protein	Midcycle Change
Albumin group	
Prealbumin	Decrease
Albumin	Decrease
α_1-Globulins	
α_1-Lipoprotein	
α_1-Orosomucoid	
α_1-Antitrypsin	Decrease
α_2-Globulins	
α_2-Haptoglobin	
α_2-Ceruloplasmin	
α_2-Lipoprotein	
β-Globulins	
Transferrin	Decrease
β_1C	
β_1C/β, A globulin	
β_1-Hemopexin	
γ-Globulins	
IgG, γ	Decrease
IgA, β_2A	Decrease
IgA Secretory	
IgM*	
Lactoferrin	

* Seen only in trace amounts in occasional samples.

protein in two basic forms, soluble proteins and glycoproteins.

a) Soluble proteins. The first group comprises 55 % of the total proteins and resembles serum proteins; albumin and γ-globulin (IgG) are the major components. By immunodiffusion and immunoelectrophoretic studies of human cervical mucus, 15 additional proteins (58, 62, 86, 101–104, 126, 129), including lactoferrin (86), secretory IgA (62), and α₁-antitrypsin have been identified [(127); Table 4]. In the bovine mucus at estrus, albumin, α₁-antitrypsin, transferrin, and IgG have been identified (97). Cyclic variation in the amount of a number of proteins in cervical mucus has been described. In general, there appears to be a preovulatory decrease and a postovulatory increase in the amount of albumin, α₁-antitrypsin and immunoglobulins (101, 126, 127).

The majority of serum proteins in the cervical mucus probably originate from blood serum (100). Intravenous administration of ¹³¹I-labeled serum albumin in women is followed by the appearance of radioactivity in the cervical secretion within 2 min. Within 1 hr the concentration of the isotope in the mucus surpasses that in the serum by several times. This indicates that the cervical epithelia concentrate and actively secrete certain materials in the mucus. Von Kaulla et al. (65), found that the ability of the cervical epithelia to concentrate ¹³¹I was impaired in some infertile patients and that pilocarpine altered the dynamics of ¹³¹I secretion. After their administration by intravenous injections, ³⁵SCN and ¹³¹I-labeled L-thyroxin have also been detected in the mucus (65).

Such soluble proteins as secretory IgA and lactoferrin are obviously synthesized by cervical epithelium since they are absent in the blood.

b) Glycoproteins. The second type of protein (45 %) in

the cervical mucus is a hydrogel rich in carbohydrates and consisting of at least two electrophoretically defined glycoproteins of the mucin type (104). Most of the physical properties of cervical mucus are due to these mucins. Variation in the structure and viscosity of macromolecules with a molecular weight of over 10^6 is responsible for periodic receptivity and inhibition of sperm penetration. For many years a controversy existed as to the chemical identity of this constituent of cervical mucus, which was variously described as a neutral mucopolysaccharide, an acid mucopolysaccharide, and a glycoprotein.

Cervical mucus does not contain hyaluronic acid (106, 131, 156). The uptake of ^{35}S-labeled sulfate by cervical glands of the guinea pig, rabbit, and man has led to the belief that cervical mucus contains a sulfated acid mucopolysaccharide, possibly a keratosulfate (157). However, the labeled sulfate is probably attached only to epithelial glycoprotein and not secreted in mucus, or it is contained in taurine, a free amino acid, which is found in large amounts in both human and bovine mucus [S. Doehr and K. S. Moghissi, unpublished data; (115)].

Shettles (131) found a 1:2 ratio for galactose and hexosamine in human cervical mucus and consequently suggested the presence of a heteropolysaccharide composed of repeating disaccharide units (galactose plus hexosamine) combined with some fucose-containing components. Werner (155, 156) suggested that cervical mucus contains a glycoprotein of the fucose (fucomucin) and sialic acid (sialomucin) types. Substantial evidence indicates that the mucins of cervical mucus conform to the common structural pattern that has evolved for epithelial glycoproteins.

Enzymatic studies and comparison of the biochemical properties of cervical mucus with saliva, purified salivary mucin, orosomucoid, synovial fluid, and chondroitin sulfate have also confirmed that the carbohydrate component of human cervical mucus is a glycoprotein or a mucin and not a mucopolysaccharide (106).

Such proteolytic enzymes as trypsin and chymotrypsin have been found to hydrolyze readily human, as well as bovine, cervical mucus and mucins and to produce certain physical and chemical changes (103, 105).

Gibbons and his associate (43, 47), in a series of studies on human and bovine cervical mucus, found that in either case this secretion contained a mucin (by definition, a carbohydrate-rich glycoprotein) consisting of 75–80% carbohydrate and 20–25% amino acid residue. The carbohydrate portion contained fucose, galactose, glucosamine, and galactosamine. The sialic acid content of the bovine estrous mucin was higher (14%) than that of human mucin (9%). Furthermore human mucin contained predominantly N-acetylneuraminic acid, whereas the sialic acid of bovine material was of the N-glycolyl type (Table 5). Gibbons' findings indicate that the gel phase of the mucus consists of two primary components: 1) an epithelial glycoprotein; and 2) a protein.

The epithelial glycoprotein is the major fraction and is

TABLE 5. *Composition of Human and Bovine Epithelial Glycoprotein Isolated From Cervical Mucus*

Constituent	Human Midcycle Mucus	Bovine Mucus	
		Estrus	Pregnancy
N*, %	6.11	6.11	5.95
Hexosamine, % as base	20.0	25.80	25.9
Galactose, %	27.0	32.00	32.80
Fucose, %	11.0	3.20	2.80
Sialic acid**			
N-acetyl, %	8.8	0.5	0.5
N-glycolyl, %	0.5	14.00	19.00

* Kjeldahl method.   ** Direct Ehrlich's reaction. [From Gibbons (43) and Gibbons & Roberts (47).]

composed of a polypeptide backbone with a characteristic amino acid residue very rich in serine, threonine, and proline. A large number of heterosaccharide side chains consisting principally of N-acetylglucosamine and galactose linked $1 \rightarrow 3$ or $1 \rightarrow 4$ are attached to the polypeptide chain via N-acetylgalactosaminyl-O-seryl or O-threonyl glycosidic bonds (Fig. 7). This linkage is responsible for the characteristic alkali lability of this class of compounds. Additionally the fucose and neuraminic acid are linked as nonreducing side branches to hexosamine-galactose chains, which may terminate in a sugar residue or sequence with blood-group specific reactivity. The entire heterosaccharide side chains may contain as many as 16 sugars. This information relates only to the primary structure. Secondary, tertiary, and quaternary structures have been difficult to establish because the physical properties of the mucus change in response to hormonal influence throughout the menstrual cycle in the human and in the bovine estrous cycle. However, flow-birefringence studies indicate that the glycoprotein fraction of cervical mucus is a random coil polymer.

According to Gibbons, the preparation of this glycoprotein does not consist of a collection of molecules that are identical replicates. The size, arrangement, and molecular weight of heterosaccharide side chains vary. There is not therefore only one glycoprotein, but in theory a large number of different glycoproteins exist, even though chemically all are of the same type. The properties of such substances therefore represent the statistical average of all molecules in the preparation which may vary continuously. This phenomenon is known as polydispersity.

The second component of the mucin is a protein (or proteins) that has been isolated from the purified mucous gel. It comprises less than 15% of the mucin fraction and may be important rheologically. The viscoelastic quality of the mucin suggests that this may be a cross-linking protein in a flexible, threadlike structure.

A recent investigation (S. Doehr & K. S. Moghissi, unpublished data) strongly suggests that disulfide bonds are responsible for interchain linkages. Reduction of these bonds results in a decrease in the sedimentation

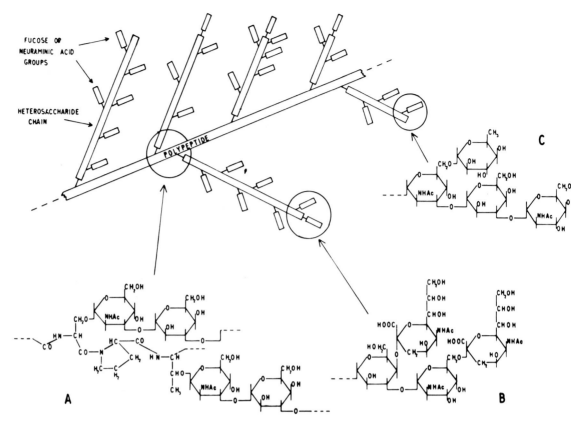

FIG. 7. Probable structure of epithelial glycoproteins, such as those present in cervical mucus. Note polypeptide chain with heterosaccharide side chains containing glucosamine, galactosamine (as N-acetyl), neuraminic acid (as N-acetyl or N-glycolyl), galactose, and fucose. [From Gibbons & Mattner (46).]

velocity to almost one-half that of the mucin in its natural state.

The strongest evidence in support of a cross-linking protein is based on studies in which proteolytic enzymes destroyed the rheological properties of the mucus but had little effect in breaking the glycoprotein into smaller residues. Such a minor protein fraction may possibly be associated with the glycoprotein through secondary forces, such as hydrogen bonding.

Both types of bonds, the covalent-disulfide linkages, as well as hydrogen bonding, no doubt function in forming the complex meshwork that can exist in an almost liquid state, at one extreme of the cycle at the time of ovulation or estrus, or as a very rubbery elastic gel during pregnancy.

pH of cervical mucus. In assessing the pH of cervical mucus it is important to distinguish between the values obtained from the vaginal pool and those obtained from the external cervical os and endocervix. The pH gradient increases toward the cervical canal; this is due to the acidity of vaginal secretions that partially contaminate cervical mucus discharged in the vagina. Bovine and human endocervical secretions are generally alkaline during the entire estrous or menstrual cycles (45, 78, 95). The range of pH reported is between 6.5 and 9. Serial determinations have revealed an increase in alkalinity at midcycle in man (see Figs. 2 and 6) and during estrus in

the cow. Human midcycle mucus has a pH range of 7–8.5. The pH of bovine estrous mucus varies between 7 and 9. The optimal pH for sperm penetration is also in the range of 7–9.

Antibacterial Activity and Bacteriology of Cervical Mucus

Cervical mucus has bacteriostatic and bactericidal properties against certain strains of bacteria. Pommerenke (118) found that the mucus had bacteriostatic qualities against staphylococci and *Streptococcus hemolyticus* (*S. pyogenes*) but enhanced the growth of certain strains of *Neisseria gonorrhoeae* in vitro. In a more recent study, Rozansky et al. (122) did not substantiate these findings but detected muramidase (lysozyme) activity in cervical secretion. Muramidase is an enzyme capable of hydrolyzing the structurally important beta 1–4 linkage between N-acetylmuramic acid and N-acetylglucosamine in the cell walls of certain bacteria. Serial determinations of muramidase show a marked decrease coinciding with the time of ovulation and a postovulatory increase (128). Bactericidal activity of the human cervical mucus is present during all phases of the menstrual cycle but is least pronounced at the time of ovulation (33).

Normal cervical mucus has been found to be sterile in one-third of the women examined. The remaining two-thirds showed rather scanty flora—lactobacilli, diphtheroids, coagulase-negative staphylococci, nonhemolytic streptococci, *Escherichia coli*, and yeasts were the most important organisms (136).

Chronic cervicitis has been incriminated as a factor contributing to infertility in women. Certain bacteria, such as *E. coli*, α-hemolytic streptococci (*S. viridans*), *Streptococci pyogenes* (*S. hemolyticus*), *Aerobacter*, and others have been found to have spermicidal properties in vitro. The bacteria most commonly cultured from the cervices of women with chronic cervicitis have been reported to include *Staphylococcus aureus*, *Aerobacter aerogenes*, *Enterococcus faecalis*, *Streptococcus viridans*, *E. coli*, and *Proteus vulgaris*. The spermicidal action of these bacteria does not appear to be an absolute deterrent to sperm transport and fertility, since conception can and does occur frequently in women who have chronic cervicitis. However, in his study of 350 infertile patients, Sobrero (136) found that treatment of chronic cervicitis significantly increased subsequent chance of the women to conceive.

Cyclic Changes of Cervical Mucus and Tests for Ovulation Detection

The secretion of cervical mucus in all species investigated is regulated by ovarian hormones. Estrogen stimulates the production of copious amounts of watery mucus, and progesterone inhibits the secretory activity of cervical epithelia (21, 57, 95, 99, 118). The physical properties and certain chemical constituents of cervical mucus show cyclic variations, and their determination may be used to evaluate indirectly the amount of circulating sex hormones, such evaluation would aid in detecting the time of ovulation or estrus. In Figures 2 and 6 serial determinations of some important properties of human cervical mucus during a normal menstrual cycle are shown. Correlation of cyclic changes in these properties with pituitary and ovarian hormone excretion demonstrates conclusively that the optimal changes in such properties of cervical mucus as greatest increase in quantity, spinnbarkeit, ferning, and pH and decrease in viscosity and cell content occur immediately before ovulation and are reversed after ovulation. Preovulatory mucus is most receptive to sperm penetration.

Knowledge of the physical changes of the mucus has been applied extensively in clinical medicine to determine the time of ovulation. Among other alterations, the preovulatory decrease of albumin and α₁-antitrypsin (127) and the relative increase in the mucins (95, 101) determined by electrophoretic or immunological methods and the increase of sodium chloride content, as utilized in the "paper spot" test (93), are worthy of mention. In women increasing levels of urinary estrogen at midcycle are associated with a decreasing content of sialic acid in the cervical mucus until a minimal value is reached about one day before presumptive ovulation (17). The decrease of sialic acid in cervical mucus as a result of increased circulating estrogen has further been demonstrated by the administration of FSH, which leads to a rise in endogenous estrogen and a decrease in sialic acid content of the mucus (16). Examination of the physical and chemical properties of cervical mucus in relation to ovarian hormone function has revealed that estrogens bring about a decrease in the specific weight of the mucus to below 1.008. In contrast, progesterone increases the specific weight of the mucus to a value greater than or equal to 1.008. A new form of pregnancy diagnosis in cattle has been based on these findings and is apparently in wide use in the USSR (49).

Cervical Mucus in Pregnancy

During pregnancy, cervical secretions form a highly viscous, thick, and turbid gel that occludes the cervical canal. This mucus plug acts as an effective barrier against spermatozoal and bacterial invasion of the uterine cavity. It has an alkaline pH between 7 and 9.6 and does not crystallize when dried on a microscope slide. Indeed, the crystallization of cervical mucus during pregnancy suggests a luteal deficiency and a need for the administration of progesterone to support the gestation. During pregnancy, mucus is highly elastic and presents a great degree of plasticity and tack; it has little or no spinnbarkeit and is very cellular.

The chemical properties of gestational mucus are also different from the mucus of nonpregnant females. During pregnancy, bovine mucus contains more sialic acid and less water than estrous mucus. Water content of human mucus during pregnancy varies between 64 and 89%. Proteins are also found in larger amounts in cervical mucus of pregnant women and range from 1 to 22%, with a mean of 6.5%; 15.6% of total proteins is albumin, 33% is globulin, and 50.6% is mucin (K. Moghissi and R. Selik, unpublished data). Immunoelectrophoretic studies of human cervical secretion during pregnancy have revealed protein patterns similar to those of nonpregnancy mucus—albumin and γ-globulin are present in most samples, and α₁-, α₂-, and β-globulins are found occasionally. Trnka et al. (148) found albumin and γ-globulin in higher concentrations and with increasing frequency in the mucus collected in early (6–10 weeks) and late (38–40 weeks) gestation.

FUNCTION OF THE CERVIX IN SPERM TRANSPORT

Marion Sims (132) in 1866 defined the role of the cervix in reproduction: "If I were asked what next to mere mechanical obstruction of the cervix uteri constitutes the greatest obstacle to conception, I would have no hesitation in saying that it was an abnormal secretion from the cervix." Numerous studies since this original observation have emphasized the importance of the uterine cervix in reproduction.

During coitus, millions of spermatozoa are usually deposited in the vagina. The actual number of spermatozoa in an ejaculate varies in different species and ranges from 200–500 million in man to 3 billion in the ram and 8 billion in the bull.

The posterior vaginal fornix forms a natural repository for the semen ejaculate. In certain rodents (mouse, rat, guinea pig) and in the rhesus monkey and chimpanzee, the ejaculated semen coagulates instantly. Human semen coagulates to a lesser extent, but many sperm cells are nonetheless trapped until seminal fibrinolytic enzymes cause liquefaction. The first portion of the ejaculate, however, contains the highest concentration of spermatozoa (3/4 in man), which quite promptly penetrate the cervical secretion (82).

Migration of Sperm Through the Cervix

In women the vaginal fluid is usually acid with a pH of about 3–4. Cervical secretions, however, provide a favorable medium for spermatozoa and appear to promote their motility and longevity.

Migration of spermatozoa through the cervix depends on their motility and density and on the composition and physical properties of cervical secretions.

Sperm penetrability of human cervical mucus begins on about day 9 of a normal cycle and increases gradually to a peak at ovulation (see Figs. 2 and 6). It is usually inhibited within 1 or 2 days after ovulation but may persist to a lesser degree for a longer period (94, 135, 138). In some women, sperm penetrability occurs only during a limited period of the menstrual cycle. Individual variations are common (95).

In cattle and sheep, sperm penetration occurs only during estrus. During pregnancy the mucus forms a formidable barrier to sperm migration (13).

IN VITRO STUDIES. In vitro sperm penetration of cervical mucus has been investigated by two different techniques: *1*) the slide method; and *2*) the capillary tube method. A good correlation has been found between results obtained by these techniques (69).

When studied in vitro (98) by the slide method, a sharp boundary separating human or bovine cervical mucus placed in juxtaposition to semen on the microscope slide is observed. At the interface, fingerlike projections or phalanges of seminal fluid develop within a few minutes and penetrate the mucus (Figs. 8–11). Sperm usually fill these canals before entering the mucus. Most sperm cells penetrate the apex of the phalangeal canal and enter the mucus. Once in the cervical mucus, spermatozoa fan out and move at random. Some return to the seminal plasma layer, but most migrate deep into the cervical mucus until they meet with resistance from cellular debris or leukocytes. They then either stop or change direction. The formation of the phalanx and interface appears to be a physical phenomenon resulting from the contact of two fluids differing in viscosity and surface tension. This formation is observed more prominently in samples obtained at the premenstrual or postmenstrual period.

Phalanges increase the surface area between seminal fluid and cervical mucus and trap small pockets of semen within the mucus, which protects a number of spermatozoa from the hostile environment of the vagina. This phenomenon may account for the passage of inert parti-

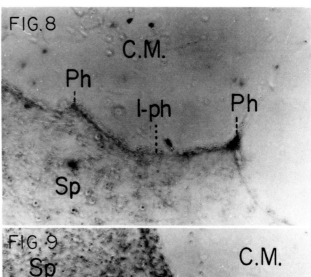

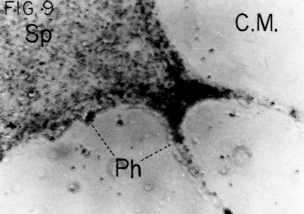

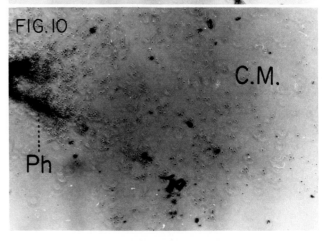

FIG. 8. In vitro cervical mucus-sperm penetration study. Typical early phalanx (*Ph*) and interface (*I-ph*) formation. *Sp*, sperm; *C.M.*, human cervical mucus. [From Moghissi et al. (98).]

FIG. 9. In vitro cervical mucus-sperm penetration study; more advanced stage of phalanx formation. Note presence of numerous spermatozoa in larger phalanges and a few within cervical mucus. Abbreviations as in Fig. 8. [From Moghissi et al. (98).]

FIG. 10. In vitro cervical mucus-sperm penetration study. Spermatozoa fanning out from the apex of phalanges and invading cervical mucus. Abbreviations as in Fig. 8. [From Moghissi et al. (98).]

cles through cervical mucus, as reported by Egli & Newton (29). Phalanx formation therefore appears to facilitate sperm migration.

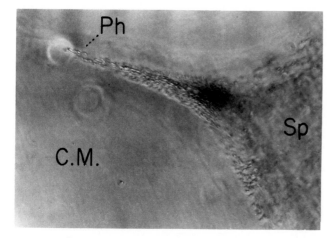

FIG. 11. In vitro sperm penetration in bovine estrous mucus (*C.M.*). Distinct phalanx (*Ph*) filled with sperm (*Sp*) is shown. [From Moghissi et al. (98).]

TABLE 6. *Human Sperm Progression in Various Media*

Medium*	Velocity, mm/min	Ref.
Normal saline	2.88	56
Ringer's solution	0.18	10
Ringer's glucose solution	0.54	10
Ringer's fructose solution	0.67	10
Ringer's galactose solution	0.27	10
Blood serum	1.7	10
Blood serum	1.1	69

* 37 C.

Cleanliness of mucus appears to be a factor favoring sperm migration. Thus cellular debris and leukocytes halt the progress of spermatozoa in mucus (98). There is no resistance to sperm migration in thin mucus, but viscous mucus forms an impenetrable barrier. Cervical mucus diluted artificially with normal saline or 5% dextrose is more readily penetrated by sperm than is undiluted mucus (98).

A decrease in the motility of bull, ram, and rabbit sperm at dilutions beyond 10^6 cells/ml in normal saline has been observed (145). In contrast, spermatozoa in cervical mucus withstand indefinite dilution. Carlborg (15) showed that in man dilution of sperm samples of good motility to 1 million/ml did not affect the rate of sperm migration in the mucus. The depression of motility at low concentration of cells appears to be due to dilution of seminal plasma and to loss of substances from the spermatozoa. Cervical mucus, like seminal plasma, appears to have a protective effect on the spermatozoa and presumably acts by preventing the escape of intracellular constituents or surface components. Spermatozoa are quite resistant to the effect of dilution in washed mucous gel freed of soluble components. However, after rheological properties of mucus are destroyed, a marked dilution effect occurs when spermatozoa are suspended in the medium (145). According to Tampion & Gibbons (145), the physical properties of glycoproteins in the mucus are the effective factors that protect sperm cells. When spermatozoa emerge from the cervical secretion, they are susceptible to the lethal effects of dilution. It appears therefore that mucins of cervical mucus, much like the glycoproteins coating the epithelial covering of the digestive and respiratory tracts, protect spermatozoa against loss of intracellular or surface components.

Spermatozoa from various species readily penetrate a number of physiological solutions and blood serum (Table 6). However, with the exception of blood serum and normal saline, the rate of progression of human sperm in these media is less than that in cervical mucus. Bull spermatozoa, in contrast, swim more slowly in cervi-

cal mucus of the cow than any other medium tested (145). Sperm cells perish instantly in distilled water (97).

The extent and depth of sperm penetration in cervical mucus bears a direct relationship to sperm density and motility. Higher sperm density and greater motility are associated with more massive penetration into the mucus (69). Dead or immotile spermatozoa do not penetrate cervical mucus. Preservation of semen by freezing also reduces the ability of spermatozoa to penetrate cervical mucus. However, when liquid nitrogen is used for storage, this reduction is limited to a degree that might still be compatible with fertility, even for storage periods approaching 3 years (38).

IN VIVO STUDIES. Most in vivo experiments in man are confined to postcoital tests and uterine aspirations and confirm in vitro findings. The significance of spermatozoa found in cervical secretions several hours after intercourse remains controversial. Some investigators have suggested that they consist mainly of sperm populations of poor quality that failed to complete their passage to the uterus. Grant (50) correlated the results of postcoital tests and endometrial aspirations in 920 women and found that motile spermatozoa were present in the uterus in 10% of the women, although they could not be demonstrated in cervical mucus. Recent evidence, however, strongly suggests that the cervical mucus functions as a reservoir in which spermatozoa are stored and thence are released slowly but continuously into the uterus for many hours after coitus (89–91). The postcoital test may provide valuable information on sperm migration and survival. Sims (132) in 1866 and Cary (19) in 1930 observed rapid postcoital penetration of sperm in cervical mucus. Sobreo & MacLeod (138) performed immediate postcoital tests in 47 couples. In 18 women, liquefaction of the semen took place in the vagina while the patient was being examined about 5 min after ejaculation. On 44 occasions, specimens were obtained both from the cervical os and from the cervical canal while the semen was still coagulated in the vaginal pool. In 39 instances, motile spermatozoa were seen in both cervical mucus specimens 1.5–3 min after ejaculation. Serial postcoital tests have shown that preovulatory improvement of cervical mucus coincides with the increased number of motile spermatozoa observed in mucus samples (140). After ovulation the quality of mucus deteriorates and only a few, if any, live sperm cells are found in the mucus

(140). Combined postcoital tests and endometrial aspirations have demonstrated that the greatest numbers of spermatozoa in the endometrial cavity are found at or near ovulation. Very few were present in the uterus during the luteal or early follicular phase of the cycle (41).

It has been suggested that during coitus the muscular activity of the uterus or respiratory efforts cause a drawing-in of semen and thus aid sperm migration (6). Krehbiel & Carstens (68) and Akester & Inkster (2) reported that the injection of radio-opaque media into the vagina of the rabbit followed by digital stimulation of the vulva during fluoroscopic examination revealed strong vaginal contractions forcing the opaque media through the cervix and uterus to the uterotubal junction. Belonoschkin (6) similarly described an inward-outward movement of the mucous column in the human cervical canal. Monitoring of intravaginal and intrauterine pressure changes during human coitus showed an increase in uterine pressure during female orgasm, which was followed by a sharp fall to a negative pressure after orgasm (40). On the basis of these and other similar data, it has been suggested that the sperm may be aspirated en mass into the uterus. A number of in vitro and in vivo studies have failed to confirm these observations (55, 87, 88, 96, 98, 137, 154). Noyes et al. (108) could not demonstrate the passage of radio-opaque oil in the reproductive tract of rabbits. Sobrero (137) was unable to observe any movement of glairy mucus emerging from the cervix in more than 100 women in the fertile period during forcible inhalation and exhalation. In another series of experiments, he fitted a group of women with a snug cervical cap containing water-soluble, opaque material and normal semen mixed with an opaque medium. Pelvic radiography before and after masturbation or coitus, or both, with and without female orgasm failed to show evidence of any radio-opaque material beyond the vagina.

Postcoital tests as early as 1.5–3 min after ejaculation have not shown any mixture of cervical mucus and semen or the presence of male urethral epithelial cells or vaginal epithelial cells in the mucus (137, 138). Furthermore distribution of the spermatozoa in the cervical mucus in these tests has been found to be uniform, and sperm cells are lower in concentration in the cervical secretion than in the vaginal pool; such findings indicate an orderly and uniform sperm penetration rather than en block insemination (138).

Masters (87) did not observe any displacement of the cervical plug during coitus, nor was he able to demonstrate the entry of radio-opaque fluid from a cervical cap into the uterus after coitus or clitoral stimulation. The only definitive response of the cervix to sexual stimulation, according to Masters and Johnson, is a minimal dilatation of the external os (88).

Although spermatozoa appear to move at random in the cervical secretion, they may move largely along strands of cervical mucus. Tampion & Gibbons (143, 145) suggested that bull spermatozoa travel in threads of

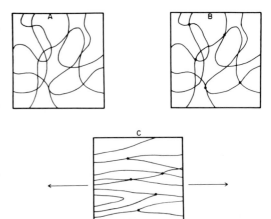

FIG. 12. Molecular anisotropy arising as a result of stress in a random cross-linked network of flexible threadlike molecules. The cross links are a combination of ionic and hydrogen bonds. They are persistent but probably not permanent. Such a structure will have all the rheological properties of mucus. Normally it will cohere (A and B). Under strain it will become anisotropic due to the extension of the threadlike molecules in the direction of strain (C). [From Gibbons & Mattner (45).]

bovine mucus; they follow the path of least resistance and are oriented along the line of strains, that is, parallel with the direction of elongation of the molecules. It is readily apparent that the shape of a sperm cell would favor its movement through mucus in this manner rather than by passing across the molecular network (Fig. 12). When forward progression of a spermatozoon in mucus is impeded, the sperm cell usually resumes its forward course with a sudden deflection onto a parallel path, as if it has broken obliquely through the laterally restraining glycoprotein strands. In vitro studies of human spermatozoa and cervical mucus confirmed this phenomenon (45, 97).

Mattner and his associate (89–91) have demonstrated that the spermatozoa in the cervices of ruminants after mating are not uniformly distributed within the lumen and tend to be aggregated at, or in, the vicinity of the mucosa. According to Mattner, under natural conditions the line of strain will originate at the mucus-secreting epithelium and pass through to the anterior portion of the vagina. On entering the mucus, spermatozoa are constrained to follow these pathways and thus pass to the mucosa of the cervix rather than penetrate directly into the uterus. Return of sperm along strain lines to the vagina is prevented by a series of intervening strain lines, each of which tends to reorient the sperm back toward the crypts (Fig. 13).

Such a process could cause aggregation of a large number of spermatozoa in the crypts and clefts of cervical mucosa where they are stored and released into the uterus at a constant rate. Thus spermatozoa are retained in the cervix, despite their continued flaggelation and despite the drainage of mucus from the cervix into the vagina. In support of this theory, Mattner (89, 90) has demonstrated that only motile spermatozoa accumulate in the crypts of the cervical canal, where additionally

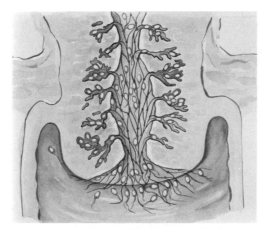

FIG. 13. Schematic representation of current concept of sperm transport through the cervix. Observe long mucous filaments, sperm penetration along the molecular line of strains, and aggregation of spermatozoa in the crypts and clefts of cervical canal.

they are protected from phagocytosis. Dead sperm cells, on the contrary, are confined to the central portion of the lumen and are eliminated from the cervix. Similarly, in the rabbit, higher numbers of sperm have been recovered from the cervix than from the uterotubal junction or oviduct at comparable times after artificial insemination (30). These data suggest that in this species, as in ruminants, the cervix, rather than the uterotubal junction, may act as a reservoir for sperm.

Rate of Sperm Migration and Energy Requirements

The rate of sperm progression in cervical mucus has been determined by several investigators with the capillary tube technique. The speed of sperm penetration into human mucus varies during the menstrual cycle from 0.1 to 3 mm/min (Table 7) and is greatest in preovulatory mucus (10, 69). The mean velocities of spermatozoa in bovine cervical mucus and in normal saline are, respectively, 6.48 and 9.78 mm/min (5 min at 37 C) (145).

Mammalian spermatozoa are highly active cells possessing the enzymes required to carry out the biochemical reactions of the Embden-Meyerhof pathway, tricarboxylic acid cycle, fatty acid oxidation, electron transport system, and perhaps the hexose-monophosphate shunt. Apparently the metabolic and glycolytic enzymes are located in the tail portion of the spermatozoon, and the respiratory enzymes are confined to the mitochondria.

Spermatozoa are capable of metabolizing a variety of exogenous and some endogenous substrates. Exogenous oxidizable substrates include such sugars as glucose, fructose, or mannose; glycerol and sorbitol; lactic, pyruvic, and acetic acids; and certain fatty acids and several amino acids (78–81, 92). Since spermatozoa possess only a negligible reserve of endogenous glycogen, they must depend on extracellular carbohydrates for energy requirements under anaerobic conditions and during their passage through the mucus. The utilization of hexoses by

TABLE 7. *Rate of Sperm Progression in Human Cervical Mucus*

Reference	Speed, mm/min
Botella-Llusia (10)	0.63
Kremer (69)	1.80 (1.0–2.8)
Lamar et al. (71)	0.1–3.0

sperm cells is carried out through the Embden-Meyerhof pathway and consists of breakdown of carbohydrates by glycolysis to pyruvic and lactic acids. In seminal plasma, fructose is the major carbohydrate and constitutes the chief source of nutrition for sperm. However, sperm can also metabolize glucose and mannose to lactic acid. Rabbit or bull sperm cannot utilize galactose, since they lack the enzyme, phosphogalactose uridyltransferase.

Seminal fluid contains about 300 mg/100 ml of reducing substances, expressed as glucose (92). The diminution of these reducing substances, when semen is allowed to stand, suggests their utilization by spermatozoa. Cervical mucus contains reducing substances throughout the cycle and at times in amounts comparable to those reported in semen. These reducing substances include glycogen, glucose, mannose, and maltose (153). Amylase, an enzyme capable of reducing glycogen to glucose, is also found in cervical mucus (118, 134).

In addition to the free reducing substances present in cervical mucus throughout the cycle as a result of hydrolysis, other carbohydrates (about one-half of which are fermentable by yeast) yield additional quantities of reducing substances (118, 153). When cervical mucus is allowed to stand for 24 hr at room temperature, the sugar content is reduced by about 12%. However, when spermatozoa washed with Ringer's solution are added to the mucus in quantities of 1 million/100 mg of solution, the resultant decrement in sugar content after standing a similar period of time is doubled (74). This finding suggests the destruction of sugar by enzymes and indicates that sugar serves a purpose useful to spermatozoal metabolism.

Bull spermatozoa (147) can oxidize three naturally occurring amino acids, L-tyrosine, L-phenylalanine, and L-tryptophan, and can oxidize other amino acids at a much slower rate. Similar oxidizing activity toward amino acids is also exhibited by spermatozoa of other species (ram and boar). Various amino acids, including L-phenylalanine, DL-alanine, L-proline, L-hydroxyproline, DL-threonine, L-arginine, and glycine have been shown to enhance or to prolong the respiration of washed boar sperm suspension (53). Human and bovine cervical secretions, as indicated previously, contain some of these amino acids that may be available to sperm cells.

Lipids and lipoproteins present in cervical mucus may also function in sperm respiration or act as protective colloids on the sperm cells (83).

Pommerenke & Viergiver (120) showed that washing human spermatozoa with Ringer's saline solution and resuspending them in the same medium does not di-

TABLE 8. *Sperm Penetration Studies in Cervical Mucus Hydrolyzed by Seminal Protein*

Sample	Mucus	Amount of Protease, units	F_1	F_2	F_3	F_4
I	C*		25	15	10	3
	D**	0.7	25	25	25	20
II	C		1	0	0	
	D	0.7	25	25	25	
III	C		25	8	0	0
	D	0.7	25	25	20	2
IV	C		2	0	0	
	D	4	25	2	0	
V	C		25	15	2	
	D	1	25	25	15	

Samples I, II, and III were each 0.4 ml, and IV and V were 0.2 ml. All were hydrolyzed by seminal protease for 5 min at room temperature. F_1, F_2, F_3, and F_4 indicate first, second, third, and fourth microscopic fields, respectively, from interface 2 min after the start of in vitro sperm-cervical mucus penetration tests.   * Control cervical mucus.   ** Digested cervical mucus. [From Moghissi & Syner (103).]

minish their in vitro ability to penetrate the mucus. Sperm motility is arrested in the absence of utilizable sugar and is restored by its addition to the saline solution. Amino acids and fatty acids do not have this effect on recovery of motility when added to washed spermatozoa (80).

The rates of sperm metabolism and motility vary with temperature. Higher temperatures increase the metabolic rate and correspondingly decrease the life-span. In vitro sperm migration tests performed at room temperature and at 37 C, however, yield similar results.

Effect of Seminal Protease on Sperm Migration

Kurzrok & Miller (70) reported digestion of normal cervical mucus by semen. Belonoschkin (6) also described the liquefaction of cervical mucus by sperm. Takamine (142) believed the lytic ability of sperm to be due to hyaluronidase. However, cervical mucus does not contain uronic acid, and the enzyme hyaluronidase has no effect on cervical mucus (106, 156). Huggins & Neal (61) demonstrated the presence of a trypsin or chymotrypsin-like enzyme in semen.

More recent investigations indicate that human seminal plasma contains a chymotrypsin-like proteolytic enzyme and two peptidases [(76); F. Syner and K. Moghissi, unpublished data]. Spermatozoa exhibit similar proteolytic activity (F. Syner and K. Moghissi, unpublished data). Seminal protease has been isolated and purified [(103); F. Syner and K. Moghissi, unpublished data]. One unit of protease obtained from seminal plasma has an activity equivalent to 2 μg of commercial pancreatic chymotrypsin. The proteolytic activity of the pooled raw samples of human seminal plasma is 1.9–2.5 units/ml. Addition of commercial pancreatic proteases in vitro to semen or cervical mucus facilitates sperm migration (98, 103).

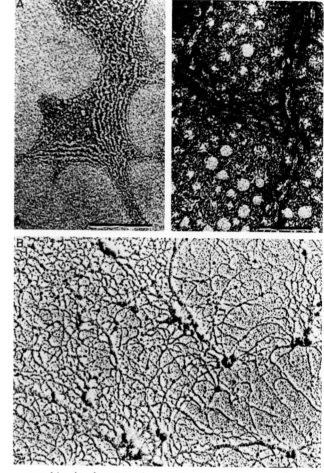

FIG. 14. *A*: electron micrograph of bovine cervical mucus negatively stained with uranyl oxalate. Scale line 0.1 μ. *B*: electron micrograph of purified bovine cervical mucin in Li buffer negatively stained with uranyl oxalate. Scale line 0.1 μ. *C*: electron micrograph of human cervical mucus rotary shadowed with platinum. Scale line 0.1 μ. [From Van Bruggen & Kremer (149).]

Incubation of cervical mucus with isolated and purified seminal protease causes hydrolysis of mucus followed by accelerated sperm migration [(103); Table 8]. The addition of seminal protease to freshly ejaculated semen also enhances sperm migration. Ferning and spinnbarkeit decrease when cervical mucus is subjected to proteolytic digestion by the addition of chymotrypsin or seminal protease (103). Hydrolysis of cervical mucus by proteolytic enzymes is also followed by a marked reduction in its viscosity and a dissolution of gel structure.

Van Bruggen & Kremer (149), in electron-microscopic studies of bovine estrous mucus and human midcycle cervical mucus, have demonstrated long, filamentous structures, often randomly aggregated in complicated networks. Digestion with the proteolytic enzyme, pronase, completely destroyed the filamentous structures (Figs. 14 and 15). These morphological observations confirm the reported biochemical and physical changes following hydrolytic digestion of the cervical mucus (103, 104, 106). Gibbons & Mattner (45, 46) suggested a model for the mucin of cervical mucus, which consists of a

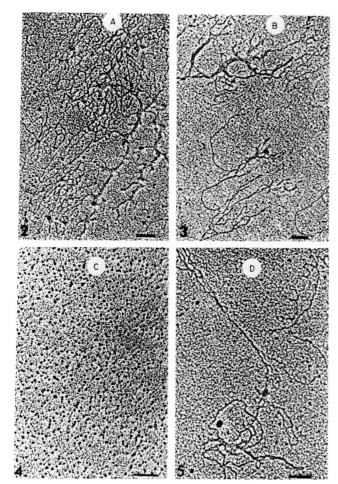

FIG. 15. Electron micrograph of bovine cervical mucus. *A*: untreated bovine cervical mucus. *B*: bovine cervical mucus treated with deoxyribonuclease. *C*: bovine cervical mucus after digestion with pronase. *D*: bovine cervical mucus treated with hyaluronidase. All preparations rotary shadowed with platinum; scale line 0.1 μ. Note lack of any effect by deoxyribonuclease and hyaluronidase and disappearance of filamentous structures as a result of hydrolysis by pronase. [From Van Bruggen & Kremer (149).]

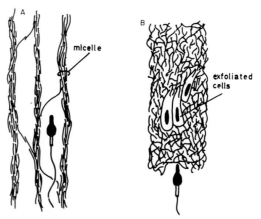

FIG. 16. Model of cervical mucus. Ovulatory- or estrogenic-type secretions (*A*) and luteal-type secretions (*B*) are shown. Estrogenic model (*A*) indicates the micelles and intermicellar space open to sperm penetration. The progestational model (*B*) shows the dense network without micellar structure, which acts as a barrier to spermatozoa. [From Odeblad (111).]

random, cross-linked network of flexible threadlike molecules. The consistency of mucus, according to these authors, may be related primarily to the degree of cross linkage [Fig. 12; (45)]. Odeblad (111), with nuclear magnetic resonance and rheological techniques, described a similar meshlike structure (Fig. 16). The meshes or micelles in midcycle seemed to be parallel and to be composed of 100–1,000 chains of glycoproteins. The distance between micelles varied between 1 and 10 μ (average 3 μ). The aqueous spaces between the micelles allow the passage of sperm, as well as diffusion of soluble substances. Estrogen is responsible for this type of mesh. During the luteal phase or under the influences of progestogens, the mesh size was significantly smaller. Odeblad substantiated the observation of Tampion & Gibbons (143) that sperm migration occurred within certain mucous channels. Proteolytic enzymes may hydrolyze the backbone protein or some of the cross linkages of the mucin and reduce the network to a less re-

sistant mesh with more open channels for the passage of spermatozoa. The escape of spermatozoa from the cervical crypts opposed by filaments of glycoprotein may depend on hydrolysis of these chains by protease in the sperm head. Cervical mucus contains α_1-antitrypsin, which may inhibit the activity of trypsin, and similar proteolytic enzymes. At midcycle, when the mucus is most receptive to sperm penetration, the α_1-antitrypsin content of cervical mucus is lowest (127).

Cervical Mucus pH and Sperm Migration

Spermatozoa are susceptible to changes in the pH of cervical mucus. Acidic mucus immobilizes spermatozoa, whereas alkaline mucus enhances their motility. Excessive alkalinity of cervical mucus (pH > 8.5) may also affect adversely the viability of spermatozoa (144). The optimal pH for sperm migration and survival in cervical mucus is between 7 and 8.50 (15, 78, 95), which is the pH range of normal midcycle or estrous cervical mucus.

The Effect of Foreign Proteins and Immune Antibodies on Sperm Migration

Cervical mucus contains IgA (β_{2A}-globulin), IgG (γ-globulin) (100, 102, 129), secretory IgA (62), and traces of IgM (β_{2M}-globulin). Gamma globulin of the IgG type is the most constant constituent and is found in most samples of cervical mucus (102, 129). Both spermatozoa and semen have antigenic properties. Animal and human studies support the view that a natural or induced immunologic incompatibility between sperm and cervical mucus may lead to infertility. Human sperm is readily agglutinated in bovine and rabbit sera and immobilized in bovine estrous mucus (97, 98). This does not occur when washed bovine mucin, from which serum proteins have been removed, is used.

Transvaginal immunization of the guinea pig with either testicular or epididymal sperm shows much higher hemoagglutinating and precipitating titers in the vaginal and uterine washings as compared to the circulating serum antibodies.

Menge (94) demonstrated that isoimmunization of heifers with bull semen and homogenized testis resulted in an induced temporary infertility. Specific sperm agglutinins were detected in the serum and uterine and vaginal mucus of the isoimmunized heifers. Lindahl and co-workers (72, 73) have described a sperm antiagglutinic factor (AAF) in the fluid of the growing follicle, in the Fallopian tubes, and in the cervical mucus of normal women, with a peak activity in midcycle. The antiagglutinins are materials that can inhibit the spontaneous agglutination of washed spermatozoa of various animals. The production of AAF was stimulated by estrogen and inhibited by progesterone. Antiagglutinic factor was found to be active only in its reduced form and to be inactive when oxidized. In four cases of unexplained infertility, these authors found AAF present only in the inactive oxidized form at the time of ovulation. After treatment with reducing agents (sodium thioglycollate), the cervical mucus showed normal antiagglutinic activity.

Fjallbrant and his associate (35–38) studied cervical mucus penetration by human spermatozoa from men with autoantibodies or from men treated with rabbit antisera against seminal plasma, seminal spermatozoa, and spermatocele spermatozoa, and with sera from men with different concentrations of naturally occurring sperm autoantibodies in the blood. He found that low concentrations of sperm antibodies reduced the sperm motility in mucus, whereas high concentrations reduced the sperm motility and the extent of sperm penetration. The antibodies responsible for this effect appeared to be of an agglutinating and immobilizing type and seemed to be of the 7S variety. The binding sites of these antibodies on spermatozoa were in the middle piece and tail of the cell membrane (37).

Parish & Ward (114) found two cytotoxic antisperm and three harmless antibodies in the cervical mucus and serum of three infertile women. The cytotoxic antibodies were of the IgG type. The addition of complement caused disruption of spermatozoal heads in one woman. The cervical mucus of another woman contained a cytotoxic antibody that reacted with spermatozoal surface antigen and caused immobilization without morphological changes. These antibodies were not neutralized by cell-free seminal plasma. The three harmless antibodies were IgM and IgA globulins that were persistent and specific for antigens in the seminal plasma, which coated spermatozoa. They were neutralized by cell-free seminal plasma. One of the antigens was a blood group A substance.

Blood group antigens and their antibodies have been found in cervical mucus (42). Behrman and co-workers (4) have suggested ABO incompatibility as a possible cause of certain cases of unexplained infertility. More recent data, however, do not show any alteration of postcoital tests of cervical mucus in patients with positive circulating isoagglutinins or ABO (H) incompatibility

(130). Other studies have demonstrated that agglutinins were actually found more frequently in cervical mucus of fertile women than in that of infertile women. This is the reverse of that which would be expected if these agglutinins were involved in the establishment of A- and B-type offspring among ABO-incompatible matings (139).

The Effect of Sex Hormones on Cervical Mucus and Sperm Penetration

Secretory activity of cervical glands is controlled by sex hormones. An increase in the amounts of endogenous estrogen during the preovulatory phase of the cycle or the administration of synthetic estrogens produces copious amounts of thin, watery, alkaline, acellular cervical secretion with intense ferning, spinnbarkeit, and sperm receptivity [see Figs. 2 and 6; Table 9; (16, 22, 57, 95, 118, 152)].

Endogenous progesterone during the luteal phase of the cycle or in pregnancy produces scanty, viscous, cellular mucus with low spinnbarkeit and no ferning. Spermatozoa are unable to penetrate progestational cervical mucus (22, 57, 95, 118). Other constituents of cervical mucus, such as proteins (95, 101, 126), enzymes (105, 134), and electrolytes, are sensitive to hormonal changes. The surface tension (75) and conductivity (117) of mucus are also controlled by estrogen and progesterone. Administration of estrogen to postmenopausal or castrated women and to those with supracervical hysterectomy and excised ovaries causes a significant increase in the amount and translucency of the mucus (51, 119). Progesterone alone had no effect in such instances. Almost all synthetic oral and parenteral progestogens alone or in combination with estrogen to some degree inhibit mucorrhea and sperm penetration through the cervical mucus [(Figs. 17 and 18; see Table 9; (23, 95, 99, 158, 159)]. Under the influence of these compounds, cervical mucus becomes highly viscous and cellular and is secreted in scant quantities. The ferning pattern disappears, and the spinnbarkeit phenomenon is markedly reduced. The normal preovulatory decrease in albumin and sialic acid and increase in mucoids are altered. The pH, however, is not significantly changed (18, 95, 99); this property of progestogens is of practical importance. The contraceptive potential of such microdose synthetic

TABLE 9. *Effect of Steroid Hormones on Cervical Mucus Production and Sperm Migration*

Hormone	Preovulatory Change	Luteal Change	Sperm Migration
Estrogen	+	−	+
Progesterone	−	+	−
Combination O.C.*	−	+	−
Sequential O.C.*	+	−	+
Pure progestogens (oral)	−	+	−
Depo-medroxyprogesterone acetate	−	+	−
Androgens	−	+	−

* Oral contraceptive.

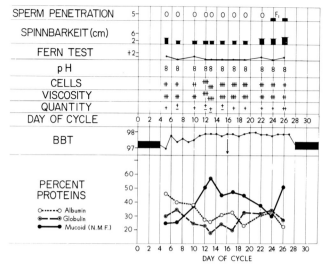

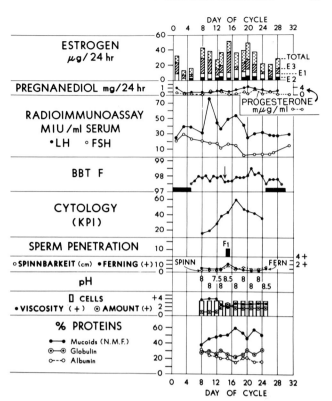

FIG. 17. Correlation of basal body temperature (*BBT*) with various properties of cervical mucus as in Fig. 2. A combination of norethindrone acetate (2.5 mg) and ethinyl estradiol (0.05 mg) is administered from day 5 through day 24 of the cycle. F_1 and F_2, the number of sperm in the first and second microscopic fields ($\times$ 200), respectively, from interface 15 min after the start of in vitro sperm-cervical mucus penetration test. *Arrow*, day of ovulation during the normal cycle. Note monophasic *BBT*, high viscosity and cellularity, lack of sperm penetration and ferning, decrease in amount, and spinnbarkeit. Typical protein changes—decrease in albumin and increase in mucins—are absent. [From Moghissi (95).]

progestogens as chlormadinone acetate (159), norgestrel (97, 121), norethindrone (K. Moghissi, unpublished data), and megestrol acetate (87) may depend largely on their ability to produce cervical mucus hostile to sperm penetration.

Sequential-type oral contraceptives do not alter the properties of the mucus and may indeed improve its quality by making it more receptive to sperm penetration (23, 159). Androgens exert inhibitory effects on cervical secretions similar to those of progestogens (159).

*Effect of Ovulation-Inducing
Agents on Cervical Mucus*

Clomiphene citrate, a synthetic ovulation-inducing compound, has a marked antiestrogenic effect on cervical secretion. During the administration of this medication, cervical mucus becomes viscous, turbid, and cellular and exhibits little or no spinnbarkeit and ferning (23, 124). Sperm penetration through the mucus is inhibited. About 5–10 days after the termination of clomiphene therapy, however, a rebound mucorrhea develops and sperm penetrability is restored.

Treatment with human menopausal gonadotrophin (HMG) usually produces increasing amounts of endogenous estrogen; this stimulates the secretion of preovulatory-type cervical mucus, which is receptive to sperm penetration (7, 16, 146).

The administration of human chorionic gonadotrophins, if followed by ovulation, brings about progestational changes with inhibition of sperm migration.

FIG. 18. Correlation of urinary estrogen excretion, urinary pregnanediol, serum gonadotrophins (*FSH* and *LH*), serum progesterone, basal body temperature (*BBT*), and karyopiknotic index (*KPI*) of vaginal cytology with cervical mucous properties as in Fig. 6. Norgestrel (75 μg daily) is administered from day 1 through day 30 of cycle. F_1 and F_2, number of spermatozoa in the first and second microscopic fields ($\times$ 200), respectively, from interface 5 min after the start of in vitro sperm-cervical mucus penetration test. Note depressed *FSH* and *LH* surges, monophasic *BBT*, increased estrogen excretion with multiple peaks, and slight rise of serum progesterone and urinary pregnanediol in the second half of the cycle. Cervical mucus is decreased in amount and is converted to a viscous, cellular secretion with no ferning and low spinnbarkeit (except for day 15); normal midcycle protein changes are abolished. Sperm migration is inhibited. A few spermatozoa penetrated the mucus on day 15 but were sluggish and did not survive. *N.M.F.*, nonmigrating fraction.

Sperm Survival in the Cervical Canal

Longevity of spermatozoa in the female genital tract is an important factor in fertility. A distinction should be made between the duration of motility and fertilizing capacity. Sperm motility is not necessarily a criterion of fertilizing potential. Live sperm have been found in the vagina up to 12 hr after coitus (41). Kremer (69) found that the motility of human spermatozoa that have remained in the vagina longer than 35 min is so compromised that their ability to penetrate cervical secretion is lost. Contamination with mucus at times alters the pH of the posterior fornix of the vagina and prolongs the survival of ejaculated sperm. A clear relationship between the pH of the intravaginal seminal pool and the motility of spermatozoa has been established. When the pH of the pool is 6 or higher, appreciable numbers of motile spermatozoa are encountered in the vagina (69). In human cervical mucus, motile spermatozoa have been found from 2 to 8 days after coitus (41, 107) and 1 week after artificial insemination (116). In the human uterus and oviducts live sperm cells have been recovered from 48 to 60 hr after sexual intercourse (34, 60, 123). It is believed, however, that spermatozoa may usually be capable of fertilization only within 48 hr after coitus (6, 69).

CONCLUSION

The uterine cervix may be compared to a biological valve that at certain periods during the reproductive cycle allows the entry of spermatozoa into the uterus and at other times bars their admission. By no means a passive organ, it is an active participant in the process of sperm migration. Most of the physiological functions of the cervix are effected by the secretion of the cervical epithelium.

Despite species variations, the cervix presents certain anatomic and histological structures common to most mammalian species. It has a rich vascular and nervous supply and epithelial components sensitive to sex hormones. The distinct columnar epithelium of the endocervix represents at least two major cell types, secretory cells and ciliated cells. At present the function of ciliated cells is not well understood.

Cervical mucus is a complex and dynamic substance that shows a number of rheological properties, such as viscosity, flow elasticity, spinnbarkeit, thixotropy, and stickiness. It has also the ability to crystallize at certain phases of the reproductive cycle. Its water content rises at midcycle or during estrus. It contains a large number of inorganic salts and organic compounds, including carbohydrates, lipids, enzymes, amino acids, and proteins. The soluble proteins include IgG, IgA, and secretory IgA, which may have immunologic importance. By far, the most important constituents of the mucus are the glycoproteins or the mucins. These macromolecules have a polypeptide backbone with oligosaccharide and sialic acid side chains. There is variability in the size and arrangement of heterosaccharide side chains and in the molecular weight of mucins within the same species, as well as in different species. A cross-linking protein has also been suggested as a part of the flexible, threadlike structure of cervical mucins. Cervical mucus is susceptible to proteolytic hydrolysis. The digestion of the mucus or its mucins by proteolytic enzymes results in marked physical and certain biochemical changes.

The glycoproteins of cervical mucus are undoubtedly responsible for its distinct physical properties, as well as its functional dynamism. The cyclic polymerization and depolymerization of these mucins are responsible for periodic receptivity or hostility of the hydrogel to sperm invasion.

From a functional point of view the following properties may be ascribed to the cervix and its secretion: a) receptivity to sperm penetration at or near ovulation (or estrus) and impedance of entry at other times; b) sperm reservoir; c) protection of sperm cells from the hostile environment of the vagina and from phagocytosis; d) supplementation of the energy requirements of spermatozoa; e) filtration; and f) possible capacitation of spermatozoa.

Current data indicate that ejaculated spermatozoa rapidly enter midcycle or estrous cervical mucus. Although subsequent migration through the cervical canal is accomplished principally by intrinsic motility, it also seems to be influenced by proteolytic activity of seminal plasma and spermatozoa and phalanx formation because of the difference in surface tension between semen and cervical mucus, as well as the orientation of strands of mucins of cervical mucus. The latter phenomenon, the orientation of strands of mucins of cervical mucus, may be responsible for the storage of spermatozoa in the cervical crypts and their gradual release over an extended period into the uterus and oviducts. Preovulatory or estrous mucus is watery, thin, acellular, alkaline, isotonic, and threadlike. It crystallizes intensely when allowed to dry, exhibits maximal spinnbarkeit, and is low in protein and antitrypsin content. Spermatozoa penetrate such mucus with extreme rapidity. Furthermore the mucus is a favorable medium for sperm survival and probably provides sperm cells with energy substances required for their motility.

Retention of spermatozoa in the mucus also protects them from the phagocytes within the female tract. Preovulatory cervical mucus contains very few, if any, leukocytes, and those that enter the mucus from the uterus and stromal phagocytes are kept physically separate from the spermatozoa. The ovum has a limited life-span, generally believed not to exceed 6–8 hr (8). Since the spermatozoa do not survive well in the uterus or oviduct and are more susceptible to phagocytosis when dead or immobilized, the protective action of cervical mucus insures a constant release of motile spermatozoa into the upper tract after the initial rapid passage, which thus increases the chance of fertilization. In vitro and in vivo observations suggest that cervical mucus functions not only as a sperm reservoir but also as a biological filter where dead, abnormal or unfit spermatozoa are retained and prevented from reaching the uterine cavity (89, 90, 140).

Capacitation of spermatozoa before fertilization has been established in a number of mammalian species and may also exist in man. The role of cervical secretion in capacitation, although not explored, remains a distinct possibility.

The occurrence of antisperm antibodies in cervical mucus may interfere with the motility or survival of spermatozoa, or both, and thus reduces or inhibits fertility.

Certain progestational steroids and related compounds bring about physical and biochemical changes of cervical mucus and interfere with sperm penetration. The determination of their value for effective and more localized contraception merits further investigation.

REFERENCES

1. ADHAM, N., AND E. A. SCHENK. Autonomic innervation of the rat vagina, cervix and uterus and its cyclic variation. *Am. J. Obstet. Gynecol.* 104: 508–516, 1969.
2. AKESTER, A. R., AND I. J. INKSTER. Cine-radiographic studies of the genital tract of the rabbit. *J. Reprod. Fertility* 2: 507–508, 1961.
3. ALLISTON, C. W., T. B. PATTERSON, AND L. C. ULBERG. Crystallization patterns of cervical mucus as related to estrus in beef cattle. *J. Animal Sci.* 17: 322–325, 1958.
4. BEHRMAN, S. J., J. BUETTNER-JANUSH, R. HEGLAR, H. GERSHOWITZ, AND W. L. TEW. ABO (H) blood incompatibility as a cause of infertility. A new concept. *Am. J. Obstet. Gynecol.* 79: 847–855, 1965.
5. BELLER, F. K., AND G. WEISS. The fibrinolytic enzyme system in cervical mucus. *Fertility Sterility* 17: 654–662, 1966.
6. BELONOSCHKIN, B. *Zeugung beim Menschen im Lichter der Spermatozoenlehre.* Stockholm: Sjoberg, 1949.
7. BLAIR, G. W. S., S. J. FOLLEY, P. M. V. COPPEN, AND F. H. MALPRESS. Rheological properties of bovine cervical secretions during the estrous cycle. *Nature* 147: 453–454, 1941.
8. BLANDAU, R. J. Gamete transport—comparative aspect. In: *The Mammalian Oviduct,* edited by E. S. E. Hafez and R. J. Blandau. Chicago: Univ. of Chicago Press, 1969, p. 141–155.
9. BLOOM, W., AND D. W. FAWCETT. *A Textbook of Histology* (8th ed.). Philadelphia: Saunders, 1957, p. 610–614.
10. BOTELLA-LLUSIA, J. Methods for determining the type and degree of spermatic motility. In: *Proceedings of the Fifth World Congress on Fertility and Sterility,* edited by B. Westin and N. Wiqvist. Amsterdam: Excerpta Medica Foundation, 1967, p. 636–644.
11. BRECKENRIDGE, M. A. B., AND W. T. A. POMMERENKE. Analysis of carbohydrates in human cervical mucus. *Fertility Sterility* 2: 29–44, 1951.
12. BRECKENRIDGE, M. A. B., AND W. T. A. POMMERENKE. Analysis of lipid constituents of the cervical secretion. *Fertility Sterility* 2: 451–458, 1951.
13. BRET, A. J., AND P. COIFFORD. Mucus cervical au cours de la grossesse. *Rev. Franc. Gynecol. Obstet.* 59: 395–443, 1964.
14. BRINBERG, C. H., R. KURZROK, AND A. LANFER. Simple test for determining ovulation time. *J. Am. Med. Assoc.* 166: 1174–1175, 1958.
15. CARLBORG, L. Determination of sperm migration rate in small samples of cervical mucus. *Acta Endocrinol.* 62: 732–746, 1969.
16. CARLBORG, L., AND C. GEMZELL. Sialic acid content and sperm receptivity of cervical mucus in relation to estrogen excretion following administration of FSH. *Acta Endocrinol.* 62: 711–720, 1969.
17. CARLBORG, L., E. D. B. JOHANSSON, AND C. GEMZELL. Sialic acid content and sperm penetration of cervical mucus in relation to total urinary estrogen excretion and plasma progesterone levels and ovulatory women. *Acta Endocrinol.* 62: 721–731, 1969.
18. CARLBORG, L., W. MCCORMICK, AND C. GEMZELL. Effect of norethisterone acetate with or without ethinylestradiol on the sialic acid concentration and sperm receptivity of cervical mucus. *Acta Endocrinol.* 59: 636–643, 1968.
19. CARY, W. H. Sterility diagnosis. The study of sperm cell migration in the female secretions and interpretation of findings. *NY State J. Med.* 30: 131–136, 1930.
20. CLIFT, A. F. Observations on certain rheological properties of human cervical secretion. *Proc. Roy. Soc. Med.* 39: 1–9, 1945.
21. COHEN, M. R. Cervical mucorrhea and spinnbarkeit in patients taking norethindrone plus mestranol (Norinyl 1-mg). *Fertility Sterility* 19: 405–410, 1968.
22. COHEN, M. R., I. F. STEIN, AND B. M. KAYE. Spinnbarkeit: a characterization of cervical mucus, significance at ovulation time. *Fertility Sterility* 3: 201–209, 1952.
23. COHEN, M. R., AND M. PEREZ PELAEZ. The effect of norethin-drone acetate-ethinyl estradiol, clomiphene citrate and dydrogesterone on spinnbarkeit. *Fertility Sterility* 16: 141–150, 1965.
24. COLBORN, G. L., J. B. WALTER, AND C. M. LANG. Observations on the cervix uteri of the squirrel monkey. *J. Morphol.* 122: 81–88, 1967.
25. COLE, H. H. A study of the mucosa of the genital tract of the cow, with special reference to the cyclic changes. *Am. J. Anat.* 46: 261–301, 1930.
26. DAVID, A., AND L. MASTROIANNI. Cervical mucus arborization in the rhesus monkey. *J. Reprod. Fertility* 17: 495–499, 1968.
28. ECKSTEIN, P., AND S. ZUCKERMAN. Morphology of the reproductive tract. In: *Marshall's Physiology of Reproduction* (3rd ed.), edited by A. S. Parkes. Boston: Little, Brown, 1960, vol. 1, part 1, p. 43–155.
29. EGLI, G. E., AND M. NEWTON. The transport of carbon particles in the human female reproductive system. *Fertility Sterility* 12: 151–155, 1961.
30. EL-BANNA, A. B. *Comparative Study of Physiology and Histology of the Female Reproductive Tract in Relation to Gamete Transport (Ph.D. thesis).* Pullman, Wash.: Washington State University, 1969, p. 68–134.
31. EMMENS, C. W. Growth of the reproductive and endocrine organs of the female rabbit. *J. Endocrinol.* 1: 409–416, 1939.
32. ENDERS, R. K. Reproduction in the mink (*Mustela vison*). *Proc. Am. Phil. Soc.* 96: 691–755, 1952.
33. ENHORNING, G., L. HULDT, AND B. MELEN. Ability of cervical mucus to act as a barrier against bacteria. *Am. J. Obstet. Gynecol.* 106: 532–537, 1970.
34. FARRIS, E. J. *Human Fertility and Problems of the Male.* White Plains, N.Y.: Author's Press, 1950.
35. FJALLBRANT, B. Sperm antibodies and sterility in men. *Acta Obstet. Gynecol. Scand.* 47, Suppl. 4: 1–38, 1968.
36. FJALLBRANT, B. Cervical mucus penetration by human spermatozoa treated with antispermatozoal antibodies from rabbit and man. *Acta Obstet. Gynecol. Scand.* 48: 71–84, 1969.
37. FJALLBRANT, B. Localization of human male antibodies on spermatozoa. *Am. J. Obstet. Gynecol.* 108: 550–556, 1970.
38. FJALLBRANT, B., AND D. R. ACKERMAN. Cervical mucus penetration *in vitro* by fresh and frozen preserved human semen specimens. *J. Reprod. Fertility* 20: 515–517, 1969.
39. FLUHMANN, C. F. *The Cervix Uteri and Its Disease.* Philadelphia: Saunders, 1961, p. 3–108.
40. FOX, C. A., H. S. WOLFF, AND J. A. BAKER. Measurement of intravaginal and intrauterine pressure during human coitus by radiotelemetry. *J. Reprod. Fertility* 22: 243–251, 1970.
41. FRENKEL, D. A. Sperm migration and survival in the endometrial cavity. *Intern. J. Fertility* 6: 285–290, 1961.
42. GERSHOWITZ, H., S. J. BEHRMAN, AND J. V. NEAL. Hemagglutinins in uterine secretions. *Science* 128: 719–720, 1958.
43. GIBBONS, R. A. Chemical properties of two mucoids from bovine cervical mucus. *Biochem. J.* 73: 209–217, 1959.
44. GIBBONS, R. A. Le mucus cervical. In: *Les Fonctions du Col Utérin (Colloque de la Société Nationale Pour l'Étude de la Sterilité et de la Fécondité).* Paris: Masson Cie, 1964, p. 57–68.
45. GIBBONS, R. A., AND P. MATTNER. Some aspects of the chemistry of cervical mucus. In: *Proceedings of the Fifth World Congress on Fertility and Sterility,* edited by B. Westin and N. Wiqvist. Amsterdam: Excerpta Medica Foundation, 1967, p. 695–700.
46. GIBBONS, R. A., AND P. E. MATTNER. The chemical and physical characteristics of the cervical secretion and its role in reproductive physiology. In: *Proceedings of the H. C. Mack Symposium on Pathways to Conception, Detroit, 1969.* Springfield, Ill.: Thomas, 1971, p. 143.
47. GIBBONS, R. A., AND G. P. ROBERTS. Some aspects of the structure of macromolecular constituents of epithelial mucus. *Ann. NY Acad. Sci.* 106: 218–232, 1963.

48. Giro, C. Contribution a l'étude du system nervaux terminaux des glandes cervicales des rongeurs et de la femme. In: *Les Fonctions du Col Utérin*. Paris: Masson Cie, 1964, p. 114–133.

49. Gorokhov, L. N. Physical and chemical analysis of cervical secretion. In: *Proceedings of the Fifth International Congress on Animal Reproduction and Artificial Insemination, Trento, 1964*, vol. VI, p. 55–59.

50. Grant, A. Cervical hostility. *Fertility Sterility* 9: 321–333, 1958.

51. Guttmacher, A. F., and L. B. Shettles. Cyclic changes in cervical mucus and its practical importance. *Human Fertility* 5: 4–9, 1940.

52. Hamilton, C. E. The cervix uteri of the rat. *Anat. Record* 97: 47–62, 1947.

53. Hammond, J. *The Physiology of Reproduction in the Cow*. New York: Cambridge Univ. Press, 1927.

54. Hammond, J., and K. Wodzicki. Anatomical and histological changes during the estrous cycle in the mare. *Proc. Roy. Soc. London, Ser. B.* 130: 1–23, 1941.

55. Hartman, C. G. How do sperms get into the uterus? *Fertility Sterility* 8: 403–427, 1957.

56. Harvey, C. The speed of human spermatozoa and the effect on it of various diluents with some preliminary observation on clinical material. *J. Reprod. Fertility* 1: 84–95, 1960.

57. Harvey, C., R. A. Linn, and M. H. Jackson. Certain characteristics of cervical mucus in relation to menstrual cycle. *J. Reprod. Fertility* 1: 157–168, 1960.

58. Heinen, G. Identifizierung der Serumeiweisskonponenten im getrennten Vaginal und Zervixsekret. *Geburtsh. Frauenheilk.* 22: 983–986, 1962.

59. Herrick, J. B. The cytological changes in the cervical mucosa of the cow (*Bos taurus*) throughout the estrous cycle. *Am. J. Vet. Res.* 12: 276–281, 1951.

60. Horne, H. W., Jr., and C. Audet. Spider cells, a new inhabitant of peritoneal fluid. *Obstet. Gynecol.* 11: 421–423, 1958.

61. Huggins, C. B., and W. Neal. Coagulation and liquefaction of semen. Proteolytic enzymes and citrate in prostatic fluid. *J. Exptl. Med.* 76: 527–541, 1942.

62. Hulka, J. F., and K. F. Omran. The uterine cervix as a potential local antibody secretor. *Am. J. Obstet. Gynecol.* 104: 440–442, 1969.

63. Iida, I., and T. Kawi. Cited by Mann, T. In: *The Biochemistry of Semen and of the Male Reproductive Tract*. London: Methuen, 1964, p. 291.

64. Jurow, H. N. Cyclic variations in the cervix of the guinea pig. *Am. J. Obstet. Gynecol.* 45: 762–774, 1943.

65. von Kaulla, K. N., J. K. Alkawa, P. D. Burns, and W. T. Wikle. Secretory function of the human uterine cervix; studies with radio-isotopes. *Fertility Sterility* 8: 444–454, 1957.

66. Kofoed, J. A., N. Blumenkrantz, A. B. Houssay, and E. Y. Yamauchi. Cervical mucus and serum ascorbic and dehydro-ascorbic acid concentration during the menstrual cycle. *Am. J. Obstet. Gynecol.* 91: 95–101, 1965.

67. Krantz, K. E., and W. P. Phillips. Anatomy of the human cervix, gross and microscopic. *Ann. NY Acad. Sci.* 93: 551–563, 1962.

68. Krehbiel, R., and H. P. Carstens. Roentgen studies of the mechanism involved in sperm transportation in the female rabbit. *Am. J. Physiol.* 125: 571–577, 1939.

69. Kremer, J. *The in Vitro Spermatozoal Penetration Test in Fertility Investigation* (Ph.D. thesis). Netherlands: Rijksuniversiteit Groningen, 1968, p. 24–102.

70. Kurzrok, R., and E. G. Miller. Biochemical studies of human semen and its relation to mucus of the cervix uteri. *Am. J. Obstet. Gynecol.* 15: 56–72, 1928.

71. Lamar, J. K., L. B. Shettles, and E. Delfs. Cyclic penetrability of the human cervical mucus to spermatozoa *in vitro*. *Am. J. Physiol.* 129: 234–241, 1940.

72. Lindahl, P. E., A. Ingelman-Sundberg, M. Furuhjelm, and A. Nilsson. The sperm anti-agglutinic factor in women. *J. Obstet. Gynecol. Brit. Empire* 63: 363–371, 1956.

73. Lindahl, P. E., and A. Nilsson. The isolation of sperm antagglutin from the follicle fluid and some of its properties. *Biochim. Biophys. Acta* 25: 22–32, 1957.

74. Lipphardt, E., and W. T. Pommerenke. Effect of addition of spermatozoa on the sugar content of cervical mucus. *Am. J. Obstet. Gynecol.* 59: 918–920, 1950.

75. Lippes, J., and L. B. Hurwitz. The dilution effect of surface tension of cervical mucus and its viability with the menstrual cycle. *Fertility Sterility* 18: 722–726, 1965.

76. Lundquist, F., T. Thorsteinsson, and O. Buus. Purification and properties of some enzymes in human seminal plasma. *Biochem. J.* 59: 69–79, 1955.

77. MacDonald, R. R. Cyclic changes in cervical mucus. *J. Obstet. Gynecol. Brit. Commonwealth* 76: 1090–1099, 1969.

78. MacDonald, R. R., and I. B. Lumley. Endocervical pH measured *in vivo* through the normal menstrual cycle. *Obstet. Gynecol.* 35: 202–206, 1970.

79. MacLeod, J. Metabolism of human spermatozoa. *Proc. Soc. Exptl. Biol. Med.* 42: 153–155, 1939.

80. MacLeod, J. Effect of glycolysis inhibitors and of certain substrates on metabolism and motility of human spermatozoa. *Endocrinology* 29: 583–591, 1941.

81. MacLeod, J. The role of oxygen in the metabolism and motility of human spermatozoa. *Am. J. Physiol.* 138: 512–518, 1943.

82. MacLeod, J., and R. S. Hotchkiss. Distribution of spermatozoa and of certain chemical constituents in the human ejaculate. *J. Urol.* 48: 225–229, 1942.

83. Mann, T. *The Biochemistry of Semen and of the Male Reproductive Tract*. London: Methuen, 1964, p. 265–307.

84. Mann, E. C., W. D. McLarn, and D. B. Hayt. The physiology and clinical significance of the uterine isthmus. *Am. J. Obstet. Gynecol.* 81: 209–222, 1961.

85. Mason, B. A., H. J. E. Cox, D. W. Mason, and V. Grant. Clinical and experimental studies with low doses of megestrol acetate. *Postgrad. Med. J. Suppl.* 40: 45–48, 1966.

86. Masson, P. I., J. F. Heremans, and J. Ferin. Clinical importance of the biochemical changes in the female genital tract. I. Studies of the proteins of cervical mucus. *Intern. J. Fertility* 14: 1–7, 1969.

87. Masters, W. H. The sexual response cycle of the human female. I. Gross anatomic considerations. *Western J. Surg.* 68: 57–72, 1960.

88. Masters, W. H., and V. E. Johnson. *Human Sexual Response*. Boston: Little, Brown, 1966, p. 114–116.

89. Mattner, P. E. Spermatozoa in the genital tract of the ewe. II. Distribution after coitus. *Australian J. Biol. Sci.* 16: 688–694, 1963.

90. Mattner, P. E. The distribution of spermatozoa and leucocytes in the female genital tract in goats and cattle. *J. Reprod. Fertility* 17: 253–261, 1968.

91. Mattner, P. E., and A. W. H. Braden. Spermatozoa in the genital tract of the ewe. I. Rapidity of transport. *Australian J. Biol. Sci.* 16: 473–481, 1963.

92. McCarthy, J. F., J. Stepita, and J. A. Killiam. Glycolysis in semen. *Proc. Exptl. Biol. Med.* 25: 54, 1927.

93. McSweeney, D. J., and A. J. Sbarra. A new cervical mucus test for hormone appraisal. *Am. J. Obstet. Gynecol.* 88: 705–709, 1964.

94. Menge, A. C. Induced infertility in cattle by isoimmunization with semen and testis. *J. Reprod. Fertility* 13: 445–456, 1967.

95. Moghissi, K. S. Cyclic changes of cervical mucus in normal and progestin treated women. *Fertility Sterility* 17: 663–675, 1966.

96. Moghissi, K. S. Human and bovine sperm migration. *Fertility Sterility* 19: 118–122, 1968.

98. Moghissi, K. S., D. Dabich, J. Levine, and O. W. Neuhaus. Mechanism of sperm migration. *Fertility Sterility* 15: 15–23, 1964.

99. Moghissi, K. S., and C. Marks. Effect of a microdose pro-

gestogen on endogenous gonadotropic and steroid hormones and cervical mucus properties. *Fertility Sterility.* 22: 424–434, 1971.

100. MOGHISSI, K. S., AND O. W. NEUHAUS. Composition and properties of human cervical mucus. II. Immunoelectrophoretic studies of the proteins. *Am. J. Obstet. Gynecol.* 83: 149–155, 1962.

101. MOGHISSI, K. S., AND O. W. NEUHAUS. Cyclic changes of cervical mucus proteins. *Am. J. Obstet. Gynecol.* 96: 91–95, 1966.

102. MOGHISSI, K. S., O. W. NEUHAUS, AND C. S. STEVENSON. Composition and properties of human cervical mucus. I. Electrophoretic separation and identification of proteins. *J. Clin. Invest.* 39: 1358–1363, 1960.

103. MOGHISSI, K. S., AND F. N. SYNER. The effect of seminal protease on sperm migration through the cervical mucus. *Intern. J. Fertility* 15: 43–49, 1970.

104. MOGHISSI, K. S., AND F. N. SYNER. Studies on human cervical mucus. *Fertility Sterility* 21: 234–239, 1970.

106. NEUHAUS, O. W., AND K. S. MOGHISSI. Composition and properties of human cervical mucus. III. A preliminary study of the mucoid component. *Fertility Sterility* 13: 550–558, 1962.

107. NICHOLSON, R. Vitality of spermatozoa in the endocervical canal. *Fertility Sterility* 16: 758–763, 1965.

108. NOYES, R. W., C. E. ADAMS, AND A. WALTON. Transport of spermatozoa into the uterus of the rabbit. *Fertility Sterility* 9: 288–299, 1958.

109. ODEBLAD, E. The physics of the cervical mucus. *Acta Obstet. Gynecol. Scand.* 38, Suppl. 1: 44–58, 1959.

110. ODEBLAD, E. Micro-NMR in high permanent magnetic fields. *Acta Obstet. Gynecol. Scand.* 45, Suppl. 2: 127–160, 1966.

111. ODEBLAD, E. The functional structure of human cervical mucus. *Acta Obstet. Gynecol. Scand.* 47, Suppl. 1: 59–79, 1968.

112. OLDS, D., AND N. L. VANDEMARK. Composition of luminal fluids in bovine female genitalia. *Fertility Sterility* 8: 345–354, 1957.

113. PAPANICOLAOU, G. N. General survey of vaginal smear and its use in research and diagnosis. *Am. J. Obstet. Gynecol.* 51: 316–324, 1946.

114. PARISH, W. E., AND A. WARD. Studies of cervical mucus and serum from infertile women. *J. Obstet. Gynecol. Brit. Commonwealth* 75: 1089–1100, 1968.

115. PEDERSON, D. P., AND W. T. POMMERENKE. Amino acids in cervical mucus. *Fertility Sterility* 1: 527–532, 1950.

116. PERLOFF, W. H., AND E. STEINBERGER. *In vivo* survival of spermatozoa in cervical mucus. *Am. J. Obstet. Gynecol.* 88: 439–442, 1964.

117. PLATT, H. A., E. B. CONNELL, AND M. L. STONE. Conductivity of cervical mucus during the menstrual cycle and pregnancy. *Fertility Sterility* 19: 85–90, 1968.

118. POMMERENKE, W. T. Cyclic changes in physical and chemical properties of cervical mucus. *Am. J. Obstet. Gynecol.* 52: 1023–1031, 1946.

119. POMMERENKE, W. T., AND E. VIERGIVER. The effect of the administration of estrogens upon the production of cervical mucus in castrated women. *J. Clin. Endocrinol.* 6: 99–108, 1946.

120. POMMERENKE, W. T., AND E. VIERGIVER. Comparison of rate of penetration of washed and unwashed spermatozoa in cervical mucus. *Proc. Soc. Exptl. Biol. Med.* 66: 161–163, 1947.

121. ROLAND, M. Norgestrel-induced cervical barrier to sperm migration. *J. Reprod. Fertility Suppl.* 5: 174–177, 1968.

122. ROZANSKY, R., S. PERSKY, AND B. BERCOVICI. Antibacterial action of human cervical mucus. *Proc. Soc. Exptl. Biol. Med.* 110: 876–878, 1962.

123. RUBINSTEIN, B. R., H. STRAUSS, M. LAZARUS, AND H. HANKIN. Sperm survival in women. *Fertility Sterility* 2: 15–19, 1951.

124. RUIZ-VELASCO, V., R. BAILON URIZA, B. I. CONDE, AND E. SALAS. Changes during clomiphene citrate therapy. *Fertility Sterility* 20: 829–839, 1969.

125. SANDYS, O. C., AND S. ZUCKERMAN. Observations on the cervix uteri and the urethra of monkeys. *J. Anat.* 72: 352–357, 1938.

126. SCHUMACHER, G. F. B. Biochemistry of cervical mucus. *Fertility Sterility* 21: 697–705, 1970.

127. SCHUMACHER, G. F. B., AND M. J. PEARL. Alpha$_1$ antitrypsin in cervical mucus. *Fertility Sterility* 19: 91–99, 1968.

128. SCHUMACHER, G. F. B., AND M. J. PEARL. Cyclic changes of muramidase in cervical mucus. *J. Reprod. Med.* 3: 171–178, 1969.

129. SCHUMACHER, G. F. B., E. K. STRAUSS, AND G. L. WEID. Serum proteins in cervical mucus. *Am. J. Obstet. Gynecol.* 91: 1035–1049, 1965.

130. SCHWIMMER, W. B., K. A. USTAY, AND S. J. BEHRMAN. An evaluation of immunologic factors of infertility. *Fertility Sterility* 18: 167–180, 1967.

131. SHETTLES, L. B. The polysaccharide composition of human cervical mucus. *Fertility Sterility* 2: 361–368, 1951.

132. SIMS, J. M. *Uterine Surgery.* New York: Woods, 1866.

133. SISSON, S. *The Anatomy of the Domestic Animals* (4th ed.). Philadelphia: Saunders, 1953.

134. SKERLAVY, M., J. EPSTEIN, AND A. J. SOBRERO. Cervical mucus amylase level in normal menstrual cycles. *Fertility Sterility* 19: 726–730, 1968.

135. SMITH, D. C., W. B. HUNTER, AND L. R. SPANDONI. Alkaline phosphatase concentration in cervical mucus. *Fertility Sterility* 21: 549–554, 1970.

136. SOBRERO, A. J. Bacteriological findings in the midcycle endocervical mucus in infertile women. *Ann. NY Acad. Sci.* 97: 591–598, 1962.

137. SOBRERO, A. J. Sperm migration in human female. In: *Proceedings of the Fifth World Congress on Fertility and Sterility,* edited by B. Westin and N. Wiqvist. Amsterdam: Excerpta Medica Foundation, 1967, p. 701–703.

138. SOBRERO, A. J., AND J. MACLEOD. The immediate postcoital test. *Fertility Sterility* 13: 184–189, 1962.

139. SOLISH, G. I. Distribution of ABO iso-hemagglutinins among fertile and infertile women. *J. Reprod. Fertility* 18: 459–474, 1969.

140. SUJAN, S., J. DANEZIS, AND A. J. SOBRERO. Sperm migration and cervical mucus studies in individual cycles. *J. Reprod. Fertility* 6: 87–97, 1963.

142. TAKAMINE, H. Role of hyaluronidase on sperm penetrability in cervical mucus of the cow. *Med. Biol. Tokyo* 18: 62, 1951.

143. TAMPION, D., AND R. A. GIBBONS. Orientation of spermatozoa in mucus of the cervix uteri. *Nature* 194: 381, 1962.

144. TAMPION, D., AND R. A. GIBBONS. Effect of pH on the swimming rate of bull spermatozoa. *J. Reprod. Fertility* 5: 249–258, 1963.

145. TAMPION, D., AND R. A. GIBBONS. Swimming rate of bull spermatozoa in various media and the effect of dilution. *J. Reprod. Fertility* 5: 259–275, 1963.

146. TAYMOUR, M. L., S. H. STURGIS, B. L. LIEBERMAN, AND D. P. GOLDSTEIN. Induction of ovulation with human postmenopausal gonadotropin. *Fertility Sterility* 17: 731–735, 1966.

147. TOSIC, J., AND A. WALTON. Metabolism of spermatozoa. The formation and elimination of hydrogen peroxide by spermatozoa and effects on motility and survival. *J. Biochem.* 47: 199–212, 1950.

148. TRNKA, V., J. REJNEK, AND A. DOLEZAL. The protein spectrum of cervical secretion during the course of pregnancy. *Am. J. Obstet. Gynecol.* 89: 215–219, 1964.

149. VAN BRUGGEN, E. F. J., AND J. KREMER. Electron microscopy of bovine and human cervical mucus. *Intern. J. Fertility* 15: 50–57, 1970.

150. VANDEMARK, N. L., AND R. L. HAYES. Rapid sperm transport in the cow. *Fertility Sterility* 5: 131–137, 1954.

151. VANDEMARK, N. L., AND A. N. MOELLER. Speed of spermatozoa transport in reproductive tract of estrous cow. *Am. J. Physiol.* 165: 674–679, 1951.

152. VIERGIVER, E., AND W. T. POMMERENKE. Cyclic variations in the viscosity of cervical mucus and its correlation with

amount of secretion and basal body temperature. *Am. J. Obstet. Gynecol.* 51: 192–200, 1946.

153. VIERGIVER, E., AND W. T. POMMERENKE. The determination of reducing substances in human cervical mucus. *Am. J. Obstet. Gynecol.* 54: 459–466, 1947.

154. WALTON, A. On the function of the rabbit cervix during coitus. *J. Obstet. Gynecol. Brit. Empire* 37: 92–95, 1930.

155. WERNER, I. Studies of glycoproteins from mucus epithelium and epithelial secretion. *Acta Soc. Med. Upsalien.* 58: 1–55, 1953.

156. WERNER, I. The chemistry of cervical mucus. *Acta Obstet. Gynecol. Scand.* 38, Suppl. 1: 39–43, 1959.

157. ZACCHARIA, F. The acid mucopolysaccharide of the cervical mucus. *Acta Obstet. Gynecol. Scand.* 38, Suppl. 1: 84–89, 1959.

158. ZANARTU, J. Effect of synthetic oral gestagens on cervical mucus and sperm penetration. *Intern. J. Fertility* 9: 225–230, 1964.

159. ZANARTU, J. Effect of natural and synthetic sex steroids in cervical mucus, penetration and ascent of spermatozoa. In: *Proceedings of the Fifth World Congress on Fertility and Sterility*, edited by B. Westin and N. Wiqvist. Amsterdam: Excerpta Medica Foundation, 1967, p. 704–709.

160. ZINSER, H. K. La vascularization du col utérin. In: *Les Fonctions du Col Utérin*. Paris: Masson Cie, 1964, p. 101–111.

161. ZONDEK, B. Cervical mucus arborization as an aid in diagnosis. In: *Progress in Gynecology*, edited by J. Meigs and S. Sturgis. New York: Grune & Stratton, 1957, vol. III, p. 86–98.

162. ZUCKERMAN, S. The menstrual cycle of the primates. I. General nature and homology. *Proc. Zool. Soc. London* 1930: 691–754, 1930.

163. ZUCKERMAN, S., AND A. S. PARKES. The menstrual cycle of the primates. V. The cycle of the baboon. *Proc. Zool. Soc. London* 1932: 139–191, 1932.

Effects of ovarian steroids on uterine metabolism

JAMES C. WARREN

ROBERT D. CRIST

Departments of Obstetrics-Gynecology and Biochemistry, Washington University School of Medicine, St. Louis, Missouri and The University of Kansas School of Medicine, Kansas City, Kansas

CHAPTER CONTENTS

METABOLISM IS THE SUM of the processes involved in the buildup and destruction of protoplasm intrinsic to life. In the uterus this includes the uptake of nutriments from the circulation and their utilization, as well as changes in the population and activity state of cellular macromolecules. Undoubtedly estrogens and progestins profoundly affect uterine metabolism to cause growth and differentiation. Although a good deal of activity has gone into study of the morphological and physiological effects of progesterone, metabolic changes have been most extensively studied with the estrogens. Previous reviews by Szego & Roberts (125), Mueller et al. (89), Hagerman & Villee (46), and Williams-Ashman & Liao (140) have delineated numerous alterations in uterine metabolism after estrogen administration. With both types of steroids

we would like not only to catalogue and understand changing metabolic events, but also to gain some insight into how these changes are brought about.

As nature's secrets have unfolded to investigation, one is always impressed with the order and logic of the systems, once they have been delineated. Thus it is natural that the ultimate hope of the reproductive biologist is to describe a system that includes the primary interaction of the steroid with one or a few receptors, which set some master program in action. Further it is attractive to assume that the master program is naturally, and possibly uniquely, present in cells of the target organ and needs only be triggered by the arrival of the appropriate hormone to initiate the numerous subsequent metabolic effects. The elucidation of this primary interaction and the ordering of these subsequent events have occupied the attention of many investigators in this decade.

Investigations have attempted to exploit various breakthroughs in biochemistry, physiology, and pharmacology and to evaluate the possible role of ovarian steroids in the uterine system. Ligand-induced conformation change, newly described metabolic pathways, membrane and soluble receptors, gene derepression, and enzyme induction have been examined as possible mechanisms for the mediation of biological activity, particularly of the estrogens. Two major strategies have directed the course of the search: *1)* finding the earliest metabolic change evident after administration of the hormone, and *2)* finding a high-affinity primary receptor, or receptors, of some type. Both strategies have their pitfalls.

We attempt to present an analysis of the numerous effects of ovarian steroids on uterine metabolism and to trace the development of several concepts and, in some cases, illustrate experimental methodology with work done in this laboratory.

EFFECT OF ESTROGENS ON UTERINE METABOLISM

The observed enlargement of the uterus after administration of estrogenic substances led to the early identification of the uterus as a target organ for estrogens.

TABLE 1. *Effects of Natural Steroids on Stability of Human Glutamic Dehydrogenases*

Steroid	Residual Activity at 120 min, %	
	With liver enzyme	With uterine enzyme
None	99 (95)	(99)
Dehydroisoandrosterone	93 (92)	(100)
Estradiol-17β	91 (97)	(99)
Testosterone	102 (100)	(108)
Progesterone	103 (90)	(102)
Cortisol	90 (95)	(99)

Each tube contained 0.5 mg glutamic dehydrogenase from human liver or 2.0 mg prepared from uterus, together with the steroid listed at a final concentration of 10 μM. Numbers outside parentheses are values for incubation in phosphate-chloride buffer. Values in parentheses are for incubation in phosphate-chloride-Mg^{2+} buffer.   [Adapted from Warren et al. (101).]

Clearly estrogens are, in essence, growth-stimulating hormones for the uterus.

The introduction of aggressive biochemical investigation came in the 1950s with a series of studies by Mueller and his associates (53, 54, 60, 78, 84, 85, 88), which demonstrated that the rapid uterine growth induced by estradiol is associated with early stimulation of various metabolic pathways involved in one-carbon metabolism, nucleic acid and protein synthesis, and increased activity of amino acid-activating enzymes. Basically these investigations revealed that estrogens caused a marked increase in uterine anabolic activity and biosynthesis of numerous metabolic compounds. An important later aspect of this work was the demonstration that levels of puromycin that blocked protein synthesis prevented these responses, suggesting that they occur secondary to the synthesis of rate-limiting enzymes involved in anabolic pathways (87). Further, Ui & Mueller (131) reported that the estrogen-induced synthesis of RNA, lipid, and protein, as well as a major portion of water imbibition, was blocked by actinomycin D.

Stability and Activity of Preformed Enzymes

The idea that a steroid may express its biological activity by interacting with a macromolecule, inducing a change of conformation in that macromolecule, has long been an attractive one. If the macromolecule is an enzyme, the induced change of conformation might be reflected in a change in activity or stability. In the early 1960s, Tomkins, Yielding, and co-workers (130, 145, 146) demonstrated that certain estrogenic compounds promote dissociation of glutamic dehydrogenase from bovine liver subunits, which resulted in diminished activity toward glutamic acid as substrate. Glucose 6-phosphate dehydrogenase from red cells (74) and mammary tissue (71) was found to be inhibited primarily by 3β-hydroxy-Δ⁵-steroids, and McKerns (79, 80) demonstrated that various steroids inhibited the enzyme from the adrenal

and pituitary. We conducted several experiments to determine the physiological significance of these effects.

GLUTAMIC DEHYDROGENASE. Glutamic dehydrogenase from human liver was purified to homogeneity (4.0 units/mg under the conditions of assay described below). The enzyme from human uterus was purified about 20-fold to 22 milliunits/mg. The effects of various steroids on the activity and stability of these preparations were evaluated (101, 135).

The stability of glutamic dehydrogenase was tested. The enzyme was preincubated at 37 C in concentrations that apparently approximate those in vivo. Usually phosphate-chloride buffer containing 75 μmole potassium-phosphate buffer (pH 7.3) and 5 μmole sodium chloride per milliliter was used. In other instances a phosphate-chloride-Mg^{2+} buffer containing, in addition to the above, 15 μmole magnesium sulfate per milliliter was used. Activity, in all cases, was evaluated spectrophotometrically by generation of reduced cofactor in a 3.0-ml solution containing 130 μmole potassium-phosphate buffer (pH 7.6), 50 μmole L-glutamate, and 2.0 μmole NAD^+. Assays were started by adding enzyme (an aliquot of the preincubation solution), and initial linear velocities were determined. Activity was determined before preincubation and after 60–120 min. The preincubation results reflect the effect of the steroids used on the stability of the enzyme. As shown in Table 1, various steroids at 10 μM concentration had little or no effect on the stability of the enzymes from the liver and uterus.

To evaluate the effects of steroids and diethylstilbestrol on enzymatic activity, they were added to the assay solution described above with NAD^+ or $NADP^+$ as cofactor. As shown in Table 2, some inhibition of the uterine enzyme was seen with 40 μM concentrations, and the biologically active 17β-compounds were more effective than the 17α-epimers. When steroid concentrations were lowered to 1.0 μM, no inhibition was observed.

GLUCOSE 6-PHOSPHATE DEHYDROGENASE. Because steroid concentrations in the placenta and ovary are known, we prepared 6-phosphate dehydrogenase from these sources. The placental enzyme was purified 15-fold to a specific

TABLE 2. *Effects of Steroids and Diethylstilbestrol on Activity of Human Uterine Glutamic Dehydrogenase*

Addition	Activity, %	
	With NAD^+	With $NADP^+$
Diethylstilbestrol	2	1
Estradiol-17β	77	67
Estradiol-17α	95	100
Testosterone	85	100
Epitestosterone	98	100

Results were obtained by using the described assay with 1 μmole cofactor and 0.2 mg enzyme. Steroids (40 μM) were added in 0.05 ml propylene glycol. Activities with NAD^+ and $NADP^+$ are expressed as percentages of a control to which only propylene glycol was added.   [Adapted from Warren et al. (101).]

activity of 348 milliunits/mg and the corpus luteum enzyme 22-fold to a specific activity of 2.72 units/mg.

Several steroid hormones inhibited the placental enzyme at 10 μM concentrations, but none were effective at 0.1 μM concentrations [Table 3; (18)]. The greatest inhibitory effects with ovarian enzyme were seen with Δ^5-3β-hydroxysteroids, but even these effects were absent at 0.1 μM concentrations (95).

The ovarian enzyme was washed three times with 70% (NH$_4$)$_2$SO$_4$ to remove essentially all bound NADP$^+$, as described by Kirkman & Hendrickson (64) for glucose 6-phosphate dehydrogenase purified from human erythrocytes. With the ovarian enzyme, 92% of the enzymatic activity was lost. Reactivation was studied by adding washed enzyme equivalent to 0.7 unit of unwashed enzyme per milliliter to each of several vials containing standard assay buffer with cofactors and steroids in the concentrations shown (Fig. 1). An aliquot was assayed immediately after addition and after 60 and 120 min of preincubation. Addition of a physiological level of NADP$^+$ (10^{-5} M) to the washed enzyme restored about 95% of the original activity at 37 C (42). The NADP$^+$-induced reactivation was about five times as rapid at 37 C as it was at 25 C. It was not retarded at either temperature by 10^{-5} M estradiol-17α, estradiol-17β, or dehydroisoandrosterone (3β-hydroxy-androst-5-ene-17-one). Rather extensive studies on the stability of the enzyme from corpus luteum and placenta also revealed no significant effects of these steroids on stability.

CONCLUSIONS. Although steroids may affect the stability and activity of preformed enzymes, the data we obtained with glucose 6-phosphate dehydrogenase and glutamic dehydrogenase from several sources lead us to doubt that these observations are of any physiological significance. Effects on stability are seen only at concentrations several times those found in the uterus. These observations certainly do not rule out the reaction of a steroid and some macromolecule as the ultimate mediator of estrogen action, but they do militate against the possibility that either of the above enzymes could be that macromolecule.

TABLE 3. *Inhibition of Placental Glucose 6-Phosphate Dehydrogenase by Steroids*

Steroid	Inhibition, %		
	10^{-5} M	10^{-6} M	10^{-7} M
Dehydroisoandrosterone	70	20	0
Pregnenolone	53	20	0
17α-Hydroxypregnenolone	20	0	0
5α-Androstane-3,17β-diol	60	30	0
Androstenedione	20	0	0
Estradiol-17β	0*	0	0

Results obtained with 80 milliunits enzyme, 0.6 μmole NADP$^+$, and steroids at concentrations shown are expressed as percent inhibition compared to controls to which only vehicle (propylene glycol) was added.   *Similar lack of inhibition obtained with 0.075 μmole NADP$^+$ (2.5 × 10^{-5} M).   [Adapted from Betz & Warren (18).]

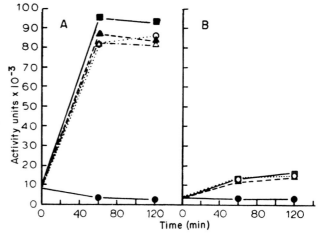

FIG. 1. Reactivation of glucose 6-phosphate dehydrogenase from bovine ovaries by exposure of washed enzyme to control (*closed circles*); 10^{-5} M NADP$^+$ (*closed triangles*); 10^{-5} M NADP$^+$ with 10^{-5} M estradiol-17α (*open circles*); 10^{-5} M NADP$^+$ with 10^{-5} M estradiol-17β (*closed squares*); and 10^{-5} M dehydroisoandrosterone (*open triangles*). A: preincubated and assayed at 37 C. B: preincubated and assayed at 25 C. Assay carried out in 0.05 M tris [tris-(hydroxymethyl)amino methane] buffer, 0.01 M MgSO$_4$, and 7.0 mM β-mercaptoethanol (pH 8.0). Reactions started by addition of enzyme (aliquots of the preincubation solutions). [Adapted from Nielson & Warren (95).]

Carbohydrate Metabolism

GLUCOSE UTILIZATION. Szego & Roberts (125) demonstrated that glucose utilization in rat uterus is increased as early as 4 hr after estrogen administration. Incorporation in the uterus in vitro of uniformly labeled glucose-^{14}C into protein, RNA, lipid, and CO$_2$ was markedly increased as early as 1 or 2 hr after estrogen administrations (93). Further, this increase was blocked by administration of actinomycin D or cycloheximide.

We examined the relationship between enzyme activity and the activity of certain metabolic pathways in rat uterus (12) after administration of estradiol-17β. Activities of glucose 6-phosphate and 6-phosphogluconate dehydrogenase were studied. The relative rates of glucose utilization via the glycolytic and hexose-monophosphate shunt pathways in rat uterine segments in Robinson's medium were assessed by following the formation of ^{14}CO$_2$ from glucose-1-^{14}C in vitro. Incorporation of the two glucose carbon atoms into lipid, protein, and RNA by these segments in vitro was also examined.

After intravenous administration of 5.0 μg estradiol-17β to a 250-g rat castrated 4 weeks previously, formation of CO$_2$ by uterine segments in vitro from carbon atoms 1 and 6 of glucose is elevated at 2 hr (Fig. 2). The ratio of carbon 1 to carbon 6 incorporated into CO$_2$ increases linearly with time after estrogen administration (Fig. 3). Nevertheless, in the first 6 hr after estrogen administration, no increase in the activity of glucose 6-phosphate and 6-phosphogluconate dehydrogenases was noted (Fig. 4). Induction of both enzymes is seen after 6 hr.

These observations suggest that estradiol controls glucose metabolism in the uterus by at least two mechanisms.

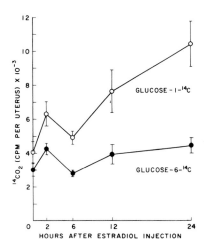

FIG. 2. Effect of estradiol on rate of incorporation of labeled glucose into $^{14}CO_2$ by rat uterine segments. *Open circles*, amounts of $^{14}CO_2$ produced in a 2-hr incubation in vitro from glucose-1-^{14}C; *closed circles*, amounts of $^{14}CO_2$ produced from glucose-6-^{14}C. Values expressed as means ± SE. [Adapted from Barker & Warren (12).]

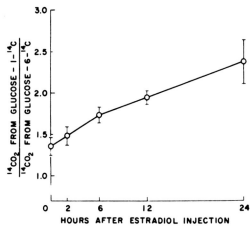

FIG. 3. Effect of estradiol on ratio per uterus of $^{14}CO_2$ produced from glucose-1-^{14}C to $^{14}CO_2$ produced from glucose-6-^{14}C. Rat uterine segments produce CO_2 in a 2-hr incubation in vitro. Values expressed as means (*open circles*) ± SE. [Adapted from Barker & Warren (12).]

The first, prominent 2 hr after administration, results in increased metabolism of glucose to CO_2 via the glycolytic and the hexose-monophosphate shunt pathways and logically results from an estrogen effect on glucose uptake or phosphorylation to glucose 6-phosphate. The second results in a linear increase in the proportion of glucose metabolized via the hexose-monophosphate shunt pathway as a function of time after estradiol injection and may reflect the observed induction of hexose-monophosphate shunt enzymes.

More direct studies of the first mechanism have been made, which indicate that it is the uptake of glucose that is enhanced by estrogen administration. Roskoski & Steiner (106) demonstrated that estradiol-17β increased the initial rate of transport of the nonmetabolized glucose analogue, 3-O-methyl-D-glucose, into uterine cells as early as 2 hr after its administration. Further they showed

that its transport obeyed Michaelis-Menten kinetics and that the effect of estrogen was to increase the maximum velocity (V_{max}) twofold with no effect on the Michaelis-Menten constant (K_m). They concluded that the uterine sugar transport system has many characteristics similar to the transport systems of other tissues but is also responsive to estrogen. Smith & Gorski (114) used 2-deoxyglucose-1-^{14}C, which is not utilized beyond the 6-phosphate stage; they demonstrated that 1 hr after treatment with 5.0 μg estradiol-17β, uterine segments showed a 135% increase in conversion of 2-deoxyglucose-1-^{14}C to the 6-phosphate. Thus a very early estrogen effect is acceleration of the transport step. Further, cycloheximide abolished the hormone effect.

ENZYME ACTIVITIES. We carried out a study on the effects of estradiol-17β on induction of dehydrogenases in the uterine supernatant (11). The total activity of these enzymes in the soluble fraction (supernatant of uteri homogenized in Robinson's medium and centrifuged at $105,000 \times g$ for 30 min) of the ovariectomized rat uterus was measured before and 12 hr after administration of 5.0 μg of estradiol-17β. All preparations were checked for the absence of endogenous NADH- and NADPH-oxidase activity, as well as the absence of activity without the appropriate substrate. Results are expressed as units per uterus. Assays were conducted by standard methods of Glock & McLean (42), Ochoa (98), Velick (133), Kornberg (66), and Abe et al. (2). Significant increases in D-glucose 6-phosphate:NADP oxidoreductase (G6PD) and 6-phospho-D-gluconate:NADP oxidoreductase (6PGD) are seen (Table 4). Other activities do not increase significantly, and L-isocitrate:NADP oxidoreductase (ICDH) decreases slightly. No estrogen-dependent

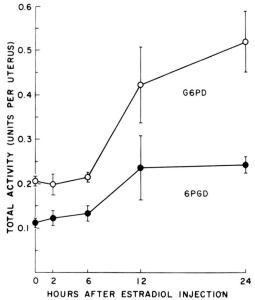

FIG. 4. Effect of estradiol on the total activity of glucose 6-phosphate dehydrogenase (*G6PD*) and 6-phosphogluconate dehydrogenase (*6PGD*) in the rat uterus. *Open circles*, units of *G6PD*; *closed circles*, units of *6PGD*. Values expressed as means ± SE. [Adapted from Barker & Warren (12).]

TABLE 4. *Effect of Estradiol on Total Activity of Several Dehydrogenases in the Uterus of the Ovariectomized Rat*

Enzyme*	Control, units/uterus per min	12-Hr Estradiol Treated		
		units/uterus per min	% of control	P
G6PD	0.131 ± 0.010	0.188 ± 0.021	143.5	<0.05
6PGD	0.075 ± 0.003	0.094 ± 0.009	125.3	<0.05
MADH	0.016 ± 0.004	0.029 ± 0.003	181.3	<0.05
ICDH	0.676 ± 0.031	0.598 ± 0.053	88.5	
GAPD	0.041 ± 0.006	0.090 ± 0.024	219.5	<0.10
LDH	1.66 ± 0.14	1.67 ± 0.15	100.6	

Each value represents average enzyme activity ± SE of 3 or 4 preparations from uterine segments, each of which was taken randomly from a pool of 16 uteri. Data statistically analyzed by the t test for nonpaired variates.   *G6PD, D-glucose-6-phosphate:NADP oxidoreductase; 6PGD, 6-phospho-D-gluconate: NADP oxidoreductase; MADH, L-malate:NADP oxidoreductase; ICDH, L-isocitrate:NADP oxidoreductase; GAPD, D-glyceraldehyde-3-phosphate:NAD oxidoreductase; LDH, L-lactate: NAD oxidoreductase.   [Adapted from Barker et al. (11).]

pyridine-nucleotide transhydrogenase could be detected in controls or after administration of estradiol-17β. These results parallel those of Mueller (86), who could not detect transhydrogenase, and those of Eckstein & Villee (38) who noted that, although pentose cycle enzymes from the uterus were increased 24 hr after estrogen administration, no increase in various Krebs cycle enzymes was noted and ICDH decreased.

Singhal and associates have shown that estradiol administered to the ovariectomized rat increases the activity of phosphohexose-isomerase (113), phosphofructokinase (112), and supernatant hexokinase (132). All these effects are seen within 4 hr after steroid administration and are inhibited by various inhibitors of protein and RNA synthesis. Therefore the authors have concluded that they represent effects on de novo synthesis of these enzymes rather than activation. Although this is a reasonable, tentative assumption, the activation could theoretically result from increased amounts of some other protein activator. Absolute conclusions on these and on the other cited increases in enzyme activity in this chapter await the demonstration of increased amounts of enzyme. One technique used for this purpose is to effect incorporation of a radioactive amino acid, then isolate the enzyme to homogeneity and determine specific activity, or to remove the enzyme with a specific antibody for quantitation. Results of such studies are presently not available for the uterus.

Baquer & McLean (9) reported that intraperitoneal administration of 10 μg estradiol benzoate to the immature rat caused within 4 hr (before an increase in total activity was seen) a change in the distribution of hexokinase activity between particulate and supernatant fractions with an 80% increase in the activity of particulate-bound type I hexokinase. It may be pertinent that this hexokinase has a lower K_m for ATP, since Aaronson et al. (1) have shown that the concentration of uterine ATP

falls about 50% within 4 hr after estrogen is administered to the castrated animal.

Bitman and co-workers (22) have shown that small increases in uterine glycogen are evident in the uterus 2 hr after estrogen administration and that glycogen steadily increases for several hours thereafter.

CONCLUSION. Estradiol definitely increases glucose utilization by the uterus. Uptake of glucose and the incorporation of glucose into CO_2, lipid, RNA, protein, and glycogen are increased. The activity of the pentose-phosphate pathway increases, and several enzymes responsible for carbohydrate metabolism display increased activity, presumably because estradiol has induced their de novo synthesis. This general activation of glucose uptake and metabolism by estradiol is exactly what one would expect from a hormone that induces growth. Although certain of these responses occur before others, all are seen in a matter of hours, not minutes, and there is no compelling evidence that these changes in carbohydrate metabolism represent a "primary response" to estradiol. Rather, they seem to represent secondary responses resulting from biological amplification, via a genomic (RNA and protein synthesis) mechanism, of the smaller (and thus more difficult to detect) primary response. For that elusive primary response, we must turn to the area of protein and RNA synthesis where responses occur in minutes instead of hours.

RNA and Protein Synthesis

That RNA synthesis is a significant and early factor in the control of uterine metabolism by estrogen was well documented in 1963 by reports from the laboratories of Ui & Mueller (131), Hamilton (47), Noteboom & Gorski (96), Wilson (141), and Talwar & Segal (127). Continued investigation has been active and parallels the general advance in the methodology of molecular biology. For a time, the overall prize in the "first metabolic event" category was held by Means & Hamilton (81). They reported that estrogen administration caused an in vivo increase of 40% in the incorporation of labeled uridine into uterine nuclear RNA of the castrated rat within 2 min.

A steroid that exerts important, direct effects in the nucleus should be expected to go there, and indeed that is the case. Localization, concentration, and persistent presence of estradiol in target organs (uterus and vagina), as compared with nontarget tissues (liver, kidney, blood, and muscle), were demonstrated by Jensen & Jacobson (58). Toft & Gorski (129) described a 9.5S cytosol receptor in the uterus and reported that the macromolecule was a protein, because it was destroyed by proteolytic enzymes but not by ribonuclease. Jensen and co-workers (59) reported that this receptor participated in the intranuclear transfer of estradiol by a process that "consumes" the 9S cytosol fraction as a nuclear 5S fraction appeared. Although several other studies have been done on this receptor, they are not detailed here, since they are discussed in the chapter by Gorski in this volume of the *Handbook*.

Evidence for concentration of estradiol in calf endometrial nuclei was presented by Maurer & Chalkley (76) who reported that it was bound to chromatin in a hormone- and tissue-specific manner. Using cesium chloride gradient centrifugation, they found the steroid bound to a protein component of the chromatin material. The binding was reversible at 37 C, and estradiol was not metabolized before binding. [For those who wish more information on the nature of chromatin, the work of Bonner et al. (23) is recommended.] Stumpf (117), with autoradiographic techniques, observed nuclear accumulation of ³H-estradiol in such target tissues as the uterus, but not in liver and adrenal.

The most attractive hypothesis for the expression of specificity in the differentiation and growth that follow estrogen administration is derepression of specific genes. Although Gorski (44) had elegantly shown that in vitro synthesis of RNA from nucleotide-triphosphate precursors by isolated uterine nuclei was elevated 1 hr after estrogen treatment of the intact immature rat, the mechanism remained unknown. It seemed pertinent to determine whether the action of estrogen in the system was due to activation of RNA polymerase, changes in nuclear membrane permeability, or derepression of DNA. Only the derepression mechanism directly provides the specificity desirable in the system.

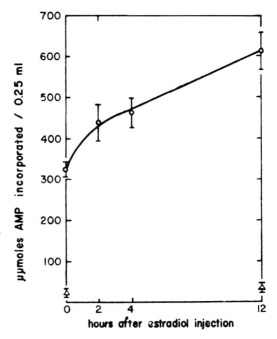

FIG. 6. *Open circles*, template capacity of purified rat uterine chromatin prepared from rats at various times after a single injection of 5.0 μg estradiol-17β. Incubations carried out as described with 12 μg DNA in the form of purified chromatin. Added polymerase was capable of incorporating 9,040 pmole AMP/0.25 ml when 50 μg purified salmon-sperm DNA was used as a primer, and the incorporation without primer (405 pmole AMP/0.25 ml) has been subtracted from the values reported. Each chromatin preparation was made from 3 or 4 uteri, and the number of preparations represented is 7, 4, 4, and 6 for the 0-, 2-, 4-, and 12-hr points, respectively. Template capacity of each chromatin preparation was determined in duplicate. *Open triangles*, incorporation without added polymerase by 12 μg DNA in the form of purified chromatin. Data presented as mean ± SEM. [Adapted from Barker & Warner (13).]

ESTRADIOL EFFECTS ON TEMPLATE CAPACITY OF UTERINE CHROMATIN. We demonstrated that estradiol-17β stimulates the capacity of purified chromatin from the uteri of castrated rats to serve as template for DNA-dependent RNA polymerase (14). The chromatin was prepared, as described by Marushige & Bonner (75), and incubated, as described by Bonner & Huang (24); DNA-dependent RNA polymerase was prepared from early log phase *Escherichia coli* cells by the method of Chamberlin & Berg (26) to a purity corresponding with their fraction 3.

Chromatin was first prepared from animals 12 hr after the injection of 5.0 μg estradiol-17β. A comparison of the template capacity of purified chromatin from control and estrogen-primed uteri is shown in Figure 5. These data indicate that in the presence of added polymerase the template capacity of chromatin (equivalent to 12 μg DNA) from estrogen-treated animals is about 75% above that from control uteri. The endogenous ribonuclease of this system was negligible. Further the addition of 3.0 μM estradiol-17β to the assay solution immediately before assay had no effect. Template capacity of uterine chromatin was significantly elevated 2 hr after the administration of estradiol-17β and increased over the entire 12-hr period of evaluation (Fig. 6). The purified chro-

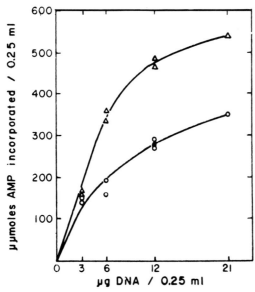

FIG. 5. Template capacity of rat uterine chromatin purified from 12 control rats (*open circles*) and that from 12 rats injected 12 hr before killing with 5.0 μg estradiol-17β (*open triangles*). Incubations were carried out as described with various concentrations of DNA in the form of purified chromatin. Added polymerase was capable of incorporating 11,640 pmole AMP/0.25 ml when 50 μg purified salmon-sperm DNA was used as a primer, and incorporation without primer (393 pmole AMP/0.25 ml) has been subtracted from the values reported. Each point represents one incubation. *Closed circle*, effect of adding 3 μM estradiol-17β to incubation mixture containing 12 μg DNA in the form of purified chromatin from control rats. [Adapted from Barker & Warren (13).]

TABLE 5. *Template Capacity of Purified Chromatin Prepared From Uterus, Lung, and Liver of Ovariectomized Rats*

Chromatin Source	pmole AMP Incorporated per 0.25 ml		
	Control	Estradiol-17β	Control, %
Uterus	144	261	181*
Lung	761	727	96
Liver	1,800	1,628	91

Chromatin was purified from tissues of 12 control and 12 estradiol-17β-treated (12 hr before killing) rats. Incubations were carried out as described with 12 μg DNA in the form of purified chromatin. Added polymerase was capable of incorporating 8,450 pmole AMP/0.25 ml when 50 μg purified salmon-sperm DNA was used as a primer, and incorporation without primer (387 pmole AMP/0.25 ml) has been subtracted from the values reported. Each chromatin preparation was assayed in duplicate.   *Significant at $P < 0.05$.   [Adapted from Barker & Warren (13).]

matin contained very little RNA-polymerase activity. The estrogen-induced increase in template activity of chromatin is specific for the uterus, since no effect was seen with chromatin from lung and liver (Table 5).

These data were the first to indicate that estradiol-17β causes a tissue-specific increase in the template capacity of uterine chromatin. They paralleled the hepatic response to cortisol detected by Dahmus & Bonner (35).

VARIATION IN TEMPLATE CAPACITY DURING THE ESTROUS CYCLE. Warren & Barker (134) investigated whether such fluctuations in template capacity of chromatin parallel physiological changes in estrogen concentration by studying the intact, cycling golden hamster in the absence of exogenous steroid. Animals were grouped according to the stage of their estrous cycle. On the morning of the experiment, uteri were taken from animals in each of the 4 days of the cycle. Chromatin was prepared from some uteri, and other uteri were cut into segments for incubation with glucose-1-^{14}C and glucose-6-^{14}C in Robinson's medium. Template activity was evaluated as above, and the RNA fractions were isolated and quantitated from the glucose incubations, as described by Gorski & Nicolette (45). As shown in Figure 7, template capacity remains essentially constant on days 1–3 of the cycle and is elevated about 50% on day 4. Incorporation of radioactivity from glucose into RNA follows the same pattern, but the increase on day 4 is 100%. Events in the extremely regular cycle of the hamster indicate that estrogen levels begin to rise on day 3 and are maximal early on day 4.

The increase in template capacity and the incorporation of ^{14}C from glucose into RNA on day 4 of the estrous cycle are results similar to those observed after administration of 5.0 μg estradiol-17β to the ovariectomized rat (12, 13). Certainly administration of this quantity of steroid to a rat ovariectomized 4 weeks previously represents a marked change in estrogen status. That changes of similar magnitude occur in the hamster between days

3 and 4 of its cycle indicates *a*) that metabolic activity of the uterus is capable of great change within the interval of one estrous cycle; *b*) that physiological amounts of estrogen are capable of eliciting marked increases in RNA synthesis and chromatin template capacity in uterine tissues that have not been estrogen deprived for long periods of time; and *c*) that a strong correlation exists between the template capacity of chromatin and RNA synthesis in the uterus.

EFFECTS IN VITRO. Although estradiol-17β causes an increase in template activity in the intact, cycling, and treated castrated animal, we were not certain whether this was a primary nuclear event and thus set out to evaluate the possibility that estradiol-17β might increase the template capacity of chromatin in vitro (14). Chromatin was prepared from the uteri and lungs of adult rats that had been castrated 4 weeks previously. This chromatin was preincubated at 37 C with and without steroids for various periods of time. Then aliquots were taken for the determination of template capacity.

Incubation of chromatin prepared from the uterus and lung of ovariectomized animals at 37 C results in a progressive (and approximately fourfold) increase in template capacity over a 12-hr period (Table 6). The presence of 5 μM estradiol-17β clearly enhances this increase with uterine chromatin but has no effect with lung chro-

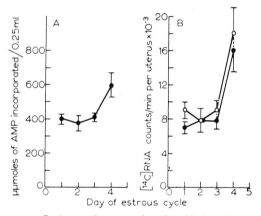

FIG. 7. *A*: template capacity of purified uterine chromatin from hamsters in different days of the estrous cycle. Reaction mixture in a final volume of 0.25 ml contained 10 μmole tris buffer (pH 8.0); 1.0 μmole MgCl₂; 0.25 μmole MnCl₂; 3.0 μmole β-mercaptoethanol; 0.1 μmole each of cytosine triphosphate (CTP), uridine triphosphate (UTP), and guanidine triphosphate (GTP); 0.1 μmole [8-^{14}C]ATP (1,000 count/min per nmole); 25 μg DNA in the form of purified chromatin and purified DNA-dependent RNA polymerase. Added polymerase was capable of incorporating 8,120 pmole AMP/0.25 ml when 50 μg purified salmon-sperm DNA was used as a primer, and incorporation without primer (374 pmole AMP/0.25 ml) has been subtracted from the values reported. Each value represents the mean ± SE of 4 preparations, each containing uterine horns from 4 animals. Template capacity of each chromatin preparation was determined in duplicate. *B*: incorporation of ^{14}C from glucose into RNA in vitro by uteri from animals in different days of the estrous cycle. Segments incubated 2 hr at 37 C in 2.0 ml Robinson's medium containing 2 mg (0.25 μc/mg) of [1-^{14}C]-glucose (*open circles*) or [6-^{14}C]glucose (*closed circles*). Each value represents the mean ± SE of 4 incubations, each containing 2 segments prepared as described in the text. [Adapted from Warren & Barker (134).]

TABLE 6. *Effect of Estradiol-17β on Template Capacity of Purified Chromatin from Rat Uterus and Lung*

Experiment	Chromatin Source	In Vitro Treatment	pmole AMP Incorporated per 0.25 ml	
			0 hr	12 hr
1	Uterus	Control	280	950
	Uterus	Estradiol-17β	272	1,750
2	Uterus	Control	270	1,245
	Uterus	Estradiol-17β	241	2,060
	Lung	Control	1,000	4,675
	Lung	Estradiol-17β	948	4,540
3	Uterus	Control	415	1,485
	Uterus	Estradiol-17β	419	1,742
	Lung	Control	817	4,475
	Lung	Estradiol-17β	910	4,570

Chromatin for each experiment was purified from tissues of 12 ovariectomized rats (no in vivo hormone treatment) and assayed for template capacity, as indicated with 12 μg DNA in the form of purified chromatin. Preincubations were carried out in tris [tris(hydroxymethyl)amino methane] buffer (0.01 M, pH 8.0) with and without 5 μM estradiol-17β for the indicated time at 37 C. Added polymerase was capable of incorporating 11,950 pmole AMP/0.25 ml when 50 μg of purified salmon-sperm DNA was used as primer, and incorporation without primer (400 pmole AMP/0.25 ml) has been subtracted from the values reported. Each value represents the mean of duplicate assays. In addition to chromatin and enzyme, the template capacity assay system contained 10 μmole tris buffer (pH 8.0); 1.0 μmole $MgCl_2$; 0.25 μmole $MnCl_2$; 2.0 μmole β-mercaptoethanol; 0.1 μmole each of cytosine triphosphate (CTP), uridine triphosphate (UTP), and guanidine triphosphate (GTP); and 0.1 μmole ATP-8-^{14}C (1,000 count/min per nmole) in a final volume of 0.25 ml. [Adapted from Barker & Warren (14).]

matin. Further, estradiol-17β effects, which are clearly evident after 12 hr of incubation, are not clearly manifest after 4 hr of incubation. The biologically inactive epimer, estradiol-17α, added in similar concentrations inhibited the increase in template capacity of uterine chromatin (Table 7). The inclusion of penicillin (10,000 units/ml) in the incubation medium had no effect on the observed activation of uterine chromatin. A DNA assay (diphenylamine) on the supernatant (10,000 × g for 30 min) of activated chromatin in the RNA-synthesis mixture (without β-mercaptoethanol) indicated that at least 95 % of the DNA added in the form of chromatin was soluble.

Response of uterine but not of lung chromatin to in vitro incubation with estradiol-17β but not estradiol-17α suggests that some inherent tissue and hormone specificity is preserved in the purified chromatin and supports the possibility that the steroid enhances the transcription of the genetic material in the nucleus. Although the physicochemical nature of chromatin activation by in vitro incubation is not presently known, the process is apparently influenced in a very specific manner by the addition of the biologically active estrogen.

In each of the five experiments with the uterine chromatin, in vitro estradiol-17β activated template capacity over that of the controls. In the two least impressive experiments (Table 6, experiment 3; and Table 7, experiment 1) the activation was only 16 and 20 % above that

of the controls. In these two experiments, the original template capacity of the chromatin preparations used was greater than those of preparations that demonstrated more impressive responses.

Two distinct limitations of these in vitro observations arise in the prolonged incubation time and high concentrations required for the estradiol-17β-induced increase in template capacity to become clearly evident. These limitations may be due to extensive removal of some component of the system (perhaps receptor protein) by the physical agitation of purification. Tissue and hormone specificities suggest that these in vitro observations may well be relevant.

The original interpretation offered for the observation that estradiol-17α decreased template activity in vitro was that it could displace small amounts of estradiol-17β remaining even in the castrated animals. Barker & Anderson (10) have recently shown that intraluminal estradiol-17α can displace, from the uterus, previously administered estradiol-17β (administered intravenously or intraluminally) and that this displacement is accompanied by a reduced template capacity of uterine chromatin.

PROTEIN SYNTHESIS. Numerous experiments cited above clearly demonstrated that increased protein synthesis was a response to estradiol. Early experiments analyzed general protein synthesis or enzyme induction often present after several hours, but more recent efforts have centered on proteins synthesized soon after estradiol was administered. This initial protein precedes the amplification step effected at the gene level and indeed may cause it. One such protein has been described by Barnea & Gorski (15) and by Manol & Thayer (77). This topic is not dis-

TABLE 7. *Effect of Estradiol-17α and Estradiol-17β on Template Capacity of Purified Chromatin from Rat Uterus*

Experiment	In Vitro Treatment	pmole AMP Incorporated per 0.25 ml	
		0 hr	12 hr
1	Control	303	925
	Estradiol-17α	324	545
	Estradiol-17β	325	1,100
2	Control	191	468
	Estradiol-17α	230	287
	Estradiol-17β	218	2,609

Chromatin for each experiment was purified from the tissues of 12 ovariectomized rats (no in vivo hormone treatment) and assayed for template capacity with 12 μg DNA in the form of purified chromatin. Preincubations were carried out in tris buffer (0.01 M, pH 8.0) with 5 μM estradiol-17α or estradiol-17β for the indicated time at 37 C. Added polymerase was capable of incorporating 8,385 pmole AMP/0.25 ml when 50 μg purified salmon-sperm DNA was used as primer, and incorporation without primer (236 pmole AMP/0.25 ml) has been subtracted from the values reported. Each value represents the mean of duplicate assays. Components of template capacity assay system are as indicated in Table 6. [Adapted from Barker & Warren (14).]

cussed further, since it is covered by J. Gorski in his chapter in Part 1 of this volume of the *Handbook*.

Another topic of particular interest has been the study of estrogen effects on RNA-polymerase activities. Hamilton et al. (50) reported that the product of Mg^{2+}-activated RNA polymerase in the uterus is similar to ribosomal RNA in terms of base composition and nearest neighbor frequencies, whereas that of $Mn^{2+}(NH_4)_2SO_4$-activated polymerase is more similar to DNA. Hamilton et al. (49) reported that, after administration of estradiol, Mg^{2+}-activated RNA polymerase is stimulated first (1 hr vs. 12 hr). They conclude that a ribosomal type of RNA is first produced. This conclusion is supported by Billing et al. (19) who reported that the earliest type of RNA to increase after estrogen administration was Q-1 RNA, the ribosomal RNA precursor.

CONCLUSIONS. All types of RNA are produced in the uterus after estrogen administration. Ultimately, increases in ribosomal, messenger, and transfer RNA occur. The evidence supports a system

$$\text{hormone} \rightarrow X \rightarrow \text{genome} \rightarrow \text{RNA} \rightarrow \text{protein}$$

A fascinating experiment by Segal and co-workers (107) shows that, 4 hr after estrogen is given to a group of castrated rats, uterine RNA could be extracted and given intraluminally to a second group of castrated rats in which it caused the classic morphological picture of estrogen stimulation. This response was not seen when RNA from untreated rats, RNA from treated rats after ribonuclease treatment, or RNA from liver was used. These observations clearly indicate that the estrogen-induced RNA is the active principle or final common pathway for the biological response.

The receptor protein of the uterine cytosol probably plays an important role in the mechanism of estrogen action in that organ. Good evidence suggests that this receptor is a component for the transfer of estradiol-17β into the nucleus and "that is where the action is"—at least some of it. The result of the intranuclear appearance of estradiol is ultimately an increase in RNA synthesis that occurs, at least in part, by gene derepression and increased template capacity of uterine chromatin. Further, estradiol action to increase RNA synthesis can be shown in vitro with chromatin, although these experiments are still somewhat inconclusive. The sequence of events between intranuclear arrival of the estrogen and the resulting outpouring of RNA remains unknown.

The rapid labeling of nuclear RNA in vivo 2 min after estrogen administration is an attractive candidate for the primary metabolic event in this system. Indeed, Hamilton in a review of the subject (48) has already concluded that binding to chromatin and stimulation of RNA synthesis in the nucleolus are primary events in early estrogen action. Nevertheless he states that the precise and primary molecular mechanisms involved in estrogen action remain undiscovered, and we are inclined to agree with him.

Nonnuclear Mechanisms

One of the striking responses of the uterus to estradiol-17β can be detected with nothing but an observing eye. Within a minute or so after intravenous estrogen administration, a distinct hyperemia is clearly evident in rat uterus. The speed and magnitude of this response and the subsequent imbibition of water are impressive and suggest that membrane phenomena occurring independently of, and prior to, nuclear responses may be a component in the mechanism whereby estrogens affect uterine metabolism. Spaziani & Szego (116) and Shelesnyak (109) noted that estrogen administration diminished uterine histamine concentrations and total content and proposed this event as the metabolic basis for the observed hyperemia and permeability change. Unfortunately they assayed hours instead of minutes after treatment. Szego and co-workers then showed that intraluminal application of histamine mimics the estradiol effect in stimulating the incorporation of radioactive amino acids into uterine protein, lipids, and purines (123) and even in the induction of endometrial mitoses (126).

Over the last decade, cyclic 3',5'-adenosine monophosphate (cyclic AMP) has been shown to function as an intracellular messenger and has been implicated as an intermediary in the mechanism of action of several protein hormones. Observations by Sutherland & Rall (118) and Kakiuchi & Rall (61) indicated that epinephrine and histamine, respectively, enhanced the accumulation of cyclic AMP in specific organs. Szego considered that estrogens might also, via histamine or even some other intermediary, affect cyclic AMP. Szego & Davis (120) demonstrated that intravenous estradiol-17β (1.0 μg/100 g body wt) caused a significant increase in rat uterine cyclic AMP within 15 sec. By doing so, they captured and now hold the all-time prize in the "first metabolic event" category that Szego had previously only shared with Means & Hamilton (81). This increase in cyclic AMP was only transient; it began to fall within 5 min and returned to normal levels 60 min after estrogen administration, as shown in Figure 8. No increase was seen with estradiol-17α, even when it was given in doses of 25 μg/100 g body wt. Szego & Davis (122) subsequently demonstrated that the estrogen-induced elevation of uterine cyclic AMP is blocked by the β-adrenergic blocking agent, propranolol, whereas the α-adrenergic blocking agents, phentolamine and dibenzyline, had no affect. They suggested that adenyl cyclase is associated with β-receptor function.

The pertinent question now was whether cyclic AMP was capable of demonstrating estrogen-like anabolic effects in uterus. Hechter and co-workers (52) reported that it did. By using uterine horns in vitro, they found that cyclic AMP increased protein and RNA synthesis and widely stimulated biosynthetic processes involving lipids and glycogen. The effects of cyclic AMP were partially, but not completely, abolished by actinomycin D. Inclusion of 10 mM glucose also stimulated several of the processes they studied, as did several other nucleotides.

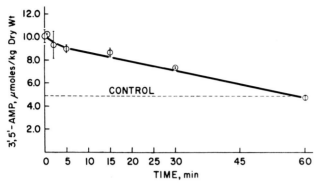

FIG. 8. Time course of estradiol effect on uterine cyclic 3′,5′-AMP. Estradiol-17β as the sodium salt (1 μg/100 g body wt) was administered intravenously at zero time. Control animals received vehicle alone. Points for estradiol-treated animals are composed of average duplicates with deviations shown. The 0.5-min group represents the mean of 6 samples and the corresponding SEM. Control values represented by a *horizontal line*. [Adapted from Szego & Davis (120).]

Sharma & Talwar (108) extended these studies by using stretched uterine horns from ovariectomized rats in vitro. They found cyclic AMP effective, even at 0.1 mM concentrations, in stimulating both uptake of radioactive uridine and leucine and their incorporation into RNA and protein. Only cyclic AMP was effective in the first 15 min, although several other nucleotides did cause similar but smaller effects within 2 hr. Because cyclic AMP appeared to facilitate primarily the uptake of the precursors they used during the first 15–30 min, Sharma and Talwar suggested that the increased labeling of RNA during this period resulted merely from the increase in intracellular uridine. On prolonged incubation (1–2 hr) the relative specific activity of RNA increased, which indicated activation of the transcription process. In this regard, Billing et al. (20) have also shown that estradiol-17β increases incorporation of radioactive uridine and guanosine into the intracellular acid-soluble fraction during the first 2 hr after its administration.

Birchall & Halkerson (21) attempted to further evaluate the intermediary role of histamine in the overall process by using antihistamines. They could draw no conclusions because all the antihistamines tried formed insoluble complexes with RNA and depressed incorporation of uridine-³H.

Szego has contended that estradiol-17β works through activation of membrane phenomena (release of histamine; activation of adenyl cyclase, which is membrane bound; and release of β-glucuronidase from lysosomes) with generalized reorientation of cytostructural surfaces (122). She has suggested that inhibition of the uterine response to estradiol-17β by actinomycin D results from its effects on the adrenal with liberation of glucocorticoids (which stabilize uterine membrane structures) rather than by a direct action of the antibiotic on RNA synthesis. This suggestion is supported by the observations that actinomycin D has little or no effect in the adrenalectomized rat (72, 124) and that glucocorticoids inhibit the estrogen-induced elevation of cyclic AMP in rat uterus (121).

Nicolette & Mueller (94) restudied the effects of actinomycin D on the uterine response to estrogen in ovariectomized rats with and without prior adrenalectomy. They found that a small but significant fraction of the responses studied (water imbibition and incorporation of radioactive glycine into protein and RNA) was indeed insensitive to the antibiotic. According to current concepts, this indicates that part of the response may not depend on RNA synthesis.

Barnea & Gorski (16) demonstrated that guanethidine inhibits the uterine water imbibition response to estrogen but has no effect on in vivo incorporation of cytidine-³H into RNA or in vitro metabolism of glucose-U-¹⁴C into CO_2. This suggests that the responses are mediated in different ways. Ferrando & Nalbandov (41) froze portions of rat uterine horns and demonstrated that estrogen would not induce implantation in these areas, whereas histamine would. They suggested that histamine may mediate the implantation response to estrogen. Of interest was the observation that frozen horns responded equally well to estrogen-induced weight and growth response. These two studies suggest that there may be more than one mediator of estrogen action.

CONCLUSION. Hyperemia, changes in permeability, and release of cytoplasmic-bound materials are early and significant features in estrogen action on the uterus. They would be expected to result in delivery of relatively more estradiol-17β, as well as a host of other metabolites valuable in the growth of the uterus. Arrival of these metabolites (delivery of the groceries) might well effect genomic derepression, as substrate induction (83) is a well-known phenomenon. In this case the specificity of the genomic response would reside in the metabolites made available.

The cytoplasmic receptor effecting the transfer of estradiol-17β into the nucleus (where the complex binds to chromatin, inducing specific increases in template activity) also provides an attractive mechanism for the specificity of the genomic response.

It seems that neither membrane nor genomic effects can be discarded or held to be exclusive of the other at this time. Both are probably important factors in estrogen action, independent but interrelated.

Affinity-Labeling Steroids

Previously cited investigations (59, 129) described a receptor molecule for uterine estrogen that is indeed a protein. Enzyme-active sites have been identified by the covalent bonding of substrate derivatives. We have undertaken the synthesis and evaluation of steroid derivatives in which the steroid moiety delivers the reagent group to the macromolecular steroid binding site. Under this circumstance, reactive amino acid residues adjacent to or within that site should be relatively favored in covalent binding. The literature relating to enzyme affinity labeling suggests that such a strategy might be successful (8, 55, 143).

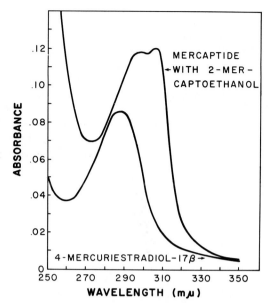

FIG. 9. Absorbance of 39 μM 4-mercuriestradiol-17β (4ME) and its mercaptide with 2-mercaptoethanol produced when 41 μM cysteine in 0.10 M sodium-phosphate buffer (pH 7.5, 25 C) was added to 4ME. [Adapted from Chin & Warren (27).]

4-MERCURI-17β-ESTRADIOL. Because of Boyer's elegant studies of the reaction of organic mercurials with sulfhydryl groups (25) and the work of Terenius (128) and Jensen and co-workers (57), which indicated that sulfhydryl groups may be pertinent in estradiol binding by the receptor, we first synthesized 4-mercuri-17β-estradiol, a steroid derivative with the mercury affixed to the aromatic A-ring of estradiol (27). When 4-mercuri-17β-estradiol (4ME) reacted with cysteine, under physiological conditions, the spectral change shown in Figure 9 was obtained. With reduced glutathione, the maximal spectral increase was also found at 305 mμ. The steroid did not react with glycine, tyrosine, cystine, or lysine. Thus it could be concluded that spectral change at 305 mμ represents mercaptide formation with a cysteine residue. One mole of egg albumin reacts with 3 moles 4ME, which indicates three reactive sulfhydryl groups in the native protein, similar to results with p-mercuribenzoate (27).

When 4ME (20–70 μM) reacts in 3.0 ml of 0.1 M sodium phosphate buffer (pH 7.5, 25 C) with 0.1 μmole reduced glutathione or 0.12 μmole egg albumin, 33 μM estradiol-17β has no effect on the rate of mercaptide formation. With 0.5 mg glutamic dehydrogenase or 1.1 mg pyruvate kinase (two enzymes with steroid binding sites of moderate affinity), mercaptide formation was significantly inhibited by estradiol-17β but not by estriol or cortisone. Finally estradiol-17β did not inhibit the rate of mercaptide formation with 0.75 mg pyruvate kinase and 37.2 μM p-chloromercuribenzoate. These observations (Table 8) are compatible with a mechanism in which the steroid moiety delivers mercury (the reagent) to the allosteric (37, 63, 144) binding sites of glutamic dehydrogenase and pyruvate kinase. The resulting increase in local concentration favors mercaptide formation with a reactive residue at or near that site. Inhibition of mercaptide formation by estradiol-17β occurs because it can occupy the binding site and thus exclude 4ME.

We next evaluated the biological activity of 4ME and its interaction with the uterine receptor protein (90). When estradiol-17β, 4ME, and its mercaptide with 2-mercaptoethanol were applied intraluminally in the uteri of ovariectomized rats, each induced glucose 6-phosphate and 6-phosphogluconate dehydrogenases. No such induction was seen with p-mercuribenzoate or its mercaptide with 2-mercaptoethanol, which suggested that the induction by 4ME is not simply a mercury effect (Table 9). Further, 4ME produced hyperemia and water imbibition, whereas p-mercuribenzoate did not. Finally 25 ng 4ME, applied daily for 4 days, produced an endometrium morphologically similar to that produced by an equal amount of estradiol-17β.

When induction of glucose 6-phosphate dehydrogenase by estradiol-17β and 4ME was studied as a function of time, the results shown in Figure 10 were obtained. For ease of comparison, data are presented as percentage increase over control values. Estradiol-17β effected maximal induction in 40 hr, then decreased rapidly. The 4ME-induced activity peaked at 24 hr but fell very slowly. After 100 hr, estradiol-induced activity was lower than 4ME-induced activity. This experiment was extended with a second group of animals. Activity of the enzyme in the uterus of animals treated with 0.1 μg estradiol-17β returned to control levels at 140 hr. Activity of the enzyme in animals treated with 0.1 μg 4ME remained at 200% of control values 140 hr after treatment and at 155% of control values even at 280 hr.

Investigation with the glycogenic response (as a parameter of estrogenicity) to intraluminally applied 4ME yielded data that supported the above results. First, p-mercuribenzoate failed to induce glycogen synthesis. Second, persistence of 4ME as an estrogen was confirmed, since glycogen levels remained at maximally stimulated values 43 hr after administration of 4ME, although the induction by estradiol-17β had fallen to about 50% of its 18-hr level.

It was conceivable that in vivo demercuration of 4ME occurred in the rat uterus. This possibility was

TABLE 8. *Effect of Steroids on Rate of Mercaptide Formation*

Sulfhydryl Donor	Reagent*	Steroid, 33 μM	Inhibition of Mercaptide Formation
Reduced glutathione	4ME	Estradiol-17β	No
Egg albumin	4ME	Estradiol-17β	No
Glutamic dehydrogenase	4ME	Estradiol-17β	Yes
Pyruvate kinase	4ME	Estradiol-17β	Yes
	4ME	Estriol	No
	4ME	Cortisol	No
	PCMB	Estradiol-17β	No

* 4ME, 4-mercuri-17β-estradiol; PCMB, p-chloromercuribenzoate. [Adapted from Chin & Warren (27).]

TABLE 9 *Enzymatic Response of Ovariectomized Rat Uterus to Intraluminal Administration of Estradiol and Several Mercury Compounds*

Treatment		Enzymatic Activity			
		Glucose-6-P Dehydrogenase		6-P-Gluconate Dehydrogenase	
Compound	Dose, μg	Units/uterus	% of control	Units/uterus	% of control
A					
1.8% Saline		0.098±0.002		0.052±0.001	
Estradiol-17β	0.05	0.224±0.001	229	0.104±0.002	200
	0.10	0.210±0.006	214		
4-Mercuri-17β-estradiol	0.05	0.136±0.002	139	0.070±0.002	135
	0.10	0.224±0.006	229		
4-(2-Hydroxy-ethyl-mer-capto)mer-curi-17β-es-tradiol	0.05	0.188±0.001	192	0.094±0.004	181
	0.10	0.198±0.004	202		
B					
1.8% Saline		0.058±0.004			
p-Mercuriben-zoate	0.0125	0.056±0.002	97		
	0.05	0.052±0.002	90		
	0.125	0.066±0.003	114		
p-Mercuriben-zoate mer-captide	0.055	0.058±0.004	100		

The experiments in (A) were performed on 350–375-g rats that were ovariectomized 5 weeks before use. Animals used in (B) weighed 200–220 g and were ovariectomized 3 weeks before use. Animals were killed 18 hr after compounds given. Each value reported is the mean of at least 6 determinations, each assayed in duplicate. Values expressed as mean ± SE. Variation from control values is significant ($P < 0.01$) for each value in (A). No significant variation from control ($P < 0.05$) was observed in any value in (B). [Adapted from Muldoon & Warren (90).]

explored, but no demercuration of 4ME was found. The estrogenic activity of 4ME was concluded to be inherent within the molecule.

Finally radioactive 4ME was incubated with the uterine cytosol and centrifuged through a 5–20% sucrose density gradient, as described by Toft & Gorski (129). Analysis of the binding revealed specific uptake in the fraction with mobility identical to that of the estradiol-17β receptor complex. Exposure of the cytosol to unlabeled estradiol-17β before the addition of 4ME prevented binding of the latter compound by the receptor (Fig. 11).

Muldoon has carried out further studies to show that 4ME is truly covalently bound to the receptor protein. He incubated uterine supernatant fractions from 21-day-old Holtzman rats under conditions described by Toft & Gorski (129). When 6,7-³H-estradiol-17β is incubated for 1 hr at 4 C, essentially all of it could be extracted into benzene. He next incubated small amounts of 6,7-³H-4ME with supernatant fractions and extracted it after 1 hr at 4 C. Unlabeled estradiol-17β (4×10^{-4} μg/ml) added 15 min before the addition

of 6,7-³H-4ME caused 2 additional picomoles of 4ME per pair of horns to be extractable into benzene, presumably by excluding it from the receptor protein binding site (T. Muldoon, personal communication). This quantity is of the same order of magnitude as the binding capacity reported by Jensen et al. (59).

These observations demonstrate that 4ME mimics estradiol-17β in the production of several biological responses and in the nature of its binding to soluble uterine receptor sites. Although the binding of steroid to receptor protein has not been proven an absolute prerequisite to the subsequent display of estrogenic

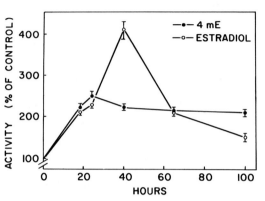

FIG. 10. Uterine glucose-6-P dehydrogenase activity at various intervals after a single intraluminal application of 0.1 μg estradiol-17β (*open circles*) or 4-mercuri-17β-estradiol (*closed circles*). Activity calculated as units/uterus for each group of 4 animals. Values are mean ± SE expressed as percentage of controls for comparison. Rats weighed 200–220 g and were 3 weeks postovariectomy. [Adapted from Muldoon & Warren (90).]

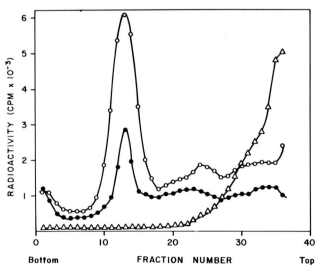

FIG. 11. Density gradient sedimentation patterns of radioactivity in uterine supernatant fractions after 15-min incubation with 1.2×10^{-8} M 17β-estradiol-6,7-³H (*open circles*); 1.3×10^{-8} M 4-mercuri-17β-estradiol-6,7-³H (*closed circles*); 1.2×10^{-8} M unlabeled estradiol-17β followed by 15-min incubation with 1.3×10^{-8} M 4-mercuri-17β-estradiol-6,7-³H (*open triangles*). Samples of 200 μliters were layered onto 5–20% sucrose gradients and centrifuged for 13 hr at 220,000 g and 2 C. Specific activity of 4-mercuri-17β-estradiol-6,7-³H was 25.1 c/mmole and that of 17β-estradiol-6,7-³H was 48.6 c/mmole. [Adapted from Muldoon & Warren (90).]

activity, suggestive evidence for the participation of some type of macromolecular receptor in the mechanism of action of 4ME results from the persistence of its effect.

ANTIESTROGENS: 4-MERCURI-17α-ESTRADIOL. Several reports (39, 40) have indicated that certain compounds that are poor estrogens or even antiestrogens when given as a single dose become good estrogens when given frequently; this suggests that their low estrogenicity is due to rapid clearance from the target organ. We considered that a derivative of estradiol-17α that could be retained in the uterus might display enhanced estrogenicity (which would indicate that inherent estrogenicity of the 17α-epimer is good if only it can be retained at the receptor site) or persistent antiestrogenicity (which would indicate that it excludes estradiol-17β from the receptor although lacking, as it is bound, significant, inherent estrogenic activity). We synthesized 4-mercuri-17α-estradiol and assured structure and purity. Doses of 50 and 100 ng/horn applied intraluminally did not display significant estrogenic activity when measured by the change in activity of glucose 6-phosphate dehydrogenase 24 hr after administration. Similarly applied, 50 ng 4-mercuri-17β-estradiol, caused a plateau response (200% of control value).

Persistence of the antiestrogenic activity of estradiol-17α and 4-mercuri-17α-estradiol was then compared by the intraluminal administration of equimolar amounts of each followed at intervals by an intraluminal dose of estradiol-17β. As shown in Table 10, both are short-term antiestrogens, but the effects of estradiol-17α dissipate with time, whereas 4-mercuri-17α-estradiol is a persistent antiestrogen. Continued presence of 4-mercuri-

17α-estradiol at the receptor site is indicated by its persistent antiestrogenic activity. Despite this continued presence, it appears to induce less than the required conformation in the receptor.

Finally we have shown that 4-mercuri-17β-estradiol can be delivered to the uterus by systemic administration and that this delivery is facilitated by shielding the mercury by reaction with β-mercaptoethanol. The mercaptide shows a persistence of estrogenic activity exceeding that of equimolar amounts of estradiol itself. This suggests that the mercaptide is concentrated at the receptor site by the reversible binding step so that mercaptide exchange can occur with a sulfhydryl residue at that site.

CONCLUSIONS. The persistent effects (estrogenic and antiestrogenic) of the affinity-labeling compounds are compatible with the existence of a macromolecular receptor and further indicate that dissipation of the biological activity of an estrogen may occur as a result of its dissociation from some form of this receptor. Indeed, estradiol is capable of this dissociation at 37 C (76).

We hope to use the affinity-labeling steroids to characterize amino acid residues participating at enzymatic steroid binding sites and to further investigate cytosol receptors. If a cytosol receptor bearing a covalently bound radioactive estrogenic steroid can be added to isolated nuclei and a radioactive nuclear receptor isolated, we have proof that one arises from the other. Further, if a cytosol receptor bearing covalently bound steroid (in the absence of free steroid) can be shown in vitro to induce nuclear RNA synthesis, that the receptor:estrogen complex initiates the intranuclear response without transfer of the steroid is indicated.

Unfortunately the mercaptide bond is only a pseudo-covalent one, and the mercuristeroids do not meet the rigorous demands of the above strategy. We have recently synthesized 2-diazoestrone derivatives that may serve the purpose (28).

TABLE 10. *Antiestrogenic Activity of 4-Mercuri-17α-Estradiol and Estradiol-17α*

Experiment	First Administration	Time, hr	Second Administration	G6PH Activity, milliunits/horn
1	Vehicle	2	Saline	106.2 ± 10.1
2	Vehicle	2	Estradiol-17β	172.5 ± 15.6
3	Estradiol-17α	2	Estradiol-17β	125.9 ± 10.2
4	4MEα	2	Estradiol-17β	131.0 ± 10.8
5	Estradiol-17α	24	Estradiol-17β	155.0 ± 11.7
6	4MEα	24	Estradiol-17β	133.5 ± 2.8
7	Estradiol-17α	48	Estradiol-17β	177.2 ± 10.1
8	4MEα	48	Estradiol-17β	132.9 ± 5.8

Steroids given by uterine intraluminal application to Holtzman rats (200–220 g) ovariectomized 4 weeks before use. Each value represents an average of 6 animals. First administration was vehicle, estradiol-17α (50 ng/horn), os 4MEα (100 ng/horn). After the times shown, saline or estradiol-17β (4 ng/horn) was applied to the same horn. Enzyme activity in injected horn was measured 24 hr after second administration. In experiment 2, enzyme activity is significantly greater (at least $P < 0.05$) than that in experiments 3, 4, 6, and 8, but not greater than that in experiments 5 and 7. Further, enzyme activity in experiment 7 is significantly greater ($P < 0.01$) than that in experiment 8. 4MEα, 4-mercuri-17α-estradiol. [Adapted from Ellis & Warren (40).]

EFFECTS OF PROGESTINS ON UTERINE METABOLISM

The pioneering studies of Corner and Allen resulted in the isolation of progesterone and demonstrated that it was a controlling factor in the maintenance of pregnancy (4, 6). This effect (for gestation) led to its designation as progesterone (5). A great deal of effort has been expended in the study of the capacity of progesterone to alter endometrial morphology, induce withdrawal bleeding in the primate, and maintain a quiescent myometrium. Extensive studies have been made of the metabolism of progesterone by target and nontarget organs, and numerous synthetic, orally active compounds have been developed and marketed. Nevertheless information relative to the molecular mechanisms whereby progesterone affects uterine metabolism is miniscule, as compared with estradiol.

It is reasonable to assume that progesterone must profoundly alter endometrial metabolism, especially in the estrogen-primed primate. Under its influence epithelial cells change form and secrete glycogen and stromal cells gather mantles of cytoplasm. Increases in uterine weight are seen, but mitosis is not prominent (97). Although progesterone modifies the uterus, its growth-promoting activity does not equal that of estradiol.

Changes in Enzyme Activity

In 1955 Lutwak-Mann (73) demonstrated that progesterone increased the activity of uterine carbonic anhydrase. Pincus (102) later devised an assay method based on this principle. Nevertheless this metabolic event is not an obligatory one, since Knudsen (65) has shown that treatment with Diamox (a carbonic anhydrase inhibitor) has no effect on the capacity of progesterone to induce the typical morphology, although it eliminates the increase in enzyme activity.

Progesterone causes the accumulation of endometrial glycogen naturally (97) and in tissue culture (56). Although a decrease in amylase may be responsible for this event (92), complete analysis of the synthetic enzymes is needed.

Lerner and co-workers (70) demonstrated that administration of progesterone to the immature rat increased the activity of uterine glucose 6-phosphate dehydrogenase, NADP$^+$-isocitric dehydrogenase, and NADP$^+$-malic enzyme, as well as total uterine RNA and DNA content. Murdoch & White (92) have reported that administration of progesterone to the castrated rabbit caused increase in the activities of succinic dehydrogenase and glucose 6-phosphate dehydrogenase and decreases in those of amylase and lactate dehydrogenase. Progesterone increased endometrial phosphatase activity, but, when given after estrogen treatment, it limited the greater response of acid and alkaline phosphatase observed with estrogen alone. Further, estradiol, which has little effect on succinic dehydrogenase, clearly inhibits the capacity of progesterone to enhance its activity (91) in the ovariectomized ewe. In the ovariectomized mouse, progesterone has no effect on alkaline phosphatase but reduces the estradiol-induced increase in its activity (3).

De Asua (36) demonstrated that estradiol induces pyruvate kinase in the uterus of the castrated rat, whereas progesterone inhibits that response. Singhal (111) confirmed this observation and also reported that progesterone (112) had no effect on uterine phosphohexose isomerase but inhibited estradiol-induced increases in activity. These examples allow the delineation of no clear pattern but do indicate that progesterone may affect enzyme activities even in the absence of estrogen and that the two steroids are often antagonisite.

The uterus increases markedly in size during pregnancy and involutes after delivery. Histological study has shown that this involution occurs by a decrease in the size of individual myometrial cells (69). Estrogen levels, which rise during pregnancy and fall postpartum, may be partially responsible; progesterone may also function in this phenomenon. Kao et al. (62) have shown that administration of progesterone to ovariectomized and estrogen-treated animals increases the activity of protocollagen hydroxylase, and hypertrophy is seen. Woessner (142) has proposed that proteolytic enzymes are responsible for involution, while Csapo's group (31) has suggested that ultimate initiation of postpartum involution results from loss of myometrial stretching. Postpartum involution of the rabbit uterus was reduced by repeated injections of progesterone (43). Coffey (29) has found that, if the uterus is removed within 3 days of delivery, tissue culture systems (explants) synthesize collagenase for 10 days. Collagenase activity in the in vitro preparations is increased slightly by 10^{-5} M estradiol, significantly decreased by the presence of 10^{-5} M progesterone, and completely abolished by 5×10^{-5} M concentrations. Whereas these levels of estradiol are clearly pharmacological, Wiest (34) has shown that progesterone concentration in the uterus of the pregnant rat approximates 10^{-6} M. These data suggest that progesterone may participate in myometrial hypertrophy. After delivery, diminishing progesterone (as well as withdrawal of estrogen and possibly stretch) facilitates postpartum involution.

Myometrial Quiescence

Progesterone causes an increase in the membrane potential and liminal stimulus required to effect contraction of the myometrial cell. Csapo (30) first proposed that progesterone served a primary role in the defense mechanism of human pregnancy by assuring myometrial quiescence and has defended this position successfully against all opposition. Kumar & Barnes (67) reported that progesterone inhibited human myometrial adenosine triphosphatase activity in vitro, but they used concentrations of 10 μg/ml of myometrial tissue, which is clearly pharmacological. They also demonstrated that progesterone is present in human myometrium (68), with amounts in subplacental regions exceeding those in antiplacental regions until the 38th week of gestation, after which the ratio fell to unity. They suggested that this fall was causally related to the onset of labor, which in the human being occurs at the 40th week. Csapo & Takeda (33) have described a uterine "pacemaker" and reported that when the progesterone "block" is in effect, electrical activity and its propagation are suppressed. Csapo & Wiest (34) studied progesterone concentrations in plasma, placenta, and uterus in the pregnant rat and observed that the maintenance of pregnancy correlates more closely with uterine than with plasma levels. When pregnancy was maintained after ovariectomy, plasma but not placental or uterine progesterone content dropped to normal preparturient levels.

Intra-amnionic injection of hypertonic saline induces abortion in the human female. Csapo, Wiest, and co-workers (32, 138) demonstrated that after such an injection, plasma progesterone levels fall before the onset of labor. No such fall occurred with isotonic saline injections, which did not induce abortion.

These studies implicate progesterone as a factor in uterine quiescence. Progesterone in pregnancy appears to function in the maintenance of endometrial integrity and prevention of withdrawal bleeding, and later in maintaining a low state of myometrial activity to avoid premature expulsion of the fetus. Although the molecular bases of these phenomena remain to be elucidated, there is little doubt that the steroid was appropriately named.

Uterine Progesterone Receptor

The administration of radioactive estradiol-17β is clearly followed by its accumulation in the uterus and other target organs (see above). Such was not the case in early studies with radioactive progesterone (17, 103, 147). Failure to localize radioactivity in the uterus may have resulted from the conversion of the steroid to numerous polar metabolites (51, 119) that distribute and bind specifically and nonspecifically in several tissues and body fluids (136). In more recent studies in which concentrations of endogenous progesterone itself were quantitated during pregnancy, values in the uterus clearly exceed those in plasma (137). This was not the case with endogenous 20α-hydroxy-4-pregnene-3-one. These observations are compatible with a binding or receptor system in the uterus that has considerably more affinity for progesterone than the more polar metabolite.

The elegant studies of O'Malley and co-workers (99, 100) have disclosed a progesterone receptor in chick oviduct, a specific target organ. Cytosol and nuclear-binding proteins have been characterized, and evidence for their participation in the intranuclear transfer of progesterone has been presented (see chapter by O'Malley in this volume of the *Handbook*). Although O'Malley's group has solved the problem of cytosol contamination by transcortin or corticosterone-binding globulin (CBG) in the oviduct, earlier studies in the uterus were clearly hampered by its presence. Milgram & Baulieu (82) demonstrated a progesterone-binding fraction in rat uterus but were unable to clearly differentiate it from CBG. Reel and co-workers (104) reported a progesterone-binding fraction in the uterus of the pregnant rat and indicated that heating abolished its ability to bind cortisone (possibly by destroying contaminating CBG) but caused little change in progesterone binding. Zimmering et al. (148) have studied a complex system in ovine endometrial cytoplasm. Fractions of 4S and 8S that bind estradiol-17β are

present. On centrifugation through sucrose density gradients, the 8S fraction did not appear to bind progesterone, but equilibrium dialysis revealed binding consistent with the formation of a complex of two molecules of the 8S-binding protein and a single molecule of progesterone. Arias & Warren (7) have also noticed that analytical grade sucrose interferes with binding of estradiol-17β by a nuclear macromolecule in chicken liver.

More recently, Wiest & Rao (139) have reported the presence of specific progesterone-binding proteins in the cytosol of human and rabbit endometrium. The uterus of a castrated rabbit contains a 4S fraction; estrogen priming induces an 8S fraction, which disaggregates in the presence of KCl. Although 5α-pregnane-3,20-dione competed with progesterone for this binding site, cortisol and several other steroids did not, which indicates that the binding protein is not CBG. These authors also found a 4S fraction in the nuclei of estrogen-primed rabbit uterus.

These studies in the uterus, which indicate the presence of cytosol and nuclear progesterone-binding proteins, have not thus far clearly indicated their role as a "receptor." Such a designation would require proof of participation in intranuclear transfer similar to that in the chick oviduct.

Protein and RNA Synthesis

Few observations on the effects of progesterone on protein and RNA synthesis are available. Rogers (105) reported that progesterone increases the incorporation of ^{14}C-labeled protein hydrolysate into glandular epithelium of the rat uterus within 6 hr but had no effect on conversion of uridine-^{3}H into RNA. Smith (115) reported that progesterone decreases the incorporation of lysine-^{14}C into epithelial nuclear proteins but causes a modest increased incorporation into stromal nuclear histones.

Conclusions

Much effort has been expended in physiological studies of progesterone and synthesis of orally effective progestins. Little information is available on the molecular mechanisms whereby progesterone affects uterine metabolism. However, after its administration, changes in enzyme activities, myometrial quiescence, and RNA and protein synthesis have been recorded. Biological effects of several steroid hormones appear to involve alteration of events at the genetic level. It is therefore attractive to suggest that this may well be the case with progesterone. Unlike the estrogens, membrane phenomena do not appear to be a significant part of its action. A firm conclusion must nevertheless await further evidence of a uterine receptor complex that transfers the steroid or a metabolite to a nuclear location.

REFERENCES

1. AARONSON, S. A., Y. NATORI, AND H. TARVER. Effect of estrogen on uterine ATP levels. *Proc. Soc. Exptl. Biol. Med.* 120: 9–10, 1965.
2. ABE, T., D. D. HAGERMANN, AND C. A. VILLEE. Estrogen-dependent pyridine nucleotide transhydrogenase of human myometrium. *J. Biol. Chem.* 239: 414–418, 1964.
3. ALDEEN, K. A. M. The influence of oestrogen and progesterone on the distribution of alkaline phosphatase in the mouse uterine endometrium. *J. Endocrinol.* 46: 405–406, 1970.
4. ALLEN, W. M. The preparation of purified progestin. *J. Biol. Chem.* 98: 591–605, 1932.
5. ALLEN, W. M., A. BUTENANDT, G. W. CORNER, AND K. H. SLOTTA. Nomenclature of corpus luteum hormone. *Science* 82: 153, 1935.
6. ALLEN, W. M., AND G. W. CORNER. Physiology of the corpus luteum. VII. Maintenance of pregnancy in rabbit after very early castration by corpus luteum extracts. *Proc. Soc. Exptl. Biol. Med.* 27: 403–405, 1930.
7. ARIAS, F., AND J. C. WARREN. An estrophilic macromolecule in chicken liver cytosol. *Biochim. Biophys. Acta* 230: 550–559, 1971.
8. BAKER, B. R. Factors in the design of active-site-directed irreversible inhibitors. *J. Pharm. Sci.* 53: 347–364, 1964.
9. BAQUER, N. A., AND P. MCLEAN. The effect of oestrogens on the activity and binding of multiple forms of hexokinase in the rat uterus. *Biochem. Biophys. Res. Commun.* 37: 158–164, 1969.
10. BARKER, K. L., AND J. M. ANDERSON. Displacement of estradiol-17β from the uterus by estradiol-17α: effect on template capacity of uterine chromatin. *Endocrinology* 83: 585–591, 1968.
11. BARKER, K. L., M. H. NEILSON, AND J. C. WARREN. Estrogen control of uterine carbohydrate metabolism: factors affecting glucose utilization. *Endocrinology* 79: 1069–1074, 1966.
12. BARKER, K. L., AND J. C. WARREN. Estrogen control of carbohydrate metabolism in the rat uterus: pathways of glucose metabolism. *Endocrinology* 78: 1205–1212, 1966.
13. BARKER, K. L., AND J. C. WARREN. Template capacity of uterine chromatin: control by estradiol. *Proc. Natl. Acad. Sci. US* 56: 1298–1302, 1966.
14. BARKER, K. L., AND J. C. WARREN. Effect of 17β-estradiol in vitro on the template capacity of uterine chromatin. *Endocrinology* 80: 536–539, 1967.
15. BARNEA, A., AND J. GORSKI. Estrogen-induced protein. Time course of synthesis. *Biochemistry* 9: 1899–1904, 1970.
16. BARNEA, A., AND J. GORSKI. Guanethidine effects on the metabolic response of the rat uterus to estrogen. *Endocrinology* 86: 909–911, 1970.
17. BERLINER, D. L., AND W. G. WIEST. The extrahepatic metabolism of progesterone in rats. *J. Biol. Chem.* 221: 449–459, 1956.
18. BETZ, G., AND J. C. WARREN. Studies with glucose 6-phosphate dehydrogenase from human placenta. *Acta Endocrinol.* 49: 47–57, 1965.
19. BILLING, R. J., B. BARBIROLI, AND R. M. S. SMELLIE. Changes in the patterns of synthesis of ribonucleic acid species in immature rat uterus in response to oestradiol-17β. *Biochem. J.* 112: 563–569, 1963.
20. BILLING, R. J., B. BARBIROLI, AND R. M. S. SMELLIE. The mode of action of oestradiol. I. The transport of RNA precursors into the uterus. *Biochim. Biophys. Acta* 190: 52–59, 1969.
21. BIRCHALL, K., AND I. D. K. HALKERSON. Effect of antihistamines on ribonucleic acid synthesis in the uterus of the ovariectomized rat. *Endocrinology* 85: 773–778, 1969.
22. BITMAN, J., H. C. CECIL, M. L. MENCH, AND T. R. WRENN. Kinetics of in vivo glycogen synthesis in the estrogen-stimulated rat uterus. *Endocrinology* 76: 63–69, 1965.
23. BONNER, J., G. R. CHALKLEY, M. DAHMUS, D. FAMBROUGH, F. FUJIMURA, R. C. HUANG, J. HUBERMAN, R. JENSEN, K.

MARUSHIGE, H. OHLENBUSCH, B. OLIVERA, AND J. WIDHOLM. Isolation and characterization of chromosomal nucleoproteins. In: *Methods in Enzymology*, edited by L. Grossman and K. Moldave. New York: Acad. Press, 1968, vol. XII, p. 3–65.
24. BONNER, J., AND R. C. HUANG. Methodology for the study of the template activity of chromosomal nucleohistone. *Biochem. Biophys. Res. Commun.* 22: 211–217, 1966.
25. BOYER, P. D. Spectrophotometric study of the reaction of protein sulfhydryl groups with organic mercurials. *J. Am. Chem. Soc.* 76: 4331–4337, 1954.
26. CHAMBERLIN, M., AND P. BERG. Deoxyribonucleic acid-directed synthesis of ribonucleic acid by an enzyme from *Escherichia coli*. *Proc. Natl. Acad. Sci. US* 48: 81–94, 1962.
27. CHIN, C. C., AND J. C. WARREN. Synthesis of 4-mercuri-17β-estradiol and study of its reaction with sulfhydryl compounds and proteins. *J. Biol. Chem.* 243: 5056–5062, 1968.
28. CHIN, C. C., AND J. C. WARREN. Synthesis of 2-diazoestrone sulfate: use for affinity labeling steroid binding sites. *Biochemistry* 9: 1917–1922, 1970.
29. COFFEY, R. J. *The Effect of Progesterone on a Specific Enzyme System: Rat Uterine Collagenase* (Ph.D.thesis). St. Louis: Washington University, 1970.
30. CSAPO, A. The mechanism of effect of the ovarian steroids. *Recent Prog. Hormone Res.* 12: 405–431, 1956.
31. CSAPO, A., T. ERDOS, C. R. deMATTOS, E. GRAMSS, AND C. MOSOCOWITZ. Stretch-induced growth, protein synthesis and function. *Nature* 207: 1378–1379, 1965.
32. CSAPO, A. I., E. KNOBIL, M. PULKKINEN, H. J. VAN DER MOLEN, I. F. SOMMERVILLE, AND W. G. WIEST. Progesterone withdrawal during hypertonic saline-induced abortions. *Am. J. Obstet. Gynecol.* 105: 1132–1134, 1969.
33. CSAPO, A. I., AND H. TAKEDA. Effect of progesterone on the electric activity and intrauterine pressure of pregnant and parturient rabbits. *Am. J. Obstet. Gynecol.* 91: 221–231, 1965.
34. CSAPO, A. I., AND W. G. WIEST. An examination of the quantitative relationship between progesterone and the maintenance of pregnancy. *Endocrinology* 85: 735–746, 1969.
35. DAHMUS, M. E., AND J. BONNER. Increased template activity of liver chromatin, a result of hydrocortisone administration. *Proc. Natl. Acad. Sci. US* 54: 1370–1375, 1965.
36. DE ASUA, L. J., E. ROZENGURT, AND H. CARMINATTI. Estradiol induction of pyruvate kinase in the rat uterus. *Biochim. Biophys. Acta* 170: 254–262, 1968.
37. DOUVILLE, A. W., AND J. C. WARREN. Steroid-protein interaction at sites which influence catalytic activity. *Biochemistry* 7: 4052–4059, 1968.
38. ECKSTEIN, B., AND C. A. VILLEE. Effect of estradiol on enzymes of carbohydrate metabolism in rat uterus. *Endocrinology* 78: 409–411, 1966.
39. ELLIS, R. W., AND J. C. WARREN. Estrogenic activity of 4-mercuri-17β-estradiol and its mercaptide following systemic administration. *Endocrinology*. In press.
40. ELLIS, R. W., AND J. C. WARREN. Estrogenic and antiestrogenic activity of 4-mercuri-17α-estradiol. *Steroids* 17: 331–344, 1971.
41. FERRANDO, C., AND A. V. NALBANDOV. Relative importance of histamine and estrogen on implantation in rats. *Endocrinology* 83: 933–937, 1968.
42. GLOCK, G. E., AND P. MCLEAN. Further studies on properties and assay of glucose 6-phosphate dehydrogenase and 6-phosphogluconate dehydrogenase of rat liver. *Biochem. J.* 55: 400–408, 1953.
43. GOODALL, F. R. Progesterone retards postpartum involution of the rabbit myometrium. *Science* 152: 356–358, 1966.
44. GORSKI, J. Early estrogen effects on the activity of uterine ribonucleic acid polymerase. *J. Biol. Chem.* 239: 889–892, 1964.
45. GORSKI, J., AND J. A. NICOLETTE. Early estrogen effects on newly synthesized RNA and phospholipid in subcellular

fractions in rat uteri. *Arch. Biochem. Biophys.* 103: 410–423, 1963.

46. HAGERMAN, D. D., AND C. A. VILLEE. A mechanism of action for estrogenic steroid hormones. In: *Mechanism of Action of Steroid Hormones*, edited by C. A. Villee and L. L. Engles. New York: Pergamon Press, 1961, vol. 1, p. 169–181.

47. HAMILTON, T. H. Isotopic studies on estrogen-induced accelerations of ribonucleic acid and protein synthesis. *Proc. Natl. Acad. Sci. US* 49: 373–379, 1963.

48. HAMILTON, T. H. Control by estrogen of genetic transcription and translation. *Science* 161: 649–661, 1968.

49. HAMILTON, T. H., C. S. TENG, AND A. R. MEANS. Early estrogen action: nuclear synthesis and accumulation of protein correlated with enhancement of two DNA-dependent RNA polymerase activities. *Proc. Natl. Acad. Sci. US* 59: 1265–1272, 1968.

50. HAMILTON, T. H., C. C. WIDNELL, AND J. R. TATA. Synthesis of ribonucleic acid during early estrogen action. *J. Biol. Chem.* 243: 408–417, 1968.

51. HASKINS, A. L., JR. Assay of circulating progesterone by ultraviolet spectroscopy. *Proc. Soc. Exptl. Biol. Med.* 73: 439–443, 1950.

52. HECHTER, O., K. YOSHINAGA, I. D. K. HALKERSTON, AND K. BIRCHALL. Estrogen-like anabolic effects of cyclic 3′,5′ adenosine monophosphate and other nucleotides in isolated rat uteri. *Arch. Biochem. Biophys.* 122: 449–465, 1967.

53. HERRANEN, A., AND G. C. MUELLER. Effect of estradiol on the metabolism of serine-3-C^{14} in surviving uterine segments. *J. Biol. Chem.* 223: 369–375, 1956.

54. HERRANEN, A., AND G. C. MUELLER. The effect of estradiol pretreatment on the serine aldolase activity of rat uteri. *Biochim. Biophys. Acta* 24: 223–224, 1957.

55. HOKIN, L. E., M. MOKOTOFF, AND S. M. KUPCHAN. Alkylation of a brain transport adenosintriphosphatase at the cardiotonic steroid site by strophanthindin-3-haloacetates. *Proc. Natl. Acad. Sci. US* 55: 797–804, 1966.

56. HUGHES, E. C., L. M. DEMERS, T. CSERMELY, AND D. B. JONES. Organ culture of human endometrium. *Am. J. Obstet. Gynecol.* 105: 707–720, 1969.

57. JENSEN, E. V., D. J. HURST, E. R. DE SOMBRE, AND P. W. JUNGBLUT. Sulfhydryl groups and estradiol-receptor interaction. *Science* 158: 385–387, 1967.

58. JENSEN, E. V., AND H. I. JACOBSON. Basic guides to the mechanism of estrogen action. *Recent Prog. Hormone Res.* 18: 387–414, 1962.

59. JENSEN, E. V., T. SUZUKI, T. KAWASHIMA, W. E. STUMPF, P. W. JUNGBLUT, AND E. R. DE SOMBRE. A two-step mechanism for the interaction of estradiol with rat uterus. *Proc. Natl. Acad. Sci. US* 59: 632–638, 1968.

60. JERVELL, K. F., C. R. DINIZ, AND G. C. MUELLER. Early effects of estradiol on nucleic acid metabolism in the rat uterus. *J. Biol. Chem.* 231: 945–959, 1958.

61. KAKIUCHI, S., AND T. W. RALL. Effects of norepinephrine (NE) and histidine (H) on levels of adenosine 3′,5′-phosphate (3,5-AMP) in brain slices. *Federation Proc.* 24: 150, 1965.

62. KAO, K. Y. T., W. M. ARNETT, AND T. H. McGAVACK. Effect of endometrial phase, ovariectomy, estradiol and progesterone on uterine protocollagen hydroxylase. *Endocrinology* 85: 1057–1061, 1969.

63. KIMBERG, D. V., AND K. L. YIELDING. Pyruvate kinase: structural and functional changes induced by diethylstilbestrol and certain steroid hormones. *J. Biol. Chem.* 237: 3233–3239, 1962.

64. KIRKMAN, H. N., AND E. M. HENDRICKSON. Glucose 6-phosphate dehydrogenase from human erythrocytes. *J. Biol. Chem.* 237: 2371–2376, 1962.

65. KNUDSEN, K. A., R. C. JONES, AND R. A. EDGREN. Effect of a carbonic anhydrase inhibitor (Diamox) on the progesterone-stimulated rabbit uterus. *Endocrinology* 85: 1204–1208, 1969.

66. KORNBERG, A. Lactic dehydrogenase of muscle. In: *Methods of Enzymology*, edited by S. P. Colowick and N. O. Kaplan. New York: Acad. Press, 1955, vol. 1, p. 441–443.

67. KUMAR, D., P. R. ADAMS, AND A. C. BARNES. Inhibitory effect of progesterone on activity of human myometrial adenosine triphosphatase. *Nature* 203: 83, 1964.

68. KUMAR, D., AND A. C. BARNES. Studies in human myometrium during pregnancy. VI. Tissue progesterone profile of the various compartments in the same individual. *Am. J. Obstet. Gynecol.* 92: 717–719, 1965.

69. KURIMITSU, C., AND L. LOEB. The involution of the uterus following labor and the influence of castration and suckling on the process of involution. *Am. J. Physiol.* 55: 422–442, 1921.

70. LERNER, L. J., R. HILF, A. TURKHEIMER, I. MICHAL, AND S. L. ENGEL. Effects of hormone antagonists on morphological and biochemical changes induced by hormonal steroids in the immature rat uterus. *Endocrinology* 78: 111–124, 1966.

71. LEVY, R. H. The interaction of mammary glucose 6-phosphate dehydrogenase with pyridine nucleotides and 3β-hydroxyandrost-5-en-17-one. *J. Biol. Chem.* 238: 775–784, 1963.

72. LIPPE, B. M., AND C. M. SZEGO. Participation of adrenocortical hyperactivity in the suppressive effect of systemic actinomycin D on uterine stimulation by estrogen. *Nature* 207: 272–274, 1965.

73. LUTWAK-MANN, C. Carbonic anhydrase in the female reproductive tract. Occurrence, distribution and hormonal dependence. *J. Endocrinol.* 13: 26–38, 1955.

74. MARKS, P. A., AND J. BANKS. Inhibition of mammalian glucose-6-phosphate dehydrogenase by steroids. *Proc. Natl. Acad. Sci. US* 46: 447–452, 1960.

75. MARUSHIGE, K., AND J. BONNER. Template properties of liver chromatin. *J. Mol. Biol.* 15: 160–174, 1966.

76. MAURER, H. R., AND G. R. CHALKLEY. Some properties of a nuclear binding site of estradiol. *J. Mol. Biol.* 27: 431–441, 1967.

77. MAYOL, R. F., AND S. A. THAYER. Synthesis of estrogen-specific proteins in the uterus of the immature rat. *Biochemistry* 9: 2484–2489, 1970.

78. McCORQUODALE, D. J., AND G. C. MUELLER. Effect of estradiol on the level of amino acid activating enzymes in the rat uterus. *J. Biol. Chem.* 232: 31–42, 1958.

79. McKERNS, K. W. Hormonal regulation of dehydrogenase enzymes of the anterior pituitary. *Biochim. Biophys. Acta* 73: 507–509, 1963.

80. McKERNS, K. W., AND E. KALEITA. Inhibition of glucose-6-phosphate dehydrogenase by hormones. *Biochem. Biophys. Res. Commun.* 2: 344–348, 1960.

81. MEANS, A. R., AND T. H. HAMILTON. Early estrogen action: concomitant stimulations within two minutes of nuclear RNA synthesis and uptake of RNA precursor by the uterus. *Proc. Natl. Acad. Sci. US* 56: 1594–1598, 1966.

82. MILGRAM, E., AND E. E. BAULIEU. Progesterone in uterus and plasma. I. Binding in rat uterus 105,000 g supernatant. *Endocrinology* 87: 276–287, 1970.

83. MONOD, J. From enzymatic adaptation to allosteric transition. *Science* 54: 475–483, 1966.

84. MUELLER, G. C. Incorporation of glycine-2-C^{14} into protein by surviving uteri from α-estradiol-treated rats. *J. Biol. Chem.* 204: 77–90, 1953.

85. MUELLER, G. C. Some biochemical studies on the mechanism of action of estrogens. *Cancer* 10: 716–720, 1957.

86. MUELLER, G. C. Discussion of "Mechanism of action of estrogens" by D. D. Hagerman and C. A. Villee. In: *Mechanism of Action of Steroid Hormones*, edited by C. A. Villee and L. L. Engles. New York: Pergamon Press, 1961, vol. 1, p. 181–187.

87. MUELLER, G. C., J. GORSKI, AND Y. AIZAWA. The role of protein synthesis in early estrogen action. *Proc. Natl. Acad. Sci. US* 47: 164–169, 1961.

88. MUELLER, G. C., AND A. HERRANEN. Metabolism of 1-

carbon fragments by surviving uteri from estradiol-treated rats. *J. Biol. Chem.* 219: 585–594, 1956.

89. MUELLER, G. C., A. M. HERRANEN, AND K. F. JERVELL. Studies on the mechanism of action of estrogens. *Recent Prog. Hormone Res.* 14: 95–139, 1958.

90. MULDOON, T. G., AND J. C. WARREN. Characterization of steroid-binding sites by affinity-labeling. II. Biological activity of 4-mercuri-17β-estradiol. *J. Biol. Chem.* 244: 5430–5435, 1969.

91. MURDOCH, R. N., AND I. G. WHITE. The effect of oestradiol and progesterone on the activity of enzymes in the endometrium and caruncles of the ovariectomized ewe. *J. Endocrinol.* 42: 187–192, 1966.

92. MURDOCH, R. N., AND I. G. WHITE. The activity of enzymes in the rabbit uterus and effect of progesterone and oestradiol. *J. Endocrinol.* 43: 167–174, 1969.

93. NICOLETTE, J. A., AND J. GORSKI. Effect of estradiol on glucose-U-C14 metabolism in the rat uterus. *Arch. Biochem. Biophys.* 107: 279–283, 1964.

94. NICOLETTE, J. A., AND G. C. MUELLER. Effect of actinomycin D on the estrogen response in uteri of adrenalectomized rats. *Endocrinology* 79: 1162–1165, 1966.

95. NIELSON, M. H., AND J. C. WARREN. Steroid effects on glucose-6-phosphate dehydrogenase from bovine corpora lutea. *Biochim. Biophys. Acta* 97: 532–541, 1965.

96. NOTEBOOM, W. D., AND J. GORSKI. An early effect of estrogen on protein synthesis. *Proc. Natl. Acad. Sci. US* 50: 250–255, 1963.

97. NOYES, R. W., A. T. HERTIG, AND J. ROCK. Dating the endometrial biopsy. *Fertility Sterility* 1: 3–25, 1950.

98. OCHOA, S. "Malic" enzyme. In: *Methods of Enzymology*, edited by S. P. Colowick and N. O. Kaplan. New York: Acad. Press, 1955, vol. I, p. 739–753.

99. O'MALLEY, B. W., W. L. McGUIRE, P. O. KOHLER, AND S. G. KORENMAN. Studies on the mechanism of steroid hormone regulation of synthesis of specific proteins. *Recent Prog. Hormone Res.* 25: 105–160, 1969.

100. O'MALLEY, B. W., M. R. SHERMAN, AND D. O. TAFT. Progesterone "receptors" in the cytoplasm and nucleus of chick oviduct target tissue. *Proc. Natl. Acad. Sci. US* 67: 501–508, 1970.

101. PETERSON, D. M., AND J. C. WARREN. Effect of steroids and cofactors on the activity and stability of human placental glutamate dehydrogenase. *Acta Endocrinol.* 51: 599–608, 1966.

102. PINCUS, G., T. MIYAKE, A. P. MERRILL, AND P. LONGO. The bioassay of progesterone. *Endocrinology* 61: 528–533, 1957.

103. PLOTZ, E. J. Studies with labelled progesterone in human pregnancy. In: *Brooklodge Symposium: Progesterone*, edited by A. C. Barnes. Augusta, Mich.: Brook Lodge Press, 1961, p. 91–104.

104. REEL, J. R., S. D. VAN DEWARK, Y. SHIH, AND M. R. CALLANTINE. A specific progestin receptor in the rat uterus. *Endocrine Soc. Meeting, 52nd, St. Louis, Mo., 1970*, Abstr. 94.

105. ROGERS, A. W., R. N. JOHN, AND K. BROWN-GRANT. Early effects of progesterone on the uterus of the ovariectomized rat. *J. Anat.* 106: 182–183, 1970.

106. ROSKOSKI, R., JR., AND D. F. STEINER. The effect of estrogen on sugar transport in the rat uterus. *Biochim. Biophys. Acta* 135: 717–726, 1967.

107. SEGAL, S. J., O. W. DAVIDSON, AND K. WADA. Role of RNA in the regulatory action of estrogen. *Proc. Natl. Acad. Sci. US* 54: 782–787, 1965.

108. SHARMA, S. K., AND G. P. TALWAR. Action of cyclic adenosine 3′,5′-monophosphate *in vitro* on the uptake and incorporation of uridine into ribonucleic acid in ovariectomized rat uterus. *J. Biol. Chem.* 245: 1513–1519, 1970.

109. SHELESNAK, M. C. Histamine releasing activity of natural estrogens. *Proc. Soc. Exptl. Biol. Med.* 100: 739–741, 1959.

110. SINGHAL, R. L., AND J. R. E. VALADARES. Metabolic control mechanisms in mammalian systems. II. Hormonal regu-

lation of uterine phosphohexose isomerase. *Biochem. Pharmacol.* 17: 1251–1260, 1968.

111. SINGHAL, R. L., AND J. R. E. VALADARES. Estrogenic regulation of uterine pyruvate kinase. *Am. J. Physiol.* 218: 321–327, 1970.

112. SINGHAL, R. L., J. R. E. VALADARES, AND M. L. GEORGE. Metabolic control mechanisms in mammalian systems. I. Hormonal induction of phosphofructokinase in the rat uterus. *J. Biol. Chem.* 242: 2593–2598, 1967.

113. SINGHAL, R. L., J. R. E. VALADARES, AND G. M. LING. Estrogen-induced increase in phosphohexose isomerase activity in the rat uterus. *Metabolism* 16: 271–278, 1967.

114. SMITH, D. E., AND J. GORSKI. Estrogen control of uterine glucose metabolism. *J. Biol. Chem.* 243: 4169–4174, 1968.

115. SMITH, J. A., L. MARTIN, AND R. J. B. KING. Effects of oestradiol-17β and progesterone on nuclear-protein synthesis in the mouse uterus. *Biochem. J.* 114: 59P, 1969.

116. SPAZIANI, E., AND C. M. SZEGO. The influence of estradiol and cortisol on uterine histamine of the ovariectomized rat. *Endocrinology* 63: 669–678, 1958.

117. STUMPF, W. E. Nuclear concentration of ³H-estradiol in target tissues. Dry-mount autoradiography of vagina, oviduct, ovary, testis, mammary tumor, liver and adrenal. *Endocrinology* 85: 31–37, 1969.

118. SUTHERLAND, E. W., AND T. W. RALL. The relation of adenosine-3′,5′-phosphate and phosphorylase to the actions of catecholamines and other hormones. *Pharmacol. Rev.* 12: 265–299, 1960.

119. SWEAT, M. L., AND M. J. BRYSON. Comparative metabolism of progesterone in proliferative human endometrium and myometrium. *Am. J. Obstet. Gynecol.* 106: 193–201, 1970.

120. SZEGO, C. M., AND J. S. DAVIS. Adenosine 3′,5′-monophosphate in rat uterus: acute elevation by estrogen. *Proc. Natl. Acad. Sci. US* 58: 1711–1718, 1967.

121. SZEGO, C. M., AND J. S. DAVIS. Inhibition of estrogen-induced cyclic AMP elevation in rat uterus. II. By glucocorticoids. *Life Sci.* 8: 1109–1116, 1969.

122. SZEGO, C. M., AND J. S. DAVIS. Inhibition of estrogen-induced elevation of cyclic 3′,5′-adenosine monophosphate in rat uterus. I. By beta-adrenergic receptor-blocking drugs. *Mol. Pharmacol.* 5: 470–480, 1969.

123. SZEGO, C. M., AND D. A. LAWSON. Influence of histamine on uterine metabolism: stimulation of incorporation of radioactivity from amino acids into protein, lipid and purines. *Endocrinology* 74: 372–381, 1964.

124. SZEGO, C. M., AND B. M. LIPPE. Mediation by adrenocortical hypersecretion of the suppressive influence of actinomycin D on uterine estrogen sensitivity. *Steroids Suppl.* II: 235–247, 1965.

125. SZEGO, C. M., AND S. ROBERTS. Steroid action and interaction in uterine metabolism. *Recent Prog. Hormone Res.* 8: 419–469, 1953.

126. SZEGO, C. M., AND S. H. SLOAN. The influence of histamine and serotonin in promoting early uterine growth in the rat. *Gen. Comp. Endocrinol.* 1: 295–305, 1961.

127. TALWAR, G. P., AND S. J. SEGAL. Prevention of hormone action by local application of actinomycin D. *Proc. Natl. Acad. Sci. US* 50: 226–230, 1963.

128. TERENIUS, L. SH-groups essential for estrogen uptake and retention in the mouse uterus. *Mol. Pharmacol.* 3: 423–428, 1967.

129. TOFT, D., AND J. GORSKI. A receptor molecule for estrogens: isolation from the rat uterus and preliminary characterization. *Proc. Natl. Acad. Sci. US* 55: 1574–1581, 1966.

130. TOMKINS, G. M., K. L. YIELDING, J. F. CURRAN, M. R. SUMMERS, AND M. W. BITENSKY. The dependence of the substrate specificity on the conformation of crystalline glutamate dehydrogenase. *J. Biol. Chem.* 240: 3793–3798, 1965.

131. UI, H., AND G. C. MUELLER. The role of RNA synthesis in early estrogen action. *Proc. Natl. Acad. Sci. US* 50: 256–260, 1963.

132. VALADARES, J. R. E., R. L. SINGHAL, AND M. R. PARULEKAR.

17β-estradiol: inducer of uterine hexokinase. *Science* 159: 990–991, 1968.

133. VELICK, S. F. Glyceraldehyde-3-phosphate dehydrogenase from muscle. In: *Methods in Enzymology*, edited by S. P. Colowick and N. O. Kaplan. New York: Acad. Press, 1955, vol. I, p. 401–406.

134. WARREN, J. C., AND K. L. BARKER. Cyclic variation in RNA synthesis potential in the uterus of the golden hamster. *Biochim. Biophys. Acta* 138: 421–423, 1967.

135. WARREN, J. C., D. O. CARR, AND S. GRISOLIA. Effect of cofactors, oestrogens and magnesium ions on the activity and stability of human glutamate dehydrogenase. *Biochem. J.* 93: 409–419, 1964.

136. WESTPHAL, U. Assay and properties of corticosteroid-binding globulin and other steroid-binding serum proteins. In: *Methods of Enzymology*, edited by R. B. Clayton. New York: Acad. Press, 1969, vol. XV, p. 761–796.

137. WIEST, W. G. Progesterone and 20α-hydroxy-pregn-4-en-3-one in plasma, ovaries and uteri during pregnancy in the rat. *Endocrinology* 87: 43–48, 1970.

138. WIEST, W. G., M. O. PULKKINEN, J. SAUVAGE, AND A. I. CSAPO. Plasma progesterone levels during saline-induced abortion. *J. Clin. Endocrinol. Metab.* 30: 774–777, 1970.

139. WIEST, W. G., AND B. R. RAO. Progesterone binding proteins in rabbit uterus and human endometrium. In: *Advances in the Biosciences 7*. Elmsford, N.Y.: Pergamon, 1971, p. 251–266.

140. WILLIAMS-ASHMAN, H. G., AND S. LIAO. Sex hormones and hydrogen transport of isolated enzyme systems. In: *Actions of Hormones on Molecular Processes*, edited by G. Litwack and D. Kritchevsky. New York: Wiley, 1964, chapt. 18, p. 482–508.

141. WILSON, J. D. The nature of the RNA response to estradiol administration by the uterus of the rat. *Proc. Natl. Acad. Sci. US* 50: 93–100, 1963.

142. WOESSNER, J. F. Catabolism of collagen and non-collagen protein in the rat uterus during post-partum involution. *Biochem. J.* 83: 304–314, 1962.

143. WOLFSY, L., H. METZGER, AND S. J. SINGER. Affinity labeling—a general method of labeling the active sites of antibody and enzyme molecules. *Biochemistry* 1: 1031–1039, 1962.

144. YIELDING, K. L., AND G. M. TOMKINS. Structural alterations in crystalline glutamic dehydrogenase induced by steroid hormones. *Proc. Natl. Acad. Sci. US* 46: 1483–1488, 1960.

145. YIELDING, K. L., G. M. TOMKINS, M. W. BITENSKY, AND N. TALAL. Reagent-induced changes in the structure and catalytic activity of glutamic dehydrogenase. *Can. J. Biochem.* 42: 727–743, 1964.

146. YIELDING, K. L., G. M. TOMKINS, J. S. MUNDAY, AND J. F. CURRAN. The effects of steroid hormones on the glutamic dehydrogenase reaction. *Biochem. Biophys. Res. Commun.* 2: 303–306, 1959.

147. ZANDER, J. Gestagens in human pregnancy. In: *Endocrinology of Reproduction*, edited by C. W. Lloyd. New York: Acad. Press, 1959, p. 255–282.

148. ZIMMERING, P. E., I. KAHN, AND S. LIEBERMAN. Estradiol and progesterone binding to a fraction of ovine endometrial cytoplasm. *Biochemistry* 9: 2498–2506, 1970.

CHAPTER 33

Effects of hysterectomy and other factors on luteal function

L. L. ANDERSON | *Department of Animal Science, Iowa State University, Ames, Iowa*

CHAPTER CONTENTS

AN ESSENTIAL FEATURE in the regulation of the reproductive cycle in many mammalian species is the functional status of the corpus luteum. One intriguing aspect of corpus luteum physiology is the influence of the uterus in controlling luteal function, particularly that of luteal regression.

This discussion deals with the effects of hysterectomy on the function of the corpus luteum and the physiological control of luteal function by the uterus. Of particular interest are the comparative aspects of uterine-luteal relationships in several mammalian species. In some species the presence of the uterus causes a marked effect on the life-span of the corpus luteum, whereas in others its presence or absence seems to have no influence on the reproductive cycle. Other factors affecting luteal function are considered. These are *a*) intrauterine devices; *b*) toxic agents within the uterus; *c*) local uterine luteolytic action; *d*) uterine transplantation; *e*) ovarian transplantation; *f*) oxytocin; *g*) prostaglandins; and *h*) uterine luteolytic factors.

INTRAUTERINE DEVICES AND CORPUS LUTEUM FUNCTION

The presence of a foreign body in the uterine lumen affects the development and maintenance of the corpus

Journal Paper No. J-6871 of the Iowa Agriculture and Home Economics Experiment Station, Ames, Iowa. Projects No. 1325 and 1712. This project was supported in part by Grant HD-01168-11 from the National Institute of Child and Health and Human Development.

luteum in several mammalian species. In species in which the foreign body seems to have no effect on luteal function (e.g., rabbit and monkey) it may provide a contraceptive action either locally or throughout the uterine lumen.

Intrauterine devices fabricated from a variety of materials (e.g., glass beads, metal cylinders, nylon or polyethylene loops, coils, and tubing) interfere with the development and maintenance of the corpora lutea as indicated by shortened estrous cycles in the ewe, cow, Indian water buffalo, guinea pig, and goat. In the rat, hamster, pig, monkey, and human being, the length of the estrous or menstrual cycle is unaffected by the intrauterine device (IUD), but implantation is prevented in these species, as well as in the rabbit (3, 56, 101).

The stage in the cycle when the IUD is inserted is an important consideration for reducing the estrous interval. When the IUD is inserted during the early part of the cycle in the guinea pig, ewe, or cow, the corpora lutea regress prematurely, but insertion later in the estrous cycle can prolong that cycle. For example, inserting an IUD (plastic beads) in the ewe on day 3 reduces that and subsequent cycles from 16 to 9–13 days, but cycles seem to be extended beyond 20 days when the bead is inserted at day 8 (147). Inserting the IUD as late as day 13 fails to alter the cycle length (149). Normal 16-day cycles resume in these animals after removal of the bead. Not only the initial but subsequent estrous intervals are either reduced or extended when the IUD remains in the animal. Occasional estrous cycles are unaltered in the presence of the IUD.

The early luteal regression is caused by a local luteolytic effect from the stimulated part of the uterus. Denervating the uterine segment that contains the IUD nullifies the shortening effect; normal cycles resume. In guinea pigs having ovulations in both ovaries, glass beads inserted in one uterine horn cause the adjacent corpora to regress early, whereas luteal regression proceeds normally in the opposite ovary (26). Furthermore, when IUD is located in the uterine horn adjacent to the ovulating ovary, it exerts a greater luteolytic effect than when it is in the opposite horn in the hamster, guinea pig, ewe, and cow.

TABLE 1. *Luteal Function After Hysterectomy*

Species	Cyclic Periodicity, days		Length of Pseudopregnancy, days		Refs.
	Before hysterectomy	After hysterectomy	Before hysterectomy	After hysterectomy	
Hamster	4	4	8–10	16–23	41, 42, 64, 71, 123, 130, 137, 156
Mouse	4–5	4–5	10–11	15–17	18, 201
Rat	4–5	4	12–14	18–25	10, 32, 33, 51, 100, 106, 129, 140, 157, 159
Rabbit			15–16	25–29	15, 52, 90, 128, 185, 188, 198
Guinea pig	15–18	80–110			40, 63, 83, 105, 126, 127, 175
Sheep	16–18	160–170			120, 144, 205, 207
Pig	20–22	>140			6, 7, 21, 72, 76, 136
Cow	18–22	>270			11, 108, 134, 205
Rhesus monkey	28–29	27–29			37, 99, 150, 197, 200
Human	27–29	27–29			13, 20, 117, 184, 202

HYSTERECTOMY

The effects of hysterectomy in different species have been reviewed extensively (3, 4, 24, 139, 173). Removal of the uterus can clearly alter the process of luteal regression in some species; it seems to have no effect on the periodicity of the estrous cycle but prolongs the duration of pseudopregnancy in the hamster, rat, and mouse (Table 1). Uterine removal in the estrous rabbit does not alter ovulation (166), but the duration of pseudopregnancy is extended. In the guinea pig, sheep, pig, and cow, hysterectomy prolongs luteal function for a period equivalent to or exceeding that of pregnancy. Removal of the uterus in these eight species maintains luteal function for an extended period. When the corpora lutea are in late stages of regression at the time of hysterectomy, they regress completely, estrus recurs, and the newly formed corpora lutea are maintained for an extended period. A repetition of a prolonged luteal phase occurs with each successive induction of pseudopregnancy in the hysterectomized rat (10, 159) and rabbit (52, 90, 107) and after spontaneous estrus and ovulation in the hysterectomized ewe (120).

In several species [13-lined ground squirrel (69); ferret (45, 62); dog (48); badger (44); opossum (98); brush possum (53); rhesus monkey (37, 150, 197, 200); human (20, 117, 184, 202)], hysterectomy does not alter ovarian function or cyclic periodicity. For example, in the opossum the gestation is shorter than the cycle, and hysterectomy does not alter the periodicity of estrus. In the ferret, pregnancy is of the same duration as is pseudopregnancy, and hysterectomy does not increase the luteal life-span.

In the monkey the earlier evidence suggested that menstrual cycles continue uninterrupted after hysterectomy (37, 99, 197, 200). Recent work clearly indicates that ovarian cycles continue after the rhesus monkey is hysterectomized (150). The duration of menstrual cycles in four animals was 27.5 ± 0.7 days before surgery and remained unchanged after hysterectomy (27.8 ± 0.6 days). Furthermore the duration of the elevated concentrations of progesterone in peripheral plasma during the luteal phase was similar in normal and hysterectomized monkeys. The rise and fall in levels of progesterone in the peripheral plasma in one hysterectomized monkey indicated a consistent periodicity similar to that of the normal menstrual cycle.

There has been no conclusive evidence that hysterectomy alters ovarian function in women, although some clinical evidence was interpreted as indicating cessation of luteal function, continuation of menstrual cycles, and early menopause. Clinical evidence on the excretion of urinary pregnanediol, vaginal smears, and basal body temperature was interpreted as indicating that hysterectomy does not affect cyclic ovarian function or hasten onset of menopause (202). Andreoli (13) found that the menstrual cycle was prolonged 2–8 days in patients hysterectomized on days 17–19, but normal cycles continued when surgery was performed on day 24 or 25. The pattern of urinary excretion of pregnanediol in seven patients suggested that cyclic ovarian function continues after hysterectomy (20).

In the rat there is little development of corpora lutea during the 4- or 5-day estrous cycle. Progesterone levels in the ovarian venous blood remain low (1–2 μg/ovary/hr), with a maximal level (4 μg/ovary/hr) at proestrus (100). After induced pseudopregnancy, corpora lutea reach maximal size by day 5 and are maintained until about day 13 (Fig. 1). After hysterectomizing a pseudopregnant rat or inducing pseudopregnancy in a hysterectomized animal, one finds the corpora are no larger than those found during normal

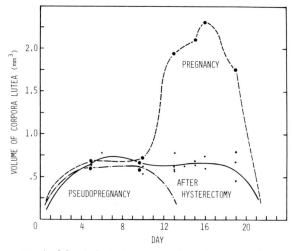

FIG. 1. Morphological changes in rat corpora lutea during different reproductive states. [Adapted from Perry & Rowlands (159).]

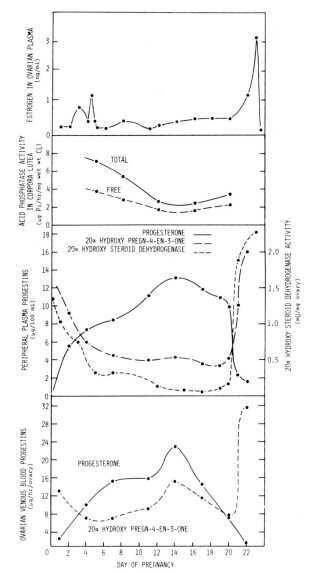

FIG. 2. Biochemical changes in ovarian function during pregnancy in the rat. Data on levels of progesterone and 20α-hydroxy-pregn-4-en-3-one in the ovarian venous blood are from Hashimoto et al. (100). The levels of progesterone, 20α-hydroxypregn-4-en-3-one, and 20α-hydroxysteroid dehydrogenase are from the data of Wiest et al. (204) and Wiest (203). Acid-phosphatase activity is expressed as inorganic phosphate (Pi) in μg/hr/mg wet wt of corpora lutea (CL). Free activity was measured after incubating the luteal tissue 1 hr at 37C. Total activity was obtained by the addition of 1% Triton X-100 before incubation. The values for acid-phosphatase activities are from Smith & Waynforth (189). Levels of estrogen in ovarian plasma were determined by an intravaginal bioassay. Data on levels of estrogen in plasma are adapted from Yoshinaga et al. (211).

venous blood (100) or peripheral blood (203) increase during the first half of gestation—levels peak at day 14 and decline thereafter; extremely low levels occur at parturition (Fig. 2).

Other reliable indicators of the functional activity of the corpus luteum in the rat are 20α-hydroxypregn-4-en-3-one (20α-OHP) and ovarian 20α-hydroxysteroid dehydrogenase activity (100, 203, 204). Secretory rates of 20α-OHP in ovarian venous blood (100) and peripheral blood (203) are inversely related to the levels of progesterone (see Fig. 2). At the termination of pregnancy, a time when the corpora are regressing, there is a marked increase in levels of 20α-OHP. The levels of 20α-hydroxysteroid dehydrogenase activity in the ovary decline initially and rise abruptly at term, changes similar to those found in 20α-OHP. Kuhn & Briley (124) suggest that the cessation of progesterone secretion (e.g., before parturition) is caused partly by a redirection of the metabolism of pregnenolone away from progesterone and toward 20α-OHP.

An additional criterion for determining the functional status of corpora lutea may be acid-phosphatase activity measured histochemically (125) or biochemically (189). During the first 12 days of pregnancy, both free and total acid-phosphatase activities decline and reach lowest levels by day 16 (see Fig. 2). As the secretory activity of the corpora begins to decline in late pregnancy, the levels of acid-phosphatase activity increase. Therefore the level of progesterone in the blood and the ratio of progesterone to 20α-OHP increase as pregnancy progresses and corresponding acid-phosphatase activities decrease. As the level of progesterone falls, acid-phosphatase activity increases.

During the course of pregnancy, levels of estrogen in plasma remain low and then increase markedly soon after parturition (see Fig. 2). This pattern of estrogen secretion may be unrelated to luteal function and thus may reflect primarily follicular development.

The duration of pseudopregnancy in intact rats is one week less than that in hysterectomized rats, though the morphological size of the corpora lutea is similar in both groups (see Fig. 1). Maximal activity of the corpora lutea in pseudopregnant rats occurs at day 6, as indicated by levels of progesterone in ovarian venous plasma (Fig. 3). Peak progesterone levels also occur at day 6 in pseudopregnant, hysterectomized animals, but at a concentration of steroid twice that found in normal pseudopregnant rats. The level of progesterone remains higher after hysterectomy, and the decline in luteal function requires a week longer than during normal pseudopregnancy. During the last week of pseudopregnancy in hysterectomized rats, plasma levels of progesterone are four- to sixfold less than during a similar period of pregnancy (see Figs. 2 and 3). There is an inverse relationship in the secretion of progesterone and 20α-OHP during pseudopregnancy and after hysterectomy (see Fig. 3).

In pseudopregnant rats, 20α-hydroxysteroid dehydrogenase activity is inversely related to progesterone levels

pseudopregnancy, though they are maintained until days 18–25. After mating, the corpora lutea are similar to those in pseudopregnant or hysterectomized animals until about day 10, increase threefold by day 16, and thereafter decline. The increased growth of corpora during the later half of gestation is caused by trophic hormones from the placentas. The levels of progesterone in ovarian

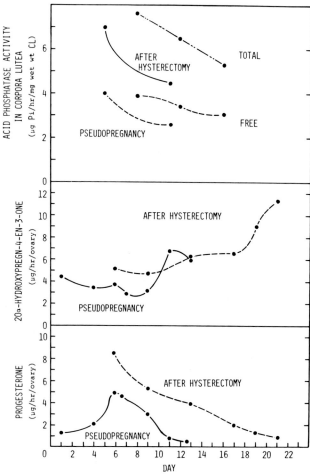

FIG. 3. Plasma levels of progestins and acid-phosphatase activity in luteal tissue of the rat are shown during pseudopregnancy and during pseudopregnancy in hysterectomized animals. Acid-phosphatase activity is expressed as inorganic phosphate (Pi) in $\mu g/hr/$ mg wet wt of corpora lutea (CL). Free activity was measured after incubation, and total activity was obtained by addition of 1% Triton X-100 before incubation. Progestin values are from data of Hashimoto et al. (100) and acid-phosphatase activities from data of Smith & Waynforth (189).

in ovarian blood (19, 100). During the first 7 days, dehydrogenase activity declines precipitously and then increases steadily to day 13. This enzyme activity remains low from days 6–17 in hysterectomized, pseudopregnant rats, but a marked increase in 20α-hydroxysteroid dehydrogenase activity occurs at the termination of this diestrous phase. Thus, during pseudopregnancy in intact and hysterectomized rats, the levels of 20α-hydroxysteroid dehydrogenase activity are inversely related to the concentrations of progesterone and directly correlated with levels of 20α-OHP in ovarian venous blood. The levels of acid-phosphatase activity (free and total) during early pseudopregnancy are similar to those of early pregnancy, though the rate of decline in activity is less marked in pseudopregnant animals between days 8 and 12 [see Figs. 2 and 3; (189)]. In hysterectomized, pseudopregnant rats, initial levels of free and total acid-

phosphatase activity are higher at day 8, but these levels decline by days 12 and 16 (see Fig. 3).

The decline in levels of progesterone near termination of pregnancy, pseudopregnancy, or pseudopregnancy in hysterectomized rats generally results in elevated levels of 20α-OHP, 20α-hydroxysteroid dehydrogenase and acid-phosphatase activities. The shift in the amounts of progesterone and 20α-OHP at this time relates to the ability of the 20α-hydroxysteroid dehydrogenase to reduce progesterone to 20α-OHP. Changes in acid-phosphatase activity may influence or control the secretion of progestational steroids, but a specific role of acid phosphatase in the regression of the corpus luteum is unknown.

In the guinea pig the estrous cycle is about 16 days; the corpus luteum attains maximal size by days 8–10 and regresses completely by day 20 (Fig. 4). After mating the volume of the corpus is threefold greater than it is by day 16 of the cycle; the corpus luteum maintains this volume until parturition (about day 68) and then regresses rapidly during lactation. If the animal is hysterectomized early in the cycle (days 4–6) the corpus luteum develops much like that of pregnancy, but it is maintained well beyond day 68, though it gradually regresses by day 120. When the uterus is removed at day 10, the corpus develops and regresses in a pattern similar to that during gestation. Removal of the uterus very late in the estrous cycle (day 15) has a detrimental effect on the life-span of the corpus. The declining corpus luteum of that cycle is spared by hysterectomy; it develops but does not attain a volume comparable with that of pregnancy. Furthermore its regression is almost complete by day 60. In some animals, estrus and ovulation occur soon after hysterectomy on day 15. The corpora lutea of that cycle regress, but the newly formed corpora develop and are maintained in a manner similar to that in animals hysterectomized on day 5 or 10 of the luteal phase (175). When corpora lutea are induced in hysterectomized animals, they develop and regress independent of the original corpora (64). Though there are characteristic changes in the morphology of corpora

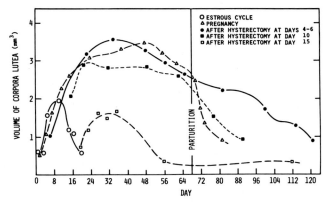

FIG. 4. Morphological changes in the corpus luteum of the guinea pig during the estrous cycle, pregnancy, and after hysterectomy at days 4–6, 10, or 15. [Adapted from (61, 63, 174–176).]

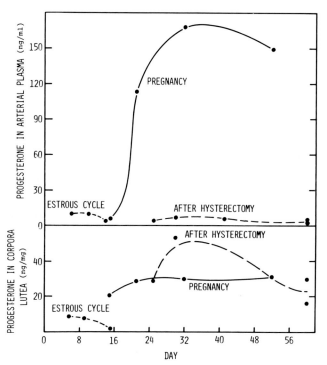

FIG. 5. Levels of progesterone in corpora lutea and arterial plasma during the estrous cycle, pregnancy, and after hysterectomy in guinea pigs. [Adapted from Heap et al. (105).]

lutea from cycling, pregnant, and hysterectomized guinea pigs, this criterion provides only a limited indication of their secretory activity.

An indicator of the physiological activity is the level of progesterone in the luteal tissue (Fig. 5). During the estrous cycle, progesterone levels, as measured by a fluorescence assay, increase at midcycle and decline gradually to extremely low levels by day 16 (105). By day 16 of pregnancy the corpus contains considerably more progesterone than at any time during the estrous cycle. This level of steroid is maintained throughout gestation. After the animal is hysterectomized, the concentrations of progesterone are similar to those found during gestation. Progesterone levels in peripheral plasma are low throughout the estrous cycle, but they increase markedly by day 20 in mated guinea pigs and remain high throughout gestation (see Fig. 5). After hysterectomy the levels of progesterone in plasma remain low, similar to those during the estrous cycle. These plasma levels of progesterone measured by a fluorescence technique (103) are higher than those determined by a gas chromatographic technique (81) for the estrous cycle. Gas chromatography defined a preovulatory peak at estrus, extremely low levels of progesterone at days 1–3, an increase to maximal values for the luteal phase from days 7 to 11, and a decline to basal levels by day 15 (81). Plasma levels of progesterone suggest that the secretory activity of corpora lutea in hysterectomized guinea pigs is similar to that of the estrous cycle. During gestation the placentas and ovaries contribute to the progesterone

content of the peripheral blood, but placental production of the steroid is relatively more important near term, as indicated by maintenance of pregnancy in ovariectomized guinea pigs (104).

Exogenous estrogen is luteolytic in cyclic guinea pigs (48), but hysterectomy prevents luteolysis (29, 112). In hemihysterectomized animals, estradiol benzoate induces luteal regression in the ovary adjacent to the remaining horn, whereas corpora in the opposite ovary are maintained (29). These results indicate that the uterus is involved in luteolytic action by exogenous estrogen; mediation of this response by the hypophysis seems unlikely.

After ovulation in the ewe the corpus luteum develops to maximal weight by day 11, maintains this weight until late in the estrous cycle (day 15), and regresses rapidly the next day (Fig. 6). After hysterectomizing ewes early in the cycle (days 3–6), Wiltbank & Casida (205) found that the same corpora lutea measured 10 and 11 mm in diameter by day 20 and were maintained at least 107 days. Luteal tissue weight at days 11 and 26 indicates maintenance of the corpus after hysterectomy (55, 207).

Progesterone in the luteal tissue increases to maximal levels by day 10 of the estrous cycle, remains at this level through day 15, and falls abruptly to nondetectable amounts by day 16 [(60, 168); see Fig. 6]. After hysterectomy the luteal tissue levels of progesterone exceed those of the cycle at day 26 (55). Progesterone levels in peripheral plasma are extremely low at estrus, increase to peak values by days 10 through 14, and decline at day 16 of the cycle (see Fig. 6). In mated ewes there is a steady increase in plasma levels of progesterone beyond day 16, which indicates maintenance of corpora lutea; these corpora remain fully functional for almost the entire gestation.

Typical fine structural and biochemical changes associated with the decline in steroid production by the corpus luteum include shrinkage of the lutein cells, swelling of mitochondria and thinning of their matrix, accumulation of lipid droplets within the cytoplasm, a decline in both Δ^5-3β-hydroxysteroid dehydrogenase and diaphorase activities, and degeneration of nuclei (60). These features are evident by day 15, when, in a brief period of 24 hr, progesterone levels in the ovarian venous plasma and luteal tissue decline rapidly. An additional characteristic feature is the abundance of lysosomes during the period of rapid involutionary changes in the ovine lutein cell (67). The fragility of these lysosomes to the stress of homogenizing the lutein cells is determined by measuring the total specific activity of acid phosphatase and acid protease. Fragility is expressed as the ratio of free activity (F) in the supernatant to the sum of the free plus lysosome-bound activity (F + B) times 100. This ratio, with acid protease and acid phosphatase as the marker enzymes, is relatively constant between days 11 and 15 but increases sharply during luteal regression within the next 24 hr (see Fig. 6).

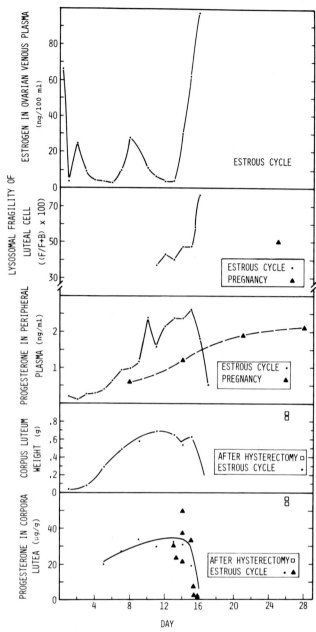

FIG. 6. Measures of ovarian function during the estrous cycle, pregnancy, and after hysterectomy in the ewe. Data on luteal tissue weight were adapted from Roche et al. (168), Woody et al. (207), and Collins et al. (55). Data on levels of progesterone in luteal tissue were adapted from Deane et al. (60) and Roche et al. (168). Plasma levels of progesterone are data from Stabenfeldt et al. (194, 195). The percentage of lysosomal activity in luteal cells is expressed as the ratio of free acid-phosphatase activity (F) to free plus bound acid-phosphatase activity (F + B). Acid-phosphatase activity is expressed as μg nitrophenol/hr/mg wet wt of tissue. These data were adapted from Dingle et al. (67). Plasma levels of estrogens in cycling ewes were measured by radioimmunoassay (179).

By contrast the lysosomes in luteal cells from pregnant ewes do not increase in fragility by the test of homogenization. There is an increase in the size of the lysosomal particles during luteal regression (days 15–16),

which may indicate the formation of autophagic vacuoles. Thus the increase in fragility of lysosomes is one of the earliest changes associated with luteal regression in the ewe. This evidence, together with maximal secretion of progesterone on day 15 to almost nondectectable levels within 24 hr (80, 186), may indicate that lysosomes function in regression of the ovine lutein cell.

The levels of estrogens in ovarian venous plasma are high at estrus (day 0), decline markedly within 24 hr, and remain low until days 15 and 16 of the cycle [see Fig. 6; (179)]. Plasma estrogens increase to peak levels near the termination of the cycle, when plasma levels of progesterone drop abruptly. That endogenous levels of estrogens lead or contribute to the demise of the corpus luteum at this time in the estrous cycle of the ewe is possible but unproven. Exogenous estrogens are luteotrophic in the ewe (65, 66), but they cause premature luteal regression when injected on days 11 and 12 of the cycle (102). Injecting estrogen at this time in hysterectomized ewes does not interfere with maintenance of corpora lutea (196). In unilaterally hysterectomized ewes having a recent ovulation point on each ovary, injections of estradiol-17β significantly reduce the weight of the corpus luteum on the side adjacent to the remaining uterine horn, as compared with luteal weight in the opposite ovary (1). These results suggest that the uterus mediates the effect of the estrogen. Hysterectomy also prevents or reduces the inhibitory action of exogenous progesterone, which suggests that the uterus may be partly responsible for mediating this action (207).

Evidence for a lytic effect of the nongravid uterus in the ewe is substantiated by experiments dealing with hysterectomy and evaluation of subsequent luteal function by measuring progesterone in ovarian venous plasma (Fig. 7). During the estrous cycle, plasma levels of progesterone are maximal at days 9 through 12, with little decline evident by day 15. With the onset of estrus, plasma progesterone drops to nondetectable levels.

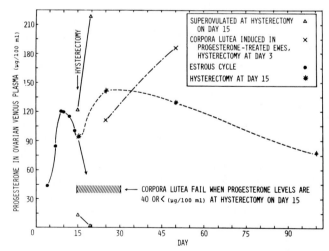

FIG. 7. Levels of progesterone in ovarian venous plasma during the estrous cycle and after hysterectomy in the ewe. [Adapted from Moor et al. (143, 144) and Short (186).]

Luteal involution can be arrested by hysterectomizing ewes on day 15, if levels of progesterone in plasma are at least 40 μg/100 ml plasma (20 animals). In such hysterectomized ewes the rescued corpus luteum is maintained at least 100 days, as indicated by substantial levels of plasma progesterone (see Fig. 7). When levels of progesterone in plasma are less than 40 μg/100 ml at hysterectomy on day 15, the corpus luteum regresses within 3 days (20 ewes). A similar situation exists in ewes superovulated at hysterectomy on day 15 (see Fig. 7). If levels of progesterone in plasma are too low, luteal regression proceeds, but, when the steroid levels are high at this time, the secretory activity of the induced corpora is increased markedly 3 days later. The life-span of induced corpora lutea in the ewe depends on that of the natural corpora of the estrous cycle (114, 143), but hysterectomy prolongs the life-span of induced corpora lutea in progesterone-blocked ewes (see Fig. 7). Plasma levels of progesterone remain high 25 and 50 days later.

Though luteal involution occurs late in the estrous cycle of the ewe, it can be arrested by removal of the uterus. The corpus luteum may have undergone marked functional and morphological regression by day 15, and yet it can be saved by hysterectomy. It seems that the nongravid uterus is essential for initiating and continuing processes that lead to death of the luteal cell.

Corpus luteum control of the diestrous interval in the pig is clearly evident by structural and functional changes in the lutein cell during the estrous cycle and pregnancy and after hysterectomy. The corpus is essential for successful completion of gestation; its life and death depend not only on the state of the uterus (whether gravid or not), but also on the presence or absence of the uterus. The structure of the corpus luteum is characterized by use of light (57, 58) and electron microscopy (21, 22, 46), and there is a close correlation between morphological changes during the reproductive cycle (e.g., estrous cycle, pregnancy, and after hysterectomy) and levels of progesterone in luteal tissue (2, 136,

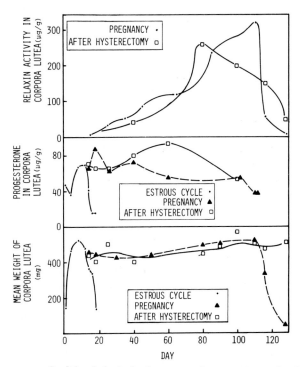

FIG. 9. Morphological changes and progesterone levels in porcine corpora lutea during the estrous cycle, pregnancy, and after hysterectomy. Relaxin activity in luteal tissue is shown during pregnancy and after hysterectomy. Relaxin activity is expressed as μg NIH porcine reference relaxin per gram luteal tissue. [Adapted from Anderson et al. (8), Belt et al. (21), Cavazos et al. (46), and Masuda et al. (136).]

171), ovarian venous plasma (89, 136), and peripheral plasma (193, 199).

Typical patterns of porcine luteal function during the estrous cycle and early stages of pregnancy are well defined by measuring levels of progesterone in peripheral plasma (Fig. 8). During the cycle, progesterone increases to peak values by days 10–14, declines slightly by day 15, and drops to low levels by days 16 through 20. In mated animals the levels of progesterone increase in a similar way, but they remain high during the first 28 days. Morphological changes in the development, maintenance, and regression of corpora lutea are shown for the estrous cycle, pregnancy, and after hysterectomy (Fig. 9). The increase and decrease in weight of corpora during the cycle correspond with similar changes in their secretory activity (see Figs. 8 and 9). By day 16 a trend of irreversible decline and eventually complete regression is indicated. In mated pigs, corpora are larger than those of the cycle at day 14, and they are maintained at this weight until parturition. After delivery they regress rapidly during lactation. When the pig is hysterectomized during the active luteal phase of the cycle or during pregnancy, the corpora lutea develop to maximal weight by day 14 and are maintained at this level well beyond day 128. They eventually regress by days 150–200; estrus and sometimes ovulations occur, but there is usually a high incidence of cystic ovarian follicles (74).

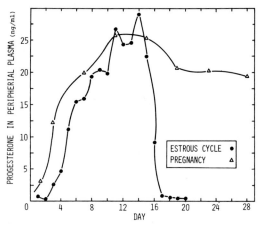

FIG. 8. Progesterone in peripheral plasma of the pig during the estrous cycle and pregnancy. [Adapted from Stabenfeldt et al. (193) and Tillson et al. (199).]

Similar changes, such as those in tissue weight, occur in the concentrations of progesterone in luteal tissue during these three reproductive states with the exception of declining levels of progesterone after day 100 of gestation, even though luteal tissue weight is maintained (see Fig. 9).

Fine structural features of the porcine lutein cell during periods of active secretion of progesterone (e.g., days 4–12 of estrous cycle) include accumulated masses of agranular endoplasmic reticulum, small coated vesicles usually near the Golgi complex, and larger coated vesicles near the plasmalemma (46). The coated vesicles may effect cellular transport. During luteal regression (days 14 through 18) there is an increase in lipid droplets, cytoplasmic disorganization, and vacuolation of agranular endoplasmic reticulum. As progesterone levels decline in the terminal phase of the cycle, there is also an increase in the number of cytoplasmic residual bodies (lysosomes) and an invasion of connective tissue. These events result in formation of the corpus albicans. Acid-phosphatase activity increases progressively during the estrous cycle, but there is an abrupt increase in activity during early phases of luteal regression (2). These changes coincide with autolytic processes in the lutein cell. During pregnancy and after hysterectomy the fine structural features of the lutein cell are similar to, and typical of, steroid-secreting cells (21). In these phases the animals' lutein cells contain a larger Golgi apparatus, more agranular and granular endoplasmic reticulum, and an immensely larger number of membrane-limited dense bodies, which are not acid-phosphatase positive, than found in lutein cells of the estrous cycle. The presence of considerable areas of granular endoplasmic reticulum in lutein cells from hysterectomized and pregnant pigs suggests an increased capacity for protein synthesis over that observed in the estrous cycle.

The porcine corpus luteum also accumulates abundant quantities of relaxin during pregnancy and after hysterectomy (see Fig. 9). In mated pigs the levels of relaxin remain low during the first 30 days and gradually increase to peak values by day 110. By 36 hr before parturition, relaxin levels begin to decline, drop to very low levels within 16 hr of delivery, and remain low during lactation. After hysterectomy there is a similar increase in relaxin activity, but maximal levels occur at day 80, and a gradual decline follows by day 128. Low levels of relaxin at day 128 are contradictory to the large size of the corpora lutea in these hysterectomized animals. Relaxin activity in porcine corpora may indicate the functional life of this ephemeral gland, for the activity increases as the age of the corpora increases. Its activity is extremely low during the estrous cycle, even though corpora lutea develop and secrete abundant amounts of progesterone during this brief period.

A significant role for endogenous estrogen in luteotrophic or luteolytic action in the pig seems doubtful. Estrone is the primary estrogen excreted in the urine of the pig. Estrone levels remain low during the luteal phase and then peak sharply during proestrous and estrous

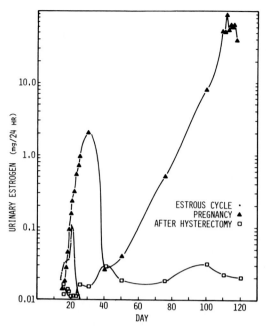

FIG. 10. Accumulation of estrone in 24-hr urine collections in pigs during the estrous cycle, pregnancy, and after hysterectomy. [Adapted from Bowerman et al. (31).]

phases of the estrous cycle [Fig. 10; (31, 132, 163)]. In mated animals an initial peak in estrogen excretion occurs at about day 30, a marked decline soon after, and a gradual increase to extremely high excretion rates just before parturition (31, 164, 169). A rapid decrease in amounts of urinary estrogen occurs after parturition (164, 169). In ovariectomized, hypophysectomized pigs having their pregnancy maintained by exogenous progesterone, the level of urinary estrone is similar to that of intact pregnant animals (82). When pigs are hysterectomized during the luteal phase of the estrous cycle, the excretion of urinary estrone remains consistently low, even though the corpora lutea are maintained as if the animals were pregnant (see Fig. 10). A similar low level of urinary estrone excretion occurs after pigs are hysterectomized at day 70 of pregnancy (170). The major source of estrogen during late gestation is the placenta in this species. Exogenous estrogen causes corpora to be maintained for prolonged periods in the nongravid pig (74, 151).

UTERINE TRANSPLANTATION

Uterine transplantation has been used to determine the importance of uterine innervation to ovarian function. Experimental evidence from several species is summarized in Table 2. The results indicate that major nervous pathways to the uterus are not essential for uterine luteolytic action. Successful transplants that induce luteal regression seem to have more viable endometrial glands and endometrial stroma than do those that fail to induce luteolysis. For example, transplanting one uterine horn or pieces of endometrium to

TABLE 2. *Ovarian Function After Uterine Transplantation*

Species	Type of Graft			Site of Graft	Duration of Luteal Function Compared with that of		Luteal Life-Span, days	Refs.
	Auto-	Homo-	Hetero-		Estrous cycle	Pseudopregnancy or pregnancy		
Rat		+		Intraperitoneal, estrous uterus		Reduced	11–16	106
	+			Abdominal skin and musculature		Reduced	16–18	140
	+			Abdominal skin and musculature	Normal		4–6	140
	+			Renal capsule		Reduced	11–19	10
	+			Renal capsule	Normal		4–6	10
Hamster	+			Cheek pouch		Reduced	11–13	41, 43, 71
		+		Cheek pouch		Reduced	9–13	41, 43, 71
			+	Cheek pouch, rat uterus		Reduced	12–16	41, 43, 71
			+	Cheek pouch, rabbit uterus		Normal	14–17	41
			+	Cheek pouch, mouse uterus		Normal	15–16	71
			+	Cheek pouch, human uterus		Normal	16–19	41
			+	Cheek pouch, human endometrium		Normal	16–19	41, 43
		+		Cheek pouch, hamster endometrium		Reduced	11–14	43, 137
			+	Cheek pouch, ovine endometrium (day 14 or 15)		Reduced	9–13	42, 43
			+	Cheek pouch, ovine endometrium (day 3 or 6)		Normal	14–21	42, 43
Rabbit	+			Viscera, endometrium		Reduced	14–17	52
	+			Abdominal musculature, endometrium			*	141, 185
	+			Omentum		Pregnancy maintained		212
Guinea pig	+			Beneath subcutaneous tissue	Prolonged		>50	127
	+			Abdominal oblique muscles	Continued		15–32	39
	+			Abdominal muscles, endometrium	Continued		24	39
	+			Abdominal wall	Continued		21–27	3
Dog	+			Beneath subcutaneous tissue	Continued		*	48
	+			Omentum		Pregnancy maintained		212
Pig	+			Abdominal muscles	Continued		22–28	7
	+			Parietal wall of peritoneum	Continued		21–23	77
	+			Small intestine	None		0	74
Sheep	+			Between flank muscles, endometrium	Continued		<40	43, 178
	+			Omentum		Pregnancy maintained		212
	+			Omentum		Pregnancy failed		152
	+			Omentum	Continued		16–18	152
	+			Ovary and uterus to neck	Continued		17	97

* Ovarian function continued as indicated by follicular development and new corpora lutea.

the cheek pouch of hysterectomized hamsters reduces pseudopregnancy to 13.5 days, as compared with 18 days in hysterectomized controls, but myometrial transplants are ineffective (41). In pigs, uterine autotransplants to abdominal muscles or to the peritoneum effectively induce luteolysis, but similar grafts to the small intestine are ineffective, because the luteolytic action of the autograft is inactivated by the liver.

Experimental evidence in the ewe is of particular interest (see Table 2). Endometrial autografts to flank muscles reduce the life-span of corpora lutea in hysterectomized ewes, but endometrial tissue grafted in the corpus luteum at hysterectomy causes only local degeneration of lutein cells and maintenance of the prolonged diestrous phase (43). Local luteolytic effects are evident

by autotransplanting the uterus or ovaries, or both, to the neck (87, 97). When the ovary is autotransplanted to the neck in unilaterally ovariectomized animals, the corpus luteum is maintained. A similar prolonged luteal phase occurs when a uterine horn is transplanted to the neck and an ovary remains in the abdomen, but putting an ovary and a uterine horn in the neck of ewes in which the other ovary and horn are removed results in estrous intervals of normal duration. These results favor a local, rather than a systemic, action of the uterus on the function of the corpus luteum.

The experimental evidence in several species suggests that the uterine luteolytic effect is mediated by local and systemic pathways, and only endometrium is essential for this action.

OVARIAN AUTOTRANSPLANTATION

Autotransplanting the ovary to a site distant from the uterus prolongs the life of the corpus luteum. Such evidence is found in the rat (10), guinea pig (27, 77), ewe (88), and heifer (93). For example, pseudopregnancies are 3–4 days longer in rats with their ovaries transplanted to the kidney capsule than are those in sham-operated animals (13 days). By removing one or both uterine horns in these autografted rats, the pseudopregnancies are extended even longer—20 and 24 days.

In contrast, autografting the ovaries to the uterus shortens pseudopregnancy to less than that in sham-operated rats (10) and reduces the duration of estrous cycles in guinea pigs (27).

TOXIC AGENTS AND LUTEAL FUNCTION

Irritants, corrosives, or bacterial infections in the uterine lumen modify luteal function. The effects of these toxic agents on ovarian function are summarized in Table 3. Irritation of the endometrium early in the estrous cycle usually induces premature regression of the corpus luteum and shortens estrous intervals. When the endometrium is infected, irritated, or destroyed later in the cycle, the corpus usually persists beyond the duration of the treatment cycle. In some cases the corpus luteum is maintained for an extended period, an effect similar to that of hysterectomy.

The infiltration of leukocytes into the endometrium is influenced by ovarian steroids. The uterus is more susceptible to infection during the progestational than during the estrogenic phase of the cycle. Infection early in the cycle may stimulate the uterus, but its introduction later may result in inactivation of the endometrium. These conditions lead to shortened and prolonged estrous intervals.

OXYTOCIN AND BOVINE LUTEAL FUNCTION

Oxytocin injected in heifers during the first week of the estrous cycle induces premature regression of the developing corpus luteum and reduces the cycle by half (14). If the ovary contains a corpus luteum at the beginning of a series of oxytocin injections, the corpus completes its pattern of development and regression, and estrous cycles

TABLE 3. *Introduction of Toxic Agents in the Uterus and Luteal Function*

Species	Intrauterine Agent	Day of Estrous Cycle Agent Introduced	Estrous Interval, days	Corpus Luteum	Refs.
Guinea pig	Bouin's fixative, picric acid, 10% phenol, or 10% silver nitrate	5	30		40
Pig	Bouin's fixative, 10% tannic acid, 12.5% phenol, or 10% silver nitrate	11 or 12	None	Maintain	6
Cow	Gelceptor F, viscous gel	1, 2 or 5	11.9		209, 210
		6	15.5		
		12	21.3		
		14 or 16	25.8		
		17 or 18	19.5		
	Iodine (Lugol's solution)	3	11.6		148
		16	26.0		
	Polyvinyl pyrrolidone iodine	3	10.8		
	Raw semen and preputial washings	0	10–12		94
	Spontaneous pyometra		None	Maintain	167
	Escherichia coli	*	None	Maintain	133
Ewe	45% propylene glycol, 15% ethanol, 15% benzyl alcohol, and 25% water in:				
	Horn near ovulating ovary	4	9		208
	Horn opposite ovulating ovary	4	16		
	Escherichia coli	1		Regress day 7	34
	Escherichia coli in:				
	Severed horn near ovulating ovary	1		Regress day 7	35
	Horn opposite ovulating ovary	1		Normal day 7	
	Ligated horn near ovulating ovary	1		Regress day 7	36
		3		Regress day 9	
		5		Regress day 11	
		7		Regress day 13	
		9		Normal day 15	
		9	<18		
		11	>21		
		13	<18		
		15	<18		
	Corynebacterium pyogenes	10	>21	Maintain	59
	Vibrio fetus	10	>21	Maintain	

* Infused twice weekly for 41 days.

are uninterrupted. If the heifer is hysterectomized at the beginning of the cycle, oxytocin fails to induce luteal regression, but premature luteolysis occurs after partial hysterectomy (5). Oxytocin effectively induces luteolysis when the uterus is opened longitudinally along the dorsal attachment from the cervix to the uterotubal junction. These results imply that the uterus is essential for inducing luteolysis by pharmacological dosages of oxytocin in the cow.

Convincing evidence that luteolytic action of oxytocin is mediated by the uterus is found in partially hysterectomized heifers (86). In animals having the retained uterine horn ipsilateral to the ovary containing the corpus luteum, oxytocin induces premature luteolysis. When the developing corpus luteum is in the ovary contralateral to the remaining horn, the same regimen of oxytocin injections fails to reduce the life of the corpus luteum; cycles in these or saline controls extend to at least 26 days. Therefore a local uterine luteolytic action is initiated by the oxytocin.

Though inhibition of uterine contractions by atropine and epinephrine blocks luteolytic action of oxytocin (23), oxytocin-induced contractions may not be a primary cause of luteolysis, since similar contractions produced by electrical stimulation fail to induce luteal regression (158). That oxytocin regulates luteal function through the hypothalamicohypophysial system by inhibiting the secretion of luteinizing hormone (93, 190) is not supported by its luteolytic action either after hypophysial stalk transection (108) or after administration of progesterone to intact animals (95). Plasma levels of luteinizing hormone remain unaffected by oxytocin until day 5 of the cycle (96).

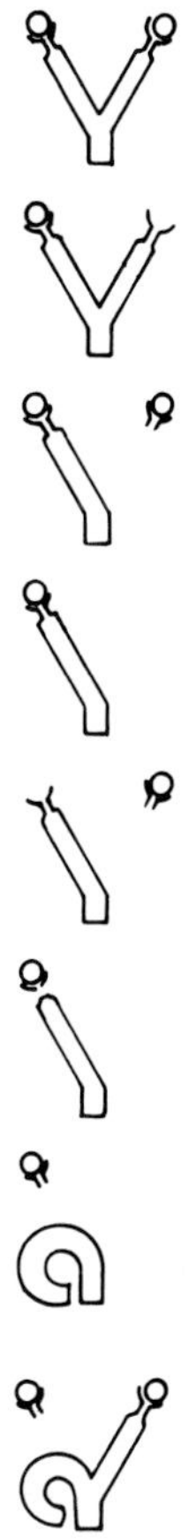

	ESTROUS INTERVALS		
	NO.	DAYS*	NO. >50 DAYS
A	12	17±0.3	0
B	12	15±0.3	0
C	5	30±2.8	7
D	9 2	17±0.5 35±2.3	0
E	4	31±4.7	8
F	2	41±3.5	9
G	1	38	10
H	8	25±1.2	4

*MEAN AND SE

FIG. 11. Local relationship of the ovary and uterus in the guinea pig. [Adapted from Butcher et al. (38).]

LOCAL EFFECT OF UTERUS ON OVARIAN FUNCTION

Luteolytic action by the uterus in several species is primarily a local response and, secondarily, a systemic response (3, 85). When one uterine horn is removed, the corpora lutea ipsilateral to the nongravid horn regress, whereas those in the opposite ovary are maintained. This local luteolytic effect is found in the partially hysterectomized hamster (155), guinea pig (25, 83), sheep (43, 113), pig (72), and cow (83), but not in the rat (17) or rabbit (111, 165). Cyclic periodicity remains normal after unilateral ovariectomy in the hamster (76, 137), rat (10, 16, 17, 38), guinea pig (16, 38, 83), and ewe (16, 113, 145). Unilateral hysterectomy or unilateral hysterectomy combined with removal of the contralateral ovary extends the luteal life-span in these four species. For example, the local relationships between the ovary and the uterus are demonstrated in the guinea pig (Fig. 11). In intact guinea pigs the estrous cycle is 17 days, and removing one ovary or an ovary and its adjacent horn does not change the length of the cycles. But removing one uterine horn or a horn and the opposite ovary causes prolonged cycle intervals. Ligating and cutting all physical connections between the remaining horn and ovary or retracting the uterine horn also maintains luteal function.

The conceptus causes maintenance of luteal function during early phases of the pregnancy in the pig (12, 71) and ewe (142, 145) by overcoming the luteolytic effect of the uterus. When a sufficient amount of nongravid uterus remains in these pregnant animals, the luteolytic action dominates, and the pregnancy fails. When one uterine horn in the pig is removed, pregnancy continues and the corpora are maintained in both ovaries, but, when only a small part of one nongravid horn remains after partial hysterectomy and the animal is mated, the corpora ipsilateral to the gravid horn are maintained and those near the nongravid segment regress (73). Increasing the amounts of one nongravid horn allows the uterine luteolytic effect to control ovarian function and thus causes luteal regression and pregnancy failure in the opposite horn (12). Niswender et al. (153) also found that corpora lutea remain functional only in the ovary near the gravid horn in pigs made unilaterally pregnant by day 2, but the corpora are maintained in both ovaries when the animal is made unilaterally pregnant after day 12. The first 12 days is the critical period in this species for uterine luteolytic action on a local or systemic level. The pregnancy can be maintained, however, by daily injections of progesterone (12) or by inducing a second set of corpora lutea before day 12 (50).

Pathways mediating local luteolytic effects are not clearly defined. By separating or ligating connections of the blood, lymphatics and nerve supplies between a uterine horn and its ovary, or both horns and ovaries, extend luteal function in the guinea pig (28, 84, 110), rat (17), hamster (155, 156), and ewe (68, 118); the proximity of the ovary containing the corpus luteum to the uterine horn seems to have no effect on histological features of the endometrium and uterine glands in the ewe (54). But the absence of the horn (hemihysterectomy) near the ovulating ovary prevents exogenous progesterone from causing luteal regression (206). A part of the effect of the exogenous progesterone on luteal regression may be mediated through the uterus; the horn must be near the ovulating ovary to convey this action. Even resection of an oviduct in the pig reduces progesterone levels in the adjacent ovary (153). The circulating blood and lymph between the uterus and ovary are important in the control of ovarian function.

PROSTAGLANDINS

Prostaglandins belong to a class of biologically active lipids, and certain ones of these (e.g., PGE_2, $PGF_{2\alpha}$) are capable, in some species, of terminating pregnancy and inducing luteolysis (Table 4). Infusion of prostaglandin ($PGF_{2\alpha}$) into pseudopregnant rats reduces progesterone and increases 20α-OHP levels in the ovaries, and pseudopregnancy is shortened. Injections of $PGF_{2\alpha}$ are equally effective in inducing luteolysis in hysterectomized (see Table 4) and in hypophysectomized rats given daily injections of prolactin (79). In ewes with ovarian autotransplants in the neck, exogenous $PGF_{2\alpha}$ abruptly reduces the secretion of progesterone from the ovary (138). The infusion of uterine vein blood into the ovarian artery in similarly prepared ewes also induces rapid

regression of the corpus luteum (B. V. Caldwell, personal communication).

In contrast to inhibitory effects of prostaglandins on luteal function in vivo, in vitro incubation of ovarian tissues with prostaglandins stimulates steroidogenesis. For example, they increase progesterone production, as well as the incorporation of acetate-1-^{14}C, in slices of bovine corpora lutea (192).

Several mechanisms whereby exogenous prostaglandin (e.g., PGE_2, $PGF_{2\alpha}$) could interrupt implantation or terminate pregnancy were suggested: a) initiating rhythmic uterine contractions; b) controlling blood flow to the ovaries and uterus; c) depressing progestin production by the corpus luteum; and d) altering sodium balance of placental fluids. In pregnant hamsters, higher levels of prostaglandin are required to induce luteolysis when gonadotrophins (e.g., follicle-stimulating hormone, prolactin) are injected (116). Similarly, higher dosages of prostaglandin are needed to induce luteolysis during later gestation, a period of placental luteotrophic support, than are required during early phases of pregnancy (116). In rhesus monkeys, $PGF_{2\alpha}$ induces luteolysis, as indicated by lowered plasma levels of progestin, at a time when progestin levels normally increase because of the trophic stimulus of the blastocyst (121). It also lowers plasma progesterone when given late in the menstrual cycle.

Exogenous prostaglandins reduce utero-ovarian vein blood flow in the rat and rabbit (161, 162). It has been suggested (160) that uterine luteolytic action may be explained as primarily a constriction of utero-ovarian veins at certain stages in the luteal phase of the cycle. Whether such a mechanism could be involved in local luteolytic action observed in several species is unknown. Involvement of prostaglandins of uterine origin in the control (local or systemic) of luteal function remains to be established.

UTERINE LUTEOLYTIC FACTORS

There have been several attempts to isolate, purify, and test uterine extracts for luteolytic activity (33, 43,

TABLE 4. *Exogenous Prostaglandins on Ovarian Function*

Species	During Pregnancy		After Hysterectomy	During Pseudopregnancy or Menstrual Cycle	Refs.
	PGE_2	$PGF_{2\alpha}$	$PGF_{2\alpha}$	$PGF_{2\alpha}$	
Rat	Block implantation	Terminate pregnancy		Induce luteolysis	79, 91, 154, 161, 162
Hamster	Block implantation	Terminate pregnancy	Induce luteolysis		79, 115, 116, 154
Guinea pig			Induce luteolysis		30
Rabbit	Block implantation	Terminate pregnancy	Induce luteolysis	Induce luteolysis	79, 91, 92, 154, 160–162, 183
Rhesus monkey	Terminate pregnancy	Terminate pregnancy		No effect on cycle	121, 122
Human	Terminate pregnancy	Terminate pregnancy		No effect on cycle	120, 172, 191

120, 135). Corpora lutea do not regress prematurely after lyophilized ovine uteri (119, 120), guinea pig uterine homogenates (110), porcine endometrial filtrates (9), or porcine uterine flushings (180) are injected into test animals of the same species, but porcine endometrial filtrates depress progesterone synthesis by luteal tissue in vitro (78). Addition of subcellular fractions of guinea pig uterus causes a marked inhibition of progesterone synthesis in an in vitro system containing substrate (pregnenolone), cofactor, and ovarian microsomes from guinea pigs, whereas extracts of intestine, skeletal muscle, and liver do not inhibit progesterone production (109).

One biological test system utilizes the hysterectomized hamster; a positive response is a reduction in the duration of pseudopregnancy (137) or a decline in luteal tissue weight and progesterone content of the corpora (131). Uterine extracts from hamsters 6 and 7 days pseudopregnant reduced pseudopregnancy in the test animals, whereas similar extracts from other stages of pseudopregnancy or pregnancy were ineffective (137). Aqueous extracts of ovine (42) or bovine (71) endometrium from the late luteal phase of the estrous cycle also induce premature luteal regression, as indicated by shortened pseudopregnancies in the hamster. Crude suspensions and aqueous extracts of bovine endometrium collected on days 10–13 of the estrous cycle reduce luteal function in the hamster, but similar preparations of myometrium, serum albumin, and skeletal muscle are not luteolytic (131).

Systems for culturing monolayers of granulosa cells (47) have been used by Schomberg and associates (180–182) to test luteolytic activity of porcine uterine flushings and endometrial preparations. Uterine flushings from the late luteal phase (days 12–18) of the cycle disrupt or destroy cell monolayers within a few hours, but flushings from days 0 to 10 and day 20 cause no lysis of these cells. Cinematography confirms lytic activity of day 16 flushings in vitro, but in vivo tests of these flushings do not produce luteolysis in the pig (182). Cultures of ovine granulosa cells have been used to test possible luteolytic activity of endometrial preparations from several stages in the estrous cycle of the ewe (43). Though two-thirds of the extracts obtained in the late luteal phase (days 14 and 15) are luteolytic, a few preparations from other stages are equally effective in causing degeneration of the granulosa cells.

Death of the lutein cell may be brought about in several ways (187). A uterine luteolysin should produce the same physiological and cytological changes in lutein cells in an in vitro system as are observed during luteal regression in vivo.

CONCLUSIONS

The physiological condition of the uterus controls the functional status of the corpus luteum in several species. This is evident under natural conditions from cyclic periodicity in nongravid females and maintenance of the corpus luteum during gestation. Premature regression or prolonged maintenance of the corpus luteum can be caused by a variety of experimental conditions in the uterus, including: a) presence of an intrauterine device; b) toxic agents within the uterus; c) exogenous oxytocin; and d) partial hysterectomy.

Hysterectomy prolongs luteal function in some species (e.g., ewe and pig) but does not interfere with cyclic periodicity in others (e.g., rhesus monkey and opossum). In those species in which hysterectomy delays luteal regression, the endometrium seems essential for inducing luteolysis. Destroying or modifying only the endometrium without affecting the myometrium usually delays luteal regression, whereas endometrial grafts induce luteolysis in hysterectomized animals.

Local luteolytic action between a uterine horn and its adjacent ovary is observed in some species. Furthermore the action of exogenous oxytocin, progesterone, or estrogen may be mediated through the uterus, for absence of the uterus usually results in maintenance of the corpus luteum under these experimental conditions.

The factors initiating the regression of the lutein cell during the estrous cycle or after parturition may be different from those affecting luteal function after experimental modification of the uterus. Even in hysterectomized animals, the corpora lutea eventually regress, but it is unlikely that the process of luteolysis in aged lutein cells is similar to that occurring during premature luteal regression.

REFERENCES

1. AKBAR, A. M., K. E. ROWE, AND F. STORMSHAK. Luteal regression by estradiol in unilaterally hysterectomized ewes. J. Animal Sci. 30: 1033, 1970.
2. AKINS, E. L., M. C. MORRISSETTE, AND P. T. CARDEILHAC. Luteal and endometrial phosphatase activities during the porcine estrous cycle. J. Animal Sci. 28: 51–56, 1969.
3. ANDERSON, L. L., K. P. BLAND, AND R. M. MELAMPY. Comparative aspects of uterine-luteal relationships. Recent Progr. Hormone Res. 25: 57–104, 1969.
4. ANDERSON, L. L., A. M. BOWERMAN, AND R. M. MELAMPY. Neuro-utero-ovarian relationships. In: Advances in Neuroendocrinology, edited by A. V. Nalbandov. Urbana: Univ. of Illinois Press, 1963, p. 345–373.

5. ANDERSON, L. L., A. M. BOWERMAN, AND R. M. MELAMPY. Oxytocin on ovarian function in cycling and hysterectomized heifers. J. Animal Sci. 24: 964–968, 1965.
6. ANDERSON, L. L., R. L. BUTCHER, AND R. M. MELAMPY. Subtotal hysterectomy and ovarian function in gilts. Endocrinology 69: 571–580, 1961.
7. ANDERSON, L. L., R. L. BUTCHER, AND R. M. MELAMPY. Uterus and occurrence of oestrus in pigs. Nature 198: 311–312, 1963.
8. ANDERSON, L. L., J. J. FORD, J. B. PETERS, R. M. MELAMPY, AND D. F. COX. Relaxin activity in porcine corpora lutea during pregnancy and after hysterectomy (Abstract). Federation Proc. 29: 705, 1970.

9. ANDERSON, L. L., AND R. M. MELAMPY. *In vivo* technique for utero-ovarian studies in the gilt. *J. Animal Sci.* 21: 1018, 1962.

10. ANDERSON, L. L., R. M. MELAMPY, AND C. L. CHEN. Uterus and duration of pseudopregnancy in the rat. *Arch. Anat. Microscop. Morphol. Exptl. Suppl.* 56: 373–384, 1967.

11. ANDERSON, L. L., F. C. NEAL, AND R. M. MELAMPY. Hysterectomy and ovarian function in beef heifers. *Am. J. Vet. Res.* 23: 794–802, 1962.

12. ANDERSON, L. L., R. P. RATHMACHER, AND R. M. MELAMPY. The uterus and unilateral regression of corpora lutea in the pig. *Am. J. Physiol.* 210: 611–614, 1966.

13. ANDREOLI, C. Corpus luteum activity after hysterectomy in women. *Acta Endocrinol.* 50: 65–69, 1965.

14. ARMSTRONG, D. T., AND W. HANSEL. Alteration of the bovine estrous cycle with oxytocin. *J. Dairy Sci.* 42: 533–542, 1959.

15. ASDELL, S. A., AND J. HAMMOND. The effects of prolonging the life of the corpus luteum in the rabbit by hysterectomy. *Am. J. Physiol.* 103: 600–605, 1933.

16. BARLEY, D. A., R. L. BUTCHER, AND E. K. INSKEEP. Local uterine regulation of luteal regression. *J. Animal Sci.* 25: 918, 1966.

17. BARLEY, D. A., R. L. BUTCHER, AND E. K. INSKEEP. Local nature of utero-ovarian relationships in the pseudopregnant rat. *Endocrinology* 79: 119–124, 1966.

18. BARTKE, A. Influence of an IUD on the leucocytic content of the uterus and on the duration of pseudopregnancy in mice. *J. Reprod. Fertility* 23: 243–247, 1970.

19. BAST, J. D., AND O. E. TAUBER. 20α-Hydroxysteroid dehydrogenase activity in ovaries of pseudopregnant and pregnant rats. *Federation Proc.* 30: 535, 1971.

20. BELING, C. G., S. L. MARCUS, AND S. M. MARKHAM. Functional activity of the corpus luteum following hysterectomy. *J. Clin. Endocrinol.* 30: 30–39, 1970.

21. BELT, W. D., L. F. CAVAZOS, L. L. ANDERSON, AND R. R. KRAELING. Fine structure and progesterone levels in the corpus luteum of the pig during pregnancy and after hysterectomy. *Biol. Reprod.* 2: 98–113, 1970.

22. BJERSING, L. On the ultrastructure of granulosa lutein cells in porcine corpus luteum. *Z. Zellforsch. Mikroskop. Anat.* 82: 187–211, 1967.

23. BLACK, D. L., AND R. T. DUBY. Effect of oxytocin, epinephrine and atrophine on the oestrous cycle of the cow. *J. Reprod. Fertility* 9: 3–8, 1965.

24. BLAND, K. P., AND B. T. DONOVAN. The uterus and the control of ovarian function. *Advan. Reprod. Physiol.* 1: 179–214, 1966.

25. BLAND, K. P., AND B. T. DONOVAN. Asymmetry in luteal size following hemi-hysterectomy in the guinea-pig. *J. Endocrinol.* 34: iii–iv, 1966.

26. BLAND, K. P., AND B. T. DONOVAN. Uterine distention and the function of the corpora lutea in the guinea-pig. *J. Physiol., London* 186: 503–515, 1966.

27. BLAND, K. P., AND B. T. DONOVAN. The effect of autotransplantation of the ovaries to the kidneys or uterus on the oestrous cycle of the guinea-pig. *J. Endocrinol.* 41: 95–103, 1968.

28. BLAND, K. P., AND B. T. DONOVAN. Observations on the time of action and the pathway of the uterine luteolytic effect of the guinea-pig. *J. Endocrinol.* 43: 259–264, 1969.

29. BLAND, K. P., AND B. T. DONOVAN. Oestrogen and progesterone and the function of the corpora lutea in the guinea-pig. *J. Endocrinol.* 47: 225–230, 1970.

30. BLATCHLEY, F. R., AND B. T. DONOVAN. Luteolytic effect of prostaglandin in the guinea pig. *Nature* 221: 1065, 1969.

31. BOWERMAN, A. M., L. L. ANDERSON, AND R. M. MELAMPY. Urinary estrogens in cycling, pregnant, ovariectomized and hysterectomized gilts. *Iowa State J. Sci.* 38: 437–445, 1964.

32. BRADBURY, J. T. Prolongation of the life of the corpus luteum by hysterectomy in the rat. *Anat. Record* 70: 51, 1937.

33. BRADBURY, J. T., W. E. BROWN, AND L. A. GRAY. Maintenance of the corpus luteum and physiologic action of progesterone. *Recent Progr. Hormone Res.* 5: 151–194, 1950.

34. BRINSFIELD, T. H., AND H. W. HAWK. Luteolytic effect of induced uterine infection in the ewe. *J. Animal Sci.* 27: 150–152, 1968.

35. BRINSFIELD, T. H., AND H. W. HAWK. Unilateral effect of induced uterine infection on luteal development in the ewe. *J. Animal Sci.* 27: 1631–1633, 1968.

36. BRINSFIELD, T. H., D. K. HIGGINBOTHAM, AND H. W. HAWK. Influence of induced uterine infection at various stages of the estrous cycle on the corpus luteum of the ewe. *J. Animal Sci.* 29: 616–618, 1969.

37. BURFORD, T. H., AND A. W. DIDDLE. Effect of total hysterectomy upon the ovary of the Macacus rhesus. *Surg. Gynecol. Obstet.* 62: 701–707, 1936.

38. BUTCHER, R. L., D. A. BARLEY, AND E. K. INSKEEP. Local relationship between the ovary and uterus of rats and guinea pigs. *Endocrinology* 84: 476–481, 1969.

39. BUTCHER, R. L., K. Y. CHU, AND R. M. MELAMPY. Effect of uterine auto-transplants on the estrous cycle in the guinea pig. *Endocrinology* 70: 442–444, 1962.

40. BUTCHER, R. L., K. Y. CHU, AND R. M. MELAMPY. Utero-ovarian relationships in the guinea pig. *Endocrinology* 71: 810–815, 1962.

41. CALDWELL, B. V., R. S. MAZER, AND P. A. WRIGHT. Luteolysis as affected by uterine transplantation in the Syrian hamster. *Endocrinology* 80: 477–482, 1967.

42. CALDWELL, B. V., R. M. MOOR, AND R. A. S. LAWSON. Effects of sheep endometrial grafts and extracts on the length of pseudopregnancy in the hysterectomized hamster. *J. Reprod. Fertility* 17: 567–569, 1968.

43. CALDWELL, B. V., L. E. A. ROWSON, R. M. MOOR, AND M. F. HAY. The utero-ovarian relationship and its possible role in infertility. *J. Reprod. Fertility Suppl.* 8: 59–76, 1969.

44. CANIVENC, R., M. BONNIN-LAFFARGUE, AND M. C. RELEXANS. L'utérus gravide a-t-il une fonction luteotrope chez le Blaireau européen *Meles meles* L.? *Compt. Rend. Soc. Biol.* 156: 1372–1375, 1962.

45. CARMICHAEL, E. S., AND F. H. A. MARSHALL. The correlation of the ovarian and uterine functions. *Proc. Roy. Soc. London, Ser. B* 79: 387–394, 1907.

46. CAVAZOS, L. F., L. L. ANDERSON, W. D. BELT, D. M. HENRICKS, R. R. KRAELING, AND R. M. MELAMPY. Fine structure and progesterone levels in the corpus luteum of the pig during the estrous cycle. *Biol. Reprod.* 1: 83–106, 1969.

47. CHANNING, C. P. Influences of the *in vivo* and *in vitro* hormonal environment upon luteinization of granulosa cells in tissue culture. *Recent Progr. Hormone Res.* 26: 589–622, 1970.

48. CHEVAL, M. Ovarian and uterine grafts. *Proc. Roy. Soc. Med.* 27: 1395–1406, 1934.

49. CHOUDARY, J. B., AND G. S. GREENWALD. Luteolytic effect of oestrogen on the corpora lutea of the cyclic guinea-pig. *J. Reprod. Fertility* 16: 333–341, 1968.

50. CHRISTENSON, R. K., AND B. N. DAY. Maintenance of unilateral pregnancy in the pig with induced corpora lutea. *J. Animal Sci.* 32: 282–286, 1971.

51. CHRISTIAN, R. M., JR., L. YUAN, AND I. ROTHCHILD. The effect of hysterectomy on parameters of luteinizing hormone secretion in pseudopregnant rats. *Acta Endocrinol.* 58: 57–66 1968.

52. CHU, J. P., C. C. LEE, AND S. S. YOU. Functional relation between the uterus and corpus luteum. *J. Endocrinol.* 4: 392–398, 1946.

53. CLARK, M. J., AND G. B. SHARMAN. Failure of hysterectomy to affect the ovarian cycle of the marsupial *Trichosurus vulpecula. J. Reprod. Fertility* 10: 459–461, 1965.

54. CLOUD, J. G., AND L. E. CASIDA. Histological changes in the uterine horns during the estrous cycle in the ewe in relation to the proximity of the corpus luteum. *J. Animal Sci.* 28: 492–495, 1969.

55. COLLINS, W. E., E. K. INSKEEP, B. E. HOWLAND, A. L. POPE, AND L. E. CASIDA. Effects of hysterectomy and corpus luteum induction on pituitary-ovarian relationships in the ewe. *J. Animal Sci.* 25: 87–91, 1966.

56. CORFMAN, P. A., AND S. J. SEGAL. Biologic effects of intra-uterine devices. *Am. J. Obstet. Gynecol.* 100: 448–459, 1968.

57. CORNER, G. W. The corpus luteum of pregnancy, as it is in swine. *Carnegie Inst. Wash. Contrib. Embryol.* 5: 69–94, 1915.

58. CORNER, G. W. On the origin of the corpus luteum of the sow from both granulosa and theca interna. *Am. J. Anat.* 26: 117–183, 1919.

59. COUDERT, S. P., AND R. V. SHORT. Prolongation of the functional life of the corpus luteum in sheep with experimental uterine infections. *J. Reprod. Fertility* 12: 579–582, 1966.

60. DEANE, H. W., M. F. HAY, R. M. MOOR, L. E. A. ROWSON, AND R. V. SHORT. The corpus luteum of the sheep: relationship between morphology and function during the oestrous cycle. *Acta Endocrinol.* 51: 245–263, 1966.

61. DEANESLY, R. Normal growth and persistence of corpora lutea of both ovaries in the unilaterally pregnant guinea-pig. *J. Reprod. Fertility* 14: 519–521, 1967.

62. DEANESLY, R., AND A. S. PARKES. The effect of hysterectomy on the oestrous cycle of the ferret. *J. Physiol., London* 78: 80–85, 1933.

63. DEANESLY, R., AND J. S. PERRY. Independent regression of normal and induced corpora lutea in hysterectomized guinea-pigs. *J. Reprod. Fertility* 20: 503–508, 1969.

64. DEFEO, V. J. Decidualization. In: *Cellular Biology of the Uterus*, edited by R. M. Wynn. New York: Appleton Press, 1967, p. 191–290.

65. DENAMUR, R., J. MARTINET, AND R. V. SHORT. Mode of action of oestrogen in maintaining the functional life of corpora lutea in sheep. *J. Reprod. Fertility* 23: 109–116, 1970.

66. DENAMUR, R., AND P. MAULEON. Contrôle endocrinien de la persistance du corps jaune chez les ovins. *Compt. Rend.* 257: 527–530, 1963.

67. DINGLE, J. T., M. F. HAY, AND R. M. MOOR. Lysosomal function in the corpus luteum of the sheep. *J. Endocrinol.* 40: 325–336, 1968.

68. DOBROWOLSKI, W., AND E. S. E. HAFEZ. The effect of destruction of utero-ovarian vascular connections on the lifespan of the corpus luteum in sheep. *J. Reprod. Fertility* 23: 165–167, 1970.

69. DRIPS, D. Studies on the ovary of the spermophile (*Spermophilus citellus tridecemlineatus*) with special reference to the corpus luteum. *Am. J. Anat.* 25: 117–184, 1919.

70. DUBY, R. T., J. W. McDANIEL, C. H. SPILMAN, AND D. L. BLACK. Utero-ovarian relationships in the golden hamster. II. Quantitative and local influences of the uterus on ovarian function. *Acta Endocrinol.* 60: 603–610, 1969.

71. DUBY, R. T., J. W. McDANIEL, C. H. SPILMAN, AND D. L. BLACK. Utero-ovarian relationships in the golden hamster. III. Influence of uterine transplants and extracts on ovarian function following hysterectomy. *Acta Endocrinol.* 60: 611–620, 1969.

72. DU MESNIL DU BUISSON, F. Regression unilaterale des corps jaunes après hysterectomie partielle chez la truie. *Ann. Biol. Animale Biochim. Biophys.* 1: 105–112, 1961.

73. DU MESNIL DU BUISSON, F. Possibilite d'un fonctionnement dissemblable des ovaries pendant la gestation chez la truie. *Compt. Rend.* 253: 727–729, 1961.

74. DU MESNIL DU BUISSON, F. Contrôle du maintien du corps jaune de la truie. *J. Reprod. Fertility* 12: 413–414, 1966.

75. DU MESNIL DU BUISSON, F. *Contribution a l'Étude du Maintien du Corps Jaune de la Truie* (D.Sc. thesis). Paris: Univ. of Paris, 1966.

76. DU MESNIL DU BUISSON, F., AND L. DAUZIER. Contrôle mutuel de l'utérus et de l'ovaire chez la truie. *Ann. Zootech.* 8, Suppl. 1: 147–159, 1959.

77. DU MESNIL DU BUISSON, F., AND P. ROMBAUTS. Effet d'auto-transplants utérins sur le cycle oestrien de la truie. *Compt. Rend.* 256: 4984–4986, 1963.

78. DUNCAN, G. W., A. M. BOWERMAN, L. L. ANDERSON, W. R. HEARN, AND R. M. MELAMPY. Factors influencing *in vitro* synthesis of progesterone. *Endocrinology* 68: 199–207, 1961.

79. DUNCAN, G. W., AND B. B. PHARRISS. Effect of nonsteroidal compounds on fertility. *Federation Proc.* 29: 1232–1239, 1970.

80. EDGAR, D. C., AND J. W. RONALDSON. Blood levels of progesterone in the ewe. *J. Endocrinol.* 16: 378–384, 1958.

81. FEDER, H. H., J. A. RESKO, AND R. W. GOY. Progesterone concentrations in the arterial plasma of guinea-pigs during the oestrous cycle. *J. Endocrinol.* 40: 505–513, 1968.

82. FÈVRE, J., P. C. LÉGLISE, AND P. ROMBAUTS. Du role du l'hypophyse et des ovaires dans la biosynthese des oestrogenes au cours de la gestation chez la truie. *Ann. Biol. Animale Biochim. Biophys.* 8: 225–233, 1968.

83. FISCHER, T. V. Local uterine regulation of the corpus luteum. *Am. J. Anat.* 121: 425–442, 1967.

84. FISCHER, T. V. Evidence for a functional local utero-ovarian pathway. *Proc. Ann. Meeting Soc. Study Reprod., 2nd, Davis, Calif., 1969,* p. 6.

85. GINTHER, O. J. Local utero-ovarian relationships. *J. Animal Sci.* 26: 578–585, 1967.

86. GINTHER, O. J., C. O. WOODY, S. MAHAJAN, K. JANAKIRA-MAN, AND L. E. CASIDA. Effect of oxytocin administration on the oestrous cycle of unilaterally hysterectomized heifers. *J. Reprod. Fertility* 14: 225–229, 1967.

87. GODING, J. R., F. A. HARRISON, R. B. HEAP, AND J. L. LINZELL. Ovarian activity in the ewe after autotransplantation of the ovary or uterus to the neck. *J. Physiol., London* 191: 129–130P, 1967.

88. GODING, J. R., J. A. McCRACKEN, AND D. T. BAIRD. The study of ovarian function in the ewe by means of a vascular autotransplantation technique. *J. Endocrinol.* 39: 37–52, 1967.

89. GOMES, W. R., R. C. HERSCHLER, AND R. E. ERB. Progesterone levels in ovarian venous effluent of the nonpregnant sow. *J. Animal Sci.* 24: 722–725, 1965.

90. GREEP, R. O. Effects of hysterectomy and of estrogen treatment on volume changes in the corpora lutea of pregnant rabbits. *Anat. Record* 80: 465–477, 1941.

91. GUTKNECHT, G. D., J. C. CORNETTE, AND B. B. PHARRISS. Antifertility properties of prostaglandin $F_{2\alpha}$. *Biol. Reprod.* 1: 367–371, 1969.

92. GUTKNECHT, G. D., G. W. DUNCAN, AND L. J. WYNGARDEN. Effect of prostaglandin $F_{2\alpha}$ on ovarian blood flow in the rabbit as measured by hydrogen desaturation. *Physiologist* 13: 214, 1970.

93. HANSEL, W., AND R. B. SNOOK. Pituitary ovarian relationships in the cow. *J. Dairy Sci.* 53: 945–960, 1970.

94. HANSEL, W., AND W. C. WAGNER. Luteal inhibition in the bovine as a result of oxytocin injections, uterine dilatation, and intrauterine infusions of seminal and preputial fluids. *J. Dairy Sci.* 43: 796–805, 1960.

95. HARMS, P. G., AND P. V. MALVEN. Modification of bovine luteal function by exogenous oxytocin and progesterone. *J. Animal Sci.* 29: 25–29, 1969.

96. HARMS, P. G., G. D. NISWENDER, AND P. V. MALVEN. Progesterone and luteinizing hormone secretion during luteal inhibition by exogenous oxytocin. *Biol. Reprod.* 1: 228–233, 1969.

97. HARRISON, F. A., R. B. HEAP, AND J. L. LINZELL. Ovarian function in the sheep after autotransplantation of the ovary and uterus to the neck. *J. Endocrinol.* 39: xiii, 1968.

98. HARTMAN, C. G. Hysterectomy and the oestrous cycle in the opossum. *Am. J. Anat.* 35: 25–29, 1925.

99. HARTMAN, C. G. Studies in the reproduction of the monkey *Macacus* (Pithecus) rhesus, with special reference to menstruation and pregnancy. *Carnegie Inst. Wash. Contrib. Embryol.* 23: 1–161, 1932.

100. HASHIMOTO, I., D. M. HENRICKS, L. L. ANDERSON, AND R. M. MELAMPY. Progesterone and pregn-4-en-20α-ol-3-one in ovarian venous blood during various reproductive states in the rat. *Endocrinology* 82: 333–341, 1968.

101. HAWK, H. W. Effect of intra-uterine devices on corpus luteum function. *J. Animal Sci.* 27, Suppl. 1: 119–128, 1968.

102. HAWK, H. W., AND D. J. BOLT. Luteolytic effect of estradiol-17β when administered after midcycle in the ewe. *Biol. Reprod.* 2: 275–278, 1970.

103. HEAP, R. B. A fluorescence assay of progesterone. *J. Endocrinol.* 30: 293–305, 1964.
104. HEAP, R. B., AND R. DEANESLY. Progesterone levels in intact and ovariectomized pregnant guinea-pigs. *J. Endocrinol.* 30: ii–iii, 1964.
105. HEAP, R. B., J. S. PERRY, AND I. W. ROWLANDS. Corpus luteum function in the guinea-pig; arterial and luteal progesterone levels, and the effects of hysterectomy and hypophysectomy. *J. Reprod. Fertility* 13: 537–553, 1967.
106. HECHTER, O., M. FRAENKEL, M. LEV, AND S. SOSKIN. Influence of the uterus on the corpus luteum. *Endocrinology* 26: 680–683, 1940.
107. HECKEL, G. P. The estrogen sparing effect of hysterectomy. *Surg. Gynecol. Obstet.* 75: 379–390, 1942.
108. HENDRICKS, D. M., S. L. OXENREIDER, AND L. L. ANDERSON. Ovarian function after hypophysial stalk transection in the cow. *Am. J. Physiol.* 216: 1213–1218, 1969.
109. HESS, M. The mechanism of action of uterine luteolytic factors. *Intern. Congr. Anat., 9th, Leningrad, 1970*, p. 52.
110. HOWE, G. R. Influence of the uterus upon cyclic ovarian activity in the guinea pig. *Endocrinology* 77: 412–414, 1965.
111. HUNTER, G. L., AND L. E. CASIDA. Absence of local effects of the rabbit uterus on weight of corpus luteum. *J. Reprod. Fertility* 13: 179–181, 1967.
112. ILLINGWORTH, D. V. Luteolytic and luteotrophic effects of oestrogen in the guinea-pig. *J. Reprod. Fertility* 18: 548–549, 1969.
113. INSKEEP, E. K., AND R. L. BUTCHER. Local component of utero-ovarian relationships in the ewe. *J. Animal Sci.* 25: 1164–1168, 1966.
114. INSKEEP, E. K., B. E. HOWLAND, A. L. POPE, AND L. E. CASIDA. Ability of corpora lutea induced experimentally in progesterone treated ewes to prevent subsequent ovulation. *J. Animal Sci.* 23: 1172–1175, 1964.
115. JOHNSTON, J. O., AND K. K. HUNTER. Prostaglandin $F_{2\alpha}$ mode of action in pregnant hamsters. *Physiologist* 13: 235, 1970.
116. JOHNSTON, J. O., AND K. K. HUNTER. *In vivo* interaction of prostaglandin $F_{2\alpha}$ with hamster luteotropic complex. *Proc. Ann. Meeting Soc. Study Reprod., 3rd, Columbus, Ohio, 1970*, p. 30.
117. JONES, G. E. S., AND R. W. TELINDE. Metabolism of progesterone in hysterectomized women. *Am. J. Obstet. Gynecol.* 41: 682–687, 1941.
118. KARIM, S. M. M., AND G. M. FILSHIE. Therapeutic abortion using prostaglandin $F_{2\alpha}$. *Lancet* 1: 157–159, 1970.
119. KIRACOFE, G. H., C. S. MENZIES, H. T. GIER, AND H. G. SPIES. Effect of uterine extracts and uterine or ovarian blood vessel ligations on ovarian functions of ewes. *J. Animal Sci.* 25: 1159–1163, 1966.
120. KIRACOFE, G. H., AND H. G. SPIES. Length of maintenance of naturally formed and experimentally induced corpora lutea in hysterectomized ewes. *J. Reprod. Ferility* 11: 275–279, 1966.
121. KIRTON, K. T., B. B. PHARRISS, AND A. D. FORBES. Luteolytic effects of prostaglandin $F_{2\alpha}$ in primates. *Proc. Soc. Exptl. Biol. Med.* 133: 314–316, 1970.
122. KIRTON, K. T., B. B. PHARRISS, AND A. D. FORBES. Some effects of prostaglandins E_2 and $F_{2\alpha}$ on the pregnant rhesus monkey. *Biol. Reprod.* 3: 163–168, 1970.
123. KLEIN, M. Relation between the uterus and the ovaries in the pregnant hamster. *Proc. Royal Soc. London, Ser. B* 125: 348–364, 1938.
124. KUHN, N. J., AND M. S. BRILEY. The roles of pregn-5-ene-3β, 20α-diol and 20α-hydroxy steroid dehydrogenase in the control of progesterone synthesis preceding parturition and lactogenesis in the rat. *Biochem. J.* 117: 193–201, 1970.
125. LOBEL, B. L., R. M. ROSENBAUM, AND H. W. DEANE. Enzymic correlates of physiological regression of follicles and corpora lutea in ovaries of normal rats. *Endocrinology* 68: 232–247, 1961.
126. LOEB, L. The effect of extirpation of the uterus on the life and function of the corpus luteum in the guinea pig. *Proc. Soc. Exptl. Biol. Med.* 20: 441–443, 1923.
127. LOEB, L. The effects of hysterectomy on the system of sex organs and on the periodicity of the sexual cycle in the guinea pig. *Am. J. Physiol.* 83: 202–224, 1927.
128. LOEB, L., AND M. G. SMITH. The effect of hysterectomy on the duration of life, retrogression of corpora lutea and secondary sex organs in the rabbit. *Am. J. Anat.* 58: 1–25, 1936.
129. LONG, J. A., AND H. M. EVANS. The oestrous cycle in the rat and its associated phenomena. *Mem. Univ. Calif.* 6: 1–148, 1922.
130. LUKASZEWASKA, J. H., AND G. S. GREENWALD. Comparison of luteal function in pseudopregnant and pregnant hamsters. *J. Reprod. Fertility* 20: 185–187, 1969.
131. LUKASZEWASKA, J. H., AND W. HANSEL. Extraction and partial purification of luteolytic activity from bovine endometrial tissue. *Endocrinology* 86: 261–270, 1970.
132. LUNAAS, T. Urinary oestrogen levels in the sow during oestrous cycle and early pregnancy. *J. Reprod. Fertility* 4: 13–20, 1962.
133. LYNN, J. E., S. H. MCNUTT, AND L. E. CASIDA. Effects of intra-uterine bacterial inoculation and suckling on the bovine corpus luteum and uterus. *Am. J. Vet. Res.* 27: 1521–1526, 1966.
134. MALVEN, P. V., AND W. HANSEL. Ovarian function in dairy heifers following hysterectomy. *J. Dairy Sci.* 47: 1388–1393, 1964.
135. MALVEN, P. V., AND W. HANSEL. Effect of bovine endometrial extracts, vasopressin and oxytocin on the duration of pseudopregnancy in hysterectomized and intact rats. *J. Reprod. Fertility* 9: 207–215, 1965.
136. MASUDA, H., L. L. ANDERSON, D. M. HENRICKS, AND R. M. MELAMPY. Progesterone in ovarian venous plasma and corpora lutea of the pig. *Endocrinology* 80: 240–246, 1967.
137. MAZER, R. S., AND P. A. WRIGHT. A hamster uterine luteolytic extract. *Endocrinology* 83: 1065–1070, 1968.
138. MCCRACKEN, J. A., M. E. GLEW, AND R. J. SCARMUZZI. Corpus luteum regression induced by prostaglandin F_2-alpha. *J. Clin. Endocrinol.* 30: 544–546, 1970.
139. MELAMPY, R. M., AND L. L. ANDERSON. Role of the uterus in corpus luteum function. *J. Animal Sci.* 27, Suppl. 1: 77–96, 1968.
140. MELAMPY, R. M., L. L. ANDERSON, AND C. L. KRAGT. Uterus and life span of rat corpora lutea. *Endocrinology* 74: 501–504, 1964.
141. MISHELL, D. R., AND L. MOTYLOFF. The effect of hysterectomy upon the ovary, with reference to a possible hormonal action of the endometrium upon the ovary. *Endocrinology* 28: 436–440, 1941.
142. MOOR, R. M. Effect of embryo on corpus luteum function. *J. Animal Sci.* 27, Suppl. 1: 97–118, 1968.
143. MOOR, R. M., W. D. BOOTH, AND L. E. A. ROWSON. Effect of hysterectomy on the life-span of corpora lutea induced artificially in progesterone-treated ewes. *J. Reprod. Fertility* 12: 385–387, 1966.
144. MOOR, R. M., M. F. HAY, R. V. SHORT, AND L. E. A. ROWSON. The corpus luteum of the sheep: effect of uterine removal during luteal regression. *J. Reprod. Fertility* 21: 319–326, 1970.
145. MOOR, R. M., AND L. E. A. ROWSON. Local uterine mechanisms affecting luteal function in the sheep. *J. Reprod. Fertility* 11: 307–310, 1966.
146. MOOR, R. M., AND L. E. A. ROWSON. Local maintenance of the corpus luteum in sheep with embryos transferred to various isolated portions of the uterus. *J. Reprod. Fertility* 12: 539–550, 1966.
147. MOORE, W. W., AND A. V. NALBANDOV. Neurogenic effect of uterine distention on the estrous cycle of the ewe. *Endocrinology* 53: 1–11, 1953.
148. NAKAHARA, T., I. DOMEKI, S. INUI, AND M. YAMAUCHI. Effects of intrauterine infusion of iodine solution on the estrous cycle of the cow. *Japan. J. Animal Reprod.* 13: 57–65, 1967.
149. NALBANDOV, A. V., W. W. MOORE, AND H. W. NORTON.

Further studies on the neurogenic control of the estrous cycle by uterine distention. *Endocrinology* 56: 225–231, 1955.

150. NEILL, J. D., E. D. B. JOHANSSON, AND E. KNOBIL. Failure of hysterectomy to influence the normal pattern of cyclic progesterone secretion in the rhesus monkey. *Endocrinology* 84: 464–465, 1969.

151. NISHIKAWA, Y., AND T. HORIE. Study on the mechanism of extraordinary maintenance of corpus luteum in sows by estrogen injection, with special reference to its relationship with potency of the anterior pituitary. *Proc. Japan. Acad.* 39: 764–769, 1963.

152. NISWENDER, G. D., P. J. DZIUK, J. GRABER, AND C. C. KALTENBACH. Function of the corpus luteum in the ewe following relocation of the uterus or embryo. *J. Animal Sci.* 30: 935–940, 1970.

153. NISWENDER, G. D., P. J. DZIUK, C. C. KALTENBACH, AND H. W. NORTON. Local effects of embryos and the uterus on corpora lutea in gilts. *J. Animal Sci.* 30: 225–228, 1970.

154. NUTTING, E. F. Antifertility activity of prostaglandin E₂ in hamsters, rabbits and rats. *Proc. Ann. Meeting Soc. Study Reprod., 2nd, Davis, Calif., 1969,* p. 1.

155. ORSINI, M. W. Discussion. *J. Animal Sci.* 27, Suppl. 1: 131–133, 1968.

156. ORSINI, M. W. Effect of hysterectomy on hamster corpora. *Anat. Record* 163: 238, 1969.

157. O'SHEA, J. D. Increased duration of pseudopregnancy associated with uterine distension in the rat. *J. Reprod. Fertility* 23: 229–236, 1970.

158. OXENREIDER, S. L. Ovarian function in the cow after induction of uterine motility. *J. Reprod. Fertility* 16: 297–300, 1968.

159. PERRY, J. S., AND I. W. ROWLANDS. Effect of hysterectomy on the ovarian cycle of the rat. *J. Reprod. Fertility* 2: 332–340, 1961.

160. PHARRISS, B. B. The possible vascular regulation of luteal function. *Perspectives Biol. Med.* 13: 434–444, 1970.

161. PHARRISS, B. B., J. C. CORNETTE, AND G. D. GUTKNECHT. Vascular control of luteal steroidogenesis. *J. Reprod. Fertility Suppl.* 10: 97–103, 1970.

162. PHARRISS, B. B., AND L. J. WYNGARDEN. The effect of prostaglandin F₂α on the progestogen content of ovaries from pseudopregnant rats. *Proc. Soc. Exptl. Biol. Med.* 130: 92–94, 1969.

163. RAESIDE, J. I. Urinary oestrogen excretion in the pig at oestrus and during the oestrous cycle. *J. Reprod. Fertility* 6: 421–426, 1963.

164. RAESIDE, J. I. Urinary oestrogen excretion in the pig during pregnancy and parturition. *J. Reprod. Fertility* 6: 427–431, 1963.

165. RATHMACHER, R. P., AND L. L. ANDERSON. Blood flow and progestin levels in the ovaries of the pregnant rabbit. *Endocrinology* 88: 821–824, 1971.

166. ROBBINS, S. L., AND J. SHEPHERD. Effect of hysterectomy on the rabbit ovary. *Am. J. Obstet. Gynecol.* 86: 367–373, 1963.

167. ROBERTS, S. J. *Veterinary Obstetrics and Genital Diseases.* Ann Arbor: Edwards Bros., 1956.

168. ROCHE, J. F., D. L. FOSTER, F. J. KARSCH, B. COOK, AND P. J. DZIUK. Levels of luteinizing hormone in sera and pituitaries of ewes during the estrous cycle and anestrus. *Endocrinology* 86: 568–572, 1970.

169. ROMBAUTS, P. Excrétion urinaire d'estrogènes chez la truie pendant la gestation. *Ann. Biol. Animale Biochim. Biophys.* 2: 151–156, 1962.

170. ROMBAUTS, P., AND F. DU MESNIL DU BUISSON. Excrétion d'oestrogènes après hysterectomie durant la gestation où pendant le cycle oestral. *Compt. Rend.* 258: 5076–5078, 1964.

171. ROMBAUTS, P., F. PUPIN, AND M. TERQUI. Évolution de la teneur en progestérone des corps jaunes de truie pendant le cycle oestral et la gestation. *Compt. Rend.* 261: 2753–2756, 1965.

172. ROTH-BRANDEL, V., M. BYGDEMAN, N. WIQVIST, AND S. BERGSTROM. Prostaglandins for induction of therapeutic abortion. *Lancet* 1: 190–191, 1970.

173. ROTHCHILD, I. Interrelations between progesterone and the ovary, pituitary, and central nervous system in the control of ovulation and the regulation of progesterone secretion. *Vitamins Hormones* 23: 209–327, 1965.

174. ROWLANDS, I. W. The corpus luteum of the guinea pig. *Ciba Found. Colloq. Aging* 2: 69–83, 1956.

175. ROWLANDS, I. W. Effect of hysterectomy at different stages in the life cycle of the corpus luteum in the guinea-pig. *J. Reprod. Fertility* 2: 341–350, 1961.

176. ROWLANDS, I. W., AND R. V. SHORT. The progesterone content of guinea-pig corpus luteum during the reproductive cycle and after hysterectomy. *J. Endocrinol.* 19: 81–86, 1959.

177. ROWSON, L. E. A., AND R. M. MOOR. Embryo transfer in the sheep: the significance of synchronizing oestrus in the donor and recipient animal. *J. Reprod. Fertility* 11: 207–212, 1966.

178. ROWSON, L. E. A., AND R. M. MOOR. The influence of embryonic tissue homogenate infused into the uterus, on the life-span of the corpus luteum in the sheep. *J. Reprod. Fertility* 13: 511–516, 1967.

179. SCARAMUZZI, R. J., B. V. CALDWELL, AND R. M. MOOR. Radioimmunoassay of LH and estrogen during the estrous cycle of the ewe. *Biol. Reprod.* 3: 110–119, 1970.

180. SCHOMBERG, D. W. Effects of pig uterine flushings on ovarian tissues *in vitro* and *in vivo.* In: *Proceedings of Third International Congress on Endocrinology,* edited by C. Gaul. Amsterdam: Excerpta Medica Foundation, 1969, p. 916–920.

181. SCHOMBERG, D. W. The concept of a uterine luteolytic hormone. In: *The Gonads,* edited by K. W. McKerns. New York: Appleton Press, 1969, p. 383–414.

182. SCHOMBERG, D. W., J. A. CAMPBELL, AND G. D. WILBANKS. Effects of uterine flushings from pigs on porcine granulosa cells growing in tissue culture. *Advan. Biosci.* 4: 429–440, 1969.

183. SCOTT, R. S., AND P. I. C. RENNIE. Factors controlling the life-span of the corpora lutea in the pseudopregnant rabbit. *J. Reprod. Fertility* 23: 415–422, 1970.

184. SESSUMS, J. V., AND D. P. MURPHY. Hysterectomy and the artificial menopause. *Surg. Gynecol. Obstet.* 55: 286–289, 1932.

185. SESSUMS, J. V., AND D. P. MURPHY. The influence of endometrium upon the rabbit ovary after hysterectomy. *Surg. Gynecol. Obstet.* 56: 600–609, 1933.

186. SHORT, R. V. Ovarian steroid synthesis and secretion *in vivo.* *Recent Progr. Hormone Res.* 20: 303–340, 1964.

187. SHORT, R. V. Reproduction. *Ann. Rev. Physiol.* 29: 373–400, 1967.

188. SIEGMUND, H. Ovarialfunktion nach Uterusexstirpation. *Arch. Gynaekol.* 157: 223–228, 1934.

189. SMITH, J. A., AND H. B. WAYNFORTH. Acid phosphatase activity in viable and regressing rat corpora lutea. *J. Endocrinol.* 47: 167–176, 1970.

190. SNOOK, R. B., M. A. BRUNNER, R. R. SAATMAN, AND W. HANSEL. The effect of antisera to bovine LH in hysterectomized and intact heifers. *Biol. Reprod.* 1: 49–58, 1969.

191. SPEROFF, L., AND P. W. RAMWELL. Prostaglandins in reproductive physiology. *Am. J. Obstet. Gynecol.* 107: 1111–1130, 1970.

192. SPEROFF, L., AND P. W. RAMWELL. Prostaglandin stimulation of *in vitro* progesterone synthesis. *J. Clin. Endocrinol.* 30: 345–350, 1970.

193. STABENFELDT, G. H., E. L. AKINS, L. L. EWING, AND M. C. MORRISSETTE. Peripheral plasma progesterone levels in pigs during the oestrous cycle. *J. Reprod. Fertility* 20: 443–449, 1969.

194. STABENFELDT, G. H., M. DROST, AND C. BEAMES. Plasma progesterone levels in the ewe during pregnancy (Abstract). *Federation Proc.* 29: 705, 1970.

195. STABENFELDT, G. H., J. A. HOLT, AND L. L. EWING. Peripheral plasma progesterone levels during the ovine estrous cycle. *Endocrinology* 85: 11–15, 1969.

196. STORMSHAK, F., H. E. KELLY, AND H. W. HAWK. Suppression of ovine luteal function by 17β-estradiol. *J. Animal Sci.* 29: 476–478, 1969.

197. TELINDE, R. W., AND W. R. WHARTON, JR. Ovarian function

following pelvic operation. *Am. J. Obstet. Gynecol.* 80: 844–862, 1960.

198. TENNY, B., F. PARKER, JR., AND S. L. ROBBINS. The effect of hysterectomy on ovarian function in the rabbit. *Am. J. Obstet. Gynecol.* 70: 889–893, 1955.

199. TILLSON, S. A., R. E. ERB, AND G. D. NISWENDER. Comparison of luteinizing hormone and progesterone in blood and metabolites of progesterone in urine of domestic sows during the estrous cycle and early pregnancy. *J. Animal Sci.* 30: 795–805, 1970.

200. VAN WAGENEN, G., AND H. R. CATCHPOLE. Hysterectomy at parturition and ovarian function in the monkey (*M. mulatta*). *Proc. Soc. Exptl. Biol. Med.* 46: 580–582, 1941.

201. WESTMAN, A. Untersuchungen uber die Ovarialfunktion nach Uterusexstirpation. *Zentr. Gynaekol.* 53: 2578–2582, 1929.

202. WHITELAW, R. G. Ovarian activity following hysterectomy. *J. Obstet. Gynaecol. Brit. Commonwealth* 65: 917–932, 1958.

203. WIEST, W. G. Progesterone and 20α-hydroxypregn-4-en-3-one in plasma, ovaries and uteri during pregnancy in the rat. *Endocrinology* 87: 43–48, 1970.

204. WIEST, W. G., W. R. KIDWELL, AND K. BALOGH, JR. Progesterone catabolism in the rat ovary: a regulatory mechanism for progestational potency during pregnancy. *Endocrinology* 82: 844–859, 1968.

205. WILTBANK, J. N., AND L. E. CASIDA. Alteration of ovarian activity by hysterectomy. *J. Animal Sci.* 15: 134–140, 1956.

206. WOODY, C. O., AND O. J. GINTHER. Effect of exogenous progesterone on corpora lutea in unilaterally hysterectomized heifers. *J. Animal Sci.* 27: 1387–1390, 1968.

207. WOODY, C. O., O. J. GINTHER, AND A. L. POPE. Effects of exogenous progesterone and hysterectomy on corpora lutea in ewes. *J. Animal Sci.* 27: 1383–1386, 1968.

208. WOODY, C. O., O. J. GINTHER, AND A. L. POPE. Unilateral effect of intrauterine injection of alcoholic solutions on the corpus luteum of the ewe. *J. Animal Sci.* 28: 63–65, 1969.

209. YAMAUCHI, M., T. NAKAHARA, AND Y. KANEDA. Effect of intrauterine administration of a viscous gel-like substance on the estrous cycle in cattle. *Japan. J. Animal Reprod.* 11: 54–62, 1965.

210. YAMAUCHI, M., T. NAKAHARA, Y. KANEDA, AND S. INUI. Effects of uterine distention on the oestrous cycle of the cow. *J. Reprod. Fertility* 13: 379–386, 1967.

211. YOSHINAGA, K., R. A. HAWKINS, AND J. F. STOCKER. Estrogen secretion by the rat ovary in vivo during the estrous cycle and pregnancy. *Endocrinology* 85: 103–112, 1969.

212. ZHORDANIA, I. F., AND O. A. GOTSIRIDZE. Autotransplantation of the uterus into the omentum. *Intern. J. Fertility* 8: 849–857, 1963.

CHAPTER 34

Anatomy and physiology of the mammalian uterotubal junction

E. S. E. HAFEZ | *Department of Gynecology-Obstetrics and Department of Physiology, Wayne State University, School of Medicine, Detroit, Michigan*

CHAPTER CONTENTS

THE UTEROTUBAL JUNCTION is an ill-defined anatomic unit separating two maternal environments, that of the isthmus and that of the uterus. It consists of an intramural portion and an extramural portion, and it develops during an early stage of postnatal life. In the rat, coiling of the oviduct begins at 3 days after birth; the uterotubal junction is sharply defined early in the first week, and cilia develop by 6 days after birth.

ANATOMY OF THE UTEROTUBAL JUNCTION

In the last four decades anatomic studies of the uterotubal junction (UTJ) have been reported for several species [rat (2); mouse (21); ungulates (34); man or primates (23, 29, 35, 44)].

Considerable differences in the morphology, gross anatomy, and histology of the uterotubal junction exist among mammals (17, 19). Differences are found in *a*) the degree of flexure and the angle at which the oviduct and uterine cornu meet; *b*) lumen size in the caudal portion of the isthmus; *c*) the number and size of mucosal folds; *d*) vascular and lymphatic supplies; *e*) the number and morphology of ciliated mucosal cells; *f*) the cytology of epithelial secretory cells and the adjacent endometrial glands; *g*) ciliary activity during different stages of the reproductive cycle; *h*) the relative thickness of longitudinal and circular muscle layers; and *i*) the degree of fusion of the oviducal muscularis with the uterine myometrium (Figs. 1 and 2).

Four types of junctions are found in litter-bearing species (Figs. 3–5). In the rabbit, pocketlike, highly ciliated diverticulae of different sizes protrude into the lumen of the UTJ. The physiological significance of these structures is not yet ascertained. In the pig similar complicated projections into the lumen form sperm reservoirs. In the hamster the lumen of the uterotubal junction resembles a corkscrew. The rat and mouse have a papilla and an arched coil. The dog has a mound with a long, slit ostium. In single-bearing species, two variations are found (Fig. 6). In cattle and sheep, there is a flexure, but no folds project from the isthmus. Primates have a long intramural portion without projecting folds (Figs. 5 and 7).

In man the intramural (interstitial) portion of the uterotubal junction, which penetrates the uterine wall and opens into the uterine cavity, has an ampullalike dilatation. However, its lumen, as determined by X-ray analysis, is a threadlike channel communicating with the uterus or separated from it by a narrow, X-ray-opaque zone. This constriction is usually designated a sphincter and is caused by an annular fold of the uterine mucosa (29).

Endometrial cells may be present in the interstitial portion of the uterotubal junction (see Fig. 7) and may respond to hormones in the same way that the endometrium does. The presence of endometrial cells here is apparently normal; it has no effect on the occurrence of pregnancy and no causal relationship to extrauterine endometriosis or salpingitis isthmica nodosa (23).

The sphincterlike structure of the uterotubal junction may depend on *a*) the physiological characteristics of oviducal ligaments, namely the mesoturbarium and mesometrium; *b*) the extent of the intramural portion and

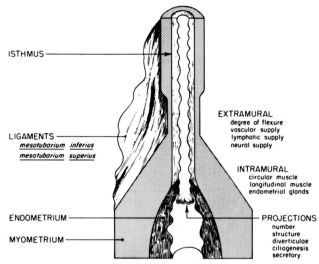

FIG. 1. Variations to be expected in the anatomy of uterotubal junction of several mammalian species. [From Hook & Hafez (19).]

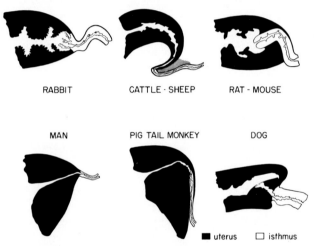

FIG. 2. Diagrammatic illustration (not drawn to scale) showing species differences in the morphology of the uterotubal junction. Varied anatomic relationships between the isthmus and the uterus are observed: the conspicuous folds in the rabbit; the flexure of the isthmus in cattle; the moundlike papilla in the dog; the archlike junction in the rat; and the intramural portion of oviduct in primates.

surrounding musculature; *c*) the arrangements of circular and longitudinal musculature at and near the uterotubal junction; and *d*) the presence and fine structure of muscle fiber spirals.

Histology

Species differences in the histology of the UTJ are found in *a*) the vascular and lymphatic supplies; *b*) cytology of epithelial secretory cells and adjacent endometrial tissue; *c*) relative thickness of longitudinal and circular musculature; and *d*) degree of fusion of oviducal muscularis with the myometrium (Figs. 8–10). In the rhesus monkey a dense layer of connective tissue is surrounded by a thick layer of circular musculature. Muscle

spirals extend within the mucosal folds. Indistinct longitudinal musculature merges with the myometrium.

The histological characteristics of the UTJ vary with the stage of the reproductive cycle. In the rabbit the elaborate processes of the UTJ adjacent to the uterine tissue obscure the lumen and become highly edematous under progesterone dominance. The nonciliated cells of the UTJ show irregular, tight microvilli; apical vesicles; and lysosomal structures. These may indicate absorptive, rather than secretory, function.

The functions of the uterotubal junction are primarily regulated by the relative thicknesses of the mucosa, submucosa, and circular and longitudinal musculature. For example, an excessive layer of muscular coating may function as a sphincter. Edema in the submucosa may cause flexure in the lumen of the uterotubal junction, or it may cause interlocking of the mucosal folds within

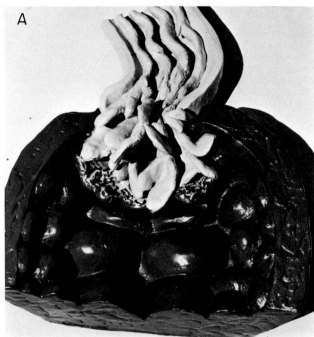

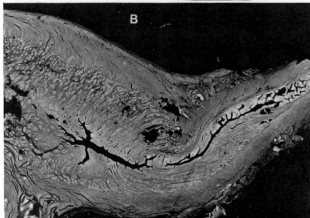

FIG. 3. Anatomic characteristics of the uterotubal junction in the domestic rabbit. Note the mucosal folds in a three-dimensional model (*A*) and in a longitudinal section (*B*).

In all species the muscular layer is thicker in the isthmic and interstitial sections than in the ampullary portion, where the longitudinal muscle bundles are rather sparse and more widely separated by loose, highly vascu-

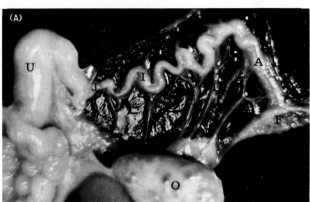

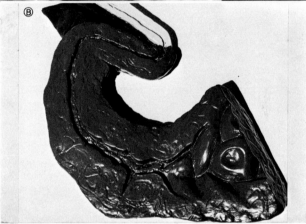

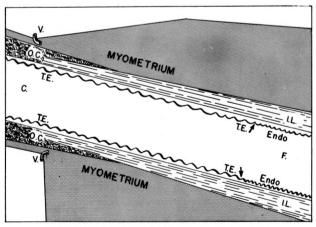

FIG. 6. Anatomic characteristics of the bovine uterotubal junction. *A*: postmortem specimen—*A*, ampulla; *F*, fimbriae; *J*, uterotubal junction; *L*, lymphatic and vascular supply; *O*, ovary; *U*, uterus. *B*: three-dimensional model in longitudinal section. Note the well-developed ligament attached to the uterotubal junction.

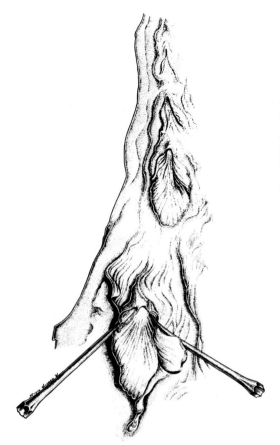

FIG. 4. Pocketlike diverticulae of different sizes found within the folds protruding into the lumen of the uterotubal junction of the rabbit. The physiological significance of these structures is not ascertained. [From Hook & Hafez (19).]

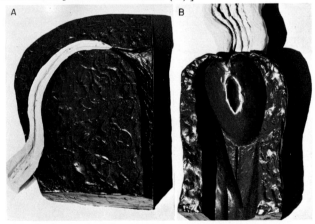

FIG. 5. Anatomic differences between the uterotubal junction of the pig-tailed monkey (*A*) and the dog (*B*). Note the interstitial portion of the oviduct in the monkey. In the dog the broadly based mound of the endometrium, which rises from the mesometrium, has a longitudinal slit about 1 mm long, parallel to the walls of the uterine horn; isthmic folds terminate in the uterine mound.

the lumen. The thicknesses and arrangement of the mucosa, submucosa, and circular and longitudinal musculature vary with the species, with the individual animal, and even within the individual at different segments of the uterotubal junction (see Figs. 8 and 10).

FIG. 7. Architectural pattern of the interstitial portion of the human oviduct. *C*, cornual end of oviduct; *Endo*, endometrium; *IL*, inner longitudinal muscle; *OC*, outer circular muscle; *TE*, tubal epithelium—internal ostium of oviduct (*arrow*); *V*, vessels at the uterotubal junction. [From Lisa et al. (23).]

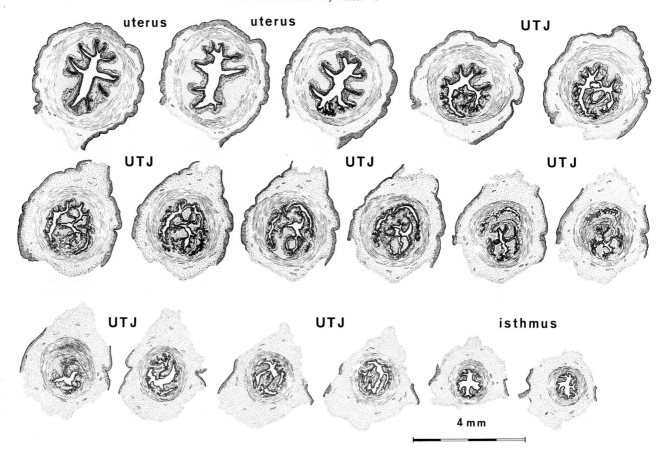

FIG. 8. Diagrammatic illustration showing the changes in the histological characteristics of cross sections of the uterotubal junction in the rabbit. Note the changes from the isthmic portion to the tip of the uterus. (From E. S. E. Hafez and A. A. El-Banna, unpublished data.)

lar connective tissues. In man the autochthonous musculature that forms the inner layer of the uterine wall consists of four bundles (see Fig. 7). This arrangement enables a constrictor effect to be placed on the larger part of the intramural tube. It may also influence the transport of the egg in the direction of the uterine cavity and that of sperm in the opposite direction (44). The autochthonous layer contains spiral fibers originating from two directions with intersections at regular levels. Each spiral traverses the inner layer from the outside inward as its convolutions gradually assume a smaller diameter.

Vasculature and Nerve Supply

The vascular supply of the uterotubal junction is derived from ovarian and uterine blood vessels that anastomose in the mesosalpinx to form a prominent uteroovarian vascular arch. The vessels that surround and supply the external uterotubal junction in man, as well as one or two vascular rings enclosing the intramural part of the oviduct, depend on uterine vasculature.

The autonomic nerves of the uterotubal junction come principally from the ovarian plexus. The hypogastric plexus also provides some nerve supply. In the isthmus, adrenergic nerve terminals gradually increase and ap-

pear to follow the smooth muscle cells of the circular layer. In the thick circular musculature, nerve terminals are abundant.

FUNCTIONS OF THE UTEROTUBAL JUNCTION

The uterotubal junction is thought to control sperm transport from the uterus to the oviduct and egg transport in the opposite direction, but the degree of control varies with the species. However, surgical removal of the uterotubal junction in the rabbit did not seem to affect sperm migration, fertilization, or egg transport (10).

The Uterotubal Junction and Sperm Transport

The uterotubal junction apparently restricts sperm transport in most species because of its extremely small lumen and complex anatomy, but its importance as a barrier depends on the site of ejaculation. If semen is ejaculated into the uterus, as in primates, the rat, mouse, and horse, the uterotubal junction may be the major barrier to sperm transport. However, if semen is deposited in the vagina, as in the rabbit and ruminants, the cervix may be a more important barrier to sperm movement.

It has been suggested that the uterotubal junction prevents foreign and dead sperm from entering the oviduct. When rats are inseminated with mixtures of motile rat, guinea pig, and bovine sperm, only the rat sperm appear in the oviducts (22). Motility, however, is not essential for sperm transport; in man both nonmotile sperm and such inert material as carbon particles pass through the uterotubal junction (12).

RATE OF SPERM TRANSPORT. Scanning electron microscopy

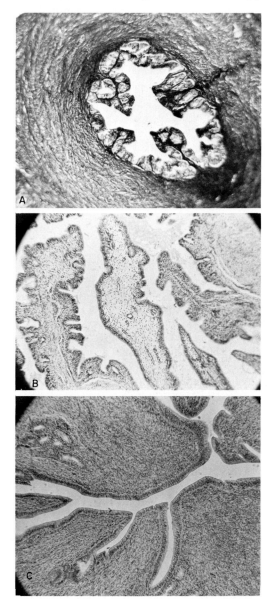

FIG. 9. Species differences in the histological characteristics of the uterotubal junction. *A*: cross section in the intramural portion of the oviduct of the rhesus monkey. Note the thick muscular layer and the arrangement of the muscle fibers within the folds. × approximately 64. *B*: longitudinal section in the uterotubal junction of the rabbit. Elaborate diverticulae obscuring the lumen of the oviduct are shown. × approximately 32. *C*: longitudinal section (rat) of the distal half of the arched coil of the isthmus terminating in a papilla that projects into the lumen of the anterior end of the uterine horn on the antimesometrial side. × approximately 32.

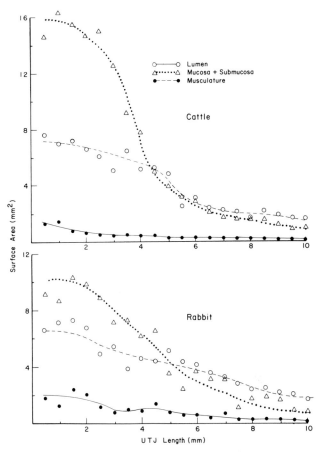

FIG. 10. Species differences in the surface area of the lumen, mucosa and submucosa, and musculature of the uterotubal junction in rabbit and cattle at 72 hr after ovulation. Each diagram represents an individual animal. The surface area of mucosa and submucosa is larger, and the narrowing toward the isthmic portion is more abrupt in cattle than in rabbits. The musculature is thicker in rabbits than in cattle. The lumen at segments 6 and 7 is wider at 72 hr after ovulation than at estrus. (From E. S. E. Hafez and A. A. El-Banna, unpublished data.)

is very useful for observing gamete transport within the reproductive tract. The narrow passage of the UTJ and the longitudinal arrangement of the epithelial folds facilitate the passage of actively migrating sperm. Irrespective of whether the uterotubal junction is the primary or only a secondary barrier to sperm transport, the number of sperm entering the oviduct is far smaller than the number that reaches the uterus. In the rat, for example, sperm are about 30,000 times more plentiful in the uterus than in the oviduct (8). The number traversing the uterotubal junction varies with the stage of the reproductive cycle.

Some of the sperm pass from the anterior uterus into the oviduct very rapidly. Sperm transport from the cervix to the oviducts requires 8 min in sheep (27) and only 2.5 min in cattle (43). Transit time, however, is prolonged if the animal is disturbed during, or soon after, copulation. For example, no sperm were found in the oviducts of disturbed ewes 15 min after copulation (25). Despite this rapid transport of some sperm, numbers sufficient for maximal fertilization may not accumulate for several hours. Although, in the rabbit, sperm reach the anterior tip of the uterus within 30 min after copulation 2–5 hr more are required for numbers sufficient to ensure maximal fertilization to enter the oviduct (1). In the pig sperm remain in the uterotubal junction for some time after copulation, perhaps because of the presence of diverticulae (33, 34).

NUMBER OF SPERM. The number of sperm transported through the uterotubal junction is affected by the hormonal condition of the female. For example, ovariectomy in sheep or pseudopregnancy in the rabbit causes a reduction in the number of sperm transported.

A decrease of spermatozoa transported through the junction—and, hence, available for fertilization—may cause the lowered fertility often observed after progestagen treatment for the synchronization of estrus in sheep and cattle (18, 31).

SPERM RESERVOIRS. The availability of sperm in the oviduct is determined by the population in other segments of the reproductive tract (25, 26). Spermatozoa in the oviduct must be continually replenished from lower regions of the reproductive tract if viable sperm are to be present at ovulation. In the pig a high concentration of spermatozoa remains for over 24 hr in the region of the uterotubal junction then disappears over the next 48 hr. Spermatozoa from the reservoir probably pass continually into the oviducts to reach the site of fertilization (33).

In ungulates and certain primates the cervix (and possibly the vagina) acts as a sperm reservoir for the uterus. The isthmus in certain species may fulfill the same function. In sheep about twice as many sperm are present in the isthmus as in the ampulla at 1 hr after copulation; at 24 hr this ratio is about 8:1 (32). At 48 hr the population in the isthmus appears almost exhausted, probably because of failure of replenishment from the uterus. On the other hand, in several laboratory mammals the isthmus is considered a barrier to the free progression of sperm. This may be due to its narrow lumen, the extensive folding of the mucosa, and the presence of forceful muscular contractions at estrus (15).

The percentage of sperm recovered in different parts of the rabbit female tract represents only the sperm "in transit" and probably does not indicate the total number transported to each site (27). Recoveries from the uterotubal junction and uterus are maximal 8–24 hr after insemination. Largest numbers appear in the oviduct 8–12 hr after insemination, the period coinciding with the time of ovulation.

Quinlivan & Robinson (32) studied the patterns of sperm distribution in the reproductive tract of sheep at the first estrus after progestagen synchronization and at normal estrus. One hour after insemination, progestagen-treated and untreated ewes differed little in total numbers of spermatozoa recovered and in their distribution among the various regions of the reproductive tract.

Thereafter, fewer live sperm were recovered from treated ewes, and a smaller percentage had reached the oviduct. Both transport and survival of spermatozoa in the oviduct of the ewe are deleteriously affected by progestagen treatment.

The number of sperm recovered from the oviducts after insemination increases with time, but the number in the whole tract decreases. However, after a given interval this ratio is reversed. For example, 12 hr after insemination in the rabbit, the number of sperm in the oviducts begins to decline sharply, more rapidly, in fact, than do total numbers in the whole reproductive tract. The average number of sperm recovered from the oviducts of rabbits 12 hr after insemination was 20,292; 4 hr later this dropped to 6,423.

PHYSIOLOGICAL MECHANISMS. Several processes enhance the transport of sperm through the uterotubal junction: antiperistaltic contractions of the isthmus (46); uterine contractions (21); and the bulk flow of oviducal fluids toward the infundibulum.

The Uterotubal Junction and Egg Transport

Several studies have been made on laboratory animals to determine the temporal pattern of egg transport through the oviduct. The fact that eggs are rarely recovered from the uterotubal junction suggests that the transport through this region is rapidly accomplished [see (14, 24)]. The movement of oil droplets in the rabbit's oviduct, studied in vitro, also indicates that eggs move through the uterotubal junction rapidly.

Thirty hours after ovulation most eggs occupy segments 4 to 6 of the 8 segments of the bovine oviduct. Ten to 30 additional hours are required for the slow traverse through these segments; very few eggs are recovered from segments 7 and 8.

Greenwald (14) used a variety of histological techniques to detect a structural basis for the "isthmic block" but found none. El-Banna & Hafez (13) measured planimetrically the lumen size of various segments of the bovine oviduct and found that of the ampullary-isthmic junction to be the smallest at all reproductive stages. However, it enlarged twofold in the 3–4 days following estrus.

In the rabbit, hamster, mouse, and guinea pig, most eggs are trapped in the ampullary-isthmic junction.

These observations suggest that the uterotubal junction is not the major barrier to egg transport in the oviduct.

PHYSIOLOGICAL ROLE OF THE AMPULLARY-ISTHMIC JUNCTION. There has been less emphasis in the literature on the ampullary-isthmic junction than on the uterotubal junction as the principal barrier to egg transport. Various mechanisms have been proposed as explanations for oviducal blocking at the uterotubal junction: closure of the oviducal lumen due to edema of subserosa and musculature; partial or complete inhibition of contractile activity of the circular musculature at the site of the block; variation in the rate and amplitude of muscular contraction; or all three. These mechanisms could be equally applicable to a functional block at the ampullary-isthmic junction.

Little is known about the transport of eggs through the isthmus of the oviduct. Peristaltic and antiperistaltic contractions have been described, but the isthmus' thick muscular wall makes the location and movement of eggs difficult to observe. Contractions move rabbit ova through the oviduct except at a critical point—the isthmic portion immediately anterior to the uterotubal junction—where movement of ova is arrested (6).

ENDOCRINE MECHANISMS. The influence of estrogens and progesterone on the passage of eggs through the oviduct has often been studied. Injection of progesterone may (2) or may not (7, 14) hasten the rate of egg transport. Similarly, ovariectomy reportedly enhances such movement in rats (2) and rabbits (30), but not in mice (45).

Egg transport through the uterotubal junction is enhanced in cattle that have been treated with pregnant mares' serum gonadotrophins to raise progesterone levels and, hence, induce multiple corpora lutea. In 72 hr the eggs of treated cattle reach the uterus, but those of untreated animals are still in segment 6 of the oviduct.

At present the literature on the endocrine basis for egg transport through the uterotubal junction contains many contradictory and confusing observations, and more investigations will be required to resolve the problem.

CLINICAL ASPECTS

The patency of the uterotubal junction has been tested with the insufflation technique in several clinical studies. Gas forced into the uterus produces an abrupt rise in pressure until it begins to leak off into the oviduct through the uterotubal junction. Then intrauterine pressure drops sharply to a new, lower plateau [see review (17)]. The pressure needed to open the uterotubal junction is commonly called the *peak pressure* or the *uterotubal opening pressure*, it differs at various stages of the reproductive cycle.

In some individuals, however, elaborate projections, such as papillae, occur at the oviducal orifice. Gas pressure apparently forces them against one another so that the opening effect of peak pressure is counteracted. If insufflation is continued after peak pressure is reached, the pressure plateau does not drop but stays at a high level with minor fluctuations.

Since it has the smallest diameter, the interstitial portion of the oviduct controls gas pressure (23, 35, 37, 38), yet pressure fluctuations occur in the uterus after the oviduct has been removed (37). However, fluctuations cease if the outer two-thirds of the intramural portion of the oviduct is also removed (28).

Since uterine muscle girdles the intramural portion of the oviduct (44), occlusion of the uterotubal junction may be created by the muscle contraction of the wall of the oviduct or of the surrounding uterus. Studies in

which microballoons were inserted into the myometrium of the uterine fundus, into the musculature of the uterine cornu near the isthmus, or into the oviducal wall suggest that uterine musculature plays an important role. Pressure changes during insufflation coincide only with pressure changes in the myometrium near the oviduct (40, 41).

The pattern of uterotubal insufflation may be influenced by several factors: *a*) uterotubal anatomic arrangement; *b*) nature of adjacent ligaments; *c*) presence of adhesions; *d*) hormonal factors; and *e*) certain reproductive disorders. For example, after smoking or administration of epinephrine, a change, mostly an increase, is observed in motility patterns associated with uterotubal insufflation.

Effects of Hormones and Drugs

Hormones also influence the opening pressure of the uterotubal junction in women. A pressure of 180–200 mm Hg is required to force gas through the uterotubal junction just before or at menstruation, whereas only 80–100 mm Hg is needed after menstruation (36). Estrogens elevate the initially low peak pressure typical of the menopausal woman (5). However, the opening of the human uterotubal junction is so variable that it has not been possible to consistently relate peak pressures with the phases of the menstrual cycle (11).

All oviducal segments respond similarly to acetylcholine, epinephrine, norepinephrine, and oxytocin. On the other hand, prostaglandin causes one-fourth of the oviduct to contract but relaxes the other three-fourths of the oviduct (39).

Anatomic Anomalies

Structural abnormalities in the uterotubal junction may result in reproductive failure. Hypertrophy of the endometrium in the interstitial segment, papillomas, endometrial polyps, or cancerous growths may cause stenosis in the uterotubal junction (23). General anomalies and diseased conditions of the oviduct have been described by Benirschke (4). Hydrosalpinges and pysosalpinges are more common in man and swine (mostly bilateral) than in cattle, sheep, and laboratory mammals (mostly unilateral). Oviducal abnormalities in women are frequently caused by infections.

CONCLUDING REMARKS

Considerable differences in the morphology, gross anatomy, and histology of the uterotubal junction exist among mammals: *a*) complex diverticulae in the rabbit and pig; *b*) a lumen resembling a corkscrew in the guinea pig; *c*) an arched coil ending in a papilla in the rat and mouse; *d*) a mound with a long, slit ostium in the dog; *e*) a flexure in cattle and sheep; and *f*) a long intramural portion in the monkey and man. The reproductive-cycle stage affects characteristics of the ciliated, nonciliated, and peg cells of the mucosa; the lamina propria; and the circular and longitudinal musculature. The sphincterlike structure of the uterotubal junction may depend on *a*) the physiological characteristics of meso- turbarium and mesometrium; *b*) the extent of the intra- mural portion and surrounding musculature; *c*) the arrangements of circular and longitudinal musculature at and near the uterotubal junction; and *d*) the presence and coiling of muscle fibers.

The UTJ prevents large numbers of sperm from enter- ing the oviduct at one time, may function in the selec- tion of vigorous sperm and their capacitation, and con- trols the transport rate of embryos to the uterus. These phenomena are essential for normal fertilization and early embryonic survival. The cervix and uterotubal junction appear to act as mechanical barriers that are able to maintain graded concentrations of sperm throughout the female reproductive duct system. The relative importance of these two barriers varies with the species.

The ampullary-isthmic junction and the uterotubal junction seem to act as barriers to regulate the transport of oviducal eggs. The relative importance of these two physiological junctions also varies with the species. Egg transport through the uterotubal junction is affected by the estrogen-progesterone balance and the development of the corpus luteum. The isthmus is partially relaxed $2\frac{1}{2}$ days after ovulation; then it becomes totally relaxed. In some species small doses of estrogen result in acceler- ated egg transport through the uterotubal junction and eventual embryonic degeneration. Uterotubal insuffla- tion is used extensively to study the patency of the uterotubal junction. Extreme care must be taken to

ensure that differences observed are not due to the tech- nique itself. With this method supposed differences be- tween species that can often be related to anatomic structure or to the endocrine state have been found. The characteristics of the UTJ affect the results of tubal in- sufflation and the radiological appearances of hystero- salpingography. Some reproductive disorders affect clini- cal evaluation of uterotubal patency.

Extensive research is needed on the anatomy, physi- ology, and pharmacology of the uterotubal junction in primates and other species. The following research areas should be emphasized: *a*) neural, vascular, and lym- phatic supply of the uterotubal junction; *b*) histological and histochemical changes following copulation at the time of egg transport to the uterus and following ovariec- tomy or administration of exogenous steroids; *c*) the architecture and fine structure of the muscle fibers in the circular and longitudinal musculature in relation to that of the oviducal mucosal folds and the myometrium; *d*) anatomic and physiological function of the ligaments attached to the oviduct and uterus; the endocrine and pharmacophysiological aspects of these ligaments; *e*) relative importance of the uterotubal junction, in com- parison with other parts of the oviduct, in controlling entry of eggs into the uterus; *f*) mechanisms involved in transport of sperm and eggs through the uterotubal junction; *g*) the effects of the reproductive cycle stages, ovarian function, and exogenous hormones on the open- ing and closing of the uterotubal junction; and *h*) neuro- endocrine control of the uterotubal junction. Further studies are also needed to clarify the effects of contra- ceptives and drugs on the pharmacophysiology of the uterotubal junction.

REFERENCES

1. ADAMS, C. E. A study of fertilization in the rabbit: the effect of post-coital ligation of the fallopian tube or uterine horn. *Endocrinology* 13: 296–308, 1956.
2. ALDEN, R. H. The oviduct and egg transport in the albino rat. *Anat. Record* 84: 137–170, 1942.
3. ANDERSON, D. H. The rate of passage of the mammalian ovum through various portions of the fallopian tube. *Am. J. Physiol.* 83: 557–569, 1927.
4. BENIRSCHKE, K. Pathogenic processes of the oviduct. In: *The Mammalian Oviduct*, edited by E. S. E. Hafez and R. J. Blandau. Chicago: Univ. of Chicago Press, 1969, p. 271–307.
5. BERNSTEIN, P., AND M. FERESTEN. Estrogenic effects upon tubal contractility and the vaginal secretion in the menopause. *Endocrinology* 26: 946–952, 1940.
6. BLACK, D. L., AND S. A. ASDELL. Transport through the rabbit oviduct. *Am. J. Physiol.* 192: 63–68, 1958.
7. BLACK, D. L., AND S. A. ASDELL. Mechanism controlling entry of ova to rabbit uterus. *Am. J. Physiol.* 197: 1275–1278, 1959.
8. BLANDAU, R. J., AND D. L. ODOR. The total number of sper- matozoa reaching various segments of the reproductive tract in the female albino rat at intervals after insemination. *Anat. Record* 103: 93–109, 1949.
9. DAVID, A., AND B. CZERNOBILSKY. A comparative histologic study of the uterotubal junction in the rabbit, rhesus monkey, and human female. *Am. J. Obstet. Gynecol.* 10: 417–421, 1968.
10. DAVID, A., G. BRACKETT, AND C. R. GARCIA. Effects of micro- surgical removal of the rabbit uterotubal junction. *Fertility Sterility* 20: 250, 1969.

11. DAVIDS, A. M. Fallopian tube motility in relation to the men- strual cycle. *Am. J. Obstet. Gynecol.* 56: 655, 1948.
12. EGLI, G. E., AND M. NEWTON. The transport of carbon par- ticles in the human female reproductive tract. *Fertility Sterility* 12: 151–155, 1961.
13. EL-BANNA, A. A., AND E. S. E. HAFEZ. Profile analysis of the oviductal wall in rabbits and cattle. *Anat. Record* 166: 469–478, 1970.
14. GREENWALD, G. S. A study of the transport of ova through the rabbit oviduct. *Fertility Sterility* 12: 80–95, 1961.
15. GREENWALD, G. S. *In vivo* recording of intraluminal pressure changes in the rabbit oviduct. *Fertility Sterility* 14: 666–674, 1963.
16. HAFEZ, E. S. E. The uterotubal junction and the luminal fluid of the uterine tube of the rabbit. *Anat. Record* 145: 7, 1963.
17. HAFEZ, E. S. E., AND D. L. BLACK. The mammalian uterotubal junction. In: *The Mammalian Oviduct*, edited by E. S. E. Hafez and R. J. Blandau. Chicago: Univ. of Chicago Press, 1969, p. 85–126.
18. HANCOCK, G. L. Fertilization in farm animals. *Animal Breeding Abstr.* 30: 285–299, 1962.
19. HOOK, S. J., AND E. S. E. HAFEZ. A comparative anatomical study of the mammalian uterotubal junction. *J. Morphol.* 125: 159–184, 1968.
20. HOWE, G. R., AND D. L. BLACK. Migration of rat and foreign spermatozoa through the utero-tubal junction of the oestrous rat. *J. Reprod. Fertility* 5: 95–100, 1963.
21. KUHLMANN, W. Uterotubal valve and the fate of the sperm in

the female tract of the mouse. *Jackson Lab. Ann. Rept., 36th, 1964–65*, p. 71–72.

22. LEONARD, S. L., AND P. L. PERLMAN. Conditions effecting the passage of spermatozoa through the utero-tubal junction of the rat. *Anat. Record* 104: 89–102, 1949.

23. LISA, J. R., J. D. GIOLA, AND I. C. RUBIN. Observations on the interstitial portion of the fallopian tube. *Surg. Gynecol. Obstet.* 99: 159–169, 1954.

24. LONGLEY, W. J., AND D. L. BLACK. Comparisons of methods for locating ova in the oviduct of the rabbit. *J. Reprod. Fertility* 16: 69–72, 1968.

25. MATTNER, P. E. Spermatozoa in the genital tract of the ewe. II. Distribution after coitus. *Australian J. Biol. Sci.* 16: 688-694, 1963.

26. MATTNER, P. E. Formation and retention of the spermatozoan reservoir in the cervix of the ruminant. *Nature* 212: 1479–1480, 1966.

27. MATTNER, P. E., AND A. W. H. BRADEN. Spermatozoa in the genital tract of the ewe. I. Rapidity of transport. *Australian J. Biol. Sci.* 16: 473–481, 1963.

28. MIKULICZ-RADECKI, F. V. Untersuchungen über die Tubenkontraktionen mit Hilfe der Pertubation. *Z. Gynaekol.* 54: 2183–2191, 1930.

29. NOVAK, J., AND I. C. RUBIN. Anatomy and pathology of the fallopian tubes. *Ciba Clin. Symp.* 4(6): 179–199, 1952.

30. NOYES, K. W., C. E. ADAMS, AND A. WALTON. The transport of ova in relation to the dosage of estrogen in ovariectomized rabbits. *J. Endocrinol.* 18: 108–117, 1959.

31. QUINLIVAN, T. D., AND T. J. ROBINSON. The number of spermatozoa in the Fallopian tubes of ewes at intervals after artificial insemination following withdrawal of SC-9880 impregnated intravaginal sponges. In: *The Control of the Ovarian Cycle in Sheep*, edited by T. J. Robinson. Sydney: Sydney Univ. Press, 1967, p. 177–193.

32. QUINLIVAN, T. D., AND T. J. ROBINSON. Numbers of spermatozoa in the genital tract after artificial insemination of progestagen-treated ewes. *J. Reprod. Fertility* 19: 73–85, 1969.

33. RIGBY, J. P. Persistence of spermatozoa at the utero-tubal junction of the sow. *J. Reprod. Fertility* 11: 153, 1966.

34. RIGBY, J. P., AND T. D. GLOVER. The structure of the utero-tubal junction of the sow. *J. Anat.* 99: 416–417, 1965.

35. ROCKER, L. The anatomy of the utero-tubal junction area. *Proc. Roy. Soc. Med.* 57: 707–709, 1964.

36. RUBIN, I. C. Most favorable time for transuterine insufflation to test tubal patency. *J. Am. Med. Assoc.* 84: 661–671, 1925.

37. RUBIN, I. C. Manometric oscillations. Discussion of paper by Stabile. *Fertility Sterility* 5: 147–153, 1954.

38. RUBIN, I. C., AND J. NOVAK. Anatomy and pathology of the fallopian tube. *Ciba Clin. Symp.* 4: 179–191, 1952.

39. SANDBERG, F., A. INGELMAN-SUNDBERG, AND G. RYDEN. The effect of prostaglandin E_1 on the human uterus and Fallopian tubes *in vitro. Acta Obstet. Gynecol. Scand.* 42: 269–278, 1963.

40. STABILE, A. Nuestra interpretacion de las alternativas ritmicas en los quimograms de insuflacion uterotubaria. *Obstet. Ginecol. Lat. Am.* 10: 40–48, 1952.

41. STABILE, A. Interpretation of manometric oscillations observed during uterotubal insufflation. *Fertility Sterility* 5: 138–147, 1954.

42. STAVORSKI, J., AND C. G. HARTMAN. Uterotubal insufflation: a study to determine the origin of fluctuations in pressure. *Obstet. Gynecol.* 11: 622–639, 1958.

43. VAN DEMARK, N. L., AND A. N. MOELLER. Speed of spermatozoan transport in reproductive tract of estrous cow. *Am. J. Physiol.* 165: 674–679, 1951.

44. VASEN, L. C. The intramural part of the fallopian tube. *Inter. J. Fertility* 4: 309–321, 1959.

45. WHITNEY, R., AND H. O. BURDICK. Effect of massive doses of an estrogen on ova transport in ovariectomized mice. *Endocrinology* 24: 45–61, 1939.

46. WINTENBERGER-TORRES, S. Movements des trompes et progression des oeufs chez la brebis. *Ann. Biol. Animale Biochim. Biophys.* 1: 121–129, 1961.

CHAPTER 35

Endocrine control of the structure and function of the mammalian oviduct

E. S. E. HAFEZ | *Department of Gynecology-Obstetrics and Department of Physiology, School of Medicine, Wayne State University, Detroit, Michigan*

CHAPTER CONTENTS

THE STRUCTURE OF the mammalian oviduct is well adapted to its multiple functions (Fig. 1). The fringelike fimbriae, together with contractions of the oviducal musculature, transport ovulated eggs from the ovarian surface to the infundibulum. The eggs are transported through the mucosal folds of the ampulla to the site of fertilization at the ampullary-isthmic junction. Contractile activity of the oviduct helps move spermatozoa through the uterotubal junction and the isthmic folds to the fertilization site. After fertilization the cleaved eggs are transported to the uterus. The mesotubarium and mesosalpinx (ligaments of the oviduct) and oviducal musculature coordinate the oviducal contractile activity. The oviducal fluid provides a suitable environment for capacitation of spermatozoa, fertilization, and cleavage of fertilized eggs.

The hormonal milieu of the female affects the structure, ultrastructure, and secretory activity of the oviducal epithelium; the contractile activity of the oviducal musculature; the quantitative and qualitative characteristics of the oviducal secretions; and the pattern and rate of gamete transport.

The endocrine control of oviducal functions has been studied by hypophysectomy or ovariectomy, with or without subsequent hormonal therapy. Histological, histochemical, and cytological techniques have been used to study the cyclic changes in structure and ultrastructure of ciliated and nonciliated cells during prenatal development, prepubertal life, phases of the reproductive cycle, pregnancy, and senescence (Table 1). The effect of hormones on the rate of egg transport through the oviduct has been evaluated by in vitro (74) and in vivo (90, 91) techniques. Techniques of flushing the reproductive tract have provided information on patterns and rates of gamete transport in the oviduct.

PRENATAL DIFFERENTIATION

Before sexual differentiation the Müllerian and Wolffian ducts are equally developed. In the female fetus, Müllerian ducts develop into their derivative structures, whereas the Wolffian ducts disappear completely or leave vestigial remnants. Organogenesis in the fetal oviduct of mammals shows a basic, orderly pattern (Fig. 2). The fimbriae develop; the oviduct becomes demarcated from the uterus; the oviducal epithelium increases in height and exhibits pseudostratification. Secretory cells appear as bulging filiform processes within the oviducal lumen (144). In the newborn human female, differentiation into ciliated and nonciliated cells is apparent (161).

The Müllerian ducts of several species respond to exogenous androgen and estrogen in vivo and in vitro. The response varies with the species, stage of development at hormone injection, and dose and type of hormone. The administration of estrogens to mammalian female fetuses causes precocious hypertrophy of the Müllerian ducts; with large doses hypertrophy may be extreme. In male fetuses, estrogens cause persistence of the Müllerian ducts and differentiation in varying degrees (46). In estrogen-treated birds, oviducts of male and female fetuses persist and hypertrophy—the right duct of the female normally

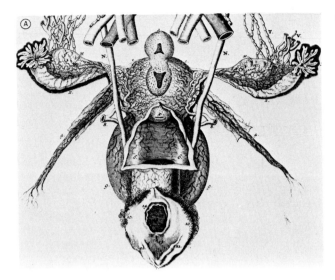

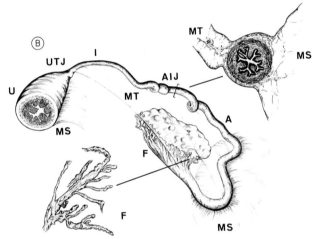

FIG. 1. *A:* human reproductive organs and their lymphatic vessels, as drawn in 1722. Note rich supply of vessels to the ovary and oviduct. [From Nuck (29, 138a), by courtesy of The Wellcome Trustees.] *B:* diagrammatic illustration of the rabbit oviduct. *A,* ampulla; *AIJ,* ampullary-isthmic junction; *F,* fimbriae; *I,* isthmus; *MS,* mesosalpinx; *MT,* mesotubarium; *U,* uterus; *UTJ,* uterotubal junction.

undergoes involution (Fig. 3). Differentiation proceeds even after hatching, and the effects become permanent. The period of susceptibility to the hormone is limited.

Androgens of fetal testes cause degeneration of Müllerian ducts in males at the beginning of sex differentiation, and testicular grafts inhibit Müllerian duct development in females. On the other hand, in a few species adult-type androgens fail to inhibit the ducts or produce only a limited and localized involution (46). The ostial portion is inhibited in the hedgehog (130), and the vaginal segment is suppressed in female opossums (44, 45) and in mice (147). Large doses of testosterone stimulate the Müllerian ducts and their derivatives in opossums (Fig. 4).

Species differences in the effect of maternal circulation on oviducal development are partly due to differences in

TABLE 1. *In Vitro and In Vivo Techniques Used to Study Effects of Hormones on Structure and Function of the Mammalian Oviduct*

Objective	Technique	Ref.
In vitro study of ciliated and secretory cells	Culture fragments of oviducal mucosa by coverslip technique and transfer of growth to special chambers	101
	Trypsinizing oviducts to harvest epithelia for culture in Rose Chamber	162
Functional differentiation of Müllerian ducts	Addition of hormones or fetal endocrine glands to tissue and organ cultures of fetal oviducts in vitro	144, 155, 156
	Grafting ovarian or testicular tissues or injecting steroid hormones into female or male embryo before or after sexual differentiation	46
	Fetal castration	
Activity of oviducal musculature	Visual observation through abdominal wall	165
	Direct kymography	23, 24, 106
	Direct perfusion with fluid	40, 104
	Uterotubal insufflation (Rubin test)	6, 53, 81, 153
	Thin catheter placed in lumen to record intraluminal pressure in unrestrained, nonanesthetized females	41
	Cineradiology	21
Collection of fluid for analysis	Extra-abdominal device	50
	Intra-abdominal device	85
	Radioisotopes	67, 176
	Flushing genital tract	100
	Stripping oviduct after slaughter	139, 140, 166
	Ligating the oviduct at the uterotubal junction and fimbriae	19, 20, 79, 120
Identification of adrenergic and cholinergic receptors	Fluorescence microscopy	42
	Studying spontaneous motility of oviduct in vitro	157
	Measuring changes in resting pressure of perfused oviduct in response to autonomic drugs	151
Detection of protein uptake in oviducal epithelium	Immunofluorescence	69, 70
Metabolism of oviducal tissue	Warburg manometry	
Cyclic changes or effects of hormones on structure and ultrastructure of oviducal epithelium	Light and electron microscopy	
	Histochemical observation of frozen-dried specimens	

placental and fetal hormones. The human placenta, fetal testes, and fetal adrenals can synthesize several steroids (27, 144, 160). On the other hand, the placenta of the guinea pig is incapable of synthesizing estrogen from car-

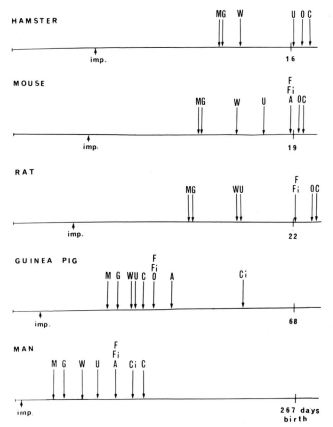

FIG. 2. Comparison of developmental sequences in several mammalian female reproductive tracts. *Arrows*, beginnings of such important events as implantation (*imp.*), Müllerian duct development (*M*), gonadal sex differentiation (*G*), and Wolffian duct degeneration (*W*), uterovaginal canal development (*U*), as well a the beginning of the following developments in oviducal differentiation: *O*, demarcation from uterus; *C*, coiling; *F*, epithelial folds; *Fi*, fimbriae; *A*, ampulla differentiation; *Ci*, ciliated cells. [From Price et al. (144).]

bon substrates (2) or converting androstenedione to dehydroepiandrosterone (28).

Organ cultures have been used to transfer the fetal reproductive tract to an environment free from placental and maternal hormones and thus allow investigation of prenatal differentiation of the oviduct under a variety of hormonal conditions. Müllerian ducts in organ culture differentiated normally with or without the presence of ovaries (143), but the muscular contractions of the ducts were inhibited in the presence of fetal testicular tissue (155, 156). Differentiation of the fetal oviduct is apparently hormone independent in the first half of pregnancy [Fig. 5; (141, 143)]. During the second half of pregnancy, the most important morphogenetic and histogenetic developments are hormone dependent.

In a variety of genetic mosaics or chimeras, particularly the true hermaphrodites, the degree of homolateral duct development is correlated with the type of gonadal differentiation (16). The true hermaphrodite mink with a chimeric diploid XX/triploid XXY chromosome makeup shows greater Müllerian duct reduction on the side containing more testicular gonad (133).

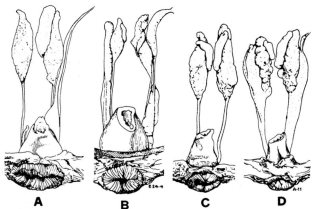

FIG. 3. Effects of sex hormones on development of the sex ducts in chick embryos. *A:* normal female embryo of 18 days; development of the left oviduct with shell gland and retrogression of the right are evident. *B:* genetic male embryo of 18 days treated with 2.0 mg estrone. Both oviducts are present and greatly hypertrophied. Compare with *C* for the normal condition. *C:* normal male embryo of 17 days; note the paired Wolffian ducts and the absence of both oviducts. *D:* genetic female embryo of 17 days after treatment with 1.0 mg androsterone. Absence of both oviducts and extreme hypertrophy of the Wolffian ducts are evident. For the normal female anatomy, compare with *A*; and for normal size of male ducts, see *C*. [Adapted from Willier (171).]

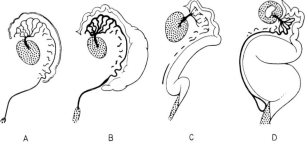

FIG. 4. Diagrammatic representation of the effects of relatively large doses of testosterone propionate, administered from birth to 50 days, on the development of reproductive ducts in opossums. *A:* sex ducts as they appear in a normal male at 50 days. The vas deferens (Wolffian duct), epididymal tubules, and remnants of mesonephric tubules are in *black*; the atrophic Müllerian duct is *unshaded*; and the testis is *stippled*. *B:* paradoxical effects of large doses of male hormone administered to males; effects of the male hormone on the male duct system appear throughout. With large doses, however, the oviducal and uterine regions of the Müllerian duct grow and develop, but the vaginal segment is absent, as in the normal male. *C:* sex ducts as they appear in a normal female at 50 days. The Wolffian duct and associated structures have disappeared, and the Müllerian duct has developed into oviducal, uterine, and vaginal segments. The contribution of the urogenital sinus to the vaginal canal is indicated in *stipple*. *D:* effects of the male hormone in a female subject. Male duct system is preserved and greatly hypertrophied, although not as large or as well differentiated as in the treated male; the effect of a large dosage of androgen on the female genital tract is much greater than on the treated male at the same dosage level (see *B*). These paradoxical effects of androgen on Müllerian duct derivatives disappear entirely at lower dosages. [From Burns (46).]

The freemartin is a female bovine twinborn with a male in which male gonads are partially developed and female reproductive organs are usually sterile. The phenomenon also occurs very rarely in sheep, goats, pigs, and

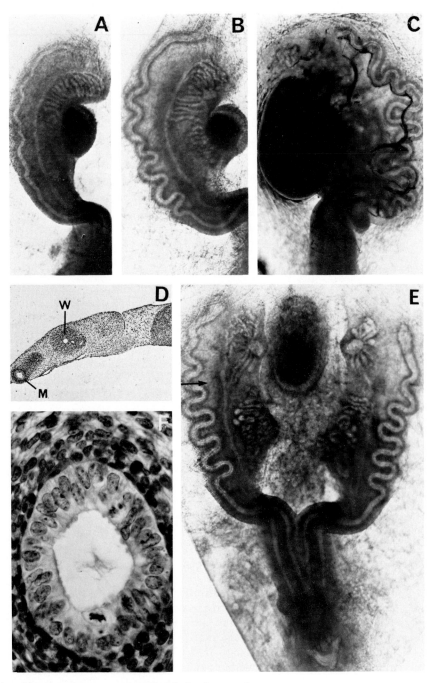

FIG. 5. Growth and coiling of the guinea pig oviduct in culture as compared with development in vivo. *A:* right side of tract explanted at 29–30 days and cultured for 3 days with 2 pieces of adrenals from the same fetus. × 16. *B:* same explant as in *A* after 9 days of culture; age, 38 days. Note maintenance of the Wolffian duct. × 16. *C:* portion of uncultured reproductive tract from female fetus; degree of oviducal growth and coiling in vivo at 38 days of age are shown. × 16. *D:* cross section of cultured tract in *E* at the level of the *arrow;* Müllerian duct (*M*) and partial maintenance of Wolffian duct (*W*) are apparent. × 35. *E:* whole female tract explanted at 29 days and cultured for 11 days with one piece of adrenal from the same fetus; age, 40 days. Compare degree of growth and coiling of the oviduct with that in vivo (*C*). × 16. *F:* high-power view of cross section of 40-day-old oviduct in *D;* about 2×-diameter increase over the initial stage at 29 days and slight crypts in the epithelium are shown. × 500. [From Price et al. (144).]

horses. The freemartin's male gonads are intra-abdominal and never descend into the pelvic cavity; they resemble the testes in structure but have more interstitial cells. Wolffian and Müllerian ducts are poorly developed (Fig.

6). The abnormality is apparent very early in embryonic life.

Development of the freemartin's gonad and reproductive duct system has been partially controlled by sub-

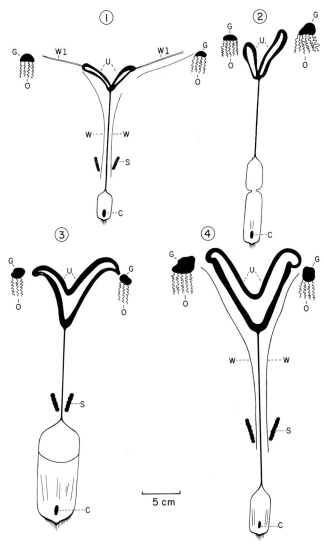

FIG. 6. Reproductive tracts of 1-year-old freemartin quintuplets (4 females and 1 male) with low degree of transformation from female to male (drawn to scale). Note the different degrees of transformation among the different animals. The male reproductive organs were normal and are not shown. *C*, clitoris; *G*, gonad; *O*, ovarian plexus; *S*, seminal vesicle; *U*, uterus; *W*, Wolffian ducts; *W1*, rudimentary oviducts. [Rajakoski & Hafez (146).]

stances received from her male twin through their fetal intercirculatory system. Two theories have been advanced to explain the freemartin condition: the *sex-chromosome mosaicism* theory and the *steroid induction* theory [reviewed by Hafez (82)]. The placentas of bovine multiple pregnancy have a common circulation as a result of the anastomosis of allantoic blood vessels. Blood group studies have shown that the inosculation may permit a reciprocal exchange of primordial hematopoietic tissues so that each twin carries more than one type of erythrocyte: erythrocytes formed by its own tissue and erythrocytes formed by alien tissue derived from its twin. Such twins are called *chimeras*, and the phenomenon of mixed blood is called *erythrocyte chimerism* or *mosaicism*. If allantoic fusion results in blood chimeras, cells other than erythrocytes may also

be exchanged. Karyotype analysis of chromosomes shows a definite chimerism in the bone marrow cells and leukocytes of bovine freemartins and their male partners—they contain a mixture of XX and XY cells. The inability to reproduce bovine freemartinism experimentally (107, 113) has raised doubt about the steroid induction hypothesis.

OVIDUCAL EPITHELIUM

Histology and Ultrastructure

The oviducal epithelium consists of ciliated cells, nonciliated cells, and peg cells—intercalary cells or Stiftchenzellen (Figs. 7 and 8). The peg cells are rodlike with a flat, compressed nucleus and practically no cytoplasm.

The density, cytological characteristics, and ultrastructure of the oviducal epithelium vary with species, segments of the oviduct, hormonal conditions, and reproductive phases (102). Peg cells are characteristic of the oviduct of the mouse but are rarely encountered in the rat. Cyclic changes in the rat oviduct are not clearly demonstrated by histological (3, 17) or histochemical (54) techniques. Cyclicality is more apparent in species with longer reproductive cycles (primates and farm animals).

SECRETORY EPITHELIUM. The cytology of the secretory cells changes through the estrous or menstrual cycle. During estrus, epithelial height and secretory activity reach their maximums. After ovulation the secretory material is evacuated from the secretory cells, and epithelial height decreases. These variations become progressively more pronounced from the isthmus to the infundibulum.

The structure and amount of the secretory granules also depend on the ovarian function. In the rabbit dense homogeneous granules are most common in estrus, whereas less dense, nonhomogeneous granules are characteristic of the postovulatory phase (135). Several types of granules (1–5 μ in diameter) are found in the secretory cells of the oviduct (Fig. 9). The granules of the postovulatory type may result from successive changes in the granules of the estrous type.

Cytological changes during the secretory cycle have been studied in the rabbit and in women. In the rabbit secretory granules form during proestrus and reach a maximum at estrus. They then bulge into the lumen of the oviduct in a goblet shape with many electron-lucent granules aggregated in the apical portion of the cell. In the presence of progesterone, these granules, usually with their encompassing membranes, are discharged 72 hr postcoitus (Fig. 10). The secretory cells then become elongated but persist to repeat the secretory cycle (37). Secretory material is sequestered in the saccules of the Golgi complex throughout the reproductive cycle. The number of saccules and vesicles associated with Golgi activity is greater in superovulated rabbits than in normal estrous rabbits (37). Se-

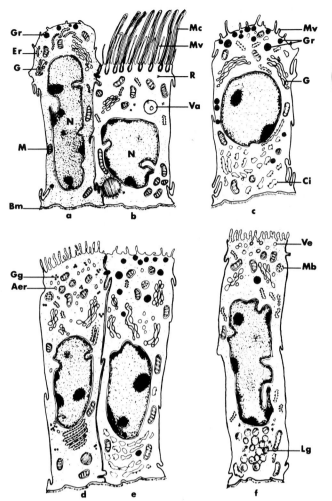

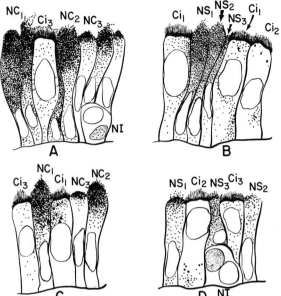

FIG. 7. Schematic drawing of the different epithelial cell types in the mouse oviduct: *a*, preampullar nonciliated cell; *b*, ciliated cell; *c*, ampullar nonciliated cell; *d* and *e*, isthmic nonciliated cells; *f*, junctural nonciliated cell. *Aer*, agranular endoplasmic reticulum; *Bm*, basal membrane; *Ci*, dilated cisternae of the endoplasmic reticulum; *Er*, endoplasmic reticulum; *G*, Golgi complex; *Gg*, glycogen granules; *Gr*, granules; *Lg*, lipid granule; *M*, mitochondrion; *Mc*, motile cilium; *Mb*, multivesicular body; *Mv*, microvillus; *N*, nucleus; *R*, ribosomes; *Va*, vacuole; *Ve*, vesicle. [From Reinius (148).]

FIG. 8. Diagrammatic illustration of the various types of epithelial cells in rabbit (*A* and *B*) and cattle (*C* and *D*) oviduct. Nonciliated cells: *NC₁*, overcrowded granulation; *NC₂*, moderately crowded granulation; *NC₃*, slightly crowded granulation; *NS₁*, abundantly scattered granulation; *NS₂*, moderately scattered granulation; *NS₃*, slightly scattered granulation; *NI*, basal cell with cell cytoplasmic inclusion. Ciliated cells: *Ci₁*, abundant granulation; *Ci₂*, scattered granulation; *Ci₃*, no granulation.

cretory granules disappear in ovariectomized rabbits, except in the isthmus, where some granules remain long after the operation (60).

In the human oviduct, definite cytological changes during the follicular phase precede secretory activity [(51, 95, 173); Table 2]. The endoplasmic reticulum of the secretory cells spreads out, the mitochondria swell as their matrices fill with a granular substance, and the Golgi apparatus becomes well developed (95). During the luteal phase, numerous secretory droplets appear, the endoplasmic reticulum dilates, mitochondria become fewer, and the Golgi apparatus expands (173).

Nuclear volume in human oviducts increases steadily from day 1 of the cycle to ovulation. During the luteal phase, nuclei are fewer but larger (116). Nuclear volumes are similar to proliferative phase volumes during early pregnancy, but in late pregnancy and the postpartum period the nuclear volumes are less than at any other time (173).

In birds the magnum portion of the oviduct secretes ovalbumin, the glycoprotein of albumin, and mucus. The conspicuous glands of this segment are built under the influence of estrogen alone but are activated by androgen or progesterone (132). The isthmus, histologically distinct from the magnum, contains tubular glands that secrete the shell membranes. Little is known about the endocrine control of the isthmus.

CILIATED EPITHELIUM. The nature and degree of cyclic changes in the ciliated epithelium vary with the species. In rabbits (31, 96, 97), rats, and mice, ciliated cells apparently remain structurally unchanged during the reproductive cycle. This apparent stability may be due partly to very short estrous cycles—sufficient time does not elapse for an extreme loss of ciliated cells. In animals with long luteal phases, such as cattle, sheep, swine, horse, dog, and cat, ciliated cells are regenerated cyclically (60). In the rhesus monkey ciliated cells increase in number and height during the follicular phase and decrease during the luteal phase. In the fimbriae and ampulla the ciliated cells not only fluctuate considerably, but also are shed and regenerated (34).

Hashimoto et al. (95) did not find any cyclic changes

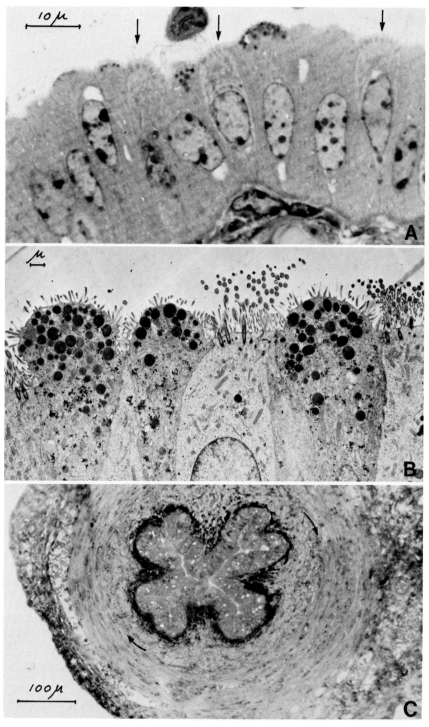

FIG. 9. *A:* guinea pig ampulla (metestrus). Ciliated (*arrows*) and nonciliated cells. In some of the nonciliated cells, granules are observed. A corona radiata cell is noticed above the epithelial membrane. Light microscopy; × 1,500. *B:* guinea pig ampulla (metestrus). Ciliated and nonciliated cells with granules are observed. Electron microscopy of an area similar to that demonstrated by light microscopy in *A.* × 4,000. *C:* guinea pig isthmus (metestrus). Cross section demonstrates the narrow, star-shaped lumen; the connective tissue of the tunica mucosa (*dark-stained*); the inner longitudinal and the outer circular muscle layer; and the tunica serosa. *Arrows* indicate the region between the two muscle layers. Light microscopy; × 160. [From Nilsson & Reinius (134).]

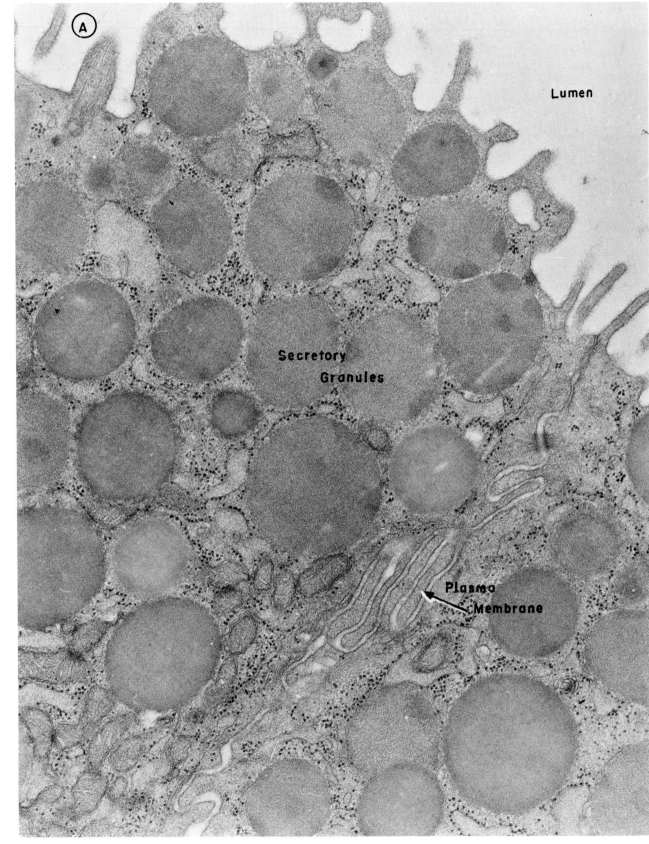

FIG. 10. Electron micrographs of secretory cells of oviducal epithelium. Cytological events associated with the secretory process in the rabbit are shown. *A:* portions of 2 preestrus secretory cells containing secretory granules. × 38,000. *B:* portions of 2 secretory cells 36 hr postcoitus with discharging and coalescing granules. × 17,750. [From Brower & Anderson (37).]

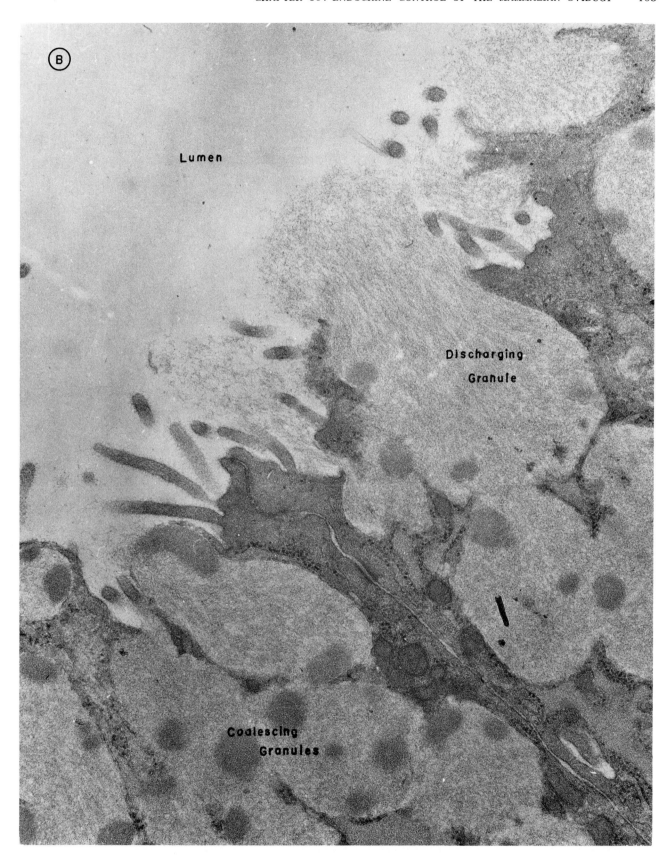

TABLE 2. *Cyclic Changes in Ultrastructure of Secretory Cells of the Human Oviduct*

Days of Menstrual Cycle	Cytological Characteristics			
	Mitochondria	Golgi apparatus	Endoplasmic reticulum	Other
1	Diminished	Small, compact	Limited	
5–7	More numerous	More tightly packed	Larger	
11				Dark, electron-dense granules
15 and 16		Enlarged		Additional large, light-grey granules; dark granules more numerous
16–18				Rupture of several cells
				Contents expelled into lumen

From Clyman (51); Hashimoto et al. (95); Woodruff & Pauerstein (173).

in the ciliated cells of the human oviduct during the menstrual cycle. However, Clyman (51) reported that the ciliated cells enlarged, their mitochondria increased, and a few cytoplasmic granules appeared as the cycle progressed. The conflicting findings are mainly due to the inherent difficulty in obtaining tissue samples from normal patients. The samples are usually secured from patients suffering from such gynecological diseases as uterine myomas, uterine cancer, or ovarian cancer. Ovarian dysfunction is associated with estrogen-progestin imbalance. Also, anxiety associated with surgery may induce ovarian malfunction, which in turn alters the histology of the oviducal epithelium.

In postparturient women the epithelium becomes increasingly lower and the ciliated cells decrease in number (5). The administration of stilbestrol, starting on the day of delivery (5 mg/day for 5–9 days), causes the ciliated epithelium to proliferate intensely. In early postmenopausal women the ciliated cells appear normal (159), but during late menopause, with minimal levels of estrogen, the ciliated cells are lost (173). In women with endometrial hyperplasia, a condition associated with hyperestrogenism, ciliated cells in the oviducts increase in number.

Ovariectomy, hypophysectomy, stalk-sectioning, or hypothalamic lesioning causes complete deciliation in the oviducts of rabbits (60) and rhesus monkeys (Fig. 11). The deciliated epithelium is completely restored with estrogen treatment. Estrogen also stimulated ciliation in ovariectomized, immature rabbits and monkeys.

Deciliation of the oviducal epithelium occurs in several ways: *a*) the entire distal third of ciliated cells becomes constricted and cast off into the lumen; *b*) whole ciliated cells are shed from the epithelium; or *c*) several cilia are shed from the ciliated cells (34).

The rate of cilia beat is partly affected by the endocrine environment. In the rabbit oviduct the cilia beat about 1,200 times per minute. Progesterone increases the rate of beat by about 20 % (32).

Histochemistry

The patterns of qualitative and quantitative histochemical response to endogenous and exogenous hormones vary with the segment of the oviduct and the animal species (Table 3). The hormonal effect on the height of the oviducal epithelium and production of periodic acid-Schiff (PAS)-positive material increases from the isthmus toward the infundibulum (Fig. 12).

Glycogen is present in the epithelial cells of most mammals (71), although absent in sheep and mice. Before ovulation it is distributed equally around the nucleus; after ovulation the supranuclear deposit becomes depleted (66). In women these changes may reflect hormone-dependent variations in ciliary activity (65).

Several enzymes were identified in homogenates of the rat oviduct by zonal electrophoresis: one alkaline phosphatase; four types of acid phosphatase; and seven different esterases (150). Most of these enzymes have been identified histochemically in the oviducal epithelium. Ovariectomy causes a decrease in the activity of two types of acid phosphatase and two esterases in the rat (150) and of oxidative enzymes in the rabbit (163). After hypophysectomy the activity of sterol-3-β-ol dehydrogenase decreases in the oviducal epithelium of the rat (118).

Esterases are found in the cytoplasm of nonciliated cells of the human and bovine oviducts. The intracellular localization of the enzyme varies with ovarian function. On the other hand, cyclic hormone changes do not alter the histochemical patterns of succinodehydrogenase, diphosphopyridine nucleotide-diaphorase in primates (61), or the patterns of alkaline phosphatase in several animals (8).

Glass (69) studied the uptake of macromolecules by the oviducal epithelium of the mouse with the fluorescent antibody technique. At ovulation the ampullary epithelium reacts more intensely than the isthmic epithelium. As pregnancy progresses, epithelial fluorescence decreases.

In the rabbit oviduct, PAS-positive and diastase-resistant mucopolysaccharides are deposited around the eggs as a tertiary membrane known as the mucin layer (13, 33). Mucin-secreting cells become progressively more abundant from the lumen to the isthmus, and at estrus mucin granules are found only in isthmian cells (78). Estrogen is responsible for the synthesis and storage of mucin in the oviducal epithelium, whereas progesterone is necessary for its discharge into the lumen (73, 75). The mucin layer around oviducal eggs becomes considerably thinner with exogenous estrogen [Fig. 13, (72)], and embryonic mortality may result.

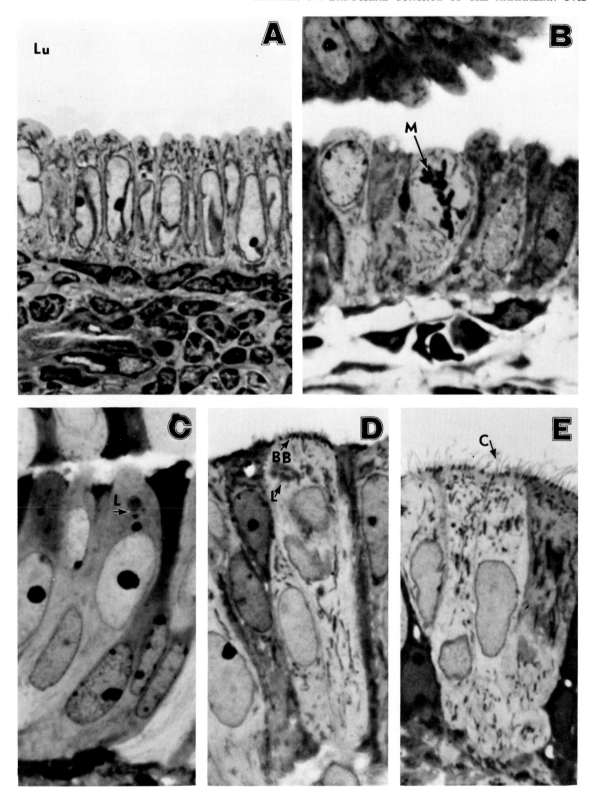

FIG. 11. Fimbriae from ovariectomized monkeys 6 weeks before estrogen treatment. × 990. *A:* fimbriae after 1-day treatment with estradiol benzoate (10 μg/day). No visible changes. Compare with Fig. 4C. *Lu,* lumen. *B:* fimbriae after 2-day treatment wtih estradiol benzoate (10 μg/day). Epithelium shows both hypertrophy and hyperplasia. Mitotic figures (*M*) are common. *C:* fimbriae after 3-day treatment with estrogen. Epithelial cells are maximally hypertrophied. *Clear cells* and *dark cells* are present. Only *clear cells,* which are the future ciliated cells, contain lipid complexes. *L,* lipid complex. *D:* fimbriae after 4-day treatment with estrogen. *Clear cells* develop basal bodies, which line up at luminal surface of the cell. *BB,* basal body. *E:* fimbriae after 5-day treatment with estrogen. Basal bodies sprout cilia, and cells appear mature. *C,* cilia. [From Brenner (34).]

OVIDUCAL MUSCULATURE

The anatomy of the oviducal musculature has been described for several primates (172). However, little is known about cyclic changes in the histology and ultra-structure of the musculature. In swine, oviducal muscle fibers are nearly twice as long at estrus as they are at di-estrus (4).

The oviducal musculature undergoes various types of complex contractions—localized peristalsis-like contractions originating in isolated segments or loops and traveling only a short distance; segmental contraction; and wormlike writhing of the entire oviduct (21, 23, 90, 91). Contractions in an abovarian direction are more common than those in an adovarian direction. In general the ampulla is less active than the isthmus throughout the sexual cycle. In the rabbit the contractions of circular musculature of the ampulla are slow and of high amplitude. The isthmic rings contract more rapidly but less vigorously.

Oviducal muscular contractions are stimulated by contractions of two major membranes that contain smooth musculature and are attached to the fimbriae, ampulla, and ovary: the mesosalpinx and the mesotubarium superius (see Fig. 1, bottom). The frequency and amplitude of spontaneous contractions vary with sexual cycle phases (Table 4). Before ovulation, contractions are gentle with some individual variations in the rate and pattern of contractility. At estrus and ovulation, contractions become most vigorous. At this time the mesosalpinx and mesotubarium superius contract vigorously, independently, and intermittently; the mesotubarium contracts more vigorously than the mesosalpinx. These contractions draw the oviduct into the form of a crescent, slide the fimbriae over the surface of the ovary, and cause continuous change in the contour of the oviduct (26). At the time of ovulation, the fringelike folds contract rhythmically and "massage" the ovarian surface. By 24 hr after ovulation, the intensity and rate of contraction in rabbit oviducts decrease. Two days after ovulation there is little further change in ampullary contractions (76).

Ovariectomy reduces the rate and amplitude of oviducal contractions. The musculature does not become completely quiescent, and the degree of reduction depends on the recency of ovariectomy. Ampullary egg transport occurred in the rabbit 167 days after ovariectomy (30).

Several investigators studied the effects of steroids on the rate, amplitude, and tonus of oviducal contractions by employing either the Rubin technique or direct observations on the oviduct (106, 165). In the rabbit, estrogens seem to stimulate, progestins to repress, contraction (48, 74, 76, 77, 92, 94). However, Blandau (26) and Boling (30) stated that progesterone stimulated the oviduct's musculature and that increased oviducal activity near ovulation is due to the withdrawal of estrogen and to the secretion of progesterone from the follicles before rupture.

Testosterone inhibits the frequency and amplitude of oviducal contractions and reduces the opening pressure of the oviduct (68, 154). These effects can be reversed by estrogen. In anovulatory women exogenous estrogen and progesterone in doses sufficient to make the endometrium secretory did not restore oviducal motility to the pattern

TABLE 3. *Summary of Effects of Hormones on Localization and Activity of Metabolites and Enzymes in Oviducal Epithelium by Histochemical Techniques*

Substrate or Enzyme	Animal Species	Qualitative and Quantitative Reaction	Refs.
Glycogen	Rat	Present in infundibulum at preovulatory phase	63
	Rabbit	Present in ampulla under estrogen influence	63
	Cattle	Absent at estrus; reaches a maximum 8 days after estrus	164
	Man	In ciliated cells, not in nonciliated cells; reaches a maximum and appears in lumen on day 22 of cycle	112
Lipid	Man	More conspicuous at ovulation; diminishes at menopause; maximal concentration at mid-luteal phase	63, 64
	Rabbit	High levels at luminal edge of epithelium at ovulation or after estrogen injections; no reaction during pseudo-pregnancy	85
Periodic acid-Schiff (PAS)	Man	At ovulation localized reaction on surface of secretory cells and in slight amounts within lumen	64
	Sheep	At estrus and metestrus reaction appears in lumen and decreases in epithelium	80
Succinic dehy-drogenase	Man	No cyclic changes	62
Esterase	Man	Follicular: reaction at apical portion of cytoplasm; Luteal: reaction at basal portion of cytoplasm	22, 64
Alkaline phos-phomonoes-terases	Rat	Greater activity during proestrus	150
Glycerylphos-phorylcho-line diesterase	Cattle Swine Rabbit Rat Mouse	Activity in fluid is highest at estrus	167
Alkaline phos-phatase	Man	Maximal levels at ovulation and minimal levels at menstruation	7
	Rat	No cyclic changes	36
		Intense reaction in fimbriae and ampulla and weak reaction in isthmus reach a maximum at estrus and metestrus, and a minimum at diestrus	8

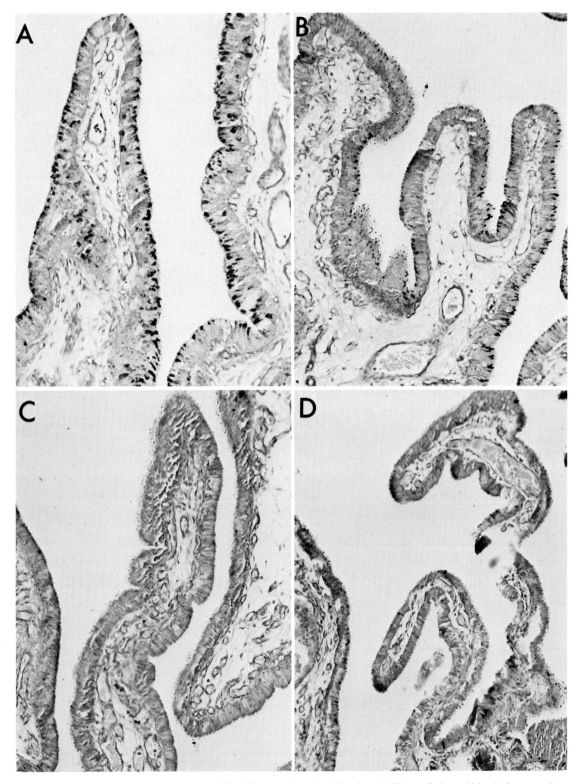

FIG. 12. Micrographs of oviducal epithelium of the rabbit during pseudopregnancy. × 122.
A: infundibulum on day 1 (ovulation) of pseudopregnancy. Note large accumulation of PAS-positive
material at outer edge of epithelium (periodic acid-Schiff base with hematoxylin stain—PASH).
B: infundibulum 5 days after ovulation (PASH). *C:* infundibulum 7 days after ovulation (PASH).
D: infundibulum 11 days after ovulation. Note degeneration of epithelium and absence of PAS-
positive material (PASH). [From Hamner & Fox (85).]

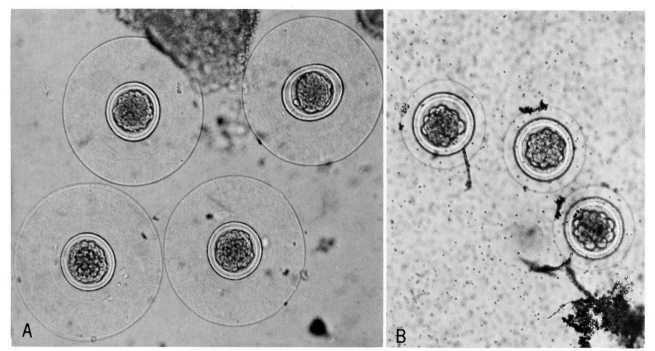

FIG. 13. *A:* normal rabbit egg 72 hr postcoitus. *B:* rabbit eggs 72 hr postcoitus after injection of 5 μg estradiol benzoate at 24 and 48 hr postcoitus. Note the thin mucin layer. [From Greenwald (72).]

exhibited during ovulation in a normally cycling patient (52).

The varying patterns of oviducal motility may be associated with cyclic changes in glycogen content of oviducal musculature. Glycogen in the human oviduct is more abundant in the inner circular musculature than in the outer longitudinal musculature (112). The incidence of glycogen is low after menstruation, higher after ovulation, and highest during pregnancy (64, 111, 112). Glycogen content in human myometrium fluctuates similarly (35).

The sympathetic nervous system controls the oviducal musculature by long adrenergic fibers arising from the hypogastric plexus and by short adrenergic waves arising from the neurons near the uterovaginal junction. The amount of adrenergic transmitter substance appears to be hormonally controlled.

The oviduct has α- and β-adrenergic receptors but no cholinergic nerve supply. In rabbits the receptors' response to epinephrine varies with the phase of the ovarian cycle. Under the influence of epinephrine the isthmus maintains a contraction for 3 days after ovulation (173). Acetylcholine stimulates the tone and amplitude of both the human (157) and rabbit oviduct in vitro (39) but reduces the tone and amplitude in women in vivo (6). The response of the rabbit oviduct to acetylcholine varies cyclically. These cyclic variations suggest that ovarian steroids may modify the activity levels of α- and β-receptors. Little is known of the possible endocrine-dependent fluctuations in adrenergic nervous activity.

The isthmus is innervated and responds differently

TABLE 4. *Cyclic Changes in Frequency and Amplitude of Contractions of Oviducal Musculature in Various Mammals*

Species	Stage of Reproductive Cycle	Frequency of Contractions, per min	Amplitude of Contractions	Ref.
Man	At ovulation	4–5	High, uniform	152
	Midcycle	1–3	Low, irregular	52
	Late in cycle	5–7		
Pig	Estrus	13–15	Shallow, irregular, or uniform	
	3 Days postovulation		Almost ceased activity	168
	Interestrus	4–6	Regular	
Rabbit	Estrus	12–18		23, 24
	3 Days postovulation	3–4	Irregular	21
	Anestrus	4–9	Variable	76

from the ampulla. In several mammals the isthmus has a noradrenergic innervation that allows it to act as a sphincter (Fig. 14). The muscular and neuronal prerequisites for a sphincter have been demonstrated in man, rat, cat, and dog (41). In nonmated rabbits the sphincteric function of the isthmus is very marked and can be further augmented by increased activity of the hypogastric nerve (40).

Prostaglandins exhibit contrasting effects on the distal and proximal segments of the human oviduct (173). Isolated from human seminal plasma, prostaglandins are

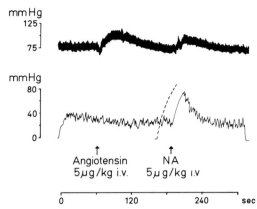

FIG. 14. Perfusion pressure curves from rabbit oviduct isthmus after injections of *angiotensin* and noradrenaline (*NA*). *Top:* training, systemic arterial blood pressure. For perfusion, saline (28 units/min) was forced toward the ovary from 0.5 cm from the uterotubal junction. Vaginal smear showed estrus. [From Brundin (41).]

TABLE 5. *Effect of Stage of Pseudopregnancy at Time of Insemination on Number of Spermatozoa Recovered in Different Regions of Reproductive Tract of Female Rabbit*

Day of Pseudo-preg-nancy	Total Number of Sperm Re-covered, × 10⁶	Total Number of Sperm Recovered as % of Sperm Inseminated	Number of Spermatozoa Recovered from Different Regions of the Tract, × 10⁶				
			Vagina	Cervix	Uterus	UTJ*	Oviduct
1	16.7	5.6	7.9	8.0	0.59	0.117	0.013
3	16.4	5.5	10.9	4.4	0.96	0.163	0.013
5	24.9	8.3	20.5	4.4	0.10	0.004	0.002
7	21.6	7.2	13.2	8.4	Nil	Nil	Nil

* Uterotubal junction.   [From Dobrowolski & Hafez (55).]

derivatives of a C_{20} acid (prostanoic acid) containing a cyclopentene ring. Prostaglandin E_1 has one double bond; prostaglandin E_2 has two double bonds; prostaglandin E_3 has three double bonds. Intravenous injections of prostaglandin E_1 cause relaxation of the isthmic circular musculature and reduce the opening pressure in the human oviduct from 31 to 5 mm Hg (40, 103). On the other hand, prostaglandin E_1 seems to cause contraction of the isthmic longitudinal musculature in vitro (158).

SPERM TRANSPORT AND CAPACITATION IN THE OVIDUCT

Sperm Transport

The pattern and rate of sperm transport through the oviduct are due to several mechanisms—peristalsis and antiperistalsis of oviducal musculature and the complex contractions of the oviducal mucosal folds, the mesotubarium, and the mesosalpinx. Their relative importance in sperm transport through the oviduct varies among species (127, 128).

The pattern and amplitude of contraction vary in different segments of the oviduct. In the isthmus, peristaltic and antiperistaltic contractions are segmental, vigorous, and almost continuous. In the ampulla strong peristaltic waves move in a segmental fashion toward the midportion of the oviduct (26). Whether sperm are transported to the ampulla by momentary relaxation of the ampullary-isthmic junction or by their own motility is not known. The ampullary-isthmic junction may not present any significant hindrance to sperm transport.

The frequency and amplitude of contraction of the different segments of the oviducal musculature are under the control of ovarian hormones (see section OVIDUCAL EPITHELIUM, *Histochemistry* in this chapter). In general the rate of sperm transport is influenced by hormones, mainly oxytocin (56, 99, 131) and progesterone (55), and may be modified in vivo by such seminal pharmacody-

namic agents as prostaglandin (59). High titers of progesterone depress contractile activity of the uterine and oviducal musculature so that sperm are detained in the uterus. The high levels of phagocytosis of spermatozoa in the uterus are probably responsible for inhibition of sperm transport. This inhibition affects fertilization rate. If female rats are mated early in estrus and each isthmus is ligated 1–5 hr after ejaculation, the majority of ova remain unfertilized (117). Similar findings have been reported for the hamster (175). During pseudopregnancy in rabbits, transport of spermatozoa to the oviduct is inhibited (9, 55), and from days 5 to 7 of pseudopregnancy inseminated spermatozoa do not reach the rabbit oviduct (Table 5).

The role of the uterotubal junction in sperm transport varies with the species. In the horse and pig a large volume of semen is ejaculated directly into the uterus. Most of the ejaculate in the pig disappears from the uterus within 2 hr, and a high concentration of sperm is left at the uterotubal junction. This sperm reservoir persists for 24 hr and then disappears within the next 48 hr (149). Sperm reservoirs may provide a continuous flow of sperm to the ampulla. In other species, such as cattle, sheep, rabbits, and primates, the volume of the ejaculate is relatively small and semen is deposited in the vagina. In these species the cervix and uterotubal junction appear to act as simple mechanical barriers that maintain a graded concentration of sperm throughout the reproductive tract from the vagina to the oviduct (Figs. 15 and 16). This pattern of distribution is altered by injection of such hormones as progesterone (Fig. 17).

Massive numbers of sperm disappear within the female reproductive tract, and only a very few viable sperm are found in the ampulla at the time of fertilization (Table 6). In certain species, some sperm become incorporated into the oviducal and uterine mucosa (12). Most sperm are phagocytized by the leukocytes that appear in massive numbers in oviducal and uterine fluids after copulation (11, 14, 105). The leukocytic influx depends partly on endocrine factors.

Little is known about the effect of the intrauterine device (IUD) on sperm transport rate and distribution in the female reproductive tract. In sheep these devices seem

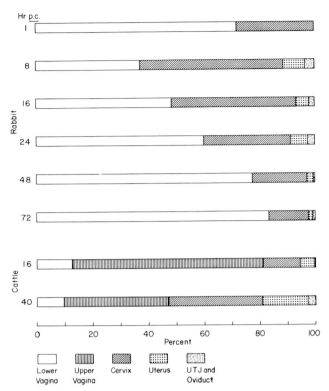

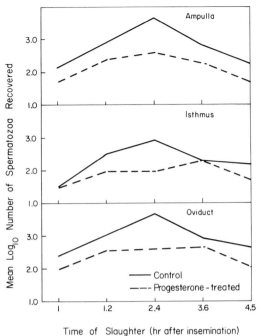

FIG. 15. Sperm distribution in different segments of female reproductive tracts in rabbit (*top*) and cattle (*bottom*) at different hours after insemination (*p.c.*) as a percentage of sperm recovered. Sperm distribution in the oviduct is not indicated separately because of the very small percentage recovered. Note the graded concentration of spermatozoa from the vagina to the oviduct. [From El-Banna & Hafez (57).]

FIG. 17. Estimated mean number of spermatozoa recovered from ampulla, isthmus, and whole oviduct of untreated and progesterone-treated sheep at intervals after insemination. Note inhibition of sperm transport after progesterone treatment. [From Quinlivan & Robinson (145).]

primates does not affect transport of spermatozoa in the oviduct.

Sperm Capacitation

Capacitation of spermatozoa refers to some unknown changes in the sperm whereby the acrosome reaction is unblocked and the sperm are rendered capable of fertilization. With the aid of lytic enzymes, the sperm can then pass through the matrix of the cumulus oophorus and the zona pellucida. These changes occur in the female tract and require several hours before completion. Present evidence suggests that capacitation in rabbit sperm is not a structural change but a process that enables the sperm to respond appropriately to surface-active factors that may well emanate from the ovum-granulosa cell mass. This response, manifested in the vesicular acrosome reaction, is a prerequisite for sperm penetration into the zona pellucida.

Species in which the need for sperm capacitation can be inferred from observations on the time relations of fertilization in vivo or the requirements for fertilization in vitro include rabbit, rat, mouse, golden hamster, Chinese hamster, ferret, sheep, cattle, and man (10, 47, 49, 129, 136).

While evidence on sperm capacitation in some species tends to favor involvement of a specific agent in the female tract, in others it supports the conception of an endogenous change in the spermatozoon produced by a precise set of maternal conditions. Factors necessary for sperm capacitation in the rabbit are present in the oviduct (1) and are specific for the female reproductive tract

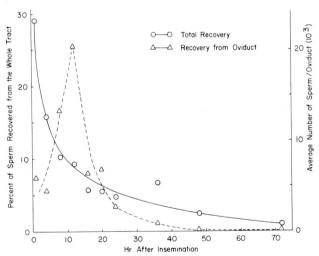

FIG. 16. Total sperm recovered from rabbit female tract in relation to the number of sperm recovered from the oviduct at different intervals after insemination. Note that the number of spermatozoa recovered from the oviducts increased with time following insemination, although total number of sperm recovered from the whole tract was decreasing. [From El-Banna & Hafez (57).]

to interfere with sperm transport. Hawk (98) could not recover sperm from oviducal flushings of inseminated ewes in which IUDs had been inserted 2–4 weeks previously. The presence of an intrauterine contraceptive in

(87). The milieu needed for sperm capacitation is dependent on ovarian hormones. In pseudopregnant or ovariectomized rabbits, capacitation in the oviduct can be achieved by treatment with estrogen or progesterone but cannot be achieved without hormones. Further study of hormonal regulation of sperm capacitation in other species is urged.

Increased metabolic activity of spermatozoa in the presence of oviducal fluids is considered a component of capacitation (88). In the rabbit this heightened production of usable energy is caused by increased O_2 uptake from a dialyzable, heat-stable bicarbonate ion (89). Oviducal fluid secreted by sheep at estrus stimulates more sperm metabolism than does an equal amount of diestrous fluid (25). Because the oviduct produces at least twice as much fluid at estrus, much more metabolic stimulation than necessary is available to spermatozoa in the oviduct.

Oviduct uptake of O_2 is not affected by the endocrine milieu in women (126) or rabbits (86). Although O_2 tension in the rabbit oviduct is significantly less under progesterone dominance than during estrus, it remains adequate to support respiration (19, 20).

EGG TRANSPORT AND DEVELOPMENT IN THE OVIDUCT

Pattern and Rate of Egg Transport

Eggs are transported from the ovarian follicles to the uterus by the action of cilia and by the peristaltic contractions of the oviducal musculature. The eggs are suspended in fluid formed by secretory cells of the oviducal epithelium, which is also the medium for capacitation of sperm and maturation of the zygote. In species with closed ovarian bursae (mouse), the eggs are picked up from the ovaries by the action of the cilia. In species with opened ovarian bursae (ungulates, primates), pick-up of eggs is due to the muscular contraction of the engorged fimbriae aided by the contractions of the mesosalpinx and mesotubarium.

Three stages are recognized in the transport of eggs from the infundibulum to the uterus: 1) rapid transport through the ampulla; 2) retention for 1–2 days at the ampullary-isthmic junction where fertilization occurs (tube locking); and 3) fairly rapid transport of eggs through the isthmus and uterotubal junction. The egg's entry into the uterus, timed to coincide with the beginning of the luteal phase, occurs 3 days after fertilization in most mammalian species.

EGG TRANSPORT IN AMPULLA. Eggs move through the upper ampulla very rapidly. The continuous, smooth pattern of transport is mainly due to ciliary action and segmenting muscular contractions, which work against the flow of ampullary fluid.

RETENTION OF EGGS AT AMPULLARY-ISTHMIC JUNCTION. For 1 or 2 days the eggs are retained at the ampullary-isthmic junction, which acts as a functional block (Fig. 18). The anatomy of this region varies with the species. In mice,

TABLE 6. *Number of Sperm Recovered from the Rabbit Oviducts at Different Intervals After Insemination*

Hour After Insemination	Number of Sperm per Oviduct	
	Range	Mean
1	40–20,600	5,836
4	331–16,000	4,303
8	300–58,000	13,320
12	2,100–133,341	20,292
16	1,000–19,322	6,423
20	110–20,300	6,701
24	200–12,080	2,793
36	338–2,100	981
48	76–334	165
72	0–410	83

From El-Banna & Hafez (57).

rats, and hamsters a narrow lumen at the ampullary-isthmic junction causes considerable quantities of oviducal fluid to accumulate and dilatate one of the ampullary loops (Fig. 19). One day after ovulation the lumen widens and releases the fluids.

Several physiological mechanisms have been suggested to explain blocking of eggs at the ampullary-isthmic junction: temporary inactivity of the epithelial cilia; localized edema of the isthmic region; adovarian activity; constriction or inactivity of the isthmic circular muscles; or tubal locking by a specific sphincteric muscle, or muscles, in the isthmus.

Brundin (38, 39) used sensitive pressure transducers to measure intraluminal pressures in both the ampulla and isthmus of the rabbit. Pressure changes within the lumen of the ampulla never exceeded 7 mm Hg, but pressure within the isthmus ranged from 16 to 50 mm Hg. These data seemed to indicate a functional occlusive mechanism at the ampullary-isthmic junction.

Several histological techniques have failed to demonstrate any isolated sphincteric structure in the isthmus of the rabbit (74) or man (119). However, El-Banna & Hafez (58) measured planimetrically the lumen size of all segments of the oviduct in rabbits and cattle and found that of the ampullary-isthmic junction to be the smallest at all reproductive stages (Figs. 20–22), although it enlarged twofold in the 3–4 days after estrus. In man (42) and other species (142), the isthmus and ampullary-isthmic junction have a rich adrenergic plexus intermingled with the circular muscle fibers. In the ampulla, adrenergic nerve distribution is sparse and confined mainly to perivascular areas and to a thin subserosal nerve plexus (40). Thus the isthmus probably functions as a physiological, if not an anatomic, adrenergic sphincter.

EGG TRANSPORT IN ISTHMUS. After leaving the ampullary-isthmic junction, eggs pass fairly rapidly through the isthmus. Egg transport through the isthmus is produced by peristaltic contractions of the circular muscle innervated by adrenergic nerve terminals. Distention of the isthmus by fluid and eggs stimulates the peristaltic contractions. The eggs are retained in the final segment of the isthmus

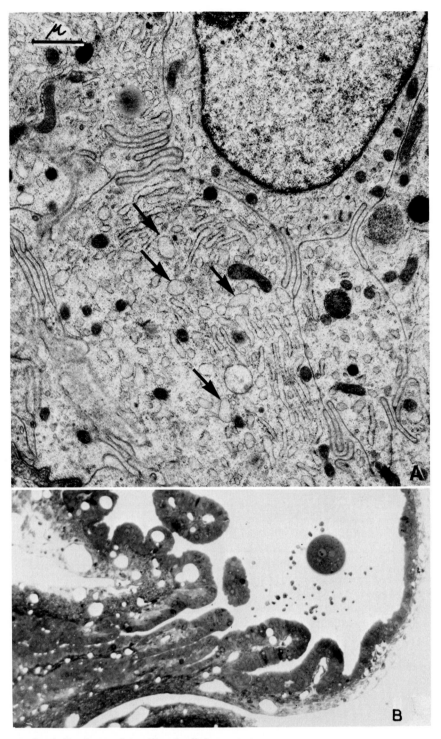

FIG. 18. *A:* mouse ampulla (day 2 after estrus, 3 PM). Basal part of nonciliated cell demonstrates granular endoplasmic reticulum with few granular cisternae. Part of the nucleus is in the *upper right* corner. × 15,000. *B:* mouse ampullary-isthmic junction (day 1 after estrus, 5 PM). Wide lumen of the ampulla is to the *right*, narrow lumen of the isthmus to the *left*. Note thin muscular layer of the ampulla and thicker muscular layer of the isthmus. A one-cell egg in pronuclear stage surrounded by dispersed granulosa cells lies in the ampulla lumen. Light microscopy; × 150. [From Nilsson & Reinius (134).]

until the uterotubal junction relaxes, and a peristaltic rush carries the eggs through the directional flow of the luminal fluid to the uterus (Fig. 23).

Near the uterotubal junction in the rabbit, most of the cells are ciliated; thus egg transport through this segment may be more rapid (74).

EFFECTS OF INTRAUTERINE DEVICES. Little is known about the physiological mechanisms whereby the intrauterine device (IUD) interferes with conception. It has been suggested that it works by altering patterns of motility in the oviducts and uterus (121, 122). The presence of these devices has been found to accelerate egg transport in the superovulated monkey with high progesterone levels (123, 124). In normally cycling monkeys, however, the presence of an IUD did not affect egg transport (114, 125). The effects of IUD's seem to be related to duration of use (138).

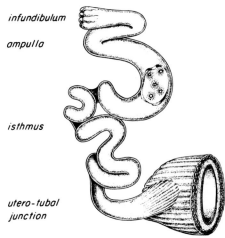

FIG. 19. Mouse oviduct. Eggs are shown in the ampulla on day 1 of pregnancy. [Redrawn from Reinius (148).]

Endocrine Control of Egg Transport

It is critical that fertilized eggs reach the uterus at an appropriate progestational stage of the ovarian cycle. Both estrogen and progesterone must be present at appropriate levels to induce the egg's normal 3-day stay in the oviduct.

The ovarian hormones control egg transport in the oviduct and the actions of the ampullary-isthmic and uterotubal junctions. These mechanisms can also be altered by exogenous synthetic and natural estrogens and progestins, certain synthetic nonsteroids, gonadotrophins, prostaglandins, and other drugs influencing the contraction of smooth musculature, such as reserpine. Such compounds may accelerate the rate of egg transport to the uterus or cause "tube-locking" of the eggs at the ampullary-isthmic junction; both alterations result in embryonic mortality. The effects of estrogen and progesterone vary with their proportions, the timing of their administration, and the animal species.

ESTROGENS. Noyes et al. (137) transferred freshly ovulated eggs into the oviducts of castrated mature rabbits whose reproductive tracts had atrophied. Some of the castrates had been treated with various amounts of estradiol. In general, as estrogen dosage increased, more eggs were found in the oviducts and fewer in the uteri. In treated and untreated castrates, eggs were transported irregularly, ejected from either side of the oviducts, and not retained normally in the uteri.

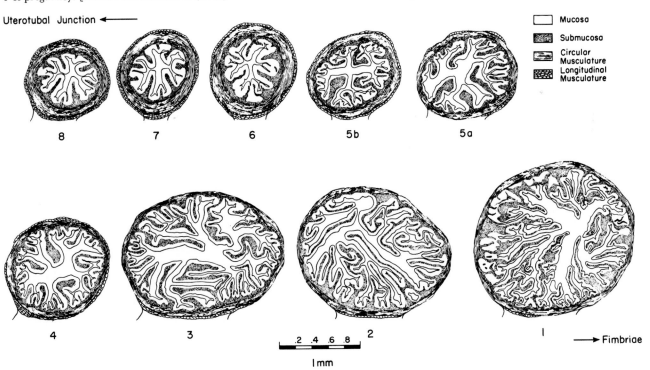

FIG. 20. Diagrammatic illustration of sections of different segments of rabbit oviduct at estrus. Figures represent the location of segments starting from the fimbriae. Note changes from the ampulla to the isthmus at segment 5. Sections 5a and 5b were taken at the beginning and end of segment 5. Ampullary-isthmic junction is located between segments 5 and 6. Segment 6 had the narrowest oviducal lumen. [From El-Banna & Hafez (58).]

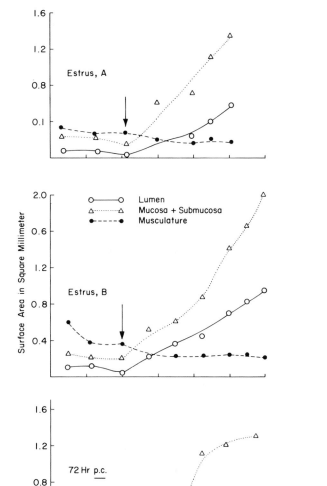

FIG. 21. Surface areas of the lumen, mucosa plus submucosa, and musculature of rabbit oviducts at estrus and *72 Hr* postcoitus (*p.c.*). Each diagram represents an individual animal. Note the differences between animals at the same reproductive stage (*Estrus A* and *Estrus B*) and the differences produced by time lapse. The narrowing of the oviducal lumen at the isthmic segment, which was apparent at estrus, is reduced by *72 Hr p.c. Arrows* indicate possible locations of ampullary-isthmic junctions (1–1.5 cm of the isthmus was excluded with the uterotubal junction). [From El-Banna & Hafez (58).]

Little is known about the endocrine mechanisms that cause the stricture of the ampullary-isthmic junction. The blocking of eggs in the oviduct can be prolonged (by injections of small doses of estrogen) or shortened (by larger doses of the same hormone). This effect has been demonstrated in rabbits (24, 74, 92, 94, 137), mice (43, 169), and rats (3).

PROGESTERONE. Harper (93) recovered newly ovulated eggs in cumulus, stained them with toluidine blue, and transferred them to rabbit oviducts. In estrus, at ovulation, and from day 2½ to day 15 of pseudopregnancy, egg transport rates were 11, 9, and 6 mm/min, respectively. Harper suggested that progestin retards egg transport by depressing ampullary-muscular activity. Chang (48) found that egg transport was delayed by administration of medroxylprogesterone acetate on the day of ovulation and for 1 or 2 days thereafter. However, Black & Asdell (23) and Greenwald (74) have claimed that progesterone treatment after mating accelerates egg transport. High levels of endogenous progesterone in superovulated cattle have accelerated egg transport (Fig. 24).

As superovulatory response to gonadotrophins increases and ovaries enlarge, more and more eggs are lost into the peritoneal cavity. The loss occurs because size of fimbriae does not increase in proportion to the increase in size of the ovaries (Fig. 25).

Development of Embryo in the Oviduct

The oviduct seems to take an active part in maintaining eggs and preparing them for fertilization and segmentation. In vitro studies indicate that it also supports blastulation. In an artificial medium, two-celled mouse eggs did not develop, except for some late two-cell embryos in which cleavage continued after the addition of lactate. Early two-cell embryos did cleave when cultured in oviducts extirpated from recently ovulated and mated mice (170); these embryos grew best in oviducts from late estrous and metestrous mice. Thus endocrine factors seem important in the early development of mouse embryos (18). The effects of endocrine environment on the qualitative and quantitative characteristics of the oviducal fluid are discussed in another chapter.

Evidence indicates that oviducal epithelium is most active near the developing embryo. In the rabbit, epithelial uptake of radioactive sulfate increases in the region containing the egg (115). Using an immunofluorescent technique, Glass (69) showed that two- to four-cell mouse eggs absorb proteins similar to those in the mother's blood serum. The oviducal epithelium accumulates serumlike proteins under hormonal control (70).

CONCLUDING REMARKS

Prenatal differentiation of the oviduct in the first half of pregnancy is hormone independent. Morphogenesis and histogenesis in the second half of pregnancy are hormone dependent. Species variations in prenatal differentiation patterns are partly related to differences in placental hormones and fetal gonads.

Ovarian estrogen and progesterone affect the height and ultrastructure of oviducal epithelium; amount and structure of the different types of secretory granules; ciliogenesis, deciliation, and rate of cilia beat (Fig. 26). Morphological and quantitative manifestations of some of the

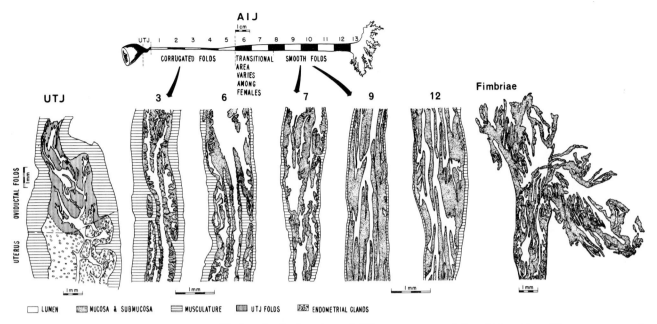

FIG. 22. Longitudinal sections of different segments of the rabbit oviduct. Figures represent the location of the segments starting from the uterotubal junction. Note corrugated mucosal folds in the isthmus and the smooth folds of the ampulla. Note also the complexity of the folds at the uterotubal junction.

cyclic histochemical reactions vary in degree with the segment of oviduct and animal species.

Cyclic changes in the histology and histochemistry of the oviducal epithelium promote nurture of gametes, before and during fertilization, and of the oviducal embryo. The endocrine milieu affects qualitative and quantitative characteristics of oviducal fluid, sperm capacitation, and O_2 uptake of oviduct. The developing embryo interacts with the adjacent oviducal epithelium.

The rate and pattern of sperm transport through the oviduct are attributed to peristalsis and antiperistalsis of musculature and contraction of mucosal folds and mesosalpinx. The relative importance of these mechanisms varies among species. The frequency and amplitude of contractions of oviducal circular and longitudinal musculature, mesosalpinx, and mesotubarium are controlled by ovarian hormones, adrenergic and noradrenergic activity, and such components of seminal plasma as prostaglandin.

Three stages are recognized in the transport of oviducal eggs: *1)* rapid transport in the ampulla; *2)* retention at the ampullary-isthmic junction; and *3)* fairly rapid transport through the isthmus. Exogenous ovarian hormones may slow or speed egg transport to result in embryonic mortality. The effect of these hormones on rate of egg transport varies with the dose, mode of injection, and animal species. The transport of material through the oviduct depends greatly on particle size. Particles as small as the spermatozoa seem to be transported in both directions. Large particles, such as the eggs, are transported at a variable rate depending on the endocrine milieu of the female.

Future research is needed in a wide spectrum of species to understand the interactions among the endocrine,

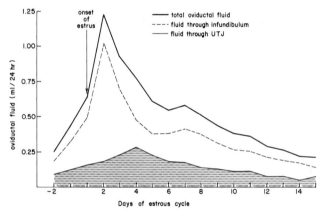

FIG. 23. Directional flow of the oviducal secretions in the ewe. Cannulae were placed in the ovarian end of the ampulla. An increase in total output of oviducal fluid began on the last day of the estrous cycle and reached a maximum on about day 2 of estrus, after which a gradual decline occurred. Most of the total fluid flowed through the ampullary end. Flow into the uterus remained low for most of the cycle but markedly increased 3.9 days after the onset of estrus, the time at which eggs enter the uterus. [From Bellve & McDonald (15).]

pharmacodynamic, and immunological aspects of gamete transport, fertilization, and early embryonic development. Additional and detailed information on estrogen and progesterone levels in several species should be provided by studies using radiologically tagged hormones (108–110) and sensitive assay methods Some suggested areas of investigation follow.

1. How do hormones affect the segmental peristaltic and antiperistaltic muscular contractions of the ampulla and isthmus and the stricture of the ampullary-isthmic junction?

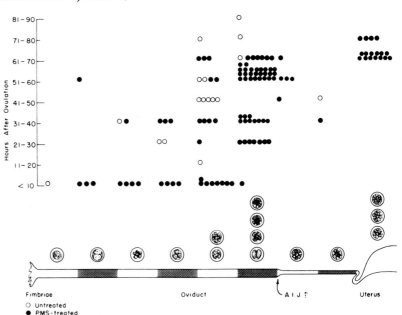

FIG. 24. *Top:* rate of egg transport in relation to time of ovulation. Number of eggs recovered from different segments in untreated (*open circles*) and pregnant mares' serum-treated (*closed circles*) cattle. *Bottom:* rate of cleavage in relation to location of oviducal segments. *A.I.J.*, hypothetical ampullary-isthmic junction. [From Hafez et al. (84).]

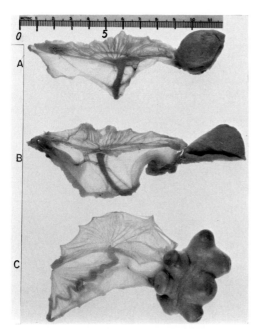

FIG. 25. Fimbriae and ovary from normally ovulating (*A* and *B*) and superovulating (*C*) cows. Note the small size of the fimbriae in relation to the ovary of superovulated cows; this causes loss of eggs and poor recovery rate. [From Hafez (83).]

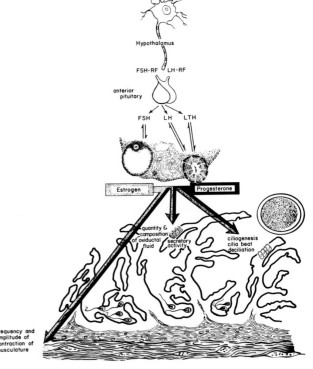

FIG. 26. Influence of hormonal factors on the structure and function of the mammalian oviduct. *FSH-RF* and *LH-RF*, releasing factors; *FSH, LH,* and *LTH,* gonadotrophins.

2. How do hormones affect the biochemical and biophysical characteristics of the oviducal ducts?

3. What is the role of mucosal folds in gamete transport? To what extent are the functions of mucosal folds regulated by the contraction of the muscle fibers within them?

4. Are the ciliated cells especially arranged on the base or tip of the folds? How does this arrangement affect sperm transport against the direction of cilia beat? Is the rate of cilia beat regulated by endocrine factors?

5. What hormonal and pharmacological factors govern the opening of the ampullary-isthmic junction? With a better understanding of such mechanisms it should be possible to cause the junction to open prematurely and thus to accelerate the transport of the fertilized egg to the uterus as a means of contraception.

REFERENCES

1. ADAMS, C. E., AND M. C. CHANG. Capacitation of rabbit spermatozoa in the Fallopian tube and in the uterus. *J. Exptl. Zool.* 151: 159–165, 1962.
2. AINSWORTH, L., AND K. J. RYAN. Steroid hormone transformations by endocrine organs from pregnant mammals. I. Estrogen biosynthesis by mammalian placental preparations *in vitro*. *Endocrinology* 79: 875–883, 1966.
3. ALDEN, R. H. The oviduct and egg transport in the albino rat. *Anat. Record* 34: 137–170, 1942.
4. ANAPOLSKY, D. Cyclic changes in the size of muscle fibers of the Fallopian tube of the sow. *Am. J. Anat.* 40: 459–469, 1928.
5. ANDREWS, M. C. Epithelial changes in the puerperal Fallopian tube. *Am. J. Obstet. Gynecol.* 62: 28–37, 1951.
6. ARTNER, J., AND H. TULZER. Über vegetativ bedingte Änderungen der Tubenmotilität. *Arch. Gynaekol.* 188: 364–375, 1957.
7. AUGUSTIN, E., AND R. HUWALD. Vorkommen und Aktivität der alkalischen Phosphatase im Eileiter des Weibes. *Arch. Gynaekol.* 187: 406–425, 1956.
8. AUGUSTIN, E., AND A. MOSER. Vorkommen und Aktivität von alkalischer Phosphatase in Eileiter der Ratte und in unbefruchteten Eiern während der Tubenwanderung. *Arch. Gynaekol.* 185: 759–780, 1955.
9. AUSTIN, C. R. Fertilization and transport of gametes in the pseudopregnant rabbit. *J. Endocrinol.* 6: 63–70, 1949.
10. AUSTIN, C. R. Observations on the penetration of the sperm into the mammalian egg. *Australian J. Sci. Res., Ser. B* 4: 581–596, 1951.
11. AUSTIN, C. R. Fate of spermatozoa in the uterus of the mouse and rat. *J. Endocrinol.* 14: 335–342, 1957.
12. AUSTIN, C. R. Fate of spermatozoa in the female genital tract. *J. Reprod. Fertility* 1: 151–156, 1960.
13. BACSICH, P., AND W. J. HAMILTON. Some observations on vitally stained rabbit ova with special reference to their albuminous coat. *J. Embryol. Exptl. Morphol.* 2: 81–86, 1954.
14. BEDFORD, J. M. Effect of environment on phagocytosis of rabbit spermatozoa. *J. Reprod. Fertility* 9: 249–256, 1965.
15. BELLVE, A. R., AND M. F. MCDONALD. Directional flow of Fallopian tube secretion in the Romney ewe. *J. Reprod. Fertility* 15: 357–364, 1968.
16. BENIRSCHKE, K. Pathologic processes of the oviduct. In: *The Mammalian Oviduct*, edited by E. S. E. Hafez and R. J. Blandau. Chicago: Univ. of Chicago Press, 1969, chapt. 11, p. 271–310.
17. BERTALANFFY, F. D., AND C. LAU. Mitotic rates, renewal times, and cytodynamics of the female genital tract epithelia in the rat. *Acta Anat.* 54: 39–81, 1963.
18. BIGGERS, J. In: *Preimplantation Stages of Pregnancy*, edited by G. E. W. Wolstenholme and M. O'Connor. Boston: Little, Brown, 1965, p. 397.
19. BISHOP, D. W. Active secretion in the rabbit oviduct. *Am. J. Physiol.* 187: 347–352, 1956.
20. BISHOP, D. W. Oxygen concentrations in the rabbit genital tract. *Proc. Intern. Congr. Animal Reprod., 3rd, Cambridge, 1956*, p. 53–55.
21. BJÖRK, L. Cineradiographic studies on the Fallopian tube in rabbits. *Acta Radiol. Suppl.* 176: 1–54, 1959.
22. BJÖRKMAN, N., AND B. FREDRICSSON. The bovine oviduct epithelium and its secretory process as studied with the electron microscope and histochemical tests. *Z. Zellforsch. Mikroskop. Anat.* 55: 500–513, 1961.
23. BLACK, D. L., AND S. A. ASDELL. Transport through the rabbit oviduct. *Am. J. Physiol.* 192: 63–68, 1958.
24. BLACK, D. L., AND S. A. ASDELL. Mechanism controlling entry of ova into rabbit uterus. *Am. J. Physiol.* 197: 1275–1278, 1959.
25. BLACK, D. L., L. V. CROWLEY, R. T. DUBY, AND C. H. SPILMAN. Oviduct secretion in the ewe and the effect of oviduct fluid on oxygen uptake by ram spermatozoa *in vitro*. *J. Reprod. Fertility* 15: 127–130, 1968.
26. BLANDAU, R. J. Gamete transport—comparative aspects. In: *The Mammalian Oviduct*, edited by E. S. E. Hafez and R. J. Blandau. Chicago: Univ. of Chicago Press, 1969, chapt. 5, p. 129–163.
27. BLOCH, E. Hormone production by the foetal adrenocortical gland. *Proc. Intern. Congr. Endocrinol., 2nd, London* 1: 785, 1964.
28. BLOCH, E., AND E. NEWMAN. Comparative placental steroid synthesis. I. Conversion of (7-³H)-dehydroepiandrosterone to (³H)-androst-4-ene-3,17-dione. *Endocrinology* 79: 524–530. 1966.
29. BODEMER, C. W. History of the mammalian oviduct. In: *The Mammalian Oviduct*, edited by E. S. E. Hafez and R. J. Blandau. Chicago: Univ. of Chicago Press, 1969, p. 3–26.
30. BOLING, J. L. Endocrinology of oviductal musculature. In: *The Mammalian Oviduct*, edited by E. S. E. Hafez and R. J. Blandau. Chicago: Univ. of Chicago Press, 1969, chapt. 6, p. 164–181.
31. BORELL, U., O. NILSSON, J. WERSALL, AND A. WESTMAN. Electron-microscope studies of the epithelium of the rabbit Fallopian tube under different hormonal influences. *Acta Obstet. Gynecol. Scand.* 35: 36–41, 1956.
32. BORELL, U., O. NILSSON, AND A. WESTMAN. Ciliary activity in the rabbit Fallopian tubes during oestrus and after copulation. *Acta Obstet. Gynecol. Scand.* 36: 22–28, 1957.
33. BRADEN, A. W. H. Properties of the membranes of rat and rabbit eggs. *Australian J. Sci. Res., Ser. B* 5: 460–471, 1952.
34. BRENNER, R. M. The biology of oviductal cilia. In: *The Mammalian Oviduct*, edited by E. S. E. Hafez and R. J. Blandau. Chicago: Univ. of Chicago Press, 1969, chapt. 8, p. 203–229.
35. BRODY, S. Hormonal influence on the glycogen content of the human myometrium. *Acta Endocrinol.* 27: 377–384, 1958.
36. BRONZETTI, P., E. MAZZA, G. MILIO, AND P. MOTTA. Su alcuni aspetti dell'attivita fosfatasica alcalina e della P. A. S.—reattivita dell'epitelio della tuba uterina di Mus Rattus albinus. *Biol. Latina* 16: 385–402, 1963.
37. BROWER, L., AND E. ANDERSON. Cytological events associated with the secretory process in the rabbit oviduct. *Biol. Reprod.* 1: 130–148, 1969.
38. BRUNDIN, J. A functional block in the isthmus of the rabbit Fallopian tube. *Acta Physiol. Scand.* 60: 295–296, 1964.
39. BRUNDIN, J. An occlusive mechanism in the Fallopian tube of the rabbit. *Acta Physiol. Scand.* 61: 219–227, 1964.
40. BRUNDIN, J. Distribution and function of adrenergic nerves in the rabbit Fallopian tube. *Acta Physiol. Scand. Suppl.* 259: 1–59, 1965.
41. BRUNDIN, J. Pharmacology of the oviduct. In: *The Mammalian Oviduct*, edited by E. S. E. Hafez and R. J. Blandau. Chicago: Univ. of Chicago Press, 1969, chapt. 10, p. 251–269.
42. BRUNDIN, J., AND C. WIRSEN. Adrenergic nerve terminals in the human Fallopian tube by fluorescence microscopy. *Acta Physiol. Scand.* 61: 505–506, 1964.
43. BURDICK, H. O., R. WHITNEY, AND G. PINCUS. The fate of mouse ova tube-locked by injections of oestrogenic substances. *Anat. Record* 67: 513–519, 1937.
44. BURNS, R. K. Hormones and experimental modification of sex in the opossum. *Biol. Symp.* 9: 125–146, 1942.
45. BURNS, R. K. Hormones and the growth of the parts of the urogenital apparatus in mammalian embryos. *Cold Spring Harbor Symp. Quant. Biol.* 10: 27–33, 1942.
46. BURNS, R. K. Role of hormones in the differentiation of sex. In: *Sex and Internal Secretions* (3rd ed.), edited by W. C. Young. Baltimore: Williams & Wilkins, 1961, vol. 1, chapt. 2, p. 76–158.
47. CHANG, M. C. The fertilizing capacity of spermatozoa deposited into the Fallopian tubes. *Nature* 168: 697–698, 1951.
48. CHANG, M. C. Effects of oral administration of medroxylprogesterone acetate and ethinyl estradiol on the transportation and development of rabbit eggs. *Endocrinology* 79: 939–948, 1966.

49. CHANG, M. C., AND R. YANAGIMACHI. Fertilization of ferret ova by deposition of epididymal sperm into the ovarian capsule, with special reference to the fertilizable life of ova and capacitation of sperm. *J. Exptl. Zool.* 154: 175–187, 1963.

50. CLEWE, T. H., AND L. MASTROIANNI, JR. A method for continuous volumetric collection of oviduct secretions. *J. Reprod. Fertility* 1: 146–150, 1960.

51. CLYMAN, M. J. Electron microscopy of the human Fallopian tube. *Fertility Sterility* 17: 281–301, 1966.

52. DAVIDS, A. M. Fallopian tubal motility in relation to the menstrual cycle. *Am. J. Obstet. Gynecol.* 56: 655–663, 1948.

53. DAVIDS, A. M., AND M. B. BENDER. Effects of adrenaline on tubal contractions of the rabbit in relation to sex hormones (study *in vivo* by Rubin method). *Am. J. Physiol.* 129: 259–263, 1940.

54. DEANE, H. W. Histochemical observations on the ovary and oviduct of the albino rat during the estrous cycle. *Am. J. Anat.* 91: 363–393, 1952.

55. DOBROWOLSKI, W., AND E. S. E. HAFEZ. Transport and distribution of spermatozoa in pseudopregnant rabbits. *Am. J. Vet. Res.* 31: 2243–2246, 1970.

56. EGLI, G. E., AND M. NEWTON. The transport of carbon particles in the human female reproductive tract. *Fertility Sterility* 12: 151–155, 1961.

57. EL-BANNA, A. A., AND E. S. E. HAFEZ. Sperm transport and distribution in rabbit and cattle female tract. *Fertility Sterility* 21: 534–540, 1970.

58. EL-BANNA, A. A., AND E. S. E. HAFEZ. Profile analysis of the oviductal wall in rabbits and cattle. *Anat. Record* 166: 469–478, 1970.

59. ELIASSON, R. Prostaglandin—properties, actions and significance. *Biochem. Pharmacol.* 12: 405–412, 1963.

60. FLERKÓ, B. Die Epithelien des Eileiters und ihre hormonalen Reaktionen. *Z. Mikroskop. Anat. Forsch.* 61: 99–118, 1954.

61. FORAKER, A. G., AND J. Z. CRESPO. Oxidative and glycogen-synthesizing enzymes in the uterine tube. *Obstet. Gynecol.* 19: 64–68, 1962.

62. FORAKER, A. G., S. W. DENHAM, AND P. A. CELL. Dehydrogenase activity. II. In the Fallopian tube. *Obstet. Gynecol.* 2: 500–507, 1953.

63. FREDRICSSON, B. Studies on the morphology and histochemistry of the Fallopian tube epithelium. *Acta Anat.* 38, Suppl. 37: 1–23, 1959.

64. FREDRICSSON, B. Proliferation of rabbit oviduct epithelium after estrogenic stimulation with reference to the relationship between ciliated and secretory cells. *Acta Morphol. Neerl. Scand.* 2: 193–202, 1959.

65. FREDRICSSON, B. Histochemical observations on the epithelium of human Fallopian tubes. *Acta Obstet. Gynecol. Scand.* 38: 109–134, 1959.

66. FREDRICSSON, B. Histochemistry of the oviduct. In: *The Mammalian Oviduct*, edited by E. S. E. Hafez and R. J. Blandau. Chicago: Univ. of Chicago Press, 1969, chapt. 12, p. 311–332.

67. FRIZ, M. Tierexperimentelle Untersuchungen zur Frage der Tubensekretion. *Z. Geburtshilfe Gynaekol.* 153: 285–294, 1959.

68. GEIST, S. H., U. J. SALMON, AND M. MINTZ. The effect of estrogenic hormone upon the contractility of the Fallopian tubes. *Am. J. Obstet. Gynecol.* 36: 67–77, 1938.

69. GLASS, L. E. Transfer of native and foreign serum antigens to oviductal mouse eggs. *Am. Zoologist* 3: 135–156, 1963.

70. GLASS, L. E., AND T. R. McCLURE. Postnatal development of the mouse oviduct: transfer of serum antigens to the tubal epithelium. In: *Preimplantation Stages of Pregnancy*, edited by G. E. W. Wolstenholme. Boston: Little, Brown, 1965, p. 294.

71. GRAUMANN, W. Ergebnisse der Polysaccharidhistochemie. In: *Handbuch der Histochemie*, edited by W. Graumann and K. Neumann. Stuttgart: Fischer, 1964, vol. 2, part 2, p. 403.

72. GREENWALD, G. S. Interruption of pregnancy in the rabbit by the administration of estrogen. *J. Exptl. Zool.* 135: 461–482, 1957.

73. GREENWALD, G. S. Endocrine regulation of the secretion of

74. GREENWALD, G. S. A study of the transport of ova through the rabbit oviduct. *Fertility Sterility* 12: 80–95, 1961.

75. GREENWALD, G. S. The role of the mucin layer in development of the rabbit blastocyst. *Anat. Record* 142: 407–415, 1962.

76. GREENWALD, G. S. *In vivo* recording of intraluminal pressure changes in the rabbit oviduct. *Fertility Sterility* 14: 666–674, 1963.

77. GREENWALD, G. S. Species differences in egg transport in response to exogenous estrogen. *Anat. Record* 157: 163–172, 1967.

78. GREENWALD, G. S. Endocrinology of oviductal secretions. In: *The Mammalian Oviduct*, edited by E. S. E. Hafez and R. J. Blandau. Chicago: Univ. of Chicago Press, 1969, chapt. 7, p. 183–202.

79. GREGOIRE, A. T., D. GONGSAKDI, AND A. E. RAKOFF. The presence of inositol in genital tract secretions of the female rabbit. *Fertility Sterility* 13: 432–435, 1962.

80. HADEK, R. The secretory process in the sheep's oviduct. *Anat. Record* 121: 187–205, 1955.

81. HAFEZ, E. S. E. Pressure fluctuations during uterotubal kymographic insufflation in pregnant rabbits. *Fertility Sterility* 13: 426–431, 1962.

82. HAFEZ, E. S. E. Reproductive failure in domestic mammals. In: *Comparative Aspects of Reproductive Failure*. New York: Springer, 1967, p. 44–95.

83. HAFEZ, E. S. E. Superovulation and preservation of mammalian eggs. *Acta Endocrinol.* 60, Suppl. 140: 44, 1969.

84. HAFEZ, E. S. E., A. A. EL-BANNA, AND J. A. LINEWEAVER. Gamete transport in beef cattle. *Congr. Intern. Reprod. Animal Insemin. Artif.*, VIᵉ, Paris 1 E: 707–709, 1968.

85. HAMNER, C. E., AND S. B. FOX. Biochemistry of oviductal secretions. In: *The Mammalian Oviduct*, edited by E. S. E. Hafez and R. J. Blandau. Chicago: Univ. of Chicago Press, 1969, chapt. 13, p. 333–372.

86. HAMNER, C. E., J. P. JONES, AND S. B. FOX. Effect of estrogen and progesterone on respiration and glycolysis of the rabbit oviduct. *Fertility Sterility* 20: 143–148, 1969.

87. HAMNER, C. E., AND N. J. SOJKA. Capacitation of rabbit spermatozoa: species specificity and organ specificity. *Proc. Soc. Exptl. Biol. Med.* 124: 689–691, 1967.

88. HAMNER, C. E., AND W. L. WILLIAMS. Effect of the female reproductive tract on sperm metabolism in the rabbit and fowl. *J. Reprod. Fertility* 5: 143–150, 1963.

89. HAMNER, C. E., AND W. L. WILLIAMS. Identification of sperm-stimulating factor of rabbit oviductal fluid. *Proc. Soc. Exptl. Biol. Med.* 117: 240–243, 1964.

90. HARPER, M. J. K. The mechanisms involved in the movement of newly ovulated eggs through the ampulla of the rabbit Fallopian tube. *J. Reprod. Fertility* 2: 522–524, 1961.

91. HARPER, M. J. K. Egg movement through the ampullar region of the Fallopian tube of the rabbit. *Proc. Intern. Congr. Animal Reprod.*, 4th, The Hague, 1961, p. 375–381.

92. HARPER, M. J. K. The effects of constant doses of oestrogen and progesterone on the transport of artificial eggs through the reproductive tract of ovariectomized rabbits. *J. Endocrinol.* 30: 1–19, 1964.

93. HARPER, M. J. K. Transport of eggs in cumulus through the ampulla of the rabbit oviduct in relation to day of pregnancy. *Endocrinology* 77: 114–123, 1965.

94. HARPER, M. J. K. The effects of decreasing doses of oestrogen and increasing doses of progesterone on the transport of artificial eggs through the reproductive tract of ovariectomized rabbits. *J. Endocrinol.* 31: 217–226, 1965.

95. HASHIMOTO, M., T. SHIMOYAMA, M. KOSAKA, A. KOMORI, T. HIRASAWA, Y. YOKOYAMA, N. KAWASE, AND T. NAKAMURA. Electron microscopic studies on the epithelial cells of the human Fallopian tube (Report III). *J. Japan. Obstet. Gynecol. Soc.* 11: 92–100, 1964.

96. HASHIMOTO, M., T. SHIMOYAMA, Y. MORI, A. KOMORI, M.

KOSAKA, AND K. AKASHI. Electronmicroscopic observations on the secretory process in the Fallopian tube of the rabbit (Report II). *J. Japan. Obstet. Gynecol. Soc.* 6: 384–391, 1959.

97. HASHIMOTO, M., T. SHIMOYAMA, Y. MORI, A. KOMORI, H. TOMITA, AND K. AKASHI. Electronmicroscopic observations on the secretory process in the Fallopian tube of the rabbit (Report I). *J. Japan. Obstet. Gynecol. Soc.* 6: 235–243, 1959.

98. HAWK, H. Inhibition of ovum fertilization in the ewe by intra-uterine plastic spirals. *J. Reprod. Fertility* 10: 267–269, 1965.

99. HAYS, R. L., AND N. L. VANDEMARK. Effects of oxytocin and epinephrine on uterine motility in the bovine. *Am. J. Physiol.* 172: 557–560, 1953.

100. HEAP, R. B. Some chemical constituents of uterine washings: a method of analysis with results from various species. *J. Endocrinol.* 24: 367–378, 1962.

101. HELLSTROM, K. E., AND O. NILSSON. In vitro investigation of the ciliated and secretory cells in the rabbit Fallopian tube. *Exptl. Cell Res.* 12: 180–201, 1957.

102. HORSTMANN, E., AND H. STEGNER. H. Tube, Vagina, und aüssere weibliche Genitalorgane. In: *Handbuch der Mikroskopischen Anatomie des Menschen.* Berlin: Springer, 1966, vol. 7/4, p. 35–85.

103. HORTON, E. W., I. H. M. MAIN, AND C. J. THOMPSON. The action of intravaginal prostaglandin on the female reproductive tract. *J. Physiol., London* 168: 54–55P, 1963.

104. HORTON, E. W., I. H. M. MAIN, AND C. J. THOMPSON. Effects of prostaglandins on the oviduct, studied in rabbits and ewes. *J. Physiol., London* 180: 514–528, 1965.

105. HOWE, G. R. Leucocytic response to spermatozoa in ligated segments of the rabbit vagina, uterus and oviduct. *J. Reprod. Fertility* 13: 563–566, 1967.

106. ICHIJO, M. Studies on the motile function of the Fallopian tube. Report I. Analytic studies on the motile function of the Fallopian tube. *Tohoku J. Exptl. Med.* 72: 211–218, 1960.

107. JAINUDEEN, M. R., AND E. S. E. HAFEZ. Attempts to induce bovine freemartinism experimentally. *J. Reprod. Fertility* 10: 281–283, 1965.

108. JENSEN, E. V., AND H. I. JACOBSON. Fate of steroid estrogens in target tissues. In: *Biological Activities in Relation to Cancer,* edited by V. Pincus. New York: Acad. Press, 1960.

109. JENSEN, E. V., AND H. I. JACOBSON. Basic guides to the mechanism of estrogen action. *Recent Progr. Hormone Res.* 18: 387–408, 1962.

110. JENSEN, E. V., H. I. JACOBSON, J. W. FLESHER, N. N. SAHA, G. N. GUPTA, S. SMITH, V. COLUCCI, D. SHIPLACOFF, H. G. NEUMANN, E. R. DE SOMBRE, AND P. W. JUNGBLUT. Estrogen receptors in target tissue. In: *Steroid Dynamics,* edited by E. G. Pincus et al. New York: Acad. Press, 1966.

111. JOEL, C. A. Zur Histologie und Histochemie der menschlichen Eileiter während Zyklus und Schwangerschaft. *Mschr. Geburtsh. Gynaekol.* 110: 252–265, 1940.

112. JOEL, K. The glycogen content of the Fallopian tubes during the menstrual cycle and during pregnancy. *J. Obstet. Gynaecol. Brit. Empire* 46: 721–730, 1939.

113. JOST, A., M. CHODKIEWICZ, AND P. MAULEON. Intersexualité du foetus de veau produite par des androgènes: comparison entre l'hormone foetale responsable du free-marinisme et l'hormone testiculaire adulte. *Compt. Rend. Acad. Sci.* 256: 274–276, 1963.

114. KELLY, W. A., AND J. H. MARSTON. Contraceptive action of intrauterine devices in the Rhesus monkey. *Nature* 214: 735–737, 1967.

115. KOESTER, H. Tierexperimentelle Untersuchungen zur Frage der Tubensekretion. *Beitr. Fertility Sterility* IV (Suppl. *Z. Geburtshilfe. Gynaekol.*) 162: 63, 1964.

116. LEHTO, L. Cytology of the human Fallopian tube: observations on the epithelial cells of the human Fallopian tube during foetal and menstrual life and on tubal cancer. *Acta Obstet. Gynecol. Scand. Suppl.* 4: 3–95, 1963.

117. LEONARD, S. L. The reduction of uterine sperm and uterine

fluid on fertilization of rat ova. *Anat. Record* 106: 607–615, 1950.

118. LEVY, H., H. W. DEANE, AND B. L. RUBIN. Visualization of steroid-3β-ol-dehydrogenase activity in tissues of intact and hypophysectomized rats. *Endocrinology* 65: 932–942, 1959.

119. LISA, J. R., J. D. GIOIA, AND I. C. RUBIN. Observations on the interstitial portion of the Fallopian tube. *Surg. Gynecol. Obstet.* 99: 159–169, 1954.

120. MARCUS, S. L. Protein components of oviduct fluid in the primate. *Surg. Forum* 15: 381–383, 1964.

121. MARGULIES, L. C. *Intrauterine Contraceptive Devices.* New York: Excerpta Medica Foundation, 1962, p. 61.

122. MARGULIES, L. C. Intrauterine contraception—a new approach. *Obstet. Gynecol.* 24: 515–520, 1964.

123. MASTROIANNI, L., AND C. HONGSANAND. Mechanism of action of the intrauterine contraceptive device in the primate. I. Tubal transport of ova and distribution of spermatozoa. In: *Intrauterine Contraception. Proceedings of the Second International Conference.* New York: Population Council, 1964, p. 194.

124. MASTROIANNI, L., AND C. ROSSEAU. Influence of the intrauterine coil on ovum transport and sperm distribution in the monkey. *Am. J. Obstet. Gynecol.* 93: 416–420, 1965.

125. MASTROIANNI, L., JR., S. SUZUKI, Y. MONABE, AND F. WATSON. Further observations on the influence of the intrauterine device on ovum and sperm distribution in the monkey. *Am. J. Obstet. Gynecol.* 99: 649–661, 1967.

126. MASTROIANNI, L., W. W. WINTERNITZ, AND N. P. LOWI. The in vitro metabolism of the human endosalpinx. *Fertility Sterility* 9: 500–509, 1958.

127. MATTNER, P. E. Spermatozoa in the genital tract of the ewe. II. Distribution after coitus. *Australian J. Biol. Sci.* 16: 688–694, 1963.

128. MATTNER, P. E. Spermatozoa in the genital tract of the ewe. III. Role of spermatozoan motility and of uterine contractions in transport of spermatozoa. *Australian J. Biol. Sci.* 16: 877–884, 1963.

129. MATTNER, P. E. Capacitation of ram spermatozoa and penetration of the ovine egg. *Nature* 199: 772–773, 1963.

130. MOMBAERTS, J. Le sinus uro-génital et les glandes annexes du Hérisson (*Erinaceus europaeus* L.). *Arch. Biol.* 55: 393–554, 1944.

131. MROUEH, A. Oxytocin and sperm transport in rabbits. *Obstet Gynecol.* 29: 671–673, 1967.

132. NALBANDOV, A. V. Role of sex hormones in the secretory function of the oviduct. In: *Comparative Endocrinology,* edited by A. Gorbman. New York: Wiley, 1959, chapt. 32.

133. NES, N. Diploid-triploid chimerism in a true hermaphrodite mink (*Mustela vison*). *Hereditas* 56: 159–170, 1966.

134. NILSSON, O., AND S. REINIUS. Light and electron microscopic structure of the oviduct. In: *The Mammalian Oviduct,* edited by E. S. E. Hafez and R. J. Blandau. Chicago: Univ. of Chicago Press, 1969, chapt. 3, p. 57–84.

135. NILSSON, O., AND U. RUTBERG. Ultrastructure of secretory granules in post-ovulatory rabbit oviduct. *Exptl. Cell Res.* 21: 622–625, 1960.

136. NOYES, R. W. The capacitation of spermatozoa. *Obstet. Gynecol. Surv.* 14: 785–797, 1959.

137. NOYES, R. W., C. E. ADAMS, AND A. WALTON. The transport of ova in relation to the dosage of oestrogen in ovariectomized rabbits. *J. Endocrinol.* 18: 108–117, 1959.

138. NOYES, R. W., T. H. CLEWE, W. A. BONNEY, S. B. BURRUS, V. J. DE FEO, AND L. L. MORGENSTERN. Searches for ova in the human uterus and tubes. I. Review, clinical methodology and summary of findings. *Am. J. Obstet. Gynecol.* 96: 157–167, 1966.

138a. NUCK, A. 1722. [Cited in Bodemer (29).]

139. OLDS, D., AND N. L. VANDEMARK. Composition of luminal fluids in bovine female genitalia. *Fertility Sterility* 8: 345–354, 1957.

140. OLDS, D., AND N. L. VANDEMARK. Luminal fluids of bovine female genitalia. *J. Am. Vet. Med. Assoc.* 131: 555–556, 1957.

141. ORTIZ, E., J. J. P. ZAAIJER, AND D. PRICE. Organ culture studies of hormone secretion in endocrine glands of fetal guinea pigs. IV. Androgens from fetal adrenals and ovaries and their influence on sex differentiation. *Koninkl. Ned. Akad. Wetenschap., Proc. Ser. C* 70: 475–488, 1967.

142. OWMAN, C. H., E. ROSENGREN, AND N.-O. SJÖBERG. Adrenergic innervation of the human female reproductive organs: a histochemical and chemical investigation. *Obstet. Gynecol.* 30: 763–773, 1967.

143. PRICE, D., E. ORTIZ, AND J. J. P. ZAAIJER. Organ culture studies of hormone secretion in endocrine glands of fetal guinea pigs. III. The relation of testicular hormone to sex differentiation of the reproductive ducts. *Anat. Record* 157: 27–41, 1967.

144. PRICE, D., J. J. P. ZAAIJER, AND E. ORTIZ. Prenatal development of the oviduct *in vivo* and *in vitro*. In: *The Mammalian Oviduct*, edited by E. S. E. Hafez and R. J. Blandau. Chicago: Univ. of Chicago Press, 1969, chapt. 1, p. 29–46.

145. QUINLIVAN, T. D., AND T. J. ROBINSON. Numbers of spermatozoa in the genital tract after artificial insemination of progestagen-treated ewes. *J. Reprod. Fertility* 19: 73–86, 1969.

146. RAJAKOSKI, E., AND E. S. E. HAFEZ. Derivatives of cortical cords in adult freemartin gonads of bovine quintuplets. *Anat. Record* 147: 457–468, 1963.

147. RAYNAUD, A. Modification expérimentale de la différenciation sexuelle des embryons de souris, par action des hormones androgènes et oestrogènes. *Actualités Sci. Ind.*, Monographs 925, 926, 1942.

148. REINIUS, S. *Morphology of Oviduct, Gametes and Zygotes as a Basis of Oviductal Function in the Mouse* (Ph. D. thesis). Sweden: Univ. of Uppsala, 1969.

149. RIGBY, J. P. The persistence of spermatozoa at the uterotubal junction of the sow. *J. Reprod. Fertility* 11: 153–155, 1966.

150. ROBBOY, S. J., AND R. H. KAHN. Electrophoretic separation of hydrolytic enzymes of the female rat reproductive tract. *Endocrinology* 75: 97–103, 1964.

151. ROSENBLUM, I., AND A. A. STEIN. Autonomic responses of the circular muscles of the isolated human fallopian tube. *Am. J. Physiol.* 210: 1127–1129, 1966.

152. RUBIN, I. C. The influence of hormonal activity of the ovaries upon the character of tubal contractions as determined by uterine insufflation. *Am. J. Obstet. Gynecol.* 37: 394–404, 1939.

153. RUBIN, I. C. *Uterotubal Insufflation.* St. Louis, Mo.: Mosby, 1947.

154. RUBIN, I. C., AND A. M. DAVIDS. Pharmacodynamic effects of testosterone propionate on tubal contractions (oviduct of rabbit) determined by CO_2 insufflation. *Endocrinology* 26: 523–525, 1940.

155. RUMERY, R. E. Fetal mouse oviducts in tissue and organ cultures. *Fertility Sterility* 20: 149–162, 1969.

156. RUMERY, R. E. The fetal mouse oviduct in organ and tissue culture. In: *The Mammalian Oviduct*, edited by E. S. E. Hafez and R. J. Blandau. Chicago: Univ. of Chicago Press, 1969, chapt. 19, p. 445–458.

157. SANDBERG, F., A. INGELMAN-SUNDBERG, L. LINDGREN, AND G. RYDEN. *In vitro* studies of the motility of the human fallopian tube. I. The effect of acetylcholine, adrenaline, nor-adrenaline and oxytocin on the spontaneous motility. *Acta Obstet. Gynecol. Scand.* 39: 506–515, 1960.

158. SANDBERG, F., A. INGELMAN-SUNDBERG, AND G. RYDEN. The effect of prostaglandin E_1 on the human uterus and Fallopian tubes *in vitro. Acta Obstet. Gynecol. Scand.* 42: 269–278, 1963.

159. SHIMOYAMA, T. Electron microscopic studies of the epithelial cells of the mucosa membrane of the human Fallopian tube in the foetus, pregnancy and menopause. *J. Japan. Obstet. Gynecol. Soc.* 15: 1307–1314, 1963.

160. SOLOMON, S. Formation and metabolism of neutral steroids in the human placenta and fetus. *J. Clin. Endocrinol. Metab.* 26: 762–772, 1966.

161. STEGNER, H. E. Elektronenmikroskopische Untersuchungen über die Sekretionsmorphologie des menschlichen Tubenepithels. *Arch. Gynaekol.* 197: 351–363, 1962.

162. VALENTI, C. Harvesting and culture of epithelial cells from hollow organs of the female reproductive system. *Z. Zellforsch. Mikroskop. Anat.* 60: 850–859, 1963.

163. VELARDO, J. T., AND C. G. ROSA. Female genital system. In: *Handbuch der Histochemie*, edited by W. Graumann and K. Neumann. Stuttgart: Fischer, 1963, vol. 7, part 3, p. 45.

164. WEETH, H. J., AND H. A. HERMAN. A histological and histochemical study of the bovine oviducts, uterus and placenta. *Res. Bull. Mo. Agr. Exptl. Sta.* No. 501, 1950.

165. WESTMAN, A. A contribution to the question of the transit of the ovum from ovary to uterus in rabbits. *Acta Obstet. Gynecol. Scand. Suppl.* 3: 1–104, 1926.

166. WHITE, I. G., AND J. C. WALLACE. Breakdown of seminal glycerylphosphorylcholine by secretions of the female reproductive tract. *Nature* 189: 843–844, 1961.

167. WHITE, I. G., J. C. WALLACE, AND G. M. STONE. Studies of the glycerylphosphorylcholine diesterase activity of the female genital tract in the ewe, cow, sow and rat. *J. Reprod. Fertility* 5: 298, 1963.

168. WHITELAW, M. J. Tubal contractions in relation to the estrus cycle as determined by uterotubal insufflation. *Am. J. Obstet. Gynecol.* 25: 475, 1933.

169. WHITNEY, R., AND H. O. BURDICK. Tube-locking of ova by oestrogenic substances. *Endocrinology* 20: 643–647, 1936.

170. WHITTEN, W. K. Culture of tubal ova. *Nature* 79: 1081–1082, 1957.

171. WILLIER, B. H. The embryonic development of sex. In: *Sex and Internal Secretions* (2nd ed.), edited by E. Allen, E. A. Doisy, and C. H. Dunforth. Baltimore: Williams & Wilkins, 1939, chapt. 3.

172. WISLOCKI, G. B. On the female reproductive tract of the gorilla with a comparison of that of other primates. *Contrib. Embryol. Carnegie Inst. Wash.* 23: 163–204, 1932.

173. WOODRUFF, J. D., AND C. J. PAUERSTEIN. *The Fallopian Tube.* Baltimore: Williams & Wilkins, 1969.

174. YAMASHITA, T., A. A. EL-BANNA, AND E. S. E. HAFEZ. Histochemical characteristics of cervical epithelia in rabbits and cattle. *Acta Histochem.* 39: 195–205, 1971.

175. YANAGIMACHI, R., AND M. C. CHANG. Sperm ascent through the oviduct of the hamster and rabbit in relation to the time of ovulation. *J. Reprod. Fertility* 6: 413–420, 1963.

176. ZACCHARIAE, F. Autoradiographic (S^{35}) and histochemical studies of sulphomucopolysaccharides in the rabbit uterus, oviducts and vagina. *Acta Endocrinol.* 29: 118–134, 1958.

CHAPTER 36

Endocrine control of ciliogenesis
in the primate oviduct

ROBERT M. BRENNER
RICHARD G. W. ANDERSON

Departments of Electron Microscopy and Reproductive Biology,
Oregon Regional Primate Research Center, Beaverton, Oregon

CHAPTER CONTENTS

THE EPITHELIUM of the primate oviduct, particularly that of the rhesus monkey, is dramatically dependent on estrogens to maintain a normal state of differentiation. The two major cell types, ciliated and secretory, which atrophy and dedifferentiate completely after ovariectomy, are restored by estrogen treatment. This response is most dramatic in the fimbriated extremity of the oviduct. This region is so sensitive to changes in hormone levels that, during the late luteal phase of a normal menstrual cycle, all the ciliated cells atrophy and shed their cilia; then, during the early follicular phase, the fimbriated region hypertrophies and regenerates ciliated cells.

Every ciliated cell possesses several hundred cilia, each with a complex ultrastructure, and attached to each cilium is one basal body of different but equally complex ultrastructure. The cyclic loss and redevelopment of these highly organized microtubular arrays is a remarkable feat of cellular engineering. Equally remarkable is the fact that estrogen-induced ciliogenesis in spayed (or juvenile) monkeys is identical with that in intact, cycling animals. The oviducts of fetal animals also show a burst of ciliogenesis late in gestation that is identical with that

Publication No. 514 of the Oregon Regional Primate Research Center. Supported by NIH Grants HD-20753 and RR 00163 and by Population Council Grant M66.110.

in adults. Thus spayed, juvenile, and fetal animals provide a rich source of experimental material for analyzing the ultrastructural details of ciliogenesis and the mechanisms that regulate this type of cellular differentiation.

In this chapter we review the details of the ciliogenic process and its endocrine control.

ENDOCRINE CONTROL OF CILIOGENESIS

Cyclic Changes During the Menstrual Cycle

Most of the reports on the primate oviduct (human and subhuman) concur that cilia are lost and regenerated cyclically (6, 14, 29, 33–35, 42, 43, 45–47). In early studies on the rhesus monkey (46, 47) and Java monkey (25), oviducal ciliated cells increase and decrease in number during the follicular and luteal phases, respectively. However, a disturbing number of more recent reports state that no cyclic changes occur in the ciliated cells of the human oviduct (15, 24, 36). Similar conflicting reports on cyclic changes in the oviducal cilia of other mammals have also been published. These discrepancies have been reviewed in detail elsewhere (9, 10).

Our own studies in the rhesus monkey show that the ciliated cells of the oviducal fimbriae completely shed and regenerate their cilia cyclically. However, in the ampullae the ciliated cells fluctuate only in height; most of the atrophied ciliated cells retain their cilia (8). These observations were based on the study of samples of the fimbriae and ampullae obtained at closely spaced intervals during the cycle from 35 mature rhesus monkeys. The ovaries were removed concurrently, and a serial-section analysis of follicular development was conducted (27).

On day 2 of the cycle (Figs. 1–6), numerous clear cells in various phases of ciliogenesis were present in the fimbriae. In many cells, the basal bodies were lined up at the cell margins, and some had sprouted tiny cilia. From menstrual days 3 through 9, the number of tall, mature ciliated cells increased. The ciliated cells remained tall

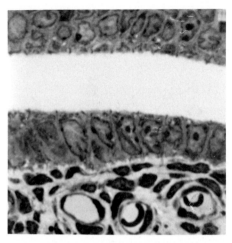

FIG. 1. Fimbriae on day 2 of menstrual cycle. Epithelium is atrophied and deciliated. × 1,200.

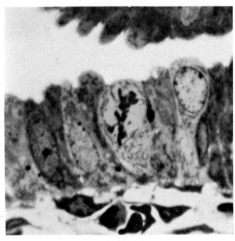

FIG. 2. Fimbriae on day 3 of menstrual cycle. Hypertrophy begins and mitotic activity prevails. × 1,200.

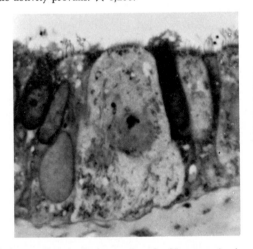

FIG. 3. Fimbriae on day 4 of menstrual cycle. Hypertrophy is maximal, and basal bodies develop. In the large clear cell, basal bodies lined up at the cell margin are shown. × 1,200.

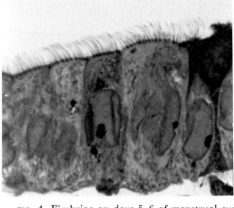

FIG. 4. Fimbriae on days 5–6 of menstrual cycle. Epithelium is now fully ciliated. × 1,200.

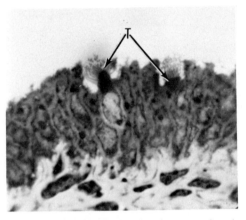

FIG. 5. Fimbriae on day 25 of menstrual cycle. The great majority of the ciliated cells shed their tips (*T*) by a pinching-off process. × 1,200.

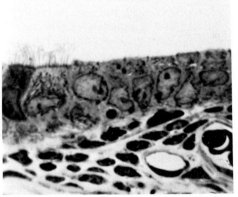

FIG. 6. Fimbriae on day 27 of menstrual cycle. Epithelium is maximally atrophied and deciliated. A few atrophied, ciliated cells persist. × 1,200.

and normal through day 18, when they began to diminish in height. Many of them became dense and shrunken; the distal third of other cells, including the entire ciliary apparatus, pinched off and was shed into the lumen, as occurs in apocrine secretion. This apocrine mechanism of deciliation has been observed in the oviducts of several species (6, 20, 23). On days 21 through 27, almost 95% of the epithelial cells were completely deciliated. Only a few atrophied ciliated cells remained, and the fimbriae resembled those from ovariectomized animals.

In the ampulla, on days 2 through 9, there were some ciliogenic cells, but not so many as in the fimbriae. The cells were tallest through the midportion of the cycle and began to shrink by day 18. Some ciliated cells became very dark and atrophied, and a number of them shed their ciliated tips, but the overall degree of ciliary loss was minimal compared with that in the fimbriae. On days 21–27, the ampullary epithelium was characteristically very low but fully ciliated.

In this study, two of the animals biopsied on days 23 and 27 had an anovulatory cycle. The ovaries had large follicles and no fresh corpora lutea, an indication that ovulation had not occurred. The fimbriae and ampullae of these two animals had fully ciliated epithelia resembling those of animals in midcycle. Presumably, the progesterone level in the blood of these two animals was abnormally low. All ovaries from the animals in which deciliation of the fimbria had occurred by days 21–27 showed normal corpora lutea. Development of corpora lutea and an increase in the progesterone level in the blood apparently are prerequisites for deciliation and atrophy. The cyclic renewal of cilia thus presumably reflects cyclic changes in estrogen-to-progestin ratios.

Ovariectomy and the Effects of Estrogen

THE RHESUS MONKEY. Allen (1, 2) was the first to show that estrogen is the stimulating agent responsible for restitution of the oviducal epithelium. He demonstrated that the oviducts of adult monkeys atrophy and deciliate after ovariectomy, that estrogen treatment stimulates reciliation, and that the cilia that regenerate are motile. We have confirmed and extended Allen's original observations.

In our original studies (9), 12 cycling female rhesus monkeys were bilaterally ovariectomized, and after 7 weeks the fimbriae were biopsied to determine whether the cilia had been lost. In all animals the epithelium had atrophied and deciliated (Fig. 7). Nine weeks later, the animals received a series of intramuscular injections of estradiol benzoate in sesame oil at a rate of 10 μg/day and were biopsied on days 1 through 6 and again on day 9 after the injections had begun. Two spayed control animals were injected with 1 cc sesame oil per day and biopsied on day 9 of treatment.

Motile cilia developed after 4–5 days of estrogen treatment; the ciliated cells hypertrophied and increased in number through day 9 (Fig. 8). The oviducts of the control animals remained atrophied and did not develop cilia.

The events of ciliogenesis were the same as in cycling oviducts (see section THE PROCESS OF CILIOGENESIS, in this chapter), and the rate of development was almost identical with that in the early follicular phase.

Furthermore we have determined that estrogen acts directly on the oviducal epithelium. Spayed monkeys were laparotomized, and on three consecutive days the fimbriated end of the left oviduct was soaked for 1 hr in a lactated Ringer's solution containing 1 μg estradiol per milliliter. Vascular connections were not disturbed. The right side was soaked in a control lactated Ringer's solution. On day 6 after the onset of treatment, both fimbriae were biopsied. Large numbers of ciliated cells were found only in the fimbriae exposed to estradiol.

Paradoxically we have not been able to demonstrate a direct estrogen effect on oviducal epithelium in vitro. Fragments of atrophied oviduct from spayed monkeys placed in an organ culture system (13) do not manufacture cilia, despite the presence of estradiol in the culture medium. However, if oviducts are prestimulated by estrogen in vivo for 3 or 4 days so that they are hypertrophied and have begun to make basal bodies and if frag-

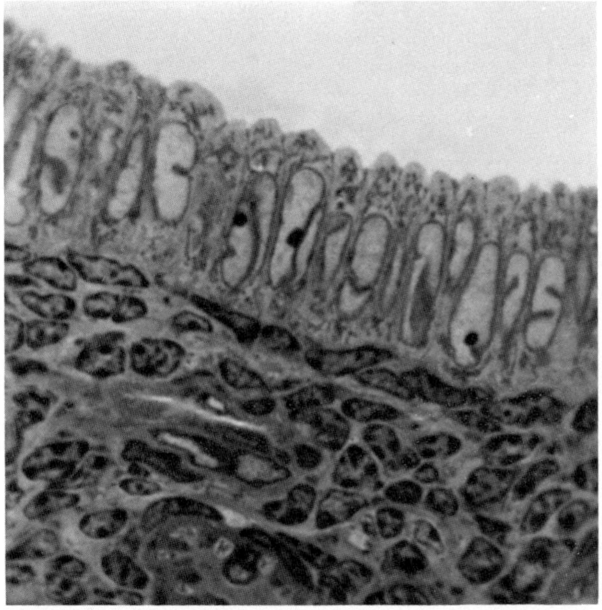

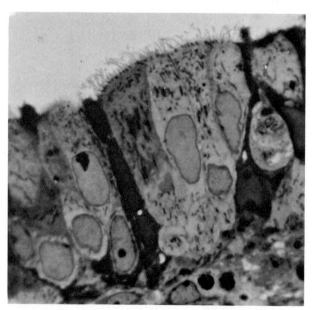

FIG. 7. Fimbriae 7 weeks after ovariectomy. Epithelium is atrophied and deciliated. Stroma is condensed, and stromal cell nuclei are hyperchromatic. × 1,200.

FIG. 8. Fimbriae from ovariectomized animal after 5 days of estrogen treatment (10 μg estradiol benzoate per day). Epithelium is hypertrophied and fully ciliated. × 1,200.

ments of such oviducts are placed in organ culture, they continue to differentiate and manufacture cilia in vitro. Such in vitro ciliation from preestrogenized oviducts occurs even in culture medium that lacks estradiol; however, the addition of estradiol helps to develop a larger crop of healthy, ciliated cells. We are currently studying the effects of different chemically defined culture media in an effort to determine the necessary conditions for a complete estrogen response.

Although a deficient estrogen supply results in the dedifferentiation of the oviduct, the cyclic loss of cilia during the menstrual cycle suggests that the normal endogenous stimulus to atrophy and deciliation is progesterone. Good & Moyer (22) have described an estrogen-progestin sequence that produces a normal secretory endometrium in spayed rhesus monkeys: estradiol-17β, 20–40 μg/day, days 1–22; and progesterone, 1–2 mg/day, days 11–22. We have treated rhesus monkeys with these dosages and sampled the oviduct on days 10 and 18 of the artificial cycle. On day 10 we found a fully hypertrophied, ciliated, and secretory oviducal epithelium; on day 18 we found an atrophied, almost fully deciliated, and still secretory epithelium. The degree of atrophy and deciliation was most pronounced in the fimbriae. These data support the hypothesis that progesterone antagonizes the cilia-maintaining effects of estradiol during the normal cycle. Either estrogen withdrawal, as after ovariectomy, or the antagonism of estradiol by progesterone induces the loss of cilia and dedifferentiation in the oviducal epithelium of the rhesus monkey. Exactly how progesterone interferes with estrogen action in the cell remains to be determined.

OTHER SPECIES. Support for the role of progesterone in atrophy and deciliation comes from a highly informative study on the behavior of oviducal cilia in women during the postpartum period (5), a time of minimal endogenous estrogen and progestin secretion. In postparturient women at the time of delivery, the oviducal epithelium is low (average height 16 μ) and becomes lower during the postpartum period (average height 10 μ), and the ciliated cells decrease in number. Women who receive stilbestrol alone, with administration starting on the day of delivery (5 mg/day for 5–9 days), show an intense proliferation of the ciliated epithelium. The cells reach 20–25 μ in height, compared with the average height of about 10 μ in untreated cases. On the other hand, women who receive stilbestrol with progesterone during the same period show an inhibition of the estrogen effect, and the ciliated epithelium resembles that at delivery. Treatment with stilbestrol or progesterone 5–10 days before delivery produces no stimulation of the ciliated epithelium.

Flerko (20) reported that 3–4 months after castration, hypophysectomy, stalk section, or hypothalamic lesioning, the oviducts of rabbits underwent a complete loss of cilia that was restored by estrogen treatment. However, other reports indicated that, although ovariectomy of rabbits caused oviducal atrophy, there was no dramatic loss of cilia (7). In the most recent study, Odor (28) found that 50% deciliation had occurred by 7 months after

ovariectomy. Estrogen treatment of these long-term spayed rabbits (estradiol benzoate, 10 μg/day for 10 days) caused a loss of cilia from the atrophied, persistent ciliated cells and then a subsequent regeneration of cilia.

The conflicting reports on the reactions of the rabbit oviduct need to be resolved. In addition, more information is needed on the effects of ovariectomy, estrogen replacement therapy, and progesterone on the oviducal cilia of such common laboratory rodents as rats, mice, guinea pigs, and hamsters. Flerko (20) stated that ciliated cells are regenerated cyclically in the oviducts of sheep, horse, pig, cow, dog, and cat, but these observations are yet to be confirmed.

The conflicting reports of the cyclic behavior of oviducal cilia in women may be at least partially due to the fact that different authors have sampled different regions of the oviduct. We have ample evidence that hormonal dependence differs strikingly in different regions of the monkey oviduct; during the cycle the ampulla never shows as great a loss of cilia as do the fimbriae. Furthermore most of the women who come to surgery suffer from uterine myomas, uterine cancer, ovarian cancer, and other diseases, all of which undoubtedly disturb ovarian function and probably interrupt the normal estrogen-progestin cyclicity in some of these patients If corpora lutea are not formed, progesterone levels will not rise high enough to induce any loss of ciliated cells from the oviduct.

Pregnancy and the Fetus

Additional evidence for the inhibitory effects of progesterone on oviducal cilia comes from our observations

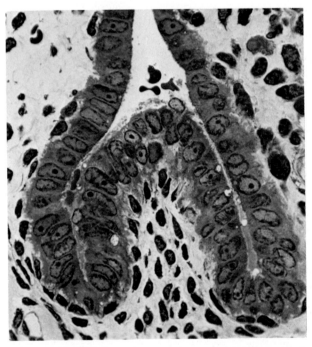

FIG. 9. Fimbriae from pregnant rhesus monkey. The epithelium is atrophied and deciliated. × 1,200.

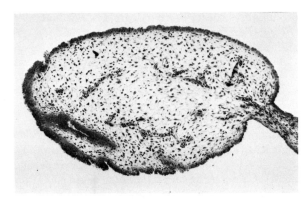

FIG. 10. Fimbriated end of 83-day-old fetal oviduct. Epithelium is low, cuboidal, and smoothly contoured. Typical villous folds of the fimbriae do not develop until 120–130 days gestation. × 80.

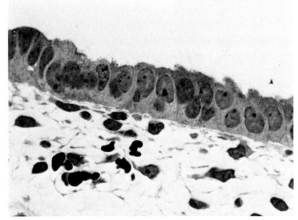

FIG. 11. A higher magnification of Fig. 10. Epithelial cells are very uniform in appearance. Ciliated and secretory cells are absent. × 800.

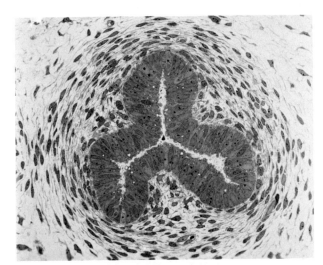

FIG. 12. Ampulla of 81-day fetal oviduct. The lumen is slitlike. Stromal elements are forming the oviducal submucosa. × 300.

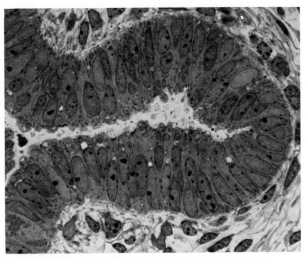

FIG. 13. Higher magnification of Fig. 12. No ciliated or secretory cells are present. × 800.

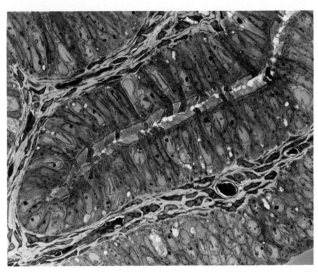

FIG. 14. Ampulla of 150-day fetal oviduct. The lumen is still slitlike, but the epithelium has become fully differentiated. Note that ciliated and secretory cells are present. × 600.

on pregnant rhesus monkeys. Biopsies of the maternal fimbriae of pregnant monkeys on days 45 through 165 of gestation have shown that all the fimbriae were completely atrophied, deciliated, and nonsecretory [(12);

Fig. 9]. Presumably the progestins of pregnancy had induced atrophy in the maternal fimbriae. However, the oviducts obtained from the fetuses of these same pregnancies showed a surprisingly different pattern of ciliation (11).

The fetal oviduct, complete with fimbriae, ampulla, and isthmus, was clearly recognizable at about 60–80 days gestation (Figs. 10–13). The lumen was slitlike and lined by a low, cuboidal epithelium. Mesenchymal elements were forming the various muscle and connective tissue layers. Villous folds developed slowly and were well differentiated by 120–130 days of gestation. At about 130 days, ciliated and secretory cells appeared and increased in number through days 150–155 (Fig. 14). At this time, the epithelium of the fetal oviduct resembled that of a mature female in the follicular phase of the menstrual cycle. Toward the end of gestation, retrogressive changes appeared in the oviducal epithelium; the ciliated cells atrophied and deciliated, and the secretory cells darkened and shrank. The epithelium then resembled that of a mature female in the luteal phase of the menstrual cycle (Fig. 15; see Fig. 6). These retrogressive changes continued into neonatal life, so that by 3 months after birth the entire oviducal epithelium was atrophied and nonciliated, except for the isthmus, where ciliated cells persisted indefinitely.

When exogenous estrogen (estradiol benzoate, 10–30 μg/day for 5 days) was administered to 3–12-month-old infants, a fully ciliated and secretory epithelium developed (Fig. 16). We have no data on the levels of estrogens or progestins in the blood of rhesus fetuses and neonates, but the waves of differentiation and dedifferentiation in the oviducal epithelium during fetal and neonatal life suggest changes in the levels of endogenous estrogens and progestins during this period. The regional differences in the state of differentiation of the fetal oviducal epithelium

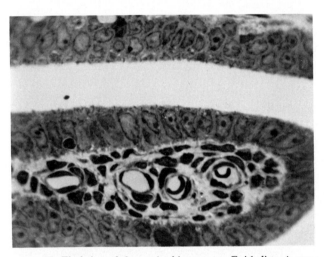

FIG. 15. Fimbriae of 3-month-old neonate. Epithelium is now low, cuboidal, and deciliated. × 1,000.

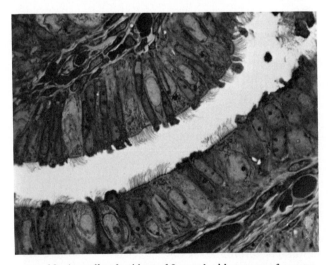

FIG. 16. Ampulla of oviduct of 3-month-old neonate after estrogen treatment (10 μg estradiol benzoate per day for 5 days). Epithelium is fully differentiated. Ciliated and secretory cells are present. × 650.

presumably reflect different degrees of hormone dependence and are analogous to those in the oviducts of sexually mature monkeys.

The maternal oviducts are atrophied and nonciliated throughout pregnancy, yet the fetal oviducts show a burst of ciliation and a wave of deciliation. We assume that in the mother progestins antagonize estrogens and cause atrophy of the oviduct, but how the fetal oviduct escapes a similar suppression is difficult to understand. Perhaps maternal progestins do not reach high enough levels in fetal blood to antagonize fetal estrogens, or perhaps the burst of differentiation in the fetal oviduct is simply an unusual aspect of embryological mechanics. These hypotheses must remain speculative until measurements of estrogens and progestins in maternal and fetal blood are correlated.

Dramatic age-related shifts in the state of epithelial differentiation seem to be restricted to the oviducts of rhesus monkeys. Studies on the tubes of human fetuses, newborns, and prepubertal children show that ciliated and secretory cells are absent during early fetal life, appear before birth, persist during neonatal life, and become most prominent at puberty (39, 40). In rodents with relatively short gestation periods, such as hamsters, mice, and rats (gestation of 16–22 days), cilia develop shortly after birth and persist into adult life. In the guinea pig (gestation of 68 days), oviducal cilia develop at about days 53–54 of gestation and then persist (30).

Life History of Oviducal Epithelium

A review of the life history of the oviducal epithelium of rhesus monkeys provides an excellent summary of the pattern of ciliogenesis in this species (Fig. 17). The epithelium in the early fetal oviduct is low, cuboidal, and undifferentiated. During late fetal life, it differentiates to a fully ciliated and secretory state. Shortly before birth the epithelium returns to the low cuboidal state and remains so until puberty. In neonatal and juvenile oviducts, exogenous estrogen induces the formation of cilia and secretory granules. At puberty, ciliated and secretory cells, which wax and wane during each cycle, develop; deciliation occurs during the luteal phase, and reciliation occurs in the early follicular phase. Ovariectomy in adults leads to dedifferentiation of the epithelium and the loss of cilia and secretory granules; estrogen treatment restores these cells to their mature state. Artificial oviducal cycles

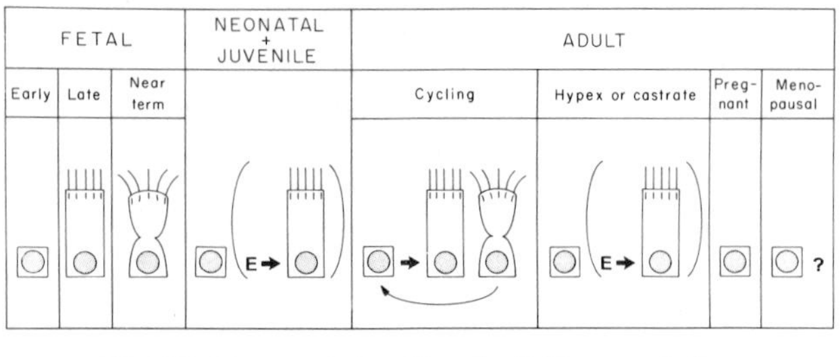

FETAL			NEONATAL + JUVENILE	ADULT			
Early	Late	Near term		Cycling	Hypex or castrate	Pregnant	Menopausal

FIG. 17. Life history of the ciliated cell illustrated diagrammatically. E, estrogen.

can be induced in spayed adults by sequential estrogen-progestin treatment. When pregnancy occurs, the epithelium dedifferentiates quickly and remains in a low cuboidal state throughout pregnancy. When cycles resume, the epithelium is restored. We have few data on senescent animals, but we strongly suspect that the oviducal epithelium atrophies and deciliates when ovarian function finally ceases.

THE PROCESS OF CILIOGENESIS

Ultrastructure of the Ciliated Cell

The fully ciliated cell found on day 14 of the menstrual cycle or after 9 days of estrogen stimulation is about 30 μ tall. The nucleus is located in the base of the cell, and the apical area contains numerous mitochondria, Golgi complexes, rough endoplasmic reticulum, and a cluster of large lipid droplets (Fig. 18). Two hundred to 300 cilia extend from the luminal surface of the cell, and each cilium is continuous with a basal body located just below the surface of the cell. The basal bodies are lined up in orderly rows directly beneath the cell membrane, extensions of which form the ciliary membranes.

Basal bodies are hollow, cylindrical structures about 0.25 μ wide and 0.5 μ long and are practically identical with the cell centriole (Fig. 19). Their walls are composed of nine equally spaced sets of three tubules (200 A each) that run from base to apex and are pitched to the left at

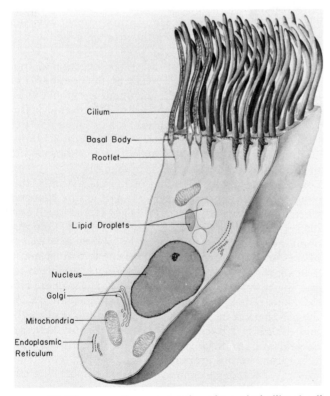

FIG. 18. Diagrammatic representation of a typical ciliated cell from oviduct of the rhesus monkey.

10–15° angles to the longitudinal axis of the organelle (3). The transverse axis of each triplet set at its basal end intersects a tangent to the luminal circumference of the basal body at an approximate 40° angle (triplet angle). As the triplet set travels its helical path from base to apex, it also twists toward the lumen on the longitudinal axis of the inner tubule. This twist causes a change in the triplet angle from 40° (basally) to 10° at the basal body-cilium junction, and this in turn causes a 65 mμ decrease in the outside diameter of the basal body. Extending from base to midregion are 50-A-thick sheets of material that connect the inner and outer tubules of adjacent triplet sets. In the midregion a similar sheet encircles the lumen and interconnects all the inner tubules. Also in the midregion a pyramidal basal foot composed of striated fibrous material projects at right angles from the basal body wall. Just distal to the midregion, sheets of material (the alar sheets) project from each outer tubule at an approximate 50° angle to the transverse axis of the triplet set. Each sheet (about 175 mμ long) merges with the cell membrane. At the basal end, each triplet set is attached to a strand of fibrous material, and the nine strands merge into a bundle (the rootlet) that gradually decreases in diameter as it extends basally into the cytoplasm of the cell. The rootlet has transversely arranged, dense bands at 110-mμ intervals, which give the overall structure a striated appearance (Fig. 20).

The basal portion of the cilium begins at the level of the cell surface (see Fig. 19). The inner and middle tubules of each triplet set in the basal body continue into the cilium to become the nine peripheral doublets. As the triplets become doublets, their helical arrangement is lost. The central pair of tubules is not present in this region, and the diameter of the lumen (120 mμ) is less than that of the basal body. The peripheral doublets are very close to each other, and interdoublet connections exist between the inner and outer tubules of each unit. In addition, fibers extend radially from the middle of the doublet complex to the ciliary membrane.

The midportion of the cilium begins with the appearance of the central pair of tubules about 200 mμ from the basal body-cilium transition (Fig. 21). The new pair of tubules begins abruptly in the center of the ciliary shaft with no defined basal plate (19), although the ground plasm often is denser in this region (see Fig. 39). The radial spacing between each peripheral doublet is greater in the midregion than at the base, and the luminal diameter is about 180 mμ. Two arms located on opposite sides of the inner tubule project toward the outer tubule of the adjacent doublet. These arms probably consist of an ATPase called dynein (21). Very delicate strands of material (50 A) connect the inner tubule of each doublet to the central pair of tubules. These radial linkers are common to most cilia. The midportion, which makes up the greatest length of the cilium (7 μ), has the typical 9 + 2 arrangement of tubules usually associated with ciliary structure (19).

In the apical (tip) region of the cilium, the ciliary diameter decreases and the tubules end at different levels.

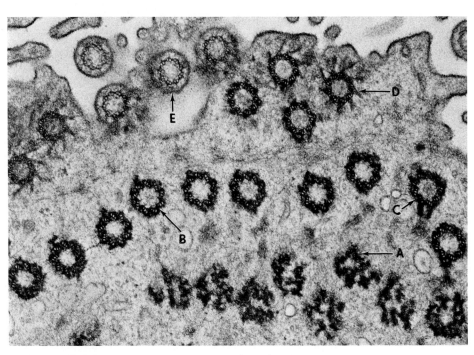

FIG. 19. Transverse section through a ciliated cell. Basal bodies and cilia are sectioned at different levels to show the tubule organization at these points: *A*, rootlet region; *B*, basal portion of basal body; *C*, midregion with basal foot; *D*, apical region with alar sheets; *E*, basal region of cilium with central pair of tubules absent and doublet to membrane linkers. × 39,700.

The outer tubules of each peripheral doublet end first, and the remaining singlets become crowded together. The various intertubular connections and the dynein arms are all lost. The spacing between the peripheral singlets and the central pair becomes very irregular, and these tubules terminate at various levels. Finally, at the very tip, all the tubules disappear, and the tip diameter reaches a minimum (see Fig. 39).

Basal Body and Cilia Formation

BASAL BODY DEVELOPMENT. Studies on serial biopsies taken during either estrogen treatment or the normal menstrual cycle reveal that the first sign of an estrogen response is an increase in mitotic activity in the oviducal epithelium 2 days after the beginning of stimulation (see Fig. 2). The epithelium becomes hypertrophied by the third day of stimulation, and clear cells (future ciliated) and dark cells (future secretory) are evident (Fig. 22). Both cell types are tall with well-developed Golgi complexes, rough endoplasmic reticulum, polysomes, and numerous enlarged mitochondria—evidence that the cells are actively synthesizing the molecules necessary for differentiation. Frequently these cells have two centrioles (the diplosomal pair) in the apical region, and the members of the pair are usually oriented at right angles to each other. A rudimentary (or primary) cilium (37) usually develops from one of the centrioles in both cell types (Fig. 23).

Late on day 3 of estrogen stimulation, 40–60-mμ granules, irregularly shaped and differing in electron density, appear in the apex of the future ciliated cells. (see Fig.

27). Stereomicroscopic and high-magnification studies reveal that the granules are composed of 40–75-A fibers embedded in an amorphous material which diminishes in amount toward the periphery of each granule. The fibers thus appear to taper as they extend from the granule center, and this gives the granule a stellate appearance.

These "fibrous granules" are often aggregated into large groups forming sheets or spheres, the boundaries of which are delimited from the surrounding cytoplasm by subtle differences in electron density. The ground plasm within the aggregate of granules contains many fibers of various lengths and thicknesses. Small groups of fibrous granules are also seen in the immediate neighborhood of the diplosomal centrioles (Figs. 24 and 25).

Within the large aggregates of fibrous granules, discrete spherical masses of fibers, 90–110 mμ in diameter when fully developed, appear (see Figs. 28 and 29). These masses, called "deuterosomes" by Sorokin (37), consist of an inner dense region composed of tightly interwoven fibers (50 A) in a surrounding matrix and an outer, more delicate corona. At the junction between the inner mass and the corona, the amorphous matrix is less dense and the fibers radiate centrifugally in a random fashion. At the periphery of the corona, the matrix is maximally light and the fibers are less numerous (Fig. 26; see Fig. 31). Several authors have suggested that deuterosomes develop from fibrous granules by a process of "condensation" (17, 37); deuterosomes certainly resemble enlarged fibrous granules.

At this time the synthesis of basal bodies begins. Our best interpretation of the formative processes involved is

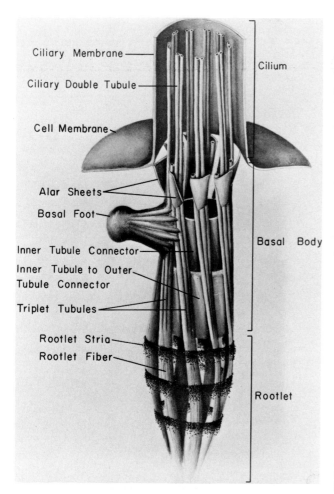

FIG. 20. Model of a basal body from the oviduct of the rhesus monkey.

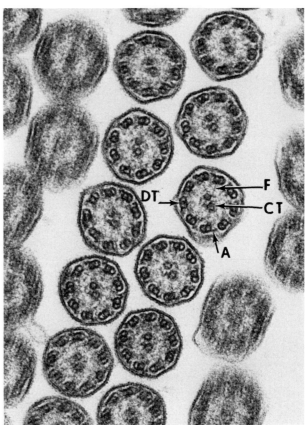

FIG. 21. Midportion of several cilia. The 9 doublet tubules (DT) and 2 central tubules (CT) are evident. The outer arm (A) on each inner tubule is prominent, and delicate fibers (F) radiate from the central tubules to the outer doublets. × 45,000.

that fibrous granules coalesce to form the material of the probasal body itself and that deuterosomes and diplosomal centrioles serve as organizing centers around which the new basal bodies develop. Most of the probasal bodies develop in contact with deuterosomes; a smaller number develop around diplosomal centrioles. We have called these two pathways of basal body development the *acentriolar* and *centriolar* pathways, respectively [(4); see Fig. 30].

Diplosomal centrioles engaged in procentriole production (the centriolar pathway) have a 40–50-mμ thick coat of flocculent material around their outer walls (see Fig. 25). This material varies from amorphous to filamentous and is not uniformly thick around the centriole. The base of the developing procentriole is enmeshed in the outer region of this corona, so that 30–40 mμ separate the parent from the daughter during the early stages of induction. Several filaments extend into the base of the procentriole from the corona, one of which is aligned with the longitudinal axis of the daughter structure (see Fig. 25). These filaments are part of the cartwheel (4), a complex central structure found only in developing basal bodies.

Generally the procentrioles form at right angles to the centriole and are distributed along the centriolar axis

from midregion to base (see Figs. 25 and 26). The number of procentrioles generated by each centriole varies from one to ten, all of which are in the same stage of development at any one time. Serial sections often show one set of three or four procentrioles encircling the midregion and another set around the basal region of the same centriole. Sometimes the procentrioles spiral up the centriole from base to midregion. A basal foot or an anomaly in the centriole structure distorts the normal perpendicular orientation of daughter to parent. In extreme cases, procentrioles project from the basal opening of the centriole lumen.

The procentrioles rapidly develop into mature basal bodies by elongation and expansion, during which the characteristic daughter-to-parent orientation is maintained (see Fig. 26). At maturity the basal bodies break away from the parent and join the population of basal bodies synthesized via the major pathway. They are indistinguishable from acentriolar-generated basal bodies (see Fig. 36).

In the acentriolar pathway, procentrioles form by fusion of fibrous granules, and each procentriole usually develops in contact with the corona of a deuterosome (Fig. 28). Most commonly, one or two procentrioles project from each sphere, but as many as four procentrioles

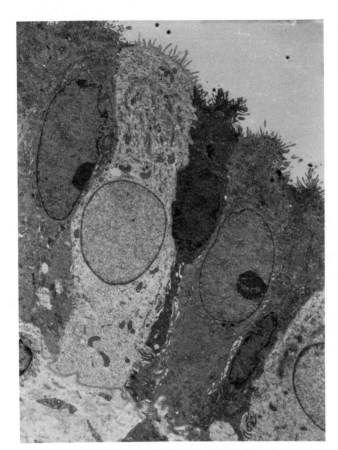

FIG. 22. Hypertrophied epithelium characteristic of day 3 of stimulation. The clear cell is a future ciliated cell, and fibrous granules are present in the distal region of the cytoplasm. ×3,000.

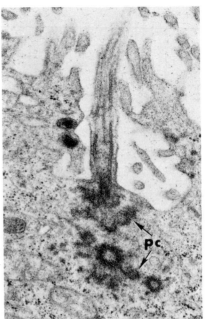

FIG. 24. Diplosomal pair with rudimentary cilium that are producing procentrioles (*pc*). × 28,000.

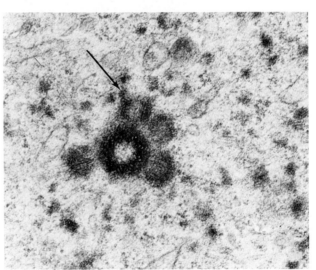

FIG. 25. Diplosomal centriole generating procentrioles. The procentrioles are in contact with a corona of flocculent material that encircles the parent. Fibrous granules appear to be deposited at the apical end of a procentriole (*arrow*). × 61,000.

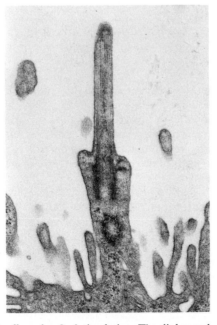

FIG. 23. Epithelial cell on day 3 of stimulation. The diplosomal centrioles have migrated to the luminal surface, and one centriole has produced a rudimentary cilium. × 28,000.

per deuterosome can occur (Fig. 29). Occasionally procentrioles develop independently of the deuterosome (Fig. 30).

Structural continuity exists between the corona of the deuterosome and the primitive cartwheel that develops within the early procentrioles (Fig. 31). The filaments of the cartwheel are similar to the fibers of the deuterosome. Similar continuity exists between the corona of the diplosomal centriole and the cartwheel of the daughter during centriolar procentriole formation.

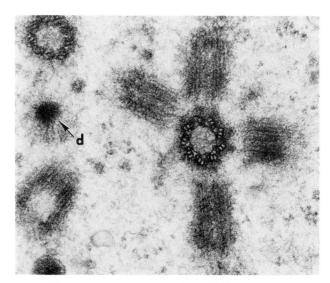

FIG. 26. Nearly complete basal bodies associated with a diplosomal centriole. This centriole is sectioned through the midregion, whereas the centriole in Fig. 25 is sectioned through the base region. The presence of maturing basal bodies and deuterosomes (d) indicated that the acentriolar pathway is at the same stage of development. × 64,000.

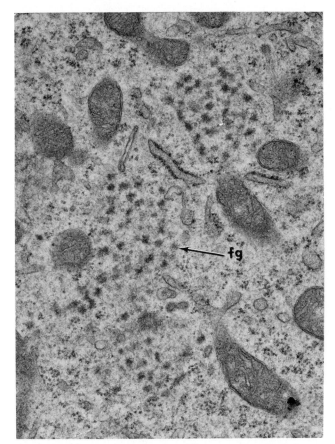

FIG. 27. Fibrous granules (fg) in the cytoplasm of a future ciliated cell. The granules are commonly aggregated into clusters, and many fine filaments traverse randomly among the granules. × 38,000.

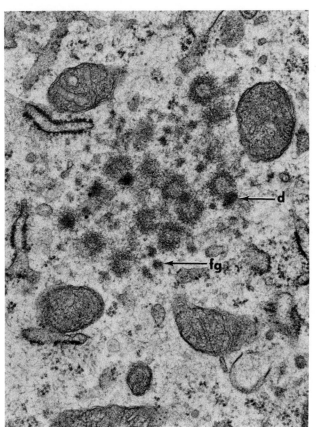

FIG. 28. Procentrioles forming in contact with a deuterosome (d). Notice that the deuterosome is similar to the fibrous granules (fg) during these early stages of development. × 31,000.

In both pathways a procentriole is first recognizable as an annulus of amorphous material with an irregular outside diameter of 100–195 mμ, a uniform luminal diameter of 85 mμ, and an approximate length of 125 mμ. Favorable sections indicate that the luminal band that demarcates the circumference of the lumen is formed from fibers of thin sheets of material similar to those associated with the granules. Fibrous granules gather around this band to form the annulus wall. The cartwheel begins to form at this stage. One end of the annulus, the future basal end of the basal body, abuts the corona of either the deuterosome or the diplosomal centriole (4).

The primitive cartwheel appears in transverse sections as a set of nine filaments (spokes) radiating from a central filamentous ring to nine equidistant points on the procentriole luminal band (Fig. 32). Longitudinal sections show the central ring as a thin-walled (∼40 A) cylinder extending from the base to the apex of the procentriole (see Fig. 31). The elements extending from the central cylinder to the luminal circumferences are rod-shaped filaments that originate at right angles to the cylinder and seem to be more numerous near the base of the procentriole (see Fig. 33).

Once the procentrioles are initiated and continuity is established between the corona and the cartwheel, the

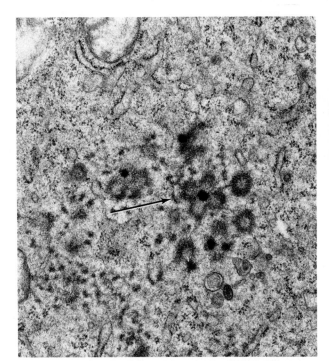

FIG. 29. A later stage of procentriole development than that shown in Fig. 28. One deuterosome is inducing formation of 4 procentrioles. Fibrous granules apparently are being deposited at the apex of one procentriole (*arrow*). × 28,000.

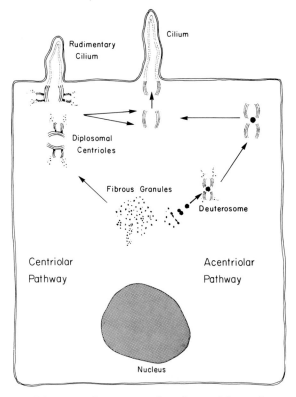

FIG. 30. Diagrammatic representation of acentriolar and centriolar pathways of basal body formation in the oviduct of the rhesus monkey.

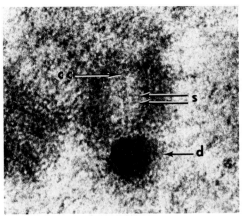

FIG. 31. Longitudinal view of a procentriole; the cartwheel structure is shown. Spokes (*s*) are oriented perpendicularly to the central cylinder (*cc*). The cylinder seems to merge with the cortex of the basally positioned deuterosome (*d*). × 120,000.

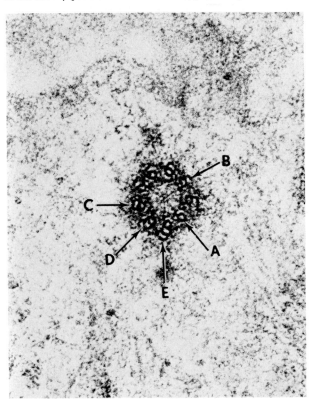

FIG. 32. Transverse view of a procentriole forming B- and C-tubules. The cartwheel with central cylinder and spokes is well developed. *A*, complete A-tubule; *B*, B-tubule forming; *C*, B-tubule complete; *D*, C-tubule forming; *E*, complete triplet. × 112,000.

tubules that form the nine triplet sets of the mature basal body begin to develop. Three-dimensional interpretations of tubule formation are depicted in Figures 33 and 34. The first tubule to form is the A (inner)-tubule of the eventual triplet set; this is also the first tubule to form in *Paramecium* (16) and in chicken tracheal cells (26). Each A-tubule begins as a half-cylinder that closes gradually from base to apex. Each developing cylinder forms be-

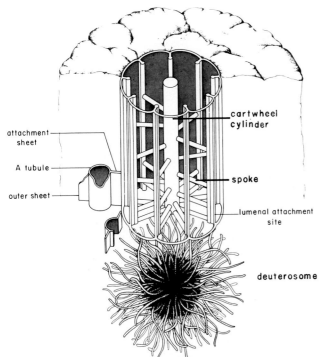

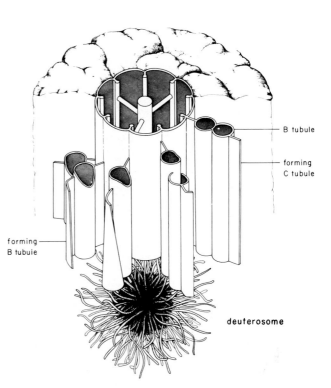

FIG. 33. Diagrammatic representation of A-tubule initiation. Cartwheel is complete, and the first A-tubule is completely initiated with its inside and outside 100-A sheets formed. Counterclockwise from the first tubule, a second A-tubule is forming. It has not become attached to the luminal attachment site.

FIG. 34. Diagrammatic representation of B- and C-tubule formation and growth.

tween two 100-A-thick sheets of material; one of these attaches the developing tubule to one spoke of the cartwheel, and the other projects freely outward. The A-tubules form in sequence around the periphery; each new tubule develops 40° of arc distant from its nearest neighbor. After all the A-tubules have been initiated, the B-tubules develop from the freely projecting 100-A sheets attached to the A-tubules. Each of these sheets forms a half-cylinder, which then closes on the wall of the A-tubule. C-tubules form similarly from sheets that project outward from the B-tubules. Thus the B-tubules share a wall with the A-tubules, and the C-tubules share one with the B-tubules (see Fig. 32).

The longitudinal growth of the A-, B-, and C-tubules proceeds unevenly. Complete and incomplete A-, B-, and C-tubules are seen at any level of the lengthening procentrioles (see Figs. 32 and 34); often the triplet sets are not all completely formed until ciliogenesis is in process.

When the basal body has almost reached its mature length, one or two (usually one) basal feet (see Fig. 20) form in the midregion at right angles to the wall by a deposition of fibrous, granulelike material. The alar sheets [(3); see Fig. 20] begin to form as extensions from the C-tubules in the apical region and assume their final arrangement when the basal body-cilium relationship is established.

As the basal body matures, the cartwheel remains a constant length and becomes a robust network of fila-

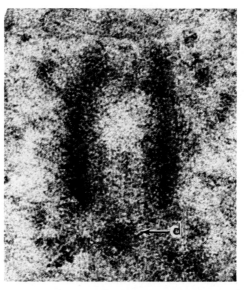

FIG. 35. Longitudinal section of a nearly complete basal body. Notice that the length of the cartwheel region has not increased from that in Fig. 31, whereas the walls of the procentriole have lengthened. A deuterosome (d) is at the base of the basal body. × 120,000.

ments. This network may act as a scaffolding upon which basal body morphology is established (Fig. 35). When the completed basal body begins to migrate to the cell surface (see Fig. 37) or while cilium formation is taking

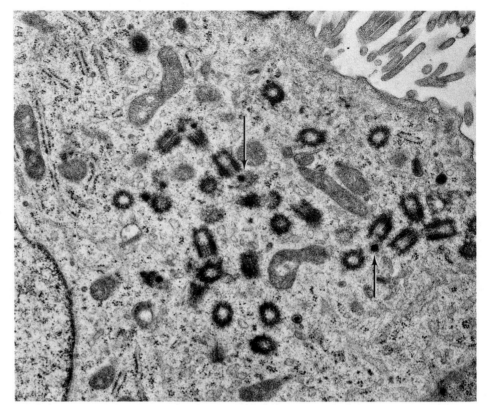

FIG. 36. Newly formed basal bodies randomly arranged in the apex of the cell. Deuterosomes are beginning to disassociate from the basal bodies (*arrows*). × 26,650.

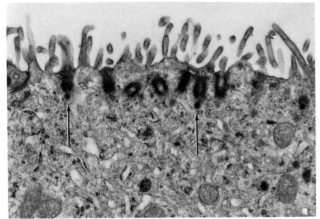

FIG. 37. Basal bodies lined up at the surface of the cell just before cilia formation begins. Deuterosomes are still attached to some of the basal bodies (*arrows*). × 13,300.

place, the cartwheel structure breaks down and forms a vesicle that remains in the lumen (see Fig. 38); a similar vesicle is commonly seen within the lumen of centrioles and basal bodies in other cell systems (37, 41). Eventually this vesicle disappears.

When the triplets are forming, the angle of the triplet set to the circumference measures 60–65°. In the corresponding region of the mature basal body, this angle is 40° (3). The angle change is gradual and incomplete until after the cartwheel disappears.

The completed basal bodies produced by both pathways are now randomly arranged within the apical cyto-

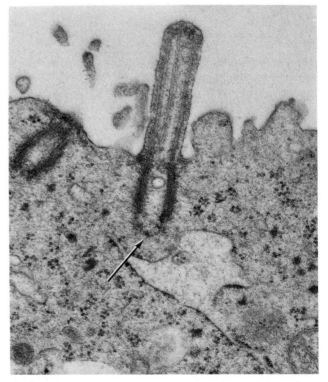

FIG. 38. A ciliary bud. The doublet tubules are in direct continuity with 2 of the triplet tubules of the basal body. Aggregates of fibrous granules appear to be added at the base of the basal body (*arrow*) to form the rootlet. The vesicle in the lumen is the remains of the broken-down cartwheel structure. × 42,000.

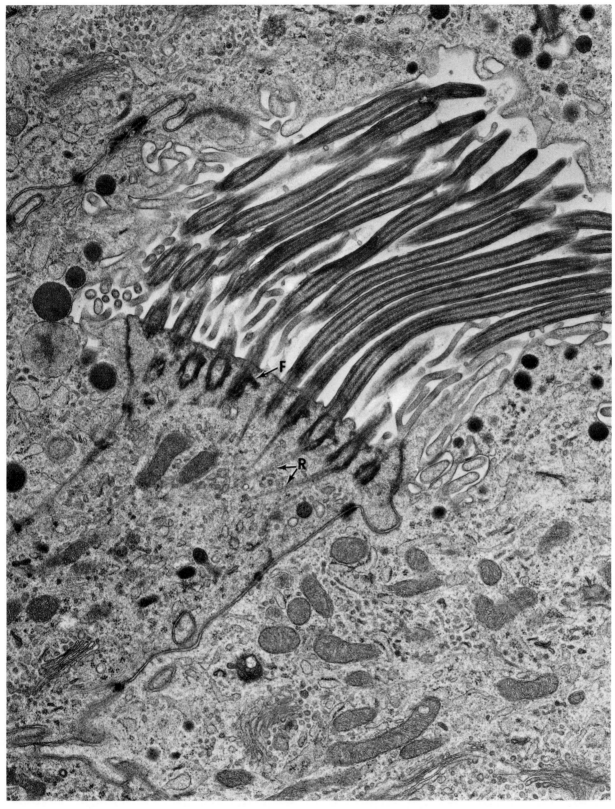

FIG. 39. Fully ciliated cell. Cilia are fully developed. Characteristic basal feet (*F*) and rootlets (*R*) of basal bodies are shown. × 20,000.

plasm of the cell (Fig. 36). Eventually they migrate to the cell surface. Their random orientation is lost as the apex of each structure comes in contact with the cell surface and cilia formation begins (Fig. 37). At the same time, fibrous granules reappear near the basal bodies, and rootlets start to form (Fig. 38). The rootlets, like the basal feet, seem to form by aggregation of fibrous granules (Fig. 38).

CILIA FORMATION. The formation of the cilia in the oviduct of the rhesus monkey is similar to that in the vertebrate rod cell (44), neural epithelium (38), various protozoa (32), and rat trachea (17, 37). The basal body fuses with the apical cell membrane, a localized bleb of cytoplasm appears directly over the apex of the basal body, and this bleb becomes a ciliary bud (see Fig. 38). The alar sheets attach where the membrane of the bleb returns to the normal plane of the cell surface. The axonemal tubules begin to form in this bud and become progressively more organized, but the tip of the growing cilium remains bulb-shaped and appears to contain disorganized axonemal precursor material (see Fig. 38). When the cilium is complete, the bulb-shaped tip is lost, and this region assumes its final conical form (Fig. 39). These morphological patterns suggest that ciliary elongation takes place in the tip region, as it does in the developing flagella of the protozoan, *Ochromonas danica* (31), and the bacterium, *Bacillus subtilis* (18).

CONTROL OF CILIOGENESIS:
IMPLICATIONS AND QUESTIONS

Estrogen-driven ciliogenesis in the oviduct of the rhesus monkey is a complex phenomenon that entails the interaction of hormones with cell regulatory mechanisms and the orderly unfolding of precise developmental sequences. Many questions remain unanswered by the data reviewed above—questions concerning the action of hormones and the mechanism of cellular differentiation. For example, does estrogen act solely on the nucleus in these cells in which such diverse cytoplasmic events occur?

Does estrogen merely initiate a nuclear program, which, once started, proceeds independently of the cytoplasmic presence of the hormone, or does estrogen interact directly with the ciliogenic precursors? By what mechanism does progesterone antagonize estradiol and inhibit ciliogenesis?

The basal body-cilium complex in the fimbriae is much more dependent on estrogen than that in the ampulla. What is the molecular basis of these regional differences in estrogen dependence? The ciliated epithelium of the respiratory tract is insensitive to estrogen. How do cells in the same organism build identical structures so that one set is hormone dependent and the other hormone independent? What is the molecular basis of these differences? Similarly, what is the molecular basis for the species differences in the hormone dependence of oviducal ciliated cells?

The mechanics of basal body and cilia formation also raise a host of interesting questions. What is the significance of the two pathways for basal body formation, centriolar and acentriolar, in the same cell? What regulates the synchrony of the basal body assembly process? What macromolecular controls are operative during the precise elaboration of the nine triplet sets of tubules in each basal body? What stimulates the migration of the newly formed basal bodies to the cell surface? What regulates their orderly lineup at fixed distances from one another at the cell membrane? What is the nature of the interaction between the basal body and the cell membrane that results in the formation of a ciliary bud, and what regulates the assembly of the nine peripheral doublets and the central pair of microtubules in the ciliary axoneme? Finally, how is the final length of the cilium controlled?

We hope that our research, which is directed toward the solution of these and related problems, will provide deeper insight into the complex phenomena of hormone action and cell differentiation so beautifully expressed in the rhythmic behavior of the female reproductive tract.

The authors would like to express their appreciation to Norma Hoskins, Carole Whortley, and Sharon Maher for their excellent assistance.

REFERENCES

1. ALLEN, E. Reactions of immature monkey (*Macacus rhesus*) to injections of ovarian hormone. *J. Morphol.* 46: 479–520, 1928.
2. ALLEN, E. Further experiments with an ovarian hormone in the ovariectomized adult monkey, *Macacus rhesus*, especially the degenerative phase of the experimental menstrual cycle. *Am. J. Anat.* 42: 467–487, 1928.
3. ANDERSON, R. G. W. The structure of the basal body from the rhesus monkey oviduct (Abstract). *Anat. Record* 166: 272, 1970.
4. ANDERSON, R. G. W., AND R. M. BRENNER. The formation of basal bodies (centrioles) in the rhesus monkey oviduct. *J. Cell Biol.* 50: 10–34, 1971.
5. ANDREWS, M. C. Epithelial changes in the puerperal fallopian tube. *Am. J. Obstet. Gynecol.* 62: 28–37, 1951.
6. BALBONI, G. Ricerche istochimische sull'epitelio tubarico della donna. *Riv. Ostet. Ginecol.* 9: 164–194, 1954.

7. BORELL, U., O. NILSSON, J. WERSÄLL, AND A. WESTMAN. Electron-microscope studies of the epithelium of the rabbit fallopian tube under different hormonal influences. *Acta Obstet. Gynecol. Scand.* 35: 36–41, 1956.
8. BRENNER, R. M. Renewal of oviduct cilia during the menstrual cycle of the rhesus monkey. *Fertility Sterility* 20: 599–611, 1969.
9. BRENNER, R. M. The biology of oviductal cilia. In: *The Mammalian Oviduct*, edited by R. J. Blandau and E. S. E. Hafez. Chicago: Univ. of Chicago Press, 1969, p. 203–229.
10. BRENNER, R. M. Hormonal control of cilia renewal in the primate oviduct: ultrastructural studies. In: *Progress in Gynecology*, edited by S. Sturgis and M. Taymor. New York: Grune & Stratton, 1970, p. 77–97.
11. BRENNER, R. M. Ciliogenesis in the primate oviduct. In: *Pathways to Conception; The Role of the Cervix and the Oviduct in Reproduction*, edited by A. I. Sherman. Springfield, Ill.: Thomas, 1971, p. 50–66.

12. BRENNER, R. M. Hormonal regulation of oviductal epithelium. In: *The Regulation of Mammalian Reproduction*, N.I.H. Conference. In press.

13. BRENNER, R. M., R. G. W. ANDERSON, AND M. J. KAMM. Estrogen-driven ciliogenesis in organ culture of rhesus monkey oviduct (Abstract). *J. Cell Biol.* 39: 16a, 1968.

14. BRUNI, A. C. L'intima struttura delle trombe uterine e il transito dell'ovulo. *Monitore Zool. Ital. Suppl.* 69: 1–36, 1950.

15. CLYMAN, J. M. Electron microscopy of the human fallopian tube. *Fertility Sterility* 17: 281–301, 1966.

16. DIPPLE, R. V. The development of basal bodies in *Paramecium*. *Proc. Natl. Acad. Sci. US* 61: 461–468, 1968.

17. DIRKSEN, E. R., AND T. T. CROCKER. Centriole replication in differentiating ciliated cells of mammalian respiratory epithelium. An electron microscopic study. *J. Microscopie* 5: 629–644, 1965.

18. EMERSON, S. U., K. TOKUYASU, AND M. I. SIMON. Bacterial flagella; polarity of elongation. *Science* 16: 190, 1970.

19. FAWCETT, D. W. Cilia and flagella. In: *The Cell*, edited by J. Brachet and A. E. Mirsky. New York: Acad. Press, 1961, vol. II, p. 217–297.

20. FLERKO, B. Die Epithelien des Eileiters und ihre hormonalen Reaktionen. *Z. Mikroskop. Anat. Forsch.* 61: 99–118, 1954.

21. GIBBONS, I. R. The structure and composition of cilia. In: *Formation and Fate of Cell Organelles*, edited by K. B. Warren. New York: Acad. Press, 1967, vol. 6, p. 99–113.

22. GOOD, R. G., AND D. L. MOYER. Estrogen-progesterone relationships in the development of secretory endometrium. *Fertility Sterility* 19: 37–49, 1968.

23. HAMPERL, H. Über die "hellen" Flimmerepithelzellen des menschlichen Uterusschleimhaut. *Arch. Pathol. Anat. Physiol.* 319: 265–281, 1950.

24. HASHIMOTO, M., T. SHIMOYAMA, M. KOSAKA, A. KOMORI, T. HIRASAWA, Y. YOKOYAMA, N. KAWASE, AND T. NAKAMURA. Electron microscopic studies on the epithelial cells of the human fallopian tube (Report II). *J. Japan. Obstet. Gynecol. Soc.* 11: 92–100, 1964.

25. JOACHIMOVITS, R. Studien zur Menstruation, Ovulation, Aufbau und Pathologie des weiblichen Genitales bei Mensch und Affe (*Pithecus fascicularis mordax*), Eileiter und Ovar. *Biol. Generalis* 11: 281–348, 1935.

26. KALNINS, V. I., AND K. R. PORTER. Centriole replication during ciliogenesis in the chick tracheal epithelium. *Z. Mikroskop. Anat. Forsch.* 100: 1–30, 1969.

27. KOERING, M. J. Cyclic changes in ovarian morphology during the menstrual cycle in *Macaca mulatta*. *Am. J. Anat.* 126: 73–101, 1969.

28. ODOR, D. L. Estrogen and ciliogenesis in the infundibulum of the rabbit oviduct (Abstract). *Anat. Record* 163: 236, 1969.

29. PERNKOPF, E., AND A. PICHLER. Systematische und topographische Anatomie des weiblichen Beckens. In: *Biologie und Pathologie des Weibes*, edited by L. Seitz and A. J. Amreich. Berlin: Urban & Schwarzerberg, 1953, p. 83–211.

30. PRICE, D., J. J. P. ZAAIJER, AND E. ORTIZ. Prenatal development of the oviduct *in vivo* and *in vitro*. In: *The Mammalian Oviduct*, edited by R. J. Blandau and E. S. E. Hafez. Chicago: Univ. of Chicago Press, 1969, p. 29–46.

31. ROSENBAUM, J. L., AND F. M. CHILD. Flagellar regeneration in protozoan flagellates. *J. Cell Biol.* 34: 345–364, 1967.

32. ROTH, J. E., AND Y. SHIGENAKA. The structure and formation of cilia and filaments in rumen protozoa. *J. Cell Biol.* 20: 249–270, 1964.

33. SCHRÖDER, R. Die mikroskopische Anatomie des Eileiters. In: *Handbuch der mikroskopischen Anatomie des Menschen*, edited by by W. v. Möllendorff. Berlin: Springer, 1930, vol. 7, pt. 1, p. 396–419.

34. SCHULTKA, R. Der Sekretionszyklus der Flimmerzellen der menschlichen Tube uterina auf Grund cytologischer und cytopochemischer Untersuchung. *Acta Histochem.* 15: 285–315, 1963.

35. SCHULTKA, R., AND J. H. SCHARF. Sekretionszyklus der Tubenepithelzelle in Abhängigkeit vom ovariellen Zyklus. *Zentr. Gynaekol.* 85: 1601–1906, 1963.

36. SHIMOYAMA, T. Electron microscopic studies of the epithelial cells of the fallopian tube mucosa in the mature woman. *J. Japan. Obstet. Gynecol. Soc.* 15: 1237, 1963.

37. SOROKIN, S. P. Reconstructions of centriole formation and ciliogenesis in mammalian lungs. *J. Cell Sci.* 3: 207–230, 1968.

38. SOTELO, J. R., AND O. TRUJILLO-CENOZ. Electron microscopic study of the development of ciliary components of the neural epithelium of the chick embryo. *Z. Zellforsch. Mikroskop. Anat.* 49: 1–12, 1958.

39. STEGNER, H.-E. Das Epithel der Tuba uterina des neugeborenen, elektronenmikroskopische Befunde. *Z. Zellforsch. Mikroskop. Anat.* 55: 247–262, 1961.

40. STEGNER, H.-E. Elektronenmikroskopische Untersuchungen über die Sekretionsmorphologie des menschlichen Tubenepithels. *Arch. Gynaekol.* 197: 351–363, 1962.

41. STUBBLEFIELD, E., AND B. R. BRINKLEY. Architecture and function of the mammalian centriole. In: *Formation and Fate of Cell Organelles*, edited by K. B. Warren. New York: Acad. Press, 1967, p. 175–218.

42. TIETZE, K. Zur Frage nach den zyklischen Veränderungen des menschlichen Tubenepithels. *Zentr. Gynaekol.* 53: 32–38, 1929.

43. TIETZE, K. Histologische Tubenveränderungen in den einzelnen Lebansphasen des Weibes und bei Ovarialtumoren. *Arch. Gynaekol.* 148: 724–737, 1932.

44. TOKUYASU, K., AND E. YAMADA. The fine structure of the retina studies with the electron microscope. IV. Morphogenesis of the outer segments of the retinal rods. *J. Biophys. Biochem. Cytol.* 6: 225–230, 1959.

45. WESTMANN, A. E. Studies of the function of the mucous membrane of the uterine tube. *Acta Obstet. Gynecol. Scand.* 10: 228–298, 1930.

46. WESTMANN, A. E. Studien über den Sexualzyklus bein Makakus-Rhesus-Affen, nebst einigen Bemerkungen über den menstruellen Blutungsmechanismus. *Acta Obstet. Gynecol. Scand.* 12: 282–328, 1932.

47. WESTMANN, A. E. Einige Bemerkungen aus Anlass des Aufsatzes von Jägeroos; die sexualzyklischen Umwandlungen in der Tube uterina beim Menschen und bei den niedrigen Primaten. *Acta Obstet. Gynecol. Scand.* 13: 263–268, 1934.

CHAPTER 37

Oviducal fluid—composition and physiology

CHARLES E. HAMNER | *Division of Reproductive Biology, Department of Obstetrics and Gynecology, University of Virginia School of Medicine, Charlottesville, Virginia*

CHAPTER CONTENTS

THE OVIDUCT HOLDS a fundamental position in reproduction—it transports the gametes and zygotes and provides an essential environment for fertilization and cleavage of the egg. During the last several years, we have come to realize that each region of the oviduct—infundibulum (preampulla), ampulla, and isthmus, as well as the uterus—provides a specific environment for the developing embryo before its implantation. The fluids rendered to the lumen of the oviduct and to the uterus by transudation and secretion are the major contributors to the total environment. This environment is influenced greatly by the hormonal state of the female, which produces alterations in the vascular system and cytology of the reproductive tract; these alterations cause changes in the composition and volume of the fluids.

FORMATION OF THE FLUID

Oviducal fluid is formed through the processes of transudation and secretion. However, information is scant concerning the specific mechanisms whereby the fluid reaches the lumen of the oviduct. Under natural conditions at ovulation, oviducal fluid may be a combination of fluids with contributions from the oviduct itself, the peritoneal fluid, uterine fluid, and follicular fluid. Animals with a periovarian sac that almost completely encloses the ovary would be expected to have a mixture of oviducal fluid and follicular fluid after ovula-

tion. The accumulation of fluid in sections of the oviduct between ligatures eliminates the possibility that the oviduct depends on influx from the peritoneal cavity for its total fluid volume (19, 44, 143).

Many facts indicate that transudation influences oviducal fluid volume and chemical composition. The oviduct has an extensive lymphatic system that greatly expands at estrus (5, 85), and a corresponding increase in volume of oviducal fluid is noticed. Dry matter content and osmolarity of the fluid in estrogen-treated rabbits decrease as the fluid volume increases. Oviducal fluid from rhesus monkeys contains albumin and α_1-, α_2-, and β-globulins in the same proportions of total protein as does their serum; γ-globulins, however, are present at lower levels (90). Transudation of these proteins from the vascular system probably accounts for their presence in oviducal fluid. Rabbit oviducal fluid contains proteins similar to those of rabbit serum, but both fluids contain proteins that are immunologically different, which indicates that selective transudation occurs and that the oviduct also produces its own characteristic proteins through secretory processes (125).

Evidence of secretory activity in the oviduct has come from cytological, histochemical, and biophysical studies. The oviducal epithelium of many mammals (rabbit, rat, mouse, sheep, cow, dog, horse, and man) produces secretory granules during estrus that are extruded into the lumen after ovulation (28, 36, 41, 51, 53, 54, 81, 112). The secretions are periodic acid-Schiff (PAS) positive and are not digested by α-amylase (10, 33, 57, 58, 82). Incorporation of radioactive sulfur into oviducal secretions indicates the synthesis of acid mucopolysaccharide (147, 148). Secretory pressure in the oviduct of the rabbit is highest during estrus (46 cm H_2O) and drops (to 11.8 cm H_2O) after ovariectomy (19).

The mechanisms involved in formation of the oviducal fluid need a great deal more study. Because the fluid is partially a transudate, specific drugs or their metabolites could be delivered to the gametes via transudation to enhance or alter physiological events. One such drug, 2-methyl-3-ethyl-4 phenyl-Δ^4-cyclohexene carboxylic acid (ORF-4563), appears in the oviducal fluid when given orally to rabbits and monkeys (146). Utilization of immune mechanisms to produce antibodies to sperm or egg antigens that pass into the oviducal fluid might be a very effective method of contraception. Immunoglobulins as a class have been identified in oviducal fluid (125), but information on selectivity of transfer of immunoglobulins into the oviducal fluid is limited.

Methods of Collection

Many approaches, including flushing and stripping of the genital tract, ligating the oviduct at distant points for fluid accumulation, and cannulating the lumen with tubing to capture the fluid from a continuous flow, have been used to obtain fluid from the female reproductive tract. Bishop (19) in 1956 was the first to cannulate the fimbriated end of the oviduct for continuous collection of fluid. He connected polyethylene tubing to a manometer and measured the secretory pressure in the rabbit oviduct. Various adaptations of his method have been developed for the continuous collection of fluid from the genital tract (25, 40, 73, 76, 115, 120). The continuous flow method allows collection of fluids from the same animal under various hormonal states for prolonged periods. Collection of fluids by the continuous flow method eliminates many of the disadvantages of the other methods. The fluid components can be quantitated, which is not possible with flushed fluids or fluids stripped from the tract. Double ligation causes stretching and flattening of the epithelium, and accumulation of fluid occludes the blood supply (167).

Hormonal Influence on Fluid Volume

Estrogen stimulates the production of fluid by the uterus and the oviduct. The highest yields of fluid in most animals (99) occur at the height of estrus. Mating triggers highest production in the rabbit, and volume is maximum during the period immediately before and after ovulation (87). Progesterone suppresses the amount of fluid in the genital tract and counteracts the stimulatory effect of estrogens (67).

The volume of oviducal fluid is highly dependent on estrogen. Intact estrous female mammals produce 1.2–5.0 ml oviducal fluid per day [rabbit, 1.2; sheep, 1.4; cow, 5.0; pig, 2.7; rhesus monkey, 3.4; and man, 1.3 ml/day (24, 26, 29–36, 48)]. Ovariectomy causes the volume to drop quickly (67, 92). If the rabbit is ovariectomized and injected with cottonseed oil alone, the volume drops to 0.5 ml/day and remains at that level indefinitely. Injection of an ovariectomized rabbit with 0.5 μg estradiol cyclopentylpropionate (ECP) per kg per day in 1.0 ml cottonseed oil causes a significant increase in fluid volume. Injection with 1.0 μg ECP per kg per day produces maximum fluid volume in the rabbit, which is equivalent to that of the intact estrous doe (Figs. 1 and 2). Higher doses of estrogen, as much as 20 μg ECP per kg per day, cause a

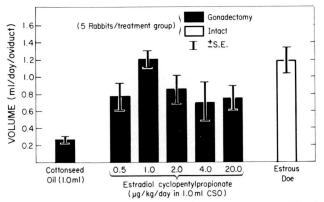

FIG. 1. Influence of estrogen treatment on rabbit oviducal fluid production rate. *CSO*, cottonseed oil. (From C. E. Hamner and A. Huckle, unpublished data.)

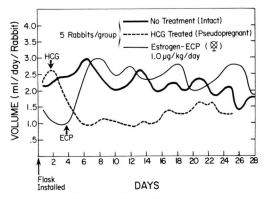

FIG. 2. Oviducal fluid production rate in nontreated, pseudopregnant, and estrogen-treated rabbits. *ECP*, estradiol cyclopentylpropionate; *HCG*, human chorionic gonadotrophin. (From C. E. Hamner and J. W. Kille, unpublished data.)

slight decrease in fluid production with no significant difference between doses of 2 and 20 μg ECP per kg per day (see Fig. 1).

A 50% drop in oviducal fluid volume from estrous level is evident by the third day of pseudopregnancy (see Fig. 2) or pregnancy in the rabbit (99). In pseudopregnancy the volume remains at about 0.5 ml/day per oviduct from 3 to 12 days postovulation and then slowly returns to the estrous level by 17 days postovulation. During pregnancy the volume continues to fall until day 24, when it is 0.3 ml/day per oviduct (19, 92, 99). Similar observations have been made with sheep (17). Injection of 0.5 mg progesterone per kg per day in cottonseed oil in combination with 0.5 μg ECP per kg to estrogen-primed rabbits also reduces the secretion rate by 50% (67).

Nearly four times as much fluid accumulates in the ampulla of the ligated rabbit oviduct as in the isthmus region of the rabbit oviduct (44). The different volumes may reflect a histological or secretory variation, or both, from one segment to another. The isthmus, with a thick, muscular wall and a small lumen, would give a great deal more resistance to fluid accumulation than the ampulla, with a thin wall and a larger lumen.

A change in the volume of oviducal fluid could assume importance if accompanied by the dilution of an essential constituent or the concentration of an inhibitor of egg cleavage. Some drugs that alter the fluid volume produced by intact animals include antiestrogens [1(p-2 diethylaminoethoxyphenyl)-1 phenyl-2 p-anisylethanol (MER-25)], which decrease volume (91), and parasympathomimetics (pilocarpine), which increase volume probably via cholinergic innervation of the oviduct (19).

Direction of Flow

Only a few attempts have been made to determine the direction of flow of oviducal fluid. In the rabbit, sheep, and cow, 90% of the fluid flows into the peritoneal cavity, except 3–6 days after ovulation when the isthmic end of the tube is relaxed and the egg passes into the uterus (17, 23, 24, 48). The rabbit isthmus relaxes again at the time of parturition, and in the immature animal the isthmus and uterotubal junction are relatively relaxed at all times (64). Bellve & McDonald (17) have demonstrated in the ewe that the volume of fluid circulating through the ampullary end of the tube closely parallels the total fluid produced for each day of the estrous cycle. Maximum flow occurs on the second day after the onset of estrus and steadily declines until day 15. Isthmic flow is very low except from days 3 to 6 after the onset of estrus, when as much as one-third of the fluid passes into the uterus, which

coincides with the passage of the egg into the uterus (17). The blockage of the isthmic end of the oviduct is estrogen dependent; induced edema and flexure of the wall of the uterotubal junction in the ewe (48) and tonic contraction of the isthmic musculature in the cow (24) are the suggested mechanisms for closure. Directional flow of oviducal fluid in the ewe at the onset of the breeding season differs markedly between the first and second ovarian cycles (Fig. 3). In the first ovarian cycle, peak isthmic flow preceded the peak ampullar flow by 1.7 ± 0.9 days; in the second ovarian cycle, peak isthmic flow followed that of ampullar flow by 1.1 ± 0.5 days (18). The sequence of flow in the first ovarian cycle was similar to that in an estrogen-treated, ovariectomized ewe (101). The sequence of flow in the second ovarian cycle was similar to that previously observed during the normal estrous cycle (17), which indicates that progesterone can prevent the increase in isthmic flow during the period of estrogen dominance before the next ovulation (18). Fluid movement probably does not play an important role in egg transport. The direction of flow is opposite to the movement of the ovum at ovulation. Later, when the eggs pass into the uterus, peristaltic movements, rather than a surge of fluid, carry the eggs through the junction (142). Thus blockage of the isthmic end of the tube appears to assure transport of the eggs to the uterus at the proper time, and the fluid simply follows the path of least resistance.

COMPOSITION OF THE FLUID

Although rabbit and sheep oviducal fluid has been analyzed extensively, fluid from cow, sow, and monkey has also been used (41, 49, 50, 73, 98, 99, 113, 114, 119).

Physical Properties

The physical properties of oviducal fluid are important to study, because they influence the composition of the fluid, the substances transported to the lumen of the oviduct, and the role of active transfer of constituents between the gametes and the fluid medium.

The osmolarity of intact estrous rabbit oviducal fluid ranges from 302 to 310 mOsm (129). Ovariectomy significantly increases osmolarity, which is reduced by estrogen (ECP) injection. Progesterone treatment after estrogen priming also increases the osmolarity of rabbit oviducal fluid (66). The dry matter content of oviducal fluid from progesterone-injected, ovariectomized rabbits is significantly higher (14.8%) than that of estrogen-treated rabbits (11.9%). There is no significant change in the specific gravity or viscosity of rabbit oviducal fluid under any of the above hormonal treatments.

Constituents

Recently the structure, metabolism, and fluid composition of each segment of the oviduct have been

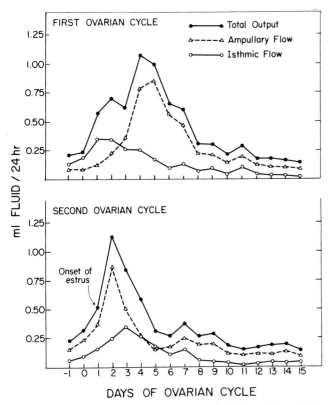

FIG. 3. Flow of tubal fluid from each end of the oviduct of the ewe at first and second ovarian cycles of the breeding season. [From Bellve & McDonald (18).]

studied (74, 100). Each segment of the oviduct, infundibulum (preampulla), ampulla, and isthmus (isthmic and uterotubal junction segments), with its own distinct structure and cytology, certainly has a specific function (118). The infundibulum is laden with cilia, which are important for transport of ova toward the ampulla. Secretory cells in the epithelium of the ampulla contain PAS-positive material that is not destroyed by α-amylase and is stained by methylene blue at various pH values; extinction occurred at pH 2.0, which indicates the presence of mucoproteins and acid mucopolysaccharides (36, 67). This secretory material is released after ovulation, when the zygote is in the ampulla (42, 53, 104). Mucopolysaccharide envelopment of the egg is very pronounced in the rabbit and opossum and has been observed in several other mammals (2, 6, 56). When mouse eggs are in the ampulla, a specific environment is formed—ampullary fluid distends the walls of the ampulla, and the ampullary-isthmic junction is closed (118). Similarly, in the isthmus of the mouse oviduct, when the lumen is distended by secretion in those loops containing the zygotes, the other loops are collapsed. The uterotubal junction, with its heavy, muscular wall and narrow lumen, probably regulates movement of the zygote to the uterus at the proper time. When the uterotubal junction of the rabbit oviduct was removed and the remaining oviduct anastomosed to the uterine horn, normal implantation occurred in only 41% of embryos, compared with 96% implantation in the intact, contralateral side of the control. Probably the best explanation for this difference is that the oviduct without a uterotubal junction fails to retain the ova until they are ready for implantation (45, 107).

Metabolic studies on the anatomic regions of the rabbit oviduct revealed that the ampulla utilizes significantly more oxygen than does the isthmus under all hormonal conditions. During progesterone treatment the ampulla produces significantly more lactate than does the isthmus but not significantly more than the infundibulum (74). Lactate is necessary for the development of the mouse blastocyst (141).

In oviducal fluid accumulated in ligated segments of the rabbit oviduct for 3 days, sodium, bicarbonate, inorganic phosphate, protein, and lactate concentrations increased significantly from the fimbriated end to the uterotubal junction, whereas chloride concentration decreased (44). Oviducal fluid from ligated segments contains higher bicarbonate and much lower lactate and protein levels than oviducal fluid collected by methods allowing free flow of the fluid to a reservoir (44, 67). Whether the differences in composition of fluid in ligated segments are due to pressure buildup, collection techniques, or functional causes remains to be clarified.

Rabbit oviducal fluid contains oxygen, sodium, chloride, potassium, magnesium, zinc, calcium, phosphate, bicarbonate, lactate, pyruvate, glucose, inositol, phospholipid, urea, amino acids (alanine, glutamic acid, glycine, serine, threonine, tryptophan, methionine, valine, taurine, glutamine, lysine, aspartic acid, and leucine), sialic acid, one or more acid mucopolysaccharides, one or more mucoproteins, and such enzymes as amylase, alkaline phosphatase, diesterase, and lysozyme (Table 1). Acetic acid and an unidentified fatty acid are present; the amount of volatile fatty acids ranges from 2.6 to 5.2 mg/ml (131).

The protein separation of rabbit oviducal fluid obtained by disc gel electrophoresis and immunoelectrophoresis demonstrates that the major proteins are from serum (125). Albumin is the most prominent protein of the rabbit oviduct, but protein species that are not found in serum and that must arise from the secretory cell of the oviducal epithelium are present [Fig. 4; (125)].

Sheep oviducal fluid contains sodium; chloride; potassium; magnesium; calcium; phosphate; bicarbonate; lactate; glucose; citrate; lipids; carbohydrates; such amino acids as lysine, histidine, arginine, aspartic acid, threonine, isoleucine, tyrosine, and phenylalanine (117); proteins; and GPC diesterase [Table 2; (77, 116, 119)].

Sodium, chloride, potassium, inorganic phosphate, reducing sugars, total fat, total protein, ash, and dry matter content have been determined in cow oviducal fluid stripped from the tubes of killed animals (113).

The amino acids in the oviducal fluid of the sow are glycine, lysine, proline, alanine, aspartic acid, ornithine, leucine, valine, glutamic acid, arginine, tyrosine, isoleucine, phenylalanine, threonine, histidine, serine, cystine, and methionine. Glycine is the predominant amino acid. The estrous sow produces 2.7 ml oviducal fluid per day with a pH of 7.9 (50).

The rhesus monkey exhibits a definite cyclic pattern of oviducal fluid volume. At the height of estrus, 3.4 ml oviducal fluid is produced per day (97). The levels of

TABLE 1. *Composition of Rabbit Oviducal Fluid*

Constituent	Amount*	Refs.	Constituent	Amount*	Refs.
pH	7.8–8.0	73	Glutamic acid	36	59, 73
Oxygen, mm Hg	45–60	19, 20, 96	Glycine	17	59, 73
Sodium, mg	32–33	19, 73	Serine	1.1	59, 73
Chloride, mg	39–41	73, 76, 99	Threonine	Trace	59, 73
Potassium	200–400	73, 76, 99	Tryptophan	Trace	59, 73
Magnesium	3.1–3.8	73	Methionine	Trace	59, 73
Zinc	6.3–6.7	73	Valine	Trace	59, 73
Calcium	160–320	73, 76	Taurine	Trace	59, 73
Phosphate (PO_4^{3-})	3.7–6.1	73	Glutamine	Trace	59, 73
Total phosphate	8.1–9.3		Lysine		73
Bicarbonate	1.7–1.9	72, 73, 133	Aspartic acid		73
			Leucine		73
Carbohydrate	60–370	73, 99	Volatile fatty	2.6–5.2	131
Lactate	31–189	21, 73, 76	acids, mg		
Pyruvate	14.5–16.7	76	Sialic acid		144
Glucose	0–257	21, 73, 76	Amylase		102
Inositol	26	60	Alkaline phosphatase		7
Phospholipid	0–80	21			
Urea	600	62	Diesterase (GPC)		137
Total protein, mg	2.1–2.7	73, 76			
Alanine	32	59, 73	Lysozyme	3.9	47

* Unless otherwise indicated, μg/ml.

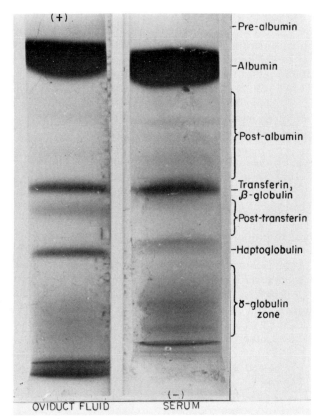

FIG. 4. Disc gel electrophoresis of proteins in oviducal fluid and blood serum from an estrous rabbit.

TABLE 2. *Composition of Sheep Oviducal Fluid*

Constituent*	Hormonal State			Refs.
	Estrus	Metestrus	Diestrus	
Sodium, mg	3.2	3.0	3.2	119
Chloride, mg	4.6	4.4	4.8	119
Potassium, μg	320	295	317	119
Magnesium, μg	19.8	21.8	24.6	119
Calcium, μg	122	114	121	119
Phosphorus (PO_4^{3-}), μg	8.7	4.6	8.4	119
Total phosphorus, μg	40.5	21.3	46.3	119
Bicarbonate, mg	1.2	1.0	1.1	119, 128
Glucose, μg	285–318	245–335		77, 128
Fructose, μg	0.52	0.89		128
Pyruvate, μg	16.2	16.3		128
Lactate, μg	150–226	114–422	382	77, 119, 128
Citrate, μg	8			77
Lipid choline, μg	10	5		77
Total protein, mg	6.7–30	4.8–28	2.1–32	77, 116, 119, 128
Carbohydrate, μg	613	437	670	
Dry matter, mg	32	40		77

* Mean values expressed as unit/ml.

sodium, potassium, calcium, lactate, glucose, hexosamine, and total proteins have been reported from preovulatory and superovulated rhesus oviducal fluid (98).

The major protein fractions of human tubal fluid are albumin, α_1-, α_2-, β_1-, β_2-, and γ-globulins; distribution of these fractions is approximately the same as that in serum (103). The oviduct produces a specific β-glycoprotein, which is absent in blood (103).

Hormonal Influence on Constituents

Significant changes occur in the concentrations of various constituents of oviducal fluid as the hormonal state of the female changes in the rabbit, sheep, and cow.

In ovariectomized rabbits, sodium content of oviducal fluid is not significantly changed by the hormonal state of the animal. Progesterone treatment (1.0 mg/kg per day in 1.0 ml cottonseed oil) significantly lowers chloride concentration after estrogen treatment (1.0 μg/kg per day in 1.0 ml cottonseed oil), and hormonal withdrawal significantly lowers the potassium content of oviducal fluid. Progesterone causes the calcium concentration of oviducal fluid to increase, whereas the lack of hormonal treatment causes a significant increase in magnesium levels. Hormonal withdrawal or progesterone treatment of estrogen-primed rabbits causes a significant increase in lactate and protein content. Zinc and phosphate levels are not influenced by the hormonal state of the female (Table 3).

No changes in potassium or chloride levels are found in rabbit oviducal fluid between estrus and pseudopregnancy, but sodium concentration is significantly lowered in the first 3 days of pregnancy (99). Calcium

TABLE 3. *Influence of Estrogen and Progesterone on Constituents in Rabbit Oviducal Fluid*

Constituents[a]	Estrogen	Progesterone plus Estrogen	Progesterone	Cottonseed Oil
Sodium, mg	2.60±0.07	2.69±0.05	2.48±0.07	2.60±0.07
Chloride, mg	2.84±0.07	2.61±0.10	2.34±0.10[b]	2.56±0.13
Potassium, μg	201±6	207±9	187±8	185±8[e]
Calcium, μg	116±9	142±8[d]	138±10	131±10
Magnesium, μg	4.0±0.2	3.9±0.1	4.1±0.2	4.6±2[e]
Zinc, μg	6.8±0.1	6.7±0.1	6.6±0.1	6.6±0.1
Phosphate (PO_4^{3-}), μg	5.6±0.8	7.1±0.5	6.4±0.5	5.7±0.3
Total phosphate, μg	7.0±0.9	9.3±0.6	9.1±0.6	8.8±0.5
Lactate, μg	181±6	214±12	257±11[f]	227±11[f]
Protein, mg	1.8±0.1	2.0±0.1	2.8±0.1[g]	2.7±0.1[g]

[a] Mean values ± SE expressed as unit/ml for 30 determinations for each hormonal treatment. [b] Chloride content with progesterone treatment significantly lower than with estrogen treatment by t test; $P < 0.05$. [Snedecor (127).] [c] Potassium content with cottonseed oil (CSO) treatment significantly lower than with estrogen treatment; $P < 0.05$. [d] Progesterone treatment significantly raised calcium content after estrogen treatment; $P < 0.05$. [e] Hormone withdrawal significantly raised magnesium level; $P < 0.05$. [f] Lactate content significantly increased with progesterone or CSO treatment; $P < 0.01$. [g] Protein content significantly increased with progesterone or CSO treatment; $P < 0.001$.

content of rabbit oviducal fluid significantly increases after ovulation (76).

Considerable variation exists among species in the electrolyte content of oviducal fluid in response to estrogen and progesterone (113, 121). In ewes the levels of sodium, potassium, and chloride are significantly lower at metestrus than at diestrus, but magnesium levels are lowest at estrus [(119); Table 2]. At estrus the oviducal fluid of the cow is lowest in sodium and potassium concentrations and highest in calcium concentration (113).

The concentration of total phosphorus, acid-insoluble phosphorus, carbohydrate, lactate, and protein in intact, normal ewes does not change significantly between stages of the cycle, but there is considerable variation among estimations within each stage (119).

The hydrogen ion concentration of rabbit oviducal fluid doubles during pregnancy (pH 7.43) compared to the estrous state in which pH is 7.75 (21). Sheep oviducal fluid at proestrus has a pH of 6.4–6.6, at estrus and metestrus a pH of 6.8–7.0, and at diestrus a pH of 6.0–6.4 (63). The alkalinity of rabbit oviducal fluid is due to a high bicarbonate content (133). Whether the source of bicarbonate is plasma or intracellular metabolism and in what form it is transported (via HCO_3^- or hydrated CO_2) are not known. Carbonic anhydrase occurs in the oviduct of a variety of mammalian species, and hydration of CO_2 is probably the mechanism of transport. Progesterone stimulates carbonic anhydrase activity in the cow and rabbit, but not in the ewe. No carbonic anhydrase is present in the nonpregnant oviduct of mice, cats, or dogs (86).

Glucose, maltose, maltotriose, maltotetrose, and fructose are present in oviducal extracts (61). Estrogen causes an increase in the oligosaccharide level, whereas progesterone and ovariectomy decrease the level. Glucose concentration (260 μg/ml) is significantly increased in rabbit oviducal fluid after ovulation (290 μg/ml), as are lactate (190–280 μg/ml) and pyruvate (16–22 μg/ml) (76). The sialic acid content of rabbit oviducal fluid is highest during estrus and drops after ovariectomy (144). After castration, hexosamine content increases beyond levels of estrus or pregnancy (144). Inositol content (26 μg/ml) in intact female rabbit oviducal fluid, which is measured by observing the turbidity produced by growth of an inositol-dependent yeast, is not influenced by estrogen or ovariectomy but is doubled by progesterone injection (60).

The total nitrogen content of rabbit oviducal secretions remains constant at 6–7% dry matter. However, the protein content of the fluid is 25% of dry weight at estrus, 30% during pregnancy, and 35% after ovariectomy (144). Urea content of oviducal fluid is 531 μg/ml in intact rabbits and is decreased to half that value by ovariectomy. Progesterone treatment has no effect on urea content (62) but causes a doubling in glycine and serine content over estrogen treatment (59).

The phospholipid content of rabbit oviducal fluid reaches 80 μg/ml at estrus (21). In human beings ovi-ducal lipids are due to fatty infiltration during the intramenstrual period and disappear during pregnancy and menopause (38, 79). Adult human oviducal lipids are confined mostly to the connective tissue cells. The human infant oviduct is free of lipids (124).

Oviducal fluid from the estrous rabbit contains 3.9 μg lysozyme per ml (47). Lysosomal sacs have been identified in the secretory cells of human oviducts and have been observed to rupture late in the menstrual cycle (41). Alkaline phosphatase occurs in the epithelium of the infundibulum and ampulla of the oviduct of several animals and is not influenced by cyclic changes (7, 29). Diesterase (glycerylphosphorylcholine-splitting enzyme) has been isolated in rabbit, sow, rat, mouse, and cow oviducal fluid (135–140). Activity of diesterase is highest at proestrus and estrus and lowest at metestrus and diestrus (139).

Peptidase activity in the rabbit oviduct is essentially constant, regardless of the hormonal state, but peptidase levels sharply increase in the rabbit endometrium during pseudopregnancy (4). This indicates that the biochemical response of the oviduct to hormonal influences may be different from that of the uterus.

PHYSIOLOGY OF SPERM IN THE FLUID

The sperm are transported from the site of deposition to the oviduct in less than 2 hr in all species studied (27). Therefore the sperm come under the influence of the oviducal environment soon after mating and must survive there for fertilization to occur. The duration of motility of sperm in the oviduct is much longer than their capacity to fertilize (22, 85, 86).

When sperm reach the uterus and oviducts, their metabolism, respiration, and morphology change. The oviduct provides a specific environment to foster maximal spermatic metabolism at estrus (15, 30, 70, 78, 114).

The oviduct has an oxygen tension well above the minimum 4–5 mm Hg necessary for motility and respiration of sperm (110). Olds & VanDemark (114) first showed that bovine oviducal fluid stimulated spermatic respiration. This observation has now been extended to the rabbit and sheep (26, 70, 72). Oviducal fluid secreted by the ewe at estrus increases spermatic respiration more than fluid produced at other times during the cycle (26). Several different factors are responsible for the stimulation of spermatic respiration and glycolysis. Wales & Restall (134) found that the oviducal fluid of the ewe stimulated spermatic respiration more than did saline in the absence of glucose and in the presence of glucose stimulated aerobic and anaerobic glycolysis, but not respiration. This effect was abolished by dialysis; they concluded that substrate alone was responsible for the stimulatory effect. Hamner & Williams (71, 72) identified bicarbonate as a stimulatory factor in the oviducal fluid of the rabbit and, because they did not consistently identify a nondialyzable factor present, concluded that bicarbonate was the sole constituent responsible for stimulation. However, a nondialyzable, heat-labile factor affecting sperm in vivo and in vitro from rabbit uterine and oviducal fluid has recently been identified (78).

Bicarbonate stimulates spermatic respiration of several species, including man (72, 108), bull (75, 80), rabbit, boar, and ram (52, 126). Rabbit sperm respire maximally at 2.36×10^{-3} M HCO_3^-, whereas human, rooster, and bull sperm respire maximally at 3.54×10^{-3} M HCO_3^-. Even though human sperm possess the components of a respiratory system (89) and actively oxidize glucose (132), their respiratory activity had been considered to be only 1–2 $\mu l/10^8$ sperm per hr (88, 122). However, washed human sperm respire at a rate of 13.7 $\mu l/10^8$ sperm per hr in the presence of 3.54×10^{-3} M HCO_3^- and only at 1.4 $\mu l/10^8$ sperm per hr without bicarbonate (72), which indicates an important role for bicarbonate in human sperm metabolism. Unwashed human sperm in whole semen containing bicarbonate respire at rates up to 9.5 $\mu l/10^8$ sperm per hr (123).

The fluids of the female reproductive tract have many constituents supporting spermatic metabolism. Glucose, lactate, inositol, hexosamines, several free amino acids, and phospholipids, as well as oxygen and carbon dioxide, are available to support oxidative respiration (22). Bicarbonate ensures an alkaline medium and furnishes a source of carbon for metabolic pathways (72). Amylase is present to digest glycogen, and a diesterase that hydrolyses glycerylphosphorylcholine from the seminal plasma is secreted by the female genital tract and may be important in uterine inseminated species (137). The environment of the female reproductive tract surrounding the sperm probably is important in maintaining the proper oxidative state, pH, and osmolarity to prevent spermatic agglutination and promote capacitation (9, 22). [Capacitation is the final maturing process that sperm undergo in the female reproductive tract to gain the ability to fertilize the egg (9).]

Factors necessary for capacitation of rabbit sperm are present in the oviduct (3) and are specific for the female reproductive tract (16, 68). Rabbit sperm are only partially capacitated after incubation in the rat oviduct or uterus for 8–18 hr (16, 68). However, among those species that have been shown to require capacitation, the females have nonspecies-specific factors in their reproductive tracts for at least part of the capacitation process. Rabbit sperm appear to be the most difficult to capacitate of any species and the hamster and sheep the easiest. Golden hamster sperm can be capacitated in oviducal fluid from the mouse and rat in 5 hr (11) and in follicular fluid from the rabbit (145). Rabbit sperm have not been capacitated in oviducal fluid (69).

The oviducts prepare sperm to fertilize eggs throughout pseudopregnancy, but the fertilization rate is lower at midpseudopregnancy than at the beginning or end. Large numbers of sperm overwhelm the ability of the oviduct to render sperm able to fertilize eggs during pseudopregnancy. These observations indicate that the ability of the oviduct to maintain and prepare the sperm to fertilize the egg is reduced by progesterone dominance. The uterus loses its ability to prepare the sperm to fertilize eggs after 6–10 days of pseudopregnancy (37).

While the sperm are being prepared to fertilize the eggs, they gain the ability to establish contact with the surface of the egg (14) and undergo an acrosomal change characterized by fusion and vesicle formation between plasma membrane and outer acrosomal membrane (15). Many mammalian sperm undergo the acrosome reaction (9, 12). Ideas about these phenomena are speculative, and many questions remain to be answered about the biochemical and morphological changes.

CONSTITUENTS SIGNIFICANT TO
ZYGOTE DEVELOPMENT

In most mammals the oviduct supports the developing blastocyst for the first 3–4 days postovulation (27, 55). The physical and biochemical conditions required for fertilization have been learned through in vitro fertilization studies (31). A simple salt solution, originally used by Hammond (65) to culture mouse ova, plus crystalline bovine albumin as a protein source, pyruvate or lactate as an energy source, and bicarbonate for buffering are required as a minimal media. The osmolarity of the synthetic medium is 280 mOsm; pH of the medium is 7.8 at 37 C under 5% CO_2-in-air atmosphere. Oxygen tension and pH seem to be especially important in fertilization. Rabbit ova are fertilized best in a medium containing bicarbonate with a pH of 7.8 and an oxygen tension of 8% (32). Hamster ova are fertilized at a maximum rate in Tyrode's solution under 5% CO_2-in-air at pH 7.6 (13). These media and conditions are very similar to the conditions in the oviduct (20, 96).

Bicarbonate ion has been identified as the dailyzable, corona cell-dispersing factor of rabbit oviducal fluid (94, 129). At 46 mEq/liter this ion will initiate corona cell dispersion, and 66 mEq/liter causes complete dispersal in 2 hr at 37.5 C without mechanical agitation. Corona cell dispersion is inhibited in vivo by acetazolamide, a carbonic anhydrase inhibitor. Acetazolamide also delays the cleavage of rabbit eggs when given at, or within 10 hr after, coitus (111). Mouse blastocysts develop in vitro in media with osmolarities of 200–354 mOsm; the optimum is 267 mOsm (34).

Austin (8) found that increasing the ratio of potassium to sodium in the culture medium causes a swelling of the blastocyst in the two-cell mouse ovum. He concludes that this is indicative of an active transport of potassium in the developing ovum. The mechanism of active transport of constituents between the oviducal fluid and the sperm and eggs needs a great deal of study.

The 16.1 ± 1.0 μg pyruvate per ml of rabbit oviducal

fluid present at estrus increases to 22.1 ± 8.0 μg/ml after ovulation (93). Pyruvate can replace lactate as an essential energy source for the development of mouse embryos in vitro; the optimum concentration is 28.8 μg/ml of medium at pH 7.4 (35). Interestingly follicular cells produce pyruvate as a metabolite of glucose (46); therefore metabolic activity of the follicular cells in the oviduct after ovulation may be an important source of energy for the fertilized ovum.

While the zygote is in the ampulla, the ampulla produces significantly more lactate because of the in-influence of progesterone (74). Rabbit oviducal epithelium produces an average of 290 μmole lactate per gram dry tissue at estrus, compared to 430 μmole 8–11 days into pseudopregnancy (99, 105, 106). The doubling of lactate level from estrus to pregnancy would account for the increase in hydrogen ion concentration during pregnancy (95).

Secretory cells produce glycogen granules that are secreted into the lumen of the isthmus (118). Two-cell mouse embryos show an increase in glycogen content while they are in the isthmus, which indicates that the secreted glycogen is produced for, and utilized by, the zygotes (130).

The first cleavage of rabbit ova occurs in amino acid-free medium, but the second cleavage requires cysteine, tryptophan, phenylalanine, lysine, arginine, and valine. Further cleavage toward the morula stage requires the addition of methionine, threonine, and glutamine (43).

Some evidence indicates that mucopolysaccharides or glycoproteins secreted by the oviducal epithelium are needed to sustain the blastocyst before implantation, but the theory is controversial (1, 2, 33, 57, 58).

CONCLUSIONS

The oviduct functions obviously and subtly in the early development of the embryo. That the oviduct is responsible for the pickup and transport of the ovum to the uterus has been known for a long time (27). However, we have recently gained an appreciation for the environment of the oviduct and for specific functions of the various segments of the oviduct (93, 113). Oviducal fluid is derived by transudation from the blood and secretion from oviducal epithelium. Both transudation and secretion are greatly influenced by estrogen and progesterone. Estrogen stimulates fluid production and secretory activity within the epithelium. Progesterone depresses fluid production and causes release of secretory materials from the epithelial cells. Except for 3–6 days postovulation, when as much as 30% of the fluid passes into the uterus, the fluid flows toward the abdominal cavity.

Oviducal fluid from six mammalian species has been biochemically analyzed. The hormonal state of the female influences the electrolyte content of oviducal fluid. This response varies considerably among species. Specific proteins which arise from secretory cells of the oviducal epithelium and serum proteins are present in oviducal fluid. Estrous oviducal fluid stimulates maximal spermatic metabolism. Several constituents, including glucose, pyruvate, lactate, bicarbonate, and an unidentified, nondialyzable, heat-labile constituent are responsible for the stimulation of respiration and glycolysis.

The contents of oviducal fluid important to fertilization and early development of the embryo have been elucidated by biochemical analysis and in vitro fertilization studies. Minimal requirements include a simple salt solution (280–300 mOsm), protein for macromolecular support, pyruvate or lactate as an energy source, bicarbonate for buffering, a reduced oxygen tension (5–8%), and an alkaline pH (7.4–7.8). Mucoproteins secreted by the oviducal epithelium appear to be needed for development and expansion of the blastocyst before its implantation.

REFERENCES

1. ADAMS, C. E. Egg development in the rabbit: the influence of postcoital ligation of the uterine tube and of ovariectomy. *Endocrinology* 16: 283–293, 1958.

2. ADAMS, C. E. Development of the rabbit eggs with special reference to the mucin layer (Abstract). *Acta Endocrinol.* 1: 687, 1960.

3. ADAMS, C. E., AND M. C. CHANG. Capacitation of rabbit spermatozoa in the Fallopian tube and in the uterus. *J. Exptl. Zool.* 151: 159–165, 1962.

4. ALBERS, H. J., J. M. BEDFORD, AND M. C. CHANG. Uterine peptidase activity in the rat and rabbit during pseudopregnancy. *Am. J. Physiol.* 201: 554–556, 1961.

5. ANDERSEN, D. H. Lymphatics of the Fallopian tube of the sow. *Contrib. Embryol. Carnegie Inst. Wash.* 19: 135–147, 1927.

6. ASSHETON, R. A re-investigation into the early stages of the development of the rabbit. *Quart. J. Microscop. Sci.* 37: 113–161, 1894.

7. AUGUSTIN, E., AND A. MOSER. Vorkommen und Aktivität von alkalischer Phosphatase im Eileiter der Ratte und in unbefruchteten und befruchteten Eiern während der Tubenwanderung. *Arch. Gynaekol.* 185: 759–780, 1955.

8. AUSTIN, C. R. *The Mammalian Egg.* Springfield, Ill.: Thomas, 1961.

9. AUSTIN, C. R. Sperm capacitation—biological significance in various species. In: *Schering Symposium on Mechanisms Involved in Conception. Advances in the Biosciences*, edited by G. Raspé. New York: Pergamon Press, 1970, vol. 4, p. 5–12.

10. BACSICH, R., AND W. J. HAMILTON. Some observations on vitally stained rabbit ova with special reference to their albuminous coat. *J. Embryol. Exptl. Morphol.* 2: 81–87, 1954.

11. BARROS, C. In vitro capacitation of golden hamster spermatozoa with Fallopian tube fluid of the mouse and rat. *J. Reprod. Fertility* 17: 203–206, 1968.

12. BARROS, C., J. M. BEDFORD, L. E. FRANKLIN, AND C. R. AUSTIN. Membrane vesiculation as a feature of the mammalian acrosome reaction. *J. Cell Biol.* 34: c1–c5, 1967.

13. BAVISTER, B. D. Environmental factors important for in vitro fertilization in the hamster. *J. Reprod. Fertility* 18: 544–545, 1969.

14. BEDFORD, J. M. The influence of the uterine environment upon rabbit spermatozoa. In: *Reproduction in the Female Mammal*, edited by G. E. Lamming and E. C. Amoroso. New York: Plenum Press, 1966, p. 478.

15. BEDFORD, J. M. Morphological aspects of sperm capacitation in mammals. In: *Schering Symposium on Mechanisms Involved in Conception. Advances in the Biosciences*, edited by G. Raspé. New York: Pergamon Press, 1970, vol. 4, p. 35–50.

16. BEDFORD, J. M., AND R. SHALKOVSKY. Species-specificity of sperm capacitation in the rabbit. *J. Reprod. Fertility* 13: 361–364, 1967.

17. BELLVE, A. R., AND M. F. McDONALD. Directional flow of Fallopian tube secretion in the Romney ewe. *J. Reprod. Fertility* 15: 357–364, 1968.

18. BELLVE, A. R., AND M. F. McDONALD. Directional flow of Fallopian tube secretion in the ewe at onset of the breeding season. *J. Reprod. Fertility* 22: 147–149, 1970.

19. BISHOP, D. W. Active secretion in the rabbit oviduct. *Am. J. Physiol.* 187: 347–352, 1956.

20. BISHOP, D. W. Oxygen concentrations in the rabbit genital tract. *Intern. Congr. Animal Reprod.* 3: 53–55, 1956.

21. BISHOP, D. W. Metabolic conditions within the oviduct of the rabbit. *Intern. J. Fertility* 2: 11–22, 1957.

22. BISHOP, D. W. Sperm physiology in relation to the oviduct. In: *The Mammalian Oviduct*, edited by E. S. E. Hafez and R. J. Blandau. Chicago: Univ. of Chicago Press, 1969, p. 231–250.

23. BLACK, D. L., AND S. A. ASDELL. Mechanism controlling entry of ova into rabbit uterus. *Am. J. Physiol.* 197: 1275–1278, 1959.

24. BLACK, D. L., AND J. DAVIS. A blocking mechanism in the cow oviduct. *J. Reprod. Fertility* 4: 21–26, 1962.

25. BLACK, D. L., R. T. DUBY, AND J. RIESEN. Apparatus for the continuous collection of sheep oviduct fluid. *J. Reprod. Fertility* 6: 257–260, 1962.

26. BLACK, D. L., L. V. CROWLEY, R. T. DUBY, AND C. H. SPILMAN. Oviduct secretion in the ewe and the effect of oviduct fluid on oxygen uptake by ram spermatozoa in vitro. *J. Reprod. Fertility* 15: 127–130, 1968.

27. BLANDAU, R. J. Gamete transport—comparative aspects. In: *The Mammalian Oviduct*, edited by E. S. E. Hafez and R. J. Blandau. Chicago: Univ. of Chicago Press, 1969, p. 129–162.

28. BORELL, U., O. NILSSON, J. WERSALL, AND A. WESTMAN. Electron-microscope studies of the epithelium of the rabbit Fallopian tube under different hormonal influences. *Acta Obstet. Gynecol. Scand.* 35: 35–41, 1956.

29. BOURNE, G., AND M. MACKINNON. The distribution of alkaline-phosphatase in various tissues. *Quart. J. Exptl. Physiol.* 32: 1–18, 1943.

30. BRACKETT, B. G. Respiration of spermatozoa after in utero incubation in estrus and pseudopregnant rabbits. In: *Proceedings of the Sixth International Congress of Animal Reproduction*, edited by C. Thibault. Paris: Institut National de la Recherche Agronomique, vol. 1, p. 43–46.

31. BRACKETT, B. G. In vitro fertilization of mammalian ova. In: *Schering Symposium on Mechanisms Involved in Conception. Advances in the Biosciences*, edited by G. Raspé. New York: Pergamon Press, 1970, vol. 4, p. 73–94.

32. BRACKETT, B. G., AND W. L. WILLIAMS. Fertilization of rabbit ova in a defined medium. *Fertility Sterility* 19: 144–155, 1968.

33. BRADEN, A. W. H. Properties of the membranes of rat and rabbit eggs. *Australian J. Sci. Res. Bull.* 5: 460–471, 1952.

34. BRINSTER, R. L. Studies on the development of mouse embryos in vitro. I. The effect of osmolarity and hydrogen ion concentration. *J. Exptl. Zool.* 158: 49–58, 1965.

35. BRINSTER, R. L. Studies on the development of mouse embryos in vitro. II. The effect of energy source. *J. Exptl. Zool.* 158: 59–68, 1965.

36. BROWER, L. K., AND E. ANDERSON. Cytological events associated with the secretory process in the rabbit oviduct. *Biol. Reprod.* 1: 130–148, 1969.

37. BROWN, S. W., AND C. E. HAMNER. Sperm capacitating ability of the female rabbit during estrus and pseudopregnancy. *Fertility Sterility* 22: 92, 1970.

38. BUTOMO, W. Zur Frage von den zyklischen Veranderungen in den Tuben (uber Tubenlipoide). *Arch. Gynaekol.* 131: 306–323, 1927.

39. CARLSON, D., D. L. BLACK, AND G. R. HOWE. Oviduct secretion in the cow. *J. Reprod. Fertility* 22: 549–552, 1970.

40. CLEWE, T. H., AND L. MASTROIANNI, JR. A method for continuous volumetric collection of oviduct secretions. *J. Reprod. Fertility* 1: 146–150, 1960.

41. CLYMAN, M. J. Electron microscopy of the human Fallopian tube. *Fertility Sterility* 17: 281–301, 1966.

42. COURRIER, R., AND H. GERLINGER. Le cycle glandulaire de l'epithelium de l'oviducte chez la chienne. *Compt. Rend. Soc. Biol.* 87: 1363–1365, 1922.

43. DANIEL, J. C., AND J. D. OLSON. Amino acid requirement for cleavage of the rabbit ovum. *J. Reprod. Fertility* 15: 453–456, 1968.

44. DAVID, A., B. G. BRACKETT, C. R. GARCIA, AND L. MASTROIANNI, JR. Composition of rabbit oviduct fluid in ligated segments of the Fallopian tube. *J. Reprod. Fertility* 19: 285–290, 1969.

45. DAVID, A., B. G. BRACKETT, AND C. R. GARCIA. Effects of microsurgical removal of the rabbit uterotubal junction. *Fertility Sterility* 20: 250–257, 1969.

46. DONAHUE, R. P., AND S. STERN. Follicular cell support of oocyte maturation: production of pyruvate in vitro. *J. Reprod. Fertility* 17: 395–398, 1968.

47. DUKELOW, W. R., H. N. CHERNOFF, AND W. L. WILLIAMS. Stability of spermatozoan decapacitation factor. *Am. J. Physiol.* 211: 826–828, 1966.

48. EDGAR, D. G., AND S. A. ASDELL. The valve-like action of the uterotubal junction of the ewe. *J. Endocrinol.* 21: 315–320, 1960.

49. EDGERTON, L. A., C. E. MARTIN, H. F. TROUT, AND C. W. FOLEY. Collection of fluid from the uterus and oviducts. *J. Animal Sci.* 25: 1265, 1966.

50. ENGLE, C. C., J. S. DUNN, R. O. HOOD, D. J. WILLIAMS, C. W. FOLEY, AND H. F. TROUT. Amino acids in sow and rabbit oviduct fluids. *J. Animal Sci.* 27: 1786, 1968.

51. ESPINASSE, P. G. The oviductal epithelium of the mouse. *J. Anat.* 69: 363–368, 1935.

52. FOLEY, C. W., AND W. L. WILLIAMS. Effect of bicarbonate and oviduct fluid on respiration of spermatozoa. *Proc. Soc. Exptl. Biol. Med.* 126: 634–637, 1967.

53. FREDRICSSON, B. Histochemical observations on the epithelium of human Fallopian tubes. *Acta Obstet. Gynecol. Scand.* 38: 109–127, 1959.

54. FREDRICSSON, B. Histochemistry of the oviduct. In: *The Mammalian Oviduct*, edited by E. S. E. Hafez and R. J. Blandau. Chicago: Univ. of Chicago Press, 1968, p. 311–332.

55. GLASS, L. E. Transfer of native and foreign serum antigens to oviductal mouse eggs. *Am. Zoologist* 3: 135–145, 1963.

56. GREENWALD, G. S. Interruption of pregnancy in the rabbit by the administration of estrogen. *J. Exptl. Zool.* 135: 461–481, 1957.

57. GREENWALD, G. S. Endocrine regulation of the secretion of mucin in the tubal epithelium of the rabbit. *Anat. Record* 130: 477–495, 1958.

58. GREENWALD, G. S. Endocrinology of oviductal secretions. In: *The Mammalian Oviduct*, edited by E. S. E. Hafez and R. J. Blandau. Chicago: Univ. of Chicago Press, 1969, p. 183–201.

59. GREGOIRE, A. T., R. GONGSAKDI, AND A. E. RAKOFF. The free amino acid content of the female rabbit genital tract. *Fertility Sterility* 12: 322–327, 1961.

60. GREGOIRE, A. T., D. GONGSAKDI, AND A. E. RAKOFF. The presence of inositol in genital tract secretions of the female rabbit. *Fertility Sterility* 13: 432–435, 1962.

61. GREGOIRE, A. T., AND R. GIBBON. Glucosyl oligosaccharides

of the rabbit genital tract: effects of ovarian hormone administration. *Intern. J. Fertility* 10: 151–155, 1965.

62. GREGOIRE, A. T., AND A. E. RAKOFF. Urea content of the female rabbit genital tract fluids. *J. Reprod. Fertility* 6: 467–469, 1963.

63. HADEK, R. Alteration of pH in the sheep's oviduct. *Nature* 171: 976–977, 1953.

64. HAFEZ, E. S. E. The uterotubal junction and the luminal fluid of the uterine tube in the rabbit. *Anat. Record* 145: 7–12, 1963.

65. HAMMOND, J. Recovery and culture of tubal mouse ova. *Nature* 163: 28–30, 1949.

66. HAMNER, C. E., AND S. B. FOX. Effect of oestrogen and progesterone on physical properties of rabbit oviduct fluid. *J. Reprod. Fertility* 16: 121–122, 1968.

67. HAMNER, C. E., AND S. B. FOX. Biochemistry of oviductal secretions. In: *The Mammalian Oviduct*, edited by E. S. E. Hafez and R. J. Blandau. Chicago: Univ. of Chicago Press, 1969, p. 333–355.

68. HAMNER, C. E., AND N. J. SOJKA. Capacitation of rabbit spermatozoa: species and organ specificity. *Proc. Soc. Exptl. Biol. Med.* 124: 689–691, 1967.

69. HAMNER, C. E., AND N. J. SOJKA. Requirements for capacitation of rabbit sperm. *Nature* 220: 1042–1043, 1968.

70. HAMNER, C. E., AND W. L. WILLIAMS. Effect of the female reproductive tract on sperm metabolism in the rabbit and fowl. *J. Reprod. Fertility* 5: 143–150, 1963.

71. HAMNER, C. E., AND W. L. WILLIAMS. Effect of bicarbonate on the respiration of spermatozoa. *Federation Proc.* 23: 430, 1964.

72. HAMNER, C. E., AND W. L. WILLIAMS. Identification of sperm stimulating factor of rabbit oviduct fluid. *Proc. Soc. Exptl. Biol. Med.* 117: 240–243, 1964.

73. HAMNER, C. E., AND W. L. WILLIAMS. Composition of rabbit oviduct secretions. *Fertility Sterility* 16: 170–176, 1965.

74. HAMNER, C. E., J. P. JONES, AND S. B. FOX. Effect of estrogen and progesterone on respiration and glycolysis of the rabbit oviduct. *Fertility Sterility* 20: 143–148, 1969.

75. HENLE, G., AND C. W. ZITTLE. Studies of metabolism of bovine epididymal spermatozoa. *Am. J. Physiol.* 136: 70–79, 1942.

76. HOLMDAHL, T. H., AND L. MASTROIANNI, JR. Continuous collection of rabbit oviduct secretions at low temperature. *Fertility Sterility* 16: 587–595, 1965.

77. IRITANI, A., W. R. GOMES, AND N. L. VANDEMARK. Secretion rates and chemical composition of oviduct and uterine fluids in ewes. *Biol. Reprod.* 1: 72–76, 1969.

78. IRITANI, A., W. R. GOMES, AND N. L. VANDEMARK. The effect of whole, dialyzed and heated female genital tract fluids on respiration of rabbit and ram spermatozoa. *Biol. Reprod.* 1: 77–82, 1969.

79. JOEL, C. A. Uber den Ascorbinsaure—Gehalt der menschlichen Tube wahrend Zyklus und Graviditat. *Schweiz. Med. Wochschr.* 71: 1286–1287, 1941.

80. JONES, E. E., AND G. W. SALISBURY. The action of carbon dioxide as a reversible inhibitor of mammalian spermatozoan respiration. *Federation Proc.* 21: 86, 1962.

81. KNEER, M., H. BURGER, AND H. SIMMER. Uber die Atmung der Schleimhaut menschlicher Eileiter. *Arch. Gynaekol.* 181: 561–574, 1952.

82. LEBLOND, C. P. Distribution of periodic acid-reactive carbohydrates in the adult rat. *Am. J. Anat.* 86: 1–25, 1950.

83. LINDAHL, P. E., AND A. NILSSON. On the occurrence of sperm antagglutin in the female rabbit. *Arkiv. Zool.* 7: 223–226, 1954.

84. LINDAHL, P. E., A. INGELMAN-SUNDBERG, M. FURUHJELM, AND A. NILSSON. The sperm anti-agglutinic factor in women. *J. Obstet. Gynaecol. Brit. Empire* 63: 363–371, 1956.

85. LOMBARD, L., B. B. MORGAN, AND S. H. McNUTT. The morphology of the oviduct of virgin heifers in relation to the estrous cycle. *J. Morphol.* 86: 1–15, 1950.

86. LUTWAK-MANN, C. Carbonic anhydrase in the female reproductive tract: occurrence, distribution and hormonal dependence. *J. Endocrinol.* 13: 26–38, 1955.

87. LUTWAK-MANN, C. Glucose, lactic acid and bicarbonate in rabbit blastocyst fluid. *Nature* 193: 653–655, 1962.

88. MacLEOD, J. The role of oxygen in the metabolism and motility of human spermatozoa. *Am. J. Physiol.* 138: 512–518, 1943.

89. MANN, T. Studies on the metabolism of semen. 7. Cytochrome in human spermatozoa. *Biochem. J.* 48: 386–388, 1951.

90. MARCUS, S. L., AND C. E. SARAVIS. Oviduct fluid in the rhesus monkey: a study of its protein components and its origin. *Fertility Sterility* 16: 785–794, 1965.

91. MASTROIANNI, L., JR., R. ABDUL-HARIM, U. SHAH, AND S. J. SEGAL. Changes in the secretion rate of the rabbit oviduct following oral administration of 1-(p-2-diethyl aminoethoxyphenyl)-1-phenyl-2p-anisylethanol. *Endocrinology* 69: 396–398, 1961.

92. MASTROIANNI, L., JR., F. BEER, U. SHAH, AND T. H. CLEWE. Endocrine regulation of oviduct secretions in the rabbit. *Endocrinology* 68: 92–100, 1961.

93. MASTROIANNI, L., JR., AND B. G. BRACKETT. Environmental conditions within the Fallopian tube. In: *Progress in Infertility*, edited by S. J. Behrmen and R. Kistner. Boston: Little, Brown, 1968, p. 195–207.

94. MASTROIANNI, L., JR., AND J. EHTESHAMZADEH. Corona cell dispersing properties of rabbit tubal fluid. *J. Reprod. Fertility* 8: 145–147, 1964.

95. MASTROIANNI, L., JR., W. FORREST, AND W. W. WINTERNITZ. Some metabolic properties of the rabbit oviduct. *Proc. Soc. Exptl. Biol. Med.* 107: 86–88, 1961.

96. MASTROIANNI, L., JR., AND R. JONES. Oxygen tension within the rabbit Fallopian tube. *J. Reprod. Fertility* 9: 99–102, 1965.

97. MASTROIANNI, L., JR., U. SHAH, AND R. ABDUL-KARIM. Prolonged volumetric collection of oviduct fluid in the rhesus monkey. *Fertility Sterility* 12: 417–424, 1961.

98. MASTROIANNI, L., JR., M. URZUA, M. AVALOS, AND R. STAMBAUGH. Some observations on Fallopian tube fluid in the monkey. *Am. J. Obstet. Gynecol.* 103: 703–709, 1969.

99. MASTROIANNI, L., JR., AND R. C. WALLACH. Effect of ovulation and early gestation on oviduct secretions in the rabbit. *Am. J. Physiol.* 200: 815–818, 1961.

100. MASTROIANNI, L., JR. W. W. WINTERNITZ, AND N. P. LOWE. The in vitro metabolism of the human endosalpinx. *Fertility Sterility* 9: 500–509, 1958.

101. McDONALD, M. F., AND A. R. BELLVE. Influence of oestrogen and progesterone on flow of fluid from the Fallopian tube in the ovariectomized ewe. *J. Reprod. Fertility* 20: 51–61, 1970.

102. McGREACHIN, R. L., L. A. HARGAN, B. A. POTTER, AND A. T. DAUS, JR. Amylase in Fallopian tubes. *Proc. Soc. Exptl. Biol. Med.* 99: 130–131, 1958.

103. MOGHISSI, K. S. Human Fallopian tube fluid. 1. Protein composition. *Fertility Sterility* 21: 321–329, 1970.

104. MOREAUX, R. Sur la morphologie et la fonction glandulaire. *Arch. Microbiol.* 14: 515–576, 1913.

105. MOUNIB, M. C., AND M. C. CHANG. Metabolism of endometrium and Fallopian tube in the rabbit. *Federation Proc.* 23: 361, 1964.

106. MOUNIB, M. S., AND M. C. CHANG. Metabolism of endometrium and Fallopian tube in the estrous and the pseudopregnant rabbit. *Endocrinology* 76: 542–546, 1965.

107. MROUCH, A. Effect of tubal implantation on rabbit fertility. *Fertility Sterility* 20: 928–932, 1969.

108. MURDOCK, R. N., AND I. G. WHITE. Studies of the metabolism of human spermatozoa. *J. Reprod. Fertility* 16: 351–362, 1968.

109. MURRAY, F. A., L. GOODE, AND A. C. LINWOOD. Effects of season, mating and pregnancy on the volume and protein content of ewe oviduct fluid. *J. Animal Sci.* 29: 727–733, 1969.

110. NEVO, A. C. Dependence of sperm motility and respiration on oxygen concentration. *J. Reprod. Fertility* 9: 103–107, 1965.

111. NORIEGA, C., AND L. MASTROIANNI, JR. Effect of carbonic anhydrase inhibitor on tubal ova. *Fertility Sterility* 20: 799–804, 1969.

112. NOVAK, E., AND H. S. EVERETT. Cyclical and other variations in the tubal epithelium. *Am. J. Obstet. Gynecol.* 16: 499–530, 1928.

113. OLDS, D., AND N. L. VANDEMARK. Composition of luminal fluids in bovine female genitalia. *Fertility Sterility* 8: 345–354, 1957.

114. OLDS, D., AND N. L. VANDEMARK. The behavior of spermatozoa in luminal fluids of bovine female genitalia. *Am. J. Vet. Res.* 18: 603–607, 1957.

115. PERKINS, J. L., L. GOODE, W. A. WILDER, JR., AND D. B. HENSON. Collection of secretions from the oviduct and uterus of the ewe. *J. Animal Sci.* 24: 383–387, 1965.

116. PERKINS, J. L., AND L. GOODE. Effects of stage of the estrous cycle and exogenous hormones upon the volume and composition of oviduct fluid in ewes. *J. Animal Sci.* 25: 465–471, 1966.

117. PERKINS, J. L., AND L. GOODE. Free amino acids in the oviduct fluid of the ewe. *J. Reprod. Fertility* 14: 309–311, 1967.

118. REINIUS, S. *Morphology of Oviduct Gametes and Zygotes as a Basis of Oviductal Function in the Mouse.* Uppsala: RK-trych, 1969, p. 1–86.

119. RESTALL, B. J., AND R. G. WALES. The Fallopian tube of the sheep. III. The chemical composition of the fluid from the Fallopian tube. *Australian J. Biol. Sci.* 19: 687–698, 1966.

120. RESTALL, B. J. The Fallopian tube of the sheep. I. Cannulation of the Fallopian tube. *Australian J. Biol. Sci.* 19: 181–186, 1966.

121. RESTALL, B. J. The Fallopian tube of the sheep. II. The influence of progesterone and oestrogen on the secretory activities of the Fallopian tube. *Australian J. Biol. Sci.* 19: 187–197, 1966.

122. ROSS, V., E. G. MILLER, AND R. KURZVOK. Metabolism of human sperm. *Endocrinology* 28: 885–893, 1941.

123. ROTHSCHILD, L. The heat production of human spermatozoa and seminal plasma; with comparative observations on bull semen. *Proc. Roy. Soc. London, Ser. B* 152: 298–310, 1960.

124. SCHEYER, H. E. Uber die Lipoide der Tube. *Virchows Arch. Pathol. Anat.* 262: 712–734, 1926.

125. SHAPIRO, S. S., J. R. JENTSCH, AND A. S. YARD. Protein composition of rabbit oviductal fluid. *J. Reprod. Fertility* 24: 403–408, 1971.

126. SHELBY, D. R., AND C. W. FOLEY. Influence of carbon dioxide absorbed and the consumption of oxygen by boar spermatozoa. *J. Animal Sci.* 25: 352–354, 1966.

127. SNEDECOR, G. W. *Statistical Methods* (5th ed.). Ames: Iowa State Press, 1961, p. 37–50.

128. SPILMAN, C. H., R. T. DUBY, AND D. L. BLACK. Effect of an intrauterine device on sheep oviduct fluids: chemical composition and stimulation of spermatozoa respiration in vitro. *Biol. Reprod.* 3: 76–81, 1970.

129. STAMBAUGH, R., C. NORIEGA, AND L. MASTROIANNI, JR. Bicarbonate ion; the corona cell dispersing factor of rabbit tubal fluid. *J. Reprod. Fertility* 18: 51–58, 1969.

130. STERN, S., AND J. D. BIGGERS. Enzymatic estimation of glycogen in the cleaving mouse embryo. *J. Exptl. Zool.* 168: 61–66, 1968.

131. SUGAWARA, S., AND S. TAKEUCHI. Identification of volatile fatty acid in genital tract of female rabbit. *Japan J. Zool. Technol. Soc.* 35: 238–242, 1964.

132. TERNER, C. Oxidation of exogenous substrates by isolated human spermatozoa. *Am. J. Physiol.* 198: 48–50, 1960.

133. VISHWAKARMA, P. The pH and bicarbonate-ion content of the oviduct and uterine fluids. *Fertility Sterility* 13: 481–485, 1962.

134. WALES, R. G., AND B. J. RESTALL. The metabolism of ram spermatozoa in the presence of genital fluids of the ewe. *Australian J. Biol. Sci.* 19: 199–209, 1966.

135. WALLACE, J. C., AND I. G. WHITE. Studies of glycerylphosphorylcholine diesterase in the female reproductive tract. *J. Reprod. Fertility* 9: 163–176, 1965.

136. WALLACE, J. C., G. M. STONE, AND I. G. WHITE. The effect of the oestrous cycle and of estradiol on the breakdown of seminal glycerylphosphorylcholine by secretions of the rat uterus. *Australian J. Biol. Sci.* 18: 88–96, 1965.

137. WHITE, I. G., AND J. C. WALLACE. Breakdown of seminal glycerylphosphorylcholine by secretions of the female reproductive tract. *Nature* 189: 843–844, 1961.

138. WHITE, I. G., J. C. WALLACE, R. G. WALES, AND T. W. SCOTT. The occurrence and metabolism of glycerylphosphorylcholine in semen and the genital tract. *Proc. Intern. Congr. Animal Reprod., 4th, The Hague* 2: 266–269, 1961.

139. WHITE, I. G., J. C. WALLACE, AND G. M. STONE. Studies of the glycerylphosphorylcholine diesterase activity of the female genital tract in the ewe, cow, sow and rat. *J. Reprod. Fertility* 5: 298, 1963.

140. WHITE, I. G., J. C. WALLACE, AND G. M. STONE. The metabolism of seminal glycerylphosphorylcholine by fluids of the female reproductive tract. *Proc. Intern. Congr. Animal Reprod., 5th, Trento* 4: 526–530, 1964.

141. WHITTEN, W. K. Culture of tubal ova. *Nature* 179: 1081–1082, 1957.

142. WINTERBERGER-TORRES, S. Movements des trompes et progression des oeuis chez la brebis. *Am. Biol. Animal Biochem. Biophys.* 1: 121–124, 1961.

143. WORKRESSENSKY, M. A. Experimentelle Untersuchungen uber die pyo- und Hydrosalpinxbildung bei den Tieren. *Zbl. Gynaekol.* 15: 849–860, 1891.

144. YAMAZAKI, K. Biochemical study of secretions from oviduct. *Japan. J. Zool. Technol. Soc.* 38: 172–180, 1965.

145. YANAGIMACHI, R. In vitro capacitation of hamster spermatozoa by follicular fluid. *J. Reprod. Fertility* 18: 275–286, 1969.

146. YARD, A. S., L. P. JUHASZ, AND R. M. GRIMES. Studies on the antifertility effect and metabolism of a new, postcoital oral contraceptive, 2-methyl-3-ethyl-4-phenyl-Δ4-cyclohexene carboxylic acid, sodium salt (ORF-4563). *J. Pharmacol. Exptl. Therap.* 167: 105–116, 1969.

147. YASUDA, M. Distribution and metabolism of acid mucopolysaccharides in the genital organs of female rabbits by hormonal influence. *Japan J. Fertility Sterility* 11: 49–56, 1966.

148. ZACHARIAE, F. Autoradiographic (^{35}S) and histochemical studies of sulphomucopolysaccharides in the rabbit uterus, oviducts and vagina. *Acta Endocrinol.* 29: 118–134, 1958.

CHAPTER 38

Gamete transport in the female mammal

RICHARD J. BLANDAU | *Department of Biological Structure, School of Medicine,*
University of Washington, Seattle, Washington

CHAPTER CONTENTS

NORMAL FERTILIZATION of a mammalian egg requires that a fully mature ovulated egg and a spermatozoon capable of penetrating it meet in the ampulla of the oviduct during a limited period of time in any single reproductive cycle.

Great effort has been expended during the past decades by many investigators exploring and resolving the morphological, endocrinological, biochemical, biophysical, and neurological factors involved in the successful meeting and fusion of the gametes. Hundreds of papers have been written on this subject. Much information has been gathered on many different species, but the fact remains that we still cannot fully explain the mechanisms involved in gamete transport for any single mammal. Only this statement can be made with absolute certainty: mature eggs are ovulated, mature spermatozoa capable of fertilizing them reach the ampulla, and, under a normally suitable environment, union of these cells is accomplished and a new life begins. Such an oversimplification of what is actually known is justified until theories of mechanisms are resolved into facts that can no longer be challenged; we but delay the full comprehension of this absorbing complexity by assumptions, guesses, and indiscriminate transfer of information from one species to another.

Unpublished observations referred to in this chapter were supported by Grant HD 0374 and Contract 70-2141 from the National Institutes of Health.

This review elaborates on the possible mechanisms involved in the complex system of gamete transport as identified in several mammalian species. Because of the limitations of space, it obviously cannot be exhaustive. Certain interpretations and conclusions reached by the reviewer may be challenged, an eventuation that substantiates the inadequacy of knowledge in this area of biology.

OVUM TRANSPORT THROUGH THE OVIDUCTS OF MAMMALS

Contrary to the general view, the oviducts have a very complex physiology: there is no other tubular system in which cells of such different dimensions as the eggs and spermatozoa are transported in opposite directions during a limited period of time; there is no tubular system in which the cellular, biochemical, and physiological changes are so specifically timed and efficiently programmed to establish an environment for the successful union of the gametes; there is no tubular system with as many anatomic subdivisions whose secretory and muscular activity vary with the endocrine status of the animal at a particular time in the reproductive cycle (35).

Egg Transport from the Ovarian Surface to the Ostium of the Infundibulum

The mechanisms by which freshly ovulated eggs are transported into the oviducts depend on *a*) the anatomic configuration of the fimbria of the infundibulum and its relationship to the surface of the ovary at the time of ovulation; *b*) the manner in which the cumulus oophorus and its contained egg are expressed from the follicle at the time of ovulation; and *c*) the physical characteristics of the antral fluids and the fluids of the matrix of the cumulus oophorus.

There is little published information on the anatomic relationship of the fimbriae of the oviducts to the ovaries at the time of ovulation (35, 76); there is even less on the anatomy and physiology of the various ovarian and oviductal ligaments and mesenteries. These structures certainly act as supports and, richly endowed with smooth muscles, play significant roles in the positioning of the ovaries in relation to the fimbriae at the time of ovulation (Fig. 1).

At ovulation in the rabbit, guinea pig, and cat the fringed, fluted, and lansiform fimbriae surround the ovaries and form the bursae ovarii (Figs. 1 and 2). Normally the ovulating eggs in these animals come into contact immediately with the ciliated cells lining the fimbriae. The intermittent contractions of the smooth muscles in the mesovaria and in the various ligaments and mesenteries attached to the ovaries and oviducts act to change the surface relationships of the ovaries and fimbriae. These rhythmic muscular contractions assure that the positioning of the fimbriae in relation to the surfaces of the ovaries is altered frequently.

In women and other primates, even though careful culdoscopic observations reveal a closer relationship between the fimbriae and ovaries than is pictured in most textbooks, it is not as intimate as in the rabbit, guinea pig, and cat. However, conclusive observations in the undisturbed pelvis of the woman are yet to be done.

Only a small portion of the relatively small fimbria of the infundibulum in the mouse, rat, and hamster comes into direct contact with the ovary. In these animals the ovary is enclosed completely by a thin-membraned periovarial sac into which the small, ciliated, medusa-like fimbria projects (Fig. 3). Since the fimbriae in these rodents make only superficial contact with the ovaries, how are the ovulated eggs transported into the oviducts? At the time of ovulation the periovarial sac is dilated with fluid, which causes the membrane to be lifted from the surface of the ovary and thus makes possible the

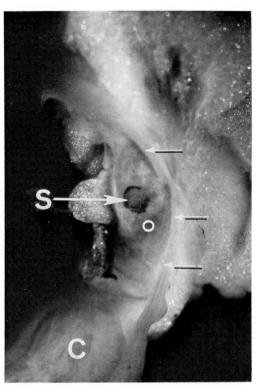

FIG. 2. Living ovary (O) of a guinea pig at the time of ovulation. The lansiform fimbria has been lifted slightly (*arrows*) to expose the stigma (S) of a recently ovulated follicle. Normally the ovary is completely enclosed in a bursa. The loops of the oviduct are embedded in adipose tissue and hidden from view. C, cornu.

movement of eggs in cumuli within the periovarial space (Fig. 4). The eggs, embedded in their cumuli, are shed completely from the follicle into the fluids filling the periovarial space (Fig. 5). Intermittent contractions of the mesovarium displace the ovary within the periovarial sac in a rotatory or spiral fashion, which in turn moves the eggs about at random within the fluids of the periovarial space. The cilia on the cells covering the fimbria beat in the direction of the ostium. When a cumulus mass comes into the sphere of influence of the fimbria, fluid currents direct the egg toward it. When contact between the fimbria and the cumulus oophorus is established, the eggs are transported quickly over the fimbrial surface, through the ostium, and then into the ampulla of the oviduct.

If the fimbriae of rabbits and cats are removed surgically and ovulation is induced by mating or injection of gonadotrophins, the cumulus mass adheres to the site of rupture for many hours. This phenomenon is particularly striking in the cat in which the highly polymerized matrix of the cumulus oophorus and antral fluid are continuous. The ovulated cumulus mass may be pulled out into a long, thin strand that returns to its original condition when the tension is released. If the fimbria of a cat that has just ovulated is lifted gently from the surface of the ovary, four to six very long, thin streamers of cumulus and matrix attached to each ovulation site

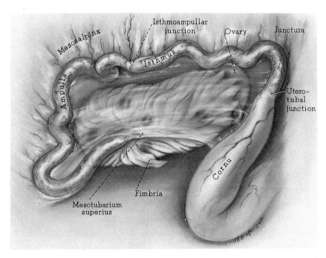

FIG. 1. Various subdivisions of the living rabbit oviduct and the mesenteries attached to it. Note arrangement of the fimbria of the infundibulum surrounding the ovary and forming the bursa ovarii. The mesotubarium superius is attached to the longitudinal axis of the fimbria and to the full antimesosalpingal border of the oviduct, as well as onto the first few millimeters of the cornu. Its intermittent contraction pulls the fimbria over the surface of the ovary.

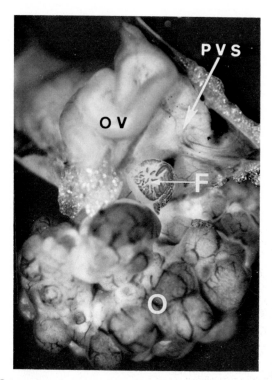

and extending into the ostium of the oviduct are apparent. Here we see a striking example of the action of the cilia of the fimbria as they sweep the sticky, ovulated materials from the surface of the ovaries. The same phenomenon occurs in rabbits and guinea pigs, although their ovulated cumuli are not as highly polymerized (Figs. 6 and 7). Hartman (38) made very similar observations for the rhesus monkey when he described the liquor folliculi of the "first order" as forming a pliable mass on which the "powerful cilia of the enveloping fimbria get hold and thus drag the imprisoned ovum out."

The manner in which eggs are transported from the surface of the ovary after ovulation varies greatly in different species. Although too few species have been examined to draw firm conclusions, there seems to be a functional relationship between the anatomic configuration of the fimbria of the infundibulum and the manner in which the eggs are ovulated and transported into the ampulla. It should be emphasized that the physical characteristics of the cumulus oophorus and whether or not the eggs are shed completely from the follicles at ovulation appear to be decisive factors.

FIG. 3. Ovary, fimbria, and oviduct of a rat killed a few hours after ovulation. Periovarial sac (*PVS*) was cut and pinned back to show the location and appearance of the fimbria (*F*). Note its small size in comparison to that of the rabbit (see Fig. 1). *O*, ovary; *OV*, coils of oviduct.

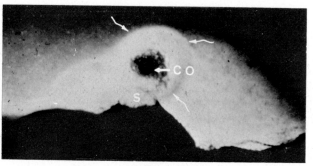

FIG. 5. Enlargement from a 16-mm motion picture film of an ovulation in the rat. Note that the cumulus oophorus (*CO*) is cast free from the stigma (*S*). *Arrows* outline the boundaries of the thin follicular fluid. Compare this type of ovulation with that of the guinea pig (see Fig. 6) and rabbit (see Fig. 7).

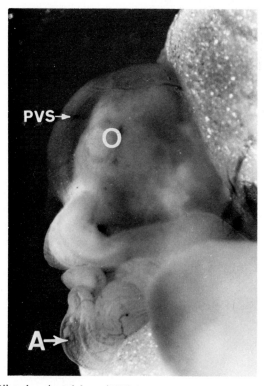

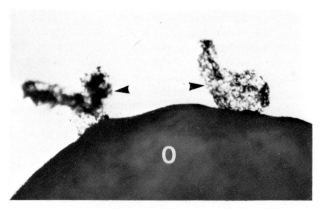

FIG. 6. Surface view of the ovary (*O*) of a guinea pig removed about 0.5 hr after ovulation. The sticky antral fluids and remnants of the cumulus oophorus (*arrowheads*) are still firmly attached to the ovulated follicles. The eggs have been transported into the ampulla of the oviduct.

FIG. 4. Dilated periovarial sac (*PVS*) from a living rat that has just ovulated. Note the dilated loop of the ampulla (*A*) containing the cumulus masses. *O*, ovary.

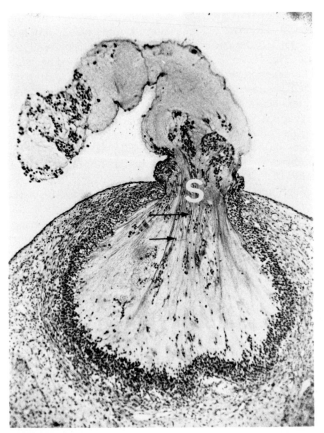

FIG. 7. Section through a recently ovulated follicle in the rabbit. A part of the cumulus oophorus and the sticky antral fluids remain attached to the stigma (*S*) and must be brushed off by the action of the ciliated cells covering the fimbria. Note the tension lines of fluid flow (*arrows*) even after ovulation has been completed.

Egg Transport Through the Ampulla

The mechanism of egg transport through the ampulla and to the isthmoampullar junction has been observed only in the living rabbit and rat (3, 11, 36, 37). At the time of ovulation in both animals, the walls of the ampulla are sufficiently thin to reveal the movements of supravitally stained cumulus masses. Egg transport through the ostium and the first few millimeters of the ampulla is effected by the action of cilia. Even though the mucosal folds of the ampulla of the rabbit are lined by numerous ciliated cells, all of which beat in the direction of the isthmoampullar junction, egg transport through this segment is effected primarily by localized, segmental, peristaltic muscular contractions. Contractions of the slightly spiraling circular musculature compress and elongate the cumulus mass. As the segmental peristaltic wave develops, the egg mass is "milked" forward. With intermittent, brief resting periods, the process continues, and the egg is carried to the isthmoampullar junction in about 6 min (14). A significant amount of fluid, the source of which has not been clearly defined, appears to be present in the rabbit ampullar lumen and may act as an important vehicle for egg transport.

A very similar pattern of egg movement through the ampulla has been observed in the living rat. At ovulation, several of the loops of the ampulla are remarkably distended with fluid. The fluid is retained by tonic contractions of the circular muscles at the isthmoampullar junction. When the cumulus masses enter the ampulla, they are propelled forward rapidly by vigorous peristaltic contractions that proceed to the junctural ring. Eventually, all the ovulated eggs are compacted into a single mass and retained above the constricted junction, the site of sperm penetration and fertilization.

Similarities in the role of the musculature in transporting eggs through the ampullae in rabbits and rats as described above may actually have been fortuitous. Preliminary observations of the cat and monkey (*Macaca nemistrina*) do not reveal the same vigorous, segmental, peristaltic waves of muscular movement of the ampulla. In these animals it is the action of the cilia that appears to play the prominent role in egg transport. Other species may transport eggs through the ampulla to the site of fertilization in significantly different ways. We reemphasize the hazards of drawing broad conclusions from observations on only a few species.

The Isthmoampullar Junction and Egg Retention

We do not know whether the isthmoampullar junction acts as a transitory constriction ring for retaining the eggs in the ampulla in all mammalian species (see Fig. 1). We do know that the physiological stricture in the mouse, rat, hamster, rabbit, and cat narrows the lumen sufficiently to prevent the cumulus masses and even denuded eggs from passing beyond it, but, again, we do not know how spermatozoa are able to pass through the constricted segment to enter the ampulla and effect fertilization in these or any other animals (19, 20). Neither do we know the nature of the constriction, its endocrinology, or its neuropharmacology (20). The assumption that the stricture is induced and maintained by the synergistic action of estrogens and progestins carries with it very tenuous scientific evidence indeed.

If spayed rabbits are injected with small doses of estrogens for 3 days and egg transport evaluated 30 hr after the last injection, we find that cumulus masses from donor animals move readily from ampulla to isthmus without evidence of a delay at the usual site of the constriction.

The number of hours eggs are retained above the isthmoampullar junction varies with the species (60). Under conditions in the wild or where males and females are housed together, mating will have occurred some hours before ovulation, and capacitated spermatozoa will be awaiting the arrival of the eggs within the ampulla. Normally sperm penetration occurs before there is evidence of cumulus cell dispersal. Within 15–18 hr after ovulation, the cumulus and corona radiata cells have disappeared from the eggs. The dispersal of the cumulus oophorus is thought to be effected by the action of enzymes present in the oviductal fluid and the cilia that brush the remaining corona cells from the zona pellucida.

Egg Transport Through the Isthmus

In most mammals several days are required for eggs to pass through the isthmi of the oviducts. Although evidence is very limited, it is assumed that eggs entering the isthmus have been freed from the cumulus and corona cells. Since these denuded eggs are not readily visible through the thicker muscular walls of the isthmus, evaluating their progress in the isthmus is more difficult than evaluating their progress in the ampulla. Egg transport through the isthmus appears to be a complex process related to a pattern of segmental peristaltic and antiperistaltic contractions that have the curious capacity of moving the eggs backward and forward in a rotatory fashion. In the rabbit, opossum, dog, and horse, tertiary membranes are deposited evenly on the zona pellucida as the eggs move through this segment. If artificial eggs made from glass or paraffin are inserted into the oviducts at the proper time in the cycle, they, too, become coated by the complex mucopolysaccharides secreted by the cells of the isthmus (33). The remarkably even deposition of the tertiary membranes certainly attests to the necessity of a rotational thrust to the forward movement. This reviewer, using fiberoptic flexible rods, has observed, by transillumination, movements within the various segments of the isthmus in anesthetized rabbits.

Continuous observation of the contractions of the various segments of the isthmus and observations for several hours after ovulation reveal the impressive complex patterns of segmental, pendular, peristaltic, and antiperistaltic contractions (5). If supravitally stained eggs in their cumuli are placed in the isthmic lumen, they may be seen to be in almost continuous motion—they sweep backward and forward from segment to segment; this rhythm is often interrupted by sudden rushes that transport the luminal contents through a number of segments. The vigorous segmental contractions may fragment the cumulus mass and propel these smaller units in the luminal fluids even more forcefully.

Between 48 and 72 hr after ovulation in the rabbit, the muscular contractions are much less vigorous but more specifically programmed. This pattern of contractions has been recorded cinematographically, and, from studying these patterns, it is obvious that the masses of cumulus cells placed in the lumen are transported in a more spiral fashion.

No one has been successful in visualizing the movements of denuded eggs in the isthmus. How they eventually move forward to the region of the junctura of the isthmus is still a mystery and a matter for conjecture. It is assumed that the eggs pass through the isthmus in single file.

Many ciliated cells line the mucosa of the isthmus in mammals. Their pattern of beat may rotate the eggs so that the tertiary membrane is deposited evenly.

Egg Movement Through the Junctural Segment of the Isthmus

Although very few observations have been made, it is assumed that the eggs are retained in the last few millimeters of the isthmus or junctura for some time before they are expelled suddenly into the uterine lumen. Such an assumption presumes that the junctura has a sphincterlike action that relaxes at a specific time and allows the fluids of the oviducts to flush the eggs into the uterus or cornua. An anatomic sphincter in the region of the junctura has never been described. Black & Asdell (9) suggest the presence of a physiological sphincter in which the resistance is decreased under the influence of progesterone. Alpha receptors predominate in the isthmus, and the injection of noradrenaline elicits contractions of the circular muscles, which may act as a sphincter.

SPERM TRANSPORT IN MAMMALS

In most mammals, copulation and the deposition of semen take place during the very restricted period of estrus or "heat." At this time the physiological and biochemical conditions of the female reproductive tract have established an environment optimal for the transport of spermatozoa.

Investigators working primarily with sheltered laboratory animals tend to forget that in the wild or natural environment the onset of behavioral estrus is the signal for the male to deposit spermatozoa and that ovulation occurs near the end of heat, whether the animals are seasonal, reflex, or cyclic ovulators. For example, in the rat, mouse, and hamster, behavioral estrus lasts about 10–13 hr during each 4–5-day cycle (15, 80). Mating usually occurs near the beginning of the period of heat. At the time of ejaculation, spermatozoa are deposited directly into the cornua, which are dilated with fluids particularly hospitable to spermatozoa. During heat the smooth muscles of the reproductive tract contract vigorously to mix and displace the sperm within the lumina. The secretory and ciliated cells are at the peak of their activities, and, since ovulation normally occurs near the end of heat, spermatozoa will have arrived within the ampulla before the eggs reach the site of fertilization. In the guinea pig a vaginal membrane seals the external orifice of the vagina during the 14–15 days of diestrus, so that mating and the deposition of spermatozoa are impossible during this interval (58, 82). In this animal the behavioral estrus lasts also for 10–12 hr; the vaginal membrane disappears at its onset, spontaneous ovulation occurs near the end of heat, and spermatozoa are deposited into a reproductive tract when the environment is optimal for their survival and transport.

Even in primates, and particularly in the human, sperm transport is effected best at about the time of ovulation (69). At this time the secretions of the cervix and other segments of the reproductive tract have biochemical and biophysical properties beneficial for sperm transport, and the inherent contractility of smooth muscles of the reproductive tract is most readily modulated and stimulated.

The volume of the ejaculate, its physical and biochemical characteristics, the site of semen deposition within the reproductive tract, the anatomy and physiology of the cervix, the pattern of mating, and the number of spermatozoa ejaculated vary greatly among mammals. All these factors must be taken into account before the mechanism of sperm transport can be appreciated for any mammal.

Some data related to these topics are summarized in Table 1. I emphasize that, although this summary is interesting and instructive, the data are exceedingly difficult to obtain; some may be suppositions, and few are without controversy. The wide variation in the time of sperm transport recorded for the ewe illustrates the inexactitude arising from present experimental procedures.

Sperm Transport Through the Cervix

The most voluminous ejaculate so far recorded is that of the pig. During a prolonged coitus, 250 ml seminal fluid containing 5 billion spermatozoa are propelled through the cervix and into the body of the uterus. By contrast, in the rat, mouse, and hamster a small compacted mass containing approximately 50 million spermatozoa is catapulted directly into the cornua at the moment of insemination. Semen is deposited into the

vagina in the rabbit, cat, cow, ewe, monkey, chimpanzee, and woman (see Table 1).

The fluidity of the ejaculate varies greatly among animals. In the dog, pig, and cow the semen remains quite liquid; in the rabbit, horse, monkey, and man it tends to form a coagulum almost immediately after ejaculation. The coagulation of the semen mass mentioned above must not be confused with the copulation plug formed simultaneously with ejaculation in such animals as the mouse, rat, hamster, and guinea pig. The copulation plug is the result of the rapid polymerization of the mixed secretions of the seminal vesicles and coagulating gland. The secretions form a hard, rubbery substance that plugs the vaginal vault within a few seconds after they are deposited.

At ejaculation some spermatozoa may be trapped in the copulation plug material; these are not released and therefore are not available for transport or fertilization. The vaginal plug with its entrapped spermatozoa is usually shed from the vagina after the end of heat.

In primates, Lagomorpha, and some other mammals, the ejaculated semen clots within several minutes and then again liquifies partially or completely within 20–30 min (43, 44, 49).

The significance of coagulum formation, the factors causing its liquifaction, and its role in insemination are poorly understood.

The cervix is not a formidable barrier to insemination in such animals as the mouse, rat, hamster, guinea pig, ferret, dog, pig, and horse in which spermatozoa may be transported at ejaculation directly into the cornua or uterus (10, 39). Sperm transport mechanisms must be much more complex in such animals as the rabbit, cat, ewe, cow, and primates in which semen is deposited into

TABLE 1. *Characteristics of Ejaculate*

Species	Volume of Ejaculate, ml	Mean Number of Sperm Ejaculated $\times 10^{-6}$	Site of Insemination	Time Between Ejaculation and Appearance of Sperm in Oviducts	Number of Sperm Reaching Ampulla	Ref.
Mouse	>0.1	50	Cornua	15 min in upper regions of oviduct	17+	48
Hamster	>0.1	80	Cornua	2 min in ampullae, 60 min in ampullae	Few	80, 81
Rat	0.1	58	Cornua	15–30 min	5–100	6, 12, 13
Guinea pig	0.15	80	Uterine body	15 min in middle of oviduct	25–50	47
Rabbit	1.0 (0.4–6.0)	250–500	Vagina	3–6 hr	250–500	1, 16, 33, 61
Cat	0.1–0.3	56	Vagina and posterior cervix	No data	40–120	71
Dog	10.0 (1.0–25.0)	125	Cornua	2 min to several hours	5–100	8, 28, 31, 77
Ewe	1.0 (0.7–2.0)	800	Vagina	2–30 min in ampullae, 4–8 hr in ampullae; average, probably 3 hr	600–5,000	7, 17, 25, 29, 53, 54, 65
Cow	4.0 (2.0–10.0)	4000–5000	Vagina	2–13 min in ampullae	4,200–27,500	30
Sow	250 (150–500)	5000	Upper cervix and uterus	30 min in oviducts, 2 hr in upper half of oviducts	Few	28a, 32
Man	3.5 (2.0–6.0)	125	Vagina	30 min in oviducts, 68 min in ampullae	Few	18, 67

the vagina. Only about 1% of the sperm in an ejaculate gets into the cornua of a rabbit. Very little specifically is known as to the manner in which spermatozoa are transported from the vagina and into the uterus in these animals. Some of the factors to consider in elucidating this problem are *a*) the role of female orgasm in effecting muscular contractility of the vagina, cervix, and uterus, which could speed the egress of sperm into the uterus; *b*) the composition and, particularly, the rheology and physical properties of the cervical fluids; *c*) the role of the directional swimming movements of the spermatozoa (78); *d*) the possible role of the pharmacologically active substances in semen, such as prostaglandins, that may modulate the contractile activity of the female reproductive tract (39).

Despite much effort, only modest and often contradictory information is available as to the manner in which spermatozoa move through the cervix. Oddly enough, more information on this phenomenon is available for woman than for any mammals in which spermatozoa are deposited in the vagina (27). It is well known that in man most of the spermatozoa are contained in the first portion of the ejaculate. One may assume, then, that at the moment of ejaculation (50) the cervix is bathed by a high concentration of spermatozoa. We must remind ourselves that human semen is deposited in the vaginal vault as an opaque coagulum that liquifies within 5–15 min (39, 69). The abundant midcycle cervical mucus comes into intimate contact with the coagulum; therefore spermatozoa may enter the cervical mucus without coming into contact with any part of the vagina (27). Sperm enter the cervical mucus of the woman in vivo within 1.5–3 min after they are deposited in the vagina.

The basic question that persists in the minds of many is whether spermatozoa are propelled through the human cervix en masse or move into and through the cervical canal by their innate motility. Rubenstein and co-workers (67) reported the recovery of spermatozoa from human oviducts within 30 min after coitus. This implies a rapid entrance of sperm into the uterus and perhaps prompted the so-called "in-suck" theory of en masse sperm transport through the cervix in the woman. This theory received credibility when Krehbiel & Carstens (45) and subsequently Akester & Inkster (2) injected radiopaque materials into the vaginae of rabbits. Digital stimulation of their vulvae caused strong vaginal contractions that forced the radiopaque materials through the cervices from whence they were transported rapidly to the uterotubal junction. The location of the radiopaque materials could be followed by cinefluorography. Such observations imply that, during intromission and orgasm, the vagina and uterus contract in such a manner that pressure within the uterus results in the in-suck of seminal fluid into the cervical canal and perhaps even into the endometrial cavity. Positive pressure may be added by the ringlike contractions of the vagina that assist in the transport. Studies of this kind

indicate that complex neurohumoral mechanisms may activate the rapid transport of sperm through the cervix in some animals.

Although there are strong proponents of the in-suck theory in the human female, the experimental evidence to validate it is exceedingly tenuous (29, 59). Observant gynecologists have examined thousands of exposed cervices in women at all times of the menstrual cycle. None has reported observing aspirations of any kind by the cervix. Amersbach (4) and others placed cervical caps containing suspensions of particulate matter of various kinds over the cervical os in human patients and recovered some of the materials from the uterus after coitus. The possibilities of artificially inducing movements of such particulate matter through the cervical canal is too great to take these conclusions seriously.

More recently, Masters & Johnson (51, 52) fitted plastic caps containing a radiopaque fluid over the cervices of six subjects at about the time of expected ovulation. The physical characteristics of the radiopaque substance simulated those of semen as closely as possible. Radiographic examinations made simultaneously with orgasmic experience and 10 min after the resolution phase failed to show even the slightest sucking effect on the artificial seminal pool.

On the basis of all available evidence, we must declare that no scientific data support the concept that contractions of the uterus or vagina play any role in effecting active sperm transport from the vaginal deposits into and through the cervix at the time of ejaculation or for any time thereafter in women (70).

The alternative that remains then is that spermatozoa, particularly in woman, move through the cervical mucus by their own innate motility. The cervical canal is looked upon by many as a *receptaculum seminis* through which platoons of spermatozoa migrate with no help from the musculature of the reproductive organs (26, 27). Unfortunately, as yet, sperm penetration of the cervical mucus has been studied only in in vitro systems. If human semen and cervical mucus from the midcycle are brought together on a glass slide so that an interface is formed between the two, the seminal plasma may be observed penetrating the mucus by the formation of phalanges. As these protrusions invade the mucus, they increase in size gradually. With time the spermatozoa appear to leave the environment of the seminal plasma and move into the cervical mucus directly (57, 63, 64). Although these reports are interesting, the observations that fluids other than seminal plasma (e.g., human serum, bromphenol blue, India ink) also form distinct interfaces and phalanges when in contact with midcycle cervical mucus demonstrate that phalanx formation appears to be a nonspecific physical phenomenon, rather than one with specific biological significance (57). The exact mechanism involved in the in vivo movement of sperm through the cervical mucus cannot yet be explained.

Fortunately there is a resurgence of interest in the

rheology, biochemistry, enzymology, and biophysical nature of the cervical mucus throughout the human menstrual cycle. Concomitantly the biophysics of sperm motility is beginning to receive its just due of attention. Interestingly, Bergman and Odeblad (unpublished observations) assert that only normal appearing spermatozoa are able to penetrate between the complex micelles of the midcycle cervical mucus.

From the available data, one may assume that, in those animals in which spermatozoa are deposited in the vagina at ejaculation, their ascent to the ampulla requires a number of hours. Braden's study (16) on the migration of spermatozoa in the rabbit emphasizes this fact. Within 3 hr after ejaculation, about 420,000 sperms were counted in the upper half of the cornua, but none had entered the oviducts. At 4 hr, 5,000 had entered the Fallopian tubes; 57% of these were found in the lower isthmus, 35% in the upper isthmus, and only 8% in the ampulla.

When spermatozoa arrive within the uterine lumen, they are still confronted with long distances to the site of fertilization in comparison to their size; with complex and constantly changing mucosal folds into which they may move or be forced; with limited access to the oviducts because of the complexities of the uterotubal junctions; with the presence of numerous ciliated cells within the oviducts, the majority of cilia beating in a direction opposite to preferred sperm transport; and finally with the physiological constriction of the isthmo-ampullar junction, which narrows the passageway into the ampulla significantly. When all the problems involved in sperm transport to the site of fertilization are considered, it is indeed remarkable that they reach the ampulla of the infundibulum at all.

The Musculature of the Female Genital Tract and Sperm Transport

In evaluating the interval of time between ejaculation or insemination and the arrival of spermatozoa in the ampulla (see Table 1), one is inclined to implicate muscular activity as a most important factor in sperm transport through the uterus and oviducts.

As early as 1840 Hausman (40) found spermatozoa throughout the uterine cornua of the dog killed during copulation. This was confirmed later by Bischoff (8). The rapid transport of sperm within the cornua or uteri of many laboratory and farm animals has been amply documented (see Table 1). The vigorous peristaltic and antiperistaltic muscular contractions of the cornua at about the time of ovulation have been observed in vivo and recorded for a number of species. These contractions result in a continuous churning of the luminal contents and the rapid mechanical movement of spermatozoa to the uterotubal junctions.

An interesting controversy has arisen concerning the remarkably rapid transport of live and dead spermatozoa, and even inert particulate matter, which is claimed to occur throughout the reproductive tracts of cows and ewes. It was assumed that sexual stimulation effected the release of oxytocin from the posterior lobe of the pituitary. The circulating oxytocin caused violent contractions of the uterus and oviducts, which swept anything within them (live or dead sperm and particulate matter) up to the ampullae in 2–15 min. In fact, the minimum time for motile sperm ascent appeared to be the same as the minimum time between ejaculation or insemination and the removal of the organs for examination (41, 42, 53–55, 68, 73–75).

The almost instantaneous ascent of spermatozoa to the oviductal ampullae could not be confirmed in ungulates by a group of French workers who reevaluated the entire problem (21–26, 72). They artificially inseminated ewes and cows in estrus by placing heat-killed sperm at the cervical os and examined the reproductive tracts for spermatozoa 8 hr later. No sperm were found within the cornua or oviducts. Mating these inseminated ewes and cows with vasectomized rams and bulls did not alter their findings. No sperm were found in the isthmus in less than 4 hr and in the ampulla in less than 8 hr, when estrous ewes were mated with vigorous rams and the location of spermatozoa evaluated at intervals thereafter by a) ligating and smearing various segments of the uterus and oviducts; b) serially sectioning various segments that had been perfused with fixative; c) aspirating total contents and examining the fluids for sperm. These workers maintain that rapid ascent of spermatozoa in the ewe, sow, and cow is not a natural phenomenon, as claimed in previous descriptions by others. They attribute the earlier results to faulty technique.

All investigators agree that sperm transport through the uterus to the uterotubal junction takes place very rapidly and is caused chiefly by muscle contractions. Endogenous oxytocin released during sexual stimulation in cattle and sheep that are not stressed during mating significantly increases the uterine tonus and the rate and amplitude of contractions. Prostaglandins in semen may function also in sperm transport, since they, too, increase uterine contractility after semination.

Fortunately the role of various hormones and pharmacological agents in normal sperm transport is receiving increasing attention (35).

The Uterotubal Junction and Sperm Transport

There are great differences in the anatomic and histological characteristics of the uterotubal junctions of different mammals. At least five different types have been recognized; some are relatively simple. Others, such as those in the pig and rabbit, have an exceedingly complex anatomy (34).

Little meaningful information on the physiology of the uterotubal junction exists. Various functions have been ascribed to it: a) a filtering or selective site for sperm entering the oviduct (66); b) a controlling mechanism for ovum transport into the uterus; c) a mechanism preventing retrograde transport of endometrial tissue, especially during menstruation; all are reasonable speculation, but none has been tested experimentally.

Despite the considerable attention observations of the passage of radiopaque substances through the uterotubal junction by cinefluoroscopy have received, it has added little to our understanding as to how spermatozoa are transported through this segment.

The mucosal lappets of the junction in the rabbit and pig interdigitate with one another to form a very complex passage. Their surfaces are covered by numerous ciliated cells in which the cilia beat in the direction opposite to the ascent of sperm (Fig. 8).

In an interesting experiment on ovulating rabbits, we were led to conclude that muscle contractions of the cornu and the intermittent opening of the lumen of the uterotubal junction may allow small numbers of sperm to enter the isthmus. The experiment was conducted by removing a cornu with a short segment of oviduct attached and immediately submerging it in a tissue culture medium maintained at body temperature. Semen from a donor rabbit was injected into a pouch made by ligating the cornu just above the cervix. The escape of sperm from the cut end of the oviduct was observed under a microscope illuminated by oblique light. Edgar & Asdell (29) demonstrated a similar valvelike action of the uterotubal colliculus in the ewe. Although the active peristaltic and antiperistaltic muscular contractions of both cornu and oviduct often make it difficult to keep the cut end of the oviduct in view, in favorable prepara-

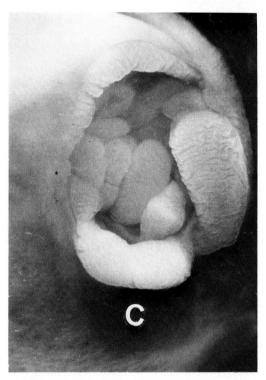

FIG. 8. An opened cornu (C) of the ovulating rabbit revealing the colliculus of the uterotubal junction. Observe the complex integrations of the lappets forming the colliculus. These polyplike processes are covered by numerous ciliated cells whose cilia beat in the direction of the cornu.

tions we were able to see small numbers of sperm escape from the oviduct in gentle spurts, which led to the conclusion that muscle contractions of the cornu and intermittent opening of the lumen of the uterotubal junction may allow small numbers of sperm to enter the isthmus.

Data conflict as to whether dead sperm may pass through the uterotubal junction and enter the oviducts in different animals. Dead sperm may pass the uterotubal junction and be transported through the oviduct in the sow (32), but not in the rat (46).

Obviously, much further investigation is needed to define the role of the uterotubal junction in transport of sperm and eggs.

Sperm Transport Through the Oviduct

We have commented on the paradoxical facility of the oviducts to propel eggs from the ovary toward the isthmoampullar junction in one direction and spermatozoa into the ampulla in the opposite direction simultaneously and discussed the manner in which eggs are transported to the site of fertilization. To do the same for transportation of spermatozoa through the isthmus is another matter, for nothing is known about it for any mammal. The formidable technical problems in following the behavior of the small, motile sperm within a thick-walled tube have so far thwarted a scientific evaluation of this process. The logical experimental approach of labeling spermatozoa with radioactive substances and following their position within the oviduct with miniature sensing devices has been tried without much success.

A small insight into this mystery has been gained for a small segment of the journey in the rabbit, namely, the isthmus. The role of muscle has been clearly defined in the transport of sperm through the isthmus through observations of the peristaltic and antiperistaltic contractions at the time of ovulation and by the movements of supravitally stained cumuli in the transilluminated isthmus, as described earlier. Until the respective roles of oviductal muscular activity, ciliary activity, rheology of the fluid, contractions of the mesosalpinx and other mesenteries, and intrinsic activity of the spermatozoa can be ascertained and their integration clarified, the mechanism of sperm transport through the oviducts will remain a mystery.

The Role of Cilia

Little can be said about the function of the numerous ciliated cells that line the mucosa of the isthmus. It was thought that in mammals all these cilia beat in the direction of the uterotubal junction. Parker (61, 62) and Yamada (79) described two ciliary systems in the oviducts of frogs, tortoises, and pigeons. Most of the luminal surfaces of their oviducts are lined by ciliated cells in which the cilia beat toward the cloaca; however, a band of ciliated cells, 2–3 mm wide, contain cilia that beat toward the ovary. Thus the ciliary beat is programmed to carry particulate matter in both directions, abovarian and adovarian. Parker suggested that the adovarian ciliated tracts may assist in the transport of spermatozoa. Recently, we repeated Parker's observations and were impressed with the ability of the adovarian tract to transport microspheres and lycopodium spores. When large tortoise eggs are dissected from the ovaries and brought to the surface of an opened oviduct, the two bands of cilia certainly play some role in rotating the yolk as the albuminous and other coatings are deposited and in impelling the egg toward the cloaca.

It was believed that such dual ciliary tracts did not exist in mammalian oviducts. Recently, we once again slit open the oviduct of an ovulating rabbit and sub-merged it in a tissue culture medium. Microspheres and stained lycopodium granules were flushed onto the ciliated mucosal surfaces of the various subdivisions of the oviducts. To our surprise the particulate matter was seen moving up and down the oviduct only in the isthmic segment. What, if any, role do these dual ciliated tracts play in sperm transport? Although we tend toward the theory that muscular contractions play the most important role in sperm transport through the isthmus and into the ampulla, we are encouraged to believe that the pattern of cilia beat may also be of some significance.

We are grateful to Mr. Roy Hayashi for his preparation of the photographs.

REFERENCES

1. ADAMS, C. E. A study of fertilization in the rabbit: the effect of postcoital ligation of the Fallopian tube or uterine horn. *J. Endocrinol.* 13: 296–308, 1956.
2. AKESTER, A. R., AND I. J. INKSTER. Cine-radiographic studies of the genital tract of the rabbit. *J. Reprod. Fertility* 2: 507–508, 1961.
3. ALDEN, R. H. The oviduct and egg transport in the albino rat. *Anat. Record* 84: 137–169, 1942.
4. AMERSBACH, R. Sterilität und Frigidität. *Muench. Med. Wochschr.* 77: 225–227, 1930.
5. ASDELL, S. A. Spermatozoan and ovum transport through the oviduct. *Zooiatria* 3: 1–4, 1961.
6. AUSTIN, C. R. Number of sperms required for fertilization. *Nature* 162: 534–535, 1948.
7. AUSTIN, C. R. Fertilization and development of the egg. In: *Reproduction in Domestic Animals*, edited by H. H. Cole and P. T. Cupps, New York: Acad. Press, 1959, chapt. 12, p. 399–432.
8. BISCHOFF, T. L. W. VON. *Die Entwicklungsgeschichte des Hunde-Eies.* Friedrich Vieweg, 1845.
9. BLACK, D. L., AND S. A. ASDELL. Mechanism controlling entry of ova into rabbit uterus. *Am. J. Physiol.* 197: 1275–1278, 1959.
10. BLANDAU, R. J. On the factors involved in sperm transport through the cervix uteri of the albino rat. *Am. J. Anat.* 77: 253–272, 1945.
11. BLANDAU, R. J. Gamete transport—comparative aspects. In: *The Mammalian Oviduct*, edited by E. S. E. Hafez and R. J. Blandau. Chicago: Univ. of Chicago Press, 1969, p. 129–162.
12. BLANDAU, R. J., AND W. L. MONEY. Observations on the rate of transport of spermatozoa in the female genital tract of the rat. *Anat. Record* 90: 255–260, 1944.
13. BLANDAU, R. J., AND D. L. ODOR. The total number of spermatozoa reaching various segments of the reproductive tract in the female albino rat at intervals after insemination. *Anat. Record* 103: 93–109, 1949.
14. BOLING, J. L. Endocrinology of oviductal musculature. In: *The Mammalian Oviduct*, edited by E. S. E. Hafez and R. J. Blandau. Chicago: Univ. of Chicago Press, 1969, p. 163–182.
15. BOLING, J. L., R. J. BLANDAU, A. L. SODERWALL, AND W. C. YOUNG. Growth of the graafian follicle and the time of ovulation in the albino rat. *Anat. Record* 79: 313–331, 1941.
16. BRADEN, A. W. H. Distribution of sperms in the genital tract of the female rabbit after coitus. *Australian J. Biol. Sci.* 6: 693–705, 1953.
17. BRADEN, A. W. H., AND C. R. AUSTIN. The number of sperms about the eggs in mammals and its significance for normal fertilization. *Australian J. Biol. Sci.* 7: 543–551, 1954.
18. BROWN, R. L. Rate of transport of spermia in human uterus and tubes. *Am. J. Obstet. Gynecol.* 47: 407–411, 1944.
19. BRUNDIN, J. An occlusive mechanism in the fallopian tube of the rabbit. *Acta Physiol. Scand.* 61: 219–227, 1964.
20. BRUNDIN, J. Distribution and function of adrenergic nerves in the rabbit fallopian tube. *Acta Physiol. Scand. Suppl.* 259: 5–56, 1965.
21. DAUZIER, L. Recherches sur les facteurs de la remontée des spermatozoïdes dans les voies génitales femelles. Étude chez le brebis (col de l'utérus). *Compt. Rend. Soc. Biol.* 147: 1556–1558, 1953.
22. DAUZIER, L. Recherches sur les facteurs de la remontée des spermatozoïdes dans les voies génitales femelles (cornes utérines). Étude chez la brebis. *Compt. Rend. Soc. Biol.* 149: 1872–1874, 1955.
23. DAUZIER, L. Recherches sur les facteurs de la remontée des spermatozoïdes dans les voies génitales femelles (trompes de Fallope). Étude chez la brebis. *Compt. Rend. Soc. Biol.* 149: 1941–1943, 1955.
24. DAUZIER, L. Physiologie du déplacement des spermatozoïdes. dans les voies génitales femelles chez la brebis et la vache. *Ann. Zootech.* 7: 281–353, 1958.
25. DAUZIER, L., AND F. DU MESNIL DU BUISSON. Les spermatozoïdes dans l'appareil génital femelle (étude chez la brebis, la vache, la truie). *Proc. World Congr. Fertility Sterility, 2nd, Naples, 1956*, p. 1149–1159.
26. DAUZIER, L., AND S. WINTERBERGER. Recherches sur la fécondation chez les mammifères: la remontée des spermatozoïdes dans le tractus génital de la brebis. *Compt. Rend. Soc. Biol.* 146: 67–70, 1952.
27. DAVAJAN, V., R. M. NAKAMURA, AND K. KHARMA. Spermatozoan transport in cervical mucus. *Obstet. Gynecol. Surv.* 25: 1–43, 1970.
28. DOAK, R. L., A. HALL, AND H. E. DALE. Longevity of spermatozoa in the reproductive tract of the bitch. *J. Reprod. Fertility* 13: 51–58, 1967.
28a. DU MESNIL DU BUISSON, F., AND L. DAUZIER. La remontée des spermatozoïdes du verrat dans le tractus génital de la truie en oestrus. *Compt. Rend. Soc. Biol.* 149: 76–79, 1955.
29. EDGAR, D. G., AND S. A. ASDELL. Spermatozoa in the female genital tract. *J. Endocrinol.* 21: 321–326, 1960.
30. EL-BANNA, A. A., AND E. S. E. HAFEZ. Sperm transport and distribution in rabbit and cattle female tract. *Fertility Sterility* 21: 534–540, 1970.
31. EVANS, E. I. The transport of spermatozoa in the dog. *Am. J. Physiol.* 105: 287–293, 1933.
32. FIRST, N. L., R. E. SHORT, J. B. PETERS, AND F. W. STRATMAN. Transport and loss of boar spermatozoa in the reproductive tract of the sow. *J. Animal Sci.* 27: 1037–1040, 1968.
33. GREENWALD, G. S. Endocrine regulation of the secretion of mucin in the tubal epithelium of the rabbit. *Anat. Record* 130: 477–496, 1958.
34. HAFEZ, E. S. E., AND D. L. BLACK. The mammalian uterotubal junction. In: *The Mammalian Oviduct*, edited by E. S. E. Hafez and R. J. Blandau. Chicago: Univ. of Chicago Press, 1969, p. 85–126.

35. HAFEZ, E. S. E., AND R. J. BLANDAU (editors). *The Mammalian Oviduct*. Chicago: Univ. of Chicago Press, 1969.

36. HARPER, M. J. K. The mechanisms involved in the movement of newly ovulated eggs through the ampulla of the rabbit Fallopian tube. *J. Reprod. Fertility* 2: 522–524, 1961.

37. HARPER, M. J. K. Egg movement through the ampullar region of the Fallopian tube of the rabbit. *Proc. Intern. Congr. Animal Reprod.*, 4th, The Hague, 1961, p. 375–380.

38. HARTMAN, C. G. Origin of ovarian adhesions from organized liquor folliculi in the rhesus monkey. *Surg. Gynecol. Obstet.* 78: 391–396, 1944.

39. HARTMAN, C. G. How do sperms get into the uterus? *Fertility Sterility* 8: 403–427, 1957.

40. HAUSMANN, U. F. *Über die Zeugung und Entstehung des mahren weiblichen Eies bei den Säugethiere*. Hanover. [Cited by Bischoff (8).]

41. HAYS, R. L., AND N. L. VANDEMARK. Effects of oxytocin and epinephrine on uterine motility in the bovine. *Am. J. Physiol.* 172: 557–560, 1953.

42. HAYS, R. L., AND N. L. VANDEMARK. Effect of stimulation of the reproduction organs of the cow on the release of an oxytocin-like substance. *Endocrinology* 52: 634–637, 1953.

43. HOSKINS, D. D., AND D. L. PATTERSON. Prevention of coagulum formation with recovery of motile spermatozoa from rhesus monkey semen. *J. Reprod. Fertility* 13: 337–340, 1967.

44. HUGGINS, C., AND W. NEAL. Coagulation and liquefaction of semen: proteolytic enzymes and citrate in prostatic fluid. *J. Exptl. Med.* 76: 527–541, 1942.

45. KREHBIEL, R. H., AND H. P. CARSTENS. Roentgen studies of the mechanism involved in sperm transportation in the female rabbit. *Am. J. Physiol.* 125: 571–577, 1939.

46. LEONARD, S. L., AND P. L. PERLMAN. Conditions effecting the passage of spermatozoa through the utero-tubal junction of the rat. *Anat. Record* 104: 89–102, 1949.

47. LEUCKART, R. Zeugung. *Wagner's Handwörterbuch der Physiolgie*. 4: 707–1000, 1853.

48. LEWIS, W. H., AND E. S. WRIGHT. On the early development of the mouse egg. *Contrib. Embryol. Carnegie Inst. Wash.* 25: 115–143, 1935.

49. MACLEOD, J. The semen specimen: laboratory examination. In: *Diagnosis in Sterility*, edited by E. T. Engle. Springfield, Ill.: C. C. Thomas, 1946, p. 3–15.

50. MACLEOD, J., AND R. HOTCHKISS. Distribution of spermatozoa and of certain chemical constituents in human ejaculate. *J. Urol.* 48: 225–229, 1942.

51. MASTERS, W. H., AND V. E. JOHNSON. *Human Sexual Response*. Boston: Little, Brown, 1966.

52. MASTERS, W. H., AND V. E. JOHNSON. Uterine response and sperm migration. In: *Human Sexual Response*. Boston: Little, Brown, 1966, chapt. 8, p. 122–126.

53. MATTNER, P. E. Spermatozoa in the genital tract of the ewe. II. Distribution after coitus. *Australian J. Biol. Sci.* 16: 688–694, 1963.

54. MATTNER, P. E. Spermatozoa in the genital tract of the ewe. III. Role of spermatozoan motility and of uterine contractions in transport of spermatozoa. *Australian J. Biol. Sci.* 16: 877–884, 1963.

55. MATTNER, P. E., AND A. W. H. BRADEN. Spermatozoa in the genital tract of the ewe. I. Rapidity of transport. *Australian J. Biol. Sci.* 16: 473–481, 1963.

57. MOGHISSI, K. S., D. DABICH, J. LEVINE, AND O. W. NEUHAUS. Mechanism of sperm migration. *Fertility Sterility* 15: 15–23, 1964.

58. MYERS, H. I., W. C. YOUNG, AND E. W. DEMPSEY. Graafian follicle development throughout the reproductive cycle in the guinea pig, with especial reference to changes during oestrus (sexual receptivity). *Anat. Record* 65: 381–401, 1936.

59. NOYES, R. H., C. E. ADAMS, AND A. WALTON. Transport of spermatozoa into the uterus of the rabbit. *Fertility Sterility* 9: 288–299, 1958.

60. OXENREIDER, S. L., AND B. N. DAY. Transport and cleavage of ova in swine. *J. Animal Sci.* 24: 413–417, 1965.

61. PARKER, G. H. The passage of the spermatozoa and ova through the oviducts of the rabbit. *Proc. Soc. Exptl. Biol. Med.* 27: 826–830, 1930.

62. PARKER, G. H. The passage of sperms and of eggs through the oviducts in terrestrial vertebrates. *Phil. Trans. Roy. Soc. London, Ser. B* 219: 381–419, 1931.

63. PERLOFF, W. H., AND E. STEINBERGER. *In vitro* penetration of cervical mucus by spermatozoa. *Fertility Sterility* 14: 231–236, 1963.

64. PERLOFF, W. H., AND E. STEINBERGER. *In vivo* survival of spermatozoa in cervical mucus. *Am. J. Obstet. Gynecol.* 88: 439–442, 1964.

65. QUINLIVAN, T. D., AND T. J. ROBINSON. Numbers of spermatozoa in the genital tract after artificial insemination of progestagen-treated ewes. *J. Reprod. Fertility* 19: 73–86, 1969.

66. RIGBY, J. P. The persistence of spermatozoa at the uterotubal junction in the sow. *J. Reprod. Fertility* 11: 153–155, 1966.

67. RUBENSTEIN, B. B., H. STRAUS, M. L. LAZARUS, AND H. HAWKINS. Sperm survival in women. *Fertility Sterility* 2: 15–19, 1951.

68. SALISBURY, G. W., AND N. L. VANDEMARK. *Physiology of Reproduction and Artificial Insemination of Cattle*. San Francisco: Freeman, 1961.

69. SOBRERO, A. J. Sperm migration in the female genital tract. In: *Mechanisms Concerned with Conception*, edited by C. G. Hartman. New York: Macmillan, 1963, p. 173–203.

70. SOBRERO, A. J. Sperm migration in the human female. *J. Sex Res.* 3: 319–322, 1967.

71. SOJKA, N. J., L. L. JENNINGS, AND C. E. HAMNER. Artificial insemination in the cat (*Felis catus* L.). *Lab. Animal Care* 20: 198–205, 1970.

72. THIBAULT, C., AND S. WINTERBERGER-TORRES. Oxytocin and sperm transport in the ewe. *Intern. J. Fertility* 12: 410–415, 1967.

73. VANDEMARK, N. L., AND R. L. HAYS. Uterine motility responses to mating. *Am. J. Physiol.* 170: 518–521, 1952.

74. VANDEMARK, N. L., AND R. L. HAYS. Rapid sperm transport in the cow. *Fertility Sterility* 5: 131–137, 1954.

75. VANDEMARK, N. L., AND A. N. MOELLER. Speed of spermatozoan transport in reproductive tract of the estrous cow. *Am. J. Physiol.* 165: 674–679, 1951.

76. WESTMAN, A. Investigations into the transport of the ovum. In: *Proceedings of the Conference Studies on Testes and Ovary, Eggs and Sperm*, edited by E. T. Engle. Springfield, Ill.: Thomas, 1952, p. 163–175.

77. WHITNEY, L. F. *How to Breed Dogs*. New York: Orange Judd, 1937.

78. WOOD, C. How spermatozoa move. *Sci. J.* 2: 44–48, 1966.

79. YAMADA, F. Studies on the ciliary movements of the oviduct. *Japan J. Physiol.* 2: 194–197, 1952.

80. YAMANAKA, H. S., AND A. L. SODERWALL. Transport of spermatozoa through the female genital tract of hamsters. *Fertility Sterility* 11: 470–474, 1960.

81. YANAGIMACHI, R., AND M. C. CHANG. Sperm ascent through the oviduct of the hamster and rabbit in relation to the time of ovulation. *J. Reprod. Fertility* 6: 413–420, 1963.

82. YOUNG, W. C., E. W. DEMPSEY, AND H. I. MYERS. Cyclic reproductive behavior in the female guinea pig. *J. Comp. Psychol.* 19: 313–335, 1935.

CHAPTER 39

Nutrition and metabolism of the ovum, zygote, and blastocyst

R. L. BRINSTER | *Laboratory of Reproductive Physiology, The School of Veterinary Medicine, University of Pennsylvania, Philadelphia, Pennsylvania*

CHAPTER CONTENTS

INTRODUCTION

Scope and Relevance

The beginning of the individual can, in some respects, be said to start with stimulation of the oocyte to undergo the maturation process. Once this stimulus occurs, the oocyte begins to mature and either completes the first meiotic division and begins the second, is ovulated and fertilized, or undergoes atresia. By far the largest number of oocytes undergo atresia, or death, before ovulation, most without even being stimulated to further their meiotic development. Many oocytes that are ovulated are never fertilized. However, the complex nuclear and cytoplasmic changes necessary for fertilization, early cleavage, and embryonic development begin with the

Financial support for the author's research is currently from PHS Grant 03071 and PHS Grant 00239 from the National Institute of Child Health and Human Development.

stimulus for ovulation, and there is no evidence for a prolonged resting stage after this stimulus. At each developmental step, the maturing oocyte and embryo must follow the correct pathway or perish.

Despite this apparent beginning of activation with the stimulus for ovulation, classic definitions of embryonic development generally begin with fertilization. For the most part, this chapter follows the classic definition and deals with the period from fertilization to implantation, partly because this is the first stage of activation and development about which there is much information. The preimplantation period in the embryo's life includes a number of important developmental and biochemical events. Some of the more obvious changes are fertilization, cleavage of the zygote, cavitation to form a blastocyst, formation of the inner cell mass, escape of the embryo from the zona pellucida, and the initiation of implantation. These phenomena appear as morphologically tangible or apparent observations, but we are most interested in the biochemical events underlying these changes and the manner in which these biochemical events are controlled—in other words, the genetic control of development.

Unfortunately we know very little about genetic control of development, and this is particularly true of the preimplantation period. We are just beginning to accumulate a foundation of biochemical information about the preimplantation embryo that can be examined for, or used to obtain, information about regulation. Most of the information is about the mouse embryo, with some about the rabbit embryo and very little about other species. From a practical standpoint, we are most interested in the human embryo and in the embryos of economically important domestic animal species. However, it seems unlikely that sufficient information can ever be obtained about these species solely from experiments on their own embryos. There simply would never be sufficient experimental material. Fortunately there is increasing evidence that many similarities exist among the preimplanted embryos of eutherian mammals. This should make possible extrapolation of much information from experiments on laboratory animals to the embryos of other species; then a few experiments with scarce embryos from valuable species will show how much extrapolation is justified in each instance. Eventually this should lead to a complete understanding of biochemical development and genetic control of that development in all species. However, at the present time we know most about the mouse and rabbit embryos, and consequently our discussion concerns predominantly the development of the early embryo of these two species.

Morphology and Chronology of Development

Despite the apparent differences among the adults of the eutherian mammalian species, one is immediately impressed, when studying the preimplantation stages of development, by the striking similarities that exist between the early embryos of different species. For instance, the release of the oocyte from the follicle follows the release of luteinizing hormone from the anterior pituitary in a large number of mammalian species. The fertilizable life of the released oocyte is 24–48 hr in most of the species about which accurate information is available (10). Despite the large differences in body size among the mammals, the oocytes released from the follicle and the zygotes of these mammals are remarkably similar in size. The field vole has the smallest ovum, which is 60 μ in diameter, and a variety of species (including man, rabbit, cow, and sheep) share the distinction of having the largest ovum, which is only 140 μ in diameter (10). In addition, the total protein content of the preblastocyst stages of mammalian embryos is relatively constant within given species and probably ranges from about 20–100 ng protein, depending on the species (22, 32, 90). After blastocyst formation the amount of protein in the embryo may *a*) not change a great deal during the few days before implantation, as in the mouse, rat, and probably man; *b*) increase considerably in the few days before implantation, as in the rabbit; or *c*) increase gradually over a period of several weeks before firm attachment, as in the pig and cow. However, the general morphological similarities in development during the first 5–7 days of development in all the species are striking.

Though the gestation period varies considerably between species, the preimplantation period, and particularly the preblastocyst period of development, are relatively constant. In man the gestation period is 270 days, and the preimplantation period is about 8 days. Yet in the mouse the gestation period is only 21 days, and the preimplantation period is still 5 days. Data for a number of species are shown in Table 1, and similarities in the timing of embryonic development, particularly in the early preimplantation period, are readily apparent. It can also be seen that in many cases the embryos spend comparable periods in the Fallopian tube. It would indeed appear from the similarities in morphology, in the time the embryos spend reaching the blastocyst stage,

TABLE 1. *Timing of Embryonic Development in Several Mammals*

Mammal	1-Cell Stage, hr	Morula Stage, hr	Blastocyst Formation, days	Entry into Uterus, days	Implantation, days	Gestation, days
Mouse	0–24	68–80	3–4	3–4	4–5	21
Rat	0–24	72–80	3–4	3–4	5–6	22
Rabbit	0–14	48–68	3–4	3–4	7–8	30
Cat			5–6	4–8	13–14	60
Sheep	0–38	96	6–7	2–4	17–18*	150
Monkey	0–24	72–96		4	9–11	164
Man			5–8	3	8–13	270
Cow	0–27	144	9	3–4	30–55*	284

Times are estimated from ovulation.   * Intimate apposition is attained earlier than this.   [From Blandau (10), Austin (6), and Boyd & Hamilton (13).]

and in their location within the reproductive tract at various stages that the developmental phenomena occurring among the various species must be quite similar. One of the most striking examples of this is the apparent requirement of all embryos so far examined for pyruvate during the first 1 or 2 days of development (see section CARBOHYDRATE AND ENERGY METABOLISM).

Metabolic Rate

The overall capability of a cell or group of cells to do work is determined by the metabolic rate of the tissue. Therefore, fundamental to an understanding of early embryonic development is knowledge of the metabolic rate of the embryos during the early period of development. Because of the small size of the mammalian embryo, it has proven difficult to make accurate measurements of oxygen consumption and such parameters of tissue mass as dry weight, wet weight, or protein content. Without these measurements no accurate judgment of overall metabolic rate of the tissue can be made. In only three species has oxygen consumption been accurately measured for most of the early developmental stages. Fridhandler (64) measured oxygen uptake of the rabbit embryo. Sugawara & Umezu (125) measured oxygen uptake of the rat embryo, and Mills & Brinster (102) measured oxygen uptake of the mouse embryo. In two of these species, the mouse and the rabbit, the protein content at different stages of embryonic development has either been measured or estimated, and this allows a calculation of Qo_2 (oxygen consumption per unit mass) to be made.

In Table 2 are shown the oxygen uptake and Qo_2 values for the developmental stages of the mouse and rabbit embryo before implantation. The newly ovulated ovum of both species has a Qo_2 of about 4 μl/mg dry wt, which is a relatively low metabolic rate, comparable to that of skin, whereas the blastocyst at the time of implantation has a Qo_2 of about 20 μl/mg dry wt, which is a relatively high metabolic rate, comparable to that of whole brain. Thus there is a dramatic increase in the overall metabolic rate of the embryos of these two species from

TABLE 2. *Oxygen Uptake and Metabolic Rate of Mouse and Rabbit Preimplantation Embryos*

Stage of Development	Mouse Embryo		Rabbit Embryo	
	Uptake, nliter/ hr per embryo	Q_{O_2}, μliter/ mg dry wt	Uptake, nliter/hr per embryo	Q_{O_2}, μliter/ mg dry wt
Unfertilized	0.156	3.95		
Fertilized	0.157	3.99	0.64	4.22
Day 2	0.150	4.08	0.60	3.96
Day 3	0.191	5.84	0.84	5.54
Day 4	0.405	13.13	5.45	
Day 5	0.535	17.61	53.00	26.76
Day 6	Embryos are implanted		214.00	22.67

Dry weight of the stages was calculated from values for the protein content of each stage assuming protein = 0.66 × dry wt (22, 32). Data on oxygen uptake for the mouse is from Mills & Brinster (102) and for the rabbit from Fridhandler and co-workers (64, 66).

the time of ovulation to implantation. The metabolic rate appears to be quite level during the first 2–3 days of development and then to increase rather sharply at about day 4 or when the blastocyst is forming. It seems quite possible that this pattern of change in the metabolic rate could be similar for the preimplantation stages of development in most mammals.

INORGANIC SUBSTANCES

Embryo Requirements in Vitro

ATMOSPHERE. The components of the atmosphere important to the embryo in vitro are water, oxygen, carbon dioxide, and nitrogen. The nitrogen is generally that part of the atmosphere remaining after the quantity of the other gases in the atmosphere is established. The relative humidity of the atmosphere is not very important if the culture medium containing the embryos is maintained under paraffin oil or liquid silicone. However, when the culture medium is exposed to the atmosphere, it is important that the atmosphere be saturated with water vapor. Otherwise, evaporation of the culture media into the atmosphere results in an increase in the osmotic pressure of the medium containing the embryos. It has been shown that hyperosmotic culture media result in poor development of the mouse embryo (16) and the rabbit embryo (111). The situation is probably similar for other embryos.

The effect of the oxygen tension of the atmosphere on the culture medium has been studied predominantly with mouse embryos. Whitten (143) showed that the eight-cell mouse embryo would develop in an atmosphere of 5% CO_2 in air or nitrogen but not in 5% CO_2 in oxygen. Using a continuous flow system, Auerbach & Brinster (3) obtained slightly different results. They found that two-cell embryos, when grown in 5% CO_2 in oxygen, degenerated within 24 hr, a finding similar to that of Whitten. However, in contrast to the findings

of Whitten, they found that the two-cell mouse embryo had a definite, measurable requirement for atmospheric oxygen during the culture period. The embryos invariably degenerated in nitrogen plus 5% CO_2 without undergoing one cleavage, and below a concentration of 1% oxygen there was a significant reduction in the number of two-cell mouse embryos developing into blastocysts (3). However, a few embryos did develop to the blastocyst stage, even at 0.5% oxygen. The fact that embryos develop in a P_{O_2} of about 7 mm Hg (in 1% oxygen) is not inconsistent with an aerobic metabolism. Chance et al. (40) demonstrated by in vivo measurements on the rat brain that the P_{O_2} of extracellular blood is much less than 4 mm Hg when electroencephalogram response and breathing stop. At this P_{O_2} the nicotinamide adenine dinucleotide in the rat brain is 80–90% reduced. This seems to be the level of reduction of pyridine nucleotide above which cellular function ceases. The intracellular P_{O_2} at this degree of nucleotide reduction, as measured in yeast, is less than 0.1 mm Hg.

Therefore it seems that very low levels of atmospheric oxygen tension are consistent with development of the embryo. However, we know from the above studies and from the studies of Thomson (130), who showed that inhibition of the cytochrome system resulted in death of mouse embryos, that oxidative metabolism is essential for development. In Thomson's studies, two respiratory chain inhibitors that were tested blocked development of two-cell embryos at fairly low concentration (cyanide at 10^{-3} M and 2,4-dinitrophenol at 10^{-4} M). Fridhandler (64) likewise found that cyanide was inhibitory to the rabbit embryo at all stages.

In 1969 Whitten (144) reported that the one-cell fertilized mouse ovum from a variety of strains would develop when cultured in test tubes containing medium under an atmosphere of 5% oxygen, 5% carbon dioxide, and the balance nitrogen. He found the development of the embryos to be retarded at 10% and 20% oxygen and suggested that his findings indicate one- and two-cell mouse embryos to be more sensitive to oxygen than are the later stages. In the rabbit, studies suggest that 10% oxygen is the best concentration in which to grow 5–7-day embryos (52).

It has been known for some time that carbon dioxide is a desirable and essential component of the atmosphere surrounding embryos in vitro. When noncarboxylic buffering compounds are substituted for bicarbonate in culture medium, development of the embryo is markedly reduced (16, 17, 27). For instance, when tris(hydroxymethyl)amino methane (Tris) or phosphate replaced bicarbonate in the medium and the gas phase was air, two-cell mouse embryos underwent only one or two cleavage divisions and then stopped dividing. Despite the need of the embryos for CO_2 in the medium, it has not been possible to demonstrate a dose-response effect on embryonic development between 1 and 10% atmospheric CO_2 (37), which suggests that, as in the case of oxygen, small but definite amounts of the gas are essential for development.

Recently, Wales et al. (139) have reported that the eight-cell mouse embryo incorporates CO_2 from radioactive bicarbonate and CO_2 in the culture medium. Graves & Biggers (76) have confirmed the findings of Wales et al. (139) and have extended the findings to other stages of early development in the mouse. These workers have provided additional evidence that carbon dioxide is an essential requirement for embryonic development.

HYDROGEN ION. Because CO_2 is an essential component of the environment of mouse embryos maintained in vitro, a bicarbonate buffer system has generally been employed in culture media used for development of the embryos. Consequently the concentration of the hydrogen ion in culture media used to support embryonic development in vitro has generally been regulated by two main factors, the amount of CO_2 in the atmosphere and the amount of bicarbonate in the medium. Therefore it has not been possible to separate the effect of bicarbonate or CO_2 concentration from the effect of pH. Whitten (142) found that development of eight-cell mouse embryos would occur between pH 6.9 and 7.7. Brinster (16) found that development of the two-cell mouse embryo into a blastocyst occurred between pH 5.87 and 7.78. He also found that the availability of the important energy sources for the embryo, pyruvate and lactate, is related to the hydrogen ion concentration of the medium (18). The lower the pH of the medium, the lower is the concentration of the substrate necessary to obtain optimum development, which suggests that the uptake of these compounds is related to the amount of the compound in the acid formed. If this is true, the membrane of the developing embryo may show selective permeability to substrates necessary for its development, and in some cases the selective permeability may depend on hydrogen ion concentration in the medium. This interaction of pH and energy source substrate has added to the difficulty of determining hydrogen ion concentration optimums for the mouse embryo in vitro. The effect of hydrogen ion is difficult to separate from the effect of energy source concentration and the effect of CO_2 concentration. Optimum hydrogen ion concentration has not been determined for the rabbit embryo or for embryos of other species.

INORGANIC IONS. The ionic composition and the osmolarity of culture media used to support development of mammalian embryos in vitro have resembled closely the ionic composition and osmolarity of blood serum. Several investigators have tried to determine the ions essential or beneficial to the embryo grown in vitro. Most of this work has been done with mouse embryos. Whitten (142) found that omission of calcium, magnesium, or potassium from the medium prevented growth and that the absence of phosphate resulted in a delay of development. The effect of calcium and magnesium on development of the mouse embryo and the interaction of the two in support of development was ex-

amined by Brinster (15), and it was shown that a reduction in the calcium concentration from 1.27 mM to 0.63 mM resulted in a significant decrease in the number of blastocysts that developed from two-cell mouse embryos in vitro. However, a reduction of the magnesium concentration from 0.59 mM to 0.15 mM did not have a significant effect on development. Furthermore there was no interaction between the effects of calcium and magnesium in these studies. Recently, Wales (136) studied the effects of potassium, magnesium, calcium, phosphate, and sulfate ions on the development of two-cell mouse embryos to blastocysts. He found potassium and calcium ions to be necessary for development and no blastocysts to be formed in the absence of either of these ions. Magnesium and phosphate ions were less important, and, even in the complete absence of these ions, development into blastocysts could occur, although the percentage of embryos forming blastocysts was decreased. Absence of sulfate ions did not affect the number of blastocysts developing. Similar studies on the effect of specific ions on development of embryos of other species have not been done, and there may be individual species variation in the effect of specific ions.

The effect of total ionic concentration or osmolarity of the culture medium has been studied in mouse and rabbit embryos. Whitten (142) found that development of the eight-cell mouse embryo would occur when osmolarity of the culture medium was reduced to 0.09. Brinster (16) found that the maximum number of two-cell mouse embryos developed into blastocysts when the osmolarity of the culture media was 0.276 osmol and that development occurred between 0.200 and 0.354 osmol. Naglee et al. (111) cultured rabbit embryos in media with osmolarities ranging from 0.230 to 0.330 and found that the number of embryos reaching the blastocyst stage in the 0.270 osmolar medium was significantly higher than those reaching the blastocyst stage in media at 0.310 and 0.330 osmol. From their studies they suggested that an osmolarity of 0.270 provided the best development for early rabbit embryos in vitro. The normal osmolarity of tissue culture medium and blood serum is about 0.308, and the reason mouse and rabbit embryos should develop more readily in vitro in hypo-osmolar culture media is not known. However, this optimal development in low osmolarity has been found for other cells grown in vitro. For instance, Eagle (56) found an optimum osmolarity of 0.277 for HeLa cells and mouse fibroblasts grown in vitro.

Recently, Whitten & Biggers (145) succeeded in cultivating one-cell-stage mouse ova to blastocysts completely in vitro in the F_1 hybrid strain C57 black/10J by SJL/J. They were unable to obtain development of the fertilized one-cell embryo to the blastocyst completely in vitro for the parent strains of this hybrid cross or for the ova of a number of other strains. The culture medium they used was similar to that previously used to cultivate two-cell mouse embryos (17, 27) with two notable differences: *1)* the concentration of crystalline bovine serum albumin was increased from 1 to 4 g/liter; and *2)* the sodium chloride was reduced to 4 g/liter, which gave the medium an osmolarity of 0.256. It appeared from the results that the hypo-osmolarity was allowing the development of the hybrid species employed. Subsequent work (8) suggests that the key to successful cultivation of the unfertilized one-cell mouse embryo for certain strains and crosses is the concentration of bovine serum albumin. If the concentration of albumin is 4 mg/ml, then the hypo-osmolarity has no effect. However, if the albumin concentration is 1 mg/ml, the hypo-osmolarity increases the number of one-cell embryos developing to blastocysts (J. D. Biggers, personal communication). This intriguing effect of hypo-osmolarity on development in general and on specific hybrid crosses remains unexplained. Perhaps the hypo-osmolarity counteracts some detrimental in vitro effect that is not yet understood. However, for cultivation of mammalian embryos in vitro, culture media of normal osmolarity (0.308 osmol) are generally used, since the increase in development is small with the hypo-osmolar media and since a physiological reason for the effect is as yet unknown. In addition, there is no indication that the osmolarity of the fluid surrounding the embryos in vivo is different from 0.308.

Blastocyst Expansion

The transition of the embryonic ball of cells known as the morula into the fluid-filled sphere known as the blastocyst has interested embryologists for a considerable time. In some species, such as the rabbit, there is a large expansion of the blastocyst before implantation. Between days 4 and 7 the volume of the rabbit embryo increases 4,000-fold. Since the dry weight of the blastocyst is only 1% of its wet weight (92), this increase in volume must be largely due to uptake of water. Studies employing radioisotopes (93) have shown that the rabbit blastocyst accumulates some ions more readily than others from the uterine fluid. These findings suggest that selective and active transport of ions is involved in the transfer phenomena and that expansion of the blastocyst could likewise result from active transport.

Little additional information about the fundamental mechanism of blastocyst expansion appeared until 1969, when Cross & Brinster (47) showed that the rabbit blastocyst maintained a potential difference (inside negative to the outside) of 7, 10, and 2 mv on days 5, 6, and 7 after mating, respectively. The maintenance of such a potential difference is very strong evidence for the active transport of ions. The existence of this negative potential has been confirmed by Gamow & Daniel (70). Smith (122) has measured the ionic composition of 6-day rabbit blastocoele fluid before and after incubation and found a net increase in sodium and chloride content. Cooling and inhibitors decreased the accumulation of these ions.

Cross & Brinster (48) reported that the transtrophoblast potential was substantially reduced by lowering the chloride concentration of the culture medium, and, when chloride was replaced by sulphate, the potential changed to a positive value. Removal of sodium ions resulted in an increase in the potential difference, the inside becoming more negative. Gamow & Daniel (70) also found that the absence of chloride reduced the potential, but they did not find an effect of sodium concentration. The maintenance of the potential difference depends on energy production, since the potential falls in the presence of metabolic inhibitors (dinitrophenol, iodoacetate, and cyanide) and in the absence of oxygen, as is shown in Figure 1. The decline in the potential under anaerobic conditions indicates that oxidative metabolism is essential for the maintenance of the potential.

Recent findings (M. H. Cross, unpublished observations) suggest that net chloride flux into the blastocyst accounts for part of the current flow from outside to inside the blastocyst. This would indicate that blastocyst development and expansion depends in part on the active transport of chloride ions from the uterine fluid into the blastocyst cavity. The movement of water would occur osmotically, and the movement of other ions could occur by exchange diffusion. There is some evidence that sodium and bicarbonate ion may be actively transported from the outside to the inside of the blastocyst cavity, but this has not yet been confirmed by ionic flux studies.

CARBOHYDRATE AND ENERGY METABOLISM

Embryo Requirements in Vitro

The carbohydrate or energy source requirements of embryos developing in vitro have been studied in some detail, particularly in the mouse embryo and, to a lesser

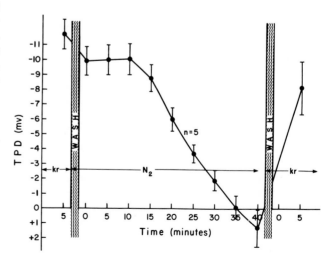

FIG. 1. Effect of anoxia on the transtrophoblast potential difference (*TPD*) in 6-day rabbit blastocyst. *mv*, millivolts (inside negative); N_2, nitrogen gas phase in medium; *kr*, Krebs-Ringer medium (20% oxygen gas phase). [From Cross & Brinster (48).]

extent, in the rabbit embryo. These studies have provided important information about embryo requirements for development. Studies by Hammond (80) and later by Whitten (142) demonstrated that the mouse embryo at the eight-cell stage could be supported in vitro by a medium containing glucose and bovine serum albumin. Later, Whitten (143) showed that development of some two-cell embryos into blastocysts occurred when the only energy source in the medium was lactate. These early studies were extended by Brinster (14, 18) who demonstrated that pyruvate, lactate, oxaloacetate, and phosphoenolpyruvate were the only substrates, of a large group of substrates tested, that would support development of the two-cell mouse embryo into a blastocyst. He also showed that there was a positive interaction between pyruvate and lactate, since the two compounds together allowed better development than did either compound alone. Glucose was not able to support development of the mouse embryo until the four-cell stage. Pyruvate appeared to be the central compound in the energy metabolism of the early mouse embryo (17, 18).

More recently, Biggers et al. (9) extended the findings of Brinster and showed that the one-cell mouse embryo would cleave to the two-cell stage and that oocyte maturation would occur in a medium containing pyruvate or oxaloacetate but not in medium containing lactate or phosphoenolpyruvate. Whittingham (147) demonstrated that embryos maintained in lactate and phosphoenolpyruvate did not undergo degeneration and that the embryos maintained in lactate would resume normal development after 24 hr if placed in a pyruvate-containing medium. It thus appears as though lactate and phosphoenolpyruvate cannot supply sufficient energy to the early embryo for development until after the two-cell stage. Although there seems little doubt that oxaloacetate is necessary for the functioning of the Krebs cycle and that the embryo must have this four-carbon compound just as other animal cells must have it, oxaloacetate is probably able to support development of the early stages because it is decarboxylated to pyruvate (17), which then acts as the energy source. Biggers et al. (9) also found that, when cumulus cells were included with oocytes, or one-cell ova, the media in which lactate, phosphoenolpyruvate, or glucose was the sole energy source were then able to support maturation of the oocyte or cleavage from the one-cell to the two-cell embryo. Subsequently, Donahue & Stern (55) demonstrated that the cumulus cells are capable of converting lactate and glucose to pyruvate, which is probably one reason for the beneficial effect of these cells.

From the above evidence it appears that, during the development of the mouse embryo, there is a gradual change in energy substrate requirement. In the beginning the oocyte needs pyruvate (or oxaloacetate) in the culture media, but when the embryo reaches the two-cell stage, it is able to develop when the energy substrate is pyruvate, oxaloacetate, lactate, or phosphoenol-

pyruvate. After the eight-cell stage the embryo is able to survive and develop in a medium in which the energy source is glucose or any of a number of other carbon chains (38). The gradual change in energy source requirement is shown in Table 3. It seems quite possible that the restrictive nature of the energy source requirements in the embryo is laid down during the early phases of oocyte development and that these restrictions, which are determined by the maternal genome, are gradually eliminated, beginning at about the time of ovulation. When the embryo reaches the blastocyst stage or at about the time of implantation, energy source requirements and energy metabolism seem to be similar to those of most adult cells.

In the rabbit embryo the energy substrate requirements are somewhat more difficult to demonstrate. The two-cell embryo (day 1) will develop into a morula in a culture medium containing only an amino nitrogen source, such as albumin (30). However, it is possible to show a beneficial effect of pyruvate, lactate, and phosphoenolpyruvate on development (30, 51). In addition it has been shown by special experimental design that the optimum concentrations for pyruvate (5×10^{-4} M) and lactate (2.5×10^{-3} M) in the culture medium are very similar for mouse and rabbit embryos (17, 30). Glucose has been shown to be beneficial for the development of rabbit blastocysts and also to increase the number of blastocysts developing from two- and four-cell-stage embryos (98).

A variety of media have been used in recent attempts to culture the early embryos of the rat (7), hamster (150), sheep (108, 148), cow (129), and man (58), but success has been very limited. In addition, different culture media have been used to study the maturation of oocytes of various species in vitro. The first attempts in this area were made by Pincus, with rabbit oocytes

TABLE 3. *Effect of Different Energy Sources on the Development of Preimplantation Mouse Embryos*

Substrate	Stage of Development at Beginning of Culture			
	Oocyte	1-Cell	2-Cell	8-Cell
Pyruvate	+	+	+	+
Oxaloacetate	+	+	+	+
Lactate	−	−	+	+
Phosphoenolpyruvate	−	−	+	+
Glucose	−	−	−	+
Malate	O	O	−	+
α-Ketoglutarate	O	O	−	+
Acetate	O	O	−	+
Citrate	O	O	−	+
Succinate	O	O	−	−
Glucose 6-phosphate	O	O	−	−
Fructose	O	O	−	−

+, development occurred when the substrate was the only energy source in medium. −, no development occurred when the substrate was the only energy source in medium. O, substrate not examined at this stage, but it probably will not support development.   [From Brinster (18), Brinster & Thomson (38), and Biggers et al. (9).]

(116, 117) and human oocytes (118) and later by Chang (42, 43) with rabbit oocytes. Recently, interest in maturation of the oocyte, has been renewed, and attempts at in vitro culture or maturation have been made with the oocytes of the mouse (9, 49), rabbit (63), and man (57, 88). In the studies involving oocytes other than those of the mouse, or embryos other than those of the mouse and rabbit, the numbers of oocytes or embryos involved have been too small to allow a critical assessment of the culture media being used or of the requirements of the cells being cultured. The best development of early embryos is generally obtained with a relatively simple medium containing as energy sources pyruvate at a concentration of about 5×10^{-4} M and glucose at a concentration of 1 mg/ml.

Whether the information on embryo requirements in vitro can be totally extrapolated to embryos developing in vivo is not known, but certainly the findings provide insight into the possibilities that exist in vivo. One indication that the information can be extrapolated, at least in part, is that development of embryos cultured in vitro appears to be normal, and transfer of the embryos to foster mothers results in subsequent normal development of a significant percentage of the embryos (41, 72, 100, 105). However, recently Bowman & McLaren (11) reported that the cleavage rate of embryos growing in vitro is lower than that of embryos growing in vivo. Part of the decrease in rate of cleavage in their investigation may have been from the low in vitro temperature (36 C). They (12) also found that, after transfer to foster mothers, only about half as many in vitro developed blastocysts as in vivo developed blastocysts underwent further development to live fetuses. Likewise, in the rabbit, Maurer et al. (98) have shown that in vitro culture of rabbit embryos decreases their chance of development after transfer to foster mothers. Some of the decrease in development after transfer to foster mothers of in vitro developed embryos may have been due to a greater problem in synchronizing recipient uterus age to in vitro developed embryos than to in vivo developed embryos. However, it seems quite possible that present knowledge does not allow as good development of embryos in vitro as normally occurs in vivo, but useful information about development still results from the in vitro culture experiments.

Embryo Permeability and Enzyme Activity

Two possible explanations might be suggested for differences in utilization of various substrates at successive developmental stages. One is the permeability of the embryo to specific substrate changes, and the second is the activity of enzymes involved in the metabolic pathway changes. If either of these changes occurs with development, the utilization of particular individual substrates will change correspondingly.

One of the first indications of selective permeability of the embryo's membrane to energy substrates was the interaction found between hydrogen ion concentration and substrate concentration (18). In these experiments, optimum concentration of the substrate (pyruvate, lactate, oxaloacetate, and phosphoenolpyruvate) was shown to be influenced by the pH of the medium. The higher the pH of the medium, the higher was the optimum concentration of the substrate required. It appeared that the embryo responded to the amount of substrate in the acid formed. More recently, studies have been made on the permeability of the mouse embryo to glucose, malate, pyruvate, and lactate at several stages of development. In the case of glucose, no significant difference in permeability was noted between two- and eight-cell embryos, although glucose is able to support development of the eight-cell, but not of the two-cell, embryo (138). Likewise, there was no difference in the permeability of one- and two-cell embryos to pyruvate and lactate, despite the fact that lactate will support the two-cell embryo but not the one-cell embryo (140). However, in the case of malate, there was a significant (sevenfold) increase in the permeability of the embryo to malate between the two- and eight-cell stage (137), which suggested that a difference in permeability may be the basis for the ability of malate to support the development of the eight-cell embryo but not that of the two-cell embryo.

Some caution should be exercised in interpreting these results on permeability since the incubation periods were relatively long (30 min) and it was not possible to determine the intracellular intermediaries. Therefore it is difficult to separate the effect of permeability from the effect of changes in enzyme activity since an increase in enzyme activity could result in increased levels of intermediaries without a change in permeability. However, in the case of malate, where we know there is little change in malate dehydrogenase activity during the period studied, it seems quite possible that a change in cell permeability accounts for the change in the embryo's response to malate in the culture medium. Recently it has been shown that permeability of the mouse embryo to α-ketoglutarate and citrate increases considerably between the two- and eight-cell stages (89). It was suggested that the changes in permeability of the embryo to these two compounds may be due to changes that occur in the mitochondrial membranes during this period of development.

The activity of a fairly large number of enzymes has now been measured in the preimplantation mouse embryo, and the activity of a few enzymes has been measured in the embryos of other species. A detailed discussion of the enzyme content of mammalian embryos has recently been published (33), and only a few of the relevant findings are discussed here. The activities of lactate dehydrogenase (LDH) and glucose 6-phosphate dehydrogenase (G6PD) are very high in the mouse embryo and sharply decrease before implantation (19, 21). The extremely high activity of these enzymes cannot specifically be related to metabolic requirements within the early embryo. The LDH in the mouse embryo is five to six thousand times the amount needed to oxidize sufficient lactate to pyruvate for embryonic development (19, 23). Likewise, G6PD activity is much higher in the mouse embryo than is needed to account for any pentose shunt activity (21, 24).

In the rabbit embryo the levels of activity of glucose 6-phosphate dehydrogenase and 6-phosphogluconate dehydrogenase (6PGD) are approximately equal, and both probably act together to regulate pentose shunt activity, which is significant during early cleavage but not during blastocyst development. On the other hand, in the mouse embryo, the pentose shunt does not appear to be very active in early development, yet the G6PD level of activity is higher in the mouse embryo than in the rabbit embryo. However, the activity of 6PGD is only about 1×10^{-2} the level of G6PD at the time of ovulation in the mouse, and therefore the 6PGD probably regulates pentose shunt activity in the mouse embryo (32). The very high levels of activity of LDH and G6PD are probably related predominantly to some requirement during oocyte development in the mouse embryo rather than to metabolism after ovulation (31).

An unusual characteristic of the lactate dehydrogenase (LDH) in the mouse embryo is that the electrophoretic isozyme pattern is predominantly type H (B subunits) during the first 5 days of development and changes to predominantly type M (A subunits) at the time of implantation (2). This finding has been confirmed by Rapola & Koskimies (119), and the identification of the LDH isozyme types has been substantiated by kinetic data (1, 119). The shift in pattern seems to be associated with the phenomena of implantation, which result in an increase in synthesis of both A and B subunits, but the A subunits are produced in much greater quantity (4). In contrast to the above studies, Gibson & Masters (73) find a predominance of type-A subunits in the early mouse embryo and suggest that a considerable amount of LDH is adsorbed from the oviduct fluid (74). However, the total LDH activity of the embryos from the strain of mice they used was very low, and their findings could indicate that strain differences exist among mice, both in LDH isozyme type and total activity.

Perhaps the most interesting enzyme measured in the preimplantation mouse embryo is hexokinase, since it has been shown to be a regulatory enzyme in many other cells. In the mouse embryo it has a very low activity at the time of ovulation, but the activity increases about sevenfold during the preimplantation period (25). The total amount of glucose converted by the embryo to lactate and CO_2 and incorporated into the embryo is very close to the total amount of carbon available from glucose through the hexokinase reaction at each of the developmental stages (see Table 4). This suggests that the hexokinase reaction is instrumental in regulating glucose availability to the early mouse embryo. The activity of phosphofructokinase (PFK), another enzyme that has been shown to be

TABLE 4. *Regulation of Glucose Utilization in the Preimplantation Mouse Embryo*

Stage of Development	Hexokinase Activity, pmole NADP reduced/ hr per embryo[a]	CO₂ Pro- duced[b,c]	Lactate Pro- duced[b,d]	Carbon Incor- pora- ted[b,e,f]	Total[b]
Unfertilized	1.23 (7.38)	0.13	0.15		
Fertilized	1.76 (10.56)	0.68	0.72		
Two-cell	1.70 (10.20)	1.19	2.10	1.65	4.94
Eight-cell	2.24 (13.44)	2.16	3.75	1.72	7.63
Morula	5.63 (33.78)	6.73	27.96		
Blastocyst	7.94 (47.64)	10.94	33.30	7.01	41.70
Late blastocyst	9.40 (56.40)	14.69	42.30	20.01	77.00

Numbers in parentheses indicate maximum intracellular glucose carbon available to the embryo.   [a] Data from Brinster (25).   [b] Values are pmole carbon from glucose per hour per embryo.   [c] Data from Brinster (24).   [d] Data from Wales (135).   [e] Values are average of previous 24 hr.   [f] Data from Brinster (28).

important in regulating glycolytic activity (113, 114), was found to be about 30 times higher than the activity of hexokinase at ovulation (34). The PFK activity remains relatively level during the preimplantation period and therefore approaches more closely the level of glycolytic activity near the time of implantation. Considering the fact that PFK activity in the cell is strongly affected by substrates and compounds in the cytoplasm, it seems reasonable that PFK could be a regulatory enzyme near the time of implantation and may, in fact, be important in regulating Embden-Meyerhof pathway activity earlier than this. However, the data suggest that hexokinase is the primary regulator of glucose utilization during the preimplantation period.

Although one needs to be cautious about interpreting the data available at the present time on embryo permeability, it is likewise important not to equate automatically changes in enzyme activity with changes in substrate utilization. The latter may, but does not always, follow the former. We need much more information on endogenous pool size of substrates and intermediates before we will understand the relative role of permeability changes and enzyme activity changes in bringing about synthetic rate changes.

Stored Substrates

In the mouse embryo, histochemical studies indicate that a substantial amount of glycogen is present at ovulation and that the amount increases until the eight-cell stage of development (132). After blastocyst formation the major part of the glycogen is utilized. There is evidence from the histochemical studies that the pathway for glycogen breakdown is operating at a very low level before blastocyst formation, since the stored glycogen does not seem to be available to the embryo for utilization (132). On the other hand, biochemical studies show that the embryo synthesizes almost all its glycogen between the one-cell and the eight-cell stages and then uses a small portion of this glycogen during blastocyst formation (124). Thus the biochemical studies suggest more synthesis early in development and less utilization later in development than do the histochemical studies.

Surprisingly, in vitro studies using radioactively labeled pyruvate and glucose do not demonstrate significant amounts of pyruvate or glucose incorporation into the carbohydrate or glycogen of the mouse embryo between the one-cell and eight-cell stages of development (28). One would expect to see such incorporation if glycogen synthesis were occurring. Perhaps the glycogen synthesis suggested by the studies of Stern & Biggers (124) occurs in vivo but not in vitro. Incorporation of pyruvate and glucose into the carbohydrate fraction of the embryo is much greater at the time of blastocyst formation and may suggest that the glycogen turnover at the blastocyst stage is high. Recent studies by Stern (123) have shown that the activity of glycogen synthetase is more than adequate to account for the total amount of glycogen synthesis at any of the developmental stages. Some of the pyruvate and glucose carbon incorporated into the carbohydrate fraction of the blastocyst could be incorporated into a polysaccharide of unknown chemical structure, which has been shown to be synthesized in large quantities by the mouse blastocyst (115). The function of this polysaccharide is unknown, but the compound is not glycogen.

Substrate Utilization

Pyruvate, as could be expected from the results of the studies described above (see subsection *Embryo Requirements in Vitro*), is oxidized very readily by the mouse and rabbit embryos. In fact, during the first 2 days of development in the mouse embryo, 90–100% of the oxygen consumption of the embryo can be attributed to pyruvate oxidation (23, 102). Glucose oxidation is very low in the newly ovulated mouse ovum, and less than 10% of the oxygen consumption can be attributed to glucose oxidation during this early period. However, glucose oxidation increases 100-fold during the preimplantation period with major increases at fertilization and blastocyst formation. Therefore, at the time of implantation, glucose is oxidized about as well as is pyruvate (24). Likewise, Wales (135) found that lactate formation from glucose by the mouse embryo increased very rapidly during the preimplantation period, and changes in lactate formation parallel very closely changes in CO_2 formation from glucose (see Table 4).

Studies on rabbit embryos also indicate that glucose is only poorly oxidized by the newly ovulated ovum (26). However, at later stages, particularly in the late morula and blastocyst stages, glucose can be oxidized in substantial amounts (26) and plays an important role in blastocyst metabolism and biosynthetic activity (67). Carbon dioxide is formed from pyruvate quite readily by the rabbit embryo at all stages and can account for over 50% of oxygen uptake throughout the

preimplantation period (29). Lactate is also oxidized very well by the preimplantation rabbit embryo (29). Therefore, despite the fact that the early rabbit embryo has only about $\frac{1}{30}$th the lactate dehydrogenase activity that the early mouse embryo contains, lactate and pyruvate are oxidized very well by the rabbit embryo.

Recent investigations on the oocyte of the rhesus monkey indicate that pyruvate is oxidized to a greater extent than is glucose in this primate species (35). Since metabolism of pyruvate and glucose by the oocyte is probably similar to metabolism of these two compounds by the early cleavage stages, the early cleavage stages of the rhesus monkey probably depend on pyruvate oxidation for their energy, just as do the early cleavage stages of the mouse and rabbit. Thus the early embryos of all three species show a marked preference for pyruvate in the early stages of development, whereas glucose is hardly oxidized at all by the oocyte, newly ovulated ovum, and fertilized ovum. The differences in amount of pyruvate oxidized by embryos of the different species seem to be related to their relative size, but, in all three species, pyruvate is oxidized to a much greater extent than is glucose.

Studies on the incorporation of pyruvate and glucose by the preimplantation mouse embryo have shown that incorporation of these two substrates increases, just as oxidation for the two substrates increases, during the preimplantation period (28). However, carbon from glucose is incorporated into the embryo to a much greater extent than is carbon from pyruvate, whereas pyruvate is oxidized to a much greater extent than is glucose throughout the preimplantation period (see Fig. 2). Carbon from glucose and pyruvate is incorporated in greater amounts before blastocyst formation than are any of the amino acids so far examined, and glucose carbon is incorporated more than is any amino acid during the entire preimplantation period (28, 36). In addition to accumulating carbon from glucose and pyruvate, the embryo converts both substrates to lactate, which is found in the culture media (135, 141). Pyruvate also is converted to alanine and aspartate by the mouse (141) and rabbit (65) blastocyst, but no evidence of substantial glutamate accumulation was found in the mouse embryo, as was found in the rabbit embryo. Glucose and pyruvate seem to play an important role in the metabolism of the mouse embryo and probably in the metabolism of all mammalian embryos during the preimplantation period.

Mouse and rabbit embryos rely on pyruvate as their primary source of energy, but the glucose they use during the first few days of development is oxidized differently. In the rabbit the pentose shunt, which could form NADPH and ribose for nucleic acid synthesis and other synthetic processes, is very active in the oxidation of glucose up to the morula stage (26, 64). After this the Embden-Meyerhof pathway and the Krebs cycle predominate. However, in the mouse embryo there is no evidence that the pentose shunt is very active at any time during the preimplantation period, and glucose

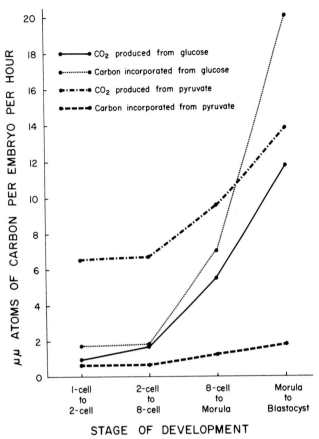

FIG. 2. Utilization of glucose and pyruvate by the preimplantation mouse embryo. [From Brinster (23, 24, 28).]

oxidation results primarily from the Krebs cycle with the formation of NADH and carbon skeletons for amino acid synthesis and other synthetic processes (24). The reason for this difference is not understood. It is important to emphasize that the energy metabolism of mouse and rabbit embryos appears to be predominantly similar, rather than different, during the preimplantation period. In both species the glycolytic pathway is relatively inactive until about the time of blastocyst formation, after which there is a sharp increase in activity. However, the Krebs cycle is the major energy-supplying pathway throughout the preimplantation period, and its activity is also markedly increased at blastocyst formation. It seems quite possible that most mammalian embryos will show this pattern of energy metabolism during the preimplantation period.

NUCLEIC ACID AND PROTEIN METABOLISM

Embryo Requirements in Vitro

A beneficial effect of nucleic acid precursors, when employed in the culture media for early cleavage stage mouse embryos, was reported in 1965 by Cole & Paul (46). However, TenBroeck (128) demonstrated that the presence of nucleic acid precursors in the culture media

either singly or in combination did not enhance development of the preimplantation mouse embryo. Since experiments with labeled nucleosides have shown that these compounds are incorporated by the early embryo (103, 104), the lack of beneficial effect cannot be due to impermeability of the embryos to the compounds. Therefore the early mouse embryo probably either contains an adequate endogenous supply of nucleic acids and precursors or is able to synthesize the components required for the formation of RNA and DNA.

On the other hand, the development of mammalian embryos is generally improved by the addition of an amino nitrogen source to the culture medium. Most of the media used in early attempts to culture embryos contained considerable amounts of serum or other undefined protein sources (5, 27). During the last few years, attempts have been made to define in more specific terms the actual requirements of mammalian embryos for amino acids and proteins. In 1956 Whitten (142) showed that the eight-cell mouse embryo would develop into a blastocyst when cultured in Krebs-Ringer bicarbonate containing 1 mg/ml of glucose and bovine serum albumin at a concentration between 0.03 and 6 %. He later showed (143) that the bovine serum albumin could be replaced with glycine or other amino acids and simple peptides. Brinster (20) examined the effect of various exogenous amino nitrogen sources on the development of the two-cell mouse embryo into a blastocyst, and he found that bovine serum albumin in concentrations between 1 and 10 mg/ml allowed maximum development. The requirement for protein could be supplied by mouse serum or bovine serum as well as by the constituent amino acids of albumin. However, it was not possible to demonstrate a group of essential amino acids necessary for the development of the early embryo. This is surprising since most other cells grown in vitro require a specific group of amino acids (essential amino acids) or a protein supplement, or both. Brinster (20) found that the removal of any single amino acid from the culture media did not prevent development of the two-cell embryo into a blastocyst. Recently, Cholewa & Whitten (44) have succeeded in culturing two-cell mouse embryos to blastocysts in media containing no amino acids or protein.

Thus the work to date suggests that the ovulated mouse ovum contains all or nearly all the amino acids it needs for development to a blastocyst. However, most studies have shown that development is substantially improved when a complement of amino acids or protein is included in the culture media. The amino acids and perhaps the protein may supplement the endogenous amino acid pool. A more probable role for the protein is to stabilize the membrane and reduce the leakage of endogenous amino acids into the culture media (20, 36). Cholewa & Whitten (44) have suggested that the beneficial effect may be due to the ability of the amino acids and albumin to remove toxic metal ions present in the culture media. The beneficial effects of exogenous amino acids and proteins seem to be greatest for development of the blastocyst and for the first cleavage division. Studies employing radioactive amino acids indicate that amino acids contained in the media are incorporated into the embryo but that protein molecules within the culture media make very little contribution to the amino acid pool and proteins of the embryo (36). This evidence also suggests that the embryo contains most of the amino acids it needs for development. Whether amino acids improve development of the mouse embryo when the medium contains albumin is not clear (20, 37). Fetal calf serum at a concentration of 10 % (v/v) appears to be beneficial for in vitro maturation of mouse oocytes (49) and often is employed in medium for the cultivation of blastocysts, particularly rabbit blastocysts. However, some recent experiments [unpublished work of P. Bowman and A. McLaren quoted by Menke & McLaren (101)] suggest that fetal calf serum may have a detrimental effect on late cleavage stages of the mouse embryo.

To what extent the preimplantation rabbit embryo requires amino nitrogen sources in the culture medium is not clear. Daniel & Olson (54) found that cystine, tryptophan, phenylalanine, lysine, arginine, and valine were essential for cleavage of the early rabbit embryo. However, Mauer et al. (97) could show no decrease in development when tryptophan or several other amino acids were omitted from the culture media of two-cell rabbit embryos, and Brinster (30) found that the early rabbit embryo would show normal cleavage for 2 days, when the only amino nitrogen source in the medium was oxidized glutathione or such single amino acids as alanine or glutamine. Therefore, under certain conditions, there is apparently no essential amino acid requirement for the preblastocyst rabbit embryo, a condition somewhat similar to the situation in the mouse embryo. However, no one has been able to obtain development of the early rabbit embryo without any amino nitrogen source in the culture medium. In fact, Kane & Foote (85–87) found that two- and four-cell-stage rabbit embryos cleaved better in media containing amino acids than in those media that did not contain amino acids. In addition, they found that, in the absence of bovine serum albumin, few blastocysts formed in a simple synthetic medium. Thus they feel that a macromolecular component (bovine serum albumin) is necessary for good development of cleavage stage rabbit embryos to blastocysts. Likewise, they feel that the addition of an amino acid complement to the medium containing bovine serum albumin improves the development of the cleavage stage embryos into blastocysts. The development of the blastocyst in the rabbit is associated with a large increase in tissue mass. Therefore it seems quite unlikely that the newly ovulated ovum contains sufficient endogenous stores to undertake such an enlargement. Consequently most studies have shown that exogenous amino nitrogen sources are needed for development of the rabbit blastocyst, and serum seems to benefit the development of the rabbit blastocyst. Some investigators have attempted to determine

if certain amino acids are essential for the blastocyst development, and Daniel & Krishnan (53) suggest that arginine, histidine, lysine, tryptophan, methionine, phenylalanine, leucine, valine, threonine, and serine are indispensible for growth of rabbit blastocyts in vitro.

Embryo Permeability and Enzyme Activity

Specific quantitative studies on the permeability of the mammalian embryo to precursors of nucleic acids and proteins have not been made. We know from the autoradiographic studies of Mintz (103, 104) that the precursors get into the embryos, but it is not possible to tell, from these studies or subsequent investigations in which counts per minute are reported, whether permeability of the embryo changes with the stage of development. In many of the studies, increases in incorporation of precursor into the embryo nucleic acid or protein have been equated with, or suggested to represent, changes in rate of synthesis. As mentioned previously, increases in incorporation may represent changes in permeability of the embryo, as well as changes in rates of synthesis.

In the absence of direct studies on permeability of the embryo to various substrates, probably the best available indication of changes in permeability is the change in acid-soluble uptake of precursors. This may provide a rough measure of the penetration of internal embryo pools by external, labeled precursor. Then a comparison of incorporated label to acid-soluble label or to total uptake should provide an estimation of changes in synthetic rate. Surely such a comparison provides a much better estimation of synthetic rate changes than do changes in incorporation taken by themselves. In the sea urchin embryo, Fry & Gross (68, 69) have shown that the rate of protein synthesis is constant from fertilization to the time of blastula formation and that the changes in precursor incorporation during this period reflect permeability changes. Most of the dramatic increase (about tenfold) seen in incorporation of protein and RNA precursors into the preimplantation mouse embryo is probably also due to changes in permeability of the embryo to the precursor. The studies of Tasca & Hillman (127) and Brinster (36) in which incorporation is compared to acid-soluble uptake or total uptake to give percentage of incorporation, as shown in Table 5, probably provide a more accurate indication of changes in overall protein synthesis than do measures of incorporation alone.

Epstein & Daentl (62) have reported that guanine uptake reaches a maximum at the eight- to 16-cell stage of the mouse embryo, in contrast to uridine for which the major increase in uptake begins 12–25 hr later. Despite the difference in the time a large increase in uptake occurred, the pattern of incorporation into the embryo for the two precursors was similar. This would suggest that the process of uptake and incorporation of the precursors is separate. Thus it appears that uptake

TABLE 5. *Carbon Accumulation from Leucine by the Preimplantation Mouse Embryo*

Period of Development	Amino Nitrogen Source in Medium	Carbon Accumulated		
		Trichloro-acetic acid precipitate incorporation, picoatoms/embryo per hr	Total uptake, pico-atoms/embryo per hr	Percent incorporation
1-Cell to 2-cell	Albumin	0.21	0.67	31
	None	0.19	0.56	34
2-Cell to 4-cell	Albumin	0.21	0.61	34
	None	0.18	0.56	32
8-Cell to morula	Albumin	1.15	2.08	55
	None	0.72	1.11	65
Morula to blastocyst	Albumin	2.15	4.56	47
	None	2.11	4.69	45

Albumin concentration 1 mg/ml.

of precursors for nucleic acids is separate from the process of incorporation, just as was suggested above for protein.

Only a few enzymes involved in nucleic acid or protein metabolism in the mammalian embryo have been measured. We know that the two-cell mouse embryo requires very few (20) or no (44) amino acids in the culture medium for in vitro development to occur, and this may suggest that the embryo has active transaminase and deaminase enzymes. Moore & Brinster (109) examined glutamic dehydrogenase and aspartate aminotransferase and found that the former decreased in activity, whereas the latter increased in activity during the preimplantation period. The increase in aspartate aminotransferase might be explained on the basis of the increase in protein synthesis and protein content that appears to occur in the 2 days before implantation. There seems to be no explanation at the present time for the fall in glutamic dehydrogenase activity.

Recently, Epstein (61) has shown that the activity of adenine phosphoribosyltransferase and hypoxanthine-guanine phosphoribosyltransferase (HGPRT) increases almost immediately after fertilization, and it is tempting to speculate that these enzymes are needed for the synthesis of nucleic acids. Epstein & Daentl (62) also found high levels of guanine deaminase (GD) in the early mouse embryo. Despite the high levels of GD, the major product formed from guanine was guanine triphosphate; this indicated that the GD was not competing effectively in vivo with the HGPRT for the guanine. This demonstrates again, as was mentioned before, that total in vitro enzyme activity does not necessarily reflect the amount of the enzyme needed by the embryo (e.g., LDH) for its metabolism or the amount of substrate converted. Some of the enzymes present in the early mammalian embryo, particularly those in high concentration, may remain from previous requirements in the oocyte. However, in certain cases, such as that of hexokinase, there is evidence that total

activity of an enzyme may influence metabolic capability.

Stored Substrates

At ovulation the mouse ovum contains about 45 pg DNA (120), which is considerably more than the 2.5 pg chromosomal DNA one would expect to be present in a haploid mouse cell. During the early cleavage stages the total DNA per embryo increases as the number of cells increases, but the DNA per cell decreases toward the normal diploid quantity of 5 pg (see Table 6). At the 16-cell stage, early on day 4, the DNA per cell is roughly one-half that found at ovulation. The nature of this excess DNA in the early mouse embryo is not known, but it appears to be in the form of oligonucleotides of low molecular weight and not highly polymerized (120). Perhaps it represents an extra chromosomal pool of DNA upon which the embryo can rely during the initial period of cell replication. Whether some of the DNA is in the form of mitochondrial DNA or associated with yolk spherules, as in the sea urchin embryo (134), is not known, but ultrastructural studies indicate that the number of mitochondria present in the early mouse embryo is small, and the internal cristae are poorly developed (39, 81).

The RNA content of the mouse ovum at ovulation is about 1,750 pg, compared to a postimplantation embryonic cell RNA average content of 20 pg/cell. The precise nature of the RNA in the embryo is not known, but its resistance to breakdown suggests that it is high-molecular-weight RNA (120). The total RNA per embryo increases slightly from the one- to the four-cell stage and then decreases steadily to the 16-cell stage (see Table 6). The RNA content per cell falls rapidly from the one- to the 16-cell stage, and the individual

TABLE 6. *Nucleic Acid and Protein Content of the Mouse and Rabbit Embryo*

Stage of Development	Mouse			Rabbit	
	DNA, pg/cell*	RNA, pg/cell*	Protein, ng/embryo**	RNA, pg/cell†	Protein, ng/embryo**
Unfertilized	45.8 (45.8)	1,750 (1,750)	26.0	20,000 (20,000)	100‡
Day 1	49.0 (49.0)	1,680 (1,680)	26.0	14,000 (28,000)	100‡
Day 2	24.0 (48.0)	905 (1,810)	24.3	2,125 (34,000)	100‡
Day 3	20.4 (163.0)	200 (1,600)	21.6	539 (69,000)	100‡
Day 4	19.3 (308.0)	50 (807)	20.4	120 (123,000)	
Day 5			20.1	46 (414,000)	1,307
Day 6	Embryos implant on day 5			35 (2,790,000)	6,235

Numbers in parentheses indicate values per embryo. *Data from Reamer (120).   **Data from Brinster (22). †Data from Manes (95).   ‡Estimated values.

cell in the 16-cell morula contains only about 50 pg RNA. The large quantity of RNA found in the newly ovulated and early cleavage stages of the mouse embryo in these biochemical studies is quite surprising in view of the small number of ribosomes present in the newly ovulated ovum and early cleavage stages of the mouse and other mammalian embryos (39, 60, 81, 99, 126, 151).

Manes & Daniel (96) have found that the early stages of the rabbit embryo also contain a considerable amount of RNA. At ovulation about 20,000 pg RNA, or about 10 times the amount present in the mouse at ovulation, is present, although the rabbit zygote is only about 3.5 times the size of the mouse zygote. The RNA content of the rabbit embryo cells gradually falls during the preimplantation period to reach a level of about 35 pg at implantation (see Table 6). As in the case of the mouse embryo, precursor incorporation data suggest that the maternal RNA of the newly ovulated ovum is supplemented by RNA synthesized by the embryo (see subsection *Substrate Utilization*). The contribution of embryo RNA is particularly noticeable after blastocyst formation in the rabbit since total RNA increases dramatically as the blastocyst grows in size.

Loewenstein & Cohen (91) determined that the one-cell mouse embryo contained 20 ng protein, 8 ng carbohydrate, and 4 ng fat. The total wet weight was estimated to be 318 ng. Brinster (22) found a slightly higher value for the protein content of the mouse embryo at ovulation (about 26 ng) and also found that the protein content decreased by 25% from ovulation to the morula stage early on day 4 (see Table 6), but after blastocyst formation protein content appeared to increase. Whether this protein that is lost by the embryo early in cleavage is used by the embryo as a source of amino acids or energy for development is not known, but it is clear that the embryo needs very few exogenous amino acids for preblastocyst development. Perhaps the protein is degraded to furnish the amino acids required for cleavage. Measurements of protein content of preblastocyst rabbit embryos have not been made; therefore we do not know how the pattern changes with development. After blastocyst formation in the rabbit, protein content increases dramatically (see Table 6).

Substrate Utilization

Little is known about the details of DNA synthesis during the preimplantation period. Tritiated thymidine is incorporated into the mouse (104) and rabbit embryos (95) at all cleavage stages, which indicates synthesis of DNA throughout this period. However, as has been mentioned above, embryos grow quite well without an exogenous source of DNA precursors; thus adequate precursors must be available in the embryo, and the embryo must be capable of whatever synthetic steps are required to make DNA from its precursor material. Reamer (120) has suggested from her studies that the large amount of extrachromosomal material

she measured as DNA existed in the form of oligonucleotides, and perhaps these serve as precursor material.

Recently, Gamow & Prescott (71) have shown that mouse embryos between the two- and 16-cell stages lack a G1 period (i.e., gap in cell cycle before DNA synthesis), and, in fact, even in the morula and blastocyst stages, the G1 period is very short and possibly absent. In most cell types the regeneration time or the rate of reproduction of the cell is controlled primarily by an extension or contraction of the time the cells are retained in the phase of the cell cycle between mitosis or interphase and subsequent synthesis of DNA (G1). Dalcq & Pasteels (50) have suggested that the early cleavage stages of the rat also have a short or completely absent G1 phase. In addition to the evidence in the mouse and rat embryos, cleavage of *Xenopus* embryos (75) and sea urchin embryos (82) takes place without a G1 phase. The absence of a G1 period means a more rapid rate of cell production and may reflect the absence of regulation of cell reproduction. Perhaps the regulation of the rate of cell reproduction is gradually imposed on different sets of cells during early differentiation of tissue from the inner cell mass.

Thymidine incorporation into DNA, at least during the blastocyst stage, is proportionate to the number of nuclei produced during the incubation period (115). The exogenous precursor (thymidine) in these experiments was shown to be rapidly incorporated, and it was estimated that 65% of the thymidine residues in the DNA of the nuclei produced during the labeling period were from labeled precursor. It appears that little or no mitochondrial DNA is synthesized by the cleaving mouse embryo (115). This is similar to the findings in the sea urchin embryos (77, 115, 134).

Although mouse embryos will develop without exogenous precursors of RNA in the medium, when tritiated uridine is present it is incorporated into the nuclei and nucleoli of cleavage stage embryos. However, there is little radioactivity seen in autoradiographic preparations of the very early embryo. Not until true nucleoli are formed after the second cleavage is much tritiated uridine taken up by the embryo (103, 104). In the late morula and blastocyst, the autoradiographs indicate very heavy labeling. The labeling appears first in the nucleus, then in the nucleoli, and finally in the cytoplasm (104). The pattern of incorporation suggested that the RNA being synthesized might be ribosomal in type.

A number of workers have tried to assess quantitatively the incorporation or uptake of labeled precursors by the developing zygote. Monesi & Salfi (107) found that uridine uptake was relatively level until about the eight-cell stage of development, and then there was a dramatic increase in uptake by the mouse embryo. Tasca & Hillman (127) measured the uptake and the incorporation of uridine by early mouse embryos. The uptake of uridine increased dramatically with the age of the embryo. Therefore, Tasca and Hillman used the ratio of incorporated uridine to total uptake as a measure of synthesis. It is essential to make some such adjustment for changes in permeability, since, as mentioned previously, changes in permeability affect pool size and may account for large differences in precursor incorporation. A summary of their results is shown in Figure 3, from which it is clear that the ratio of uridine incorporation to uptake increases between the two-cell and morula stages. This suggests that the rate of synthesis of RNA is increasing during this period.

The effect of inhibitors of RNA metabolism on the in vitro development of the preimplantation embryo has been examined, and it was found that these compounds will inhibit development of the embryo, as well as the uptake and incorporation of precursors by the embryo. For instance, it was found that the dose of dactinomycin (which inhibits DNA-dependent RNA synthesis) required to prevent cleavage of the mouse embryo is only about 1×10^{-4} the dose required to inhibit cleavage of the sea urchin embryo (77–79, 131). This suggests that the mouse embryo relies much more than does the sea urchin embryo on DNA-dependent RNA synthesis during the early cleavage stages.

Tasca & Hillman (127) found that dactinomycin did not affect leucine incorporation during a 3-hr in vitro incubation. However, Monesi et al. (106) found that dactinomycin at a concentration of 0.1 μg/ml (the same concentration used in the Tasca and Hillman studies) caused a rapid and almost complete inhibition of the incorporation of tritiated uridine at all developmental stages (see Fig. 3) and decreased incorporation of leucine into protein to about 50% of the control incorporation during a 12–16-hr incubation. Longer incubation with the antibiotic did not further depress the relative incorporation of tritiated leucine with respect to the control. The differences between the amount of amino acid incorporation in the presence of dactinomycin in the studies of Tasca & Hillman (127) and Monesi (106) must be due to differences in techniques, such as the length of cultivation. Taken together these results can be interpreted to indicate that protein synthesis in the cleaving mouse embryo depends partially on RNA with a very long half-life and partially on RNA with a

short half-life (less than 16 hr). At the present time we do not know how much of the long-half-life RNA is synthesized before ovulation by maternal genome and how much is synthesized after fertilization. In the sea urchin embryo, protein synthesis during the early cleavage stages up to gastrulation depends almost entirely on RNA synthesized before ovulation (78, 79). Very high levels (20 μg/ml) of dactinomycin do not suppress amino acid incorporation during early cleavage in the sea urchin. Thus present evidence indicates that protein synthesis in the mouse embryo is much more dependent on new RNA than is protein synthesis in the sea urchin embryo.

It has also been reported that treatment of cleavage stage mouse embryos with very low levels of dactinomycin (10^{-3} μg/ml) does not interfere with immediate development but affects differentiation (protein synthesis) at a later time (121, 127). This is similar to the situation found in the sea urchin, where treatment of the cleavage stages with dactinomycin does not affect cleavage but affects differentiation at a later stage of development. Such evidence suggests that some of the RNA synthesized during cleavage is stored and used later in development.

There is only a small amount of information available about nucleic acid metabolism in the rabbit embryo. Recently, Manes and Daniel (95, 96), on the basis of precursor incorporation studies in the rabbit embryo, suggested that the protein synthetic apparatus necessary to carry the mammalian embryo through cleavage is totally present in the zygote and is merely parceled out to each blastomere with cleavage division. They interpreted their data as indicating that the embryonic genome is not utilized for protein synthesis occurring during preblastocyst cleavage in the rabbit. Manes & Daniel (96) feel that the inhibitory effect of dactinomycin seen in a number of other studies on mammalian embryos is a side effect of dactinomycin and that its depression of RNA synthesis is not the cause of inhibition of embryonic development. Although the fundamentals of nucleic acid metabolism are probably similar in most species and it is appealing to believe that mammals are similar to invertebrates relative to their nucleic acid synthesis during the preimplantation period, considerably more evidence certainly is needed to substantiate this hypothesis of Manes and Daniel, since the bulk of the work to date suggests that important differences do exist between the embryos of invertebrates and mammals. One of the important differences is the early developmental age at which nucleoli appear and at which ribosomal and 4S RNA genes are activated in the mouse embryo (149). The information about the rabbit embryo to date suggests that it resembles the mouse embryo in its nucleic acid metabolism to a much greater extent than it resembles the sea urchin.

Several workers have attempted to examine the synthesis of specific nucleic acid fractions by studying the incorporation of uridine into RNA. Ellem & Gwatkin

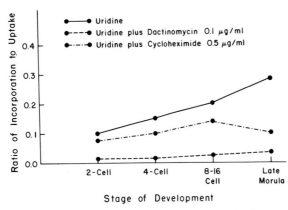

FIG. 3. Ratio of incorporation to uptake of uridine by the preimplantation mouse embryo. Embryos were incubated for 3 hr in the medium containing uridine or uridine plus the inhibitor.

(59) found that in all the stages, from the eight-cell stage to the blastocyst, uridine incorporation into ribosomal RNA was very high, which may reflect an increased synthesis of RNA necessary to increase the ribosome pool of the embryo. In addition, large amounts of exogenous uridine were incorporated into soluble RNA, whereas incorporation into messenger-like RNA was low. Incorporation into soluble and ribosomal RNA was greater and incorporation into messenger RNA much less in mouse embryo cells than occurs in diploid cells grown in vitro. Ellem & Gwatkin (59) further found that dactinomycin severely inhibited uridine incorporation into ribosomal RNA and soluble RNA but did not affect incorporation into messenger RNA in the mouse embryo.

Woodland & Graham (149) also examined the species of RNA into which labeled uridine was incorporated. They were able to study incorporation at slightly earlier stages with their techniques than were Ellem and Gwatkin. They found that at the two-cell stage most of the activity is incorporated into a low-molecular-weight RNA (5S). During succeeding cleavage stages, incorporation shifts into high-molecular-weight RNA. By the eight-cell stage of development, pronounced radioactive peaks appear at the same positions as 28S and 16S ribosomal RNA. A low-molecular-weight RNA can be identified in the four-cell stage as 4S RNA (soluble RNA). These studies show very clearly the initiation of synthesis of specific types of RNA and indicate that mice are quite different from nonmammalian embryos studied (sea urchin and frog) in the extremely early stages of development, at which they begin to synthesize 4S RNA and ribosomal RNA. It seems quite probable that the genes for 4S RNA and ribosomal RNA both become activated at the four-cell stage and during the same cell cycle. This is quite different from the sea urchin, in which 4S RNA synthesis begins a considerable time before ribosomal RNA synthesis can be detected and in which synthesis of both types of RNA begins much later in cleavage.

Pikó (115) has confirmed and extended the observations of Ellem & Gwatkin (59) and Woodland & Graham (149). He estimated that the half-life of the 39S RNA (precursor of ribosomal RNA) was 15 min and that the half-life of the heterodisperse RNA (probably containing messenger RNA and precursors of messenger RNA) was 10 min or less in the blastocyst just before implantation. He also estimated that the minimum rate of production of ribosomes was 6×10^5/min in a blastocyst consisting of 60 cells. This minimum rate of ribosome production is comparable on a per cell basis to that estimated for HeLa cells (94).

Recently, Church (45) has examined the contribution of exogenously supplied precursors to soluble RNA, ribosomal RNA, and DNA-like RNA (dRNA). His results on sRNA and rRNA are similar to the results of previous workers, but Church used the very sensitive RNA-DNA hybridization technique to identify the dRNA fraction. The results of his studies are summarized

in Figure 4. Since only incorporation was measured, we do not know the relative importance of variations in permeability and synthetic rates in causing the changes in incorporation. However, at least two points seem evident from the illustration. First, precursors appear in dRNA (which contains messenger RNA) as early as the two-cell stage, and, second, the pattern of incorporation into sRNA and rRNA is different from the pattern of incorporation into dRNA during the preimplantation period in the mouse.

We know from the work of Reamer [(120); see subsection *Stored Substrate*] that the distribution of the RNA contained in the newly ovulated mouse ovum to succeeding cells of the cleavage stages results in a cellular content of RNA of about 50 pg/cell at the 16-cell stage of development. Since this is close to the approximately 20 pg RNA found in normal postimplantation embryonic cells, we would expect to see an increase in the embryo's ability to synthesize RNA to prevent the depletion of cellular RNA. The studies we have just discussed relating to RNA synthesis and metabolism in the embryo seem to suggest that such an increase in the embryo's ability does occur. Beginning at about the four-cell stage, the embryo's ability to synthesize RNA appears to increase gradually, and then, at about the eight- to 16-cell stage of development, there is a marked increase in incorporation of RNA precursors. Since we have no measure of the change in permeability to substrate, we do not know exactly how much of the increase in incorporation results from an increased synthetic rate. The primary species of RNA being synthesized have been identified as ribosomal RNA and soluble RNA. Since the newly ovulated ovum and early mouse embryo cleavage stages do not contain very many polyribosomes

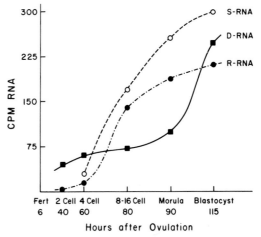

FIG. 4. Incorporation of precursors into mouse embryo RNA. Ribonucleic acid incorporation into mouse embryos cultivated in vitro for 24 hr is summarized. Soluble RNA (*S-RNA*) and ribosomal RNA (*R-RNA*) were identified by sedimentation velocity. The DNA-like RNA (*D-RNA*) was determined by utilizing unique mouse DNA sequences in the solution renaturation of the 24-hr pulse-labeled RNA with sheared DNA. The RNA/DNA hybrid was eluted from a hydroxyapatite column. *CPM*, counts/min. [From Church (45).]

or ribosomes (39, 81), it seems logical that ribosomal RNA should be one of the first types of RNA synthesized by the embryo, and, indeed, the cells of the blastocyst contain a considerable number of ribosomes. In addition, since we know that protein synthesis is occurring in the mouse embryo from fertilization onward and there is an indication that protein synthesis increases at about the time of implantation (day 5), we can expect an increase in the need of the embryo for soluble RNA. The embryo seems to meet the need by synthesizing this species of RNA beginning at the four-cell stage.

The mass of the rabbit embryo begins to increase shortly after blastocyst formation. Therefore we might expect RNA synthesis to increase in this animal species just before blastocyst formation, as it does in the mouse embryo. The studies of Manes (95) with the rabbit embryo actually show a substantial increase in uridine incorporation into RNA and in RNA content at the time of late morula and early blastocyst formation, and thus his data suggest that the rabbit embryo is similar to the mouse embryo in respect to the time at which a sharp change in RNA metabolism occurs during early development. The morula stage or the transition to a blastocyst seems to be an important time in the preimplantation period of mammalian embryos. Many aspects of metabolism, including RNA metabolism, as well as energy and protein metabolism, seem to show a marked increase at about this time.

During the preimplantation period, the number of cells in the embryo doubles approximately every 10–12 hr; however, the size and protein content of most embryos are relatively constant before blastocyst formation. After blastocyst formation, there is probably an increase in protein content, which may be relatively small or quite large, depending on the animal species. The absence of protein content increase or size increase in the early stages does not mean that there is no protein synthesis. In fact, incorporation of radioisotopically labeled amino acids into protein of the embryo can be demonstrated throughout the preimplantation period in the mouse (104) and rabbit (96). The level of incorporation is generally low in the early cleavage stages but increases markedly between the eight- and 16-cell stages and continues at a high level in the morula and blastocyst. Monesi & Salfi (107) measured quantitatively the incorporation of leucine and lysine during the early developmental stages of the mouse embryo. They found that incorporation was relatively level until about the eight-cell stage, and then there was a dramatic increase (about tenfold) in the incorporation of the amino acids by the embryo.

Tasca & Hillman (127) measured the total counts taken up by the embryo and in the acid-insoluble fraction of embryos incubated in radioactive leucine from the two-cell to blastocyst stage, and Brinster (36) determined the amount of amino acid carbon incorporated into acid-soluble and acid-insoluble fractions of the embryo throughout the cleavage period for leucine, as well as for a number of other amino acids (see Table

5). They found dramatic changes in uptake of amino acid precursors into the acid-soluble fraction during the preimplantation period and suggest that these changes in uptake have significant effects on incorporation rate into protein (see subsection *Embryo Permeability and Enzyme Activity*). They consider that the ratio of incorporation of precursor to total uptake was related more to changes in synthetic rate than was the rate of incorporation alone. Studies of Tasca & Hillman (127) show that the percentage of incorporated precursor rises from about 40 % to 80 % between the two-cell stage and the morula stage. Brinster's studies (36) show that the rate of incorporation rises from about 30 % to 50 % from the one-cell stage to the morula stage. Although the percentage of incorporation is slightly different between the studies, it is quite clear that in both studies changes in ratio are dramatically different from the changes in incorporation rate alone. Recently, Fry & Gross (68, 69) have shown that the rate of protein synthesis in the sea urchin embryo is constant up to blastula development. This is in marked contrast to earlier claims of an increase in protein synthetic rate during cleavage of the sea urchin embryo, which were based on increases in incorporation rate.

Tasca & Hillman (127) showed that cycloheximide inhibits leucine and uridine incorporation into the early cleavage stages of the mouse embryo. One would expect cycloheximide, which has been shown to inhibit leucine incorporation into other cell systems, to inhibit leucine incorporation into the early mouse embryo. However, the inhibition of uridine incorporation by cycloheximide (see Fig. 3) was somewhat unexpected and suggests that the inhibitor is blocking the formation of a protein that is necessary for uridine incorporation and RNA synthesis. This protein could be RNA polymerase or perhaps the proteins associated with ribosome formation.

Manes & Daniel (96) have studied incorporation of labeled amino acids into the preimplantation rabbit embryo and found a situation similar to that found for the mouse embryo. The incorporation of amino acid into the embryo is relatively level between the one- and eight-cell stages and then increases markedly. The increase is more rapid in the rabbit embryo, perhaps because there is a larger increase in tissue mass in the rabbit embryo than in the mouse embryo. It would be interesting to be able to compare carbon incorporated per gram of embryo protein in the rabbit and mouse, but specific amounts of carbon incorporated have not been reported for the rabbit. Unfortunately, in the Manes and Daniel study the total amount of uptake by the embryos was not reported. Therefore it is not possible to tell if uptake is changing dramatically at the same time incorporation into the embryo is changing dramatically.

Evidence of the adequacy or completeness of endogenous amino acid stores for protein metabolism in the mouse embryo comes from experiments in which incorporation of leucine by the mouse embryo was measured in the presence or absence of bovine serum albumin or fetal calf serum (36). Neither bovine serum albumin (see Table 5) nor fetal calf serum significantly affected uptake of leucine. This suggests that the macromolecules tested make a small or negligible contribution to the amino acid pool of the embryo, which is surprising, since we know that the embryos will undergo normal development when albumin is the only exogenous amino nitrogen source (20). The macromolecules must exert their beneficial effect primarily through the physical-chemical action on the cells, rather than through a combination of this and their amino acid contribution, as was suggested earlier (20). Perhaps they prevent leakage of the endogenous amino acids from the embryo by stabilizing the cell membrane.

One of the interesting observations on amino acid incorporation and uptake by cleavage stage embryos is that there is little difference in uptake or incorporation of amino acid during the early cleavage stages (see Table 5), despite the fact that cell number is doubling every 10–12 hr (36, 107). Since the genome is doubling with each cleavage, whereas cytoplasmic mass remains relatively constant, it appears that incorporation during the first few cleavages is related more to the cytoplasm than to the genome. This suggests that protein synthesis in the early mouse embryo might be occurring to a considerable extent on maternal ribosomes in conjunction with maternal messenger RNA, both of which are stored in the cytoplasm. The embryo genome seems to have little control over this synthesis, which may go on for a short time, even in the absence of cleavage (36). Perhaps maternal control predominates over embryogenesis in the mouse before the four- to eight-cell stage with increasing embryonic control thereafter. There is evidence that the embryonic genome does begin to function soon after fertilization since a paternal effect on cleavage rate has been demonstrated (146), and it seems that the X chromosome is necessary for early cleavage (110). Regardless of the details of the mechanism for control of protein synthesis, some protein synthesis must be essential for development of preimplantation embryos since low levels of puromycin will block cleavage (131).

The studies of Monesi & Salfi (107) with the mouse and Manes & Daniel (96) with the rabbit suggest an increase in amino acid incorporation at the time of fertilization, but it is not possible to determine from their data whether the increase is significant since no estimates of variance were given. However, Brinster (36) found no significant change in incorporation and only a small increase in uptake of leucine with fertilization in the mouse (see Table 7). This similarity in the incorporation of leucine between unfertilized and fertilized mouse ova is in sharp contrast to the situation in invertebrate embryos where fertilization is characterized by a marked increase in incorporation of amino acids (83, 84, 112, 133). The absence of an increase in amino acid incorporation at fertilization of the mouse ovum suggests that an enhancement of protein synthesis is not a characteristic of fertili-

TABLE 7. *Uptake and Incorporation of Carbon from Leucine by Unfertilized and Fertilized Mouse Ova*

Experiment	Unfertilized		Fertilized	
	TCA ppt	Total uptake	TCA ppt	Total uptake
1	0.378	1.466	0.417	1.870
2	0.404	1.315	0.367	1.953
3	0.346	1.542	0.348	1.555
4	0.394	1.845	0.334	2.046
5	0.360	1.140	0.277	1.729
Mean	0.376	1.462	0.348	1.831
SEM	±0.012	±0.118	±0.022	±0.087

Values expressed as picoatoms of carbon per ovum per hour. Culture medium contained 1 mg/ml albumin and 10^{-2} M leucine. Incubation time was 1 hr.   TCA, trichloroacetic acid. [From Brinster (36).]

zation in the mouse embryo, as it is in the sea urchin embryo.

SUMMARY

Among the preimplantation stages of the eutherian mammals there appears to be considerable similarity in morphology and general developmental characteristics. The similarity is particularly noticeable before blastocyst development, and it seems quite possible that the general developmental similarity during this period may indicate that the embryos have similar nutritional requirements and metabolism.

Studies on embryo requirements in vitro have contributed considerably to our knowledge of embryo metabolism and development. In general, they have indicated that the embryos need an environment similar to the environment found necessary for other mammalian cells grown in vitro. One of the interesting findings in this respect is the embryo's requirement for carbon dioxide in its environment. This requirement goes beyond the general maintenance of pH, and the carbon is actually incorporated by the embryo. In respect to ions in general, it has been demonstrated that active transport of specific ions is probably essential for the formation and development of the blastocyst and that the ability to perform this specialized form of metabolic work is developed by the embryo very early in life.

Pyruvate appears to be the central energy substrate in those species (mouse, rabbit, and monkey) in which energy source requirements of the embryo have been examined. During the first day or two of the embryo's life, the Embden-Meyerhof pathway has a very low capability, but after blastocyst formation there is a sharp increase in glycolytic ability. The Krebs cycle is the main source of energy throughout the preimplantation period. Large increases in oxygen consumption and uptake and incorporation of carbon occur at about the time of blastocyst formation. The embryo goes from a relatively inactive metabolic tissue at ovulation to a rapidly metabolizing tissue at implantation.

There is evidence that protein and nucleic acid synthesis occurs in the mammalian embryo from the time of fertilization onward, but the rate is slow during the early cleavage stages. The largest increase in incorporation of protein and RNA precursors occurs at about the time of blastocyst formation or slightly before. This corresponds to a general increase in metabolism, but also probably to an increased activity of the embryo genome at this time in development. However, since in most cases we have no measure of the change in permeability to substrate, we must be cautious in interpreting the results of changes in incorporation alone as indicative of changes in synthetic rate. In general, though, there is evidence that synthetic ability of the embryo increases during the preimplantation period and that there is a rather sharp increase in this synthetic ability in most areas of metabolism near the time of blastocyst formation.

Most of the embryos used in studies on early developmental stages have come from the mouse or rabbit, but it seems probable that the information obtained will be in the most part applicable to the embryos of other mammalian species. In fact, if we are ever going to understand the development of such scarce embryos as the human embryo, we will have to rely to a considerable degree on extensive foundation studies in laboratory animals to provide the background knowledge upon which to base crucial experiments on scarce embryos.

I thank Miss Mildred Combs for assistance in preparation of the manuscript.

REFERENCES

1. AUERBACH, S. *Lactate Dehydrogenase Isozymes in the Early Mouse Embryo* (Thesis). Philadelphia: Univ. of Pennsylvania, 1969.
2. AUERBACH, S., AND R. L. BRINSTER. Lactate dehydrogenase isozymes in the early mouse embryo. *Exptl. Cell Res.* 46:89–92, 1967.
3. AUERBACH, S., AND R. L. BRINSTER. Effect of oxygen concentration on the development of two-cell mouse embryos. *Nature* 217:465–466, 1968.
4. AUERBACH, S., AND R. L. BRINSTER. Lactate dehydrogenase isozymes in mouse blastocyst cultures. *Exptl. Cell Res.* 53:313–315, 1968.
5. AUSTIN, C. R. *The Mammalian Egg.* Springfield, Ill.: Thomas, 1961.
6. AUSTIN, C. R. Fertilization and transport of the ovum. In: *Mechanisms Concerned with Conception*, edited by C. G. Hartman. New York: Macmillan, 1963, p. 285–320.
7. BENNETT, J. P., AND C. STEWART. *In vitro* culture and manipulation of rat ova. *Proc. Study Reprod., 2nd Ann. Meeting Soc. Davis, Calif., Abstr.*, 1969, p. 30.
8. BIGGERS, J. D. New observations on the nutrition of the oocyte and the preimplantation embryo. In: *The Biology of the Blastocyst*, edited by R. Blandau. Chicago: Univ. of Chicago Press, 1971, p. 319–327.
9. BIGGERS, J. D., D. G. WHITTINGHAM, AND R. P. DONAHUE. The pattern of energy metabolism in the mouse oocyte and zygote. *Proc. Natl. Acad. Sci. US* 58:560–567, 1967.
10. BLANDAU, R. J. Biology of eggs and implantation. In: *Sex and Internal Secretions*, edited by W. C. Young and G. W. Corner. Baltimore: Williams & Wilkins, 1961, p. 797–882.
11. BOWMAN, P., AND A. McLAREN. Cleavage rate of mouse embryos *in vivo* and *in vitro*. *J. Embryol. Exptl. Morphol.* 24:203–207, 1970.
12. BOWMAN, P., AND A. McLAREN. Viability and growth of mouse embryos after *in vitro* culture and fusion. *J. Embryol. Exptl. Morphol.* 23:693–704, 1970.
13. BOYD, J. D., AND W. J. HAMILTON. Cleavage, early development and implantation of the egg. In: *Marshall's Physiology of Reproduction* (3rd ed.), edited by A. S. Parkes. London: Longmans, 1952, p. 1–110.
14. BRINSTER, R. L. A method for *in vitro* cultivation of mouse ova from two-cell to blastocyst. *Exptl. Cell Res.* 32:205–208, 1963.
15. BRINSTER, R. L. *Studies on the Development of Mouse Embryos in Vitro* (Thesis). Philadelphia: Univ. of Pennsylvania, 1964.
16. BRINSTER, R. L. Studies on the development of mouse embryos in vitro. I. The effect of osmolarity and hydrogen ion concentration. *J. Exptl. Zool.* 158:49–58, 1965.
17. BRINSTER, R. L. Studies on the development of mouse embryos in vitro. IV. Interaction of energy sources. *J. Reprod. Fertility* 10:227–240, 1965.
18. BRINSTER, R. L. Studies on the development of mouse embryos in vitro. II. The effect of energy source. *J. Exptl. Zool.* 158:59–68, 1965.
19. BRINSTER, R. L. Lactic dehydrogenase activity in the preimplanted mouse embryo. *Biochim. Biophys. Acta* 110:439–441, 1965.
20. BRINSTER, R. L. Studies on the development of mouse embryos in vitro. III. The effect of fixed-nitrogen source. *J. Exptl. Zool.* 158:69–78, 1965.
21. BRINSTER, R. L. Glucose 6-phosphate dehydrogenase activity in the preimplantation mouse embryo. *Biochem. J.* 101:161–163, 1966.
22. BRINSTER, R. L. Protein content of the mouse embryo during the first five days of development. *J. Reprod. Fertility* 13:413–420, 1967.
23. BRINSTER, R. L. Carbon dioxide production from lactate and pyruvate by the preimplantation mouse embryo. *Exptl. Cell Res.* 47:634–637, 1967.
24. BRINSTER, R. L. Carbon dioxide production from glucose by the preimplantation mouse embryo. *Exptl. Cell Res.* 47:271–277, 1967.
25. BRINSTER, R. L. Hexokinase activity in the preimplantation mouse embryo. *Enzymologia* 34:304–308, 1968.
26. BRINSTER, R. L. Carbon dioxide production from glucose by the preimplantation rabbit embryo. *Exptl. Cell Res.* 51:330–334, 1968.
27. BRINSTER, R. L. Mammalian embryo culture. In: *The Mammalian Oviduct*, edited by E. S. E. Hafez and R. Blandau. Chicago: Univ. of Chicago Press, 1969, p. 419–444.
28. BRINSTER, R. L. The incorporation of carbon from glucose and pyruvate into the preimplantation mouse embryo. *Exptl. Cell Res.* 58:153–158, 1969.
29. BRINSTER, R. L. Radioactive carbon dioxide production from pyruvate and lactate by the preimplantation rabbit embryo. *Exptl. Cell Res.* 54:205–209, 1969.
30. BRINSTER, R. L. Culture of two-cell rabbit embryos to morulae. *J. Reprod. Fertility* 21:17–22, 1970.
31. BRINSTER, R. L. Glucose 6-phosphate dehydrogenase activity in the early rabbit and mouse embryo. *Biochem. Genet.* 4:669–676, 1970.
32. BRINSTER, R. L. Activity of 6-phosphogluconate dehydrogenase in the preimplantation mouse and rabbit embryo. *Experientia* 27:371–372, 1971.
33. BRINSTER, R. L. Protein synthesis and enzyme constitution of the preimplantation mammalian embryo. In: *Regulation of Mammalian Reproduction*, edited by S. J. Segal, R. Crozier, P. A. Corfman, and P. Condliffe. Springfield, Ill.: Thomas. In press.
34. BRINSTER, R. L. Phosphofructokinase activity in the preim-

plantation mouse embryo. *Wilhelm Roux Arch.* 166: 300–302, 1971.

35. BRINSTER, R. L. Oxidation of pyruvate and glucose by oocytes of the mouse and rhesus monkey. *J. Reprod. Fertility* 24: 187–191, 1971.

36. BRINSTER, R. L. Uptake and incorporation of amino acids by the preimplantation mouse embryo. *J. Reprod. Fertility* 27: 329–338, 1971.

37. BRINSTER, R. L. *In vitro* culture of the embryo. In: *Pathways to Conception*, edited by A. Sherman. Springfield, Ill.: Thomas, 1971, p. 245–277.

38. BRINSTER, R. L., AND J. L. THOMSON. Development of eight-cell mouse embryos *in vitro*. *Exptl. Cell Res.* 42: 308–315, 1966.

39. CALARCO, P. G., and E. H. BROWN. An ultrastructural and cytological study of preimplantation development of the mouse. *J. Exptl. Zool.* 171: 253–284, 1969.

40. CHANCE, B., B. SCHOENER, AND F. SCHINDLER. The intracellular oxidation-reduction state. In: *Oxygen in the Animal Organism*, edited by F. Dickens and E. Neil. New York: Macmillan, 1964, p. 367–392.

41. CHANG, M. C. Transplantation of fertilized rabbit ova: the effect on viability of age, *in vitro* storage period, and storage temperature. *Nature* 161: 978–979, 1948.

42. CHANG, M. C. The maturation of rabbit oocytes in culture and their maturation, activation, fertilization and subsequent development in the fallopian tubes. *J. Exptl. Zool.* 128: 379–405, 1955.

43. CHANG, M. C. Fertilization and normal development of follicular oocytes in the rabbit. *Science* 121: 867–869, 1955.

44. CHOLEWA, J. A., and W. K. WHITTEN. Development of two-cell mouse embryos in the absence of a fixed-nitrogen source. *J. Reprod. Fertility* 22: 553–555, 1970.

45. CHURCH, R. B. Differential gene activity. In: *Congenital Malformations*, edited by F. C. Fraser and V. A. McKusick. Amsterdam: Excerpta Medica Foundation, 1970, p. 18–28.

46. COLE, R. J., AND J. PAUL. Properties of cultured preimplantation mouse and rabbit embryos, and cell strains derived from them. In: *Preimplantation Stages of Pregnancy*, edited by G. E. W. Wolstenholme and M. O'Connor. London: Churchill, 1965, p. 82–112.

47. CROSS, M. H., AND R. L. BRINSTER. Trans membrane potential of the rabbit blastocyst trophoblast. *Exptl. Cell Res.* 58: 125–127, 1969.

48. CROSS, M. H., AND R. L. BRINSTER. Influence of ions, inhibitors and anoxia on transtrophoblast potential of rabbit blastocyst. *Exptl. Cell Res.* 62: 303–309, 1970.

49. CROSS, P. C., AND R. L. BRINSTER. *In vitro* development of mouse oocytes. *Biol. Reprod.* 3: 298–307, 1970.

50. DALCQ, A., AND J. PASTEELS. Détermination photometrique de la tenure relative DNA de noyaux dans l'oeuf en segmentation du rat et de le fouris. *Exptl. Cell Res. Suppl.* 3: 72–97, 1955.

51. DANIEL, J. C. The pattern of utilization of respiratory metabolic intermediates by preimplantation rabbit embryos *in vitro*. *Exptl. Cell Res.* 47: 619–624, 1967.

52. DANIEL, J. C. Oxygen concentrations for culture of rabbit blastocysts. *J. Reprod. Fertility* 17: 187–190, 1968.

53. DANIEL, J. C., AND R. S. KRISHNAN. Amino acid requirements for growth of the rabbit blastocyst *in vitro*. *J. Cell Physiol.* 70: 155–160, 1967.

54. DANIEL, J. C., AND J. D. OLSON. Amino acid requirements for cleavage of the rabbit ovum. *J. Reprod. Fertility* 15: 453–455. 1968.

55. DONAHUE, R. P., AND S. STERN. Follicular cell support of oocyte maturation: production of pyruvate *in vitro*. *J. Reprod. Fertility* 17: 395–398, 1968.

56. EAGLE, H. The salt requirements of mammalian cells in tissue culture. *Arch. Biochem. Biophys.* 61: 356–365, 1956.

57. EDWARDS, R. G., B. D. BAVISTER, AND P. C. STEPTOE. Early stages of fertilization *in vitro* of human oocytes matured *in vitro*. *Nature* 221: 632–635, 1969.

58. EDWARDS, R. G., P. C. STEPTOE, AND J. M. PURDY. Fertiliza-

tion and cleavage *in vitro* of preovulator human oocytes. *Nature* 227: 1307–1309, 1970.

59. ELLEM, K. A. O., AND R. B. L. GWATKIN. Patterns of nucleic acid synthesis in the early mouse embryo. *Develop. Biol.* 18: 311–330, 1968.

60. ENDERS, A. C., AND S. SCHLAFKE. A morphological analysis of the early implantation stages in the rat. *Am. J. Anat.* 120: 185–226, 1967.

61. EPSTEIN, C. J. Phosphoribosyltransferase activity during early mammalian development. *J. Biol. Chem.* 245: 3289–3294, 1970.

62. EPSTEIN, C. J., AND D. L. DAENTL. Developmental changes in guanine uptake and utilization by preimplantation mouse embryos. *J. Cell Biol.* 47: 57a, 1970.

63. FOOTE, W. D., AND C. THIBAULT. Recherches experimentales sur la maturation in vitro des ovocytes de truie et de veau. *Ann. Biol. Animal Biochim. Biophys.* 9: 329–349, 1969.

64. FRIDHANDLER, L. Pathways of glucose metabolism in fertilized rabbit ova at various pre-implantation stages. *Exptl. Cell Res.* 22: 303–316, 1961.

65. FRIDHANDLER, L. Intermediary metabolic pathways in preimplantation rabbit blastocysts. *Fertility Sterility* 19: 424–434, 1968.

66. FRIDHANDLER, L., E. S. E. HAFEZ, AND G. PINCUS. Developmental changes in the respiratory activity of rabbit ova. *Exptl. Cell Res.* 13: 132–139, 1957.

67. FRIDHANDLER, L., W. B. WASTILA, AND W. M. PALMER. The role of glucose in metabolism of the developing mammalian preimplantation conceptus. *Fertility Sterility* 18: 819–829, 1967.

68. FRY, B. J., AND P. R. GROSS. Patterns and rates of protein synthesis in sea urchin embryos. I. Uptake and incorporation of amico acids during the first cleavage cycle. *Develop. Biol.* 21: 105–124, 1970.

69. FRY, B. J., AND P. R. GROSS. Patterns and rates of protein synthesis in sea urchin embryos. II. The calculation of absolute rates. *Develop. Biol.* 21: 125–146, 1970.

70. GAMOW, E., AND J. C. DANIEL, JR. Fluid transport in the rabbit blastocyst. *Wilhelm Roux Arch.* 164: 261–278, 1970.

71. GAMOW, E., AND D. M. PRESCOTT. The cell life cycle during early embryogenesis of the mouse. *Exptl. Cell Res.* 59: 117–123, 1970.

72. GATES, A. H. Rate of ovular development as a factor in embryonic survival. In: *Preimplantation Stages of Pregnancy*, edited by G. E. W. Wolstenholme and M. O'Connor. London: Churchill, 1965, p. 270–288.

73. GIBSON, C., AND C. J. MASTERS. On the lactate dehydrogenase of preimplantation mouse ova. *FEBS Letters* 7: 277–279, 1970.

74. GIBSON, C., AND C. J. MASTERS. Oviductal lactate dehydrogenase. *J. Reprod. Fertility* 22: 157–159, 1970.

75. GRAHAM, C. F., AND R. W. MORGAN. Changes in the cell cycle during early amphibian development. *Develop. Biol.* 14: 439–460, 1966.

76. GRAVES, C. N., AND J. D. BIGGERS. Carbon dioxide fixation by mouse embryos prior to implantation. *Science* 167: 1506–1508, 1970.

77. GROSS, P. R. The immediacy of genomic control during early development. *J. Exptl. Zool.* 157: 21–38, 1964.

78. GROSS, P. R., AND G. H. COUSINEAU. Effects of actinomycin D on macromolecule synthesis and early development in sea urchin eggs. *Biochem. Biophys. Res. Commun.* 10: 321–326, 1963.

79. GROSS, P. R., AND G. H. COUSINEAU. Macromolecule synthesis and the influence of actinomycins on early development. *Exptl. Cell Res.* 33: 368–395, 1964.

80. HAMMOND, J. Recovery and culture of tubal mouse ova. *Nature* 163: 28–29, 1949.

81. HILLMAN, N., AND R. J. TASCA. Ultrastructural and autoradiographic studies of mouse cleavage stages. *Am. J. Anat.* 126: 151–174, 1969.

82. HINEGARDNER, R. T., B. RAO, AND D. E. FELDMAN. The DNA

synthetic period during early development of the sea urchin egg. *Exptl. Cell Res.* 36: 53–61, 1964.

83. HULTIN, T. Incorporation of N^{15}-labeled glycine and alanine into the proteins of developing sea urchin eggs. *Exptl. Cell Res.* 3: 494–496, 1952.

84. HULTIN, T., AND A. BERGSTRAND. Incorporation of C^{14}-L-leucine into protein by cell-free systems from sea urchin embryos at different stages of development. *Develop. Biol.* 2: 61–75, 1960.

85. KANE, M. T., AND R. H. FOOTE. Fractionated serum dialysate and synthetic media for culturing 2- and 4-cell rabbit embryos. *Biol. Reprod.* 2: 356–362, 1970.

86. KANE, M. T., AND R. H. FOOTE. Culture of two- and four-cell rabbit embryos to the blastocyst stage in serum and serum extracts. *Biol. Reprod.* 2: 245–250, 1970.

87. KANE, M. T., AND R. H. FOOTE. Culture of two- and four-cell rabbit embryos to the expanding blastocyst stage in synthetic media. *Proc. Soc. Exptl. Biol. Med.* 133: 921–925, 1970.

88. KENNEDY, J. F., AND R. P. DONAHUE. Human oocytes: maturation in chemically defined media. *Science* 164: 1292–1293, 1969.

89. KRAMEN, M. A., AND J. D. BIGGERS. Selective permeability by preimplantation mouse embryos to citric acid cycle intermediates. *Proc. Soc. Study Reprod., 3rd Ann. Meeting, Columbus, Ohio, Abstr.*, 1970, p. 2.

90. LEWIS, W. H., AND E. S. WRIGHT. On the development of the mouse. *Contrib. Embryol. Carnegie Inst. Wash.* 25: 113–146, 1935.

91. LOWENSTEIN, J. E., AND A. I. COHEN. Dry mass, lipid content and protein content of the intact and zona-free mouse ovum. *J. Embryol. Exptl. Morphol.* 12: 113–121, 1964.

92. LUTWAK-MANN, C. Biochemical approach to the study of ovum implantation in the rabbit. In: *Implantation of Ova*, edited by P. Eckstein. Cambridge: Cambridge University Press, 1959, p. 35–49.

93. LUTWAK-MANN, C., J. C. BOURSNELL, AND J. P. BENNETT. Blastocyst uterine relationships: uptake of radioactive ions by the early rabbit embryo and its environment. *J. Reprod. Fertility* 1: 169–185, 1960.

94. MADEN, B. E. H. Ribosome formation in animal cells. *Nature* 219: 685–689, 1968.

95. MANES, C. Nucleic acid synthesis in preimplantation rabbit embryos. *J. Exptl. Zool.* 172: 303–310, 1969.

96. MANES, C., AND J. C. DANIEL, JR. Quantitative and qualitative aspects of protein synthesis in the preimplantation rabbit embryo. *Exptl. Cell Res.* 55: 261–268, 1969.

97. MAUER, R. E., E. S. E. HAFEZ, M. H. EHLERS, AND J. R. KING. Culture of two cell rabbit eggs in chemically defined media. *Exptl. Cell Res.* 52: 293–300, 1968.

98. MAURER, R. R., H. ONUMA, AND R. H. FOOTE. Viability of cultured and transferred rabbit embryos. *J. Reprod. Fertility* 21: 417–422, 1970.

99. MAZANEC, K., AND M. DVORAK. On the submicroscopical changes of the segmenting ovum in the albino rat. *Morfologie* 11: 103–110, 1963.

100. McLAREN, A., AND J. D. BIGGERS. Successful development and birth of mice cultivated *in vitro* as early embryos. *Nature* 182: 877–878, 1958.

101. MENKE, T. M., AND A. McLAREN. Mouse blastocysts grown *in vivo* and *in vitro*: carbon dioxide production and trophoblast outgrowth. *J. Reprod. Fertility* 23: 117–127, 1970.

102. MILLS, R. M., AND R. L. BRINSTER. Oxygen consumption of preimplanted mouse embryos. *Exptl. Cell Res.* 47: 337–342, 1967.

103. MINTZ, B. Incorporation of nucleic acid and protein precursors by developing mouse eggs (Abstract). *Am. Zoologist* 2: 432, 1962.

104. MINTZ, B. Synthetic processes and early development in the mammalian egg. *J. Exptl. Zool.* 157: 85–100, 1964.

105. MINTZ, B. Mammalian embryo culture. In: *Methods in Developmental Biology*, edited by J. P. Trinkaus. New York: Thomas Y. Crowell, 1967, p. 379–400.

106. MONESI, V., M. MOLINARO, E. SPALLETTA, AND C. DAVOLI. Effect of metabolic inhibitors on macromolecular synthesis and early development in the mouse embryo. *Exptl. Cell Res.* 59: 197–206, 1970.

107. MONESI, V., AND V. SALFI. Macromolecular syntheses during early development in the mouse embryo. *Exptl. Cell Res.* 46: 632–635, 1967.

108. MOORE, N. W. Preliminary studies on *in vitro* culture of fertilized sheep ova. *Australian J. Biol. Sci.* 23: 721–724, 1970.

109. MOORE, R. W., AND R. L. BRINSTER. Transamination and deamination in mouse preimplantation embryos. *Proc. Soc. Study Reprod., 3rd Ann. Meeting, Columbus, Ohio, Abstr.*, 1970, p. 3.

110. MORRIS, T. The XO and OY chromosome constitutions in the mouse. *Genet. Res. Cambridge* 12: 125–137, 1968.

111. NAGLEE, D. L., R. R. MAURER, AND R. H. FOOTE. Effect of osmolarity on *in vitro* development of rabbit embryos in a chemically defined medium. *Exptl. Cell Res.* 58: 331–333, 1969.

112. NAKANO, E., AND A. MONROY. Incorporation of S^{35}-methionine in the cell fractions of sea urchin eggs and embryos. *Exptl. Cell Res.* 14: 236–243, 1958.

113. PASSONNEAU, J. V., AND O. H. LOWRY. P-fructokinase and the control of the citric acid cycle. *Biochem. Biophys. Res. Commun.* 13: 372–379, 1963.

114. PASSONNEAU, J. V., AND O. H. LOWRY. The role of phospho-fructokinase in metabolic regulation. *Advan. Enzyme Regulation* 2: 265–274, 1964.

115. PIKÓ, L. Synthesis of macromolecules in early mouse embryos cultured *in vitro*: RNA, DNA and a polysaccharide component. *Develop. Biol.* 21: 257–279, 1970.

116. PINCUS, G., AND E. V. ENZMANN. Can mammalian eggs undergo normal development *in vitro*? *Proc. Natl. Acad. Sci. US* 20: 121–122, 1934.

117. PINCUS, G., AND E. V. ENZMANN. The comparative behavior of mammalian eggs *in vivo* and *in vitro*. I. The activation of ovarian eggs. *J. Exptl. Med.* 62: 665–675, 1935.

118. PINCUS, G., AND B. SAUNDERS. The comparative behaviour of mammalian eggs *in vivo* and *in vitro*. VI. The maturation of human ovarian ova. *Anat. Record* 75: 537–545, 1939.

119. RAPOLA, J., AND O. KOSKIMIES. Embryonic enzyme patterns: characterization of the single lactate dehydrogenase isozyme in preimplanted mouse ova. *Science* 157: 1311–1312, 1967.

120. REAMER, G. R. *The Quantity and Distribution of Nucleic Acids in the Early Cleavage Stages of the Mouse Embryo* (Thesis). Boston: Boston University, 1963.

121. SKALKO, R. G., AND J. M. D. MORSE. The differential response of the early mouse embryo to actinomycin D treatment *in vitro*. *Teratology* 2: 47–54, 1969.

122. SMITH, M. W. Active transport in the rabbit blastocyst. *Experientia* 26: 736–738, 1970.

123. STERN, S. The activity of glycogen synthetase in the cleaving mouse embryo. *Proc. Soc. Study Reprod., 3rd Ann. Meeting, Columbus, Ohio, Abstr.*, 1970, p. 3.

124. STERN, S., AND J. D. BIGGERS. Enzymatic estimation of glycogen in the cleaving mouse embryo. *J. Exptl. Zool.* 168: 61–66, 1968.

125. SUGAWARA, S., AND M. UMEZU. Studies on metabolism of the mammalian ova. II. Oxygen consumption of the cleaved ova of the rat. *Tohoku J. Agr. Res.* 12: 17–25, 1961.

126. SZOLLOSI, D. Modification of the endoplasmic reticulum in some mammalian oocytes. *Anat. Record* 158: 59–73, 1967.

127. TASCA, R. J., AND N. HILLMAN. Effects of actinomycin D and cycloheximide on RNA and protein synthesis in cleavage stage mouse embryos. *Nature* 225: 1022–1025, 1970.

128. TENBROECK, J. T. Effect of nucleosides and nucleoside bases on the development of preimplantation mouse embryos in vitro. *J. Reprod. Fertility* 17: 571–573, 1968.

129. THIBAULT, C. La culture in vitro de l'oeuf de vache. *Ann. Biol. Animal Biochim. Biophys.* 6: 159–164, 1966.

130. THOMSON, J. L. Effect of inhibitors of carbohydrate metabolism on the development of preimplantation mouse embryos. *Exptl. Cell Res.* 46: 252–262, 1967.

131. THOMSON, J. L., AND J. D. BIGGERS. The effect of inhibitors

of protein synthesis on the development of mouse embryos *in vitro*. *Exptl. Cell Res.* 41: 411–427, 1966.

132. THOMSON, J. L., AND R. L. BRINSTER. Glycogen content of preimplantation mouse embryos. *Anat. Record* 155: 97–102, 1966.

133. TIMOURIAN, H., AND G. WATCHMAKER. Protein synthesis in sea urchin eggs. II. Changes in amino acid uptake and incorporation at fertilization. *Develop. Biol.* 23: 478–491, 1970.

134. TYLER, A. Masked messenger RNA and cytoplasmic DNA in relation to protein synthesis and processes of fertilization and determination in embryonic devlopment. *Develop. Biol. Suppl.* 1: 170–226, 1967.

135. WALES, R. G. Accumulation of carboxylic acids from glucose by the pre-implantation mouse embryo. *Australian J. Biol. Sci.* 22: 701–707, 1969.

136. WALES, R. G. Effects of ions on the development of the preimplantation mouse embryo *in vitro*. *Australian J. Biol. Sci.* 23: 421–429, 1970.

137. WALES, R. G., AND J. D. BIGGERS. The permeability of two- and eight-cell mouse embryos to L-malic acid. *J. Reprod. Fertility* 15: 103–111, 1968.

138. WALES, R. G., AND R. L. BRINSTER. The uptake of hexoses by mouse embryos. *J. Reprod. Fertility* 15: 415–422, 1968.

139. WALES, R. G., P. QUINN, AND R. N. MURDOCH. The fixation of carbon dioxide by the 8-cell mouse embryo. *J. Reprod. Fertility* 20: 541–543, 1969.

140. WALES, R. G., AND D. G. WHITTINGHAM. A comparison of the uptake and utilization of lactate and pyruvate by one- and two-cell mouse embryos. *Biochim. Biophys. Acta* 148: 703–712, 1967.

141. WALES, R. G., AND D. G. WHITTINGHAM. Metabolism of specifically labelled pyruvate by mouse embryos during culture from the two-cell stage to the blastocyst. *Australian J. Biol. Sci.* 23: 877–887, 1970.

142. WHITTEN, W. K. Culture of tubal mouse ova. *Nature* 176: 96–97, 1956.

143. WHITTEN, W. K. Culture of tubal ova. *Nature* 179: 1081–1082, 1957.

144. WHITTEN, W. K. The effect of oxygen on cleavage of mouse eggs in vitro. *Proc. Soc. Study Reprod., 2nd Ann. Meeting, Davis, Calif., Abstr.*, 1969, p. 29.

145. WHITTEN, W. K., AND J. D. BIGGERS. Complete development *in vitro* of the pre-implantation stages of the mouse in a simple chemically defined medium. *J. Reprod. Fertility* 17: 399–401, 1968.

146. WHITTEN, W. K., AND C. P. DAGG. Influence of spermatozoa on the cleavage of mouse eggs. *J. Exptl. Zool.* 148: 173–183, 1961.

147. WHITTINGHAM, D. G. The failure of lactate and phosphoenolpyruvate to support development of the mouse zygote *in vitro*. *Biol. Reprod.* 1: 381–386, 1969.

148. WINTENBERGER, S., L. DAUZIER, AND C. THIBAULT. La développement *in vitro* de l'oeuf de la Brebis et de celui de la Chèvre. *Compt. Rend. Soc. Biol.* 147: 1971–1974, 1953.

149. WOODLAND, H. R., AND C. F. GRAHAM. RNA synthesis during early development of the mouse. *Nature* 221: 327–332, 1969.

150. YANAGIMACHI, R., AND M. C. CHANG. *In vitro* fertilization of golden hamster ova. *J. Exptl. Zool.* 156: 361–376, 1964.

151. ZAMBONI, L. Ultrastructure of mammalian oocytes and ova. *Biol. Reprod. Suppl.* 2: 44–63, 1970.

CHAPTER 40

Endocrine control of egg implantation

ALEXANDRE PSYCHOYOS | *Centre de Recherches de l'Hôpital de Bicêtre, Institut National de la Santé et de la Recherche Médicale, Bicêtre, France*

CHAPTER CONTENTS

THE MANNER in which the egg implants in the endometrium varies among species (18, 45, 50). In rabbits, carnivores, and some monkeys, the egg increases in volume and fills the space between the uterine walls. In mice and rats it remains small and becomes progressively covered during the transformation of the endometrium in contact with it. In the guinea pig, chimpanzee, and human being, it actively penetrates the mucosa. Whatever the manner of egg implantation, one condition is common to all mammals: the ovoendometrial interactions leading to egg implantation can only be initiated when the egg and the endometrium have reached a precise stage of maturity. The egg has to be at the blastocyst stage, and hormone-dependent changes leading to what could be called *receptive endometrium* need to have been fulfilled.

Failure of synchronism in the development of the egg

Investigations by the author and his collaborators were supported by grants from the Centre National de la Recherche Scientifique, the Lalor Foundation, the Population Council, and the Ford Foundation.

and the endometrium results in the cancellation or the postponing of egg implantation. The egg degenerates when it contacts a uterus having developed earlier. If, when the egg reaches the blastocyst stage, the uterus has yet to become receptive, the blastocyst degenerates or its growth is arrested until the endometrium becomes receptive. This latter phenomenon occurs naturally in a large variety of species. In most mammals the endometrium becomes receptive at about the moment of blastulation.

Although the initiation of the ovoendometrial interactions requires strict synchronism, several facts demonstrate the relative independence of the two partners. The egg can proliferate and embed in extrauterine sites and can also proliferate in vitro in relatively simple media. On the other hand, production of decidual tissue, the maternal component of the placenta, can be initiated by stimuli other than those offered by the blastocyst. The rigorous synchronization of the ovoendometrial interactions ensures embryonic development under adequate conditions, while the maternal tissues are protected from the uncontrolled invasion of a foreign aggressive tissue, the trophoblast.

Therefore the regular development of all the events associated with egg implantation requires precise timing. This timing, at least in the rat and mouse, is under the command of the hypothalamic-hypophysial axis and is determined by a progesterone-estrogen interplay at the cellular level. Although several gaps exist in our knowledge of the hormonal control of egg implantation in other species and particularly of the necessity of estrogen (3, 55, 85, 93, 95, 154, 160, 271, 272, 289), the information already acquired about rodents reveals a controlling mechanism that may be generally valid for mammals.

EVENTS ASSOCIATED WITH EGG IMPLANTATION

Theories about the initiation of the egg implantation process were divided in the past between those considering the egg as the active agent (383) and those attributing this function to the endometrium (171, 186). The opinion accepted before the classic studies of

Mossman (252) in Sciuroidea and of Blandau (40) in the rat was that, in the species in which decidualization precedes the epithelial degeneration, the blastocysts implant in preformed decidual crypts. Blandau (40) was the first to distinguish an early stage during which the blastocyst establishes tenuous but superficial contact with the uterine epithelium and thereby initiates decidualization of the underlying stroma cells. Blastocyst and epithelium have overlapping roles, and the early stage coincides with a period of optimal endometrial sensitivity for decidualization and with alterations in the permeability of the endometrial capillaries that are induced by the blastocyst and precede any morphological evidence of egg implantation by several hours.

Timing of Optimal Uterine Sensitivity for Decidualization

Formation of decidual tissue is the most specific function of the progestational endometrium. Decidualization involves the stroma cells (99, 193), or it may concern the epithelial cells, as in the rhesus monkey (170, 326). Decidualization is induced by the blastocyst's presence, or it may occur spontaneously, as it does in the human being during the menstrual cycle (263). Decidual metamorphosis of the progestational endometrium can also be induced experimentally by a large variety of systemically (86, 191, 192, 293, 352) or locally applied stimuli (96, 138, 175, 193, 207, 268). A new organ with specific functions (185, 350) is formed by the enlargement of the individual cells and by rapid mitotic activity (99, 193). The concentration in the stroma of such enzymes as alkaline phosphatase increases soon after the endometrial stimulation (136, 137, 141, 157, 205, 206, 214); an increase in the amount and complexity of the endoplasmic reticulum and a ballooning of the mitochondria occur in the enlarged cells (178). The uterine ribonucleic acid (RNA) and deoxyribonucleic acid (DNA) rise sharply (354, 355); the RNA-to-DNA ratio increases, and proteins that were not present before appear (205, 206), probably because of the transcription of new genetic information (332).

Beginning with Loeb's classic work (207) on the guinea pig early in the century, investigations have shown that the decidual reaction can be obtained only during a limited period of pregnancy or pseudopregnancy (209, 273). In the rat and mouse, traumatic stimuli induce a decidual response when applied during a relatively long period (3–4 days), but stimuli of short duration can only induce this response when applied during a short period on a precise day. Shelesnyak and Kraicer (192, 351) administered pyrathiazine intraperitoneally to pseudopregnant rats as a deciduogenic inducer; they found that deciduomata were obtained only when the drug was given during a 6-hr period on day 5 of pseudopregnancy. (In this chapter, days of pregnancy are determined by counting the day of detection of

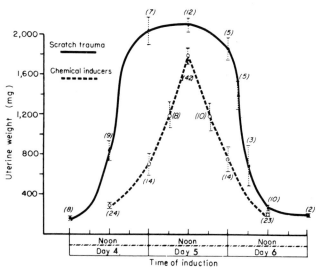

FIG. 1. Comparison of onset, magnitude, and decline of uterine sensitivity, as revealed by 2 methods of deciduoma induction. All responses measured 120 ± 0.25 hr after induction. Numbers in parentheses, number of uteri. Days of pseudopregnancy adapted to counting method described in text. [Adapted from De Feo (98).]

spermatozoa in the vaginal smear as day 1; for pseudopregnancy, day 2 is the day of the appearance of leukocytes in the smear.) De Feo (97–99) used standard light conditions (125, 382) and intraluminal injections of chemical inducers on rats and obtained similar estimates of the sensitive period with the maximal endometrial response at noon on day 5 (Fig. 1). An analogous, short increase in the uterine sensitivity to deciduoma formation also occurred in mice in the afternoon of day 4 (137, 169) and is presumed to have occurred on this same day in the hamster (99, 159).

Morphological Correlates of Uterine Sensitivity

The most pronounced stromal change during the period of uterine sensitivity for decidualization is the appearance of a transient edematous phase (99, 127, 309). This change occurs in the rat on day 5 of pregnancy or pseudopregnancy and at about noon on this day develops into a generalized edema dispersing the stroma cells. Under the effect of the edema the uterine lumen progressively occludes (309). The edematous phase seems to be a preimplantation phenomenon common to a large variety of mammals, from the armadillo (117) to the human being (263). Its occurrence was found to be independent of the blastocysts' presence, at least in the rat, rabbit, and human being. In the human being it occurs on about the 19th to 20th day of the cycle, that is, about 5 days after the presumed time of ovulation; the spontaneous decidualization of the human endometrium follows 3–4 days after this edematous phase (263). It is interesting to note that, from the 16th day of the cycle, the nucleolus of the epithelial cells differentiates to a system of tubules, the nucleolar channel system (373), which reaches maximum development on about day 20 of the cycle and disappears thereafter (73, 74).

In the pregnant and pseudopregnant rat, just before noon of day 5, the nuclei of the epithelial cells change their position and are found several hours later localized close to the epithelial basal membranes (8, 380). Large lipid drops (4) that were adjacent to the basal pole of the nuclei until noon of this day can be seen no more; instead, the cytoplasm is filled with small vacuoles giving it a spongy appearance. Ultrastructural studies by transmission electron microscopy show regular, digitiform microvilli with bulbous cytoplasmic projections among them on the luminal surface of the epithelial cells. In the afternoon on day 5 of pregnancy, the microvilli become more squat and assume irregular, clumsy profiles (257, 259, 284). Large, bulbous cytoplasmic projections were observed on the surface epithelium of the human endometrium on days 20–22 of the cycle (256) and also on the surface of the mouse epithelium on day 5 of pregnancy (256). A recent electron-microscopic study of the endometrial surface of the rat on days 4 and 5 of pregnancy (Figs. 2 and 3) reveals that these projections are well-organized formations whose function needs to be determined. Visible on day 5, they are particularly abundant on the antimesometrial luminal surface and look as if they consist of several flat and irregular tentacles formed by, and projecting from, a basal body with a hollowing center (319).

Biochemical Profile of the Sensitive Uterus

The content of nucleic acids and the pattern of their synthesis change profoundly in the receptive endometrium (166, 354, 355). An increase in the incorporation of tritiated uridine in the pseudopregnant rat endometrium shows that the RNA synthesis rises on day 3, remains high until day 5, and decreases sharply on day 6 [(267); Fig. 4]. The incorporation of ^{32}P into nucleic

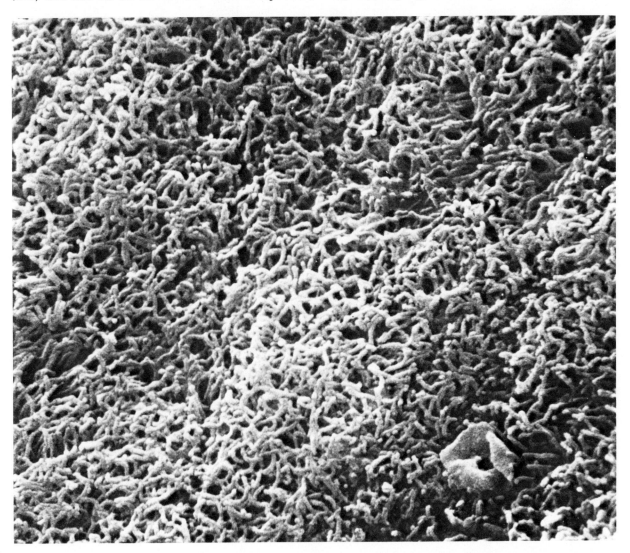

FIG. 2. Electron micrograph of luminal surface of the rat uterine epithelium. Specimen obtained from an animal killed at 3 PM on day 4 of pregnancy. Note formation protruding among the microvilli on the *right*. × 8,000. [From Psychoyos & Mandon (319).]

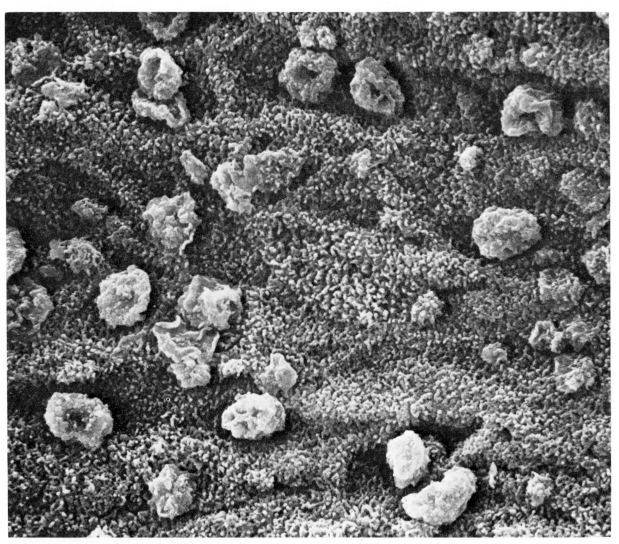

FIG. 3. Scanning electron micrograph of luminal surface of the rat uterine epithelium. Animal killed at 3 PM on day 5 of pregnancy. Note abundance and organization of formations protruding among the microvilli. × 4,000. [From Psychoyos & Mandon (319).]

acids also increases between days 3 and 5 in the rabbit (379). Measurement of in vitro synthesis of nucleic acids by the human endometrium at various days of the menstrual cycle shows an increased synthetic activity on day 16 for RNA and on day 18 for DNA and a sharp decrease on day 21 (260).

A high concentration of zinc and copper associated with low manganese concentration was detected in the human endometrium at about this time (155) and reflects modifications of enzymatic activities (210); the progress of the luteal phase of the cycle is accompanied by a gradual increase in alkaline phosphatase concentration (145). Acid cathepsin, the enzyme involved in collagen breakdown, was also found to increase during the early midsecretory phase of the human cycle (402). In the rat (401) this enzyme was found to increase on day 5, whereas other hydrolytic enzymes, such as β-glucuronidase or acid phosphatase, did not show any significant change at this time. Among several enzymatic

activities studied histochemically in this species (70), that of adenosine triphosphatase (ATPase) increases markedly between days 4 and 5. Some alkaline phosphatase activity was also detected during these days in the luminal epithelium and glands (70, 136). Electron-microscopic investigations of the subcellular localizations of these two enzymes in the rabbit have shown a pronounced activity in the microvilli of the luminal epithelium and also around some secretory droplets (168). It is generally accepted that alkaline phosphatase may play a role in the transfer of metabolites across the cell membranes, whereas ATPase seems linked with the active transport of Na^+ and K^+.

The character of endometrial metabolism changes gradually during the first 5 days of pseudopregnancy (330, 331) or pregnancy (366, 367) from one of anaerobiosis to one of aerobiosis with an increased need for exogenous material. Oxygen consumption by the uterine tissue increases. Glucose incorporation reaches a

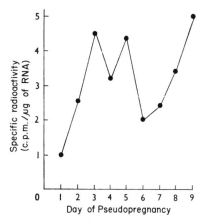

FIG. 4. Incorporation of ³H-labeled uridine into RNA of rat uterine tissue during pseudopregnancy. [From O'Grady et al. (267).]

peak on day 5 of pseudopregnancy (405). Until day 4 of pregnancy, malate dehydrogenase and isocitrate dehydrogenase gradually increase; by day 5 the levels of these enzymes decline (366).

Early Embryo-Maternal Contact

Egg transport through the oviduct takes 3–4 days in most species (6, 41, 167, 174). In the rat the eggs enter the cornua on day 4 (99), at the morula stage. They remain surrounded by their zona pellucida until early noon of day 5 (102, 106, 296). Before noon of this day, the eggs are at the blastocyst stage; they are located along the uterine horns in large crypts of the anti-mesometrial surface but are apparently still free. Between noon and 4 PM, they invariably adhere to the anti-mesometrial epithelium by their embryonic pole, while the antimesometrial and mesometrial walls of the swelling endometrium approach each other (Fig. 5). The end of this period coincides with the dispersion of the lipid droplets located at the base of the epithelial cells; later, between 4 and 6 PM, the nuclei of these cells are located basally and touch the basal membrane [(308); (Fig. 6)].

Ultrastructural information on early stages of egg implantation is available for several species (115, 116, 119, 198, 199, 283, 284, 323). In the rat on day 5 of pregnancy during the preattachment stage, the trophoblast surface nearly touches the tips of the epithelial microvilli; a gap of up to 1 μ separates the embryo from the maternal tissue. In the early afternoon the microvilli flatten, and the contact between the epithelial cells and the trophoblast becomes closer. The cytoplasmic projections of the epithelial cells can be seen attached to the blastocyst. Later during this day the microvilli can no longer be distinguished, and the attachment of the blastocyst to the epithelium becomes more intimate. The trophoblast interdigitates with epithelial cells; the trophoblastic cytoplasm surrounds cytoplasmic processes of the epithelium. By noon of day 6 the invasion stage starts with insinuation of the tro-

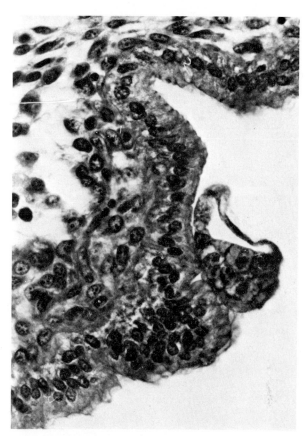

FIG. 5. Longitudinal section of a rat uterus at noon on day 5 of pregnancy. Blastocyst adheres to the antimesometrial epithelium. Note the contraction of the trophoblast, the stromal edema, and the central position of the epithelial nuclei. × 400. [From Psychoyos (308).]

phoblastic cytoplasm into the adjacent epithelial cells (118, 223, 258, 282, 284, 369).

Predecidual Capillary Response of the Endometrium

Increase in the permeability of the endometrial capillaries is a sine qua non condition for decidualization and the earliest known response of the sensitive endometrium to any kind of deciduogenic stimuli (293, 295, 312). Macromolecular dyes intravenously injected leave the circulation only in areas of highly increased capillary permeability (238). When a macromolecular colorant (Evans's blue, Geigy blue, or Pontamine blue) is injected into an animal two or more hours after the application of a deciduogenic stimulus, macroscopically visible blue areas appear in the endometrium 15 min after the injection of the colorant (293) because of the permeability of the area in which the process of decidualization has been induced; the first decidual cells appear about 20 hr later. The increase in capillary permeability can be quantitatively estimated by the use of ¹³¹I-labeled protein (37, 295). By this method the degree of capillary permeability was found to vary according to the intensity of the deciduogenic stimulus and to parallel the endometrial potential for decidualization (295).

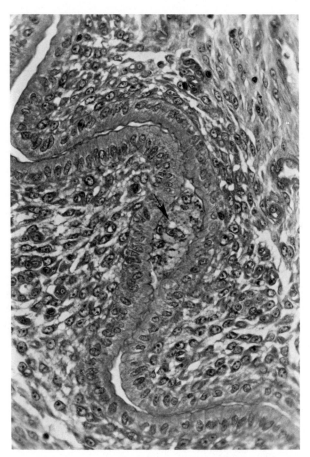

FIG. 6. Longitudinal section of a rat uterus through the region of a blue spot at 5 PM on day 5 of pregnancy. The uterine stroma, having reached a maximum edematous stage, obliterates the lumen and compresses the blastocyst within the epithelial surface. The blastocyst is contracted, and the blastocoele has disappeared (*arrow*). The epithelial nuclei have moved to the basal membrane. × 280. [From Psychoyos (308).]

In the pregnant rat, injection of a macromolecular colorant on the afternoon of day 5, that is 110 hr after the estimated time of ovulation, produces colored spots indicating an increased capillary permeability at the sites where the blastocysts are present (266, 294, 337). As shown by electron microscopy, thorotrast particles leak from the capillaries at about this moment (118). In the hamster (269) and mouse (141), the first blue-positive uteri are recovered about 90 hr after the expected time of ovulation, and in the sheep recovery can be made on the 15th day of pregnancy (48). In the species studied, the increase in the permeability of the capillaries that surround the blastocysts has thus been found to precede by 20–24 hr any morphological evidence of egg implantation.

In efforts made to identify a factor responsible for decidualization, particular attention has been given to histamine, which has been proposed as a specific factor for inducing decidualization (347, 349). Chambon & Lefrein (66) in the rabbit and Shelesnyak (347) in the rat found that histamine introduced into the uterine lumen at the proper time induced massive decidualiza-

tion, whereas histamine antagonists, also directly applied, suppressed the decidual formation. The hypothesis of a specific participation of this amine on decidualization was, however, seriously compromised when various other vasoactive substances were found to induce deciduomata when instilled into the uterine lumen at the onset of uterine sensitivity (65, 99, 175, 218, 309). Furthermore deciduoma formation can be prevented by compounds with no antihistaminic properties but with a marked inhibitory effect on the permeability of the capillaries (293, 309). Nevertheless the possibility that histamine alone, or in connection with other vasoactive amines, is implicated in decidualization should not be overlooked. Histamine is formed in cells in or near the vascular system through an inducible form of histidine decarboxylase. Although the stimulus for the induction of histidine decarboxylase seems to be nonspecific, a basic part of the mechanism through which the capillaries exert autonomous actions is presumed to result from the activity of this enzyme (335). Increased permeability after intraluminal instillation of various substances, which leads to decidualization, appears only after a latent period of at least 2 hr (A. Psychoyos, unpublished observations); histidine decarboxylase also requires more than 2 hr to acquire its induced form.

That the functional integrity of the epithelium is essential before the endometrial changes of decidualization can occur and that these changes can only be induced through processes undergone by the stimulated epithelium seem certain. In fact, exposure of the luminal uterine surface to −20 C for 2–3 min abolishes the ability of the endometrium to respond to traumatic stimuli (134), and the insertion of a thread into the endometrium fails to induce a decidual response when this thread does not reach the luminal epithelium (127).

The Egg Stimulus

In his studies on melanoma invasion, Wilson (398) observed that, despite the penetration of this malignant tissue into the antimesometrial wall of a sensitive endometrium, there is no deciduoma formation. It has been suggested that the difference between the melanoma and the trophoblast cells must be attributed to the fact that the former are separated into single, rapidly migrating units, whereas the latter are united by tight junctions, present a continuous front, and adhere to many maternal cells (399).

As shown by the insertion of inert objects about the size of a blastocyst into the lumen of the rat uterus, the slightest pressure against the sensitive endometrium is enough to induce decidualization (40, 41). However, in the mouse, plastic beads (231) or 4- or 8-cell morulae from rabbit, hamster, guinea pig, rat, and mouse do not induce any decidual response (184), whereas, in the hamster, formation of deciduoma by unfertilized ova is a frequent phenomenon (269). The degree of the endometrial sensitivity, at its onset, differs among

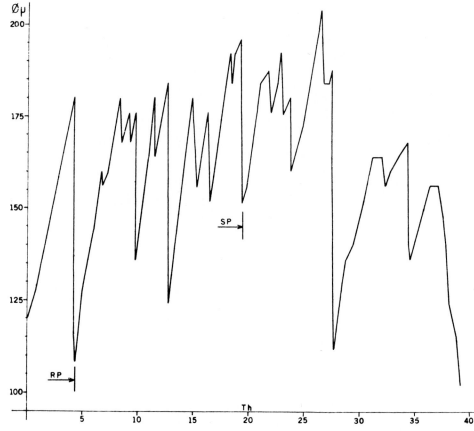

FIG. 7. Frequency and magnitude of a blastocyst's movements recorded by time-lapse cinematography. Blastocyst recovered from uterus at 4 PM on day 5 of pregnancy and cultured in vitro for 40 hr. *RP*, rupture of the zona pellucida; *SP*, emergence from zona pellucida; *Th*, time of in vitro life (hr); ∅μ, diameter of blastocyst (μ). [From Bitton-Casimiri et al. (35).]

species. Unfertilized ova, two-cell eggs, or blastocysts with no viable blastomeres are unable to initiate decidualization in the rat (5, 342), unless a progesterone treatment, which probably renders the endometrium still more sensitive, is given (10). Furthermore, in the mouse, where the degree of sensitivity appears low, decidualization can be induced by eggs from various species at the blastocyst stage (184). Blastocysts seem, therefore, to possess particular properties that enable them to induce decidualization under conditions in which inert bodies or younger eggs fail.

Time-lapse cinematography of the in vitro behavior of rodent blastocysts has been most useful in revealing the possible nature of the blastocyst's advantage over that of younger eggs. The blastocyst undergoes pulsating movements in the form of a rhythmic series of dilatations and contractions [(35, 47, 77, 78); Fig. 7]. In the rat blastocyst, these movements result in the emergence of the blastocoele content as vesicles containing a granular material [(35); Fig. 8]. In fixed material from about 84 hr after mating, Wilson (397) observed richly basophilic bodies with an eosinophilic shell around them, which, although initially within the inner cell mass, later migrated around the inner surface of the trophoblast. One hundred hours postcoitus, such

bodies can be seen protruding between the trophoblast cells and penetrating the epithelium through which, after being fragmented, they migrate into the mucosa.

The term *Wilson bodies* now refers to these strange structures whose basophilia result from their high RNA content. Doubts about the embryonic origin of these bodies were raised by observations suggesting a similarity between them and degenerating epithelial cells (139). However, Wilson & Smith (400) reported an autoradiographic demonstration of transfer of an RNA-like material from the blastocyst to the endometrial stroma cells. Time-lapse cinematography of in vitro developing rat blastocysts shows round, cell-like formations similar to the bodies described by Wilson; they detach from the inner cell mass, enter the blastocoele, and are occasionally seen to traverse the trophoblast and emerge into the culture medium (36).

Together with the pressure that the blastocyst should exert on the epithelium during its dilatation phase, components of the material emerging from the blastocysts could act as inducers of the decidualization process. Such material could be promptly captured by the luminal epithelium, which, at the moment of its optimal sensitivity, shows a high absorptive activity, as demon-

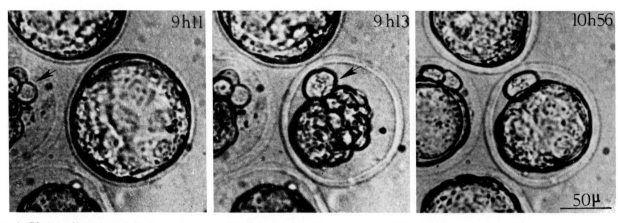

FIG. 8. Blastocoele content emerging in the form of vesicles (*arrows*) after a strong, rapid contraction of the rat blastocyst, as recorded by time-lapse cinematography. (From V. Bitton-Casimiri, J. L. Brun, and A. Psychoyos, unpublished data.)

strated by the absorption of intraluminally injected macromolecular substances (380, 381).

HORMONAL CONTROL OF EGG IMPLANTATION

In 1898 Prenant (290), using morphological criteria, recognized the endocrine nature of the corpus luteum and suggested that it protects pregnancy by inhibiting ovulation. In the same period, Knauer (188), working with adult rabbits, prevented the atrophy of the uterus after ovariectomy by regrafting fragments of the removed ovaries. He suggested that these fragments produce "something" that is transported via the blood system to the uterus. Halban (156) grafted adult ovaries into immature guinea pigs and observed the uteri growing rapidly to adult size. He concluded that the ovaries produce a substance promoting uterine development. The first 15 years of the 20th century brought an avalanche of discoveries. While exploring the role of the corpora lutea in the gestation of the rabbit, Fraenkel and Cohn (142, 143) found that the destruction of these bodies leads to the arrest of pregnancy. This made an enormous impression on the gynecologists of the time and raised many questions; Halban (156a) asked, "How does the corpus luteum know that there is a pregnancy?"

Loeb (207, 208) and Bouin and Ancel (19, 49) established that the capacity of the endometrium for progestational development and decidualization is independent of the presence of the fertilized ovum, and they recognized the role of the corpus luteum in the realization of these phenomena. In 1928 Weichert (385) obtained traumatic deciduomata in the castrated rat and guinea pig treated with a corpus luteum extract. The next year, Allen & Corner (9) extracted from the pig corpus luteum an active principle able to maintain pregnancy in ovariectomized rabbits. The isolation, structural determination, and synthesis of progesterone soon followed.

In 1912 Iscovesco (176) found in ovarian extracts an active substance soluble in alcohol and ether, but not in acetone, which, when injected into young rabbits, caused marked growth of their uteri. However, it was only after the availability of the vaginal smear criterion that the existence in the ovarian follicle of a hormone promoting estrus could be unquestionably demonstrated by Allen & Doisy (6, 7) and Courrier (80). The implication of the follicle as hormonal source resulted in great confusion, but soon the role of the follicle was clarified; the two phases of the ovarian cycle, the follicular and the luteal, were distinguished (81), and Courrier (82, 83) established the fundamental idea of the synergic or antagonistic relationship between the two ovarian hormones.

Two phenomena have become precious tools for the study of the functional relationships between progesterone and estrogen during early pregnancy: *1*) the possibility of suspending the egg implantation process in the rat and mouse by experimentally inducing delay of implantation; and *2*) the existence of a precise timing in the evolution of the uterine receptivity for nidation.

Delayed Implantation

That a seasonal arrest of blastocyst development occurs in a large variety of species belonging to several orders of mammals (56, 60, 92, 94, 112, 117, 254, 357) has been known since Bischoff's observation (34) in the roe deer. In rats, mice, and some insectivores and marsupials, the normally short preimplantation period is extended when pregnancy is associated with lactation (112, 117, 359). The lactation delay was first observed by Lataste (200, 201) in rodents. He postulated that the arrest of embryonic development occurs after the ova reach the uterus. He also observed that the length of the delay is proportional to the number of young nursing. In fact, the prolongation of pregnancy during lactation is due to the extension of the prenidatory period, while the fertilized eggs at the blastocyst stage remain in diapause within the uterus (22, 51, 120, 186, 217). Although the hormonal basis of the lactation delay was specified as soon as the purified ovarian hormones were made available, the conclusions drawn have been confusing (84), each of the ovarian hormones being found to shorten the delay period in animals nursing a large litter (43, 57, 194, 196, 386–388, 395, 396, 406).

Chambon (63) first reported that delayed implantation in the rat could also occur after early ovariectomy. Canivenc & Laffargue (58) ovariectomized their animals on day 4 and found that the implantation was delayed even when as much as 10 mg progesterone per day was given; implantation could only be induced when estradiol was added to the progesterone treatment. Cochrane & Meyer (75) ovariectomized their rats on day 3 and obtained an implantation delay in progesterone-treated animals, but their results were not consistent when the ovariectomy was performed on day 4. The contradictions were explained by the observation that, whenever ovariectomy was performed on any day before noon of day 4 of pregnancy, progesterone used alone was unable to permit implantation (264, 265, 294, 317).

The results obtained by the transfer of blastocysts to ovariectomized virgin hosts treated with progesterone alone left no doubt that estrogen is indispensable for the induction of nidation in this species (296). The transferred blastocysts were taken from normal, pregnant females on the morning of day 5, on the afternoon of this same day when the blue reaction is positive, or even in the morning of day 6 when some trophoblastic giant cells (107) are present. Whatever the origin and age of the blastocysts, they remained unimplanted for several days in the host's uterus, until the addition of estrogen to the progesterone treatment. It has been determined that 20–50 ng estradiol-17β injected subcutaneously is the threshold dosage that induces implantation [(297); Table 1]. When the estrogen is injected locally into the periuterine fat (406), the threshold dosage is reduced to 5 ng and even to 2.5 ng if progesterone is injected locally at the same time (299). This last observation of a synergic effect of progesterone and estrogen led to the suggestion (299, 306) that during lactation the ovary secretes negligible amounts of estrogen; this explains why implantation

can be induced in this case only by locally administered progesterone (57, 406). In fact, in animals in lactation delay, progesterone alone is not sufficient to induce implantation if the ovaries are removed; the addition of estrogen is, again, indispensable (44).

Hypophysectomy during the first days of pregnancy induces a delay in implantation interrupted only when both progesterone and estrogen are administered (11, 16, 33, 75, 410). Rats hypophysectomized on day 1 of pregnancy and treated daily with highly purified prolactin do not implant, though their corpora lutea show the typical luteotrophic stimulation; the implantation occurs normally in these animals when follicle-stimulating hormone (FSH) and luteinizing hormone (LH) are combined with the daily luteotrophin (LTH) treatment (1). In the mouse, inhibition of pituitary LTH function by an olfactory stimulation from alien males during the first days of pregnancy (52, 274) or by injection of ergocornine (61, 377) leads to the blocking of egg implantation because of progesterone deficiency. Prolactin release, essential in the rat for luteal maintainance (21, 121) and, hence, progesterone secretion, requires a permissive effect of the hypothalamus on the pituitary (122, 125, 235). Hypophysectomy with grafting of the pituitary under the kidney capsule increases the prolactin secretion and decreases the release of FSH and LH (125, 235, 279). When the pituitary autotransplantation is performed early in pregnancy, the corpora lutea continue to secrete progesterone, but implantation does not occur, because there is a deficiency of FSH-LH function in the grafted pituitary, and therefore estrogen is not secreted (16, 76, 123, 240, 242); under these conditions, egg implantation can be realized by the administration of estrogen (16, 62, 76, 123, 242) or by LH in a depot vehicle, which ensures a slow resorption (212, 213).

Lesions of the median eminence and induction of analogous deficiencies in pituitary function (224), when introduced on day 1 of pregnancy, also lead to a delay of implantation that can be interrupted by estrogen (144). It would be interesting to know if, in these cases in which egg implantation is delayed by the failure of the hypothalamus to stimulate FSH-LH release, the administration of the highly purified hypothalamic factors [FSH-releasing factor (FSH-RF) and LH-releasing factor (LH-RF)] reported to stimulate this release (334) could remedy the endocrine disorder. Daily treatment with certain phenothiazine derivatives also induces a delay in implantation (31, 64, 292, 301, 311, 376) that may be interrupted by exogenous estrogen (69, 292, 301), by pituitary extracts (304), or by human chorionic gonadotrophin (HCG) (69). As with median eminence lesions or pituitary autografts, there is no need for an exogenous progesterone supply. The pharmacological separation of the hypothalamus from the pituitary induced by these compounds assures the maintenance of functioning corpora lutea through a continuous release of pituitary prolactin (25, 235, 291, 311). Rothchild (327) suggested that the suckling stimulus

TABLE 1. *Effect of Various Doses of Estradiol-17β in Inducing Implantation in Rats Ovariectomized Early in Pregnancy and Treated with Progesterone*

Dose, μg	Animals Showing Implantation, %
0.01*	0
0.025*	42.8
0.05*	87.5
0.1*	100
0.0025**	0
0.005**	75
0.0025 + 50 μg progesterone**	54.5
50 μg progesterone*	0

* Subcutaneously injected. ** Local injection into periuterine fat. [From Psychoyos (297, 299).]

also suppresses the hypothalamic centers controlling the prolactin and FSH-LH functions; prolactin release is stimulated, whereas FSH-LH release is inhibited. Presumably inhibition sufficient to decrease estrogen secretion to less than the amount needed for egg implantation must be realized when more than three young are suckling. Delay or prevention of egg implantation can also result from steroid (24, 108, 371) or immunologic (202, 214) inhibition of the pituitary gonadotrophin function and from the use of compounds with antiestrogen properties (110, 113, 161, 162, 173, 280, 288, 337, 342).

It may be concluded from the above that estrogen is as indispensable as is progesterone for the initiation of egg implantation and that any procedure interfering temporarily or permanently with its presence is bound to postpone or prevent implantation.

Prenidatory Release of Estrogen

The results obtained by ovariectomy performed at different times during early pregnancy have shown that ovariectomy followed by progesterone treatment from the evening of day 4 can be performed in the rat (294, 410) and from the morning of day 4 in the mouse (172, 408) without disturbing the normal occurrence of implantation. As reported above, animals ovariectomized earlier show delay in implantation until estrogen is added to the progesterone treatment. Alloiteau (11) established that, although hypophysectomy on the afternoon of day 3 of pregnancy blocks implantation in progesterone-treated rats, when this surgery is carried out on the afternoon of day 4, progesterone treatment alone is enough to permit implantation at the normal time. A minimal dose of LH antiserum injected at 10 AM on day 4 results in delayed implantation, an effect counteracted by estrogen (212). Zeilmaker (411) avoided lactation delay by removal of the litter (constant number of 10 offspring) before 1 PM of day 4; the litter had to remain with the mother until 4 PM of this day for delay to occur. This same author, comparing the time-limits for hypophysectomy and ovariectomy in inducing delay, determined that for hypophysectomy these limits are about 7 hr shorter than those for ovariectomy (410).

To explain the transient period of optimal uterine sensitivity to deciduogenic stimuli occurring in the rat on day 5 of pseudopregnancy or pregnancy, Shelesnyak (349, 351, 353, 356) suggested that an estrogen surge occurs at the time when a proestrous rise would have occurred if the rats had not been in progestation. However, hypophysial LH content in pregnant rats shows a gradual rise without the alterations that would have indicated a release similar to that of proestrus on day 4 (147, 338, 339). Further, lesions of the anterior hypothalamus, effective in blocking ovulation by suppressing the proestrous LH rise, do not affect the normal occurrence of egg implantation (189, 304). Various pharmacological agents, such as tranquilizers, phenobarbital, and atropine, that are effective in blocking ovulation also

have no effect when injected on day 4 of pregnancy (301, 336, 410).

Treatment with tranquilizers or atropine to induce delay in implantation must be applied on day 3 (301, 336). When trifluoperazine is administered on this day, the period in which an ovariectomy can induce delay is extended for 24 hr (301, 311); if animals are injected with the drug at 10 AM or 8 PM on day 3, ovariectomy can induce delay if performed up to the evening of day 5 of pregnancy. Such animals ovariectomized later on day 5 implant with progesterone alone, but with a 1-day delay (Table 2). Thus, though procedures that inhibit the proestrous LH release do not intervene in the normal occurrence of egg implantation, the 24-hr periodicity in the induced delay by the tranquilizers' postponement of egg implantation suggests that the release of estrogen is discontinuous, subject to a circadian rhythmicity.

Estimation of the estrogen secretion during the estrous cycle and early pregnancy was made recently by intravaginal bioassay (409) and by radioimmunoassay (346). During the cycle (409), a detectable concentration of estrogen in the ovarian venous plasma appears only at about noon of each day; during a period beginning the day before proestrus and including the day of proestrus, the estrogen in the ovarian venous plasma shows a continuous rise, with its maximum (5 ng/ml) at noon on proestrus. In early pregnancy (409) this continuous rise in estrogen is missing, and the 24-hr periodicity persists; at noon, however, a gradual increase occurs with a maximum (2 ng/ml) on day 4. These data are therefore consistent with the expected 24-hr periodicity in estrogen secretion during the preimplantation period (Fig. 9).

This 24-hr rhythmicity in estrogen secretion may be connected to diurnal FSH fluctuations; for example, FSH levels in human plasma increase by midnight (129). In the rat and mouse a significant fall in pituitary FSH was observed in the evening of day 3 (32). The critical moment at which trifluoperazine must be obtained to induce delay appears to coincide with the period during which FSH falls. It has been shown that this drug causes delay only when administered up to midnight of day 3 (31). Much more information is needed to confirm the suggestion that delay induced by tran-

TABLE 2. *Effect of Trifluoperazine Pretreatment on Implantation Delay in Ovariectomized Pregnant Rats*

TFP* Treatment, Day 3 (noon) of Pregnancy	Ovariectomy Performed		Rats Showing Delay, %
	Day	Time	
−	4	9 AM–noon	95
−	4	7 PM–8 PM	56
−	5	10 AM–noon	0
+	5	10 AM–noon	100
+	5	7 PM–8 PM	37
+	6	10 AM–noon	0

* Trifluoperazine.   [From Psychoyos (294, 301).]

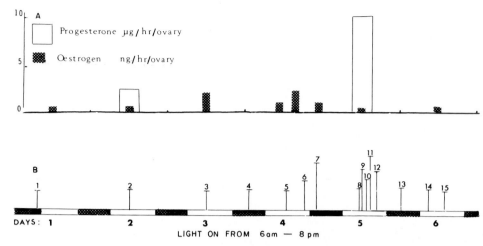

FIG. 9. *A*: changes in the levels of ovarian hormonal secretion at different stages of early pregnancy. [Data from Hashimoto et al. (164) and Yoshinaga et al. (409).] *B*: timing and sequential relationships of the various events preceding the final attachment of the egg to the endometrium in the rat. Numbered vertical lines: *1*, ovulation–fertilization; *2*, first segmentation; *3*, second segmentation; *4*, end of the period during which tranquilizers are effective in inducing delay; *5*, end of the period during which hypophysectomy induces delay; *6*, entry of morula into the cornua; *7*, end of the period during which ovariectomy induces delay; *8*, occurrence of the edematous phase; *9*, the blastocyst attaches loosely to the antimesometrial wall; *10*, onset of uterine sensitivity to decidualization; *11*, loss of the zona pellucida; *12*, the blue reaction becomes positive; *13*, end of the period of optimal sensitivity for decidualization; *14*, appearance of decidual cells; *15*, trophoblastic invasion and final attachment of the blastocysts.

quilizers is due to a blocking of FSH release. However, data suggesting such an effect have been reported for reserpine (197) and chlorpromazine (163).

Consideration of the very small amount of estrogen released on day 4, probably from the nonluteal tissues (190, 315), leads to the suggestion that only processes resulting in the complete blockade of the hypothalamic-hypophysial activity responsible for estrogen secretion would be effective in suppressing egg implantation (304). [In the rat, excess of estrogen on day 3 or 4 may cause expulsion of the egg from the genital tract and may inhibit decidualization (135, 158, 365) and egg implantation (15, 158). The same effects are obtained by administration of the so-called antiprogestins (280, 281).] This activity, differing from the one involved in the proestrous phenomena, should be linked to a basic pattern of gonadotrophin secretion sufficient to cover the needs of egg implantation for estrogen. Nevertheless the circadian rhythmicity of this activity suggests that the timing of the events associated with egg implantation depends on neurogenic timing factors analogous to those operating in spontaneous ovulation (125, 236, 311).

Specific Effects of the Ovarian Hormones
on the Ovoendometrial Relationships

In the rat during lactational or experimental delay, the dormant blastocysts were believed to be free in the lumen at a distance from the epithelium. The use of adequate fixatives that avoid shrinkage of the material reveals that the blastocysts during delay are in close contact with the antimesometrial epithelium, tenuously attached to it by their embryonic pole, or, when the delay is prolonged, enclosed between the approached uterine walls (308, 309). Ultrastructural studies (117, 224, 259, 284–286, 384) revealed that during delay the morphological relationships between the embryo and the epithelium are similar to those in the pre-attachment stage of a normally occurring implantation previously described; the luminal surface of the epithelium is covered by numerous regular, short microvilli with occasional thin pseudopodia-like protrusions among them, which should correspond to the formations recently observed in electron micrographs (318). During the delay the plasma membranes of the trophoblast and epithelial cells are generally separated by a distance of 1 μ, and the trophoblast cells occasionally possess microvilli similar to those of the epithelium (Fig. 10).

Flattening of the microvillous surface of the luminal epithelium cannot be induced by estrogen unless this hormone intervenes in a progesterone preparation; estrogen injected into ovariectomized rats not treated with progesterone (128) increases the frequency and length of the microvilli. In ovariectomized animals pretreated with progesterone 8–18 hr after the injection of estradiol-17β (285), the pseudopodia-like protrusions enlarge and form a close contact with the plasma membrane of the trophoblast cells. The epithelial cells at this time show irregular and flattened microvilli. By electron microscopy (28) the trophoblast cells of mouse blastocysts are shown to have a surface with microvillous projections, which later become flattened also. About 24 hr after estrogen administration (284, 285),

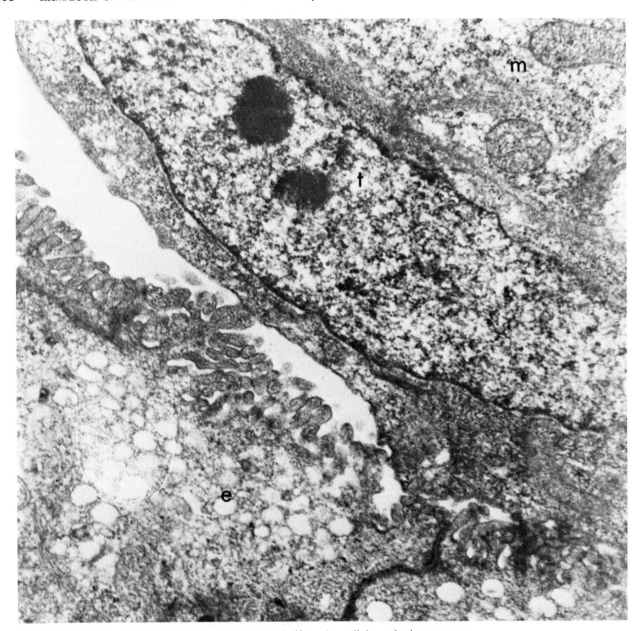

FIG. 10. Portion of an epithelial cell (*e*), a trophoblast cell (*t*), and a cell from the inner mass (*m*) from a rat uterus in delayed implantation induced by early ovariectomy followed by daily progesterone treatment. Note the microvillous surface of the epithelium and the regular border of the nucleoli of the trophoblast cell. × 24,000. [From Potts & Psychoyos (285).]

the plasma membranes of the two cellular systems run parallel and in close contact, as in normal pregnancy at the attachment stage.

In the dormant blastocysts, marked changes are observed after estrogen injection, including the development of certain dense cytoplasmic inclusions, which probably correspond to the Wilson bodies. Changes also occur in the nucleolus, which is dense and prominent during delay and appears pale with diffused borders 21 hr after the estrogen injection. A large increase of free RNA particles in the cytoplasm is also observed at this moment [(285); Fig. 11].

Weitlauf & Greenwald (394), in studying protein synthesis in mouse blastocysts by in vivo incorporation of ^{35}S-labeled methionine (148), found that, whereas in normal pregnancy uptake of the amino acid by the blastocysts increases between days 4 and 5, in lactation delay it does so only when implantation is imminent (391). These authors also found that mouse blastocysts from animals ovariectomized early in pregnancy do not incorporate ^{35}S-labeled methionine, and they showed that an activation of protein synthesis in these blastocysts occurs only after a combined progesterone and estrogen treatment (Table 3) and never in the absence of either hormone (389, 390, 394).

Histochemical studies have shown that the RNA

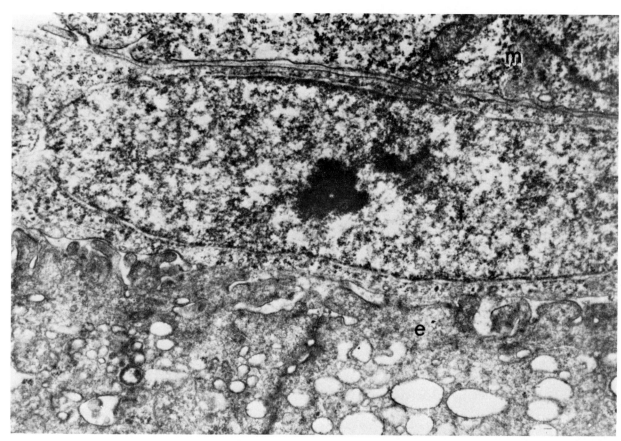

FIG. 11. Section from a rat uterus in delayed implantation induced by early ovariectomy followed by daily treatment with progesterone. In this case, the uterus was taken 21 hr after the injection of 0.1 μg estradiol-17β. Note the flattening of the epithelial surface and the irregular borders of the nucleoli of the trophoblast cell. Abbreviations as in Fig. 10. × 24,000. [From Potts & Psychoyos (285).]

TABLE 3. *Temporal Relationship Between Estradiol and Incorporation of* ^{35}*S-Labeled Methionine by Blastocysts in Ovariectomized, Progesterone-Treated Mice*

Group	Time After Estradiol Injection,* hr		Number of Animals	Blastocysts		Positive Pontamine-Blue Reactions	
	Methi-onine injected	Blasto-cysts re-covered		Reac-tivity	Num-ber	%	Intensity
1	0	2	3	0 ±	22 1	0	
2	6	8	4	0 ±	8 10	0	
3	12	14	3	+	32	0	
4	18	20	4	+	34	100	++++
5	24	26	14	+	50	100	++++

* Injection of 2 mg progesterone + 0.025 μg estradiol on day 9. [Adapted from Weitlauf & Greenwald (394).]

content of the blastocyst cells during the delay is very poor and increases soon after the addition of estrogen to the progesterone treatment (308, 310). As shown by the intraluminal instillation of the labeled precursors of proteins, RNA, and DNA in ovariectomized, progesterone-treated rats, dormant blastocysts give no evidence of protein, RNA, or DNA synthesis (287). Subcutaneous injection of estradiol rapidly results in the incorporation of the RNA precursor; a marked incorporation of labeled amino acids is observed 18 hr later and that of the DNA precursor 42 hr later (91, 287, 333). A stimulation of RNA synthesis in the blastocyst and uterus was also observed (248) after intraluminal injection of adenosine 3′,5′-monophosphate (cyclic AMP), which seems to mediate various hormonal actions.

Among the events occurring because of the effect of both ovarian hormones, is the in utero lysis of the zona pellucida (15, 102, 230, 403). In normal pregnancy the zona is lost by a lytic process; in the rat this process occurs during the early afternoon of day 5 (102, 106, 296) and in the mouse shortly before midnight of day 4 (229, 230, 270). It was shown in these species that the retention of the blastocyst in the oviduct by ligation of the uterotubal junction or early ovariectomy postpones the loss of the zona for 2–3 days (15, 270, 307). Naked blastocysts that apparently emerged from the zona on their own are then found; the lytic process seems to be absent because most of the abandoned zonae persist for several days (15, 307). The living blastocyst emerges by hatching—the process by which they also leave the pellucida in vitro (35, 36, 77, 78). In ovariectomized rats treated with progesterone, 24 hr after estrogen injection, no zonae are found either shed by, or surrounding, the blastocyst (15, 307). Thorough investigations by McLaren (227, 228, 230) show that, in the mouse during lactation delay, the loss of the zona is postponed for 24 hr and the discarded zonae persist until implantation is imminent. The lysis of the zona seems therefore to occur through modifications of the uterine milieu, realized under the same hormonal conditioning that initiates egg implantation.

It may be concluded that the known specific embryo-maternal changes leading to egg implantation can be induced only by the combined effect of the two ovarian hormones, progesterone and estrogen.

Biphasic Effect of Ovarian Hormones on Uterine Receptivity

Though the relatively short and discrete estrogen release on day 4 does not have the same quantitative importance as that accompanying proestrus, the timing of its occurrence constitutes one of the two elements dictating the moment at which the events leading to egg implantation are to begin; the other element is the moment at which the endometrial preparation by progesterone can be considered complete. In the absence of progesterone the blastocyst remains in diapause [(54, 58, 100, 111, 350, 361, 393); Fig. 12].

In the pregnant rat ovariectomized on day 4 and started on the daily progesterone treatment as soon as the operation is performed, estrogen induces implantation at the normal time when given late in the evening on this day and has no effect if given in the morning.

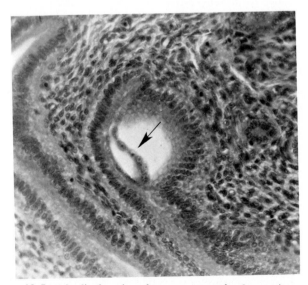

FIG. 12. Longitudinal section of a rat uterus on day 9 postcoitus. The animal received no progesterone treatment after the ovariectomy on day 4. The blastocyst (*arrow*) is encysted in the pseudostratified endometrium in a round crypt probably formed under the effect of the blastocyst motility. × 280. [From Psychoyos (308).]

Under the same conditions, but with progesterone given also on day 1 of pregnancy to hasten progestational preparation, estrogen injected in the morning of day 4 succeeds in inducing implantation (305, 306). In pregnant rats ovariectomized on day 2 and treated daily with both ovarian hormones starting on day 5 postcoitus, the blue reaction cannot be evoked earlier than the third day after the beginning of the hormonal treatment (306). Furthermore animals ovariectomized the day after estrus and treated daily with both ovarian hormones show the same timing in the onset of sensitivity as do the intact, pseudopregnant animals (404).

Many other examples show that only when the basic endometrial preparation by progesterone, which requires at least 48 hr, has been completed, is estrogen effective in inducing a state of receptivity that allows the endometrial response to stimuli of low intensity, as well as the further development of the blastocyst (220–222, 306, 309).

Calculations of the secretion rate of estrogen per ovary and per hour estimated (409) from noon of day 4 of pregnancy show that the rate of estrogen secretion should be equivalent to about 5 ng estradiol by the two ovaries per hour. Since the dose of exogenous estrogen necessary for the induction of egg implantation is about 30–50 ng (297), it can be presumed that more than 6 hr are needed for the release of this amount. Therefore during the evening of day 4 the endometrium should receive the amount needed for its transformation.

Progesterone secretion in the rat, after a short preovulatory rise, is almost nonexistent during estrus and starts to rise again by noon of the first day of diestrus (324, 375); then, in pregnancy or pseudopregnancy, it gradually increases (130, 164). Therefore a 48-hr preparation of the endometrium by this hormone is achieved by the afternoon of day 4. [During the first days of pregnancy the ovary secretes more 20α-dihydroprogesterone (20-DHP) than progesterone (130, 164, 165, 407). The 20-DHP is not a true progestational hormone, since it does not support pregnancy in ovariectomized mice, nor does it support the decidual reaction in rats. However, the decline of 20-DHP may be important for the normal preparation of the endometrium by progesterone.] The time at which this preparation is completed thus coincides with the moment at which the estrogen required for the induction of egg implantation is also available. In the rat the completion of the basic hormonal sequence is therefore realized within the last 6 hr of day 4 of pregnancy or pseudopregnancy and results in the receptive state that occurs at about noon on day 5.

The occurrence of the receptive state is invariably followed by an endometrial refractory period manifested by the complete loss of the endometrial potential for deciduoma formation (14, 98, 243, 325, 328) and by the hostility of the uterus toward blastocysts, younger eggs (46, 105, 109, 232, 261, 262, 302), and tumor growth (358). Thus the same hormonal sequence that promotes the endometrial changes leading to egg implantation is responsible for the subsequent state of nonreceptivity (305,

306, 309). In the ovariectomized virgin rat treated with various sequences of progesterone and estrogen, blastocysts in diapause implant if transferred within 24 hr after the completion of the basic hormonal sequence but fail to implant if transferred later [(302); Table 4]. Similarly, blastocysts that are normal on day 5 fail to develop when transferred into the uteri of pseudopregnant animals on day 6 (262, 306).

In rats in which ovulation has been assured by exogenous gonadotrophins, daily treatment with progesterone for the 2 days preceding a fecund coitus blocks implantation (303). Since the basic progesterone-estrogen sequence has been completed earlier, the receptive period occurs while the ova are still in the oviduct; when they reach the lumen the uterus has already progressed to the state of nonreceptivity. It has been suggested (303) that progestogens given for antiovulatory purposes should also inhibit egg implantation by creating asynchrony in the embryo-maternal relationships. In fact, a contraceptive effect independent of the occurrence of ovulation has been demonstrated in human beings with small dosages of oral progestins given daily (223) or contained in silastic capsules (S. J. Segal and H. B. Croxatto, unpublished data) implanted subcutaneously (89). Progestins given during the preovulatory period also interfere with normal implantation in the rabbit (68). A contraceptive action of progesterone, contained in silastic capsules and placed directly in the uterine cavity, was demonstrated in the rabbit (378), the rhesus monkey (340), and the human being (340).

In the rat, maintenance of the nonreceptive state for a minimum of 11 days (243) does not require any more than the minute amount of estrogen given once for the completion of the basic progesterone sequence leading to this state (14, 141, 243, 328). However, the maintenance requires daily treatment with progesterone; an arrest of this treatment for 48 hr allows the endometrium to again develop its progestational potential [(243); Table 5].

Asynchronous Implantation

Any procedure postponing the completion of the progesterone-estrogen sequence responsible for the induction of the receptive and nonreceptive uterine states allows the endometrium to remain in a neutral state; thereby its capacity for decidualization with no time limits is retained, but its sensitivity is reduced (306, 309). In rats ovariectomized before day 5 of pregnancy and treated thereafter with progesterone and in ovariectomized virgin rats treated with progesterone, traumatic stimuli induce decidualization throughout the period of the progesterone treatment (12, 13, 16, 124, 225, 241, 328). Other stimuli, such as systemic injection of pyrathiazine (87, 294) or intraluminal instillation of various substances (87, 175), remain ineffective. Decidualization can be obtained throughout lactation delay (211), but, as Krehbiel (195) demonstrated, the stimulus required is more intense than that needed when the uterus is in the state of receptivity (53).

TABLE 4. *Implantation of Blastocysts Transferred to Virgin Ovariectomized Rats Pretreated with Ovarian Hormones in Different Sequences*

Day 1	Day 2	Day 3	Day 4	Day 5	Implanted Blastocysts, %
		P	P	PE	44
P	P	P	P	PE	71
P	P	P	PE	P	66
P	P	PE	P	P	0
P	P	PE	P	PE	0
		PE	P	PE	63

Broken line indicates the basic progesterone-estrogen sequence. P, progesterone, 5 mg subcutaneously injected; E, estradiol-17β, 0.1 μg subcutaneously injected. [From Psychoyos (302).]

TABLE 5. *Effect of a Single Injection of Estradiol or of an Interruption of the Progesterone Treatment on the Uterine Capacity for Decidualization by Trauma of Ovariectomized, Progesterone-Treated Rats*

1	2	3	4	5	6	7	8	9	10	Animals with Decidual Response, %	Wt of Uterine Cornua,* mg ± SEM
P	P	PE	Tr							100	540 ± 17
P	P	PE	P	Tr						12.5	146 ± 18
P	P	P	P	Tr						100	513 ± 80
P	P	P	P	P	P	P	P	P	Tr	100	507 ± 89
P	P	PE	P	P	P	P	P	P	Tr	0	101 ± 5
P	P	PE		P	P	P	Tr			0	112 ± 2
P	P	PE			P	P	P	Tr		87.5	425 ± 23
P	P	PE				P	P	P	Tr	87.5	398 ± 70

* 96 hr after trauma. Broken line indicates basic progesterone-estrogen sequence. P, progesterone, 2.5 mg subcutaneously injected. E, estradiol-17β, 0.2 μg. Tr, trauma. [Data from Meyers (243).]

During the neutral state that exists until estrogen intervenes to complete the progesterone-estrogen sequence and to induce the succession of the receptive and nonreceptive states, decidualization can be induced at different times in the same uterus (12, 79). Peckham & Greene (275, 276) obtained two sets of deciduomata in lactating animals and in animals ovariectomized before day 5 of pregnancy and treated with progesterone alone; animals receiving the latter treatment but ovariectomized on day 5 do not produce deciduomata. Asynchronous implantation has been observed to occur spontaneously in lactating animals (386). Some cases were also reported in hypophysectomized rats with pituitary autografts (62, 76) and in pregnant rats treated with tranquilizers (311). One animal treated with chlorpromazine contained three asynchronous sets of well-developed, living embryos (292).

Asynchrony in implantation has been experimentally obtained during lactation delay by the local application of progesterone (57, 406) or estrogen (406). This treatment induces the implantation of a first set of embryos; the implantation of the second set follows spontaneously. Furthermore experimentally induced implantation of two sets of embryos was achieved in animals ovariectomized early in pregnancy and then treated with progesterone; implantation of the first set of embryos was obtained by the local injection of a minute amount (5 ng) of estradiol and implantation of the second set by systemic administration of 100 ng estradiol (299, 300). With these latter experimental conditions, the age difference between the two sets of embryos depends on the interval between the two injections (Fig. 13). When this interval exceeds 6 days, second set implantations can no longer be obtained in the same horn but only in the opposite horn. With an interval longer than 10 days, second set implantations are not possible, even in the opposite horn (300); the reason for this failure is as yet unknown.

Experimentally induced asynchronous implantation has been obtained in animals in delayed implantation after early hypophysectomy (17) or after treatment with tranquilizers (321, 322). In these cases, however, it is not necessary to induce the implantation of the second set by exogenous estrogen: 6 days after the induction of the implantation of the first set, the implantation of the second set may occur spontaneously, presumably induced by estrogen secreted by the ovary stimulated by the placental gonadotrophins. In intact experimental animals bearing two asynchronous sets of fetuses, parturition of the first set is postponed until the second set is at term; the corpora lutea remain functional throughout this period (322).

In all the above cases a minute dose of estrogen applied locally may be enough to induce the receptive state in a treated region only, whereas the rest of the uterus remains in the neutral state until the estrogen required for the total transition of the endometrium to the receptive state is made available, either exogenously or endogenously. Removal of the ovaries before the release of the amount of estrogen needed for the transformation of the endometrium to the receptive state permits implantation of some blastocysts (410). The estrogen requirements essential for the transition of the endometrium to the receptive state

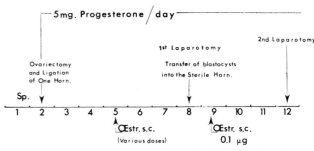

FIG. 14. An experimental procedure for the induction of asynchronous implantation demonstrates that estrogen administration after progesterone treatment induces the uterine state of receptivity followed by nonreceptivity. *Sp*, day of detection of spermatozoa in the vaginal smear; *OEstr. s.c.*, subcutaneously administered estradiol-17β.

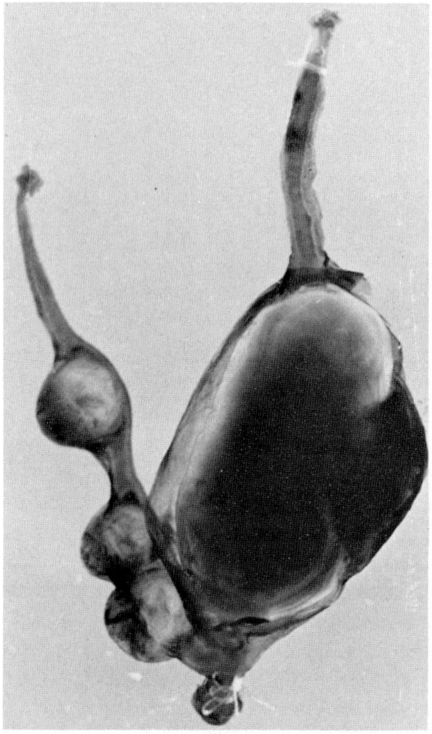

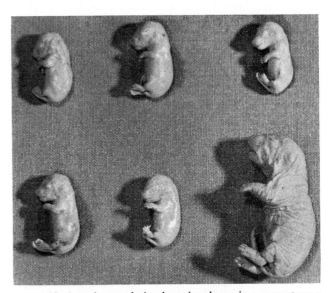

FIG. 15. Asynchronously implanted embryos in a progesterone-treated rat ovariectomized early in pregnancy. The implantation of a first embryo occurred after the administration of 30 ng estradiol on day 5 postcoitus; the second subcutaneous injection of 100 ng estradiol on day 9 induced in the normal horn, which until this time had been in delay, the implantation of 2 blastocysts, and in the sterile horn the implantation of transferred blastocysts. See Fig. 14. [From Psychoyos (298).]

FIG. 13. Experimental asynchronous implantation in the ovariectomized, progesterone-treated rat. In the right horn the implantation was induced by local injection of 5 ng estradiol-17β. In the left horn implantations were induced by another administration 10 days later of 100 ng subcutaneously injected estradiol. The uterus was cleared by the method of Orsini (269). [From Psychoyos (306).]

seem to vary along the length of the uterine horn. Asynchronous implantation may therefore also be obtained in animals in which some of the blastocysts implant first in response to an initial subthreshold systemic dose of estrogen, which induces the receptive state in limited endometrial areas. Implantation of the other blastocysts is brought about some days later by a second, stronger dose that permits the transition of the total endometrium to the receptive state (298, 305, 313).

Local induction of the receptive state leads to local manifestation of the nonreceptive state. This is demonstrated by the following experiment. Various doses of estrogen were injected on day 5 postcoitus into animals that had had one horn sterilized by ligation of the utero-tubal junction and had been ovariectomized early in pregnancy and treated daily with progesterone. A laparotomy performed on day 8 verified the occurrence of implantations in the normal horn. Foreign blastocysts were transferred into the sterile horn. A second dosage of estradiol (0.1 μg) was injected on the day after the transfer day, and the animals were laparotomized again 3 days later [(298); Fig. 14]. The number of normal horns with implantations induced by the first injection of estrogen increases according to the injected dose; for the same treatment, the number of sterile horns with implantations induced by the second injection of estrogen decreases (Figs. 15 and 16). Apparently, by increasing the dosage of estrogen given on day 5, the part of the

endometrium remaining in the neutral state is correspondingly reduced.

COMMENTS ON THE HORMONAL ACTION

Uterine Receptivity and Estrogen Receptors

The theory that the specificity of a target tissue's response to a hormone is due to the existence in this tissue of a specific intracellular receptor for this hormone is, at least for estrogen, proved valid by numerous experimental observations. Estradiol is rapidly concentrated in the endometrium and remains there unchanged for at least 6 hr bound to subcellular macromolecules considered specific estrogen receptors (2, 239, 343, 370, 372, 374).

Capacity of the endometrium to bind estradiol varies according to its functional state [(133, 312, 320); Fig. 17]. In ovariectomized, progesterone-treated rats, uptake of tritiated estradiol given to complete the progesterone-estrogen sequence is significantly high; it is extremely low when the radioactive hormone is administered 48 hr after the sequence has been completed by a previous estrogen administration. We may assume that the high affinity for estradiol shown by the neutral endometrium and the loss of this affinity when the uterus becomes nonreceptive demonstrate that the endometrial changes leading to the receptive and nonreceptive states appear after the saturation of the receptor sites by estradiol. If this is the case, the amount of available receptor molecules for estradiol, high before the induction of the receptive state, should decrease thereafter; the local manifestation of the different functional states in the same uterus could then be attributed to local variations in this amount. The ratio between saturated and unsaturated receptor sites may account for the local differences in the uterine responsiveness to estrogen given at subthreshold doses, the possibil-

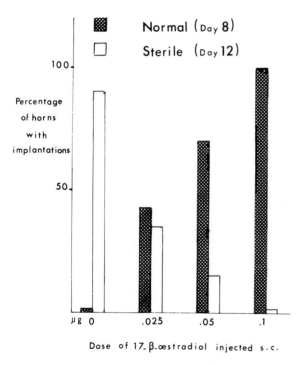

FIG. 16. Uterine receptivity to blastocysts modified by a single subcutaneous (s.c.) injection of estradiol at various dosages in the progesterone-treated, ovariectomized rat. Open columns, sterile horns implanted with transferred blastocysts. Hatched columns, normal horns implanted with the host's own blastocysts. See Fig. 14. [From Psychoyos (313).]

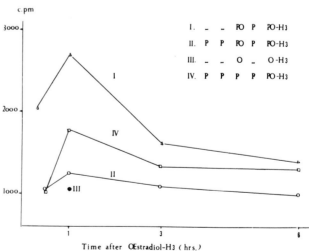

FIG. 17. Uptake of ³H-labeled estradiol by the endometrium of ovariectomized rats treated with various hormonal sequences. cpm, counts/min per rat endometrium; P, 5 mg subcutaneously injected progesterone; O, 0.1 μg subcutaneously injected estradiol-17β; O-H³, 0.1 μg subcutaneously injected tritiated estradiol. [From Psychoyos et al. (320).]

ity for the induction of the receptive state to a given area increasing with an increase in this ratio.

The markedly low uptake of tritiated estradiol administered 48 hr after a first injection of estradiol in ovariectomized rats untreated with progesterone could be assumed to be due also to the previous saturation of the receptor sites (see Fig. 17, III). The daily injection of progesterone during this 48-hr period (see Fig. 17, I) completely modifies the binding capacity of the endometrium; it allows the endometrium to develop a high affinity for estradiol. Progesterone appears therefore to increase the number of the available estrogen receptors. However, these may not be the same as those operating in the animals not treated with progesterone.

Changes in the rate of estrogen inactivation within the uterus could also account for the increased amount of estradiol found in the progesterone-treated endometrium. The rat uterus contains an enzyme that in the presence of H_2O_2 can catalyze the inactivation of estradiol and certain other estrogens in vitro (187). This enzyme appeared in the uterus of ovariectomized animals after estrogen administration, whereas progesterone decreased the accumulation of the enzyme. Klebanoff (187) studied the activity of this enzyme in uterine extracts prepared from pregnant animals from day 7 postcoitus and found it reduced compared with extracts from the estrous uteri. There is no information for days 4 and 5 of pregnancy. However, uterine peroxidase seems to be, to a large extent, peroxidase from eosinophils, and eosinophils should be involved in the endometrial receptivity; they are abundant in the rat at proestrus and estrus but also on day 5 of pseudopregnancy (38, 203, 204). Alloiteau (13) suggested that their existence in the endometrium announces the endometrial potentiality for deciduoma formation.

RNA Biosynthesis and Uterine Receptivity

In the ovariectomized adult rat and mouse or in the immature rat, estrogen stimulates the rate of incorporation of precursors into RNA within a few minutes after estrogen is injected (234, 244, 343). In ovariectomized animals pretreated with progesterone, the rate of stimulation varies according to the length of the progesterone treatment: until 48 hr after the beginning of this treatment, the stimulatory effect of estradiol does not change, whereas after this period stimulation increases suddenly (312, 314). The quantitative difference in the stimulation by estrogen may indicate qualitative differences between the RNA produced in untreated uteri and in uteri treated with progesterone. Involvement of DNA-dependent RNA synthesis in the manifestation of the receptive uterine state is suggested by the suppression of uterine sensitivity for decidual response by actinomycin D (146), which is known to affect this synthesis. Qualitatively different RNA appears at about the time the changes associated with egg implantation occur in rabbit endometrium (379). However, both phenomena may involve RNA produced under the effect of estradiol alone. Several estrogen-like phenomena, including the induction of egg

implantation in rats ovariectomized early in pregnancy and treated with progesterone, have been induced by RNA extracted from uteri treated with estrogen (343–345). This last finding suggests that all the primary steps of estrogen action in inducing egg implantation are independent of the progesterone pretreatment and are similar to those induced by estrogen in animals not pretreated with progesterone.

Most of the uterine changes occurring after the completion of the basic progesterone-estrogen sequences are among those usually characterizing the uterus when stimulated only by estrogen (114, 253, 343, 362, 363, 368). The changes include histamine release (219, 348, 364), decrease in the number of mast cells (99, 349), increase of eosinophilic leukocytes (203, 204), vasodilatation (30, 37, 278), edema (127, 309), and increase in precursor incorporation into RNA (245, 249, 267, 312) and proteins (148, 249). However, the changes specific to the initiation of egg implantation (i.e., the structural and metabolic changes concerning the embryo-maternal contact that permit the blastocyst to develop or the zona pellucida to undergo lysis) require the combined effect of progesterone and estrogen. Progesterone contribution therefore must be considered specific and essential for these changes, but the manner in which this contribution is expressed remains completely unknown.

Hormone-Dependent Factors Involved in Uterine Receptivity and Egg Development

Serious gaps exist in our present knowledge of the correlation of the various functional uterine states with factors specifically involved either in their induction or in their manifestations. Evidence for hormonal regulation in the synthesis of a cell surface factor is offered by studies in hepatoma cells showing that certain steroid hormones promote flattening, coherence, and adhesiveness of these cells to the glass by inducing the synthesis of a macromolecule (23). In the modification of the trophoblast and epithelial surfaces occurring during the state of receptivity, an analogous inducible system may respond to the ovarian hormones and this response may lead to the formation of new surface components. The structural changes of the surface of the luminal epithelium and the modification of the physicochemical properties they reflect must certainly account for the differences in the behavior of the endometrium toward the unimplanted blastocyst. The eventual synthesis of specific proteins implicated in these surface changes may be one of the essential steps in the hormonal control of the embryo-maternal relationships.

Changes in the electrolytic permeability of the plasma membranes of the epithelial and trophoblast cells should certainly play a part in the early embryo-maternal relationships (88). The electrolytic composition of uterine fluids, which probably reflects analogous endometrial changes, was found to depend on ovarian hormones (71). On the other hand, a specific property of the progestational endometrium is absorption of electronegative colloidal substances from the lumen and their retention in the cytoplasm of the epithelial cells (380, 381). This phenomenon, athrocytosis, appears in the rat nearly 60 hr after the beginning of diestrus and becomes more intense as diestrus advances; it has been detected also in the human female between days 19 and 23 of the menstrual cycle (380). In the rat this phenomenon is especially apparent in the epithelium of the antimesometrial area. The cytoplasmic formations of the epithelial surface seen by scanning electron microscopy are particularly abundant in this area; it may be that they are involved in the athrocytosis phenomenon by representing electropositive sites. Recent findings have shown that the rat blastocyst behaves like a negatively charged body that is moving to the positive pole of an electrolytic chamber (72).

The suggestion that estrogen has a direct effect on the blastocyst has been advanced; mouse blastocysts previously exposed in vitro to estradiol and subsequently well washed were found to implant when transferred to ovariectomized, progesterone-treated animals (251). These data are not consistent with what has been shown in many cases (104, 296, 389), that is, even blastocysts from 6-day-old rats do not implant when transferred to such uteri until exogenous estrogen is offered (296). During in vitro exposure of the blastocysts to estradiol, the hormone may be bound with no specific proteins, and, being thus accumulated in the blastocoele fluid, estradiol may be dispersed with this fluid to the host's epithelium.

It can be proposed that changes limited to the immediate environment of the blastocyst are enough to promote, delay, or cancel egg implantation. Since some blastocysts in the same uterine horn can be stimulated to develop, whereas others remain in diapause, it is hard to believe that activation of the blastocyst's metabolic activity is induced by some component of the uterine secretion; such a component would surely reach other blastocysts, even if it were produced only in a limited part of the endometrium. This does not necessarily mean that during the intrauterine development the embryo does not find in the uterine secretory products substances favoring its normal growth (42, 137). At the moment of uterine receptivity, periodic acid-Schiff (PAS)-positive material is found in the glands and on the luminal surface of the epithelium (137). It presumably corresponds to the polysaccharides found in the uterine washings of pseudopregnant rabbits; the role of the latter, however, is uncertain. A protein secretion specific to the uterus, uteroglobin (26, 27, 277) or blastokinin (150), was identified in the rabbit and found to exert a favorable effect on the development of the rabbit egg. A beautiful example of what has been called *uterine milk* (45) occurs in the cat (82); during its preimplantation life, which is relatively long in this species, the blastocyst is located in regions that show an intense secretory activity. Kirby's (182) experiments in the mouse suggest a favorable effect of the uterine environment on the development of normal embryonic tissue.

However, the best proof that none of the substances eventually produced by the uterus has any specificity in activating the blastocyst growth is that the mouse and rat ovum is able to proliferate in extrauterine sites (29, 39, 131, 132, 179–181, 233, 255, 329) or in relatively simple media in vitro (36, 78, 151, 153, 236, 237). This is the case not only for normal blastocysts but also for blastocysts in diapause. Such blastocysts, transferred from the uterus to the anterior chamber of the eye of the donor (310) or under the kidney capsule (183), start to proliferate, whereas the blastocysts that remain in the uterus continue to be in diapause. Presumably either an active inhibition is exerted by the endometrium (51, 149, 310, 313, 396) or the immediate uterine environment of the blastocyst is deficient in some essential metabolites under the hormonal conditions causing the diapause (42, 151).

The transfer of eggs at various cleavage stages into the uterus of ovariectomized rats shows that, if such an inhibition exists or if a factor is missing, it probably concerns only the egg at the blastocyst stage. Morulae (101, 103) or even two-cell eggs (317) can develop normally in uteri of ovariectomized animals until the blastocyst stage is reached. Once they reach this stage, they remain in diapause until the completion of the estrogen-progesterone sequence (317). The metabolic activity of the egg during the early stages differs from that of the blastocyst. In vitro incorporation of RNA and protein precursors is at a minimum up to the morula stage and rises sharply at the blastocyst stage (215, 246, 247, 250, 392). It has been mentioned that this rise in metabolic activity is not present in the blastocysts in uteri of lactating animals or those undergoing experimentally induced delay (287, 391, 394).

The outgrowth of the blastocysts when in vitro requires some essential amino acids (90, 151), and it has been suggested that delayed implantation may result from a selective restriction of those amino acids by the uterus in delay (151). However, contrary to what was expected, amino acid concentration was higher in the fluid of uteri in delay than in the fluid of normally pregnant uteri (152). Labeled methionine injected into mice showing delay is secreted into the uterus and is incorporated by normal 5-day-old blastocysts transferred to the uterus just before the amino acid injection (394). This incorporation decreases and finally, after prolonged exposure to the delayed uterus, stops completely (389).

Rat blastocysts from normal pregnancies incorporate in vitro protein, RNA, and DNA precursors; those from lactation or experimental delay, during the first hours of their recovery from the uterus at the most, do not incorporate the precursors (149, 177, 333). After being cultured in vitro for 22 hr and then exposed for 2 hr to tritiated uridine, blastocysts in diapause show a highly increased uptake of the RNA precursor [(313, 316); Fig. 18]. These data suggest that the withdrawal of the blastocysts from the environment of the uterus in delay enhances their activity for RNA synthesis. It has been proposed that the diapause of the blastocyst is due, at least in rodents, to an inhibition exerted on the blasto-

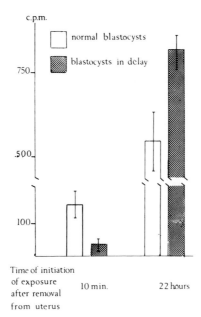

FIG. 18. Uptake of ^{3}H-labeled uridine by normal and delayed blastocysts 10 min and 22 hr after their recovery and their culture in vitro. Uptake of the radioactively labeled uridine was determined for both delayed and normal blastocysts 2 hr after the exposure of the eggs to the radioactive precursor (10 μc/ml). [From Psychoyos & Bitton-Casimiri (316).]

cyst's metabolic activity by the uterus in the absence of one or both ovarian hormones.

The supernatant liquid from the uteri of ovariectomized, progesterone-treated rats was found to contain a thermolabile factor able to inhibit the uptake of uridine by normal rabbit and rat blastocysts in vitro (313). Through such a factor the uterus may switch off the metabolic activity of the blastocyst; by removing this factor the ovarian hormones may promote the activation of the blastocyst. Further studies are needed to test this suggestion.

SUMMARY

In most mammals the ovum reaches the uterine lumen 3–4 days after fertilization as a blastocyst. The period during which the blastocyst remains in the uterus waiting to be implanted varies from a few days in most species to several months in others. In rats and mice this period, normally short, is extended when pregnancy is associated with lactation. This phenomenon, delayed implantation, has provided precious material for the study of egg im-

plantation and its hormonal conditioning. The experimental induction of delayed implantation in rats and mice by means of ovariectomy at various times in early pregnancy has provided the basis for analysis of the hormonal interplay that controls implantation.

Implantation in the rat depends on the completion of a basic hormonal sequence composed of two elements: *1*) a 48-hr period of progesterone preparation, and *2*) the presence of estrogen at the end of this period. When this sequence is completed (in normal pregnancy within the last 6 hr of day 4 postcoitus), the uterus undergoes specific modifications leading, within 24 hr, to a receptive state. This state, which in normal pregnancy covers the second half of day 5, is characterized by a high sensitivity of the endometrium for decidualization together with transient specific changes in the morphology and the biochemical profile of the endometrium. At this time an increased permeability occurs in the endometrial capillaries surrounding the blastocyst, which is about to implant. This local vascular change seems to be the sine qua non condition for decidualization, but no precise information exists on the nature of the embryonic stimulus inducing this change.

The receptive state lasts but a few hours; the endometrium gradually loses its capacity for decidualization, and the uterine environment becomes hostile to blastocysts. If the period of the progesterone preparation is shorter than 48 hr or if the estrogen intervention is postponed, the specific uterine modifications leading to the receptive state do not occur. The uterus maintains its potency for decidualization, and blastocysts, if present, are retained unimplanted but with their viability unimpaired. When the progesterone background is assured, a minute dose of estradiol applied locally to the uterus induces the receptive state in the treated region, while the rest of the uterus remains neutral.

Changes in the endometrial uptake of estradiol were found to parallel the functional states of the uterus, and changes in the number of available receptor molecules for estradiol presumably have a determining role on the induction of these states. The major component of the action of estrogen in inducing implantation of embryos must be related to its effect in promoting the synthesis of new proteins through elaboration of new genetic information in the endometrium; during delayed implantation, the synthesis of protein, RNA, and DNA in the blastocysts of rats and mice is repressed. This repression ceases under the effect of both ovarian hormones or when the blastocysts are withdrawn from the uterine environment.

REFERENCES

1. AHMAD, N., W. R. LYONS, AND H. PAPKOFF. Maintenance of gestation in hypophysectomized rats with highly purified pituitary hormones. *Anat. Record* 164: 291–304, 1969.
2. ALBERGA, A., AND E. E. BAULIEU. Concentration élective de l'oestradiol dans l'endomètre chez la ratte. *Compt. Rend.* 261: 5226, 1965.
3. ALDEEN, K. M., AND C. A. FINN. The implantation of blastocysts in the Russian Steppe lemming (*Lagurus-lagurus*). *J. Exptl. Zool.* 173: 63–78, 1970.
4. ALDEN, R. H. Implantation of the rat egg. II. Alteration in osmiophilic epithelial lipids of the rat uterus under normal and experimental conditions. *Anat. Record* 97: 1–19, 1947.

5. ALDEN, R. H., AND J. SMITH. Implantation of the rat egg. IV. Some effects of artificial ova on the rat uterus. *J. Exptl. Zool.* 142: 215–225, 1959.

6. ALLEN, E., AND E. A. DOISY. An ovarian hormone. *J. Am. Med. Assoc.* 81: 819–821, 1923.

7. ALLEN, E., AND E. A. DOISY. The extraction and some properties of an ovarian hormone. *J. Biol. Chem.* 61: 711–727, 1924.

8. ALLEN, W. M., I. Cyclical alterations of the endometrium of the rat during the normal cycle, pseudopregnancy and pregnancy. II. Production of deciduomata during pregnancy. *Anat. Record* 48: 65–103, 1931.

9. ALLEN, W. M., AND G. W. CORNER. Physiology of corpus luteum. III. Normal growth and implantation of embryos after very early ablation of the ovaries, under the influence of extracts of the corpus luteum. *Am. J. Physiol.* 88: 340–346, 1929.

10. ALLOITEAU, J. J. L'oeuf non fécondé peut-il provoquer une réaction déciduale chez la ratte? *Rev. Fran. Etudes Clin. Biol.* 3: 974–976, 1958.

11. ALLOITEAU, J. J. Hypophysectomie au début de la gestation et nidation de l'oeuf chez la ratte. *Compt. Rend.* 253: 1348–1350, 1961.

12. ALLOITEAU, J. J. Obtention de déciduomes traumatiques à tous les stades de la gestation chez la ratte. *Compt. Rend. Soc. Biol.* 157: 1153–1157, 1963.

13. ALLOITEAU, J. J. Déciduome chez la ratte cyclique ou en début de gestation malgré un traitement oestrogénique dans les jours précédant le traumatisme. Importance de la préparation oestrogénique dans cette résistance à l'oestradiol. *Compt. Rend. Soc. Biol.* 157: 1204–1207, 1963.

14. ALLOITEAU, J. J., AND G. ACKER. Résistance durable au déciduome traumatique après injection unique d'oestradiol chez la ratte. *Compt. Rend.* 262: 3043–3045, 1962.

15. ALLOITEAU, J. J., AND A. PSYCHOYOS. Y-a-t-il pour l'oeuf de la rat deux façons de perdre sa zone pellucide? *Compt. Rend.* 262: 1561–1564, 1966.

16. ALLOITEAU, J. J., A. PSYCHOYOS, AND G. ACKER. Durée de la vie fonctionnelle du corps jaune gestatif chez la ratte hypophysectomisée. *Compt. Rend.* 256: 4284–4287, 1963.

17. ALLOITEAU, J. J., AND A. VIGNAL. Seuils progestéroniques permettant, en l'absence de préparation oestrogénique, le déciduome traumatique chez la ratte privée d'ovaires, de surrénales ou d'hypophyse. *Compt. Rend. Soc. Biol.* 155: 1878–1881, 1961.

18. AMOROSO, E. C. Placentation. In: *Marshall's Physiology of Reproduction*, edited by A. S. Parkes. New York: Longmans, 1952, vol. II, p. 127.

19. ANCEL, P., AND P. BOUIN. Sur la fonction du corps jaune (4 notes préliminaires). *Compt. Rend. Soc. Biol.* 66: 454–456, 505–507, 605–607, 689–690, 1909.

20. ANDERSEN, D. H. The rate of passage of the mammalian ovum through various portions of the fallopian tube. *Am. J. Physiol.* 82: 557–569, 1927.

21. ASTWOOD, E. B. The regulation of corpus luteum function by hypophyseal luteotrophin. *Endocrinology* 28: 309–320, 1941.

22. BAEVSKY, U. B. The effect of embryonic diapause on the nuclei and mitotic activity of mink and rat blastocysts. In: *Delayed Implantation*, edited by A. C. Enders. Chicago: Univ. of Chicago Press, 1963, p. 141–154.

23. BALLARD, P. L., AND G. M. TOMKINS. Hormone induced modification of the cell surface. *Nature* 224: 344–345, 1969.

24. BARNES, L. E., AND R. K. MEYER. Delayed implantation in intact rats treated with medroxyprogesterone acetate. *J. Reprod. Fertility* 7: 139–143, 1964.

25. BARRACLOUGH, C. A., AND C. H. SAWYER. Induction of pseudopregnancy in the rat by reserpine and chlorpromazine. *Endocrinology* 65: 563–571, 1959.

26. BEIER, H. Uteroglobin: a hormone-sensitive endometrial protein involved in blastocyst development. *Biochim. Biophys. Acta* 160: 289–291, 1968.

27. BEIER, H. Biochemisch-entwicklungs-physiologische Unter-

suchungen am Protein milieu für die Blastozystentwicklung des Kanincheus (*Oryctolagus cuniculus*). *Zool. J. Anat.* 85: 72–190, 1968.

28. BERGSTROM, S., AND O. NILSSON. Morphological changes of the trophoblast surface at implantation in the mouse. *J. Reprod. Fertility* 23: 339–340, 1970.

29. BILLINGTON, W. D., C. F. GRAHAM, AND A. McLAREN. Extra-uterine development of mouse blastocysts cultured *in vitro* from early cleavage stages. *J. Embryol. Exptl. Morphol.* 20: 391–400, 1968.

30. BINDON, B. M. Blood flow in the reproductive organs of the mouse after hypophysectomy, after gonadotrophin treatment, during the oestrus cycle and during early pregnancy. *J. Endocrinol.* 44: 523–536, 1969.

31. BINDON, B. M. The role of the pituitary gland in implantation in the mouse: delay of implantation by hypophysectomy and neurodepressive drugs. *J. Endocrinol.* 43: 225–235, 1969.

32. BINDON, B. M. Follicle-stimulating hormone content of the pituitary gland before implantation in the mouse and rat. *J. Endocrinol.* 44: 349–356, 1969.

33. BINDON, B. M., AND D. R. LAMOND. Effect of hypophysectomy on implantation in the mouse. *J. Reprod. Fertility* 18: 43–50, 1969.

34. BISCHOFF, T. L. W. *Entwicklungsgeschichte des Rehes*. Giessen, 1854.

35. BITTON-CASIMIRI, V., J. L. BRUN, AND A. PSYCHOYOS. Comportement *in vitro* des blastocysts du 5e jour de la gestation chez la ratte. Etude micro-cinematographique. *Compt. Rend.* 270: 2979–2982, 1970.

36. BITTON-CASIMIRI, V., AND A. PSYCHOYOS. Développement du blastocyst du rat *in vitro*. *Compt. Rend.* 267: 762–764, 1968.

37. BITTON-CASIMIRI, V., G. VASSENT, AND A. PSYCHOYOS. Réponse vasculaire de l'utérus au traumatisme au cours de la pseudogestation chez la ratte. *Compt. Rend.* 261: 3474–3477, 1965.

38. BJERSING, L., AND N. E. BORGLIN. Effect of hormones on incidence of uterine eosinophilia in rats. *Acta Pathol. Microbiol. Scand.* 60: 27–35, 1964.

39. BLAND, K. P., AND B. T. DONOVAN. Experimental ectopic implantation of eggs and early embryos in guinea-pigs. *J. Reprod. Fertility* 10: 189–196, 1965.

40. BLANDAU, R. J. Embryo-endometrial interrelationship in the rat and guinea-pig. *Anat. Record* 104: 331–360, 1949.

41. BLANDAU, R. J. Biology of eggs and implantation. In: *Sex and Internal Secretions* (3rd ed.), edited by W. C. Young. Baltimore: Williams & Wilkins, 1961, vol. II, p. 797.

42. BLOCH, S. Contributions to research on the female sex hormones. The implantation of the mouse egg. *J. Endocrinol.* 1: 399–408, 1939.

43. BLOCH, S. Zum Problem der Nidationsvergögerung bei der sängeden Mous. *Bull. Schweiz. Akad. Med. Wiss.* 4: 309–332, 1948.

44. BLOCH, S. Experimentelle Untersuchunger über die hormonalen Grundlagen der Implantation des Säugerkeimes. *Experientia* 14/12: 447, 1958.

45. BONNET, R. *Die Uterinmilch unf ihre Bedentung für die Frucht*. Stuttgart, 1882.

46. BOOT, L. M., AND O. MUHLBOCK. Transplantations of ova in mice. *Acta Physiol. Pharm. Neerl.* 3: 133, 1953.

47. BORGESE, E., AND A. CASSINI. Cleavage of mouse egg. In: *Cinemicrography in Cell Biology*, edited by G. G. Rose. New York: Acad. Press, 1963, p. 274–282.

48. BOSHIER, D. P. The Pontamine blue reaction in pregnant sheep uteri. *J. Reprod. Fertility* 22: 595–596, 1970.

49. BOUIN, P., AND P. ANCEL. Recherches sur les fonctions du corps jaune gestatif. I. Sur le déterminisme de la préparation d'utérus à la fixation de l'oeuf. *J. Physiol. Pathol. Gen.* 12: 1–16, 1910.

50. BOYD, J. D., AND W. J. HAMILTON. Cleavage, early development and implantation of the egg: In: *Marshall's Physiology of Reproduction*, edited by A. S. Parkes. London: Longmans, 1952, chapt. 14, p. 1.

51. BRAMBELL, F. W. R. The influence of lactation on the implantation of the mammalian embryo. *Am. J. Obstet. Gynecol.* 33: 942–953, 1937.

52. BRUCE, H. M. Time relations in the pregnancy-block induced in mice by strange males. *J. Reprod. Fertility* 2: 138–142, 1961.

53. BRUMLEY, L. E., AND V. J. DE FEO. Quantitative studies on deciduoma formation and implantation in the lactating rat. *Endocrinology* 75: 883–892, 1964.

54. BUCHANAN, G. D. Blastocyst survival in ovariectomized rats. *J. Reprod. Fertility* 19: 279–284, 1969.

55. BUCHANAN, G. D. Reproduction in ferret (*Mustela furo*). II. Changes following ovariectomy during early pregnancy. *J. Reprod. Fertility* 18: 305–316, 1969.

56. CANIVENC, R. L'ovo-implantation différée des animaux sauvages. In: *Les Fonctions de Nidation Utérine et leurs Troubles*, edited by G. Masson. Paris: Masson, 1960, p. 33.

57. CANIVENC, R., C. DROUVILLE, AND G. MAYER. Developpement simultané d'embryons d'âges différents chez la ratte: réalisation expérimentale. *Compt. Rend.* 237: 1036–1038, 1953.

58. CANIVENC, R., AND M. LAFFARGUE. Survie prolongée d'oeufs fécondés non implantés dans l'utérus de rattes castrées et injectées de progestérone. *Compt. Rend.* 242: 2857–2860, 1956.

59. CANIVENC, R., AND M. LAFFARGUE. Survie des blastocysts de rat en l'absence d'hormones ovariennes. *Compt. Rend.* 245: 1752–1754, 1957.

60. CANIVENC, R., AND M. LAFFARGUE. Inventory of problems raised by the delayed ova implantation in the European badger (*Meles-meles*). In: *Delayed Implantation*, edited by A. C. Enders. Chicago: Univ. of Chicago Press, 1963, p. 115.

61. CARLSEN, R. A., G. H. ZEILMAKER, AND M. C. SHELESNYAK. Termination of early (pre-nidation) pregnancy in the mouse by single injection of ergocornine methanesulphonate. *J. Reprod. Fertility* 2: 369–373, 1961.

62. CARPENT, G., AND L. DESCLIN. Effet de l'hypophysectomie et de la transplantation pituitaire suivies de l'injection d'oestradiol sur l'évolution de la grossesse et la morphologie foetale chez la rat. *Compt. Rend.* 260: 4618–4620, 1965.

63. CHAMBON, Y. Réalisation du retard de l'implantation par des faibles doses de progestérone chez la ratte. *Compt. Rend. Soc. Biol.* 143: 753–756, 1949.

64. CHAMBON, Y. Influence de la chlorpromazine sur la fonction lutéotrophe de l'hypophyse dans la réalisation du déciduome et de l'ovoimplantation chez le rat. *Bull. Acad. Natl. Med., Paris* 142: 243–248, 1958.

65. CHAMBON, Y. Phénothiazines, ovoimplantation et décidualisation. *Bull. Soc. Roy. Belge Gynecol. Obstet.* 30: 573–584, 1960.

66. CHAMBON, Y., AND H. LEFREIN. Des effets morphogènes de l'histamine administrée *in situ* sur l'utérus de la lapine en phase progestative artificielle. *Compt. Rend. Soc. Biol.* 146: 821–824, 1952.

67. CHANG, M. C. Development and fate of transferred rabbit ova or blastocyst in relation to the ovulation time of recipients. *J. Exptl. Zool.* 114: 197–225, 1950.

68. CHANG, M. C. Fertilization, transportation and degeneration of the egg in pseudopregnant or progesterone-treated rabbits. *Endocrinology* 84: 356–361, 1969.

69. CHATTERJEE, A., AND J. K. HARPER. Interruption of implantation and gestation in rats by reserpine, chlorpromazine and ACTH; possible mode of action. *Endocrinology* 87: 966–969, 1970.

70. CHRISTIE, G. A. Implantation of the rat embryo: glycogen and alkaline phosphatase. *J. Reprod. Fertility* 12: 279–294, 1966.

71. CLEMETSON, C. A. B., V. R. MALLIKARJUNESWARA, M. M. MOSHFEGHI, J. J. CARR, AND J. H. WILDS. The effects of oestrogen and progesterone on the sodium and potassium concentrations of rat uterine fluid. *J. Endocrinol.* 47: 309–319, 1970.

72. CLEMETSON, C. A. B., M. M. MOSHFEGHI, AND V. R. MALLIKARJUNESWARA. Electrophoretic mobility of the rat blastocyst. *Contraception* 1: 357–360, 1970.

73. CLYMAN, M. J. Electron microscopic changes produced in the human endometrium by acetate and ethinyl estradiol. *Fertility Sterility* 14: 353–364, 1963.

74. CLYMAN, M. J. Fine structure of the nucleolus of the human endometrium at the time of nidation. *Excerpta Med. Found. Intern. Congr. Ser.* 133: 400–403; 1967.

75. COCHRANE, R. L., AND R. K. MEYER. Delayed implantation in the rat induced by progesterone. *Proc. Soc. Exptl. Biol. Med.* 96: 155–159, 1957.

76. COCHRANE, R. L., M. R. N. PRASAD, AND R. K. MEYER. Delayed nidation in the rat induced by autografts of the hypophysis with a case report "asynchronous" implantation. *Endocrinology* 70: 228–232, 1962.

77. COLE, R. J. Cinemicrographic observations on the trophoblast and zona pellucida of the mouse blastocyst. *J. Embryol. Exptl. Morphol.* 17: 481–490, 1967.

78. COLE, R. J., AND J. PAUL. Properties of cultured pre-implantation mouse and rabbit embryos and cell strains derived from them. In: *Preimplantation Stages of Pregnancy*, edited by G. E. W. Wolstenholme and M. O'Connor. London: Churchill, 1965, p. 82.

79. CONSTANTINIDES, P. Formation of secondary deciduomata in spayed mice and lactating rats. *Endocrinology* 43: 380–388, 1948.

80. COURRIER, R. Le cycle sexuel des mammifères. Etude de la phase folliculaire. *Arch. Biol., Liege* 34: 369–477, 1924.

81. COURRIER, R. Nouvelles recherches sur les hormones ovariennes. Unicisme ou dualisme. *Bull. Histol. Appl.* 5: 393–404, 1928.

82. COURRIER, R. *Endocrinologie de la Gestation*. Paris: Masson, 1945.

83. COURRIER, R. Interactions between estrogens and progesterone. *Vitamins Hormones* 8: 179–214, 1950.

84. COURRIER, R., AND M. BACLESSE. L'équilibre hormonal au cours de la gestation. In: *Troisème Réunion des Endocrinologists de la Langue Française*, edited by G. Masson. Paris: Masson, 1955, p. 1–16.

85. COURRIER, R., AND A. JOST. La prégneninolone assure le maintien de la grossesse chez la lapine gestante castrée. *Compt. Rend. Soc. Biol.* 130: 1162–1163, 1939.

86. COURRIER, R., AND R. KEHL. Sur les gains périvasculaires de la muqueuse utérine chez la lapine. *Bull. Assoc. Anat. 26e Reunion*, 144–150, 1931.

87. COURRIER, R., AND A. PSYCHOYOS. Recherches sur la réaction déciduale expérimentale. *Compt. Rend.* 250: 2486–2488, 1960.

88. CROSS, M. H., AND R. L. BRINSTER. Transmembrane potential of the rabbit blastocyst trophoblast. *Exptl. Cell Res.* 58: 125–127, 1969.

89. CROXATTO, H., S. DIAZ, R. VERA, M. ETHART, AND P. ATRIA. Fertility control in women with a progestagen released in microquantities from subcutaneous capsules. *Am. J. Obstet. Gynecol.* 105: 1135–1138, 1969.

90. DANIEL, J. C., AND R. S. KRISHNAN. Amino acid requirements of growth of the rabbit blastocyst *in vitro*. *J. Cell Physiol.* 70: 155–160, 1967.

91. DASS, C. M., S. MOHLA, AND M. R. PRASAD. Time sequence of action of estrogen on nucleic acid and protein synthesis in the uterus and blastocyst during delayed implantation in the rat. *Endocrinology* 85: 528–536, 1969.

92. DEANESLY, R. Delayed implantation in the stoat (*Mustela mustela*). *Nature* 151: 365, 1943.

93. DEANESLY, R. The corpus luteum hormone during and after ovo-implantation: an experimental study of its mode of action in the guinea-pig. In: *Delayed Implantation*, edited by A. C. Enders. Chicago: Univ. of Chicago Press, 1963, p. 253.

94. DEANESLY, R. Observations on reproduction in the mole (*Talpa europea*). *J. Reprod. Fertility* 9: 385–386, 1965.

95. DEANESLY, R. The role of the fertilized egg: reactions in the guinea-pig uterus at ovo-implantation and after thread traumatization. *J. Reprod. Fertility* 14: 243–248, 1967.

96. DE FEO, V. J. Comparative effectiveness of several methods

for the production of deciduomata in the rat. *Anat. Record* 142: 226, 1962.

97. DE FEO, V. J. Temporal aspect of uterine sensitivity in the pseudopregnant or pregnant rat. *Endocrinology* 72: 305–316, 1963.

98. DE FEO, V. J. Determination of the sensitive period for the induction of deciduomata in the rat by different inducing procedures. *Endocrinology* 73: 488–497, 1963.

99. DE FEO, V. J. Decidualisation. In: *Cellular Biology of the Uterus*, edited by R. M. Wynn. New York: Appleton-Century-Crofts, 1967, p. 192–290.

100. DICKMAN, Z. Can the rat blastocyst survive in the absence of stimulation by the ovarian hormones? *J. Endocrinol.* 42: 605–606, 1968.

101. DICKMAN, Z. Hormonal requirements for the transformation of morula to blastocyst in the rat: effects of long-term ovariectomy. *Steroids* 14: 385–388, 1969.

102. DICKMAN, Z. Shedding of the zona pellucida. *Advan. Reprod. Physiol.* 4: 187–206, 1969.

103. DICKMAN, Z. Effects of progesterone on the development of the rat morula. *Fertility Sterility* 21: 541–548, 1970.

104. DICKMAN, Z., AND V. J. DE FEO. The rat blastocyst during normal pregnancy and during delayed implantation including an observation on the shedding of the zona pellucida. *J. Reprod. Fertility* 13: 3–9, 1967.

105. DICKMAN, Z., AND R. W. NOYES. The fate of ova transferred into the uterus of the rat. *J. Reprod. Fertility* 12: 197–212, 1960.

106. DICKMAN, Z., AND R. W. NOYES. The zona pellucida at the time of implantation. *Fertility Sterility* 12: 310–318, 1961.

107. DICKSON, A. D. Trophoblastic giant cell transformation of mouse blastocysts. *J. Reprod. Fertility* 6: 456–466, 1963.

108. DICKSON, A. D. Effectiveness of 6α-methyl-17-acetoxyprogesterone, in combination with oestradiol benzoate, in inducing delayed implantation in the mouse. *J. Reprod. Fertility* 18: 227–233, 1969.

109. DOYLE, L. L., A. H. GATES, AND R. W. NOYES. Asynchronous transfer of mouse ova. *Fertility Sterility* 14: 215–225, 1963.

110. DUNCAN, G. W., AND A. D. FORBES. Blastocyst survival and nidation in rats treated with oestrogen antagonists. *J. Reprod. Fertility* 10: 161–167, 1965.

111. DZIUK, P. J., AND M. N. RUNNER. Recovery of blastocysts and induction of implantation following artificial insemination of immature mice. *J. Reprod. Fertility* 1: 321–331, 1960.

112. ECKSTEIN, P., M. C. SHELESNYAK, AND E. C. AMOROSO. A survey of the physiology of ovum implantation in mammals. *Mem. Soc. Endocrinol.* 6: 3–12, 1959.

113. EMMENS, G. W. Oestrogenic, anti-oestrogenic and antifertility activities of various compounds. *J. Reprod. Fertility* 9: 277–283, 1965.

114. EMMENS, W. The action of oestrogens. In: *Advances in Reproductive Physiology*, edited by A. McLaren. London: Logos Press, 1967, p. 213.

115. ENDERS, A. C. Fine structural studies of implantation in the armadillo. In: *Delayed Implantation*, edited by A. C. Enders. Chicago: Univ. of Chicago Press, 1963, p. 281.

116. ENDERS, A. C. Electron microscopy of an early implantation stage, with a postulated mechanism of implantation. *Develop. Biol.* 10: 395–410, 1964.

117. ENDERS, A. C. The uterus in delayed implantation. In: *Cellular Biology of the Uterus*, edited by R. M. Wynn. New York: Appleton-Century-Crofts, 1967, p. 151.

118. ENDERS, A. C., AND S. SCHLAFKE. A morphological analysis of the early implantation stages in the rat. *Am. J. Anat.* 120: 185–226, 1967.

119. ENDERS, A. C., AND S. SCHLAFKE. Cytological aspects of trophoblast-uterine interaction in early implantation. *Am. J. Anat.* 125: 1–30, 1969.

120. ENZMANN, E. V., N. R. SAPHIR, AND G. PINCUS. Delayed pregnancy in mice. *Anat. Record* 54: 325–338, 1932.

121. EVANS, H. M., M. E. SIMPSON, W. R. LYONS, AND K. TERPEINER. Anterior pituitary hormones which favor the production of traumatic uterine placentomata. *Endocrinology* 28: 933–945, 1941.

122. EVERETT, J. W. Luteotrophic function of autografts of the rat hypophysis. *Endocrinology* 54: 685–690, 1954.

123. EVERETT, J. W. Maintenance of pregnancy in rats by hypophyseal autografts. *Anat. Record* 124: 287–288, 1956.

124. EVERETT, J. W. Functional corpora lutea maintained for months by autografts of rat hypophysis. *Endocrinology* 58: 786–896, 1956.

125. EVERETT, J. W. Central neural control of reproductive functions of the adenohypophysis. *Physiol. Rev.* 44: 373–431, 1964.

126. EVERETT, J. W., AND C. H. SAWYER. A 24-hour periodicity in the "LH-release" apparatus in female rats disclosed by barbiturate sedation. *Endocrinology* 47: 198–218, 1950.

127. FAINSTAT, T. Extracellular studies of uterus. I. Disappearance of the discrete collagen bundles in endometrial stroma during various reproductive states in the rat. *Am. J. Anat.* 112: 337–370, 1963.

128. FAINSTAT, T., AND G. B. CHAPMAN. Microvilli of endometrial epithelium in relation to ovo-implantation. *Am. J. Obstet. Gynecol.* 112: 852–861, 1965.

129. FAIRMAN, C., AND R. J. RYAN. Diurnal cycle in serum concentrations of follicle-stimulating hormone in men. *Nature* 215: 857, 1967.

130. FAJER, A. B., AND C. A. BARRACLOUGH. Progestin secretion in pseudopregnant, pregnant and androgen-sterilized rats. *Proc. Intern. Congr. Hormonal Steroids, 2nd, Milan. Excerpta Med. Found. Intern. Congr. Ser.* 111: 364, 1966.

131. FAWCETT, D. W. The development of mouse ova under the capsule of the kidney. *Anat. Record* 108: 71–92, 1950.

132. FAWCETT, D. W., G. B. WISLOCKI, AND C. M. WALDO. The development of mouse ova in the anterior chamber of the eye and the abdominal cavity. *Am. J. Anat.* 81: 413–444, 1947.

133. FEHERTY, P., D. M. ROBERTSON, U. B. WAYNFORTH, AND A. E. KELLIE. Changes in the concentration of high affinity oestradiol receptors in rat uterine supernatant preparations during the oestrus cycle, pseudopregnancy, pregnancy, maturation and after ovariectomy. *Biochem. J.* 120: 837–844, 1970.

134. FERRANDO, G., AND A. V. NALBANDOV. Relative importance of histamine and estrogen on implantation in rats. *Endocrinology* 83: 933–937, 1968.

135. FINN, C. A., AND C. W. EMMENS. The effect of dimethylstilboestrol and oestradiol on deciduoma formation in the rat. *J. Reprod. Fertility* 2: 528–529, 1961.

136. FINN, C. A., AND J. R. HINCHLIFFE. Reaction of the mouse during implantation and deciduoma formation as demonstrated by changes in the distribution of alkaline phosphatase. *J. Reprod. Fertility* 8: 331–338, 1964.

137. FINN, C. A., AND J. R. HINCHLIFFE. Histological and histochemical analysis of the formation of implantation chambers in the mouse uterus. *J. Reprod. Fertility* 9: 301–309, 1965.

138. FINN, C. A., AND P. M. KEEN. Studies on deciduomata formation in the rat. *J. Reprod. Fertility* 4: 215–216, 1962.

139. FINN, C. A., AND A. M. LAWN. Transfer of cellular material between the uterine epithelium and trophoblast during early stages of implantation. *J. Reprod. Fertility* 15: 333–336, 1968.

140. FINN, C. A., L. MARTIN, AND J. CARTER. A refractory period following oestrogenic stimulation of cell division in the mouse uterus. *J. Endocrinol.* 44: 121–126, 1969.

141. FINN, C. A., AND A. McLAREN. A study of the early stages of implantation in mice. *J. Reprod. Fertility* 13: 259–267, 1967.

142. FRAENKEL, L. Die Funktion des Corpus luteum. *Arch. Gynaekol.* 68: 438, 1910.

143. FRAENKEL, L., AND F. COHN. Experimentelle Untersuchungen über des Einfluss des Corpus luteum auf die Insertion des Eies. *Anat. Anz.* 20: 294, 1902.

144. GALE, C. C., AND S. M. McCANN. Hypothalamic control of pituitary gonadotrophins impairment in gestation, parturition and milk ejection following hypothalamic lesions. *J. Endocrinol.* 22: 107–117, 1961.

145. GAUTRAY, J. P., P. COUDERC, M. C. COLOMB, H. SIBUT, AND C. MAUREL. Biochemical determination of alkaline phosphatase activity in the human endometrium during the menstrual cycle. *Am. J. Obstet. Gynecol.* 104: 818–822, 1969.

146. GLASSER, S. R. Biochemical studies on a cellular receptor mechanism for uterine sensitivity. *Proc. Pan. Am. Congr. Endocrinol., 6th, Mexico. Excerpta Med. Found. Intern. Congr. Ser.* 99: 335, 1965.

147. GREENWALD, G. S. Ovarian follicular development and pituitary FSH and LH content in the pregnant rat. *Endocrinology* 79: 572–578, 1966.

148. GREENWALD, G. S., AND N. B. EVERETT. The incorporation of S³⁵ methionine by the uterus and ova of the mouse. *Anat. Record* 134: 171–184, 1959.

149. GULYAS, B. J., AND J. C. DANIEL. Incorporation of labelled nucleic acid and protein precursors by diapausing and non-diapausing blastocysts. *Biol. Reprod.* 1: 11–16, 1969.

150. GULYAS, B. J., J. C. DANIEL, JR., AND R. S. KRISHNAN. Incorporation of labelled nucleosides *in vitro* by rabbit and mink blastocysts in the presence of blastokinin or serum. *J. Reprod. Fertility* 20: 255–262, 1969.

151. GWATKIN, R. B. L. Amino-acid requirements for attachment and outgrowth of the mouse blastocyst *in vitro*. *J. Cell Physiol.* 68: 335–344, 1966.

152. GWATKIN, R. B. L. Nutritional requirements for post-blastocyst development in the mouse. *J. Fertility* 14: 101–105, 1969.

153. GWATKIN, R. B. L., AND R. LOVE. Nucleolini of mouse trophoblast cells *in vitro*. *Exptl. Cell Res.* 53: 686–690, 1968.

154. HAFEZ, E. S. E. Gestation in salpingoectomized-ovariectomized progesterone treated rabbits. *Proc. Soc. Exptl. Biol. Med.* 114: 604–607, 1963.

155. HAGENFELDT, K., L. O. PLANTIN, AND E. DICZFALUSY. Trace elements in the human endometrium. I. Zinc, copper, manganese, sodium and potassium concentrations at various phases of the normal menstrual cycle. *Acta Endocrinol.* 65: 541–551, 1970.

156. HALBAN, J. Ueber den Einfluss der Ovarien und die Entwicklung des Genitales. *Mschr. Geburtsh. Gynäkol.* 12: 496–505, 1900.

156a.HALBAN, J. Discussion of L. Fraenkel's report. *Centr. J. Gynäkol.* 28: 657, 1904.

157. HALL, K. Uterine mitosis, alkaline phosphatase and adenosine triphosphatase during development and regression of deciduomata in pseudopregnant mice. *J. Endocrinol.* 44: 91–100, 1969.

158. HARPER, M. J. K. Interference with early pregnancy in rats by estrogen: mechanism of action of dienestrol. *Anat. Record* 162: 433–452, 1968.

159. HARPER, M. J. K. Deciduomal response of the golden hamster uterus. *Anat. Record* 163: 563–573, 1969.

160. HARPER, M. J. K., D. DOWD, AND A. ELLIOT. Implantation and embryonic development in ovariectomized-adrenalectomized hamster. *Biol. Reprod.* 1: 253–257, 1969.

161. HARPER, M. J. K., AND A. L. WALPOLE. Mode of action of I.C.I.46 474 in preventing implantation in rats. *J. Endocrinol.* 37: 83–92, 1967.

162. HARPER, M. J. K., AND A. L. WALPOLE. A new derivative of triphenylethylene; effect on implantation and mode of action in rats. *J. Reprod. Fertility* 13: 101–119, 1967.

163. HARRINGTON, F. E., F. J. BEX, R. L. HELTON, AND J. B. ROACH. The ovulatory effects of follicle stimulating hormone treated with chymotrypsin in chlorpromazine blocked rats. *Acta Endocrinol.* 65: 222–228, 1970.

164. HASHIMOTO, I., D. M. HENRICKS, L. L. ANDERSON, AND R. M. MELAMPY. Progesterone and pregn-4-en-20-ol-3-one in ovarian venous blood during various reproductive states in the rat. *Endocrinology* 82: 333–341, 1968.

165. HASHIMOTO, I., AND W. G. WIEST. Correlation of the secretion of ovarian steroids with function of a single generation of corpora lutea in the immature rat. *Endocrinology* 84: 873–885, 1969.

166. HEALD, P. J., AND J. E. O'GRADY. The uptake of ³H(uridine)

167. HENDRICKX, A., AND D. C. KRAEMER. Pre-implantation stages of baboon embryos. *Anat. Record* 162: 111–120, 1968.

168. HENZL, M., R. F. SMITH, R. E. MAGOUN, AND R. HILL. The influence of estrogens on rabbit endometrium. *Fertility Sterility* 19: 915–935, 1968.

169. HETHERINGTON, C. M. The development of deciduomata induced by two non-traumatic methods in the mouse. *J. Reprod. Fertility* 17: 391–393, 1968.

170. HISAW, F. L. The physiology of menstruation in *Macacus rhesus* monkeys. *Am. J. Obstet. Gynecol.* 29: 638–659, 1935.

171. HUBER, G. C. The development of the albino rat (*Mus norvegicus albinus*). I. From the pronuclear stage to the stage of the mesoderm anlage; end of the first to the end of the ninth day. *J. Morphol.* 26: 247–358, 1915.

172. HUMPHREY, K. W. The induction of implantation in the mouse after ovariectomy. *Steroids* 10: 591–600, 1967.

173. HUMPHREY, K. W. The effects of some anti-oestrogens on the deciduoma reaction and delayed implantation in the mouse. *J. Reprod. Fertility* 16: 201–209, 1968.

174. HUMPHREY, K. W. Observations on transport of ova in the oviduct of the mouse. *J. Endocrinol.* 40: 267–273, 1968.

175. HUMPHREY, K. W., AND L. MARTIN. Attempted induction of deciduomata in mice with mast-cell, capillary permeability and tissue inflammatory factors. *J. Endocrinol.* 42: 129–141, 1968.

176. ISCOVESCO, H. Le lipoide uterostimulant de l'ovaire, Propriétés physiologiques. *Compt. Rend. Soc. Biol.* 63: 104–106, 1912.

177. JACOBSON, M. A., M. K. SANYAL, AND R. K. MEYER. Effect of oestrone on RNA synthesis in pre-implantation blastocyst of gonadotrophin-treated rats. *Endocrinology* 86: 982–987, 1970.

178. JOLLIE, W. P., AND S. A. BENCOSME. Electron microscopic observations on primary decidua formation in the rat. *Am. J. Anat.* 116: 217–236, 1965.

179. KIRBY, D. R. S. Development of mouse eggs beneath the kidney capsule. *Nature* 187: 707–708, 1960.

180. KIRBY, D. R. S. The development of mouse blastocysts transplanted to the scrotal and cryptorchid testis. *J. Anat.* 97: 119–130, 1963.

181. KIRBY, D. R. S. Development of the mouse blastocyst transplanted to the spleen. *J. Reprod. Fertility* 5: 1–12, 1963.

182. KIRBY, D. R. S. The role of the uterus in the early stages of mouse development. In: *Ciba Foundation Symposium on Pre-implantation Stages of Pregnancy*, edited by G. E. W. Wolstenholme and M. O'Connor. London: Churchill, 1965, p. 325–517.

183. KIRBY, D. R. S. Ectopic autografts of blastocysts in mice maintained in delayed implantation. *J. Reprod. Fertility* 14: 515–517, 1967.

184. KIRBY, D. R. S. Immunological aspects of implantation. In: *Ovoimplantation, Human Gonadotrophins and Prolactin*, edited by P. O. Hubinont et al. Basel: Karger, 1970, p. 86–100.

185. KIRBY, D. R. S., AND T. P. COWELL. Trophoblast-host interactions. In: *Epithelial-Mesenchymal Interactions*, edited by R. Fleischmajer. Baltimore: Williams & Wilkins, 1968, p. 64–77.

186. KIRKHAM, W. B. The prolonged gestation in suckling mice. *Anat. Record* 11: 31–40, 1916.

187. KLEBANOFF, S. J. Inactivation of estrogen by rat uterine preparations. *Endocrinology* 76: 301–311, 1965.

188. KNAUER, E. Die Ovarientransplantation. Experimentelle Studie. *Arch. Gynaekol.* 60: 322–376, 1900.

189. KORDON, C. A., AND A. PSYCHOYOS. Effet de lesions hypothalamiques sur l'ovo-implantation du rat. *J. Physiol., Paris* 48: 547–548, 1966.

190. KRAICER, P. F. Secretion of the prenidation estrogen surge by the nonluteal ovarian tissues. *Endocrinology* 85: 177–178, 1969.

191. KRAIGER, P. F., AND M. C. SHELESNYAK. The induction of

deciduomata in the pseudopregnant rat by systemic administration of histamine and histamine releasers. *J. Endocrinol.* 17: 324–328, 1958.

192. KRAICER, P. F., AND M. C. SHELESNYAK. Détermination de la période de sensibilité de l'endomètre à la décidualisation au moyen de déciduomes provoqués par un traitement empruntant la voie vasculaire. *Compt. Rend.* 248: 3213–3215, 1959.

193. KREHBIEL, R. H. Cytological studies of the decidual reaction in the rat during early pregnancy and in the production of deciduomata. *Physiol. Zool.* 10: 212–233, 1937.

194. KREHBIEL, R. H. The effects of lactation on the implantation of ova of a concurrent pregnancy in the rat. *Anat. Record* 81: 43–65, 1941.

195. KREHBIEL, R. H. The production of deciduomata in the pregnant lactating rat. *Anat. Record* 81: 67–77, 1941.

196. KREHBIEL, R. H. The effects of theelin on delayed implantation in the pregnant lactating rat. *Anat. Record* 81: 381–392, 1941.

197. LABHSETWAR, A. P. Differential effects of reserpine on pituitary luteinizing hormone and follicle-stimulating hormone levels in the female rat. *Endocrinology* 81: 357–362, 1967.

198. LARSEN, J. F. Electron microscopy of the implantation site in the rabbit. *Am. J. Anat.* 109: 319–334, 1961.

199. LARSEN, J. F. Electron microscopy of nidation in the rabbit and observations on the human trophoblastic invasion. In: *Ovoimplantation, Human Gonadotropins and Prolactin*, edited by P. O. Hubinont et al. Basel: Karger, 1970, p. 38–51.

200. LATASTE, M. F. *Recherches de Zoo-éthique sur les Mammifères de l'Ordre des Rongeurs.* Cadillac: Vital Raoul Lataste, 1887.

201. LATASTE, M. F. Des variations de durée de la gestation chez les mammifères et des circonstances qui déterminent ces variations: théorie de la gestation retardée. *Compt. Rend. Soc. Biol.* 9: 21–31, 1891.

202. LAURENCE, K. A., AND S. ICHIKAWA. The effects of antiserum to bovine luteinizing hormone on the oestrus cycle and early pregnancy in the female rat. *Intern. J. Fertility* 14: 8–15, 1969.

203. LOBEL, B. L., E. LEVY, E. S. KISCH, AND M. C. SHELESNYAK. Studies on the mechanism of nidation. XXVIII. Experimental investigation on the origin of eosinophilic granulocytes in the uterus of the rat. *Acta Endocrinol.* 55: 451–471, 1967.

204. LOBEL, B. L., L. TIC, AND M. C. SHELESNYAK. Studies on the mechanism of nidation. XVII. Histochemical analysis of decidualisation in the rat. 1. Framework: oestrus cycle and pseudopregnancy. *Acta Endocrinol.* 50: 452–468, 1965.

205. LOBEL, B. L., L. TIC, AND M. C. SHELESNYAK. Studies on the mechanism of nidation. XVII. Histochemical analysis of decidualisation in the rat. 2. Induction. *Acta Endocrinol.* 50: 469–485, 1965.

206. LOBEL, B. L., L. TIC, AND M. C. SHELESNYAK. Studies on the mechanism of nidation. XVII. Histochemical analysis of decidualisation in the rat. 3. Formation of deciduomata. *Acta Endocrinol.* 50: 517–536, 1965.

207. LOEB, L. The production of deciduomata and the relation between the ovaries and the formation of the decidua *J. Am. Med. Assoc.* 50: 1897–1901, 1908.

208. LOEB, L. The experimental production of the maternal part of the placenta in the rabbit. *Proc. Soc. Exptl. Biol. Med.* 5: 102–105, 1908.

209. LONG, J. A., AND H. M. EVANS. The oestrus cycle in the rat and its associated phenomena. *Mem. Univ. Calif.* 6: 1–148, 1922.

210. LUTWAK-MANN, C., AND J. A. McINTOSH. Zinc and carbonic anhydrase in the rabbit uterus. *Nature* 221: 1111–1114, 1969.

211. LYON, R. A., AND W. M. ALLEN. Duration of sensitivity of the endometrium during lactation in the rat. *Am. J. Physiol.* 122: 624–626, 1938.

212. MACDONALD, G. J., D. T. ARMSTRONG, AND R. O. GREEP. Initiation of blastocyst implantation by luteinizing hormone. *Endocrinology* 80: 172–176, 1967.

213. MACDONALD, G. J., AND R. O. GREEP. Role of LH in blastocyst implantation. *Federation Proc.* 25: 316, 1966.

214. MADHWA, RAJ, H. G., M. R. SAIRAM, AND N. R. MOUDGAL. Involvement of luteinizing hormone in the implantation process of the rat. *J. Reprod. Fertility* 17: 335–431, 1968.

215. MANES, C., AND J. C. DANIEL, JR. Quantitative and qualitative aspects of protein synthesis in the pre-implantation rabbit embryo. *Exptl. Cell Res.* 55: 261–268, 1969.

216. MANNING, J. P., B. STEINETZ, AND T. GIANNINA. Decidual alkaline phosphatase activity in the pregnant and pseudopregnant rat. *Ann. NY Acad. Sci.* 166: 482–509, 1969.

217. MANTALENAKIS, S., AND M. KETCHEL. Frequency and extent of delayed implantation in lactating rats and mice. *J. Reprod. Fertility* 12: 391–394, 1966.

218. MARCUS, G. J., P. F. KRAICER, AND M. C. SHELESNYAK. Studies on the mechanism of nidation. II. Histamine-releasing action of pyrathiazine. *J. Reprod. Fertility* 5: 409–415, 1963.

219. MARCUS, G. J., AND M. C. SHELESNYAK. Studies on the mechanism of nidation. XX. Relation of histamine release to oestrogen action in the progestational rat. *Endocrinology* 80: 1028–1031, 1967.

220. MARTIN, L., AND C. A. FINN. Duration of progesterone treatment required for a stromal response to oestradiol-17β in the uterus of the mouse. *J. Endocrinol.* 44: 279–280, 1969.

221. MARTIN, L., AND C. A. FINN. Interactions of oestradiol and progestins in the mouse uterus. *J. Endocrinol.* 48: 109–115, 1970.

222. MARTIN, L., C. A. FINN, AND J. CARTER. Effects of progesterone and oestradiol-17β on the luminal epithelium of the mouse uterus. *J. Reprod. Fertility* 21: 461–469, 1970.

223. MARTINEZ-MANAUTOU, J., V. CORTEZ, J. GINER, R. AZNAR, J. CASASOLA, AND H. W. RUDEL. Low doses of progesterone as an approach to fertility control. *Fertility Sterility* 17: 49–57, 1966.

224. MAYER, G., O. NILSSON, AND S. REINUS. Cell membrane changes of uterine epithelium and trophoblast during blastocyst attachment in rat. *J. Anat.* 126: 43–48, 1967.

225. MAYER, G., A. J. THEVENOT-DULUC, AND J. M. MEUNIER. Déciduomes et ovo-implantation chez la ratte. Les blastocystes ne s'implantent-ils pas au cours de la phase de vie lattente parce que l'endomètre utérin ne peut se décidualiser? *Compt. Rend. Soc. Biol.* 153: 602–604, 1959.

226. McCANN, S. M., AND H. M. FRIEDMAN. The effect of hypothalamic lesions on the secretion of luteotrophin. *Endocrinology* 67: 597–608, 1960.

227. McLAREN, A. Delayed loss of the zona pellucida from blastocyst of suckling mice. *J. Reprod. Fertility* 14: 159–162, 1967.

228. McLAREN, A. A study of blastocysts during delay and subsequent implantation in lactating mice. *J. Endocrinol.* 42: 453–463, 1968.

229. McLAREN, A. Can mouse blastocysts stimulate a uterine response before losing the zona pellucida? *J. Reprod. Fertility* 19: 199–201, 1969.

230. McLAREN, A. The fate of zona pellucida. *J. Embryol. Exptl. Morphol.* 20: 1–19, 1970.

231. McLAREN, A. Early embryo-endometrial relationships. In: *Ovoimplantation, Human Gonadotropins and Prolactin*, edited by P. O. Hubinont et al. Basel: Karger, 1970, p. 18–37.

232. McLAREN, A., AND D. MICHIE. Studies on the transfer of fertilized mouse eggs to uterine foster-mothers. I. Factors affecting the implantation and survival of native and transferred eggs. *J. Exptl. Biol.* 33: 394–416, 1956.

233. McLAREN, A., AND A. K. TARKOWSKI. Implantation of mouse eggs in the peritoneal cavity. *J. Reprod. Fertility* 6: 385–392, 1963.

234. MEANS, A. R., AND T. H. HAMILTON. Early oestrogen action: concomitant stimulations within two minutes of nuclear RNA synthesis and uptake of RNA precursor by the uterus. *Proc. Natl. Acad. Sci. US* 56: 1594–1598, 1966.

235. MEITES, J., C. S. NICOLL, AND P. K. TALWALKER. The central nervous system and the secretion and release of prolactin. In: *Advances in Neuroendocrinology*, edited by A. V. Nalbandov. Urbana: Univ. of Illinois Press, 1963, p. 238–288.

236. MENKE, T. M., AND A. McLAREN. Carbon dioxide production by mouse blastocysts during lactational delay of implantation or after ovariectomy. *J. Endocrinol.* 47: 287–294, 1970.

237. MENKE, T. M., AND A. McLAREN. Mouse blastocysts grown in vivo and in vitro; carbon dioxide production and trophoblast outgrowth. *J. Reprod. Fertility* 23: 117–127, 1970.

238. MENKIN, V. *Dynamics of Inflammation.* New York: Macmillan, 1940.

239. MESTER, J., D. M. ROBERTSON, P. FEHERTY, AND A. E. KELLIE. Determination of high-affinity oestrogen receptor sites in uterine supernatant preparations. *Biochem. J.* 120: 831–836, 1970.

240. MEUNIER, J. M., AND G. MAYER. Autogreffes d'hypophyse et nidation de l'oeuf chez la ratte. *Compt. Rend.* 251: 1043–1045, 1960.

241. MEYER, R. K., AND R. L. COCHRANE. Effect of induced deciduomata on ovo-nidation in progesterone-treated ovariectomized rat. *J. Reprod. Fertility* 4: 67–79, 1962.

242. MEYER, R. K., M. R. N. PRASAD, AND R. L. COCHRANE. Delayed implantation in the rat induced by autografts of the hypophysis. *Anat. Record* 130: 339, 1958.

243. MEYERS, K. Hormonal requirements for the maintenance of oestradiol-induced inhibition of uterine sensitivity in the ovariectomized rat. *J. Endocrinol.* 46: 341–346, 1970.

244. MILLER, B. G., AND C. W. EMMENS. The incorporation of tritiated uridine in the genital tract of the oestrogen-treated mouse. *J. Endocrinol.* 39: 474–484, 1967.

245. MILLER, B. G., AND C. V. EMMENS. The effect of oestradiol and progesterone on the incorporation of tritiated uridine into the genital tract of the mouse. *J. Endocrinol.* 43: 427–436, 1969.

246. MINTZ, B. Synthetic processes and early development in the mammalian egg. *J. Exptl. Zool.* 157: 85–100, 1964.

247. MINTZ, B. Nucleic acid and protein synthesis in the developing mouse embryo. In: *Preimplantation Stages of Pregnancy,* edited by G. E. W. Wolstenholme and M. O'Connor. Boston: Little, Brown, 1965, p. 145–155.

248. MOHLA, S., AND M. R. N. PRASAD. Stimulation of RNA synthesis in the blastocyst and uterus of the rat by adenosine 3′,5′-monophosphate (cyclic AMP). *J. Reprod. Fertility* 23: 327–330, 1970.

249. MOHLA, S., M. R. N. PRASAD, AND C. M. S. DASS. Nucleic acid and protein synthesis in the blastocyst and uterus during early pregnancy in the rat. *Endocrinology* 87: 383–393, 1970.

250. MONESI, V., AND V. SALFI. Macromolecular synthesis during early development in the mouse embryo. *Exptl. Cell Res.* 46: 632–635, 1967.

251. MOORE SMITH, D. The effect on implantation of treating cultured mouse blastocysts with oestrogen in vitro and the uptake of (^{3}H) oestradiol by blastocysts. *J. Endocrinol.* 41: 17–29, 1968.

252. MOSSMAN, H. W. Comparative morphogenesis of the fetal membranes and accessory uterine structures. *Carnegie Inst. Wash. Contrib. Embryol.* 26: 133–247, 1937.

253. MUELLER, G. C. The role of RNA and protein synthesis in estrogen action. In: *Mechanisms of Hormone Action,* edited by P. Karlson. New York: Acad. Press, 1965, p. 228–245.

254. NEAL, E. G., AND R. J. HARRISON. Reproduction in European badger (*Meles meles*). *Trans. Zool. Soc. London* 29: 67–131, 1958.

255. NICHOLAS, J. S. The growth and differentiation of eggs and egg-cylinders when transplanted under the kidney capsule. *J. Exptl. Zool.* 90: 41, 1942.

256. NILSSON, O. Correlation of structure to function of the luminal cell surface in the uterine epithelium of mouse and man. *Z. Zellforsch. Mikroskop. Anat.* 56: 803–808, 1962.

257. NILSSON, O. Structural differentiation of luminal membrane in rat uterus during normal and experimental implantations. *J. Anat.* 125: 152–159, 1966.

258. NILSSON, O. Attachment of rat and mouse blastocysts to uterine epithelium. *Excerpta Med. Found. Intern. Congr. Ser.* 133: 378–384, 1967.

259. NILSSON, O. Some ultrastructural aspects of ovo-implantation. In: *Ovoimplantation, Human Gonadotropins and Prolactin,* edited by P. O. Hubinont et al. Basel: Karger, 1970, p. 52–72.

260. NORDQVIST, S. The synthesis of DNA and RNA in normal human endometrium in short-term incubation *in vitro* and its response to oestradiol and progesterone. *J. Endocrinol.* 48: 17–28, 1970.

261. NOYES, R. W., AND Z. DICKMAN. Relation of ovular age to endometrial development. *J. Reprod. Fertility* 1: 186–196, 1960.

262. NOYES, R. W., Z. DICKMAN, L. DOYLE, AND A. H. GATES. Ovum transfers synchronous and asynchronous in the study of implantation. In: *Delayed Implantation,* edited by A. C. Enders. Chicago: Univ. of Chicago Press, 1963, p. 197–212.

263. NOYES, R. W., A. T. HERTIG, AND J. ROCK. Dating the endometrial biopsy. *Fertility Sterility* 1: 3–25, 1950.

264. NUTTING, E. F., AND R. K. MEYER. Implantation delay, nidation and embryonal survival in rats treated with ovarian hormones. In: *Delayed Implantation,* edited by A. C. Enders. Chicago: Univ. of Chicago Press, 1963, p. 233–252.

265. NUTTING, E. F., AND R. K. MEYER. Effect of oestrone on delay of nidation, implantation and foetal survival in ovariectomized rats. *J. Endocrinol.* 29: 235–242, 1964.

266. O'GRADY, J. E., AND P. J. HEALD. The position and spacing of implantation sites in the uterus of the rat during early pregnancy. *J. Reprod. Fertility* 20: 407–412, 1969.

267. O'GRADY, J. E., P. J. HEALD, AND A. O'HARE. Incorporation of ^{3}H-uridine into the ribonucleic acid of rat uterus during pseudopregnancy and in the presence of I.C.I. 46474 [trans-1-(p-β-dimethylamino-ethoxyphenyl)-1,2-diphenylbut-1-ene]. *Biochem. J.* 119: 609–613, 1970.

268. ORSINI, M. W. Induction of deciduomata in hamster and rat by injected air. *J. Endocrinol.* 28: 119–121, 1963.

269. ORSINI, M. W. Morphological evidence on the intra-uterine career of ovum. In: *Delayed Implantation,* edited by A. C. Enders. Chicago: Univ. of Chicago Press, 1963, p. 155–170.

270. ORSINI, M. W., AND A. McLAREN. Loss of the zona pellucida in mice and the effect of tubal ligation and ovariectomy. *J. Reprod. Fertility* 13: 485–499, 1967.

271. ORSINI, M. W., AND R. K. MEYER. Implantation of the castrate hamster in the absence of exogenous estrogen. *Anat. Record* 134: 619–620, 1959.

272. ORSINI, M. W., AND A. PSYCHOYOS. Implantation of blastocysts transferred into progesterone treated virgin hamsters previously ovariectomized. *J. Reprod. Fertility* 10: 300–301, 1965.

273. PARKES, A. S. The functions of the corpus luteum. II. The experimental production of placentomata in the mouse. *Proc. Roy. Soc., London, Ser. B* 104: 183–188, 1929.

274. PARKES, A. S., AND H. M. BRUCE. Olfactory stimuli in mammalian reproduction. Odor excites neurohormonal responses affecting oestrus, pseudopregnancy and pregnancy in the mouse. *Science* 134: 1049–1054, 1961.

275. PECKHAM, B. M., AND R. R. GREENE. Production of secondary deciduomata in the castrated and lactating rat. *Endocrinology* 41: 273–276, 1947.

276. PECKHAM, B. M., AND R. R. GREENE. Endocrine influence on implantation and deciduomata formation. *Endocrinology* 46: 489–493, 1950.

277. PETRY, G., W. KUHNEL, AND H. M. BEIER. Studies on hormonal regulation of pre-implantation stages in pregnancy. I. Histological topochemical and biochemical studies in the normal rabbit uterus. *Cytobiologie* 2: 1–32, 1970.

278. PHELPS, D. Endometrial vascular reactions and the mechanism of nidation. *Am. J. Anat.* 79: 167, 1946.

279. PIACSEK, B. E., D. T. ARMSTRONG, AND R. O. GREEP. Hypothalamic stimulation of follicle stimulating hormone (FSH) secretion from transplanted pituitaries following exposure to constant light. *Endocrinology* 84: 1184–1192, 1969.

280. PINCUS, G. *The Control of Fertility.* New York: Acad. Press, 1965.

281. PINCUS, G., U. BANIK, AND J. JACQUES. Further studies on implantation inhibitors. *Steroids* 4: 657–676, 1964.

282. POTTS, M. Early development and implantation in the rat. *J. Anat.* 101: 622, 1967.

283. POTTS, M. The ultrastructure of implantation in the mouse. *J. Anat.* 103: 77–90, 1968.

284. POTTS, M. The ultrastructure of egg-implantation. *Advan. Reprod. Physiol.* 4: 241–267, 1969.

285. POTTS, M., AND A. PSYCHOYOS. Evolution de l'ultrastructure des relations ovo-endométriales sous l'influence de l'oestrogène chez la ratte en retard expérimental de nidation. *Compt. Rend.* 264: 370–373, 1967.

286. POTTS, M., AND A. PSYCHOYOS. L'ultrastructure des relations ovo-endométriales au cours du retard expérimental de nidation chez la souris. *Compt. Rend.* 264: 956–958, 1967.

287. PRASAD, M. R. N., C. M. S. DASS, AND S. MOHLA. Action of oestrogen on the blastocyst and uterus in delayed implantation. An autoradiographic study. *J. Reprod. Fertility* 16: 97–104, 1968.

288. PRASAD, M. R. N., AND S. P. KALRA. Mechanism of anti-implantation action of clomiphene. *J. Reprod. Fertility* 13: 59–66, 1967.

289. PRASAD, M. R. N., M. W. ORSINI, AND R. K. MEYER. Nidation in progesterone-treated, estrogen-deficient hamsters, *Mesocricetus auratus* (Waterhouse). *Proc. Soc. Exptl. Biol. Med.* 104: 48–51, 1960.

290. PRENANT, A. La valeur morphologique du corps jaune, son action physiologique et thérapeutique possible. *Rev. Gen. Sci. Pures Appl.* 9: 646–650, 1898.

291. PSYCHOYOS, A. Considérations sur les rapports de la chlorpromazine et de la lutéotrophine hypophysaire. *Compt. Rend. Soc. Biol.* 152: 918–920, 1958.

292. PSYCHOYOS, A. Retard de la nidation de l'oeuf chez la ratte à l'aide de la chlorpromazine; action de l'oestrogène. *Compt. Rend.* 248: 3216–3218, 1959.

293. PSYCHOYOS, A. La réaction déciduale est précédée de modifications précoces de la perméabilité capillaire de l'utérus. *Compt. Rend. Soc. Biol.* 154: 1384–1387, 1960.

294. PSYCHOYOS, A. Nouvelle contribution à l'étude de la nidation de l'oeuf chez la ratte. *Compt. Rend.* 251: 3073–3075, 1960.

295. PSYCHOYOS, A. Perméabilité capillaire et décidualisation utérine. *Compt. Rend.* 252: 1515–1517, 1961.

296. PSYCHOYOS, A. Nouvelles recherches sur l'ovoimplantation. *Compt. Rend.* 252: 2306–2307, 1961.

297. PSYCHOYOS, A. La nidation chez la ratte et la dose d'oestrogène necessaire. *Compt. Rend.* 253: 1616–1617, 1961.

298. PSYCHOYOS, A. Production expérimentale des superimplantations ovulaires chez le rat. *Compt. Rend.* 254: 1504–1506, 1962.

299. PSYCHOYOS, A. Nouvelles remarques sur le déterminisme de l'ovoimplantation. *Compt. Rend.* 254: 4360–4362, 1962.

300. PSYCHOYOS, A. Le déterminisme de l'ovoimplantation; recherches complémentaires. *Compt. Rend.* 254: 775–777, 1962.

301. PSYCHOYOS, A. A study on the hormonal requirements for the ovum implantation in the rat by means of delayed nidation-inducing substances (chlorpromazine, trifluoperazine). *J. Endocrinol.* 27: 337–343, 1962.

302. PSYCHOYOS, A. Précisions sur l'état de "non-réceptivité" de l'utérus. *Compt. Rend.* 257: 1153–1156, 1963.

303. PSYCHOYOS, A. Nouvelles remarques sur l'état utérin de "non-réceptivité." *Compt. Rend.* 257: 1367–1369, 1963.

304. PSYCHOYOS, A. Neurohormonal aspects of implantation. *Excerpta Med. Found. Intern. Congr. Ser.* 83: p. 508–512, 1964.

305. PSYCHOYOS, A. Control de la nidation chez les mammifères. *Arch. Anat. Microscop. Morphol. Exptl.* 54: 85–104, 1965.

306. PSYCHOYOS, A. Recent research on egg-implantation. In: *Ciba Foundation Study Group on Egg Implantation*, edited by G. E. W. Wolstenholme and M. O'Connor. London: Churchill, 1966, p. 4–28.

307. PSYCHOYOS, A. Influence of oestrogen on the loss of the zona pellucida in the rat. *Nature* 211: 5051, 1966.

308. PSYCHOYOS, A. Etude des rélations de l'oeuf et de l'endomètre au cours du retard de la nidation ou des premières phases du processus de la nidation chez la ratte. *Compt. Rend.* 263: 1755–1758, 1966.

309. PSYCHOYOS, A. The hormonal interplay controlling egg-implantation in the rat. In: *Advances in Reproductive Physiology*, edited by A. McLaren. London: Logos Press, 1967, p. 257–277.

310. PSYCHOYOS, A. Mecanismes de la nidation. *Arch. Anat. Microscop. Morphol. Exptl.* 56: 616–623, 1967.

311. PSYCHOYOS, A. The effects of reserpine and chlorpromazine on sexual functions. *J. Reprod. Fertility Suppl.* 4: 47–59, 1968.

312. PSYCHOYOS, A. Hormonal factors governing decidualisation. *Excerpta Med. Found. Intern. Congr. Ser.* 184: 935–938, 1969.

313. PSYCHOYOS, A. Hormonal requirements for egg-implantation. In: *Advances in Biosciences. IV. Mechanisms Involved in Conception*, edited by G. Raspé. London: Pergamon Press, 1969, p. 275–290.

314. PSYCHOYOS, A. Conditionnement hormonal de la receptivité utérine pour la nidation. In: *Ovoimplantation, Human Gonadotropins and Prolactin*, edited by P. O. Hubinont et al. Basel: Karger, 1970, p. 101–107.

315. PSYCHOYOS, A., AND J. J. ALLOITEAU. Castration précoce et nidation de l'oeuf chez la ratte. *Compt. Rend. Soc. Biol.* 254: 46–49, 1962.

316. PSYCHOYOS, A., AND V. BITTON-CASIMIRI. Captation *in vitro* d'un précurseur d'acide ribonucléique (ARN) (uridine 5-³H) par le blastocyste du rat; différences entre blastocystes normaux et blastocystes en diapause. *Compt. Rend.* 268: 188–190, 1969.

317. PSYCHOYOS, A., AND F. C. CHRETIEN. Transfert d'oeufs tubaires dans l'utérus des rattes castrées; effet des hormones ovariennes. *Proc. Intern. Congr. Animale Reprod. Insemination Artificielle, 6ᵉ, Paris* 1: 463–465, 1968.

318. PSYCHOYOS, A., AND P. MANDON. Scanning electron microscopy of the surface of the rat uterine epithelium during delayed implantation. *J. Reprod. Fertility* 26: 137–138, 1971.

319. PSYCHOYOS, A., AND P. MANDON. Etude de la surface de l'epithelium utérin au microscope électronique à balayage. Observations chez la ratte au 4ᵉ et au 5ᵉ jour de la gestation. *Compt. Rend.* 272: 2723–2725, 1971.

320. PSYCHOYOS, A., A. ALBERGA, AND E. E. BAULIEU. Incorporation de l'oestradiol par l'endomètre de rattes castrées prétraitées par différentes séquences hormonales. *Compt. Rend.* 266: 1407–1409, 1968.

321. PSYCHOYOS, A., J. J. ALLOITEAU, AND G. ACKER. Evolution de deux lots de foetus d'âge différent chez la ratte normale traitée par la trifluopérazine. Prolongation fonctionnelle des corps jaunes et rétention des premiers foetus *in utero*. *Compt. Rend.* 256: 4980–4984, 1963.

322. PSYCHOYOS, A., J. J. ALLOITEAU, AND G. ACKER. Delayed parturition in asynchronous implantation in the rat. *J. Reprod. Fertility* 12: 419–420, 1966.

323. REINIUS, S. Ultrastructure of blastocyst attachment in the mouse. *Z. Zellforsch. Mikroskɔ. Anat.* 77: 257–266, 1967.

324. ROSER, S., AND R. B. BLOCH. Variations du taux de la progésterone plasmatique au cours de cycles de 5 jours chez la ratte. *Compt. Rend.* 268: 1318–1320, 1969.

325. ROSSI CARTONI, C., AND G. BIGNAMI. Pre-trauma oestrogen requirements for induction of decidualisation in spayed, progesterone-treated rats. *Acta Endocrinol.* 53: 212–224, 1966.

326. ROSSMAN, I. The decidual reaction in the rhesus monkey (*Macaca mulatta*). I. The epithelial proliferation. *Am. J. Anat.* 66: 277–367, 1940.

327. ROTHCHILD, I. The corpus luteum-pituitary relationship. The association between the cause of luteotrophin secretion and the cause of follicular quiescence during lactation; the basis for a tentative theory of the corpus luteum pituitary relationship in the rat. *Endocrinology* 67: 9–41, 1960.

328. ROTHCHILD, I., AND R. K. MEYER. Studies of the pretrauma factors necessary for placentomata formation in the rat. *Physiol. Zool.* 15: 216–223, 1942.

329. RUNNER, M. N. Development of mouse-eggs in the anterior chamber of the eye. *Anat. Record* 98: 1–13, 1947.

330. SALDARINI, R. J., AND J. M. YOCHIM. Metabolism of the uterus of the rat during pseudopregnancy and its regulation by oestrogen and progestogen. *Endocrinology* 80: 453–466, 1967.

331. SALDARINI, R. J., AND J. M. YOCHIM. Glucose utilisation by endometrium of the uterus of the rat during early pseudopregnancy and its regulation by estrogen and progestogen. *Endocrinology* 82: 511–512, 1968.

332. SANANES, N., AND A. PSYCHOYOS. Effet de l'actinomycine-D sur le developpement du déciduome chez la ratte. *Compt. Rend.* 271: 430–433, 1970.

333. SANYAL, M. K., AND R. K. MEYER. Effect of estrone on DNA synthesis in preimplantation blastocysts of gonadotropin-treated immature rats. *Endocrinology* 86: 976–981, 1970.

334. SCHALLY, A. V. Hypothalamic regulation of FSH and LH secretion. In: *Research in Reproduction*, edited by R. G. Edwards. London: Intern. Planned Parenthood Federation, 1970, p. 2–3.

335. SCHAYER, R. W. Histidine decarboxylase in mast cells. *Ann. NY Acad. Sci.* 103: 164–178, 1963.

336. SCHLOUGH, J. S. Delayed implantation in the rat induced by atropine. *Biol. Reprod.* 1: 315–319, 1969.

337. SCHLOUGH, J. S., AND R. K. MEYER. The effect of antiestrogens on pre-implantation capillary permeability in the rat. *Fertility Sterility* 20: 439–442, 1969.

338. SCHWARTZ, N. B., AND I. ROTHCHILD. Changes in pituitary LH concentration during pseudopregnancy in the rat. *Proc. Soc. Exptl. Biol. Med.* 116: 107–110, 1964.

339. SCHWARTZ, N. B., AND W. L. TALLEY. Daily measurement of pituitary LH content during pregnancy in the rat: Do cyclic changes persist? *J. Reprod. Fertility* 15: 39–45, 1968.

340. SCOMMEGNA, A., N. G. PANDYA, C. M. LEE, M. CHRIST, AND M. R. COHEN. Intrauterine administration of progesterone by slow releasing device. *Fertility Sterility* 21: 201–210, 1970.

342. SEGAL, S. J., AND W. O. NELSON. An orally active compound with antifertility effects in rats. *Proc. Soc. Exptl. Biol. Med.* 98: 431–436, 1958.

343. SEGAL, S. J., AND W. SCHER. Estrogens, nucleic acids and protein synthesis in uterine metabolism. In: *Cellular Biology of the Uterus*, edited by R. M. Wynn. New York: Appleton-Century-Crofts, 1967, p. 114–150.

344. SEGAL, S. J., O. W. DAVIDSON, AND K. WADA. Role of RNA in the regulatory action of estrogen. *Proc. Natl. Acad. Sci. US* 54: 782–787, 1965.

345. SEGAL, S. J., K. WADA, AND E. SCHUCHNER. Role of RNA in estrogen-induced nidation of blastocysts. *Proc. Ann. Meeting Endocrine Soc., 47th*, 1965, p. 26.

346. SHAIKH, A. A., AND G. E. ABRAHAM. Measurement of estrogen surge during pseudopregnancy in rats by radioimmunoassay. *Biol. Reprod.* 1: 378–380, 1969.

347. SHELESNYAK, M. C. Aspects of reproduction. Some experimental studies on the mechanism of ovo-implantation in the rat. *Recent Progr. Hormone Res.* 13: 269–322, 1957.

348. SHELESNYAK, M. C. Fall in uterine histamine associated with ovum implantation in pregnant rats. *Proc. Soc. Exptl. Biol. Med.* 100: 380–381, 1959.

349. SHELESNYAK, M. C. Nidation of the fertilized ovum. *Endeavour* 19: 81–86, 1960.

350. SHELESNYAK, M. C. Decidualisation: the decidua and the deciduoma. *Perspectives Biol. Med.* 5: 503–518, 1962.

351. SHELESNYAK, M. C., AND P. F. KRAICER. Time-limits of uterine sensitivity to decidualisation during progestation. *Proc. Intern. Congr. Endocrinol., 1st, Copenhagen, 1960*, p. 547.

352. SHELESNYAK, M. C., AND P. F. KRAICER. A physiological method for inducing experimental decidualization of the rat uterus: standardization and evaluation. *J. Reprod. Fertility* 2: 438–446, 1961.

353. SHELESNYAK, M. C., AND P. F. KRAICER. The role of oestrogen in nidation. In: *Delayed Implantation*, edited by A. C. Enders. Chicago: Univ. of Chicago Press, 1963, p. 265–279.

354. SHELESNYAK, M. C., AND L. TIC. Studies on the mechanism of decidualization. IV. Synthetic processes in the decidualizing uterus. *Acta Endocrinol.* 42: 465–472, 1963.

355. SHELESNYAK, M. C., AND L. TIC. Studies on the mechanism of decidualisation. V. Suppression of synthetic processes of the uterus (DNA, RNA and protein) following inhibition of decidualisation by an antioestrogen, ethanoxytriphetol. *Acta Endocrinol.* 43: 462–468, 1963.

356. SHELESNYAK, M. C., P. F. KRAICER, AND G. H. ZEILMAKER. Studies on the mechanism of decidualisation. I. The oestrogen surge of pseudopregnancy and prograviddity and its role in the process of decidualisation. *Acta Endocrinol.* 42: 225–232, 1963.

357. SHORT, R. V., AND M. T. HAY. Delayed implantation in the roe deer (*Capreolus capreolus*). *J. Reprod. Fertility* 9: 372–374, 1965.

358. SHORT, R. V., AND K. YOSHINAGA. Hormonal influences of tumour growth in the uterus of the rat. *J. Reprod. Fertility* 14: 287–293, 1967.

359. SMITH, M. J., AND G. B. SHARMAN. Development of dormant blastocysts induced by oestrogen in the ovariectomized marsupial *Macropus eugenii*. *Australian J. Biol. Sci.* 22: 171–180, 1969.

360. SMITHBERG, M., AND M. N. RUNNER. The induction and maintenance of pregnancy in prepuberal mice. *J. Exptl. Zool.* 133: 441–457, 1956.

361. SMITHBERG, M., AND M. N. RUNNER. Retention of blastocysts in nonprogestational uteri of mice. *J. Exptl. Zool.* 143: 21–30, 1960.

362. SPAZIANI, E. Relationship between early vascular responses and growth in the rat uterus; stimulation of cell division by estradiol and vasodilating amines. *Endocrinology* 72: 180–191, 1963.

363. SPAZIANI, E., AND R. P. SUDDICK. Hexose transport and blood flow rate in the uterus: effects of oestradiol, pyromycin and actinomycin D. *Endocrinology* 81: 205–212, 1967.

364. SPAZIANI, E., AND M. C. SZEGO. Further evidence for mediation by histamine of oestrogenic stimulation of the rat uterus. *Endocrinology* 64: 713–723, 1959.

365. STONE, G. M., AND C. W. EMMENS. The action of oestradiol and dimethylstilboestrol on early pregnancy and deciduoma formation in the mouse. *J. Endocrinol.* 29: 137–145, 1964.

366. SURANI, M. A. H. *The Metabolism of Carbohydrate by Rat Uterus Tissue in Early Pregnancy* (M.Sc. thesis). Scotland: Univ. of Strathclyde, 1970.

367. SURANI, M. A. H., AND P. J. HEALD. The metabolism of glucose by rat uterus tissue in early pregnancy. *Acta Endocrinol.* 77: 16–24, 1971.

368. SZEGO, C. M. Role of histamine in mediation of hormone action. *Federation Proc.* 24: 1343–1352, 1965.

369. TACHI, S., C. TACHI, AND H. R. LIDNER. Ultrastructural features of blastocyst attachment and trophoblastic invasion in the rat. *J. Reprod. Fertility* 21: 37–56, 1970.

370. TALWAR, G. P., S. J. SEGAL, A. EVANS, AND O. DAVINSON. The binding of oestradiol in the uterus: a mechanism for derepression of RNA synthesis. *Proc. Natl. Acad. Sci. US* 52: 1059–1066, 1964.

371. TAUBERT, H. D. Maintenance of delayed implantation in the rat by single dose injection of depot 6-α-methyl-17-acetoxy-progesterone. *Endocrinology* 80: 218–220, 1967.

372. TERENIUS, L. The effect of steroidal hormones on the binding of 17β-estradiol by the mouse uterus and vagina. *Steroids* 13: 311–325, 1969.

373. TERZAKIS, J. A. The nucleolar channel system of human endometrium. *J. Cell Biol.* 27: 293–304, 1965.

374. TOFT, D., AND J. GORSKI. A receptor molecule for estrogens; isolation from the rat uterus and preliminary characterization. *Proc. Natl. Acad. Sci. US* 55: 1574–1581, 1966.

375. UCHIDA, K., M. KADOWAKI, AND T. MIYAKE. Ovarian secretion of progesterone and 20-α-hydroxypregn-4-en-3-one

during rat estrous cycle in chronological relation to pituitary release of luteinizing hormone. *Endocrinol. Japon.* 16: 227–237, 1969.

376. VARAVUDHI, P. Induction by androgens of nidation in pregnant rats deprived of gonadotrophin secretion by trifluoperazine injections and by lactation. *J. Endocrinol.* 43: 237–245, 1969.

377. VARAVUDHI, P., B. L. LOBEL, AND M. C. SHELESNYAK. Studies on the mechanism of nidation. xxiii. Effect of ergocornine in pregnant rats during experimentally induced delayed nidation. *J. Endocrinol.* 34: 425–430, 1966.

378. VICKERY, B. H., G. I. ERICKSON, J. P. BENNET, N. S. MUELLER, AND J. K. HALEBLIAN. Antifertility effects in the rabbit by continuous low release of progestin from an intrauterine device. *Biol. Reprod.* 3: 154, 1970.

379. VITTORELLI, M. L., R. A. P. HARRISON, AND C. LUTWAK-MANN. *Nature* 214: 980, 1967.

380. VOKAER, R. Recherches histophysiologiques sur l'endomètre du rat, en particulier, sur le conditionnement hormonal de ses propriétés athrocytaires. *Arch. Biol., Liege* 63: 1–84, 1952.

381. VOKAER, R., AND F. LEROY. Experimental study on local factors in the process of ova implantation in the rat. *Am. J. Obstet. Gynecol.* 83: 141–148, 1962.

382. VON BERSWORDT-WALLRABE, I., H. F. GELLER, AND U. HERLYN. Temporal aspects of decidual cell reaction. ii. Peak of sensitivity to decidual cell reaction in lactogenic hormone treated rats under rhythmical and permanent illumination. *Acta Endocrinol.* 47: 314–320, 1964.

383. VON SPEE, F. Die Implantation des Meerschweincheneies in die Uteruswand. *Z. Morphol. Anthropol.* 3: 130–182, 1901.

384. WARREN, R. H., AND A. C. ENDERS. An electron microscope study of the rat endometrium during delayed implantation. *Anat. Record* 148: 177–195, 1964.

385. WEICHERT, C. K. Production of placentomata in normal and ovariectomized guinea-pigs and albino rats. *Proc. Soc. Exptl. Biol. Med.* 25: 490–491, 1928.

386. WEICHERT, C. K. The experimental shortening of delayed pregnancy in the albino rat. *Anat. Record* 77: 31–48, 1940.

387. WEICHERT, C. K. The effectiveness of estrogen in shortening delayed pregnancy in the rat. *Anat. Record* 81: 106, 1941.

388. WEICHERT, C. K. The experimental control of prolonged pregnancy in the lactating rat by means of estrogen. *Anat. Record* 83: 1–17, 1942.

389. WEITLAUF, H. M. Temporal changes in protein synthesis by mouse blastocysts transferred to ovariectomized recipients. *J. Exptl. Zool.* 171: 1969.

390. WEITLAUF, H. M. Protein synthesis by blastocysts in the uteri and oviducts of intact and hypophysectomized mice. *J. Exptl. Zool.* 176: 35, 1971.

391. WEITLAUF, H. M., AND G. S. GREENWALD. A comparison of ³⁵S-methionine incorporation by the blastocysts of normal and delayed implanting mice. *J. Reprod. Fertility* 10: 203–208, 1965.

392. WEITLAUF, H. M., AND G. S. GREENWALD. A comparison of the *in vivo* incorporation of ³⁵S-methionine by two-celled mouse eggs and blastocysts. *Anat. Record* 159: 249–253, 1967.

393. WEITLAUF, H. M., AND G. S. GREENWALD. Survival of blastocysts in the uteri of ovariectomized mice. *J. Reprod. Fertility* 17: 515–520, 1968.

394. WEITLAUF, H. M., AND G. S. GREENWALD. Influence of estrogen and progesterone on the incorporation of ³⁵S-methionine by blastocysts in ovariectomized mice. *J. Exptl. Zool.* 169: 463–470, 1968.

395. WHITTEN, W. K. Endocrine studies on delayed implantation in lactating mice. *J. Endocrinol.* 13: 1–6, 1955.

396. WHITTEN, W. K. Endocrine studies on delayed implantation in lactating mouse. Role of the pituitary in implantation. *J. Endocrinol.* 16: 435–440, 1958.

397. WILSON, I. B. A new factor associated with the implantation of the mouse egg. *J. Reprod. Fertility* 5: 281–282, 1963.

398. WILSON, I. B. A tumor tissue analogue of the implanting mouse embryo. *Proc. Zool. Soc. London* 141: 137–151, 1963.

399. WILSON, I. B., AND D. M. POTTS. Melanoma invasion in the mouse uterus. *J. Reprod. Fertility* 22: 429, 1970.

400. WILSON, I. B., AND M. S. R. SMITH. Isotopic labeling of the mouse blastocyst. *J. Reprod. Fertility* 16: 305–307, 1968.

401. WOOD, J. C., AND A. PSYCHOYOS. Activité utérine de certains enzymes hydrolytiques au cours de la pseudogestation chez la ratte. *Compt. Rend.* 265: 141–144, 1967.

402. WOOD, J. C., E. A. WILLIAMS, D. L. BARLEY, AND R. H. GODWELL. The activity of hydrolytic enzymes in the human endometrium during the menstrual cycle. *J. Obstet. Gynecol.* 76: 724–728, 1969.

403. YASUKAWA, J. J., AND R. K. MEYER. Effect of progesterone and oestrone on the pre-implantation and implantation stages of embryo development in the rat. *J. Reprod. Fertility* 11: 245–255, 1966.

404. YOCHIM, J. M., AND V. J. DE FEO. Hormonal control of the onset, magnitude and duration of uterine sensitivity in the rat by steroid hormones of the ovary. *Endocrinology* 72: 317–326, 1963.

405. YOCHIM, J. M., AND R. J. SALDARINI. Glucose utilisation by the myometrium during early pseudopregnancy in the rat. *J. Reprod. Fertility* 20: 481–489, 1969.

406. YOSHINAGA, K. Effect of local application of ovarian hormones on the delay in implantation in lactating rats. *J. Reprod. Fertility* 2: 35–41, 1961.

407. YOSHINAGA, K. Progestin secretion by the rat ovary. *Arch. Anat. Microscop. Morphol. Exptl.* 56: 273–280, 1967.

408. YOSHINAGA, K., AND C. E. ADAMS. Delayed implantation in spayed, progesterone treated adult mouse. *J. Reprod. Fertility* 12: 593, 1966.

409. YOSHINAGA, K., R. A. HAWKINS, AND J. F. STOCKER. Estrogen secretion by the rat ovary *in vivo* during the estrous cycle and pregnancy. *Endocrinology* 85: 103, 1969.

410. ZEILMAKER, G. H. Experimental studies on the effects of ovariectomy and hypophysectomy on blastocyst implantation in the rat. *Acta Endocrinol.* 44: 355–366, 1963.

411. ZEILMAKER, G. H. Quantitative studies on the effect of the suckling stimulus on blastocyst implantation in the rat. *Acta Endocrinol.* 46: 483–492, 1964.

CHAPTER 41

Hormonal maintenance of pregnancy

R. B. HEAP

J. S. PERRY

J. R. G. CHALLIS

A. R. C. Institute of Animal Physiology,
Babraham, Cambridge, United Kingdom

CHAPTER CONTENTS

IN THIS CHAPTER the concern is with the hormonal conditions that apply in maintaining the physiological state of the animal during a normal pregnancy. *Pregnancy* is defined as the period from fertilization to parturition, and the emphasis is on the role of hormones in maintaining gestation and in the arrest of the estrous or menstrual cycles. Aspects of fertilization, blastocyst nutrition, implantation, and parturition are the subjects of other chapters.

The amount of literature on this subject is large; to limit the bibliography to manageable proportions, not all the original sources consulted have been cited, and the reader is referred to review articles in which individual references can be found.

The physiological changes affecting the female reproductive tract during pregnancy are those that control the transport of fertilized ova through the oviduct, the retention of the embryo within the uterus, the formation and function of the placenta, and the final expulsion of the fetus. In 1901 the role of the ovary in the maintenance of pregnancy was first intimated by Fränkel's demonstration that the corpus luteum is necessary for implantation and the maintenance of embryos in the uterus. It was some 20 years later that the hormonal nature of pregnancy maintenance became evident. [For history of discovery in this field, see (277).]

The state of pregnancy affects not only the reproductive tract, but also induces other maternal adjustments. It is difficult to distinguish between changes that represent physiological adaptation of the organism to the condition of pregnancy and others that contribute more directly to the optimal development of the embryo. Although our present concern is with changes in the female reproductive tract, general effects, such as hemodynamics, electrolyte balance, and appetite, are relevant to the consideration of what we have defined as normal pregnancy and are briefly considered in the succeeding sections.

It has long been recognized that a first requirement of pregnancy in eutherian mammals, with which we are primarily concerned, is a prolongation of the estrous cycle and a delay in the recurrence of ovulation. There has been speculation as to whether the course of events in pregnancy diverged from the normal cycle immediately at the time of fertilization or at some subsequent stage. In recent years this has come to be thought of as the maternal recognition of gestation, and it has been shown that in some species, at least, it occurs relatively late and that the embryos occupy the uterus for some time before ovarian function is modified in response to their presence. One of the best illustrations of this phenomenon is to be found in the sheep, in which ovulation is resumed at the normal time unless embryos have been present in the uterus up to within a day or two before. The divergence between the pregnant and nonpregnant animal becomes clear at the time of implantation. It has generally been assumed that the passage of the eggs down the oviduct is unaffected by their being fertilized, but in the horse unfertilized eggs are apparently retained in the oviduct, which is presumably able by some means to discriminate between fertilized and unfertilized eggs (367). To this extent maternal recognition of pregnancy may occur very early in gestation.

The duration of pregnancy is remarkably constant within a species and remarkably variable among species. Gestation length can be shortened by accidents leading to abortion, and in certain cases it can be prolonged, as in some genetic abnormalities or under the influence of specific dietary factors (173, 218) and in human anencephaly (14). With respect to the species differences in gestation length, the shortest and longest recorded are those of the hamster (14 days) and the elephant (22 months). In the broadest term gestation length is related to the normal adult body size of the species, but this relationship is not a consistent one. Pregnancy lasts about a year in the largest whales, as it does in the horse. At the other end of the scale, gestation is 30–32 days in the rabbit, whereas, in the viscachas of similar body weight, pregnancy lasts 145 days (20). These inconsistencies are related to differences in the stage of development the fetuses reach before birth but can only partially be accounted for in this way.

ENDOCRINE ORGANS IN PREGNANCY

Ovary

The formation of the corpus luteum and its maintenance for the whole or part of pregnancy, the secretory activity of this transient endocrine gland, and coincidental changes in follicles and interstitial tissue constitute the main ovarian events associated with the transport of the fertilized egg into the uterus, with implantation, and with placentation. The corpus luteum, a dominant feature in mammalian pregnancy, receives special emphasis because of its role in the secretion of progesterone, the most active of naturally occurring gestagens. It has become clear that we must consider as distinct phenomena the survival of the corpus luteum as a histological entity, its function in terms of progesterone synthesis, and its activity in terms of the secretion of

progesterone and other metabolites. (The abbreviation CL is used for the corpus luteum, and "lutein" or "luteal" is used as the adjective.)

FORMATION OF THE CORPUS LUTEUM. A corpus luteum is invariably formed from the ruptured follicle after ovulation. There is thus normally one CL of pregnancy in monotocous species, such as man, whereas there may be as many as 20 or 30 in a polytocous species, such as the pig. In some species a variable number of follicles are converted into accessory CL either at the time of ovulation or during the course of pregnancy. In all cases studied so far these CL also secrete progesterone. The total quantity of functional lutein tissue in the ovary during part of pregnancy may thus be made up in several ways. In some cases, as is usual in man, a single follicle ovulates and is converted into a "corpus luteum of pregnancy," which thereafter comprises the sole progesterone-producing tissue of the ovary. In another monotocous species, the mare, the CL of pregnancy is supplemented by several others that are formed possibly by ovulation (10) during the fifth week of pregnancy. The sheep and the cow have typically one or two young, and the number of CL in pregnancy closely corresponds to the number of follicles that ovulate. In a number of species, such as the mountain viscacha, accessory CL are formed from atretic follicles during the course of pregnancy. In the elephant shrew (Insectivora) and in the plains viscacha (Hystricomorpha), large numbers of follicles ovulate and give rise to a mass of CL, but only a few blastocysts, normally two, implant and develop. In the water shrew the whole ovary, with the exception of a peripheral region into which the oocytes are crowded, is converted into a solid block of luteal tissue [(296); for further details, see (9, 91, 288)].

In many species follicular growth is not suppressed during pregnancy. A notable case is that of the guinea pig, in which ovulation can be induced at any stage of pregnancy by a single intravenous injection of 50 IU chorionic gonadotrophin (315). In some animals mating (and presumably estrus) during pregnancy is not uncommon (91), but cases of superfetation have very rarely been reported.

During the follicular phase of the cycle the active endocrine tissue is that of the theca interna, the granulosa being called into play only after the disruption of the basement membrane that separates theca and granulosa and the subsequent vascularization of the latter. The thecal cells are the main, and probably the only, source of estrogen in the follicular phase, and they may also undergo morphological changes and begin to produce progesterone before ovulation. After ovulation and the formation of the corpus luteum the bulk of lutein secretory tissue is apparently derived from the granulosa in all species so far examined. Thecal elements also enter into the composition of the CL in some, probably most, species as a result of the invasion of the granulosa by the thecal blood supply and attached thecal cells. In those species in which the CL secretes both progesterone and estrogen, the former steroid may be contributed by the cells of granulosa origin and the latter by the cells derived from the theca (338). The problem of distinguishing between the two cell types has precluded an accurate assessment of their relative contributions to the formation of the CL in most species.

The actively secreting lutein cell has a characteristic appearance under optical microscopy, as well as under electron microscopy (39, 43, 73). The cytoplasm of these large, rounded cells is packed with whorls of smooth endoplasmic reticulum, which mainly replaces the rough form. The ribosomes of the developing CL are more dispersed on the membrane, and the cisternal endoplasmic reticulum is more tubular. The most extensive development of the smooth endoplasmic reticulum is found in the cells of the CL of pregnancy, which form closed networks of tubules often referred to as "fenestrated cisternae." These features, together with the accumulation of a large number of lipid droplets and an increase in the size of the Golgi complex, are characteristic of all steroid-secreting cells. It is believed that the lipid droplets constitute intracellular stores of steroid precursors, including cholesterol and cholesterol esters, that may be depleted in conditions of maximum steroid synthesis. During regression of the CL, the smooth endoplasmic reticulum loses its tubular appearance and becomes vesicular, and lipid and membrane-bound granules resembling lysosomes accumulate (73). After losing its endocrine activity, the CL of pregnancy is always greatly reduced in size but persists as a corpus albicans for a varying time before it is eliminated from the structure of the ovary.

A well-developed vascular and lymphatic drainage soon becomes established in the newly formed CL. A complex network of capillaries is formed in close proximity to, but separated by a pericapillary space from, the lutein cells. Gaps in the capillary endothelium are found, notably in the CL of the sheep, when large amounts of progesterone are being secreted. Attention has been drawn to the high rate of ovarian lymph flow in this species, and the filtration rate of proteins per unit weight of tissue in the CL has been calculated at about 1,500 mg/g, compared with about 30 mg/g in the liver, which has one of the most permeable vascular beds in the body (261). The permeability of the lutein capillaries may be directly influenced by the concentration of progesterone within the CL (261). The concentrations of progesterone in the ovarian lymphatic drainage may reach values comparable with those in ovarian venous plasma. After correcting for the rate of lymph flow, however, this route of secretion could account for not more than 20% of the daily ovarian secretion, the major portion of which was transported by the vascular route (220).

Apart from the follicles and CL, the ovary contains a third steroid-secreting tissue, the interstitial tissue, which is derived during adult life from the thecal cells of atretic follicles (154). The prominence of this tissue varies greatly in different species. It is perhaps most prominent in the ovaries of the rabbit, where it is most active (see below), whereas it is absent or inconspicuous in many species, such as the sheep and pig.

GROWTH AND LIFE-SPAN OF THE CORPUS LUTEUM. The life-span and growth of the CL of pregnancy may follow one of several patterns, according to the species. It may survive longer and grow larger than the CL of the normal cycle (as in the rat, mouse, guinea pig, and hamster). In other species the CL of pregnancy is maintained, without undergoing any additional growth (as in the domestic animals, sheep, cow, and pig, and in the human female), for a longer period than is that of the estrous cycle. Yet other eutherian species, notably among the Mustelidae and in the dog, resemble the marsupials in that the CL of pregnancy is indistinguishable from that of the cycle in terms of its life-span and growth. In the ferret, for instance, the CL of pregnancy is similar to that of pseudopregnancy in size and duration of function. In marsupials the life-span during pregnancy may be even shorter than that of the estrous cycle, except in one species, the grey kangaroo, *Macropus canguru*, in which it is slightly prolonged (332). Examples of these three patterns of growth and function are depicted for the hamster, pig, and ferret, respectively, in Figure 1.

In the rat (227, 374) the CL of pregnancy resembles that of pseudopregnancy until the 10th day after mating. It maintains this size for 3–4 days, after which there is a sudden acceleration in growth, presumably because of a placental luteotrophic stimulation, and a maximum size is reached 4–5 days later (gestation, 21 days). In the guinea pig the CL of the cycle reaches its maximum size in 9 or 10 days, but in pregnancy its growth continues and its maximum size is attained shortly after the 20th day (gestation, 68–70 days). The fact that the CL grows at about the same rate in hysterectomized, nonpregnant, as well as in hypophysectomized, pregnant, animals implies that in this species, unlike the rat, luteal growth depends more on the suppression of a uterine inhibitory factor than on the production of a pituitary or placental luteotrophin (163). The regulation of the life-span of the CL in nonpregnant guinea pigs by a uterine luteolytic mechanism has been postulated (125), and the developing embryo probably permits the growth of the CL to continue in pregnancy by eliminating the luteolytic effect of the uterus in a way comparable with that demonstrated in the sheep (259).

The sheep (177) and pig (56) are examples of species in which the CL grows to about the same size in the nonpregnant and pregnant animal. In the sheep the CL is unaffected by the presence of embryos in the uterus during the first 12 days after mating. Thereafter its further survival depends on the embryo, which either "protects" it from the luteolytic influence of the uterus or prevents the uterus from acquiring luteolytic properties. This "antiluteolytic" effect of the embryo has the very important role of prolonging the life of the CL though not affecting its growth. It seems that the state of pregnancy is in this manner signaled to the ewe on or about the 13th day and before the time of attachment to the endo-

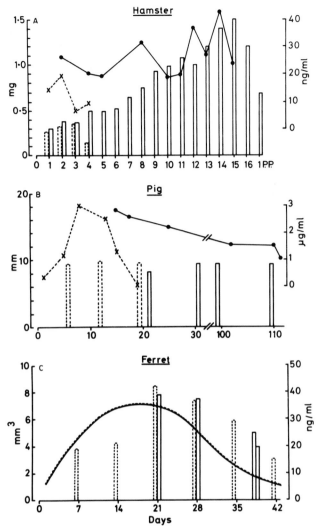

FIG. 1. Growth and life-span of CL, and plasma progesterone levels, in pregnancy (*solid lines* and *solid columns*) and in the nonpregnant animal (*dashed lines* and *dashed columns*). P.P., postpartum. *A*: hamster; gestation length, 16 days. Average CL size measured by weight (mg). Plasma progesterone levels measured in peripheral plasma (ng/ml). [From Lukaszenska & Greenwald (229).] *B*: pig; gestation length, 113 days. Average CL size measured by diameter (mm). Plasma progesterone levels measured in ovarian venous plasma (μg/ml). [From Masuda et al. (241).] *C*: ferret; gestation length, 42 days. Average CL size measured by the cube of the diameter (mm³). Plasma progesterone levels measured in peripheral plasma (ng/ml). [From B. T. Donovan and J. Oxbrow, personal communication; J. Hammond, Jr. and R. B. Heap, unpublished data; Hammond & Marshall (148).]

metrium, which occurs some 2 days later (44). The nature of the mechanism by which the embryo overcomes the uterine luteolytic factor is not yet known. Evidence suggesting a local effect, in that unilateral luteal regression is induced in pregnant sheep by the presence of an isolated, nongravid uterine horn, has been obtained. Further, the antiluteolytic capacity develops at a particular time of embryonic life; it is species specific and survives the manipulations of homogenization, freezing, and thawing. Thus daily intrauterine infusions of 14-day

sheep embryos homogenized and stored at −20 C caused a significant prolongation of the life-span of the CL (319).

In a sheep bearing a single embryo, the nongravid horn can retain its luteolytic capacity for at least the first 50 days of pregnancy, provided it is isolated from the horn occupied by the developing embryo. In the normal animal, however, the fetal membranes of the single embryo rapidly grow into both uterine horns and abolish the luteolytic effect of the nongravid horn. In the pig a minimum of four embryos in the uterus is normally required to maintain the functional activity of the CL beyond early pregnancy (292). This is achieved by a mechanism broadly similar to that found in the sheep, except that the isolated, nongravid horn remains lytic for only about the first 16 days of pregnancy (259).

Further variants of the growth and function of the CL of pregnancy are to be found in species that exhibit the phenomenon of "delayed implantation" or "embryonic diapause" (91). A special case is that of the marsupials, in which a blastocyst may remain dormant in the uterus for many months while the "joey" is suckled in the pouch (331, 332). This delay of implantation associated with lactation is observed to a lesser extent in eutherian mammals, as with the facultative delay found in lactating rats and mice mated at the postpartum estrus. In these animals the delay is proportionate to the number of young suckled and does not usually occur with litters of less than five in the rat or three in the mouse (45). The lifespan of the CL can be considerably prolonged in lactating marsupials. In the wallaby, *Setonyx brachyurus*, which in the absence of lactation has a 27-day pregnancy, the period of delay during which the CL of pregnancy persists when there is a joey in the pouch can be 4–6 months. In rats and mice the prolongation is considerably less but may be as long as 20 days, almost the length of a normal gestation period.

In some animals delayed implantation is not facultative, but obligatory. The blastocysts remain unimplanted in the uterus for long intervals, and postimplantation pregnancy may occupy less than a quarter of the time between fertilization and parturition. These species are found in the orders, Artiodactyla, Edentata, and Carnivora (Mustelidae, Pinnipedia, and Ursidae) (91).

In some animals that show delayed implantation, the CL grows and probably increases in secretory activity at the end of the period of delay (115). This occurs in the armadillo (209), in the badger (57), and in the spotted skunk, *Spilogale putorius*, which has geographically distinct breeding populations in North America. The eastern population mates in April and has a short gestation period of 50–65 days. The western population mates in September and has a long pregnancy of 210–230 days, with implantation delayed for up to 200 days. Thus in some species implantation coincides with a sudden increase in CL size and in peripheral progesterone levels [(244); Fig. 2]. However, in other species the fact that some blastocysts remain dormant in the uterus cannot be attributed simply to a deficiency in corpus luteum func-

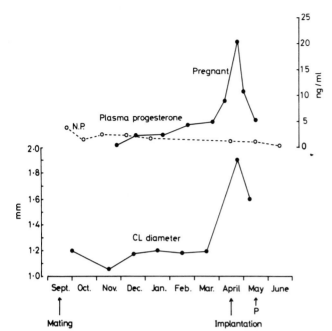

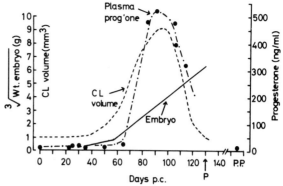

FIG. 3. Growth of CL and embryo, and plasma progesterone levels, during pregnancy in the coypu (nutria). *Prog'one*, progesterone; *P.P.*, postpartum; *p.c.*, postcoitus. [From Newson (270); Rowlands & Heap (317).]

FIG. 2. Growth of CL, and plasma progesterone levels, in the western form of the spotted skunk (*Spilogale putorius*). Note that implantation is delayed for up to 200 days. Pregnant, *solid line*; nonpregnant (*N.P.*), *dashed line*. P, parturition. [From Mead & Eik-Nes (244).]

tion. In rats and mice, implantation has been successfully induced by injections of estrogen (91). In the roe deer (342) the CL of the delay period is histologically indistinguishable from that found after implantation. In the roe deer it has been concluded that, when implantation occurs (November–December) 5 months after fertilization, it is not connected with any marked difference in either the growth or secretory activity of the corpus luteum.

Yet another variant of the patterns of growth of the CL of pregnancy is found in the coypu (*Myocastor coypus*), a hystricomorph rodent. During the first third of the 130-day pregnancy, the rate of growth of embryos and of the CL is very slow. Thereafter the growth rate of both and the secretory function of the CL increase sharply until the 100th day, after which the CL involutes [Fig. 3; (270, 317)].

In summary, the growth and maintenance of the CL of pregnancy follow many patterns; in some species the maximum size of the CL differs little from that attained in the cycle, whereas in others the CL grows considerably larger; in some instances, implantation may be delayed, and in some species this is related to a suppression of the growth of the CL.

SECRETORY ACTIVITY OF THE CORPUS LUTEUM. The biosynthesis and secretion of steroids by the CL of pregnancy have been studied by the estimation of steroid concentrations in lutein tissue and ovarian venous blood and by in vitro experiments to establish pathways of synthesis and metabolism. One of the earliest determinations of steroids

in ovarian venous blood was that of progesterone during the reproductive cycle of the ewe under acute surgical conditions (113). Since then progesterone has been identified and measured in high concentration in the ovarian venous blood of many species during pregnancy (235). An indication of the range of values is given in Table 1. The secretion rates in pregnancy are always high when the ovary contains lutein tissue, and, although there have been a few earlier reports of high concentrations in blood draining ovaries containing no CL, these have not been confirmed by more specific chemical procedures [Table 1; (222); for a detailed survey of progesterone concentrations in a wide range of tissues, see (214)].

The rates of progesterone production by individual lutein cells have been compared in different species. In the mare a value of 300 pg progesterone per cell per day has been calculated; secretion rate was 78.7 μg/min; weight of CL, 5 g; luteal cell diameter, 33 μ; and specific gravity assumed to be 1 (68). In the pregnant guinea pig the value obtained is 419 pg/cell per day, derived from a secretion rate of 0.83 μg/min and four CL of average diameter, 3 mm³ (180, 315). In the pregnant goat, for which the data are less complete, a rather lower figure of 71 pg/cell per day may be calculated by combining results from different sources (154, 162, 222).

In some animals (e.g., rat and rabbit) the reduced form of progesterone, 20α-hydroxypregn-4-en-3-one (20α-dihydroprogesterone, 20α-diHP), is an important secretory product of the ovary in pregnancy (118, 170). The interrelationships of this steroid and progesterone have an important bearing on pregnancy maintenance in some species, which is considered in greater detail below.

In a number of species the concentration of progesterone in lutein tissue is a close reflection of secretory activity (134, 241). The weight and size of the gland, on the other hand, are not always good indicators of function, particularly during the time of lutein regression in late pregnancy when the failure or reduction of progesterone secretion frequently precedes any decrease in the size of the CL (241). In common with most steroid-producing tissues, the gland itself provides little intracellular stor-

TABLE 1. *20α-Dihydroprogesterone and Progesterone During Peak Luteal Activity in Ovarian Venous Blood in Pregnancy*

Species	Progesterone		20α-Dihydroprogesterone		Ref.
	Concentration, µg/ml plasma	Secretion rate, µg/min per ovary	Concentration, µg/ml plasma	Secretion rate, µg/min per ovary	
Horse	8.4	79	0.2	1.8	339
Pig	4.7	28*			241
Cow	4.5	27**			116
Sheep	2.8	11			152
Human female	0.8				254
Goat	0.3	4.2 (1 CL)			222
	0.02	0.01 (no CL)			
Rabbit		1.1*		1.8	172
Dog		1.1*			362
Guinea pig	0.2	0.8*			268
Rat	3.9	0.4*	2.8	0.3	155

* Values may be overestimates, since no correction has been made for arterial progesterone concentrations; this is probably only important in the rat and guinea pig where peripheral levels are high in gestation. Concentrations in the rat are µg/ml blood.   ** Ovarian blood flow taken, 100 ml/100 g per min; ovarian weight, 10 g.

TABLE 2. *Maximum Concentrations of Progesterone in Luteal Tissue of Various Species*

Species*	Progesterone, ng/mg tissue	Reproductive State	Ref.
Grant's zebra (*Equus burchelli böhmi*)	233.9	Pregnant	197
Grey's zebra (*Equus grevyi*)	203.0	Pregnant	197
Badger (*Meles meles*)	89.2	Pregnant	57
Pig (*Sus scrofa*)	87.0	Pregnant	241
Dog (*Canis familiaris*)	83.0	Luteal phase	361
Egyptian buffalo (*Bubalus bubalis*)	70.0	Pregnant	114
Cow (*Bos taurus*)	42.0	Pregnant	134
Sheep (*Ovis aries*)	50.0	Luteal phase	89
Human (*Homo sapiens*)	49.8	Pregnant	391
Horse (*Equus caballus*)	46.0		334
Ferret (*Mustela putorius furo*)	40.0	Pregnant	Hammond and Heap, unpublished data
Coypu (*Myocastor coypus*)	39.0	Pregnant	317
Rat (*Rattus norvegicus*)	38.0**	Nonpregnant	382
Guinea pig (*Cavia porcellus*)	37.6	Pregnant	318
Whale (various spp.)	33.0		295
Roe deer (*Capreolus capreolus*)	30.0	Pregnant	342
Armadillo (*Dasypus novemcinctus*)	26.0	Pregnant	209
Alpaca (*Lama pacos*)	22.0	Pregnant	122
Rabbit (*Oryctolagus cuniculus*)	21.0	Pregnant	144
Hippopotamus (*Hippopotamus amphibius*)	19.0	Pregnant	216
Wallaroo (*Macropus robustus*)	15.2		Short and Sharman, unpublished data
Hyrax (*Procavia* spp.)	9.9		Short, unpublished data
Red kangaroo (*Megaleia rufa*)	9.2		Short and Sharman, unpublished data
Seal (*Phoca vitulina*)	7.1	Pregnant	334
African elephant (*Loxodonta africana*)	0.18	Pregnant	347

* See (347).   ** Concentration expressed as ng/mg ovarian tissue.

age of steroid. In contrast to cells that secrete proteins, the Golgi complex of steroid-secreting cells gives no visible evidence that it accumulates secretory granules or that steroids are expelled from the cells by this mechanism (121). Thus it is not surprising that experimental work in many animals suggests that the corpus luteum contains at any one time the equivalent of only a few minutes' secretion (179, 337). Steroid-secreting cells, on the other hand, contain appreciable stores of steroid precursors, such as cholesterol and cholesterol esters, and they probably have developed the enzymatic capacity for a high rate of steroid synthesis from stored and plasma precursors, as well as the facility for rapid release of the secretory product into general circulation. Even so, perusal of a list of the maximum progesterone concentration in CL of different animals reveals a very wide range of values (Table 2). The most striking are those found in the CL of the zebra, which are high, and those reported in the elephant, which are inexplicably low. So far as the elephant is concerned, attempts to demonstrate significant levels of progesterone in the blood or in the ovaries have hitherto failed (347). Whether this is because low concentrations in blood are adequate to maintain pregnancy in this species or because a previously unidentified progestagen is present is a tantalizing question that demands an answer.

The variation in progesterone concentration of lutein tissue raises a further question concerning the mechanism by which progesterone is released from its site of synthesis. The high concentrations found in the CL of some animals suggest that transport of steroid down a diffusion gradient into blood is not the only mechanism involved. For example, intracellular binding to tissue pro-

teins may regulate the rate at which steroid products are released from the endocrine tissue.

After the first demonstration of the in vitro synthesis of progesterone de novo by lutein tissue from the pig (110), subsequent experiments have elucidated pathways of biosynthesis. Progesterone can be synthesized from cholesterol in vitro by using CL homogenates, tissue slices, or mitochondria (17). Incubations of tissue slices with labeled substrates (acetate and cholesterol) show conclusively small but significant conversions to pregnenolone and 20α-diHP, as well as progesterone. Progesterone is also produced by lutein tissue incubated with other substrates, including pregnenolone, pregnenolone acetate, or 20α-hydroxycholesterol (103). The most probable biosynthetic pathway in CL appears to consist of the conversion of acetate to cholesterol through the intermediates mevalonic acid, squalene, lanosterol, and C_{29} and C_{28} sterols; cholesterol to pregnenolone by hydroxylation at $C_{20α}$ and C_{22} and side-chain cleavage; and finally the conversion of pregnenolone to progesterone by the action of the enzyme complex, $Δ^5$-$3β$-hydroxysteroid dehydrogenase, involving the $Δ^4$–$Δ^5$-isomerase and $3β$-reduction (17, 104). Alternative pathways have been proposed, but their quantitative significance in vivo is difficult to assess. The chief drawback of in vitro studies is the inability to reproduce adequately the dynamic state that exists in the body. Without a knowledge of the pool size of intracellular substrates and intermediates, such as cholesterol, which is considered to exist as metabolically "active" and "inactive" forms within the tissue, conclusions are mainly limited to a description of the steroids formed rather than of the rate at which they are synthesized. The limitations of this experimental approach have been discussed in detail elsewhere (17, 323).

In addition to progesterone, other steroids that can be formed in vitro by lutein tissue from precursors, including labeled acetate, dehydroepiandrosterone (DHA), or DHA sulfate, include 17α-hydroxyprogesterone, androstenedione, estradiol, and estrone (103, 104, 323).

REGULATION OF THE CORPUS LUTEUM. The formation of the CL appears to follow inevitably upon the rupture of the follicle, an event primarily controlled by the release of pituitary luteinizing hormone (LH). The subsequent persistence and function of the CL are also controlled in its initial stages by a pituitary hormone or complex of hormones that may be regarded as luteotrophic. This luteotrophic hormone (LTH) is predominantly prolactin in some species, such as the rat, and LH in others, such as the cow, although both hormones, working together in different proportions, probably play a part in most, if not all, species. In the later stages of gestation in some species the placenta assumes a luteotrophic role and maintains progesterone secretion by the CL. In others this assumption of endocrine activity by the placenta is extended still further in that the placenta itself produces progesterone and thus directly performs the original role of the CL.

The concern in this section is with the regulation of the CL in pregnancy. In addition to prolonging the life and possibly increasing the growth of the CL, luteotrophic activity implies an ability to stimulate the biosynthesis of progesterone by the CL and to extend the period of secretory function if necessary. The extent to which this activity is attributable to the pituitary can be evaluated from the following evidence. Hypophysectomy before midpregnancy frequently leads to fetal death and resorption due to the loss of anterior lobe secretions. If the operation is performed before the time of implantation, pregnancy terminates in all species in which the CL fails to develop, but it can be maintained by hormone replacement therapy or by a hypophysial autograft acting on the ovaries (119). Hypophysectomy in the second half of gestation has different effects in different species. In some it is followed by abortion, as in the rabbit (307, 350), ferret (237), goat (81), dog (174), and pig (109), which indicates that in these species LTH derives from the pituitary and the placenta does not secrete an adequate amount of progesterone to maintain pregnancy. When the pituitary is removed after a critical time in gestation, pregnancy survives and CL persist in some species [rat (283), mouse (72), guinea pig (163, 284),

and sheep (340)]. In these species, although pituitary LTH initially has an essential role in CL maintenance, later support resides in the production of a placental LTH and placental progesterone. A third group consists of those species in which either the pituitary or the ovaries are dispensable from a relatively early stage of gestation; in these the main site of progesterone synthesis for the greater part of gestation is placental [human female (192, 224), monkey (348)]. These species differ from those of other groups in that the CL regress at an early stage of pregnancy and play no further part in the maintenance of gestation. Lutein regression is less abrupt than that found just before parturition in other animals in which involution is rapid, and it is presumably due to the withdrawal or the inhibition of some luteotrophic stimulus. Although these categories are not intended to be comprehensive, they illustrate the variability of the mechanism whereby the maintenance of gestation is hormonally regulated. In some species the CL is the chief endocrine organ concerned in pregnancy maintenance, whereas in others this role has been transferred to the placenta; those species in which the placenta acts by supporting the CL may perhaps be regarded as occupying an intermediate position. We now consider in greater detail the regulation of the CL in species in each of these groups.

Rabbit. In the rabbit ovulation is induced by mating. It is brought about by a sudden release of LH after coitus, which causes a rapid release of 20α-diHP from the ovarian interstitial tissue very largely by mobilization of substrate from tissue stores of intracellular cholesterol (351). The high blood levels of 20α-diHP, characteristic of early pregnancy, apparently reinforce the release of pituitary LH and thereby ensure ovulation by a positive feedback (171). During the next 3 or 4 days of pregnancy the ovary is refractory and fails to respond to further stimulation by LH. From about the time of implantation 2 days later, the ovarian secretion rates of progesterone and 20α-diHP increase rapidly, and only between days 15 and 20 postcoitus does the amount of progesterone secreted exceed that of 20α-diHP. The ratio of progesterone to 20α-diHP and the secretion rates of both progestagens decrease markedly in the last 5 days of pregnancy [(172); Fig. 4].

Experiments in hypophysectomized animals have led to the view that pituitary LH and prolactin have an important influence on the interstitial tissue of the ovary—the former by stimulating cholesterol mobilization and steroidogenesis and the latter by facilitating cholesterol storage and maintaining a normal tissue structure (18). During most of pregnancy, LH release is suppressed by the inhibitory feedback of progesterone. The synthesis of progesterone is largely governed by the circulating level of estrogens produced by ovarian follicles (149, 172, 196). Thus, X-irradiation of pregnant does causes follicular destruction and results in regression of CL and abortion (196); pregnancy and CL can be maintained in hypophysectomized rabbits by chronic treatment with follicle-stimulating hormone (FSH)

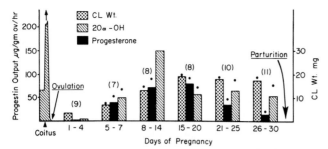

FIG. 4. Corpus luteum weights and secretion rates of progesterone and 20α-dihydroprogesterone (20α-OH) during pregnancy in the rabbit. SEM shown. [From Hilliard et al. (172).]

and prolactin (172). Therefore it seems that, in the pregnant rabbit, prolactin and FSH and possibly low levels of LH (18, 105, 354) have an important but indirect role in supporting CL function because they stimulate the synthesis of estrogen, which has a direct (but not a local) effect on luteal cells. When progesterone secretion rates fall, LH production increases; this causes raised 20α-diHP levels and hastens lutein tissue regression by decreased synthesis and esterification of cholesterol and increased conversion of cholesterol to progestagens. This hypothesis of CL maintenance in pregnant rabbits is consistent with many earlier findings; hypophysectomy at any time in pregnancy causes abortion, but CL can be maintained for at least 14 days by estrogen treatment (375); stalk-section also causes CL degeneration followed by abortion (376); LH fails to stimulate progesterone synthesis by CL slices in vitro but produces a marked increase in 20α-diHP synthesis by interstitial tissue (105). The secretion of 20α-diHP in vivo probably contributes little to the maintenance of pregnancy, since it has only about one-tenth the potency of progesterone in permitting implantation in ovariectomized rabbits (301). The chief function of the luteotrophic complex, which involves at least two and probably three pituitary protein hormones, as well as ovarian estrogens, is to maintain the circulating level of progesterone, the principal hormone of gestation. Progesterone alone can maintain pregnancy in the hypophysectomized rabbit, but the CL degenerate (307).

What regulates the secretion of follicular estrogen toward the end of gestation and ultimately brings about CL regression and the onset of parturition? The hypothesis that there may be an increased metabolism of estrogens by target tissues, such as the uterus, has been proposed; this could decrease circulating levels in late pregnancy and so lead to lutein regression (165, 172). It is also probable that alterations in LH regulation of ovarian estrogen secretion may contribute to the changes associated with parturition (353). This aspect of the regulation of the CL in pregnancy awaits definitive experiments on the secretion and metabolism of estrogens in the rabbit with the techniques now available for the assay of small amounts of these steroids.

Rat. It has been known for many years that prolactin is the principal, though probably not the only, luteo-

trophic hormone in the rat. As in the rabbit, the ovary secretes predominantly 20α-diHP at estrus, but it is derived from involuting CL rather than from interstitial tissue. By the time of implantation on day 3–4 the rate of ovarian progesterone secretion has started to increase and reaches maximum values on about day 15, whereas that of 20α-diHP decreases to low values (118, 155). The decrease of the latter is related to the regression of involuting CL from preceding cycles and is correlated with a declining 20α-hydroxysteroid dehydrogenase (20α-OH-SDH) activity (383). Between days 12 and 15 of pregnancy the ovarian secretion of both progestagens is temporarily increased, probably because of an increased production of placental gonadotrophin (23, 75). Within 48 hr before parturition there is a pronounced rise in the ovarian secretion rate of 20α-diHP, which is the result of an enhanced enzymatic activity; coincidentally, there is a more gradual fall in the secretion of progesterone (Fig. 5).

Luteotrophic control in the rat appears to differ according to the extent to which the CL are actively synthesizing progesterone (138). After hypophysectomy in unmated cyclic rats, CL regress only slowly, although they rapidly lose their ability to secrete progesterone, just as they do in the intact animal. After hypophysectomy in pseudopregnancy, when the CL are functional, regression is rapid unless the animals receive a continuous support of prolactin, as may be derived from a pituitary transplanted to an ectopic site. After hypophysectomy in pregnancy, CL regress unless the operation is performed later than day 11 postcoitus, when their maintenance is placental. It is clear therefore that functional CL depend on a continuous supply of pituitary LTH in the first half of gestation. There is further evidence from early work that placental LTH is produced in the second half. Pregnancy can be maintained in rats

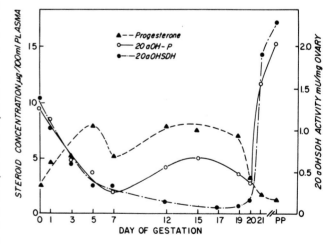

FIG. 5. Plasma concentrations of progesterone and 20α-dihydroprogesterone (20αOH-P) in the ovarian vein, and activity of 20α-hydroxysteroid dehydrogenase (20αOHSDH) in the ovarian tissue during gestation in the rat. *PP*, postpartum. [From Wiest & Kidwell (383).]

hypophysectomized on day 6 if they receive daily implants of placentas removed from other rats on day 12 of gestation (24); similarly the retention of placentas after fetal ablation maintains functional CL for the duration of pregnancy (199).

The exact nature of LTH in early pregnancy is still a matter of controversy. Although prolactin is certainly important in early pregnancy maintenance in the rat because of its LTH influence, there is experimental evidence that the LTH is complex even in this species (138). Prolactin appears to have a metabolic effect on CL rather than an influence on specific organelles, whereas luteal growth is increased when estrogen is given with prolactin. In the rat, as in the rabbit, there is conflicting evidence concerning the contribution of LH to the LTH complex. It has been observed that administration of LH in an agent that ensures a slow but continuous release to hypophysectomized rats from days 8 to 13 maintained pregnancy (5). In recent experiments, specific rabbit antisera to ovine LH injected into rats before, but not after, day 12 of pregnancy resulted in abortion. This abortifacient effect of anti-LH serum could not be reversed by giving ovine prolactin, ectopic homotransplantation of pituitaries, extracts of day-12 rat placentas, or 0.25–5.0 μg estradiol-17β, but it was overcome by 4 mg progesterone (226, 299). It has been proposed therefore that in the first half of gestation the CL are maintained by LH and prolactin. Subsequently placental luteotrophin is predominant; it resembles prolactin and possibly also LH in its action. Immediately before parturition the low blood levels of progesterone and the high estrogen levels [(390); see Fig. 13] may trigger the increased plasma levels of LH found after parturition and associated with postpartum ovulation (248). In addition to the effects of the protein hormones of the LTH complex, the role of estrogens in maintaining the CL cannot be ignored. These steroids, secreted by the ovaries probably as a transient surge (330), are necessary for implantation in the rat (333) and may also stimulate prolactin secretion, suppress LH and its paradoxical luteolytic effect, and synergize with prolactin to act directly on the CL (138).

An ingenious hypothesis has been formulated concerning the way in which ovarian progesterone secretion is regulated in the pregnant rat (156, 384). According to this concept, the total progestational activity of ovarian secretions is controlled by the extent to which progesterone is metabolized to the less active 20α-diHP, which by itself will not maintain pregnancy. It has been observed that the enzyme responsible (20α-OH-SDH) is inhibited, progesterone secretion is maintained, and CL regression is prevented. Hypophysectomy or the stimulus of suckling inhibits 20α-OH-SDH activity, whereas LH treatment, placental dislocation, or hysterectomy stimulates it and promotes the regression of lutein tissue. In summary, the regulation of the CL in the pregnant rat requires that 20α-OH-SDH activity remains at a low level to permit a relatively high rate of ovarian progesterone secretion to maintain gestation. The inhibition

of this key enzyme may be achieved by the synergistic actions of prolactin, which antagonizes the enzyme directly and aids cholesterol synthesis, and of LH, which stimulates steroidogenesis. After day 12 the function of these hormones is assumed by the placenta, and toward the end of gestation the withdrawal of placental LTH is postulated as leading to a fall in progesterone production and an increase in 20α-OH-SDH activity.

These conclusions find further support in the fact that the delay of parturition found with prolactin administration (245) is accompanied by inhibition of ovarian 20α-OH-SDH activity. The nature of the stimulus that normally increases 20α-OH-SDH activity prepartum is not known, but it probably relates to the stimulation of pituitary LH release, as well as the removal of a placental luteotrophin (383).

An abrupt change in progesterone metabolism in the rat ovary preceding parturition has been conclusively demonstrated, and it has been argued that increased 20α-OH-SDH activity in the rat ovary leads to the formation of 20α-diHP from pregnenolone mainly through the intermediate, pregn-5-ene-3β,20α-diol, rather than through progesterone [(207); Fig. 6]. Under conditions of high 20α-OH-SDH activity the secreted 20α-diHP-to-progesterone ratio approaches a value limited by the free NADP+-to-NADPH concentration ratio of the cytoplasm. A scheme relating these different pathways of biosynthesis and subcellular compartmentation of steroid dehydrogenases within the lutein cell proposes that 3β-hydroxy-Δ⁵-steroid dehydrogenase may synthesize these steroids vectorially into a "storage" compartment possibly associated with the tubules of the endoplasmic reticulum or the Golgi apparatus.

The paradoxical effects of some components of the luteotrophic complex in the rat have been discussed in papers on the luteolytic effects of LH (138, 314) and prolactin (238) and on the LH stimulation in vitro of progesterone synthesis in luteal slices (19). In many

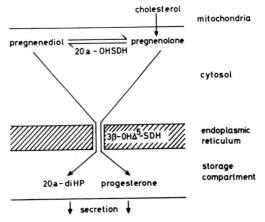

FIG. 6. A proposed subcellular compartmentation of steroid dehydrogenases (SDH) concerned with progesterone and 20α-dihydroprogesterone (20α-diHP) synthesis in the CL of the rat. 20α-OHSDH, 20α-hydroxysteroid dehydrogenase; 3β-OHΔ⁵-SDH, Δ⁵-3β-hydroxysteroid dehydrogenase. [From Kuhn & Briley (207).]

instances, however, some of these contradictory results may have been due to the different endocrine environment to which the CL were previously exposed.

As in the rat, hypophysectomy in the hamster in early pregnancy leads to involution of the CL and resorption of fetuses, and placental LTH secretion is implicated in the maintenance of later pregnancy (138). The pituitary LTH appears to consist of the synergistic action of at least two protein hormones. Prolactin and FSH, when administered concurrently, will support pregnancy in the hypophysectomized animal, the former supporting cellular integrity and the latter the secretory activity of lutein cells (137). Luteinizing hormone, at low levels, and estrogen probably contribute to the endogenous LTH complex as they synergize with prolactin and FSH in affecting the size and vascularity of the CL. In the nonpregnant mouse, prolactin and LH are luteotrophic (50, 51), but growth hormone (GH) has also been implicated because of its interaction with prolactin and exogenous LH to allow deciduoma formation after hypophysectomy (206). Prolactin alone will not maintain pregnancy after hypophysectomy on day 7 (184).

Guinea pig. An unusual feature of the luteotrophic regulation of the CL in the guinea pig is the fact that, after the release of the pituitary gonadotrophins associated with ovulation and CL formation, pregnancy can proceed even when the pituitary is removed within the first 3 days of pregnancy (163). Furthermore the number of corpora lutea does not decline, although embryonic survival is reduced by about 25%. Unlike the CL of most species, the CL of nonpregnant guinea pigs persist for a long time after hypophysectomy performed within 10 days of ovulation. Nevertheless pituitary luteotrophin clearly plays some part in the maintenance of normal luteal growth in the unmated animal since the number of corpora lutea decreases and luteal growth is retarded, though not abolished, if hypophysectomy is performed early in the cycle. The removal of both the pituitary and uterus leads to the formation of large corpora lutea comparable with those found in hysterectomized or in intact pregnant females.

It appears therefore that the growth and function of the CL after its early formation in pregnancy is probably more dependent on the suppression of a uterine factor that otherwise inhibits it than on a continuous pituitary secretion. Thus, in 27 animals hypophysectomized before the expected time of implantation, ovoimplantation proceeded normally in 20, and normal conceptuses ranging in number from 1 to 6 were found in 16 of these 20 killed up to 28 days after the operation. When conceptuses, whether normal or regressing, were present in the uterus at autopsy, the CL were comparable in size and histological appearance to those of intact animals at corresponding times in pregnancy. Arterial progesterone levels, however, were only within the expected range when normal conceptuses were present. In this work the completeness of hypophysectomy was assessed by several criteria, including macroscopic and histological examination of the sella turcica, the absence of normal vesicular

follicles, and the significant decline in uterine weight relative to body weight presumably related to the cessation of ovarian estrogen secretion after pituitary ablation.

After the 20th day of pregnancy the ovaries may be dispensed with since the placenta produces an adequate secretion of progesterone for pregnancy support [(80); see Fig. 10]. The surgical removal of conceptuses at any time of pregnancy is followed by the rapid regression of the corpora lutea (201), but it is not known if this is due to an interference with the production of a placental luteotrophin or placental progesterone. It is surprising that hypophysectomy caused resorption when carried out between days 34 and 36 but, unless resorption resulted from differing susceptibilities to operative trauma, hypophysectomy did not always interrupt pregnancy when performed 6 days later (284).

In summary, although the CL of the pregnant guinea pig is capable of an appreciable degree of autonomous development, embryonic survival may only be optimal when hypophysial LTH support is available. Experiments in nonpregnant animals indicate that FSH may have a LTH-like action (71), but it is equally probable that prolactin plays a significant role, in view of the recent demonstration that stalk-section causes an increase in the growth and progesterone content of CL, and prolactin administration accelerates luteal growth after hypophysectomy (181).

Farm animals. Already considered has been the manner in which the conceptus "protects" the CL in pregnancy from "murder" by some luteolytic agent from the uterus. This luteolysin, which may be prostaglandin $F_{2\alpha}$ (102), acts initially by some local mechanism in a number of animals (including sheep, pig, cow), but there may also be some spillover that results in a generalized systemic effect. The period over which the conceptus influences the establishment of the CL in a local manner is short in the pig but persists for at least 50 days in the sheep (259). The conceptus is unable to produce sufficient LTH to maintain the CL during the first 50 days of pregnancy in the sheep, but thereafter it is presumably capable of secreting both LTH and progesterone, since hypophysectomy no longer causes abortion or luteal regression and ovariectomy no longer terminates pregnancy. In the pig, however, the conceptus does not secrete either LTH or progesterone, since both these ablations always terminate pregnancy (107, 340).

When the nature of the LTH complex in these two species is considered, it is apparent that reference must be made to experiments on the control of the CL in the nonpregnant animal. In the hypophysectomized sheep, prolactin will maintain the function of the CL if the animal is also hysterectomized so that the overriding local influence of the uterine luteolytic agent is removed. Treatment with prolactin and appropriate levels of LH, however, will more accurately reproduce the effects of the endogenous LTH in terms of the secretory function of the CL (93, 94). Other workers, however, have found that in early pregnancy (20th day) a crude preparation of FSH and LH infused continuously maintains gestation for at least 7 days in hypophysectomized sheep (189).

In the pig there is compelling evidence that the hormonal needs for the maintenance of pregnancy change with the age of the CL. Thus at first the CL appears to be autonomous, not influenced by hypophysectomy or stalk-section, but, after about day 14 of the 112-day pregnancy, its maintenance requires several hormones. Up to about day 40, LH seems to be a predominant component of LTH action, but thereafter prolactin becomes increasingly important. Consequently the maintenance of CL after pituitary stalk-section on day 70 or later and the effect of estradiol benzoate after stalk-section on day 50 (estrogen stimulates prolactin secretion in many species) indicate that prolactin supports the CL at this stage in pregnancy (108). It may be significant that the pig placenta manufactures large amounts of estrogen throughout pregnancy (230, 298, 309).

The regulation of the CL in the pregnant cow has not yet been studied as exhaustively as in other species. There is convincing evidence from a variety of experiments to suggest that LH must be considered a major component of the LTH complex in the cow. It stimulates progesterone synthesis in vitro by the CL. It causes a very significant rise in the specific activity of progesterone when bovine CL of pregnancy are incubated with labeled acetate—unlike the response obtained with human CL of the menstrual cycle or pregnancy. The effect of LH on progesterone production by bovine CL is perhaps exerted at two sites on the steroid biosynthetic pathway, one before cholesterol formation and the other at the cholesterol-pregnenolone conversion, although the evidence for the former site of action has been disputed (17, 323). The ability of $3',5'$-cyclic AMP to mimic the action of LH in promoting steroidogenesis in the bovine CL is striking (239) and strongly suggests that LH may act by stimulating adenyl cyclase activity in lutein cells. Many other observations also suggest that LH is luteotrophic in the cow: a) the transient increase in plasma progesterone levels observed after human chorionic gonadotrophin (HCG) injections in the nonpregnant cow (328); b) the luteotrophic properties of LH, as shown after treatment with oxytocin to inhibit normal lutein development, or in prolonging the normal estrous cycle (150); c) reversal by LH administration of the action of estrogens, which in the cow (unlike the sheep and pig) are luteolytic (93). Nevertheless there is every indication that in the cow, as in all previous examples so far considered, LTH almost by definition consists of a complex of several hormones interacting to regulate the normal growth and function of CL. The survival of active CL after stalk-section in hysterectomized cows indicates that prolactin may be an important component of LTH in this species, as in others, and experiments in which in vitro and perfusion techniques are used point to its probable synergism with LH (30).

Human female. In the human being the pituitary or ovaries can be dispensed with from an early stage of gestation. As in the rhesus monkey, the role of the human CL in terms of its hormonal contribution to pregnancy maintenance is relatively brief and is concerned with the maternal recognition of gestation, implantation, and placentation. The major role in pregnancy maintenance has been transferred to the placenta, which synthesizes sufficient amounts of progesterone to support pregnancy from an early stage. After the transient ovulatory increase in LH secretion (249, 250, 313), the CL develops rapidly and is probably maintained by small amounts of LH. Within 3 to 4 days after implantation on day 6, HCG appears in the maternal urine and can be detected in blood by the 15th day postcoitus (133). In nonpregnant women the CL begins to regress about 14 days after ovulation; in pregnancy therefore HCG appears some 4–5 days earlier than the expected time of lutein regression, and its effect may be that of a secondary stimulus to maintain an otherwise failing CL (366). The conclusion that HCG is luteotrophic and steroidogenic in the human female has been challenged in recent years (340), and attention has been directed to the possibility that a synergistic interaction between more than one placental hormone may be equally important. The most probable component, elaborated early in pregnancy, is human placental lactogen (HPL) produced in large quantities from an early time in gestation. On the other hand, the decline of CL activity some 50–60 days after ovulation, as indicated by its secretion of 17α-hydroxyprogesterone [(389); see Fig. 10], occurs at a time when HCG and HPL concentrations are still rising. Nevertheless the importance of relative concentrations in synergistic interactions is well known, and explanations of the regulation of the CL in early pregnancy cannot be soundly formulated on the limited evidence available.

The essential contribution of the CL to circulating progesterone levels in early pregnancy is clearly short lived. As early as the 35th day after ovulation the ovaries have been removed without interrupting pregnancy, and there are claims that the operation may be performed even earlier (364). The prolonged life-span of the functional CL in pregnancy may be due to the removal of a uterine inhibitory agent. It has been reported that hysterectomy extended the life-span of the human corpus luteum, but later work has shown that this is not so and that the uterus does not influence the CL in either the human female or rhesus monkey by the local luteolytic mechanism demonstrated in some other species (35, 340).

Mare. The Equidae do not fall conveniently into any of the four groups described above partly because of lack of information about experimental treatments, such as hypophysectomy in pregnancy, and partly because the regulation of the CL in pregnancy in Equidae poses a series of unique and, to a large degree, unresolved questions. The single CL formed at the beginning of gestation, the CL of conception, survives for only about 40–50 days of the 330-day gestation period. Subsequently a number of accessory CL are formed by luteinization of a second crop of follicles, and, although they last longer than the CL of conception, they disappear by midpregnancy. Blood progesterone levels measured throughout gestation have shown that the concentration is comparable with that of other ungulates during the first 3–4 months but then falls dramatically to extremely low values (335). In contrast to the unusually low circulating levels, high concentrations of progesterone are found in the placenta (337), and presumably this local source of progesterone is utilized by the uterus, rather than being released in significant amounts into the blood stream. Such a local activity may be promoted by the diffuse epitheliochorial type of placentation found in the mare.

A feature peculiar to the Equidae is the occurrence of pregnant mares' serum gonadotrophin (PMSG), a potent hormone manufactured in specialized regions of the endometrium, the endometrial "cups." Although these cups have long been considered maternal in origin, very recently it has been claimed that this "decidual" tissue is actually fetal (trophoblastic) in origin (4).

A detailed analysis of the hormones that regulate CL function in the mare is not yet possible, and in the absence of experimental information a chronological description of the sequence of these early changes must serve. It is not known by what means the life and function of the CL of conception are prolonged, nor is it known why the CL should survive for only 6–7 weeks. Plasma progesterone levels decline from about day 20, and this decline is followed by endometrial cup formation as a result of a specific fetal stimulus transmitted to the mother between days 34 and 40 (2). The secretion of PMSG, first detected in maternal blood on day 35, reaches maximum levels around the 60th to 65th day (see Fig. 14). Within this period, accessory CL are formed in the ovary, presumably as a result of gonadotrophin stimulation, and the plasma progesterone concentrations are restored to a level comparable with that of the first peak but then decline to nondetectable values in midpregnancy. The pattern of progesterone and PMSG levels differs markedly in the case of a mare crossed with a donkey so that the fetus is a mule; there are yet other differences when a stallion is crossed with a female donkey (3).

Placenta

"Pregnancy is characterized by an endocrine readjustment on the part of the mother in which the placenta holds a key position" (13). In the preceding section of this chapter we indicated the extent to which progesterone synthesis and pregnancy maintenance have been transferred to the placenta in several species. In some species the placenta has little or no enzymatic capacity to produce progesterone but nevertheless has a very important endocrine function, for when it is removed by hysterectomy the function of the CL is terminated [rabbit (147); rat, hamster, and guinea pig (200, 201); cat (13)]. In contrast to the prompt regression of the CL after removal of the placenta is the well-established observation that in a number of species removal of the fetuses alone, while the placentas are left in situ, does not alter the course of pregnancy [rabbit, rat, mouse, monkey, cat (13)]. This so-called placental pregnancy is normal in that maternal body weight is maintained, placentas continue to grow, and mammary development is not affected. In the mouse, however, separation of the pubic symphysis fails, parturition is protracted, and lactation is occasionally suppressed (273). In view of the recent work on the role of the fetus in the sheep just before parturition (see below), it would be interesting to perform a similar experiment in the sheep. In this species a neural response arising from uterine distension occurs in certain circumstances, and it is conceivable that the placenta may also exert its control by some neural reflex activity (182, 265). However, experimental distension of the uterine horn in nonpregnant guinea pigs causes premature regression of the CL (41), and it has no endocrine effect on the duration of pregnancy in murine rodents (243).

FETOPLACENTAL INTERRELATIONS. There is increasing evidence that, although the placenta plays a major role in the hormonal regulation of gestation length, in some species the fetus is not simply a passenger. Some of the most direct evidence has been obtained by Liggins (218) in the sheep, where the removal of either the pituitary or the adrenals of the fetal lamb prolongs gestation. In the last 2 weeks of pregnancy, hypertrophy of the fetal adrenal is a normal occurrence (76), fetal corticosteroid secretion increases (32), and parturition may be induced by the injection of glucocorticoids or ACTH into the hypophysectomized fetus (218). Liggins has postulated that the onset of parturition in the sheep is regulated by an increasing secretion of glucocorticoids by the fetus, which results in a chain of events, as yet incompletely defined, that finally terminates in parturition. Other support for this view is derived from studies of pathological and genetic malformations of the pituitary in the fetal lamb or calf, which often result in prolonged gestation. Whether this hypothesis applies in other species is as yet not known, but it is supported by the finding that in women the incidence of prolonged gestation appears to be associated with the occurrence of fetal anencephaly involving the absence of gross malformation of the hypophysis. Also, it has recently been shown that pregnancy is prolonged in rhesus monkeys after fetal hypophysectomy (70). However, to say that the placenta has only a minor role in the control of gestation length in these species is not yet justified. Recent work in the sheep shows that, within 48 hr before parturition, uterine production of estrogens rises sharply (63, 66). The increased activity of the fetal adrenal may be associated with this dramatic increase in steriod production immediately before parturition, and it is conceivable that estrogens are important in triggering parturition.

We have seen that in the sheep the conceptus has an early role in suppressing the luteolytic activity of the uterus; that the fetal placenta later becomes a dominant factor in maintaining gestation, mainly by progesterone production but also by its LTH activity; and finally that the fetus, or fetoplacental system, triggers the onset of parturition by a mechanism involving both the fetal pituitary and fetal adrenals. In the rat the conceptus regulates the maintenance of gestation in a different manner. As we have discussed above, ovarian 20α-OH-SDH activity is inhibited during pregnancy, but, as soon as this inhibition is withdrawn, the CL of pregnancy regress and parturition occurs. The inhibition of the ovarian 20α-OH-SDH originates from the pregnant uterus, for, when the placentas are totally dislocated or the uterus is removed in hypophysectomized pregnant animals, ovarian 20α-OH-SDH activity increases and the CL regress (383). Thus in the rat the fetal placenta is responsible for the secretion of an enzyme inhibitor, possibly a placental LTH, that regulates the activity of ovarian 20α-OH-SDH, which has a key position in the control of ovarian steroid biogenesis. It has also been shown to produce enough progesterone to maintain pregnancy in the absence of the ovaries from about day 18 (86).

A question that has occupied the interest of many investigators is the relative contribution of fetal and maternal components to placental endocrinology. The maternal placenta is regarded as equivalent to the maternal deciduoma, and in rats with a massive deciduomal reaction pseudopregnancy is prolonged (369). This is not so in mice and hamsters in which the rather small deciduomata formed as a result of uterine trauma are not luteotrophic. In general the site of placental endocrine activity, however, is fetal (chorionic) rather than maternal (decidual). This has been shown in many ways: by histochemistry, by fluorescent antibodies to protein hormones, and by cell or organ culture. [For descriptions of ultrastructural, functional, and biochemical changes in the placenta during gestation, see (40, 48, 203).]

A SOURCE OF HORMONES. It was observed many years ago that most substances sought in the placenta can be found there (272). This astute comment, which has been subsequently confirmed many times, raises the question of whether the placenta produces hormones de novo or whether it stores circulating compounds. There is convincing evidence that the placenta in many species contains appreciable amounts of steroid and protein hormones. Those unique to the placenta include HCG, HPL, and PMSG, but there is reasonable doubt about whether the placenta can produce other compounds, such as ACTH, melanocyte-stimulating hormone (MSH), and vasopressin, which have also been identified in it (48). Placental production of steroids has been deduced by several methods: a) measurements of the increased urinary excretion in pregnancy after other steroid-producing glands, such as the ovaries and adrenals, have been removed (97, 151); b) studies of the interrelations of fetoplacental steroid metabolism (98,

352); and c) direct measurements of steroid concentrations across the placenta or fetus, or both (98, 222, 365, 391–393). In the human female it is now firmly established that much of the steroid biogenesis of pregnancy takes place in two interdependent compartments, the fetus and placenta (98). Whether this is true of other mammals is not entirely clear. Intriguing contrasts exist between species, like those between the human being, guinea pig, and sheep, which produce placental progesterone, and the pig and goat, which do not (98, 159, 222), and between such species as the pregnant human in which estrogen (estriol) excretion in pregnancy is 1,000 times the nonpregnant level and the sheep in which the 16α-hydroxylation pathway is lacking and estriol excretion is negligible (123). These two species also contrast with each other in that the human fetal adrenal possesses a high sulfokinase activity, whereas the sheep fetal adrenal contains none (15, 98). Conversely the human placenta possesses little sulfokinase activity (98), whereas the sheep placenta exhibits appreciable activity (124).

The placenta is unique among naturally occurring organs or tissues, since elements of differing genetic constitution are combined in it. The fetal component bears something of the nature of an allograft yet withstands the immunologic rejection an allograft may expect. It has the capacity in some species to synthesize steroid and protein hormones simultaneously. Steroidogenesis in the placenta reveals some significant differences from that found elsewhere in the body, but steroids so formed are, of course, chemically identical with those produced elsewhere. Placental gonadotrophins, on the other hand, in species where they have been identified, are chemically distinct from the corresponding pituitary hormones, although their biological properties are similar. Thus the biological properties of HCG, HPL, and PMSG resemble those of pituitary LH, prolactin (and GH), and FSH, respectively. They may represent evolutionary steps in the adoption of pituitary, as well as luteal, function by the placenta. In rodents their main influence is a luteotrophic one concerned with the support of gestation, in the mare they are characterized by a follicle-stimulating component, and in women they possess luteinizing activity. Placental gonadotrophins have not been found in the cow, sheep, or pig (13).

CAPACITY OF HORMONE PRODUCTION. The maximum concentrations of protein and steroid hormones produced by the placenta are summarized in Table 3. At least 85 enzymes have been identified, many of which are concerned with placental hormone production and others with metabolic pathways, including glycolysis, the pentose-phosphate pathway, and fatty acid and triglyceride synthesis (145). The concentration of hormones stored in placental tissue is generally low and for HCG and progesterone represents less than a 5-min supply. An exception is to be found in the mare in which the PMSG content of endometrial cups is considerable (Table 3). As is to be expected, the placental concentra-

TABLE 3. *Hormone Concentrations in Placenta of Various Species*

Hormone	Species	Concentration*	Ref.
HCG	Human	2–500 IU/g	48
HPL	Human	100–200	128
PMSG	Mare	8,600 IU/g**	316
Progesterone	Human and chimpanzee	0.5–10	337
	Mare	0.06–0.37	337
	Rhesus monkey	0.05	337
	Common seal	0.04	337
	Indian rhinoceros	0.04	337
	Dog	0.02	337
	Giraffe	0.01	337
	Sheep	0.006	337
	Rat	0.02	86
	Guinea pig	0.02	159
	Coypu	0.02	317
	Rabbit, goat, pig, cow, dog	<0.02	337
Estradiol-17β	Human	1.13	98
	Cow	0.02	135
Estrone	Human	0.35	98
	Cow	0.01	135
Estriol	Human	2.02	198

* Values expressed as μg/g, unless otherwise noted.   **Endometrial cup tissue.

tions vary with the stage of gestation and with the species. In the human being the maximum progesterone concentration is about 6 μg/g, and placental production can be as high as 250 mg/day; in the guinea pig and sheep, tissue concentrations are very low, although the production rate of placental progesterone is appreciable (67, 344). Whether these differences are due to excessive placental production in the human being or simply reflect a higher requirement for pregnancy maintenance is unclear, but the possible significance of these species differences is discussed in the last section of this chapter. As far as the guinea pig is concerned, progesterone production rates apparently exceed the requirements of a normal pregnancy. The guinea pig was the first species, excluding man, in which it was shown that pregnancy could continue normally after ovariectomy (168). In the intact animal, plasma progesterone levels rise to maximum values between the 30th and 45th days of pregnancy and then decline, but, in pregnant animals ovariectomized on the 28th day or later, progesterone levels remain lower, except in the last 2 weeks of gestation (see Fig. 10). The fact that pregnancy continues in about half the guinea pigs ovariectomized at about the 28th day of gestation, even though circulating levels of progesterone are much lower, suggests that a small placental contribution is adequate, probably because its action is local or because its turnover is much reduced. Even so, it is surprising that placental progesterone concentration is so low.

Because of the large placental production of hormones in man, the question of whether the fetus is exposed to high concentrations of placental hormones arises. There is an effective barrier to the transfer of some protein hormones, such as HPL (128), though not HCG (52). There is, however, an appreciable transfer of large quantities of progesterone (365) and estrogens (98) across the placental barrier. Placental progesterone synthesized from maternal cholesterol is transferred to the fetus and metabolized by the adrenals, liver, and peripheral tissues (352). The transfer of estrogens from mother to fetus is limited, but the transport in the opposite direction is considerable (98).

Information about the transfer of hormones in other species is not extensive. In the sheep (222) and guinea pig [(180); see Table 4] the amount of progesterone in fetal blood is very low, which suggests a barrier to placental transfer. In the sheep, however, this may be explained by the high activity of 20α-hydroxysteroid dehydrogenase demonstrated in fetal red cells (266), but conclusive proof of this point is not yet available. In a recent study on the diffusion resistance of the placenta in the sheep, cortisol passed into the maternal circulation from the fetus, but apparently there was little transfer in the opposite direction (34).

In pathological modifications of human pregnancy, placental hormone production may be augmented or suppressed. In multiple pregnancies and toxemias, as well as in cases of hydatidiform mole, and in choriocarcinomas, very high levels of HCG have been reported; moderate increases occur in the serum of some patients with diabetes, eclampsia, and preeclampsia [see (13)].

Pituitary

It has been emphasized already that the pituitary has an indispensible role in the secretion of hormones concerned with the initial events of pregnancy and that in some, but not all, species the subsequent endocrine role of the pituitary in pregnancy maintenance is transferred to the placenta. Examples have been discussed previously to illustrate the way in which the deleterious effects of removing the pituitary can be overcome by the administration of the essential trophic agents it normally secretes. The enlargement of the pituitary in pregnancy as it is related to secretory activity is therefore not unexpected. The initial observation was made in the human being in which the hypophysis increases in size by both hypertrophy and hyperplasia (78). The amount of enlargement depends on parity (300). Similar findings of increases in pituitary weight have been reported in other animals, including the mouse, cat, bitch, sow, ewe, and mare. In contrast, the pituitary of the rat, guinea pig, rabbit, and cow seems to vary little in weight during pregnancy (12).

In view of the secretory activity of the pituitary during gestation, cytological changes in acidophils, basophils, and chromophobes have received considerable study. Prolactin and GH are thought to be the products of acidophil cells in most mammalian hypophyses, whereas thyrotrophs, corticotrophs, and gonadotrophs (FSH and LH) are most concentrated in basophil zones. Detailed descriptions of the cellular changes in the anterior hypophysis associated with pregnancy are found elsewhere (297). The appearance of specialized "pregnancy cells" in the pituitary of the gravid female has been confirmed in several mammalian species. These cells are believed to originate from the "chief" or chromophobe cells; they possess a characteristic eosinophilic staining reaction, which increases in pregnancy. Whether their development is associated with high circulating levels of progesterone is uncertain, but their presence in the guinea pig pituitary at least 3 months after hysterectomy, which prolongs the life of the CL, and in the rat after the injection of CL extracts suggests that this may be so. Amoroso & Porter (12) indicate that they may play some part in the secretion of pituitary LTH in response to progesterone stimulation. According to immunofluorescence studies, very few pregnancy cells contain either human growth hormone (HGH) or HPL antigens, but so far it has not been possible to say if they contain prolactin (157).

It will be recalled from our earlier discussion on the pituitary regulation of the CL in pregnancy that this seems to be achieved by a complex interaction of several hypophysial hormones, including prolactin, LH, FSH, and possibly GH. Few systematic studies of the pituitary content of hormones are available. The interpretation of some of the early findings is influenced by doubts about the specificity of the assays employed, but useful information has nevertheless been obtained. The pituitary of the adult human female contains equal activity of FSH and LH, although the ratio in urine favors a higher activity of the former gonadotrophin (25). The gonadotrophic activity of the human pituitary in pregnancy, however, is low, and this was considered by some workers to be a strong argument, albeit indirect, in favor of a placental, rather than a pituitary, production of hormone. It is certainly consistent with the finding that hypophysectomy as early as the 12th week does not terminate pregnancy (192). In the cow, there is conflicting evidence about the pituitary content of gonadotrophic activity in pregnancy. On balance, a gradual decrease seems probable (264), and the use of the more specific radioimmunoassay procedures now available may reveal whether significant differences exist.

The gonad-stimulating potency of the pituitary is greatly elevated in early pregnancy in the mare but diminishes in the second half of pregnancy presumably due to the appearance of estrogens in circulation (12, 61, 166). Changes have also been reported in the rat, rabbit, and mouse, but in all instances the difficult questions of hormone synthesis and storage as opposed to hormone release prevent adequate interpretation of the data. For these reasons more recent investigation has been concentrated on the circulating levels rather than on tissue content.

Our knowledge about the pituitary content of prolactin has been limited hitherto by the absence of a specific and highly sensitive assay. Bioassays of the lactogen content of the anterior pituitary have shown that marked increases occur about the time of parturition (rat, guinea pig, and rabbit), but in some instances the increase has been observed at other times in pregnancy (mouse, goat, sow). There is little evidence that the sharp increases in prolactin activity are correlated with changes in the weight of the gland during pregnancy or lactation (12, 60). Few systematic assays are available for other trophic hormones (ACTH, GH, thyrotrophin) in pregnancy, but it is very probable that these hormones may contribute to metabolic changes associated with gestation.

Other Maternal Endocrine Organs

The function of the adrenals in pregnancy has been studied by a number of investigators. Evidence about adrenal-gonadal interrelations has accumulated from various sources, including experiments on the influence of sex hormones on the adrenals of normal, gonadectomized, and hypophysectomized animals, and experiments on the effect of adrenalectomy on reproductive processes (79, 91). In several species, including man, the adrenals of the female are heavier than those of the male, and this sexual dimorphism reflects the endocrine balance and adrenocortical activity of the animals. In castrated male rats, adrenal weights are greater than in intact males, but in females gonadectomy has little effect (277). During pregnancy in the mouse the adrenals become more active and enlarge, but in the rat there are no striking changes in adrenal weight or histology. Perhaps the most outstanding structural change observed so far is that seen in species in which a fetal X-zone, a large, lipoid-free, juxtamedullary region, persists through early life but disappears during the first pregnancy. In the adult female mouse, involution occurs during the 10th to 20th days of gestation. At this time the zone is much larger than that in the male, in which regression occurs at about 5 weeks of age. Several explanations have been advanced to explain this phenomenon. The X-zone involutes either when androgen production increases, as at puberty in the male, or when stimulated experimentally in the female by LH, or when androgen is administered to mice of either sex. This is interpreted to mean that the X-zone itself normally secretes androgen but undergoes disuse atrophy when the titer of circulating androgens increases. Thus, in the second half of gestation in primiparous mice, the maternal adrenals undergo a striking morphological change apparently because of increased levels of androgens. In contrast to that of the mouse, the fetal X-zone in the human being involutes shortly after birth in both sexes. The evidence suggests that its initial development is autonomous but that subsequent growth depends on a trophic stimulus, probably fetal pituitary LH. The withdrawal of fetal LH at parturition may account for the rapid postnatal involution (88).

Two aspects of adrenal physiology in pregnancy, which at first sight appear contradictory, are now considered. The first concerns the well-established fact that the maternal adrenals of many species appear to be capable of producing appreciable amounts of gonadal steroids, including androgens, estrogens, and progestagens (161, 235, 336). Under conditions of acute operative stress or when the adrenal is stimulated by ACTH, it secretes considerable amounts of these three types of steroid. However, whether this secretion is equally great in the conscious animal and whether it contributes significantly to pregnancy maintenance are in doubt. Short (336) suggests that the secretory activity reported only reflects the activity of a "leaky" gland hyperstimulated by ACTH and secreting many corticosteroid intermediates, including estrogens, androgens, and progestagens, that may have little consequence. According to another view, the increased secretory activity of the adrenal may manifest itself during occasions of physiological crisis. With regard to the adrenal production of progesterone in pregnancy, studies in the unstressed, conscious sheep with an autotransplanted adrenal show that secretion rates are low (152). Similar conclusions have been reached in the dog in which under conditions of operative stress the secretion rates of adrenal steroids, including progesterone and androgens, are high but fall, after the removal of the source of endogenous ACTH by hypophysectomy, to values similar to those reported in conscious, unstressed animals (161).

If gonadal hormones of adrenal origin played a major part in pregnancy maintenance, adrenalectomy would be expected to result in the termination of gestation at an early time after the operation. Parkes & Deanesly (277) have discussed the intriguing results of experiments first performed in the dog, which show that, despite the evidence of potential adrenal activity in pregnancy, many animals tolerate adrenalectomy even better when pregnant than at other times. It has been deduced that, in the rat, cat, dog, and ferret, survival after adrenalectomy in pregnancy is probably due to the secretory activity of the CL. In this connection it is of particular interest that progesterone administered in moderate dosage promotes the survival of adrenalectomized rats and ferrets, probably through a DOCA-like activity.

The significance of changes in the thyroid, parathyroids, and pancreas during pregnancy is obscure. Pregnancy can be tolerated in the absence of these organs, but, on the other hand, several workers report obvious changes in their function during gestation (91).

Fetus

Far from having only a passive role, the fetus contributes actively to the endocrinology of pregnancy and undergoes very marked changes in hormonal activity during gestation. The fetal endocrine glands develop characteristic functions, in some instances quite different from those found in neonatal or adult life. In some respects the fetus apparently acquires a degree of autonomy in the control of its own development and metabolic processes, but, at the same time, its metabolism and endocrinology may be profoundly affected by maternal hormones, some of which are readily transported across the fetoplacental barrier. Hence it is evident that fetal endocrinology is a complex interaction of fetal and maternal factors.

PITUITARY. It is very probable that the fetal pituitary is capable of producing most of, if not all, the trophic hormones normally associated with the adult gland. In addition to its trophic influence on target endocrine organs discussed below, it also produces growth hormone (GH), which has been found in fetal pituitaries by bioassay (302) and immunoassay (193). Moreover, higher concentrations of human growth hormone (HGH) are found in the umbilical artery than in umbilical and maternal venous blood, which supports the view that it is of fetal, rather than placental, origin (388). Thus it is distinct from HPL, which is derived from the trophoblast rather than the fetus and has GH-like properties. The function of fetal GH, however, is uncertain. Anencephalic human fetuses, in which the pituitary gland is absent or malformed, may attain normal birth weights at term. In the rat and rabbit, fetal decapitation does not affect somatic growth, although it delays testicular and thyroid differentiation and produces hypoplasia of the adrenal cortex (187), effects that can be prevented by ACTH injections into the mother (198). In contrast, destruction of the fetal hypophysis in sheep retards somatic growth (219). At 50 days of gestation the fetal sheep pituitary contains GH (356) and its concentration in fetal blood disappears after hypophysectomy of the fetus (33), which indicates that it is not produced by the placenta. In late pregnancy the plasma concentration of GH in fetal lambs is 10 times that of the mother but falls rapidly immediately before birth (33).

ADRENALS. By the fourth month of gestation the human fetal adrenal is one of the largest fetal organs and exceeds the size of the fetal kidney. By term, however, its relative size has decreased to one-third that of the kidney. The changes in size and function of the fetal adrenals are clearly influenced by trophic factors, such as ACTH and HCG (371). In the human being the adrenals of anencephalic fetuses involute prematurely (37); in other species the destruction of the fetal pituitary results in partial atrophy of the adrenals (187, 198, 219). The demonstration that ACTH is present in the human fetal pituitary by the 10th week of gestation (360), the implication that fetal ACTH is responsible for inducing the rapid increase in fetal adrenal weight associated with parturition in the sheep (218), and the finding that ACTH given to fetal dogs increases fetal cortisol secretion (183), all indicate that the fetal adrenal is probably regulated by the trophic influence of fetal ACTH. The inability of ACTH injected into the mother to cause a similar change in fetal adrenal weight in the sheep probably indicates that it fails to cross the placental barrier.

The steroidogenic activity of the human fetal adrenal

develops at an early stage in pregnancy and exhibits some characteristic features (42, 88, 371). These include a much reduced capacity to metabolize Δ^5-3β-hydroxy-steroids to Δ^4-3-keto compounds compared with adrenals in adults. This is probably associated with a repression of 3β-hydroxysteroid dehydrogenase by the high circulating levels of progesterone derived from the human placenta. Progesterone itself is actively metabolized by the fetal adrenals, as well as by other fetal organs, such as the liver (371). However, the transfer of placental progesterone (and of maternal glucocorticoids) to the fetus ensures a source of adrenal steroids that probably safeguards the fetus prenatally from the severe adrenal insufficiency that would normally arise from a deficiency in Δ^5-3β-hydroxysteroid dehydrogenase. A detailed description of steroidogenesis in the fetoplacental unit is found in the chapter by Ryan in this *Handbook*.

There are considerable differences among species in the degree of prenatal development of the adrenal medulla and in its ability to synthesize catecholamines. The ratio of epinephrine to norepinephrine is higher in the adrenal medulla of the fetal lamb than in that of the fetal calf, and shortly before parturition the adrenal has acquired more of the characteristics of the adult gland (76, 77). It is not known whether, in the fetal adrenal, medullary cells influence steroid secretion by the cortex, as in the adult.

GONADS. The hormonal activity of the fetal gonads is apparently directed more specifically toward the processes of sexual differentiation than those of pregnancy maintenance. Whether fetal or maternal gonadotrophins provide the stimulus for this activity, however, is not clear, since in human anencephalics gonadal development may be normal (234). Present theories about sex determination appear to favor the concept of gonadal corticomedullary antagonism whereby chromosomally determined substances result in testicular differentiation arising from medullary development and cortical suppression or ovarian differentiation from the reverse (188). The female or neutral pattern of development is modified in males by androgen secreted from the testicular tissue, which encourages the growth of the male Wolffian duct, whereas an unidentified substance from the same source inhibits growth of the female Müllerian duct. Any interference, natural or experimental, with this normal process of sexual differentiation leads to intersexuality of differing degrees. Administration of testosterone propionate to the mother at a particular stage of gestation in the monkey, *Macacus mulatta*, produces female pseudo-hermaphroditism. In the case of bovine twins a genetic female is masculinized in the presence of a male twin, but the explanation of this effect, though presumably related to an exchange of testosterone, is still not fully understood (341).

It seems probable that the fetal pituitary or HCG, or both, are involved in controlling Leydig cell activity in the fetal testis (371). There is abundant biochemical evidence that the fetal testis can synthesize testosterone. In addition, it appears to share some similarities with the fetal adrenal in its 17α- and 21-hydroxylase activities, as well as possessing 20α- and 20β-reductase enzymes (234). In contrast to the testis, the fetal ovary possesses little steroidogenic activity, even in the mare, in which there is striking hypertrophy and hyperplasia of the interstitial cells in both the fetal ovary and testis, which seem to parallel the changing concentrations of maternal urinary estrogens (8). Fetal gonadal growth is at a maximum when the urinary excretion of equilin, a steroid peculiar to the fetoplacental unit of this species, reaches its highest levels [(231); see Fig. 14]. A similar development of interstitial tissue has also been reported in the seal (11) and elephant (285).

OTHER FETAL ENDOCRINE ORGANS. A variety of changes in fetal endocrine organs have been described during pregnancy (234, 371). The fetal pituitary-thyroid interrelationship is demonstrable in intrauterine life, and atrophy after hypophysectomy can be reversed by thyrotrophin (TSH) administration (91). It appears, however, that thyroid function, as reflected by the accumulation of radioactively labeled iodine, develops at definite times in fetal life: near term in the mouse and rat, at mid-pregnancy in the pig, at about 3 months in the cow, and at the beginning of the second trimester in man. Whereas the placenta is relatively impermeable to TSH (204), whether triiodothyronine and thyroxine cross the barrier depends on the amount bound to the transport protein, thyroxine-binding globulin.

Insulin production by the β-cells of the fetal pancreas again varies with different species. In the rat and mouse it begins relatively late in gestation, but in fetal calves and human beings it begins at about the 4th to 5th month (234). In the sheep (1), unlike the rat, rhesus monkey, and human being, the fetus is virtually autonomous in its regulation of blood glucose, for there is no transfer of insulin across the placental barrier. In the fetal lamb, fructose acts as a carbohydrate reserve to glucose, which is the major metabolite of fructose. Acetate, acetoacetate, and free fatty acids are utilized by the fetus, but, since they do not cross the placenta, they appear to contribute little to the nutrition of the fetus.

ACTIONS OF HORMONES IN PREGNANCY MAINTENANCE

The interpretation of the effect of endocrine changes in gestation is complicated by the complex interactions of different hormones, some with an active role and others that are probably permissive, and by the range of variation among species. Progesterone, the hormone of pregnancy, appears to have a key role in all species so far studied, with the possible exception of the elephant (347). It has also been designated "the useless hormone," because in normal conditions it rarely, if ever, acts alone. It is necessary for target organs, such as the uterus, vagina, and mammary gland, to be primed with estrogen before the physiological effects of progesterone are apparent.

Progesterone and Estrogens

UTERINE GROWTH. In pregnancy the uterus enlarges, and its chemical composition changes, due in part to the action of hormones and also to the stimulus of an enlarging conceptus. The uterus of the prepubertal human female weighs about 10–15 g; its weight increases five- to sixfold with the onset of sexual activity, and in pregnancy it may reach weights of 800–1,000 g. The myometrial growth is almost entirely brought about by hypertrophy, rather than by hyperplasia, and the RNA-to-DNA ratio has been found to increase in the uterus of the pregnant rat, mouse, and human being (47, 267).

One of the most impressive effects of hormones on uterine growth is seen after treatment with estrogen. Within 30 min of injection in rats, uterine hyperemia is observed (22), and progressive increases occur during the next 48 hr in wet and dry weight, amino acid incorporation, nitrogen deposition, phosphorus uptake, and glycogen deposition. This long-established effect of estrogens has been studied in detail. Naturally occurring estrogens have been placed in the following order of uterotrophic activity in rats: estradiol-17β > estrone > 16α-hydroxyestrone > $16\,\beta$-hydroxyestrone > estriol > 16-epiestriol. The growth-promoting properties of each steroid can be modified by other estrogens, suppressed by testosterone and corticoids, and enhanced by large doses of progesterone (368). The uterotrophic effect of estrogens is direct, unaffected by either hypophysectomy or adrenalectomy, and closely related to an increase in protein synthesis. As the detailed analysis of the latter progresses, the molecular action of estrogen in the mammalian uterus is becoming increasingly understood.

The action of progesterone is greatly influenced by the extent to which the uterus has been primed by estrogen. One of the best examples of this interaction of ovarian steroid hormones is found in the rabbit, where the proliferation of the epithelium and glands of the endometrium in preparation for the reception of the fertilized ovum is associated with the synergism of estrogen and progesterone. This progestational proliferation of the endometrium can be seen also in the cat and ferret, but it is much less pronounced in other species, including mouse, rat, guinea pig, cow, sheep, and pig. Progesterone alone, however, will produce progestational changes in the uterus when given in adequate amounts, though results are sometimes inconsistent.

Several contractile proteins, including actomyosin, myosin, actin, and tropomyosin, have been isolated from the mammalian uterus (58, 82, 267). Higher concentrations of actomyosin are found in the pregnant, compared with the nongravid, uterus. In the pregnant rabbit, uterine concentrations of actomyosin decrease at first but later increase to reach maximum values toward the end of gestation. The tension measured in the longitudinal muscle follows a similar pattern. One aim of these latter experiments was to discover whether myometrial hypertrophy and the synthesis of contractile proteins were caused by hormones or by the increased stretch due to the growing fetus and its membranes. The conclusion drawn from these studies and from observations in the human being is that, although hormones, particularly estrogens, can influence the concentration of at least one contractile protein, actomyosin, the stretch induced by the growing fetus is a major stimulus of uterine growth (84, 242, 247). In some species it is probable that the local placental production of steroid hormones directly influences uterine growth.

In a recent review, Carsten (59) describes the multiple effects of estrogen and progesterone on the biochemistry of the myometrium. These include effects on DNA, RNA, and protein synthesis, on respiratory and energy-supplying systems, and on carbohydrate metabolism, particularly the regulation of uterine glycogen content. Despite all this work it remains difficult to form a comprehensive picture of the sequence of biochemical changes that occur throughout gestation and especially of those critical changes associated with main events, such as implantation. For instance, much is known about the estrogen-induced biochemical changes in the rat uterus associated with ovulation, but relatively little is known about biochemical changes during the next few days, which prepare the uterus for implantation on days 3–4.

PROGESTERONE INHIBITS MYOMETRIAL ACTIVITY. Uterine physiology is markedly altered in pregnancy, and, among the changes associated with gestation, the reduction in myometrial activity is outstanding. This allows implantation to proceed normally and prevents the expulsion of fertilized eggs. It is related to high levels of plasma progesterone, which, when removed, as in the rabbit just before parturition, allows trains of action potentials, regular in amplitude and frequency and leading to synchronous myometrial contraction, to develop (59, 83, 85, 327).

The evidence in support of the conclusion that inhibition of myometrial activity ("progesterone block") is a principal function of progesterone in pregnancy includes the following observations (208). If progesterone secretion is abolished or impaired by ovariectomy or by placental dislocation in the pregnant rabbit (day 25 postcoitus), the electrical and mechanical activity of the myometrium increases within 48 hr. If progesterone is injected, activity can be abolished for 48 hr. When a strip of uterus from a postpartum rabbit is marked off into segments with a nontoxic dye, uterine movements can be observed. After electrical stimulation, induced activity spreads throughout the length of the strip, except when it is progesterone-dominated, when only the immediate segment stimulated contracts. If the rabbit uterus is progesterone-dominated, the relation of stimulus frequency to tension developed shows a negative staircase phenomenon, but, with estrogen dominance, there is a positive staircase effect (325).

These observations derive from work on one species,

and whether progesterone inhibition of the myometrium occurs in all is still controversial. In the human female it is claimed that the progesterone block can be demonstrated in vitro, but the results appear to be particularly dependent on the steroid concentration used (208). It has also been claimed that myometrial contractility of the human uterus can be inhibited by progesterone treatment in nonpregnant but not in late pregnant or parturient subjects (83). In the ewe the pattern of myometrial response to estrogen and progesterone appears to be similar to that of the rabbit, but in the rat only a negative staircase phenomenon has been demonstrated at any time of the reproductive cycle (326). In the guinea pig the finding that any dose of progesterone is without effect on myometrial contraction, even when given into the uterine lumen (294), is one of the most perplexing observations in a field already contradictory.

Widely differing explanations have been advanced to explain the way in which progesterone acts on the myometrial cell. Csapo believed initially that progesterone depolarized the myometrial cell membrane, but later he suggested that the effect was one of hyperpolarization. Thus, because of a higher resting potential in pregnancy, it was more difficult to depolarize the cell to the threshold level for spike generation. When the progesterone effect declined near term, a decreased resting potential facilitated excitation.

This view has been challenged by Kao (191) on the grounds that the current explanations of the progesterone block are not supported by recent work on the electrophysiological properties of the myometrial cell. A detailed study of the myometrial resting potential in nonpregnant rabbits revealed no significant difference between estrogen- and progesterone-treated animals, but in pregnancy (rat, rabbit, and mouse) higher resting potentials have been reported, especially in those areas overlying the placenta. But whether a higher resting potential is necessarily a deterrent to spike production and impulse propagation is in doubt; in fact, spike amplitudes were highest, overshoot greatest, and the maximum rate of rise most rapid when the resting potential was at its maximum during midpregnancy. It is improbable that the higher resting potentials are caused by differences in the intracellular Na^+, K^+, or Cl^-, since in the rat uterus these are similar on the 15th and 19th to 20th days of pregnancy and on the first day after parturition. Therefore it has been postulated that changes in ionic permeability may underlie the different resting potentials observed. The effect of estrogens and progesterone on the permeability of phospholipid membranes has recently been studied in experiments on model membranes (liposomes). After the liposomes had been fully equilibrated with the steroids, estrogens had a pronounced stabilizing action—they reduced the permeability of the membrane to $^{42}K^+$, whereas progesterone had a labilizing effect—it increased permeability (164).

PROGESTERONE AND PARTURITION. If myometrial activity is blocked in pregnancy by progesterone, it is to be expected that an increase in contractility associated with parturition be related to a withdrawal of this inhibition. One way in which this could be detected is by measuring the reduction of plasma progesterone levels before the onset of parturition. This is considered in greater detail in the chapter by Goldman and Zarrow in Part 1 of this *Handbook*, but it is relevant to the hypothesis that the pregnancy-maintaining action of progesterone is largely due to an inhibition of myometrial activity. As shown in Figures 4, 13, and 14, the plasma progesterone levels in circulating blood of several species (rabbit, rat, horse) are low at the time of parturition, but they do not always show a precipitate fall before the onset of labor. In contrast, levels in the human female and guinea pig (see Fig. 10) are high in pregnancy, there is no decrease either in uterine vein or peripheral blood levels, and labor may begin even when maternal progesterone levels are still rising (343, 365, 386). The progesterone levels fall precipitately only after the removal of the placenta and not necessarily after the death or removal of the fetus. When therapeutic abortions are induced by intraamniotic hypertonic saline, progesterone concentrations in systemic blood decrease gradually by about one-half, after which uterine activity increases and pregnancy is terminated (385). Thus the view that parturition is initiated by a sudden fall in circulating levels of progesterone is not supported by work on those species in which the placenta secretes appreciable amounts of progesterone, as in the human being, sheep, and guinea pig (see Figs. 10 and 11; Table 4). Results in sheep are not consistent, for in about half the animals studied a marked decrease was observed (31, 129).

On the other hand, experiments in rabbits provide convincing evidence that myometrial activity is inhibited by progesterone before parturition. If oxytocin is given to a rabbit before the 30th day of gestation, parturition is not induced, but, when it is injected 24 hr later, normal delivery occurs. This effect can be prevented, however, if progesterone (1 mg/kg) is given parenterally a day earlier [(85); Fig. 7] or if progesterone is applied locally to the uterus by an intraluminal injection (293). Thus, when the uterus is dominated by progesterone, the response to oxytocin is blocked; the effect of progesterone is to reduce coordinated myometrial contractions and perhaps also to block the hypothalamic release of oxytocin.

To account for this inconsistency in the progesterone block hypothesis, attention has been directed to the possibility of two opposing intrauterine events in species where placental progesterone production is appreciable. On the one hand, the increasing uterine volume associated with the growing conceptus stimulates myometrial activity, but, on the other hand, this is opposed by placental progesterone production acting locally (83). Evidence to support the idea that the "volume-to-progesterone ratio" is critical has been derived from several sources: *a*) the myometrial cells are less contractile and impulses are not propagated in regions adjacent to the placenta when compared with interplacental areas; and *b*) the delivery of twins in the human female 12 weeks

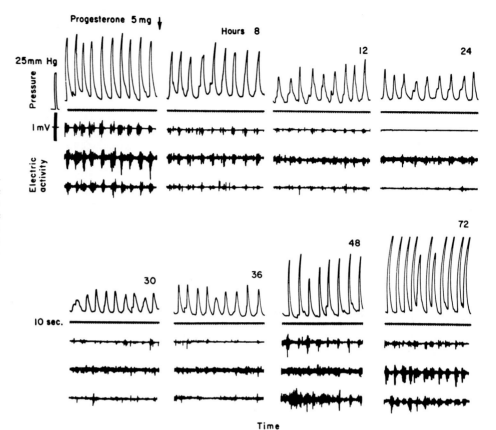

FIG. 7. Effect of intramuscularly administered progesterone (5 mg) on intrauterine pressure and electrical activity of the uterus in the conscious rabbit after the removal of the ovaries and placenta in late pregnancy. [From Csapo & Takeda (85).]

apart presumably reflects the local withdrawal of the progesterone block from one area of the uterus rather than another. In addition to this explanation, it seems probable that in those species in which the production of intrauterine progesterone occurs at a high level, the complex interaction of other factors, such as the binding of progesterone to tissue and plasma proteins and the pattern of its local metabolism, may also have important regulatory roles.

PROGESTERONE METABOLISM IN THE UTERUS. It has been known for some time that progesterone in the rat is rapidly metabolized by extrasplanchnic tissues. In uterine tissue the predominant metabolites of progesterone have a 5α-orientation resulting from oxidation in ring A by Δ^4-5α-reductase and 3α-hydroxysteroid dehydrogenase (380, 381). These enzymes are located in particulate cell fractions of whole uterus homogenates, whereas 20α-OH-SDH, present in the myometrium of the pregnant rat near term, is in the soluble fraction. The rate of progesterone metabolism is rapid, and, within 10 sec of an intravenous injection of 4-^{14}C-progesterone, labeled allopregnanedione is found in the myometrium even of eviscerated animals. In the latter preparation the amount of labeled allopregnanolone is less than that in intact rats, which indicates hepatic metabolism followed by myometrial uptake of the labeled compound. Although the rat myometrium is an active site of progesterone metabolism, it appears to retain a certain amount of unchanged progesterone

located in the nuclear-myofibrillar fraction. After the injection of labeled 17α-hydroxyprogesterone, however, highest radioactivity is found in the light microsome and soluble fractions (380).

The metabolism of progesterone in the human uterus (nonpregnant) differs quantitatively and qualitatively between the myometrium and endometrium (54, 55). In myometrial tissue the rate of metabolism in vitro is only one-sixth that found in endometrial incubations. A highly polar dihydroxy compound, a major product of endometrial metabolism, is not found in myometrial incubations. The 5α-orientated dihydro compounds are preferentially formed, as in the rat, but the capacity for reduction of the C3 keto group is not found in the human being.

ESTROGEN STIMULATES MYOMETRIAL ACTIVITY. The response of the quiescent, immature uterus to estrogen stimulation is striking. The resting membrane potential of 35 mv (inside negative) and the threshold potential are significantly raised and spike activity increased within a day of treatment in a number of species. This is followed by trains of action potentials of high amplitude and low frequency and the initiation of regular, rhythmic contractions of the myometrium. The characteristic action potentials appear in irregular bursts, and the form of the spikes is complex, presumably due to asynchronous discharge of neighboring cells. At or near parturition the release of oxytocin increases the frequency and amplitude of spikes but does not affect the resting potential. Overall, this brings about synchronous and single spikes, which are associated with the increasing activity of the myometrium (59, 191).

ESTROGENS AND PARTURITION. It has been argued that the high production of estrogen by the fetoplacental unit in the human female is not essential for the initiation of labor and increased myometrial activity. After fetal death, estrogen production is drastically reduced and labor can be readily induced without estrogen therapy—either by the injection of hypertonic solutions or by a small increase in uterine volume. However, this does not preclude the probability that estrogens play a very important part in the initiation of normal parturition. Such a role could be postulated from the following experimental evidence in the sheep. During the course of gestation plasma progesterone levels rise to a maximum at about day 130 postcoitus and in most animals fall gradually until parturition (see Fig. 11). Estrogen concentrations in the urine (total estrogens) increase from about day 70 and reach maximum levels near term (123), but the plasma concentration of unconjugated estrogens increases very sharply only 24–48 hr before parturition (63). It has recently been reported that estrogen treatment of sheep considerably increases the release of oxytocin in response to vaginal distension, whereas in goats progesterone has the opposite effect (304, 305). Moreover the prepartum rise in estrogen levels coincides with the time at which spontaneous uterine activity and myometrial reactivity to oxytocin show dramatic increases (372). These findings support a hypothesis that the sharp rise in estrogens constitutes an important component of the trigger to parturition. The extremely high concentrations of unconjugated estrogens in uterine venous blood just before parturition, when progesterone levels are declining, are consistent with a concept of removal of a myometrial progesterone block by estrogen dominance. It has been recognized for many years that estrogen treatment in pregnancy causes abortion or premature parturition; however, this is not true in all species.

The hypothesis, discussed above, that the fetus plays a major role in the initiation of parturition in the sheep must also take into consideration the striking hormonal changes observed in the mother and in particular the high circulating levels of estrogen found just before labor. The long-established interaction of ovarian steroids by which the physiological effects of estrogen and progesterone are enhanced or inhibited by each other deserve special mention in this context. In the human being, laborlike contractions have been recorded from the nonpregnant uterus near the time of menstruation. Attempts to produce these contractions experimentally were only successful when treatment with both estrogen and progesterone was stopped; no contractions were recorded when the treatment consisted of only one of the steroids (36).

MODE OF ACTION. The mammalian uterus has become a focus of research into the molecular action of estrogens

and, more recently, of progesterone. So far the primary action of these growth and regulatory hormones has not been defined, and in many instances their biochemical actions have been investigated in the nonpregnant, rather than the pregnant, uterus. Estradiol is initially bound to a cytoplasmic and then to nuclear receptor protein or proteins; this effect may constitute its primary action on the uterus, which is followed by a sequence of metabolic changes concerned with the growth of tissue. Some of the physical and chemical characteristics of the receptor proteins have been described (136, 185). The subsequent changes in tissue metabolism include an early stimulation of RNA synthesis and of the production of specific uterine proteins (29). It has been postulated that steroid hormones regulate protein synthesis by a modulation of messenger RNA (mRNA) synthesis, in much the same way as repressors and inducers control microbial protein synthesis (195). However, several processes in the protein synthesis of nucleate cells are independent of the rate of mRNA transcription (358), and it has been suggested that an important part of the primary action of steroid hormones such as estradiol may be the very rapid adjustment of the permeability of the uterus toward nucleotides and amino acids.

The consequent stimulation of general protein synthesis that is concerned with uterine growth and is closely associated with the changes that occur at the time of implantation is, not surprisingly, related to a hormonal stimulation of RNA synthesis. The long-term biochemical effects of estrogen action on the uterus, as distinct from a short-lasting pulse, have not been studied in such detail.

The biochemistry of the action of progesterone on the uterus is not yet clear, and it raises several fundamental questions about the actions of steroid hormones in general. Although radioactive estradiol is concentrated in target tissues, there has been little evidence hitherto that progesterone is similarly retained by target cells. On the contrary, progesterone is rapidly metabolized in the body and in target tissues. Thus labeled progesterone infused close-arterially into the mammary gland of pregnant and nonpregnant goats is rapidly metabolized; mammary extraction, calculated from the arteriovenous difference and expressed as a percentage of the arterial concentration, is greater than 60%; the concentration of labeled metabolites in this target tissue, however, was extremely low (162, 345). Despite a high rate of metabolism within target tissues, more recent work has revealed that small amounts of unmetabolized progesterone are retained. Thus, in the chick oviduct, which is a progesterone-sensitive tissue, a macromolecular component that has a high affinity for progesterone has been identified in the cytoplasm. After the injection of labeled progesterone into the chick, a major fraction of the labeled steroid in the oviduct was associated with this component [(275); and the chapter by O'Malley and Strout in Part 1 of this *Handbook*].

Similarly, recent work with progesterone of high specific activity shows that tissue binding of progesterone does occur in the mammalian uterus (120, 257) and probably plays an important part in pregnancy maintenance (86, 381). In the rat, from a comparison of progesterone and 20α-diHP levels in arterial plasma with those in ovarian, placental, and uterine tissues, it appears that uterine tissue is capable of concentrating progesterone in early and midpregnancy (see Fig. 13). This may be relevant to the biological action of progesterone, particularly during the time of implantation and placentation. In contrast, its 20α-metabolite, a weak progestagen, is not concentrated. During late pregnancy a progesterone concentration in uterine tissue of 2 μg/100 g prevents parturition, but, if 20α-diHP levels are greater than 3 μg/100 g, normal delivery occurs. Moreover, when both ovaries are removed or when the placentas in one horn are dislocated on day 17 postcoitus, there is unilateral abortion of the conceptuses from the uterine horn of lower progesterone concentration. These results provide further evidence for the theory discussed above that an increase in uterine volume without an increase in uterine progesterone is a prerequisite for the onset of parturition (86).

It has been claimed that progestational activity resides solely in the unchanged progesterone molecule (381), unlike the androgenic activity of testosterone, which also resides in its immediate metabolite, 5α-dihydrotestosterone. No significant progestational activity of 20α-diHP or 5α-pregnanedione has been found after injection in vivo. This does not exclude the possibility that in target cells progestational action may involve the rapid metabolism of progesterone to its 5α-metabolites, for these epimers, rather than the 5β-compounds comprising the urinary products, are preferentially formed in target tissues, such as the uterus, mammary gland, and hypothalamus. However, pregnanolone, a short-acting, potent, hypnotic steroid with a 5β-configuration, also has a pronounced action on the uterus. It is more potent than progesterone in preventing either oxytocin-induced contractions of isolated strips of rat uteri or contractions of the isolated rat duodenum produced by barium chloride (143).

Protein Hormones

The role of pituitary gonadotrophins in the maintenance of lutein function in pregnancy has been discussed above, but, as in the case of such placental protein hormones as HCG, HPL, and PMSG, our knowledge of their mechanism of action is rudimentary. The physiological effects of these hormones are here briefly summarized in so far as they contribute to an understanding of the hormonal requirements of pregnancy maintenance [for more detailed information, see (48, 127, 128)].

Secreted by the human placenta throughout pregnancy, HCG affects a number of endocrine organs, including the ovary, adrenal, and the placenta itself. Many of these effects have been observed in animals, in which HGG is a distinctly foreign substance, and consequently the results cannot be readily applied to the

human subject. Human chorionic gonadotrophin causes luteinization of ovarian interstitial and thecal cells, but its ability to cause follicular growth is still in doubt. Recent work with anti-HCG serum has shown that, although it will quantitatively neutralize the FSH-like activity of HCG, it does not eliminate all HCG activity (308). Thus the FSH-like properties of HCG preparations are not due to a contamination by pituitary FSH and may be attributable to a separate hormone different from HCG but cross-reacting with its antiserum. That HCG has luteotrophic potency in the human female and monkey has been recognized for many years, but whether this is its major role in human pregnancy is doubtful. This has led to a reconsideration of the question of how the life of the CL is prolonged in pregnancy and whether other placental protein hormones, such as HPL, may have a luteotrophic action. In this connection it may be noted that the CL of pregnancy is still capable of secreting a small amount of progesterone at term (217).

One intriguing suggestion about the function of the large amounts of protein hormones produced by the human placenta is that they perhaps act in regulating its metabolic and steroidogenic functions. Such an integrative role of HCG or HPL, or both, would be consistent with the autonomous nature of placental function, but it can hardly be thought to apply to those species in which the placenta appears to produce neither of these hormones. Since high levels of HCG in the last trimester are more frequently associated with the birth of female fetuses, it has been suggested that its placental synthesis may be influenced by the fetus (48).

Human placental lactogen is immunologically and biologically similar to HGH. It has been shown to have growth-promoting properties in several test systems, including the incremental weight gain found in hypophysectomized rats, as well as in hypopituitary human dwarfs given large doses of hormone. Its metabolic effects resemble those of HGH; it increases the level of circulating ketone bodies in fasted rats and the incorporation of glucose into fat and plasma fatty acids in the fasted monkey or rabbit; it causes hyperglycemia and hypertriglyceridemia in rabbits after 25 days of treatment. To add to an already complex range of activities, it has also been reported that this placental hormone is diabetogenic and that it antagonizes insulin and thereby increases the amount of glucose and amino acids available to the fetus (128).

Thus HPL, the "growth hormone" of late pregnancy, appears to possess multiple actions in human gestation. It seems highly probable that it plays more than a permissive role in the humoral maintenance of gestation, especially since low HPL levels have been found in blood in cases of placental insufficiency. In addition to its important effects on growth and body metabolism, it has also a prolactin-like activity, which, according to the results of certain assays, is pronounced. Whether such proteins are also produced in other species during pregnancy remains to be seen.

Pregnant mares' serum gonadotrophin, a glycoprotein with a molecular weight of 68,000, possesses a particularly high FSH activity. This activity was first shown by Cole and Hart in 1930 who found that pregnant mares' serum stimulated follicular growth and ovulation in the immature rat, unlike human pregnancy urine, which only stimulated luteinization and ovulation of follicles already well developed. In the pregnant mare the biological action of PMSG remains obscure. It is present in blood between about 40 and 150 days of gestation, which coincides with the time when accessory follicles first appear and become the secondary CL of pregnancy. After this period in pregnancy, the ovaries contain neither CL nor large follicles, and they contribute little to the maintenance of gestation, since ovariectomy no longer causes abortion (13). However, before this period (i.e., before PMSG is produced), large follicles may be found in the ovary. Whether PMSG has a luteotrophic role in the mare is not yet resolved. In recent experiments in which the fetus has been removed at different times during pregnancy, a return of normal estrus and ovulation is delayed so long as PMSG can be detected in blood; this suggests that PMSG may in some way inhibit these events in a normal pregnancy (3).

Relaxin is a polypeptide hormone of low molecular weight; it is stable to heat but can be inactivated at its disulfide bridges and free carboxy groups. In serum it is associated with the pseudoglobulin fraction. It is produced in the ovaries (CL) and placentas and has been located in the blood and reproductive organs of a number of species; it increases from very low levels early in gestation to a peak in mid- or late pregnancy but then declines. The levels in a number of species have been assayed by the guinea pig symphysis-pubis test.

Relaxin is devoid of estrogenic or progestagenic activity but acts synergistically with steroids in causing relaxation of the pelvic ligaments in late pregnancy. In terms of pregnancy maintenance it is important to note that relaxin inhibits spontaneous uterine contractions in vivo and in vitro and reduces the contractility of the myometrium in nonpregnant women after estrogen priming. The effects of relaxin treatment include softening and increased distensibility of the cervix and lower uterine segments of sows and heifers, increased myometrial glycogenesis and alkaline phosphatase activity in the mouse, and lobular-alveolar growth of the rat mammary gland. Relaxin also acts synergistically with progesterone in maintaining pregnancy in the ovariectomized mouse, as well as in facilitating the delivery of live young.

There are many problems requiring investigation before the role of this peptide in pregnancy maintenance and parturition is fully understood. Relaxin apparently consists of two active principles and has only slight antigenic properties. Parturition can occur in guinea pigs both hypophysectomized and ovariectomized, which indicates a placental source, but, as slight pubic separation also occurs at estrus in the nonpregnant guinea pig,

the placenta cannot be the only site of production (91, 146).

Other Humoral Factors

Several humoral factors show striking changes in their circulating and tissue concentrations during gestation. The role of oxytocin is a special case in point and is concerned with the onset of parturition; it is discussed in detail elsewhere in the *Handbook*. Brief reference should also be made to 5-hydroxytryptamine (5-HT, serotonin), prostaglandins, and renin—each has been implicated in the mechanism of parturition. An efficient regulatory mechanism of these humoral factors appears to be an essential feature of the maintenance of the normal pregnant state. If monoamine oxidase inhibitors are administered to pregnant rats, 5-HT metabolism is blocked and there is a high percentage of abortions (291). Prostaglandin $F_{2\alpha}$ ($PGF_{2\alpha}$) concentration apparently rises in peripheral blood during uterine contractions and, along with PGE_2, induces normal labor or terminates prenancy when infused into human subjects (194). Renin concentrations in blood are raised during human pregnancy, probably because of increased production by the uterus or kidneys (131). However, whether it has a role in pregnancy maintenance or in parturition remains obscure.

Metabolic Changes

During pregnancy the balance of maternal metabolism is shifted toward anabolism; in addition to uterine and fetal growth, the increases in mammary development, in blood volume, and probably in the weight of other organs, such as the liver, indicate a retention of water, protein, and fat. It appears that maternal weight gain in pregnancy is under endocrinological control and that it is related to the higher metabolic activity of the mother throughout pregnancy and does not simply represent an accumulation of "excess" reserves so that the maternal organism is not deprived to supply the fetus (95, 178). The early work on this subject was performed in mice, and it was revealed that the pregnancy weight gain was associated with the presence of the placenta, rather than the fetus (271). Subsequent work has been concentrated on the nature of this weight gain in different species, including the human female, and on its endocrine control.

The effect of hormones on maternal body weight gain during pregnancy has been studied in detail in the mouse (95) and rat (169). Progesterone, but not estrogen, is considered to have an important role, but the mode of its action appears to be very different in the two species. In the mouse, ovarian progesterone secretion is responsible for the extrauterine retention of protein, water, and fat. Even when food intake is restricted to maintenance or submaintenance levels, the anabolic effect of the steroid can still be demonstrated. All these experiments were conducted with the use of a "total metabolism technique" in which the balance of weight, water, fat, protein, and total energy expenditure was monitored daily. Progesterone apparently has a triple influence on body weight in pregnancy: it induces water retention, possibly by a DOCA-like action; it stimulates appetite and consequently food intake; and it has a protein anabolic effect. The weight gain produced by progesterone in the rat (nonpregnant) is associated with increased accumulation of water, fat, and other solids, as in the mouse. It only occurs in females, however, and, unlike the response in the mouse, ovariectomy has an effect very similar to progesterone treatment. The conclusion reached is therefore that progesterone increases body weight in the rat because when administered exogenously it suppresses ovarian function.

In an analysis of the components of weight gain during normal pregnancy in women, less than half the increase can be accounted for in terms of the contribution of the products of conception and the increase in weight of mammary glands and maternal blood. The still unexplained "maternal store" is probably fat, since it is water-free and stored in considerable quantity (4 kg) [(178); Fig. 8]. An explanation of these findings is complicated by the results of investigations in women, in whom progesterone has been found to be protein catabolic and natriuretic (213), although there is some evidence that women taking oral contraceptives containing progestagens may gain weight. The discrepancies between these results and those of experiments in which rats or mice are used may be due to the experiments being carried out at different times during gestation, because there is some evidence that in mice progesterone can have anabolic and catabolic effects, depending on the stage of pregnancy (95).

Vascular Changes

UTERINE BLOOD FLOW. The total blood flow to the pregnant uterus increases progressively throughout gestation, but many technical obstacles are associated with such measurements, particularly with respect to the distribution of the vascular supply within the uterus and placenta during a time when uterine weight is increasing rapidly (262). Uterine blood flow per unit weight of tissue has

been measured in goats by the 4-aminoantipyrine technique (176); it is high in the nonpregnant animal and in early pregnancy (610 ml/kg per min) but decreases in mid-pregnancy to fairly stable levels of 277 ml/kg per minute, which are maintained until parturition. These results are at variance with those of some other studies, and the reasons for the discrepancies have not been completely resolved.

Uterine blood flow in the pregnant sheep has been measured by square-wave electromagnetic flow probes and zero occlusion loops (140). Estrogens have a striking effect on the uterine vascular bed. Uterine blood flow in nonpregnant ewes increases 8-fold to 20-fold at estrus over that in the luteal phase of the cycle. The sharp rise corresponds exactly with the time at which ovarian estrogens are secreted (139, 175, 260). In pregnancy, conjugated estrogens (Premarin, 0.55–0.92 mg/kg per hr) infused intravenously 106–134 days after mating produced a marked rise in uterine blood flow (138 and 134 % greater than controls infused with saline) between the second and eighth hours of the experiment [(141); Fig. 9]. In early pregnancy, after the high rate of uterine blood flow observed at estrus, there is a rapid decrease per unit weight of tissue similar to the pattern usually observed in the luteal phase of the estrous cycle. On the

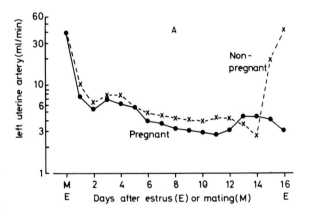

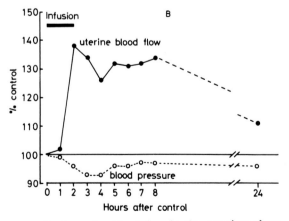

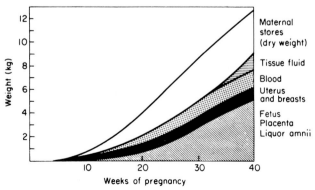

FIG. 8. The components of weight gain in normal human pregnancy. [From Hytten & Thomson (178).]

FIG. 9. *A:* uterine blood flow in the conscious sheep. [From Greiss & Anderson (140).] *B:* effect of estrogens (Premarin, 0.55–0.92 mg/kg per hr) infused intravenously on uterine blood flow and blood pressure in the conscious, pregnant sheep 106–134 days postcoitus. [From Greiss & Marston (141).]

17th or 18th day of gestation another sharp rise occurs, particularly noticeable if the conceptus is in the uterine horn ipsilateral to the monitored artery. As in the goat, uterine blood flow in the sheep per unit weight of tissue then declines to midpregnancy values. It appears probable that uterine blood flow in this species increases dramatically at term as a result of the greatly elevated levels of blood estrogens (21).

These observations raise several questions concerning the regulation of uterine blood flow in pregnancy. It can be seen that the changes parallel the greater requirements associated with the gravid horn, though the studies in sheep indicate that the resistance of the uterine capillary bed is highly sensitive to the action of estrogens. The circulating levels of estrogens in the nonpregnant sheep at estrus are probably less than 10 pg/ml; nevertheless these levels cause striking increases in uterine blood flow and decreases in uterine resistance. It seems that the response of the uterus in terms of increased blood flow is considerably more marked than that of other tissues. The ovary presents a special case in that both ovarian blood flow and lymph flow are considerably greater when the CL is present and secreting progesterone, rather than when estrogen secretion is high. The regulation of uterine blood flow, however, is unusual in that, unlike many of the vital organs, autoregulation in the uterus, whether pregnant or not, is absent. The low-resistance placenta is probably the major factor in reducing the response of the maternal and fetal cardiovascular systems to vasoactive stimuli (210). The mechanism of the uterine vascular response to hormonal stimuli, such as estrogens, is not yet clarified, but the presence of adrenergic α-receptors may be a contributory factor (240).

Information on uterine blood flow in human beings is mainly restricted to the time immediately before parturition. The available results suggest that it is considerably lower than in sheep and goats, whether expressed as total uterine blood flow or per unit of tissue weight. When measured by the nitrous oxide technique, no significant changes were observed throughout pregnancy—average blood flow was 8.9 ml/100 g tissue per minute (21). This value contrasts with that of the pregnant rat in which uterine blood flow per gram of tissue (minus uterine contents) measured by Sapirstein's indicator fractionation method was found to increase with cardiac output on the 21st day. It was maintained at a high level until parturition and then fell to a very low level within an hour (221).

The problems concerning measurements of uterine blood flow, to which we have already referred, have been attacked by experiments in which isotope-labeled microspheres and macroaggregated albumin were used to determine the partition of the vascular supply within the gravid horn. In the pregnant rabbit about 60% of uterine arterial blood goes to the placenta, 27% to the myometrium, and 13% to the vagina (111, 112). In the pregnant sheep, more than 84% of uterine flow goes to the placental cotyledons. In the work on the pregnant rabbit, attention was drawn to the more frequent occurrence of abortions and runts in the cervical part of the uterine horn, whereas oversize fetuses are usually found near the ovary. It has been suggested that this is related to the fact that blood flow within the placenta is highest in those placentas nearest the ovary.

OTHER VASCULAR CHANGES. Changes in blood volume and composition during human pregnancy are appreciable. They consist of an increase in plasma volume from about the end of the first trimester, an increase in red cell volume, and a decrease in hemoglobin concentration and hematocrit—the so-called physiological anemia of pregnancy. Plasma composition also changes; many plasma lipid fractions increase, as do some enzymes, including alkaline phosphatase (specific placental production), glutamic oxaloacetic transaminase, and lactic dehydrogenase; there is a notable fall in serum cholinesterase. The concentration of plasma protein decreases dramatically, though the concentration of the α-globulin fraction rises slightly, possibly in view of its role as a transport component of hormones and nutrients (178).

Cardiac output increases in pregnancy in many species, including the human, in whom a seeming fall the last few weeks of pregnancy is thought to be a technical artifact. Cardiac output is probably maintained at its midpregnancy level with no fall in renal blood flow and only a small decrease in lower limb blood flow. The increases that also occur in oxygen consumption and in renal clearances arising from a more effective glomerular filtration rate do not appear at present to be clearly related to hormonal control.

EMBRYONIC MORTALITY

In an animal bearing more than a single embryo, the loss of one or more does not necessarily entail the complete failure of pregnancy. Indeed a proportion of embryonic mortality is commonly regarded as normal in polytocous species, such as the pig, at least in domestic breeds in which the average litter is very large. The uterine environment is seen to be capable of supporting some of the fetuses, and it is natural to suppose that there must be something wrong with those that die or that sheer numbers may result in such competition for the available nutriment or accommodation that some fail to receive food and lodging.

There is no doubt that the fault may lie in the genome of the embryo itself (38). It may involve a lethal mutation, aneuploidy, or a disability that enhances the embryo's susceptibility to risk at various stages of development. There is, on the other hand, a great deal of evidence that embryonic loss may be due to maternal factors, and in such cases it represents a partial failure of pregnancy maintenance. This may be an inherited trait of the mother (287), or it may be attributed to more immediate causes, such as maternal nutrition (212) or the stress of a high ambient temperature (346).

It is evident that embryonic and fetal death, in pregnancies in which one or more siblings survive to term, is very unevenly distributed with respect to the stage of gestation. A high proportion of the loss, in the species studied, occurs early (290) in gestation—probably, in the pig and sheep, before the uterine luteolytic factor has been "switched off" and before any placental connection has been established between mother and embryo. Failure at a much later stage of gestation accounts for some further embryonic loss, which produces the "mummified fetuses" sometimes seen in domestic animals, and stillbirths account for yet another fraction of the total incidence of prenatal mortality. These three components of the total—early, late, and terminal—loss are differently distributed within the population, at least in the pig, the species most thoroughly investigated in this respect. Early loss is linearly related to the number of ova ovulated; later loss is not related to litter size but is concentrated within individuals (i.e., the loss of one fetus is usually associated with the loss of others in the same animal, usually within the same uterine horn); and stillbirths, which are nonlinearly related to litter size, are most frequent in very small and very large litters (286, 289).

Attention has been directed at various times to the observation that, in polytocous species with bicornuate uteri, certain positions along the uterine horn are especially favorable to embryonic development. This has been found in rabbits, mice, guinea pigs, and pigs, and in all cases the most favored position was the ovarian end of the uterine horn, the cervical end being the next best, and the intermediate positions the least favorable. It has been suggested on anatomic grounds that the relative position of placentas in the uterine arterial arcade is the cause of differences in placental weight and fetal survival (236), but this seems unlikely to apply to the pig (289). The recent finding, already referred to, that in the rabbit placental blood flow is highest in the conceptus nearest to the ovary (111), appears a more plausible explanation.

An explanation of the causes of prenatal death, especially the large fraction incurred very early in pregnancy, probably before implantation, would have great practical value and theoretical interest. On both counts the problems have received a considerable amount of attention, but very little progress has been made beyond the descriptive phase. The incidence of embryonic loss in several species has been studied in relation to genetics, nutrition, and other external factors and to such internal factors as hormonal levels, as well as litter size, parity, and body weight, but little has been learned of how the loss is imposed by the uterine environment. It seems that explanation of the abnormal must await the elucidation of the normal, and, rather than the analysis of pregnancy failure being useful in the investigation of pregnancy maintenance, the various categories of prenatal mortality probably will not be explained until we have a clearer understanding of the humoral mechanisms of normal, successful pregnancy maintenance.

HORMONE LEVELS IN PREGNANCY

Discussed here are the changes in the levels of hormones found in pregnancy, particularly the levels of steroid and protein hormones in blood, for they represent more closely than do urinary levels the secretory activity of the endocrine organs during gestation and reflect the hormone concentrations transported to target tissues. The situation is complicated by the fact that some of the target tissues may be affected by hormones produced in their immediate vicinity, as in the placenta. It also becomes apparent that even the hormone concentrations in circulating blood do not necessarily reflect either the amount available to, or the quantity required by, target tissues. However, it is evident in this chapter's next section that, with a knowledge of these levels and their variations during gestation, experiments can be carried out to define more precisely the hormonal requirements of pregnancy maintenance and the different ways in which they are supplied.

During the past five years new highly sensitive techniques allowing the rapid estimation of steroid and protein hormones in small samples of blood taken serially have been developed. Advances in the steroid field have included gas-liquid chromatography with electron capture detection, competitive protein binding, and radioimmunoassay procedures. In the last two techniques, the protein used may be a specific transport protein such as transcortin (CBG), or a specific uterine protein, such as that binding estradiol-17β, from the uterine endometrial cytosol, or an antiserum raised against a steroid-protein conjugate. Advances in the protein hormone field have included the development of highly sensitive radioimmunoassays.

In blood, steroids may be present in different physicochemical forms of unequal biological activity. Because of the high partition coefficient and the low aqueous solubilities of most of the steroids being considered here (164), only a very small fraction is to be found free in the aqueous phase; another fraction (usually small) may be bound to the erythrocyte membrane, whereas the remaining and normally much larger fraction is bound to plasma proteins. Albumin has a high capacity and a low affinity for steroids, whereas other plasma proteins (globulins), such as transcortin, sex hormone-binding globulin, and progesterone-binding protein (PBP), have a small capacity but high affinity (see Table 5). Much of the steroid found in circulating blood is conjugated in the liver with sulfuric or glucuronic acid residues. Conjugated steroids, or steroids bound to high-affinity proteins, are frequently regarded as very largely inactive biologically. Whereas this is a convenient form of classification, it should be noted that the conjugated compounds are readily utilized in some active pathways of steroid biogenesis and may possess biological actions of their own. It will be necessary to consider each of these physicochemical forms not in isolation but rather in dynamic equilibrium.

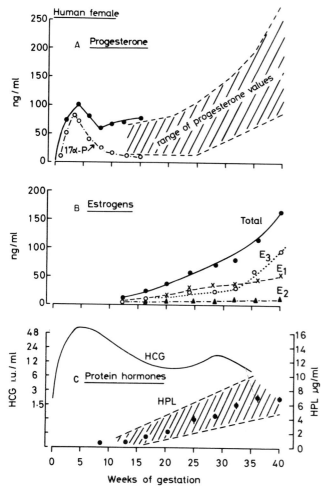

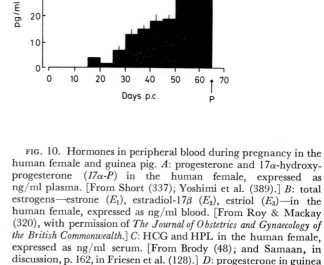

FIG. 10. Hormones in peripheral blood during pregnancy in the human female and guinea pig. *A*: progesterone and 17α-hydroxyprogesterone (*17α-P*) in the human female, expressed as ng/ml plasma. [From Short (337); Yoshimi et al. (389).] *B*: total estrogens—estrone (E_1), estradiol-17β (E_2), estriol (E_3)—in the human female, expressed as ng/ml blood. [From Roy & Mackay (320), with permission of *The Journal of Obstetrics and Gynaecology of the British Commonwealth*.] *C*: HCG and HPL in the human female, expressed as ng/ml serum. [From Brody (48); and Samaan, in discussion, p. 162, in Friesen et al. (128).] *D*: progesterone in guinea pig; ng/ml plasma; mean ±SE is indicated. Intact guinea pigs, *shaded columns*; ovariectomized guinea pigs, *open columns*. [From Heap & Deanesly (159).] *E*: total unconjugated estrogens in guinea pig; pg/ml plasma; mean ±SE is indicated. P, parturition. [From Challis et al. (67).]

It is generally supposed that the free and bound hormone fractions are distinguishable by target cells and that membrane permeability is restricted to the free hormone. Thus the relatively high concentrations of steroids to which cells are exposed may be more apparent than real, since there is probably little dissociation from the high-affinity binding proteins during transit through tissues.

With this proviso consideration can now be given to the changes in maternal levels of steroid and protein hormones during the gestation period of several species (Figs. 10–14).

HORMONE PRODUCTION RATES AND
KINETICS OF METABOLISM

Earlier sections of this chapter have dealt with the changes in endocrine organs that are associated with the secretion of hormones involved in pregnancy maintenance, the action of steroid and protein hormones insofar as they are concerned with producing an environment conducive to the growth and development of the conceptus, and the levels of hormones in blood and tissues during normal pregnancy. As will be seen, the absolute blood

levels of a particular hormone when considered alone can be misleading; they are the product of a dynamic equilibrium resulting from the rate at which the hormone is being produced, its biological half-life, and its distribution within the body. By the use of tracer techniques, much more information is being obtained about each of these factors, and experimental procedures that allow the kinetics of metabolism and production rates to be measured in the conscious animal or human subject have been developed. These data can be used to compute the compartmentation of steroids within the body and the rates of transfer from one compartment to another. In this section we concentrate on the relatively few kinetic studies that have so far been carried out during pregnancy. For clarity, the term *production rate* describes the total amount of hormone produced in the body and is synonymous with entry rate or turnover rate.

In these experiments it is necessary to assume steady-state conditions in which the amount of steroid in the system is constant and the rate of secretion into a particular pool is equal to its rate of removal. In practice there are likely to be diurnal variations of steroid secretion, as revealed in studies on estrone and cortisol in man (27). Nevertheless, if the rate of metabolism is high and the

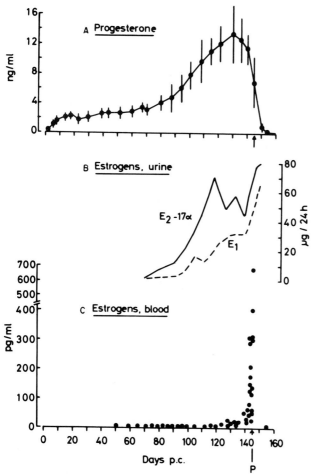

FIG. 11. Steroid hormones in the pregnant sheep. *A*: peripheral plasma progesterone ±SD. [From Bassett et al. (31).] *B*: urinary estrogens—estrone (E_1) and estradiol-17α (E_2-*17α*). [From Fevre et al. (123).] *C*: total unconjugated estrogens in peripheral plasma. *P*, parturition. [From Challis (63).]

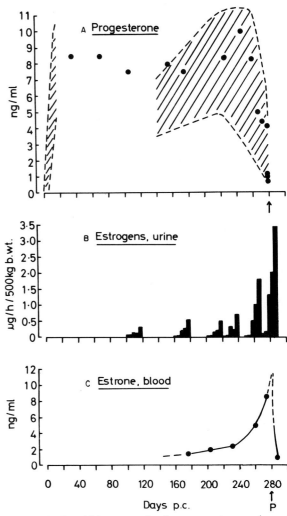

FIG. 12. Steroid hormones in the pregnant cow. *A*: peripheral plasma progesterone. [From Short (337); Stabenfeldt et al. (355).] *B*: urinary estrogens—*columns* from left to right represent estriol, estradiol-17β, estrone, estradiol-17α, and total estrogens, respectively. [From Erb et al. (117).] *C*: estrone, expressed as ng/ml blood. *P*, parturition. [From Robinson et al. (306).]

variations in steroid secretion are slow, it is probably safe to assume that the changes are too small to perturb the steady state during an experiment.

In order to arrive at an accurate measurement of the rate at which a hormone is produced in pregnancy, it is necessary to measure the rate at which it is cleared from blood—its metabolic clearance rate (MCR)—and its concentration in peripheral blood. The concept of MCR (357) is derived from classic renal physiology in which kidney clearance is the product of the percentage of the substance extracted and the blood flow through the organ. In the case of an unconjugated steroid, MCR is the sum of individual organ and tissue clearances and is defined as the irreversible clearance from the unconjugated fraction in the blood compartment expressed as the volume of blood completely cleared per unit time. Experimentally MCR may be arrived at by several methods. In one method a small amount of labeled steroid is injected intravenously and its rate of disappearance from blood is monitored in samples taken at frequent intervals. From the concentration of specifi-

cally isolated steroid in blood, it is possible by extrapolation to zero time to determine the theoretical concentration at the moment of the injection. This value can be related to the amount injected in order to calculate MCR. Although this technique has been successfully applied to the study of several steroids in man, it did not provide a satisfactory basis for the study of cortisol metabolism in the sheep, probably because labeled steroid was metabolized too rapidly immediately after injection to allow adequate mixing with endogenous cortisol (153). The method of choice is that of constant isotope infusion, in which the tracer is infused continuously until its concentration and specific activity in blood have reached steady-state conditions; MCR can then be calculated from the rate of isotope infusion divided by the concentration of specifically isolated steroid; interconversions are measured under steady-state conditions, and random

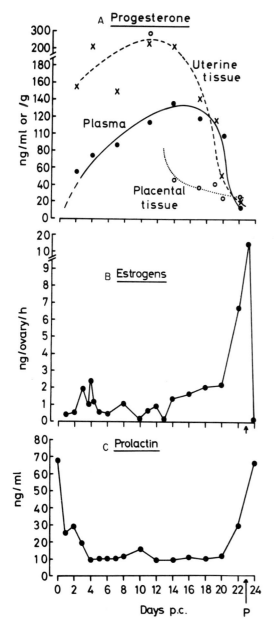

FIG. 13. Hormones in the pregnant rat. *A*: progesterone concentrations. [From Wiest (382).] *B*: estrogen secretion rate. [From Yoshinaga et al. (390).] *C*: prolactin concentration, expressed as ng/ml serum. *P*, parturition. [From Amenomori et al. (6).]

errors can be calculated more accurately. Moreover the rate of disappearance from blood can be monitored after the infusion has stopped, so that the half-life and distribution of the steroid within body compartments can be studied (27, 357).

The production rate (PR) of a hormone can be calculated from the product of MCR (liters of blood/min) and the endogenous concentration of the steroid (μg/liter of blood). It is the sum of endocrine organ secretion and the amount formed in extraendocrine tissues from precursors or prehormones (26). A *prehormone* is a substance normally present in the body but with low biological activity,

which is converted peripherally to a compound of greater biological activity. Examples of such interconversions are androstenedione to testosterone and estrone to estradiol-17β. The conversion of pregnenolone to progesterone in man (223) is considered an example of hormone production from an immediate precursor rather than from a prehormone, since only a small amount (2.4%) of the PR of progesterone is derived from pregnenolone. Interconversions in peripheral tissues, such as target tissues, may depend on the local NADPH-to-NADP ratio, as demonstrated by Talalay (363) for estrogen metabolism in the placenta. Such reactions, however, may be difficult to detect experimentally, unless a sufficient amount of the product is released into the general circulation.

Progesterone

We have seen that the plasma concentration of progesterone rises to a high level in pregnancy in some species (human, guinea pig) but remains low in others (ferret, rhesus monkey, sheep, cow, and pig) [(241, 269); see Figs. 1, 10, 11, and 12]. In the former group, plasma levels in pregnancy reach values of 100 ng/ml, and at certain times even higher concentrations have been observed (see Fig. 10). This 100-fold increase over values in nonpregnant animals contrasts with the smaller 10-fold increase observed in the sheep (see Fig. 11) and with the absence of any increase in the pregnant ferret (see Fig. 1). Recent studies of the dynamics of progesterone metabolism reveal that, although a classification into two groups of species, high and low plasma progesterone levels, respectively, is convenient, it obscures other differences that are probably fundamental to the process of pregnancy maintenance.

The human female and guinea pig serve to illustrate two extremes of what may eventually prove to be a wide range of mechanisms whereby different species meet their progesterone requirements in pregnancy. As indicated above, the sources of progesterone production in pregnancy are similar in man and guinea pig. In early pregnancy the CL forms the main secretory unit, but the placenta becomes increasingly important as the CL regresses in the human being or wanes in activity in the guinea pig. In both species the maximum plasma progesterone levels are of the same order; in the human being the levels continue to rise throughout gestation, whereas in the guinea pig they increase sharply after day 15 postcoitus, decline after about day 40, and rise again in the last stage of gestation (Fig. 15).

Notwithstanding these similarities, the dynamics of progesterone metabolism in these two species are markedly different. The MCR in pregnant women is similar to that in nonpregnant females, but the production rate in pregnant women is about 10 times greater than that in the luteal phase of the menstrual cycle and at least 100 times greater than that in the follicular phase [(223, 225); see Table 4]. Before these more precise estimates of progesterone production were available, urinary

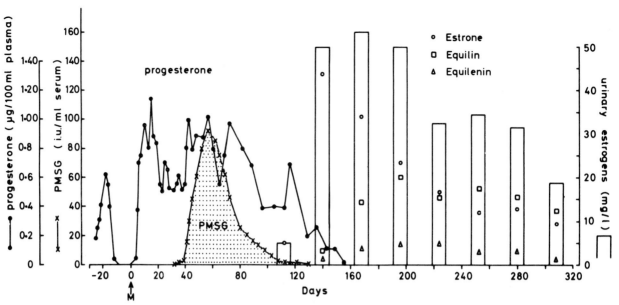

FIG. 14. Hormones in the pregnant mare—progesterone, PMSG, and estrogens. [From Allen (3) and Savard (322).]

pregnanediol estimations had been used as an index of progesterone production. In a detailed investigation of pregnanediol precursors, however, it was found that, in normal individuals, pregnenolone and possibly also pregnenolone sulfate are secreted in significant amounts and may make an important contribution to urinary pregnanediol. In consequence the secretion rate of progesterone cannot be accurately estimated from measurements of urinary pregnanediol after the administration of labeled progesterone (16). Nevertheless, in late pregnancy, when progesterone production is high, production rates measured by urinary excretion or in blood are similar—250 and 297 mg/day, respectively (223, 281).

In the pregnant guinea pig the rate of progesterone clearance is much less than that in the nonpregnant animal (160, 180). In ovariectomized, nonpregnant guinea pigs implanted with progesterone tablets, plasma levels are low (7–23 ng/ml), as in the normal cycle. But in pregnant guinea pigs ovariectomized in the first week after mating and killed on or before the 30th day of gestation, progesterone implants result in plasma levels at least 20-fold greater than in nonpregnant animals. In this study (160) animals were killed during the first 30 days of pregnancy, when the actual production of placental progesterone is far less than that of the ovary and is well below that reached in later stages (159). Since the absorption from progesterone implants is similar in pregnant and nonpregnant animals, it is concluded that the rate of progesterone clearance differs between the two groups. When MCR is measured by a continuous infusion technique in anesthetized guinea pigs, it is found to decrease by about 90% between the 15th and 20th days of gestation and to remain low until after parturition. Simultaneously with the change in MCR, plasma pro-

gesterone concentrations increase about 100-fold, whereas progesterone production rates increase only about 10-fold (Fig. 15 and Table 4).

Thus it appears that the hormonal maintenance of pregnancy, a primary function of progesterone, can be ensured in more than one way. In the human female the increased progesterone concentration in blood and placental tissue required in pregnancy is achieved by an increase in the amount produced by the placenta. In the guinea pig the increase in production rate is not sufficient to account for the whole of the rise in circulating levels, a great part of which is attributable to a progesterone-conserving mechanism involving a drop in MCR and mediated through a specific binding protein. A concomitant of this mode of control found in the guinea pig is a very low concentration of progesterone in placental tissue. When allowance is made for the difference in body weight, a slightly lower value is found in the guinea pig (about 3 mg/kg per day) compared with that found in the human being in pregnancy (about 5 mg/kg per day).

Experiments in several species have shown that labeled progesterone disappears rapidly from blood. Its rapid disappearance can be described by a double exponential function, as would be expected in a model where the steroid was distributed between two compartments. In nonpregnant women the volume of the inner compartment has been calculated as 12 liters and that of the outer compartment, 15–27 liters. These relative volumes indicate that the rapid removal of progesterone from blood is related to its rapid metabolism, rather than to its being distributed into a large volume throughout the body. The half-life of the first exponent is short (0.96 min) and that of the second exponent is much longer (10.7 min) in ovariectomized women (225). In pregnancy the initial fast rates of loss in the sheep (half-life 2.29 min) and guinea pig (2.4 min) are similar, whereas the half-lives of the slow component are 49 and 28 min, respectively (179, 344).

From a knowledge of the MCR and hepatic clearance, the question of whether progesterone is metabolized mainly by the liver or by extrahepatic tissues can be considered. In nonpregnant women the amount of progesterone metabolized in the liver is similar to that

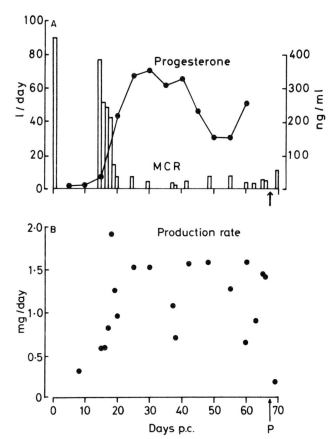

FIG. 15. The kinetics of progesterone metabolism in the pregnant guinea pig. *A*: mean progesterone levels in arterial plasma, and metabolic clearance rate (MCR_{plasma}) in individual animals. [From Challis et al. (67); Illingworth et al. (180).] *B*: production rates calculated from values in *A*. [From Challis et al. (67).]

metabolized in extrahepatic tissues (225). Similarly in the nonpregnant guinea pig, assuming hepatic extraction approaches 100%, extrahepatic clearance is appreciable and possibly as great as hepatic clearance. In contrast the greatly reduced MCR in the pregnant guinea pig implies that clearance in both hepatic and extrahepatic tissues is much less, because of the increased production of a high-affinity transport protein (180, 256). In the pregnant sheep, in which splanchnic extraction of progesterone is about 90%, the proportion cleared by extrasplanchnic tissues is also considerable, and there is an appreciable extraction by the tissues of the head (344).

Estrogens

As has been shown above, the increasing titers of urinary and blood estrogens during human pregnancy are very largely due to a greatly increased production of estriol, quantitatively the most important estrogen in gestation and used clinically as an indicator of fetal well-being (202). This is because the fetus plays a major part in estriol synthesis, since, in cases of anencephaly, production is reduced and, according to the direct estimations made by Diczfalusy's group, dehydroepinandrosterone sulfate (DHAS), produced mainly in the fetal adrenals, is hydroxylated at the 16α-position in the fetal liver before aromatization to estriol in the placenta (98). A large fraction of the estrone and estradiol-17β in pregnancy urine results from the maternal metabolism of DHAS derived from the maternal adrenals (49). There may also be some maternal metabolism to estriol, since its urinary excretion is lower in adrenalectomized pregnant women (69).

Changes in estrogen excretion in pregnant women can be produced by treatments that affect the activity of either the maternal or fetal adrenals, or both. The maternal administration of corticosteroids suppresses estriol excretion (186), whereas intramuscular ACTH (87) or metapyrone (274) stimulates it, provided the fetus is normal. Such treatments probably affect the fetal adrenal secretion of neutral steroid precursors for placental aromatization and thus alter the urinary levels of estriol. In studies in which estriol excretion was elevated above

TABLE 4. *Typical Values of Plasma Concentration, Metabolic Clearance Rate (MCR), and Production Rate (PR) of Progesterone in Pregnancy*

Species	Concentrations, ng/ml						MCR, liters/min	PR, μg/min
	Arterial or peripheral venous	Ovarian vein	Uterine vein	Adrenal vein	Umbilical			
					Vein	Artery		
Human female	100–250[a]	87–790 (254)	260 (393)	50–60 (336)	680 (223)	430 (223)	1.633[b] (223)	203 (223)
Guinea pig	140–264[a]	86–185 (268)	294–650 (159)		<1[c]	<1[c]	0.006[d]	0.3–1.4[d]
Sheep	8, 18 (222)	783–1,500 (222)	36–75 (222)	8, 19 (222)	0–9 (222)	0–7 (222)	3.321[e] (344)	8–69 (344)

Numbers in parentheses indicate references.   [a] See Fig. 10.   [b] Plasma MCR.   [c] D. V. Illingworth, personal communication.   [d] See Fig. 15.   [e] Blood MCR corrected for 25% extraction of progesterone by the tissues of the head.

the normal range, it was associated with fetal or maternal adrenal hyperplasia (46).

Isotope dilution studies have been used to calculate the production rate of estradiol-17β in pregnant women after crystallization of urinary metabolites to constant specific activity (126, 142). From the figures obtained for the excretion of radioactivity as estrone and estradiol-17β in urine, PR of estradiol-17β appears to be about 20–30 mg/day in the ninth month of pregnancy. In pregnancies with an anencephalic fetus, production rates are only one-tenth this value (233), but with hydatidiform mole they are rather higher (232).

In human pregnancy, single-injection experiments show that there is a substantial conversion of radioactive estradiol-17β to estrone (126). This observation may be related to the results obtained from in vitro incubations, which showed that the placental 17β-hydroxysteroid oxidoreductase system is activated with advancing pregnancy (62, 349). The rates of interconversions of estradiol-17β and estrone could not be measured by the single-injection technique referred to above, and so far they have only been determined for nonpregnant subjects. The transfer constant $[\rho]_{BB}$ (228) for the conversion of estradiol-17β to estrone is greater (15 %) than that of the reverse reaction (5 %) in contrast with the MCR_{blood} of estrone, which is higher (1,910 liters/day per m²) than that of estradiol-17β (1,360 liters/day per m²). Since these figures exceed hepatic blood flow (1,200 liters/day per m²), they indicate that, even in nonpregnant human subjects, extrahepatic metabolism of estrogens occurs (167, 228). A similar observation has been made in the nonpregnant rat (92).

The high clearance observed for estrogens in nonpregnant women is characteristic for steroids largely bound to albumin, although, in plasma, estrogens may also be bound to high-affinity proteins, such as sex hormone-binding globulin (SBP) [(310, 359); see Table 5] or testosterone-binding globulin (TBG) (28, 282). The testosterone-binding capacity of blood increases with an elevated concentration of TBG in the third trimester of pregnancy (370), but it falls dramatically at term (282). Since estradiol-17β is also bound by this protein, similar changes in estrogen binding may lead to differences in estrogen metabolism just before parturition. Conjugated estrogens may also be bound by the globulin fraction of plasma, but with a lower association constant than for the free steroid (132).

The kinetics of estrogen metabolism in pregnancy have been studied in detail in the sheep (64–66). Metabolic clearance rates of estrone and estradiol-17β in blood are 3.533 and 2.426 liters/min, respectively, and these values increase in late pregnancy to 3.867 and 3.287 liters/min, respectively. Comparisons between species show that the MCR of both estrogens corrected for body weight ($W^{0.75}$) is appreciably greater in sheep than in nonpregnant women (228) or in adult female rats (92). In the sheep the PR of estrone and estradiol-17β increase sharply just before parturition. During gestation, production rates are about 140–240 ng/min (estrone) and 6–105 ng/min

(estradiol-17β), but within 48 hr of parturition the values increase at least 10-fold. A large proportion of this increase could be attributed to an elevated secretion of estrogens by the gravid uterus (65, 66). In an ovariectomized pregnant animal with a catheter chronically implanted into a uterine vein, the ratio of labeled estrone to estradiol-17β in the uterine vein was greater than in the jugular vein during the continuous intravenous infusion of labeled estradiol-17β. This indicates that metabolism of estradiol-17β to estrone occurs in the gravid uterus.

Cortisol

The blood level of this glucocorticoid changes markedly in pregnancy in the human female, and it is finely regulated by a complex control system (387). During the third trimester the values for plasma cortisol are two- to threefold higher than in the nonpregnant subject, although the concentration of plasma corticosterone is unchanged. Transcortin (CBG) reaches its highest concentrations during this time due to enhanced heaptic synthesis, probably in response to estrogen stimulation. Experimentally its production can be increased by estrogen administration to nonpregnant subjects (99, 321).

Since CBG has a high affinity for cortisol, a reduction of the circulating level of free cortisol leads to increased ACTH secretion by activation of the negative feedback pathway. The question of whether the level of free cortisol changes in pregnancy is controversial. Some workers report that the free cortisol fraction increases in pregnancy or after estrogen therapy, but others have failed to find such changes (321). Recent studies, however, indicate that some of these differences may be due to the time of day when samples were taken. The unbound cortisol may be elevated in pregnancy at 900 hr and 2100 hr, but after estrogen therapy the elevation is observed only at 900 hr (100).

As in nonpregnant subjects, there is a diurnal variation in plasma cortisol in pregnancy or during estrogen therapy. The variation is due to changes in adrenal secretion rates, since similar but slightly delayed variations occur in the urinary 17-hydroxycorticosteroids, plasma disappearance constants do not fluctuate during the 24-hr period, and no changes are found in protein binding (99).

In pregnancy the rate of corticosteroid metabolism is decreased significantly; the half-life of labeled cortisol after intravenous injection is 140 min (252) compared with normal values of 60–114 min (258). A longer half-life of 114–205 min is also found after estrogen therapy (258). In nonpregnant subjects, MCR_{blood} estimated by the single-injection technique is 0.188 liters/min, and the maximum hepatic extraction is 13 %. After estrogen therapy, however, MCR is only 0.042 liters/min and the maximum hepatic extraction is 2.6 % (357). The reduction in cortisol metabolism in pregnancy may largely be attributed to an increase in the plasma concentration of CBG stimulated by the high levels of endogenous estrogens, though it is also possible that estrogens affect liver enzyme systems concerned with cortisol metabolism. Recent studies show that, in addition to a decreased clearance, cortisol production and 17-hydroxycorticosteroid excretion are lower in pregnant women but both increase during labor (253).

Experiments on the kinetics of corticosteroid metabolism have also been performed in other species during pregnancy. In the rat there is increased secretion near term and no decrease in MCR. This is associated with hyperactivity of the fetal and maternal adrenals and with the secretion of fetal corticosterone into the maternal compartment (190). In contrast, in the pregnant sheep the MCR of cortisol measured by continuous isotope infusion is relatively constant (0.60–0.66 liter plasma/min) between early pregnancy and 29 days before lambing and is similar to that found in the normal cycle (0.61 liter plasma/min). Between 16 and 3 days before parturition, however, MCR rises (0.86 liter/min) (278, 279). This is related to a fall in the transcortin-binding capacity of plasma (280). Thus, despite a relatively constant rate of cortisol secretion throughout pregnancy (10.5–11.0 μg/min), there is a fall in plasma cortisol concentration before parturition, attributed partly to the expansion of plasma volume (279).

By following the specific activity of cortisol in peripheral blood after a 4-hr isotope infusion in the pregnant sheep, Paterson & Harrison (278, 279) showed that the rate of disappearance of labeled cortisol in plasma could be described as a double exponential function and that the data could be interpreted in terms of a two-compartment model of cortisol distribution. The outer compartment, possibly corresponding to extravascular spaces, contained 130 μg cortisol, and the inner compartment, approximately the same volume as the vascular pool, contained 42 μg. In this model the half-lives of cortisol from the inner and outer pools were 1.4 min and 19 min, respectively, which reflects a more rapid clearance than that reported for the pregnant woman. This is almost certainly due to the fact that in sheep, unlike women, transcortin-binding capacity does not rise during pregnancy (280).

Aldosterone

In the last trimester of pregnancy, the secretion rate of aldosterone reaches its highest levels (74). This is shown by studies on urinary excretion and secretion rates, which both rise, and measurements of MCR and plasma protein binding, which show little change. The enhanced production is a function of the maternal adrenal, but whether this is as a result of estrogen stimulation is questionable.

It is unlikely that the raised secretion rates of aldosterone in pregnancy are directly concerned with pregnancy maintenance, since women with Addison's disease or patients bilaterally adrenalectomized may have a normal pregnancy (106). The elevated secretion of aldosterone probably results from an increase in progesterone production in pregnancy, since the administration

of progesterone to normal pregnant women increases the secretion rate further. Patients with severe preeclampsia or with a dead fetus in utero have markedly depressed aldosterone levels, similar to those in nonpregnant women, but whether this is associated with a reduction in placental progesterone secretion is unknown (373). The observed change in aldosterone secretion rate in pregnancy has been interpreted as an inhibition by progesterone of the action of mineralocorticoid on the absorptive mechanism of the renal tubule and may be a compensatory response to the natriuretic action of the high levels of progesterone in pregnancy (106, 211, 213).

Protein Hormones

Radioimmunoassay is providing information about the metabolic clearance rate and production rate of protein hormones. The clearance rate of human chorionic gonadotrophin (HCG), measured in serum and urine immediately after delivery or after an injection into a nonpregnant subject, is only about 1 ml/min. The rate of HCG removal comprises two linear components with surprisingly long half-lives of 8.9 and 37.2 hr, respectively (251). Assays of HCG in urine indicate that the production rate is about 400,000 IU/24 hr. An even longer half-life has been estimated for another placental protein hormone, pregnant mares' serum gonadotrophin (PMSG). In the gelding the half-life of exogenous PMSG is 6 days, whereas in the rabbit and rat it is shorter, about 24 hr (13). In contrast, the results obtained for pituitary protein hormones show that the clearance rate is greater and the half-life shorter than those of HCG and PMSG. Human luteinizing hormone (LH) has a MCR of 24.4 and 25.6 ml/min and a production rate of 734 and 2,400 milliunits/min in premenopausal and postmenopausal women, respectively (205). In adult men, follicle-stimulating hormone (FSH) has a half-life of only 24–38 min (7), comparable with that of HGH (276). This value is also simliar to that obtained for prolactin in other species (53,324).

FUNCTIONS OF BLOOD TRANSPORT PROTEINS IN PREGNANCY

The concept that serum proteins transport steroid hormones from their site of synthesis to the target organ in which they act has become increasingly accepted as specific proteins that possess a high affinity for a particular compound have been isolated and identified (321, 329, 377, 378). The discovery of CBG (transcortin), an α-globulin with a high affinity but low capacity for cortisol and corticosterone, transferred the emphasis of studies on the protein binding of steroids from the low-affinity, high-capacity albumin to such specific transport proteins.

The function of these transport proteins as regulators of steroid hormone action is a topic of growing interest. It has been proposed that the protein-steroid complex may provide a reservoir of steroid that is slowly disso-ciated in accord with its high K value. Thus a dominant role of a high-affinity binding protein, such as CBG or PBP, is in regulating to a greater extent the total, rather than the unbound, steroid concentration in blood. It therefore maintains at least a minimal level of steroid if secretion is suppressed and may buffer the effects of diurnal variations in secretion. In addition, the "long-term inertia" of the system, which has been defined as three times the plasma half-life (357), is increased. For example, should steroid secretion fail or be drastically reduced, the time required for the plasma concentration of a steroid bound to transcortin to fall to zero will be appreciably longer than that for a steroid not bound to high-affinity protein. A further result of the presence of a pool of steroid firmly bound to a transport protein is that the steroid is protected against metabolism. Thus, if the protein shields the steroid from hepatic metabolism, it is to be expected that the amount of steroid extracted by the liver is very similar to that fraction not protein bound or that the steroid is only weakly bound to albumin, as suggested by results obtained for testosterone, cortisol, androstenedione, progesterone, and aldosterone (27). Similarly, as already indicated earlier in this section, when the concentration of binding protein increases, the MCR of the steroid it binds decreases conspicuously. Since the biological activity of steroids bound to high-affinity proteins is much reduced (378), another function of such protein-steroid associations is probably to prevent the steroid from accumulating in an unbound form in extravascular spaces where its physiological effects may by deleterious. An example of this role is perhaps to be found in the extremely high binding activity of serum proteins for progesterone and testosterone in the pregnant guinea pig, which may protect the mother and the female

fetuses from masculinization by androgens produced in pregnancy (96). A similar mechanism has been suggested in women, in whom most of the increased amount of testosterone produced in pregnancy is protein bound (303).

The characteristics of known steroid transport proteins are summarized in Table 5, and several important aspects of such steroid-protein interactions call for further consideration in relation to their probable contribution to the hormonal maintenance of gestation. In human pregnancy the appreciable rise in the concentration of CBG is claimed to be related to the increase in blood estrogens, and exogenous estrogens stimulate the production of several steroid-binding proteins, such as CBG (321), ceruloplasmin, and TBG (263). Since CBG also has a high affinity for progesterone, as well as for cortisol and corticosterone, the possibility exists, at least in the human being, of complex interactions between estrogens, CBG, and progesterone, which all increase in late pregnancy. Recent estimates show that, like cortisol, the absolute amount of progesterone bound to transcortin and to uni-dentified high-affinity proteins is elevated in pregnancy, but the relative distribution among free, albumin-bound, and high-affinity-bound fractions remains the same (Fig. 16). The picture is complicated by the finding that estrogens also cause a fall in orosomucoid (215). This blood protein has a high affinity for progesterone (130), but its biological significance has not yet been elucidated.

Exogenous estrogen fails to increase CBG concentra-tion in the blood of guinea pigs (312). This raises a funda-mental question about the nature of the endogenous stimulus of transport protein synthesis. In the guinea pig at least three transport proteins with high affinities for cortisol, progesterone, and testosterone, respectively appear to increase appreciably during pregnancy (96).

TABLE 5. *Steroid Hormone-Binding Proteins in Plasma During Pregnancy*

Protein	Mol Wt	Concentration,* $M \times 10^7$	Steroid	Association Constant, M^{-1}	
				4 or 5 C	37 C
Albumin (human)	69,000	5,500	Aldosterone	2.6×10^3	1.7×10^3
			Estrone	4.4×10^4	
			Estradiol	1.6×10^5	
			Corticosterone	0.9×10^4	1.2×10^4 (25 C)
			Cortisol	0.6×10^4	
			Progesterone	8.9×10^4	6.1×10^4
			Testosterone	3.4×10^4	5.4×10^4 (25 C)
α_1 Acid glycoprotein, AAG (human)	41,000	180	Estradiol	0.14×10^5	0.19×10^5
			Corticosterone	0.87×10^5	
			Cortisol	0.16×10^5	0.32×10^5
			Progesterone	9.0×10^5	3.5×10^5
			Testosterone	7.3×10^5	3.0×10^5
Transcortin, CBG (human, monkey, guinea pig, rat, rabbit)	52,000	14	Corticosterone	$1-10 \times 10^8$	$0.4-4.0 \times 10^7$
			Cortisol	$0.5-10 \times 10^8$	$0.14-1.4 \times 10^8$
			Progesterone	$3-48 \times 10^8$	$0.9-3.9 \times 10^8$
Progesterone-binding protein, PBP (guinea pig)		1.4	Progesterone	$2-5 \times 10^8$	
Sex steroid-binding protein, SBP (human)	52,000	0.32	Estradiol	0.5×10^9	$0.4-1.35 \times 10^8$ (25 C)
			Testosterone	1.2×10^9	4.5×10^8 (25 C)

* Typical values.   Data from refs. 158, 246, 256, 321, 329, 378, 379.

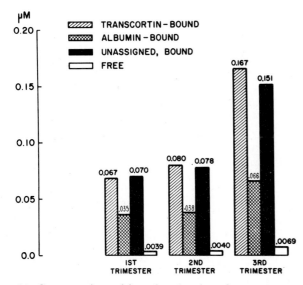

FIG. 16. Concentrations of bound and unbound progesterone in plasma of pregnant women. [From Rosenthal et al. (311).]

The most striking increase observed is that of the PBP (158, 256), a binding component that increases rapidly in early pregnancy when the MCR of progesterone falls dramatically (180). This protein, which has a high specificity for progesterone, is not stimulated by exogenous estrogen administration (160), but its concentration can be increased by testosterone injections (96). It is striking that the increased synthesis of PBP is first apparent when the definitive allantochorionic placenta is first formed. Its synthesis depends on an adequate progesterone supply and the presence of a viable fetus, but it occurs independently of the maternal pituitary (163). Thus pregnancy maintenance in the guinea pig is related not so much to an increase in progesterone production as to an increased progesterone-conserving mechanism almost certainly brought about by the increased synthesis of PBP, which markedly reduces MCR. It seems probable that the conceptus provides a signal for PBP synthesis and thereby protects its own future. Whether such a signal occurs at a precise time in the embryo's development is not yet known. It may be related to Deanesly's finding that, in guinea pigs ovariectomized 3 or 4 days postcoitus, embryos usually survive for an additional 10 days, after which their survival depends on progesterone treatment (90).

Thus far in this discussion we have been concerned with species that have hemochorial placentation in which maternal blood bathes fetal tissue. There appears to be a good correlation between this structural feature and the occurrence of elevated CBG levels in pregnancy in the relatively few mammalian species so far studied (329). It is too early to tell whether immunological reactions between maternal and fetal tissue are involved. It is interesting to note that evidence of a transmissible low CBG level in human beings has already been reported (101).

A final question of considerable importance in the study of the physiological role of transport proteins is that of their localization in the body. According to kinetics experiments in which labeled CBG was injected into blood, there is evidence for an extravascular CBG compartment, which confirms earlier work in which the concentration of CBG in lymph was found to be similar to that of plasma (321) and is consistent with later research showing CBG to have a molecular weight of 50,000–60,000. In recent experiments, it has been claimed that an intracellular protein identical with CBG can be isolated from the rat uterus. The concentration is elevated by estrogen adimnistration, and it binds progesterone and corticosterone (255). This observation is consistent with the results of experiments already discussed, which favor the existence of progesterone-binding receptors in the target tissues. In this connection it is also relevant to note the finding that rat CBG in the presence of corticosterone forms a complex with a sedimentation constant of 3.45S; when the steroid is removed, polymers (di-, tetra-, and octameric) are observed in addition to the original monomeric form (379). This reversible polymerization, perhaps the first example of the control of transport protein conformation by a steroid, may mean that the function of these carrier proteins may not be limited to steroid conservation. They may contribute to a cellular receptor mechanism and also, perhaps by steroid-induced conformational changes, aid in the process whereby a steroid is transported from endocrine cells where it is synthesized and into target cells where it is active.

The authors are indebted to Mr. A. Henville for assistance in preparing the illustrations, to Mr. D. W. Butcher and the library staff for their help in the compilation of the bibliography, and to Dr. R. M. C. Dawson for his helpful and constructive criticisms of the manuscript.

REFERENCES

1. ALEXANDER, D. P., H. G. BRITTON, N. M. COHEN, AND D. A. NIXON. Foetal metabolism. In: *Foetal Autonomy*, edited by G. E. W. Wolstenholme and M. O'Connor. London: Churchill, 1969, p. 95–111.
2. ALLEN, W. R. Factors influencing pregnant mare serum gonadotrophin production. *Nature* 223: 64–66, 1969.
3. ALLEN, W. R. *Equine Gonadotrophins* (Ph.D. thesis). Cambridge: Univ. of Cambridge, 1970.
4. ALLEN, W. R., AND R. M. MOOR. The origin of the equine endometrial cups. 1. Production of PMSG by fetal trophoblast cells. *J. Reprod. Fertility* 29: 313–316, 1972.
5. ALLOITEAU, J. J., AND J. BOUHOURS. Poursuite de la gestation chez la ratte hypophysectomisée recevant de l'hormone luteinisante. Reflexions sur les mecanismes successifs assurant le maintien fonctionnel du corps jaune gestatif. *Compt. Rend.* 261: 4230–4233, 1965.
6. AMENOMORI, Y., C. L. CHEN, AND J. MEITES. Serum prolactin levels in rats during different reproductive states. *Endocrinology* 86: 506–510, 1970.
7. AMIN, H. K., AND W. M. HUNTER. Human pituitary follicle-stimulating hormone: distribution, plasma clearance and urinary excretion as determined by radioimmunoassay. *J. Endocrinol.* 48: 307–317, 1970.

8. Amoroso, E. C. Endocrinology of pregnancy. *Brit. Med. Bull.* 11: 117–125, 1955.

9. Amoroso, E. C., and C. A. Finn. Ovarian activity during gestation, ovum transport and implantation. In: *The Ovary*, edited by S. Zuckerman. New York: Acad. Press, 1962, vol. I, p. 451–537.

10. Amoroso, E. C., J. L. Hancock, and I. W. Rowlands. Ovarian activity in the pregnant mare. *Nature* 161: 355–356, 1948.

11. Amoroso, E. C., and L. H. Matthews. The growth of the grey seal [*Halichoerus grypus* (Fabricius)] from birth to weaning. *J. Anat.* 85: 427–428, 1951.

12. Amoroso, E. C., and D. G. Porter. Anterior pituitary function in pregnancy. In: *The Pituitary Gland*, edited by G. W. Harris and B. T. Donovan. London: Butterworths, 1966, vol. 2, p. 364–411.

13. Amoroso, E. C., and D. G. Porter. The endocrine functions of the placenta. In: *Scientific Foundations of Obstetrics and Gynaecology*, edited by E. E. Philipp, J. Barnes, and M. Newton. London: Heinemann, 1970, p. 556–586.

14. Anderson, A. B., K. M. Laurence, and A. C. Turnbull. The relationship in anencephaly between the size of the adrenal cortex and the length of gestation. *J. Obstet. Gynaecol. Brit. Commonwealth* 76: 196–199, 1969.

15. Anderson, A. B. M., C. G. Pierrepoint, T. Jones, K. Griffiths, and A. C. Turnbull. Steroid biosynthesis *in vitro* by foetal and adult sheep adrenal tissue. *J. Reprod. Fertility* 22: 99–107, 1970.

16. Arcos, M., E. Gurpide, R. L. Vande Wiele, and S. Lieberman. Precursors of urinary pregnanediol and their influence on the determination of the secretory rate of progesterone. *J. Clin. Endocrinol. Metab.* 24: 237–245, 1964.

17. Armstrong, D. T. *In vitro* synthesis of progesterone. *J. Animal Sci.* 27, Suppl. 1: 181–203, 1968.

18. Armstrong, D. T., T. M. Jackanicz, and P. L. Keyes. Regulation of steroidogenesis in the rabbit ovary. In: *The Gonads*, edited by K. W. McKerns. Amsterdam: North-Holland, 1969, p. 3–26.

19. Armstrong, D. T., J. O'Brien, and R. O. Greep. Effects of luteinizing hormones on progestin biosynthesis in the luteinized rat ovary. *Endocrinology* 75: 488–500, 1964.

20. Asdell, S. A. *Patterns of Mammalian Reproduction* (2nd ed.). London: Constable, 1964.

21. Assali, N. C., P. V. Dilts, Jr., A. A. Plentl, T. H. Kirschbaum, and S. J. Gross. Physiology of the placenta. In: *Biology of Gestation*, edited by N. S. Assali. New York: Acad. Press, 1968, vol. I, p. 186–289.

22. Astwood, E. B. A six-hour assay for the quantitative determination of estrogen. *Endocrinology* 23: 25–31, 1938.

23. Astwood, E. B., and R. O. Greep. A corpus luteum-stimulating substance in the rat placenta. *Proc. Soc. Exptl. Biol. Med.* 38: 713–716, 1938.

24. Averill, S. C. E., E. W. Ray, and W. R. Lyons. Maintenance of pregnancy in hypophysectomized rats with placental implants. *Proc. Soc. Exptl. Biol. Med.* 75: 3–6, 1950.

25. Bahn, R. C., N. Lorenz, W. A. Bennett, and A. Albert. Gonadotrophins of the pituitary gland and the urine of the adult female. *Endocrinology* 52: 135–139, 1953.

26. Baird, D. T., R. Horton, C. Longcope, and J. F. Tait. Steroid prehormones. *Perspectives Biol. Med.* 11: 384–419, 1968.

27. Baird, D. T., R. Horton, C. Longcope, and J. F. Tait. Steroid dynamics under steady-state conditions. *Recent Progr. Hormone Res.* 25: 611–664, 1969.

28. Barlow, J. J., J. A. Maclaren, and L. Pothier. *In vivo* observations on testosterone and estradiol-17β protein binding in women. *J. Clin. Endocrinol. Metab.* 29: 767–776, 1969.

29. Barnea, A., and J. Gorski. Estrogen-induced protein. Time course of synthesis. *Biochemistry* 9: 1899–1904, 1970.

30. Bartosik, D. B., and E. B. Romanoff. The luteotrophic process: effects of prolactin and LH on sterol and progesterone metabolism in bovine luteal ovaries perfused *in vitro*. In: *The Gonads*, edited by K. W. McKerns. Amsterdam: North-Holland, 1969, p. 211–244.

31. Bassett, J. M., T. J. Oxborrow, I. D. Smith, and G. D. Thorburn. The concentration of progesterone in the peripheral plasma of the pregnant ewe. *J. Endocrinol.* 45: 449–457, 1969.

32. Bassett, J. M., and G. D. Thorburn. Foetal plasma corticosteroids and the initiation of parturition in the sheep. *J. Endocrinol.* 44: 285–286, 1969.

33. Bassett, J. M., G. D. Thorburn, and A. L. C. Wallace. The plasma growth hormone concentration of the foetal lamb. *J. Endocrinol.* 48: 251–263, 1970.

34. Beitins, I. Z., A. Kowarski, D. W. Shermeta, R. A. De Lemos, and C. J. Migeon. Fetal and maternal secretion rate of cortisol in sheep: diffusion resistance of the placenta. *Pediat. Res.* 4: 129–134, 1970.

35. Beling, C. G., S. L. Marcus, and S. M. Markham. Functional activity of the corpus luteum following hysterectomy. *J. Clin. Endocrinol. Metab.* 30: 30–39, 1970.

36. Bengtsson, L. P. Progesterone and the myometrium in human pregnancy. In: *Advances in Obstetrics and Gynecology*, edited by S. L. Marcus and C. C. Marcus. Baltimore: William & Wilkins, 1967, p. 103–115.

37. Benirschke, K. Adrenals in anencephaly and hydrocephaly. *Obstet. Gynecol.* 8: 412–425, 1956.

38. Bishop, M. W. H. Paternal contribution to embryonic death. *J. Reprod. Fertility* 7: 383–396, 1964.

39. Björkman, N. A study of the ultrastructure of the granulosa cells of the rat ovary. *Acta Anat.* 51: 125–147, 1962.

40. Björkman, N. *An Atlas of Placental Fine Structure*. London: Baillière, Tindall, and Cassell, 1970.

41. Bland, K. P., and B. T. Donovan. The uterus and the control of ovarian function. In: *Advances in Reproductive Physiology*, edited by A. McLaren. London: Logos Press, 1966, vol. 1, p. 179–214.

42. Bloch, E. Foetal adrenal cortex: function and steroidogenesis. In: *Functions of the Adrenal Cortex*, edited by K. W. McKerns. Amsterdam: North-Holland, 1968, vol. II, p. 721–772.

43. Bloom, W., and D. W. Fawcett. *A Textbook of Histology* (9th ed.). Philadelphia: Saunders, 1968.

44. Boshier, D. P. The pontamine blue reaction in pregnant sheep uteri. *J. Reprod. Fertility* 22: 595–596, 1970.

45. Brambell, F. W. R. The influence of lactation on the implantation of the mammalian embryo. *Am. J. Obstet. Gynecol.* 33: 942–953, 1937.

46. Breborowicz, H., and W. Biniszkiewicz. Relation between urinary oestriol and 17-ketosteroid levels and state of maternal and foetal adrenals. In: *Intra-uterine Dangers to the Foetus*, edited by J. Horsky and Z. K. Stembera. Amsterdam: Excerpta Medica Foundation, 1967, p. 283–286.

47. Brody, S. Hormonal influence on the nucleic acid and protein contents of the human myometrium. *Exptl. Cell Res.* 14: 149–159, 1958.

48. Brody, S. Protein hormones and hormonal peptides from the placenta. In: *Foetus and Placenta*, edited by A. Klopper and E. Diczfalusy. Oxford: Blackwell, 1969, p. 299–411.

49. Brown, J. B., N. A. Beischer, and M. A. Smith. Excretion of urinary oestrogens in pregnant patients treated with cortisone and its analogues. *J. Obstet. Gynaecol. Brit. Commonwealth* 75: 819–828, 1968.

50. Browning, H. C., G. A. Larke, and W. D. White. Action of purified gonadotropins on corpora lutea in the cyclic mouse. *Proc. Soc. Exptl. Biol. Med.* 111: 686–690, 1962.

51. Browning, H. C., and W. D. White. Luteotropic response in pituitary-ovarian autografts in male mice. *Proc. Soc. Exptl. Biol. Med.* 119: 1224–1227, 1965.

52. Bruner, J. A. Distribution of chorionic gonadotrophin in mother and fetus at various stages of pregnancy. *J. Clin. Endocrinol. Metab.* 11: 360–374, 1951.

53. Bryant, G. D., J. L. Linzell, and F. C. Greenwood. Plasma prolactin in goats measured by radioimmunoassay: the effects of teat stimulation, mating behavior, stress, fasting

and of oxytocin, insulin and glucose injections. *Hormones* 1: 26–35, 1970.

54. BRYSON, M. J., AND M. L. SWEAT. Metabolism of progesterone in human proliferative endometrium. *Endocrinology* 81: 729–734, 1967.

55. BRYSON, M. J., and M. L. SWEAT. Metabolism of progesterone in human myometrium. *Endocrinology* 84: 1071–1075, 1969.

56. BURGER, J. F. Sex physiology of pigs. *Onderstepoort J. Vet. Res. Suppl.* 2: 1–218, 1952.

57. CANIVENC, R., R. V. SHORT, AND M. BONNIN-LAFFARGUE. Etude histologique et biochemique du corps jaune du blaireau européen (*Meles meles* L.) *Ann. Endocrinol.* 27: 401–414, 1966.

58. CARSTEN, M. E. Tropomyosin from smooth muscle of the uterus. *Biochemistry* 7: 960–967, 1968.

59. CARSTEN, M. E. Regulation of myometrial composition, growth, and activity. In: *Biology of Gestation*, edited by N. S. Assali. New York: Acad. Press, 1969, vol. 1, p. 355–425.

60. CATCHPOLE, H. R. Hormonal mechanisms during pregnancy and parturition. In: *Reproduction in Domestic Animals*, edited by H. H. Cole and P. T. Cupps. New York: Acad. Press, 1969, p. 415–440.

61. CATCHPOLE, H. R., AND W. R. LYONS. The gonad-stimulating hormone of pregnant mares. *Am. J. Anat.* 55: 167–227, 1934.

62. CEDARD, L., T. VARANGOT, AND S. YANNOTTI. Biosynthèse et métabolisme des oestrogènes dans la placenta humain perfusé ou incubé in vitro. *European J. Steroids* 1: 287–307, 1966.

63. CHALLIS, J. R. G. Sharp increase in free circulating oestrogens immediately before parturition in sheep. *Nature* 229: 208, 1971.

64. CHALLIS, J. R. G., F. A. HARRISON, AND R. B. HEAP. Oestrogen metabolism in the ewe during late pregnancy. *J. Physiol., London* 210: 93–95P, 1970.

65. CHALLIS, J. R. G., F. A. HARRISON, AND R. B. HEAP. Uterine production of oestrogens and progesterone at parturition in the sheep. *J. Reprod. Fertility* 25: 306–307, 1971.

66. CHALLIS, J. R. G., F. A. HARRISON, AND R. B. HEAP. The kinetics of oestrogen metabolism in the pregnant sheep. In: *Endocrinology of Pregnancy and Parturition*, edited by C. G. Pierrepoint. Cardiff: Alpha Omega Alpha, 1972.

67. CHALLIS, J. R. G., R. B. HEAP, AND D. V. ILLINGWORTH. The plasma concentrations of oestrogen and progesterone in non-pregnant, pregnant and lactating guinea-pigs. *J. Endocrinol.* 51: 333–345, 1971.

68. CHANNING, C. P. The use of tissue culture of granulosa cells as a method of studying the mechanism of luteinization. In: *The Gonads*, edited by K. W. McKerns. Amsterdam: North-Holland, 1969, p. 245–275.

69. CHARLES, D., R. A. HARKNESS, F. M. KENNY, E. MENINI, A. A. A. ISMAIL, J. W. DURKIN, AND J. A. LORAINE. Steroid excretion patterns in an adrenalectomized woman during successive pregnancies. *Am. J. Obstet. Gynecol.* 106: 66–74, 1970.

70. CHEZ, R. A., D. L. HUTCHINSON, H. SALAZAR, AND D. H. MINTZ. Some effects of fetal and maternal hypophysectomy in pregnancy. *Am. J. Obstet. Gynecol.* 108: 643–650, 1970.

71. CHOUDARY, J. B., AND G. S. GREENWALD. Reversal by gonadotrophins of the luteolytic effect of oestrogen in the cyclic guinea-pig. *J. Reprod. Fertility* 19: 503–510, 1969.

72. CHOUDARY, J. B., AND G. S. GREENWALD. Ovarian activity in the intact or hypophysectomized pregnant mouse. *Anat. Record* 163: 359–372, 1969.

73. CHRISTENSEN, H. K., AND S. W. GILLIM. The correlation of fine structure and function in steroid-secreting cells, with emphasis on those of the gonads. In: *The Gonads*, edited by K. W. McKerns. Amsterdam: North-Holland, 1969, p. 415–488.

74. COGHLAN, J. P., AND J. R. BLAIR-WEST. Aldosterone. In: *Hormones in Blood* (2nd ed.), edited by C. H. Gray and A. L. Bacharach. London: Acad. Press, 1967, vol. II, p. 391–489.

75. COHEN, R. M., AND R. R. GALA. Detection of luteotropic and mammotropic activity in the serum of rats in mid-pregnancy. *Proc. Soc. Exptl. Biol. Med.* 132: 683–685, 1969.

76. COMLINE, R. S., AND M. SILVER. The release of adrenaline and noradrenaline from the adrenal glands of the foetal sheep. *J. Physiol., London* 156: 424–444, 1961.

77. COMLINE, R. S., AND M. SILVER. Development of activity in the adrenal medulla of the foetus and new-born animal. *Brit. Med. Bull.* 22: 16–20, 1966.

78. COMTE, L. *Contribution à l'Étude de l'Hypophyse Humaine* (Thèse de doctorat). Lausanne, 1898. [Cited by Amoroso & Porter (12).]

79. COURRIER, R., M. BACLESSE, AND M. MAROIS. Rapports de la cortico-surrénale et de la sexualité. *J. Physiol., Paris* 45: 327–374, 1953.

80. COURRIER, R., R. KEHL, AND R. RAYNAUD. Neutralisation de l'hormone folliculaire chez la femelle gestante castrée. *Compt. Rend. Soc. Biol.* 100: 1103–1105, 1929.

81. COWIE, A. T., P. M. DANIEL, M. M. L. PRICHARD, AND J. S. TINDAL. Hypophysectomy in pregnant goats, and section of the pituitary stalk in pregnant goats and sheep. *J. Endocrinol.* 28: 93–102, 1963.

82. CSAPO, A. I. Actomyosin content of the uterus. *Nature* 162: 218–219, 1948.

83. CSAPO, A. I. The four direct regulatory factors of myometrial function. In: *Progesterone: Its Regulatory Effect on the Myometrium*, edited by G. E. W. Wolstenholme and J. Knight. London: Churchill, 1969, p. 13–42.

84. CSAPO, A. I., T. ERDOS, C. E. R. DE MATTOS, E. GRAMMS, AND C. MOSCOWITZ. Stretch-induced uterine growth, protein synthesis and function. *Nature* 207: 1378–1379, 1965.

85. CSAPO, A. I., AND H. TAKEDA. Effect of progesterone on the electric activity and intrauterine pressure of pregnant and parturient rabbits. *Am. J. Obstet. Gynecol.* 91: 221–231, 1965.

86. CSAPO, A. I., AND W. G. WIEST. An examination of the quantitative relationship between progesterone and the maintenance of pregnancy. *Endocrinology* 85: 735–746, 1969.

87. DÄSSLER, C.-G. Effect of ACTH on maternal oestriol excretion pattern in normal pregnancy and in cases of intrauterine foetal death. In: *Intra-uterine Dangers to the Foetus*, edited by J. Horsky and Z. K. Stembera. Amsterdam: Excerpta Medica Foundation, 1967, p. 280–282.

88. DEANE, H. W. The anatomy, chemistry, and physiology of adrenocortical tissue. In: *Handbuch der Experimentellen Pharmakologie. The Adrenocortical Hormones. Their Origin, Chemistry, Physiology and Pharmacology*, edited by H. W. Deane. Berlin: Springer, 1962, vol. XIV, part 1, p. 1–185.

89. DEANE, H. W., M. F. HAY, R. M. MOOR, L. E. A. ROWSON, AND R. V. SHORT. The corpus luteum of the sheep: relationships between morphology and function during the oestrous cycle. *Acta Endocrinol.* 51: 245–263, 1966.

90. DEANESLY, R. Early embryonic growth and progesterone function in ovariectomized guinea-pigs. *J. Reprod. Fertility* 6: 143–152, 1963.

91. DEANESLY, R. The endocrinology of pregnancy and foetal life. In: *Marshall's Physiology of Reproduction* (3rd ed.), edited by A. S. Parkes. London: Longmans, 1966, vol. 3, p. 891–1063.

92. DE HERTOGH, R., E. EKKA, I. VANDERHEYDEN, AND J. J. HOET. Metabolic clearance rates and the interconversion factors of estrone and estradiol-17β in the immature and adult female rat. *Endocrinology* 87: 874–880, 1970.

93. DENAMUR, R. Formation and maintenance of corpora lutea in domestic animals. *J. Animal Sci.* 27, Suppl. 1: 163–180, 1968.

94. DENAMUR, R., J. MARTINET, AND R. V. SHORT. Sécrétion de la progestérone par les corps jaunes de la brebis après hypophysectomie, section de la tige pituitaire et hystérectomie. *Acta Endocrinol.* 52: 72–90, 1966.

95. DEWAR, A. D. The mechanism and nature of the extra-uterine weight gain of pregnancy in the mouse. *J. Reprod. Fertility Suppl.* 9: 17–26, 1969.

96. DIAMOND, M., N. RUST, AND U. WESTPHAL. High-affinity

binding of progesterone, testosterone and cortisol in normal and androgen-treated guinea pigs during various reproductive stages: relationship to masculinization. *Endocrinology* 84: 1143–1151, 1969.

97. DICZFALUSY, E., AND U. BORRELL. Influence of oophorectomy on steroid excretion in early pregnancy. *J. Clin. Endocrinol. Metab.* 21: 1119–1126, 1961.

98. DICZFALUSY, E., AND S. MANCUSO. Oestrogen metabolism in pregnancy. In: *Foetus and Placenta*, edited by A. Klopper and E. Diczfalusy. Oxford: Blackwell, 1969, p. 191–248.

99. DIXON, P. E., M. BOOTH, AND J. BUTLER. The corticosteroids. In: *Hormones in Blood* (2nd ed.), edited by C. H. Gray and A. L. Bacharach. London: Acad. Press, 1967, vol. 2, p. 306–390.

100. DOE, R. P., P. DICKINSON, H. H. ZINNEMAN, AND U. S. SEAL. Elevated nonprotein-bound cortisol (NPC) in pregnancy, during estrogen administration and in carcinoma of the prostate. *J. Clin. Endocrinol. Metab.* 29: 757–766, 1969.

101. DOE, R. P., F. LOHRENZ, AND U. S. SEAL. Familial decrease in corticosteroid-binding globulin. *Metabolism* 14: 940–943, 1965.

102. DONOVAN, B. T. The control of ovarian function. *Acta Endocrinol.* 66: 1–15, 1971.

103. DORFMAN, R. I. The biochemistry of gonadal hormones. In: *Reproduction in Domestic Animals*, (2nd ed.), edited by H. H. Cole and P. T. Cupps. New York: Acad. Press, 1969, p. 113–153.

104. DORFMAN, R., AND F. UNGAR. *Metabolism of Steroid Hormones.* New York: Acad. Press, 1965.

105. DORRINGTON, J. H., AND R. KILPATRICK. Effects of pituitary hormones on progestational hormone production by the rabbit ovary *in vivo* and *in vitro*. *J. Endocrinol.* 35: 53–63, 1966.

106. DRUCKER, W. D., A. HENDRIKX, J. H. LARAGH, N. P. CHRISTY, AND R. L. VANDE WIELE. Effect of administered aldosterone upon electrolyte excretion during and after pregnancy in two women with adrenal cortical insufficiency. *J. Clin. Endocrinol. Metab.* 23: 1247–1255, 1963.

107. DU MESNIL DU BUISSON, F., AND L. DAUZIER. Influence de l'ovariectomie chez la truie pendant la gestation. *Compt. Rend. Soc. Biol.* 151: 311–313, 1957.

108. DU MESNIL DU BUISSON, F., AND R. DENAMUR. Mécanismes du contrôle de la fonction lutéale chez la truie, la brebis et la vache. *Proc. Intern. Congr. Endocrinol., 3rd, Mexico, 1968. Excerpta Med. Intern. Congr. Ser.* 157: 927–934, 1968.

109. DU MESNIL DU BUISSON, F., P. C. LEGLISE, L. L. ANDERSON, AND P. ROMBAUTS. Maintien des corps jaunes et de la gestation de la truie, au cours de la phase préimplantatoire après hypophysectomie. *Proc. Intern. Congr. Animal Reprod. Insémination Artificial, Trento* 3: 571–575, 1964.

110. DUNCAN, G. W., A. M. BOWERMAN, W. R. HEARN, AND R. M. MELAMPY. *In vitro* synthesis of progesterone by swine corpora lutea. *Proc. Soc. Exptl. Biol. Med.* 104: 17–19, 1960.

111. DUNCAN, S. L. B. The partition of uterine blood flow in the pregnant rabbit. *J. Physiol., London* 204: 421–434, 1969.

112. DUNCAN, S. L. B., AND B. S. LEWIS. Maternal placental and myometrial blood flow in the pregnant rabbit. *J. Physiol., London* 202: 471–482, 1969.

113. EDGAR, D. G. The progesterone content of body fluids and tissues. *J. Endocrinol.* 10: 54–64, 1953.

114. EL-SHAIKH, A. S., F. B. SAKLA, AND S. O. AMIN. Changes in the density and progesterone content of luteal tissue in the Egyptian buffalo during pregnancy. *J. Endocrinol.* 43: 1–8, 1969.

115. ENDERS, A. C. (editor). *Delayed Implantation.* Chicago: Univ. of Chicago Press, 1963.

116. ERB, R. E., V. L. ESTERGREEN, JR., W. R. GOMES, E. D. PLOTKA, AND O. L. FROST. Progestin levels in corpora lutea and progesterone in ovarian venous, and jugular vein blood plasma of the pregnant bovine. *J. Dairy Sci.* 51: 401–410, 1968.

117. ERB, R. E., R. D. RANDEL, T. N. MELLIN, AND V. L.

ESTERGREEN, JR. Urinary estrogen excretion rates during pregnancy in the bovine. *J. Dairy Sci.* 51: 416–419, 1968.

118. ETO, T., H. MASUDA, Y. SUZUKI, AND T. HOSI. Progesterone and pregn-4-ene-20α-ol-3-one in rat ovarian venous blood at different stages in the reproductive cycle. *Japan J. Animal Reprod.* 8: 34–40, 1962.

119. EVERETT, J. W. Functional corpora lutea maintained for months by autografts of rat hypophysis. *Endocrinology* 58: 786–796, 1956.

120. FALK, R. J., AND C. W. BARDIN. Uptake of tritiated progesterone by the uterus of the ovariectomized guinea-pig. *Endocrinology* 86: 1059–1063, 1970.

121. FAWCETT, D. W., J. A. LONG, AND A. L. JONES. The ultrastructure of endocrine glands. *Recent Progr. Hormone Res.* 25: 315–368, 1969.

122. FERNANDEZ-BACA, S., W. HANSEL, AND C. NOVOA. Corpus luteum function in the Alpaca. *Biol. Reprod.* 3: 252–261, 1970.

123. FEVRE, J., C. PITON, AND P. ROMBAUTS. Etude des oestrogènes urinaires chez la brebis gestante. *Compt. Rend. Acad. Sci.* 261: 2517–2520, 1965.

124. FINDLAY, J. K., AND R. F. SEAMARK. The biosynthesis of oestrogens in the ovine foeto-placental unit. *J. Reprod. Fertility* 24: 141–142, 1971.

125. FISCHER, T. V. Local uterine regulation of the corpus luteum. *Am. J. Anat.* 121: 425–441, 1967.

126. FISHMAN, J., J. B. BROWN, L. HELLMAN, B. ZUMOFF, AND T. F. GALLAGHER. Estrogen metabolism in normal and pregnant women. *J. Biol. Chem.* 237: 1489–1494, 1962.

127. FORSYTH, I. A. The role of primate prolactins and placental lactogens in lactogenesis. In: *Lactogenesis*, edited by M. Reynolds and S. J. Folley. Philadelphia: Univ. of Pennsylvania, 1969, p. 195–205.

128. FRIESEN, H. G., S. SUWA, AND P. PARE. Synthesis and secretion of placental lactogen and other proteins by the placenta. *Recent Progr. Hormone Res.* 25: 161–205, 1969.

129. FYLLING, P. The effect of pregnancy, ovariectomy and parturition on plasma progesterone level in the sheep. *Acta Endocrinol.* 65: 273–283, 1970.

130. GANGULY, M., R. H. CARNIGHAM, AND U. WESTPHAL. Steroid-protein interactions. 14. Interaction between human α₁-acid glycoprotein and progesterone. *Biochemistry* 6: 2803–2814, 1967.

131. GEELHOED, G. W., AND A. J. VANDER. Plasma renin activities during pregnancy and parturition. *J. Clin. Endocrinol. Metab.* 28: 412–415, 1968.

132. GIORGI, E. P., AND P. G. CROSIGNANI. Competitive binding of free and conjugated oestrogens to plasma proteins. *J. Endocrinol.* 44: 219–230, 1969.

133. GOLDSTEIN, D. P., T. AONO, M. L. TAYMOR, K. JOCHELSON, R. TODD, AND E. HINES. Radioimmunoassay of serum chorionic gonadotropin activity in normal pregnancy. *Am. J. Obstet. Gynecol.* 102: 110–114, 1968.

134. GOMES, W. R., AND R. E. ERB. Progesterone in bovine reproduction: a review. *J. Dairy Sci.* 48: 314–330, 1965.

135. GORSKI, J., AND R. E. ERB. Characterization of estrogens in the bovine. *Endocrinology* 64: 707–712, 1959.

136. GORSKI, J., D. TOFT, G. SHYAMALA, D. SMITH, AND A. NOTIDES. Hormone receptors: studies on the interaction of estrogen within the uterus. *Recent Progr. Hormone Res.* 24: 45–72, 1968.

137. GREENWALD, G. S. Luteotropic complex of the hamster. *Endocrinology* 80: 118–130, 1967.

138. GREENWALD, G. S., AND I. ROTHCHILD. Formation and maintenance of corpora lutea in laboratory animals. *J. Animal Sci.* 27, Suppl. 1: 139–162, 1968.

139. GREISS, F. C., JR., AND S. G. ANDERSON. Uterine vascular changes during the ovarian cycle. *Am. J. Obstet. Gynecol.* 103: 629–640, 1969.

140. GREISS, F. C., JR., AND S. G. ANDERSON. Uterine blood flow during early ovine pregnancy. *Am. J. Obstet. Gynecol.* 106: 30–38, 1970.

141. GREISS, F. C., JR., AND E. L. MARSTON. The uterine vascular

bed: effect of estrogens during ovine pregnancy. *Am. J. Obstet. Gynecol.* 93: 720–722, 1965.

142. GURPIDE, E., M. ANGERS, R. L. VANDE WIELE, AND S. LIEBERMAN. Determination of secretory rates of oestrogens in pregnant and non-pregnant women from the specific activity of urinary metabolites. *J. Clin. Endocrinol. Metab.* 22: 935–945, 1962.

143. GYERMEK, L. Effects of pregnanolone and progesterone. *Lancet* 2: 1195, 1968.

144. HAFEZ, E. S. E., Y. TSUTSUMI, AND M. A. KAHN. Progestin levels in the ovaries and ovarian effluent blood in pregnant rabbits. *Proc. Soc. Exptl. Biol. Med.* 120: 75–78, 1965.

145. HAGERMAN, D. D. The enzymology of the placenta. In: *Foetus and Placenta*, edited by A. Klopper and E. Diczfalusy. Oxford: Blackwell, 1969, p. 413–469.

146. HALL, K. Relaxin. *J. Reprod. Fertility* 1: 368–384, 1960.

147. HAMMOND, J. On the causes responsible for the developmental progress of the mammary glands in the rabbit during the latter part of pregnancy. *Proc. Roy. Soc., London, Ser. B* 89: 534–546, 1917.

148. HAMMOND, J., AND F. H. A. MARSHALL. Oestrus and pseudopregnancy in the ferret. *Proc. Roy. Soc., London, Ser. B* 105: 607–630, 1929.

149. HAMMOND, J., JR., AND J. M. ROBSON. Local maintenance of the rabbit corpus luteum with oestrogen. *Endocrinology* 49: 384–389, 1951.

150. HANSEL, W., AND K. H. SEIFART. Maintenance of luteal function in the cow. *J. Dairy Sci.* 50: 1948–1958, 1967.

151. HARKNESS, R. A., E. MENINI, D. CHARLES, F. M. KENNY, AND R. ROMBAUT. Studies of urinary steroid excretion by an adrenalectomized woman during and after pregnancy. *Acta Endocrinol.* 52: 409–415, 1966.

152. HARRISON, F. A., AND R. B. HEAP. Progesterone secretion by the autotransplanted adrenal and ovary in a pregnant sheep. *J. Physiol., London* 196: 43–45P, 1968.

153. HARRISON, F. A., AND J. Y. F. PATERSON. The specific activity of plasma cortisol in sheep after rapid intravenous injection of [1,2-³H₂]cortisol, and its relation to the rate of cortisol secretion. *J. Endocrinol.* 33: 477–490, 1965.

154. HARRISON, R. J. The structure of the ovary. In: *The Ovary*, edited by S. Zuckerman. New York: Acad. Press, 1962, vol. 1, p. 143–187.

155. HASHIMOTO, I., D. M. HENRICKS, L. L. ANDERSON, AND R. M. MELAMPY. Progesterone and pregn-4-en-20α-ol-3-one in ovarian venous blood during various reproductive states in the rat. *Endocrinology* 82: 333–341, 1968.

156. HASHIMOTO, I., AND W. G. WIEST. Luteotrophic and luteolytic mechanisms in rat corpora lutea. *Endocrinology* 84: 886–892, 1969.

157. HAUGEN, O. A., AND J. S. BECK. Immunofluorescence studies with antisera to human growth hormone and human placental lactogen on adenohypophyses of pregnant and parturient women. *J. Pathol.* 98: 97–104, 1969.

158. HEAP, R. B. The binding of plasma progesterone in pregnancy. *J. Reprod. Fertility* 18: 546–548, 1969.

159. HEAP, R. B., AND R. DEANESLY. Progesterone in systemic blood and placentae of intact and ovariectomized pregnant guinea-pigs. *J. Endocrinol.* 34: 417–423, 1966.

160. HEAP, R. B., AND R. DEANESLY. The increase in plasma progesterone levels in the pregnant guinea-pig and its possible significance. *J. Reprod. Fertility* 14: 339–341, 1967.

161. HEAP, R. B., M. HOLZBAUER, AND H. M. NEWPORT. Adrenal secretion rates of C-19 and C-21 steroids before and after hypophysectomy in the pig and the dog. *J. Endocrinol.* 36: 159–176, 1966.

162. HEAP, R. B., AND J. L. LINZELL. Arterial concentration, ovarian secretion and mammary uptake of progesterone in goats during the reproductive cycle. *J. Endocrinol.* 36: 389–399, 1966.

163. HEAP, R. B., J. S. PERRY, AND I. W. ROWLANDS. Corpus luteum function in the guinea-pig; arterial and luteal pro-

gesterone levels, and the effects of hysterectomy and hypophysectomy. *J. Reprod. Fertility* 13: 537–553, 1967.

164. HEAP, R. B., A. M. SYMONS, AND J. C. WATKINS. An interaction between oestradiol and progesterone in aqueous solutions and in a model membrane system. *Biochim. Biophys. Acta* 233: 307–314, 1971.

165. HECKEL, G. P. The estrogen sparing effect of hysterectomy. *Surg. Gynecol. Obstet.* 75: 379–390, 1942.

166. HELLBAUM, A. A. The gonad-stimulating activity of pituitary glands from horses of different ages and sex types. *Anat. Record* 63: 147–157, 1935.

167. HEMBREE, W. C., C. W. BARDIN, AND M. B. LIPSETT. A study of estrogen metabolic clearance rates and transfer factors. *J. Clin. Invest.* 48: 1809–1819, 1969.

168. HERRICK, E. H. Duration of pregnancy in guinea-pigs after removal of and also after transplantation of ovaries. *Anat. Record* 39: 193–200, 1928.

169. HERVEY, E., AND G. R. HERVEY. The effects of progesterone on body weight and composition in the rat. *J. Endocrinol.* 37: 361–381, 1967.

170. HILLIARD, J., J. N. HAYWARD, AND C. H. SAWYER. Postcoital patterns of secretion of pituitary gonadotropin and ovarian progestin in the rabbit. *Endocrinology* 75: 957–963, 1964.

171. HILLIARD, J., R. PENARDI, AND C. H. SAWYER. A functional role for 20α-hydroxypregn-4-en-3-one in the rabbit. *Endocrinology* 80: 901–909, 1967.

172. HILLIARD, J., H. G. SPIES, AND C. H. SAWYER. Hormonal factors regulating ovarian cholesterol mobilization and progestin secretion in intact and hypophysectomized rabbits. In: *The Gonads*, edited by K. W. McKerns. Amsterdam: North-Holland, 1969, p. 55–92.

173. HOLM, L. W. Prolonged pregnancy. In: *Advances in Veterinary Science*, edited by C. A. Brandly and E. L. Jungherr. New York: Acad. Press, 1967, vol. 2, p. 159–205.

174. HOUSSAY, B. Action de l'hypophysectomie sur la grossesse et la sécrétion lactée chez la chienne. *Compt. Rend. Soc. Biol.* 120: 496–497, 1935.

175. HUCKABEE, W. E., C. CRENSHAW, L. B. CURET, L. MANN, AND D. H. BARRON. The effect of exogenous oestrogen on the blood flow and oxygen consumption of the uterus of the non-pregnant ewe. *Quart. J. Exptl. Physiol.* 55: 16–24, 1970.

176. HUCKABEE, W. E., J. METCALFE, H. PRYSTOWSKY, AND D. H. BARRON. Blood flow and oxygen consumption of the pregnant uterus. *Am. J. Physiol.* 200: 274–278, 1961.

177. HUTCHINSON, J. S. M., AND H. A. ROBERTSON. The growth of the follicle and corpus luteum in the ovary of the sheep. *Res. Vet. Sci.* 7: 17–24, 1966.

178. HYTTEN, F. E., AND A. M. THOMSON. Maternal physiological adjustments. In: *Biology of Gestation*, edited by N. S. Assali. New York: Acad. Press, 1969, vol. 1, p. 449–479.

179. ILLINGWORTH, D. V. Kinetics of progesterone metabolism in pregnant and non-pregnant guinea-pigs. *J. Physiol., London* 210: 99–100P, 1970.

180. ILLINGWORTH, D. V., R. B. HEAP, AND J. S. PERRY. Changes in the metabolic clearance rate of progesterone in the guinea-pig. *J. Endocrinol.* 48: 409–417, 1970.

181. ILLINGWORTH, D. V., AND J. S. PERRY. The effect of hypophyseal stalk-section upon the corpus luteum of the guinea-pig. *J. Endocrinol.* 50: 625–635, 1971.

182. INSKEEP, E. K., M. M. OLOUFA, B. E. HOWLAND, A. L. POPE, AND L. E. CASIDA. Effect of experimental uterine distension on estrual cycle lengths in ewes. *J. Animal Sci.* 21: 331–332, 1962.

183. JACKSON, B. T., AND G. J. PIASECKI. Fetal secretion of glucocorticoids. *Endocrinology* 85: 875–880, 1969.

184. JAITLY, K. D., J. M. ROBSON, F. M. SULLIVAN, AND C. WILSON. Hormonal requirements for the maintenance of gestation in hypophysectomized mice. *J. Endocrinol.* 34: iv, 1966.

185. JENSEN, E. V., T. SUZUKI, M. NUMATA, S. SMITH, AND E. DE SOMBRE. Estrogen-binding substances of target tissues. *Steroids* 13: 417–427, 1969.

186. JØRGENSEN, P. I. Influence of corticosteroids on the excretion of oestrogens in pregnancy. *J. Steroid Biochem.* 1: 33–46, 1969.

187. JOST, A. The extent of foetal endocrine autonomy. In: *Foetal Autonomy*, edited by G. E. W. Wolstenholme and M. O'Connor. London: Churchill, 1969, p. 79–89.

188. JOST, A. Hormonal factors in the sex differentiation of the mammalian foetus. *Phil. Trans. Roy. Soc., London, Ser. B* 259: 119–131, 1970.

189. KALTENBACH, C. C., J. W. GRABER, G. D. NISWENDER, AND A. V. NALBANDOV. Luteotrophic properties of some pituitary hormones in nonpregnant or pregnant hypophysectomized ewes. *Endocrinology* 82: 818–824, 1968.

190. KAMOUN, A. Activité cortico-surrénale au cours de la gestation, de la lactation et du développement pré et postnatal chez le rat. I. Concentration et cinétique de disparition de la corticostérone. *J. Physiol., Paris* 62: 5–32, 1970.

191. KAO, C. Y. Ionic basis of electrical activity in uterine smooth muscle. In: *Cellular Biology of the Uterus*, edited by R. M. Wynn. Amsterdam: North-Holland, 1967, p. 386–448.

192. KAPLAN, N. M. Successful pregnancy following hypophysectomy during the twelfth week of gestation. *J. Clin. Endocrinol. Metab.* 21: 1139–1145, 1961.

193. KAPLAN, S. L., AND M. M. GRUMBACH. Serum chorionic "growth hormone-prolactin" and serum pituitary growth hormone in mother and fetus at term. *J. Clin. Endocrinol. Metab.* 25: 1370–1374, 1965.

194. KARIM, S. M. M. Appearance of prostaglandin $F_{2\alpha}$ in human blood during labour. *Brit. Med. J.* 4: 618–621, 1968.

195. KARLSON, P., AND C. E. SEKERIS. Biochemical mechanisms of hormone action. *Acta Endocrinol.* 53: 505–518, 1966.

196. KEYES, P. L., AND A. V. NALBANDOV. Maintenance and function of corpora lutea in rabbits depend on estrogen. *Endocrinology* 80: 938–946, 1967.

197. KING, J. M. *Comparative Aspects of Reproduction in Equidae* (Ph.D. thesis). Cambridge: Cambridge University, 1965.

198. KITCHELL, R. L., AND L. T. WELLS. Functioning of the hypophysis and adrenals in fetal rats: effects of hypophysectomy, adrenalectomy, castration, injected ACTH and implanted sex hormones. *Anat. Record* 112: 561–592, 1952.

199. KLEIN, M. Recherches sur le role du placenta dans l'arrêt des manifestations du cycle ovarien au cours de la grossesse. *Arch. Anat. Microscop.* 31: 397–416, 1935.

200. KLEIN, M. Sur les facteurs qui maintiennent l'activité fonctionnelle du corps jaune gravidique. *Hormones Sexuelles, Colloque Singer Polignac.* Paris: Herman, 1938, p. 151–166.

201. KLEIN, M. Action du placenta sur le corps jaune gravidique et sur le cycle vaginal chez le cobaye. *Compt. Rend. Soc. Biol.* 130: 1392–1395, 1939.

202. KLOPPER, A. The assessment of placental function in clinical practice. In: *Foetus and Placenta*, edited by A. Klopper and E. Diczfalusy. Oxford: Blackwell, 1969, p. 471–555.

203. KLOPPER, A., AND E. DICZFALUSY (editors). *Foetus and Placenta.* Oxford: Blackwell, 1969.

204. KNOBIL, E., AND J. B. JOSIMOVICH. Placental transfer of thyrotrophic hormones, thyroxine, tri-iodothyronine and insulin in the rat. *Ann. NY Acad. Sci.* 75: 895–904, 1959.

205. KOHLER, P. P., G. T. ROSS, AND W. D. ODELL. Metabolic clearance and production rates of human luteinising hormone in pre- and postmenopausal women. *J. Clin. Invest.* 47: 38–47, 1968.

206. KOVACIC, N. Biological characteristics of pituitary and placental hormones. *J. Reprod. Fertility* 8: 165–186, 1964.

207. KUHN, N. J., AND M. S. BRILEY. The roles of pregn-5-ene-3β, 20α-diol and 20α-hydroxysteroid dehydrogenase in the control of progesterone synthesis preceding parturition and lactogenesis in the rat. *Biochem. J.* 117: 193–201, 1970.

208. KUMAR, D. Hormonal regulation of myometrial activity: clinical implications. In: *Cellular Biology of the Uterus*, edited by R. M. Wynn. Amsterdam: North-Holland, 1967, p. 449–474.

209. LABHSETWAR, A. P., AND A. C. ENDERS. Progesterone in the corpus luteum and placenta of the armadillo, *Dasypus novemcinctus. J. Reprod. Fertility* 16: 381–387, 1968.

210. LADNER, C., C. R. BRINKMAN, III, P. WESTON, AND N. S. ASSALI. Dynamics of uterine circulation in pregnant and non-pregnant sheep. *Am. J. Physiol.* 218: 257–263, 1970.

211. LAIDLAW, J. C., J. L. RUSE, AND A. G. GORNALL. The influence of estrogen and progesterone on aldosterone excretion. *J. Clin. Endocrinol. Metab.* 22: 161–171, 1962.

212. LAMMING, G. E. Nutrition and the endocrine system. *Nutr. Abstr. Rev.* 36: 1–13, 1966.

213. LANDAU, R. L., AND K. LUGIBIHL. The catabolic and natriuretic effects of progesterone in man. *Recent Progr. Hormone Res.* 17: 249–281, 1961.

214. LANGECKER, H., AND L. DAMROSCH. Der Stoffwechsel des Progesterons. In: *Handbuch der Experimentellen Pharmakologie. Die Gestagene*, edited by K. Junkmann. Berlin: Springer, 1968, vol. XXII, part 1, p. 45–263.

215. LAURELL, C.-B. Orosomucoid and α_1-antitrypsin in maternal and fetal sera at parturition. *Scand. J. Clin. Lab. Invest.* 21: 136–138, 1968.

216. LAWS, R. M., AND G. CLOUGH. Observations on reproduction in the hippopotamus, *Hippopotamus amphibius. Symp. Zool. Soc. London.* 15: 117–140, 1966.

217. LE MAIRE, W. J., P. W. CONLY, A. MOFFETT, AND W. M. CLEVELAND. Plasma progesterone secretion by the corpus luteum of term pregnancy. *Am. J. Obstet. Gynecol.* 108: 132–134, 1970.

218. LIGGINS, G. C. The foetal role in the initiation of parturition in the ewe. In: *Foetal Autonomy*, edited by G. E. W. Wolstenholme and M. O'Connor. London: Churchill, 1969, p. 218–231.

219. LIGGINS, G. C., AND P. C. KENNEDY. Effects of electrocoagulation of the foetal lamb hypophysis on growth and development. *J. Endocrinol.* 40: 371–381, 1968.

220. LINDNER, H. R. Participation of lymph in the transport of gonadal hormones. In: *Proc. Intern. Congr. Hormonal Steroids, 2nd, Milan, 1966*, p. 821–827.

221. LINZELL, J. L. Cardiac output and organ blood flow in late pregnancy and early lactation in rats. In: *Lactogenesis*, edited by M. Reynolds and S. J. Folley. Philadelphia: Univ. of Pennsylvania Press, 1969, p. 153–156.

222. LINZELL, J. L., AND R. B. HEAP. A comparison of progesterone metabolism in the pregnant sheep and goat: sources of production and an estimation of uptake by some target organs. *J. Endocrinol.* 41: 433–438, 1968.

223. LITTLE, B., AND R. B. BILLIAR. Progesterone production. In: *Progress in Endocrinology*, edited by C. Gual and F. J. Ebling. Amsterdam: Excerpta Medica Foundation, 1968, p. 871–879.

224. LITTLE, B., O. W. SMITH, A. G. JESSIMAN, H. A. SELENKOW, W. VAN T'HOFF, J. M. EGLIN, AND D. F. MOORE. Hypophysectomy during pregnancy in a patient with cancer of the breast: case report with hormone studies. *J. Clin. Endocrinol. Metab.* 18: 425–443, 1958.

225. LITTLE, B., J. F. TAIT, S. A. S. TAIT, AND F. ERLENMEYER. The metabolic clearance rate of progesterone in males and ovariectomized females. *J. Clin. Invest.* 45: 901–912, 1966.

226. LOEWIT, K. Zur Bedeutung des hypophysären Luteinisierungs-hormons für Schwangerschaft, Geburt und Lactation bei der Ratte. *Acta Endocrinol.* 65, Suppl. 149, 1970.

227. LONG, J. A., AND H. M. EVANS. The oestrous cycle in the rat and its associated phenomena. *Mem. Univ. Calif.* 6: 1–111, 1922.

228. LONGCOPE, C., D. S. LAYNE, AND J. F. TAIT. Metabolic clearance rates and interconversions of estrone and 17β-estradiol in normal males and females. *J. Clin. Invest.* 47: 93–106, 1968.

229. LUKASZENSKA, J. H., AND G. S. GREENWALD. Progesterone levels in the cyclic and pregnant hamster. *Endocrinology* 86: 1–9, 1970.

230. LUNAAS, T. Urinary oestrogen levels in the sow during oestrous cycle and early pregnancy. *J. Reprod. Fertility* 4: 13–20, 1962.

231. MacArthur, E., R. V. Short, and V. J. O'Donnell. Formation of steroids by equine foetal testis. *J. Endocrinol.* 38: 331–336, 1967.

232. MacDonald, P. C., and P. K. Siiteri. Study of estrogen production in women with hydatidiform mole. *J. Clin. Endocrinol. Metab.* 24: 685–690, 1964.

233. MacDonald, P. C., and P. K. Siiteri. Origin of estrogen in women pregnant with an anencephalic fetus. *J. Clin. Invest.* 44: 465–474, 1965.

234. MacNaughton, M. C. Endocrinology of the foetus. In: *Foetus and Placenta*, edited by A. Klopper and E. Diczfalusy. Oxford: Blackwell, 1969, p. 557–602.

235. McCracken, J. A., and D. T. Baird. The study of ovarian function by means of transplantation of the ovary in the ewe. In: *The Gonads*, edited by K. W. McKerns. Amsterdam: North-Holland, 1969, p. 175–209.

236. McLaren, A. Genetic and environmental effects on foetal and placental growth in mice. *J. Reprod. Fertility* 9: 79–98, 1965.

237. McPhail, M. K. Studies on the hypophysectomized ferret. 9. The effect of hypophysectomy on pregnancy and lactation. *Proc. Roy. Soc., London, Ser. B* 117: 34–44, 1935.

238. Malven, P. V. Hypophysial regulation of luteolysis in the rat. In: *The Gonads*, edited by K. W. McKerns. Amsterdam: North-Holland, 1969, p. 367–382.

239. Marsh, J. M., R. W. Butcher, K. Savard, and E. W. Sutherland. The stimulatory effect of luteinizing hormone on adenosine 3′,5′-monophosphate accumulation in corpus luteum slices. *J. Biol. Chem.* 241: 5436–5440, 1966.

240. Marshall, J. M. Adrenergic innervations of the female reproductive tract: anatomy, physiology and pharmacology. In: *Ergeb. Physiol., Biol. Chem. Exptl. Pharmakol.* 62: 6–67, 1970.

241. Masuda, H., L. L. Anderson, D. M. Henricks, and R. M. Melampy. Progesterone in ovarian venous plasma and corpora lutea of the pig. *Endocrinology* 80: 240–246, 1967.

242. Mattos, C. E. R. de, R. L. Kempson, T. Erdos, and A. I. Csapo. Stretch-induced myometrial hypertrophy. *Fertility Sterility* 18: 545–556, 1967.

243. Mayer, G., and M. Klein. Les hormones du placenta. In: *Rapport de la IIIe Réunion des Endocrinologistes de Langue Française*. Paris: Masson, 1955, p. 47–86.

244. Mead, R. A., and K. Eik-Nes. Seasonal variations in plasma levels of progesterone in western forms of the spotted skunk. *J. Reprod. Fertility Suppl.* 6: 397–403, 1969.

245. Meites, J., and M. C. Shelesnyak. Effects of prolactin on duration of pregnancy, viability of young and lactation in rats. *Proc. Soc. Exptl. Biol. Med.* 94: 746–749, 1957.

246. Mercier-Bodard, C., A. Alfsen, and E. E. Baulieu. Sex steroid binding plasma protein (SBP). *Karolinska Symp. Res. Methods Reprod. Endocrinol., 2nd, Stockholm, 1970*, p. 204–224.

247. Michael, C. A., and B. M. Schofield. The influence of the ovarian hormones on the actomyosin content and the development of tension in uterine muscle. *J. Endocrinol.* 44: 501–511, 1969.

248. Midgley, A. R., Jr., V. L. Gay, L. S. C. Caligaric, R. W. Rebar, S. E. Monroe, and G. D. Niswender. Radio-immunologic studies of rat LH. In: *Gonadotropins*, edited by E. Rosenberg. Los Altos, Calif.: Geron-X, 1968, p. 307–312.

249. Midgley, A. R., Jr., and R. B. Jaffe. Human luteinizing hormone in serum during the menstrual cycle: determination by radioimmunoassay. *J. Clin. Endocrinol. Metab.* 26: 1375–1381, 1966.

250. Midgley, A. R., Jr., and R. B. Jaffe. Regulation of human gonadotropins. IV. Correlation of serum concentrations of follicle stimulating and luteinizing hormones during the menstrual cycle. *J. Clin. Endocrinol. Metab.* 28: 1699–1703, 1968.

251. Midgley, A. R., Jr., and R. B. Jaffe. Regulation of human gonadotropins. II. Disappearance of human chorionic gonadotropins following delivery. *J. Clin. Endocrinol. Metab.* 28: 1712–1718, 1968.

252. Migeon, C. J., J. Bertrand, and P. E. Wall. Physiological disposition of 4-C^{14}-cortisol during late pregnancy. *J. Clin. Invest.* 36: 1350–1362, 1957.

253. Migeon, C. J., F. M. Kenny, and F. H. Taylor. Cortisol production rate. VIII. Pregnancy. *J. Clin. Endocrinol. Metab.* 28: 661–666, 1968.

254. Mikhail, G., and W. M. Allen. Ovarian function in human pregnancy. *Am. J. Obstet. Gynecol.* 99: 308–312, 1967.

255. Milgrom, E. Progesterone binding in the rat uterus cytosol. *Excerpta Med. Found. Intern. Congr. Ser. 210. Abstr.* 318: 155, 1970.

256. Milgrom, E., M. Atger, and E.-E. Baulieu. Progesterone binding plasma protein (PBP). *Nature* 228: 1205–1206, 1970.

257. Milgrom, E., and E.-E. Baulieu. Liaison spécifique de la progestérone à un perotéine dans l'utérus. *Compt. Rend., Ser. D* 267: 2005–2007, 1968.

258. Mills, I. H. Transport and metabolism of steroids. *Brit. Med. Bull.* 18: 127–133, 1962.

259. Moor, R. M. Effect of embryo on corpus luteum function. *J. Animal Sci.* 27, Suppl. 1: 97–128, 1968.

260. Moore, N. W., S. Barrett, J. B. Brown, I. Schindler, M. A. Smith, and B. Smyth. Oestrogen and progesterone content of ovarian vein blood of the ewe during the oestrous cycle. *J. Endocrinol.* 44: 55–62, 1969.

261. Morris, B., and M. B. Sass. The formation of lymph in the ovary. *Proc. Roy. Soc., London, Ser. B* 164: 577–591, 1966.

262. Morris, J. A. Vascular physiology of the uterus. In: *Cellular Biology of the Uterus*, edited by R. M. Wynn. Amsterdam: North-Holland, 1967, p. 53–70.

263. Musa, B. U., R. P. Doe, and U. S. Seal. Serum protein alterations produced in women by synthetic estrogens. *J. Clin. Endocrinol. Metab.* 27: 1463–1469, 1967.

264. Nalbandov, A. V., and L. E. Casida. Gonadotrophic action of pituitaries from pregnant cows. *Endocrinology* 27: 559–566, 1940.

265. Nalbandov, A. V., W. W. Moore, and H. W. Norton. Further studies on the neurogenic control of the estrous cycle by uterine distension. *Endocrinology* 56: 225–231, 1955.

266. Nancarrow, C. D., and R. F. Seamark. Progesterone metabolism in fetal blood. *Steroids* 12: 367–380, 1968.

267. Needham, D. M., and C. F. Shoenberg. The biochemistry of the myometrium. In: *Cellular Biology of the Uterus*, edited by R. M. Wynn. Amsterdam: North-Holland, 1967, p. 291–352.

268. Neill, J. D., B. N. Day, G. W. Duncan, and L. J. Wyngarden. Gas-chromatographic determination of progestins in tissue and blood. *Steroids* 4: 699–712, 1964.

269. Neill, J. D., E. D. B. Johansson, and E. Knobil. Patterns of circulating progesterone concentrations during the fertile menstrual cycle and the remainder of gestation in the rhesus monkey. *Endocrinology* 84: 45–48, 1969.

270. Newson, R. M. Reproduction in the feral coypu (*Myocastor coypus*). *Symp. Zool. Soc. London* 15: 323–334, 1966.

271. Newton, W. H. 'Pseudo-parturition' in the mouse, and the relation of the placenta to *post-partum* oestrus. *J. Physiol., London* 84: 196–207, 1935.

272. Newton, W. H. Hormones and the placenta. *Physiol. Rev.* 18: 419–446, 1938.

273. Newton, W. H., and F. J. Lits. Criteria of placental endocrine activity in the mouse. *Anat. Record* 72: 333–345, 1938.

274. Oakey, R. E., and R. F. Heys. Regulation of the production of oestrogen precursors in the foetus. *Acta Endocrinol.* 65: 502–508, 1970.

275. O'Malley, B. W., W. L. McGuire, P. O. Kohler, and S. G. Korenman. Studies on the mechanism of steroid hormone regulation of synthesis of specific proteins. *Recent Progr. Hormone Res.* 25: 105–152, 1969.

276. Parker, M. L., R. D. Utiger, and W. H. Daughaday. Studies on growth hormone. 2. The physiological disposition and metabolic fate of human growth hormone in man. *J. Clin. Invest.* 41: 262–268, 1962.

277. PARKES, A. S., AND R. DEANESLY. The ovarian hormones. In: *Marshall's Physiology of Reproduction* (3rd ed.), edited by A. S. Parkes. London: Longmans, 1966, vol. III, p. 570–828.

278. PATERSON, J. Y. F., AND F. A. HARRISON. The specific activity of plasma cortisol in sheep during continuous infusion of [1,2-³H₂] cortisol and its relation to the rate of cortisol secretion. *J. Endocrinol.* 37: 269–277, 1967.

279. PATERSON, J. Y. F., AND F. A. HARRISON. The specific activity of plasma cortisol in sheep after intravenous infusion of [1,2-³H₂] cortisol, and its relation to the distribution of cortisol. *J. Endocrinol.* 40: 37–47, 1968.

280. PATERSON, J. Y. F., AND F. HILLS. The binding of cortisol by ovine plasma proteins. *J. Endocrinol.* 37: 261–268, 1967.

281. PEARLMAN, W. H. [16-³H] Progesterone metabolism in advanced pregnancy and in oophorectomized-hysterectomized women. *Biochem. J.* 67: 1–5, 1957.

282. PEARLMAN, W. H., I. F. F. FONG, AND J-S. H. TOU. A further study of a testosterone-binding component of human pregnancy serum. *J. Biol. Chem.* 244: 1373–1380, 1969.

283. PENCHARZ, R. I., AND J. A. LONG. Hypophysectomy in the pregnant rat. *Am. J. Anat.* 53: 117–139, 1933.

284. PENCHARZ, R. I., AND W. R. LYONS. Hypophysectomy in the pregnant guinea-pig. *Proc. Soc. Exptl. Biol. Med.* 31: 1131–1132, 1934.

285. PERRY, J. S. The reproduction of the African elephant, *Loxodonta africana*. *Phil. Trans. Roy. Soc. London, Ser. B* 237: 93–149, 1953.

286. PERRY, J. S. Observations on reproduction in a pedigree herd of Large White pigs. *J. Agr. Sci.* 47: 332–343, 1956.

287. PERRY, J. S. The incidence of embryonic mortality as a characteristic of the individual sow. *J. Reprod. Fertility* 1: 71–83, 1960.

288. PERRY, J. S. *The Ovarian Cycle of Mammals.* Edinburgh: Oliver & Boyd, 1971.

289. PERRY, J. S., AND J. G. ROWELL. Variations in foetal weight and vascular supply along the uterine horn of the pig. *J. Reprod. Fertility* 19: 527–534, 1969.

290. PERRY, J. S., AND I. W. ROWLANDS. Early pregnancy in the pig. *J. Reprod. Fertility* 4: 175–188, 1962.

291. PFEIFER, Y., E. SADOWSKY, AND F. G. SULMAN. Prevention of serotonin abortion in pregnant rats by five serotonin antagonists. *Obstet. Gynecol.* 33: 709–714, 1969.

292. POLGE, C., L. E. A. ROWSON, AND M. C. CHANG. The effect of reducing the number of embryos during early stages of gestation on the maintenance of pregnancy in the pig. *J. Reprod. Fertility* 12: 395–397, 1966.

293. PORTER, D. G. The local effect of intra-uterine progesterone treatment of myometrial activity in rabbits. *J. Reprod. Fertility* 15: 437–445, 1968.

294. PORTER, D. G. The failure of progesterone to affect myometrial activity in the guinea-pig. *J. Endocrinol.* 46: 425–434, 1970.

295. PRELOG, V., AND P. MEISTER. Untersuchungen über Organextrakte und Harn, über die Isolierung von Progesteron aus dem Corpus Luteum des Wales. *Helv. Chim. Acta* 32: 2435–2439, 1949.

296. PRICE, M. The reproductive cycle of the water shrew, *Neomys fodiens bicolor* Shaw. *Proc. Zool. Soc. London* 123: 599–621, 1953.

297. PURVES, H. D. Cytology of the adenohypophysis. In: *The Pituitary Gland*, edited by G. W. Harris and B. T. Donovan. London: Butterworths, 1966, vol. 1, p. 147–232.

298. RAESIDE, J. I. Urinary oestrogen excretion in the pig during pregnancy and parturition. *J. Reprod. Fertility* 6: 427–431, 1963.

299. RAJ, H. G. M., AND N. R. MOUDGAL. Hormonal control of gestation in the intact rat. *Endocrinology* 86: 874–879, 1970.

300. RASMUSSEN, A. T. The weight of the principal components of the normal hypophysis cerebri of the adult human female. *Am. J. Anat.* 55: 253–276, 1934.

301. RENNIE, P., AND J. DAVIES. Implantation in the rabbit following administration of 20α-hydroxypregnen-3-one and 20β-hydroxypregnen-3-one. *Endocrinology* 76: 535–537, 1965.

302. RICE, B. F., R. PONTHIER, AND W. STERNBERG. Luteinizing hormone and growth hormone activity of the human fetal pituitary. *J. Clin. Endocrinol. Metab.* 28: 1071–1072, 1968.

303. RIVAROLA, M. A., M. G. FOREST, AND C. J. MIGEON. Testosterone, androstenedione, and dehydroepiandrosterone in plasma during pregnancy and at delivery: concentration and protein binding. *J. Clin. Endocrinol. Metab.* 28: 34–40, 1968.

304. ROBERTS, J. S., AND L. SHARE. Effects of progesterone and estrogen on blood levels of oxytocin during vaginal distension. *Endocrinology* 84: 1076–1081, 1969.

305. ROBERTS, J. S., AND L. SHARE. Inhibition by progesterone of oxytocin secretion during vaginal distention. *Endocrinology* 87: 812–815, 1970.

306. ROBINSON, R., R. D. BAKER, P. A. ANASTASSIADAS, AND R. H. COMMON. Estrone concentrations in the peripheral blood of pregnant cows. *J. Dairy Sci.* 53: 1592–1595, 1970.

307. ROBSON, J. M. Maintenance of pregnancy and of the luteal function in the hypophysectomized rabbit. *J. Physiol., London* 90: 145–166, 1937.

308. ROBYN, C., P. PERTRUSZ, AND E. DICZFALUSY. Follicle stimulating hormone-like activity in human chorionic gonadotrophin preparations. *Acta Endocrinol.* 60: 137–156, 1969.

309. ROMBAUTS, P. Excrétion urinaire d'oestrogènes chez la truie pendant la gestation. *Ann. Biol. Animale Biochim. Biophys.* 2: 151–156, 1962.

310. ROSENBAUM, W., N. P. CHRISTY, AND W. G. KELLY. Electrophoretic evidence for the presence of an estrogen-binding β-globulin in human plasma. *J. Clin. Endocrinol. Metab.* 26: 1399–1403, 1966.

311. ROSENTHAL, H. E., W. R. SLAUNWHITE, JR., AND A. A. SANDBERG. Transcortin: a corticosteroid-binding protein of plasma. x. Cortisol and progesterone interplay and unbound levels of these steroids in pregnancy. *J. Clin. Endocrinol. Metab.* 29: 352–367, 1969.

312. ROSENTHAL, H. E., W. R. SLAUNWHITE, JR., AND A. A. SANDBERG. Transcortin: a corticosteroid-binding protein of plasma. xi. Effects of estrogens on pregnancy in guinea-pigs. *Endocrinology* 85: 825–830, 1969.

313. ROSS, G. T., W. D. ODELL, AND P. L. RAYFORD. Luteinizing hormone activity in plasma during the menstrual cycle. *Science* 155: 1679–1680, 1967.

314. ROTHCHILD, I. The corpus luteum-hypophysis relationship: the luteolytic effect of luteinizing hormone (LH) in the rat. *Acta Endocrinol.* 49: 107–119, 1965.

315. ROWLANDS, I. W. The corpus luteum of the guinea-pig. *Ciba Found. Colloq. Ageing* 2: 69–83, 1956.

316. ROWLANDS, I. W. Levels of gonadotropins in tissues and fluids with emphasis on domestic animals. In: *Gonadotropins*, edited by H. H. Cole. San Francisco: W. H. Freeman, 1964, p. 74–107.

317. ROWLANDS, I. W., AND R. B. HEAP. Histological observations on the ovary and progesterone levels in the coypu, *Myocastor coypus*. *Symp. Zool. Soc. London* 15: 335–352, 1966.

318. ROWLANDS, I. W., AND R. V. SHORT. The progesterone content of the guinea-pig corpus luteum during the reproductive cycle and after hysterectomy. *J. Endocrinol.* 19: 81–86, 1959.

319. ROWSON, L. E. A., AND R. M. MOOR. The influence of embryonic tissue homogenate, infused into the uterus, on the life-span of the corpus luteum in the sheep. *J. Reprod. Fertility* 13: 511–516, 1967.

320. ROY, E. J., AND R. MACKAY. The concentration of oestrogens in blood during pregnancy. *J. Obstet. Gynaecol. Brit. Commonwealth* 69: 13–17, 1962.

321. SANDBERG, A. A., H. ROSENTHAL, S. I. SCHNEIDER, AND W. R. SLAUNWHITE, JR. Protein-steroid interactions, and their role in the transport and metabolism of steroids. In: *Steroid Dynamics*, edited by T. Nakao, G. Pincus, and J. F. Tait. New York: Acad. Press, 1966, p. 1–59.

322. SAVARD, K. The estrogens of the pregnant mare. *Endocrinology* 68: 411–416, 1961.

323. SAVARD, K., W. LE MAIRE, AND L. KUMARI. Progesterone synthesis from labeled precursors in the corpus luteum. In:

The Gonads, edited by K. W. McKerns. Amsterdam: North-Holland, 1969, p. 119–136.

324. SCHAMS, D., AND H. KARG. Untersuchungen über Prolaktin im Rinderblut mit einer radioimmunologischen Bestimmungsmethode. *Zentl. Vetmed. A.* 17: 193–212, 1970.

325. SCHOFIELD, B. M. The influence of the ovarian hormones on myometrial behaviour in the intact rabbit. *J. Physiol., London* 129: 289–304, 1955.

326. SCHOFIELD, B. M. The staircase effect shown by the myometrium. *J. Physiol., London* 154: 48–49P, 1960.

327. SCHOFIELD, B. M. Parturition. In: *Advances in Reproductive Physiology,* edited by A. McLaren. London: Logos Press, 1968, vol. III, p. 9–32.

328. SCHOMBERG, D. W., S. P. COUDERT, AND R. V. SHORT. Effects of bovine luteinizing hormone and human chorionic gonadotrophin on the bovine corpus luteum *in vivo. J. Reprod. Fertility* 14: 277–286, 1967.

329. SEAL, U. S., AND R. P. DOE. Corticosteroid-binding globulin: biochemistry, physiology and phylogeny. In: *Steroid Dynamics,* edited by T. Nakao, G. Pincus, and J. F. Tait. New York: Acad. Press, 1966, p. 63–88.

330. SHAIKH, A. A., AND G. E. ABRAHAMS. Measurement of estrogen surge during pseudopregnancy in rats by radioimmunoassay. *Biol. Reprod.* 1: 378–380, 1969.

331. SHARMAN, G. B. Delayed implantation in marsupials. In: *Delayed Implantation,* edited by A. C. Enders. Chicago: Univ. of Chicago Press, 1963, p. 3–14.

332. SHARMAN, G. B., J. H. CALABY, AND W. E. POOLE. Patterns of reproduction in female diprotodont marsupials. *Symp. Zool. Soc. London* 15: 205–232, 1966.

333. SHELESNYAK, M. C., AND P. F. KRAICER. The role of estrogen in nidation. In: *Delayed Implantation,* edited by A. C. Enders. Chicago: Univ. of Chicago Press, 1963, p. 265–274.

334. SHORT, R. V. *Progesterone in Tissues and Body Fluids* (Ph.D. Thesis). Cambridge: Cambridge University, 1958.

335. SHORT, R. V. Progesterone in blood. IV. Progesterone in the blood of mares. *J. Endocrinol.* 19: 207–210, 1959.

336. SHORT, R. V. The secretion of sex hormones by the adrenal gland. *Biochem. Soc. Symp.* 18: 59–84, 1960.

337. SHORT, R. V. Progesterone. In: *Hormones in Blood,* edited by C. H. Gray, and A. L. Bacharach. London: Acad. Press, 1961, p. 379–437.

338. SHORT, R. V. Steroids in the follicular fluid and the corpus luteum of the mare. A 'two-cell type' theory of ovarian steroid synthesis. *J. Endocrinol.* 24: 59–63, 1962.

339. SHORT, R. V. Ovarian steroid synthesis and secretion *in vivo. Recent. Progr. Hormone Res.* 20: 303–333, 1964.

340. SHORT, R. V. Implantation and the maternal recognition of pregnancy. In: *Foetal Autonomy,* edited by G. E. W. Wolstenholme and M. O'Connor. London: Churchill, 1969, p. 2–26.

341. SHORT, R. V. Bovine freemartin: a new look at an old problem. *Phil. Trans. Roy. Soc. London, Ser. B* 259: 141–148, 1970.

342. SHORT, R. V., AND M. F. HAY. Delayed implantation in the roe deer, *Capreolus capreolus. Symp. Zool. Soc. London* 15: 173–194, 1966.

343. SHORT, R. V., G. WAGNER, A.-R. FUCHS, AND F. FUCHS. Progesterone concentrations in uterine venous blood after intra-amniotic injection of hypertonic saline in mid-pregnancy. *Am. J. Obstet. Gynecol.* 91: 132–136, 1965.

344. SLOTIN, C. A., F. A. HARRISON, AND R. B. HEAP. Kinetics of progesterone metabolism in the pregnant sheep. *J. Endocrinol.* 49: xxx–xxxii, 1971.

345. SLOTIN, C. A., R. B. HEAP, J. C. CHRISTIANSEN, AND J. L. LINZELL. Synthesis of progesterone by the mammary gland of the goat. *Nature* 225: 385–386, 1970.

346. SMITH, I. D., G. H. BELL, AND G. DE CHANEET. Embryonic mortality in merino ewes exposed to high ambient temperatures. *Australian Vet. J.* 42: 468–470, 1966.

347. SMITH, J. G., J. HANKS, AND R. V. SHORT. Biochemical observations on the corpora lutea of the African elephant, *Loxodonta africana. J. Reprod. Fertility* 20: 111–117, 1969.

348. SMITH, P. E. Continuation of pregnancy in rhesus monkeys (*Macaca mulatta*) following hypophysectomy. *Endocrinology* 55: 655–664, 1954.

349. SMITH, S. W., AND L. R. AXELROD. Studies on the metabolism of steroid hormones and their precursors by the human placenta at various stages of gestation. II. In vitro metabolism of 3β-hydroxyandrost-5-en-17-one. *J. Clin. Endocrinol. Metab.* 29: 1182–1190, 1969.

350. SMITH, P. E., AND W. E. WHITE. The effect of hypophysectomy on ovulation and corpus luteum formation in the rabbit. *J. Am. Med. Assoc.* 97: 1861–1863, 1931.

351. SOLOD, E. A., D. T. ARMSTRONG, AND R. O. GREEP. Action of luteinizing hormone on conversion of ovarian cholesterol stores to steroids secreted *in vivo* and synthesized *in vitro* by the pseudopregnant rabbit ovary. *Steroids* 7: 607–620, 1966.

352. SOLOMON, S., AND E. V. YOUNGLAI. Neutral steroids in human pregnancy. Isolation, formation and metabolism. In: *Foetus and Placenta,* edited by A. Klopper and E. Diczfalusy. Oxford: Blackwell, 1969, p. 249–298.

353. SPIES, H. G., L. L. COON, AND H. T. GIER. Luteolytic effects of LH and HCG on the corpora lutea of pseudopregnant rabbits. *Endocrinology* 78: 67–74, 1966.

354. SPIES, H. G., AND S. K. QUADRI. Regression of corpora lutea and interruption of pregnancy in rabbits following treatment with rabbit serum to ovine LH. *Endocrinology* 80: 1127–1132, 1967.

355. STABENFELDT, G. H., B. I. OSBURN, AND L. L. EWING. Peripheral plasma progesterone levels in the cow during pregnancy and parturition. *Am. J. Physiol.* 218: 571–575, 1970.

356. STOKES, H., AND J. M. BODA. Immunofluorescent localization of growth hormone and prolactin in the adenohypophysis of fetal sheep. *Endocrinology* 83: 1362–1366, 1968.

357. TAIT, J. F., AND S. BURSTEIN. In vivo studies of steroid dynamics in man. In: *The Hormones,* edited by G. Pincus, K. V. Thimann, and E. B. Astwood. New York: Acad. Press, 1964, vol. V, p. 441–557.

358. TATA, J. R. Regulation of protein synthesis by growth and developmental hormones. In: *Biochemical Actions of Hormones,* edited by G. Litwack. New York: Acad. Press, 1970, vol. 1, p. 89–133.

359. TAVERNETTI, R. R., W. ROSENBAUM, W. G. KELLY, N. P. CHRISTY, AND M. S. ROGINSKY. Evidence for the presence in human plasma of an estrogen-binding factor other than albumin: abnormal binding of estradiol in men with hepatic cirrhosis. *J. Clin. Endocrinol. Metab.* 27: 920–926, 1967.

360. TAYLOR, N. R. W., J. A. LORAINE, AND H. A. ROBERTSON. The estimation of ACTH in human pituitary tissue. *J. Endocrinol.* 9: 334–341, 1953.

361. TELEGDY, G., AND E. ENDRÖCZI. Progesterone content of the dog's ovarian venous blood and ovarian tissue. *Acta Physiol. Acad. Sci. Hung.* 20: 277–283, 1961.

362. TELEGDY, G., E. ENDRÖCZI, AND K. LISSAK. Ovarian progesterone secretion during the oestrous cycle, pregnancy and lactation in dogs. *Acta Endocrinol.* 44: 461–466, 1963.

363. TOMKINS, G. M., AND E. S. MAXWELL. Some aspects of steroid hormone action. *Ann. Rev. Biochem.* 32: 677–708, 1963.

364. TULSKY, A. S., AND A. K. KOFF. Some observations on the role of the corpus luteum in early human pregnancy. *Fertility Sterility* 8: 118–130, 1957.

365. VAN DER MOLEN, H. J., AND A. AAKVAAG. Progesterone. In: *Hormones in Blood* (2nd ed.), edited by C. H. Gray and A. L. Bacharach. New York: Acad. Press, 1967, vol. 2, p. 221–305.

366. VANDE WIELE, R. L., J. BOGUMIL, I. DYRENFURTH, M. FERIN, R. JEWELEWICZ, M. WARREN, T. RIZKALLAH, AND G. MIKHAIL. Mechanisms regulating the menstrual cycle in women. *Recent Progr. Hormone Res.* 26: 63–104, 1970.

367. VAN NIEKERK, C. H., AND W. H. GERNEKE. Persistance and parthenogenetic cleavage of tubal ova in the mare. *Onderstepoort J. Vet. Res.* 33: 195–231.

368. VELARDO, J. T. The actions of steroid hormones on estradiol-17β in uterine growth and enzymorphology. In: *Proceedings of the First International Congress on Hormonal Steroids,* edited by

L. Martini and A. Pecile. New York: Acad. Press, 1964, vol. I, p. 463–490.

369. VELARDO, J. T., F. L. HISAW, AND A. B. DAWSON. Comparison of deciduomata in intact and progesterone-estrogen treated ovariectomized pseudo-pregnant rats. *Anat. Record* 113: 593, 1952.

370. VERMEULEN, A., L. VERDONCK, M. VAN DER STRAETEN, AND N. ORIE. Capacity of testosterone-binding globulin in human plasma and influence of specific binding of testosterone on its metabolic clearance rate. *J. Clin. Endocrinol. Metab.* 29: 1470–1480, 1969.

371. VILLEE, D. B. Development of endocrine function in the human placenta and fetus. *New Engl. J. Med.* 281: 473–484, 1969.

372. WARD, W. R. *Structure and Function of Ovine Cervix Uteri* (Ph.D. Thesis). Liverpool: Univ. of Liverpool, 1968.

373. WATANABE, M., C. I. MEEKER, M. J. GRAY, E. A. H. SIMS, AND S. SOLOMON. Aldosterone secretion rates in abnormal pregnancy. *J. Clin. Endocrinol. Metab.* 25: 1665–1670, 1965.

374. WEICHERT, C. K., AND A. W. SCHURGAST. Variations in size of corpora lutea in the albino rat under normal and experimental conditions. *Anat. Record* 83: 321–334, 1942.

375. WESTMAN, A., AND D. JACOBSOHN. Über Oestrin-Wirkungen auf die Corpusluteum Funktion. *Acta Obstet. Gynecol. Scand.* 17: 1–23, 1937.

376. WESTMAN, A., AND D. JACOBSOHN. Endokrinologische Untersuchungen an Kaninchen mit durchtrenntem Hypophysenstiel. *Acta Obstet. Gynecol. Scand.* 20: 392–433, 1940.

377. WESTPHAL, U. Steroid-protein interactions. XIII. Concentrations and binding affinities of corticosteroid-binding globulins in sera of man, monkey, rat, rabbit and guinea-pig. *Arch. Biochem.* 118: 556–567, 1967.

378. WESTPHAL, U. Binding of hormones to serum proteins. In: *Biochemical Actions of Hormones*, edited by G. Litwack. New York: Acad. Press, 1970, vol. 1, p. 209–266.

379. WESTPHAL, U. Preparation and characteristics of corticosteroid-binding globulin (CBG, transcortin). *Karolinska Symp. Res. Methods Reprod. Endocrinol., 2nd, Stockholm, 1970,* p. 122–140.

380. WICHMANN, K. On the metabolism and subcellular distribution of progesterone in the myometrium of the pregnant rat. *Acta Endocrinol. Suppl.* 116, 1967.

381. WIEST, W. G. Progesterone interactions in the rat uterus. In: *Progesterone: Its Regulatory Effect on the Myometrium*, edited by

G. E. W. Wolstenholme and J. Knight. London: Churchill, 1929, p. 56–72.

382. WIEST, W. G. Progesterone and 20α-hydroxypregn-4-en-3-one in plasma, ovaries and uteri during pregnancy in the rat. *Endocrinology* 87: 43–48, 1970.

383. WIEST, W. G., AND W. R. KIDWELL. The regulation of progesterone secretion by ovarian dehydrogenases. In: *The Gonads*, edited by K. W. McKerns. Amsterdam: North-Holland, 1969, p. 295–325.

384. WIEST, W. G., W. R. KIDWELL, AND K. BALOGH, JR. Progesterone catabolism in the rat ovary: a regulatory mechanism for progestational potency during pregnancy. *Endocrinology* 82: 844–859, 1968.

385. WIEST, W. G., M. O. PULKKINEN, J. SAUVAGE, AND A. I. CSAPO. Plasma progesterone levels during saline-induced abortion. *J. Clin. Endocrinol. Metab.* 30: 774–777, 1970.

386. YANNONE, M. E., J. R. MUELLER, AND R. H. OSBORN. Protein binding of progesterone in peripheral plasma during pregnancy and labor. *Steroids* 13: 773–781, 1969.

387. YATES, F. E., R. D. BRENNAN, AND J. URQUHART. Adrenal glucocorticoid control system. *Federation Proc.* 28: 71–83, 1969.

388. YEN, S. S. C., O. H. PEARSON, AND S. STRATMAN. Growth hormone levels in maternal and cord blood. *J. Clin. Endocrinol. Metab.* 25: 655–660, 1965.

389. YOSHIMI, T., C. A. STROTT, J. R. MARSHALL, AND M. B. LIPSETT. Corpus luteum function in early pregnancy. *J. Clin. Endocrinol. Metab.* 29: 225–230, 1969.

390. YOSHINAGA, K., R. A. HAWKINS, AND J. F. STOCKER. Estrogen secretion by the rat ovary *in vivo* during the estrous cycle and pregnancy. *Endocrinology* 85: 103–112, 1969.

391. ZANDER, J. Gestagens in human pregnancy. In: *Recent Progress in the Endocrinology of Reproduction*, edited by C. W. Lloyd. New York: Acad. Press, 1959, p. 255–277.

392. ZANDER, J., T. R. FORBES, A. M. VON MÜNSTERMANN, AND R. NEHER. 3-keto-4-pregnen-20α-ol and 3-keto-4-pregnen-20β-ol, two naturally occurring metabolites of progesterone. Isolation, identification, biologic activity and concentration in human tissues. *J. Clin. Endocrinol. Metab.* 18: 337–353, 1958.

393. ZANDER, J., AND A. M. VON MÜNSTERMANN. Progesteron in menschlichem Blut und Geweben. III. Progesteron in der Placenta, in der Uterusschleimhaut und im Fruchtwasser. *Klin. Wochschr.* 34: 944–953, 1956.

CHAPTER 42

Fine structure of the placenta

RALPH M. WYNN | *Department of Obstetrics and Gynecology, Abraham Lincoln School of Medicine, University of Illinois at the Medical Center, Chicago, Illinois*

CHAPTER CONTENTS

BECAUSE OF THE WIDE VARIATIONS in gross, histological, and submicroscopic structure of the placenta among even closely related species, detailed anatomic knowledge of this organ is a prerequisite to the interpretation of its manifold functions. The trophoblast, in particular, demonstrates the widest diversity of morphological adaptations to its unique role in the formation of both steroid and peptide hormones and in simultaneous function as fetal lung, liver, gut, and kidney. Striking anatomic variations, furthermore, may be found within the same organ at various stages of development and in various specialized regions. Physiological interpretation of placental fine structure is therefore logically preceded by a discussion of comparative anatomy and morphogenesis.

COMPARATIVE ANATOMY

Types of Placentation

Unilaminar placentation, the simplest form, consists of trophoblast (blastocystic ectoderm) in contact with maternal tissue, usually endometrium. Addition of endo-

This work was supported in part by Research Grant HD-04152 from the U.S. Public Health Service.

derm forms a bilaminar blastocyst, the fetal component of simple bilaminar placentation. Development of mesoderm results in a trilaminar blastocyst; the vascularized trilaminar blastocyst is the essential fetal component common to all mammalian placentas (2, 27, 28, 34, 42).

The true chorion, which consists of trophoblast and mesenchymal tissue, is basically avascular. Although it is absent in higher rodents and man, avascular chorionic placentation occurs in many animals. It entails apposition of true chorion (extraembryonic somatopleure other than that of the amnion) to the endometrium. Its trophoblast may form multinucleate giant cells or syncytial masses. Secondarily avascular chorionic or chorioallantoamnionic placentation occurs in middle and late gestation in anthropoid apes and man. In some rodents and rabbits this true chorion may be functional. In man the chorion laeve or "smooth chorion," although apparently similar superficially to the true chorion of the rabbit, arises through devascularization of the decidua capsularis and chorion laeve and forms secondarily avascular chorioamnionic placentation.

Vascularization of the chorion by the vitelline (yolk sac) vessels results in choriovitelline placentation; in chorioallantoic placentation the fetal blood supply is received through allantoic, or umbilical, vessels. Choriovitelline placentation, the more primitive variety, is the principal means of fetomaternal exchange in most marsupials, and it coexists with the allantoic placenta in many Eutheria, such as lagomorphs and rodents. In man true choriovitelline placentation is never well established because of the precocious development of the extraembryonic celom, which prevents contact of the yolk sac with the trophoblast.

In the typical eutherian blastocyst the early segregation of ectodermal tissue destined to form the trophoblast limits the formation of the endoderm and the intraembryonic mesoderm to a restricted group of cells. According to Mossman (28), formation of endoderm in all mammals is basically similar to that in the avian egg in that the cells are delaminated from the deep surface of the inner cell mass. These endodermal cells may, in part, become intimately related to the trophoblast in formation of the bilaminar yolk sac. The origin of the extraembryonic mesoderm has generated considerable controversy. In the human placenta it may arise, at least in part, by delamination from the cytotrophoblast (20–22), but comparative studies suggest that part of this layer may be derived from the same source as the intraembryonic mesoderm (27, 28).

Chorioallantoic Placentation

GROSS ANATOMY. Because the chorioallantoic placenta is the principal organ of fetomaternal exchange in most higher mammals, including man, its classification, on the basis of gross shape, histological "barrier," presence or absence of decidua, and other anatomic criteria, has been attempted frequently; however, frequent exceptions to all these criteria have been made. The definitive shape of the placenta is usually determined by the initial distribution of the villi over the chorionic surface, although, according to Wimsatt (34), the shape is occasionally secondarily derived. In the sow and mare the distribution of villi over almost the entire chorionic surface produces a diffuse placenta. In the cow and sheep, villi are restricted to separate tufts that are widely scattered over the chorion to form a cotyledonary, or multiplex, placenta. In most carnivores the grouping of villi in bands around the equator of the chorioallantoic sac results in a zonary placenta. In man, apes, rodents, bats, and most insectivores, the placenta forms a single disk; double disks may be commonly found in certain monkeys, such as the macaque. The definitive shape of the human placenta is a result of the disappearance of villi from all but a circumscribed locus on the chorion. Villi may arise primarily as outgrowths from the chorionic plate or secondarily from the basal plate as protrusions of cytotrophoblast that grow into a preformed syncytial mantle (34). The initially solid villous protrusions are subsequently vascularized by ingrowth of allantoic mesenchyme and vessels. Although deferred formation of villi usually results in a labyrinthine condition, the human placenta, according to Hamilton & Boyd (17), is derived from an earlier labyrinthine stage. Conversely the lamelliform placenta of the carnivores represents a secondary modification of the original villous condition brought about by fusion of the small villous branches of the chorion (2).

Placentas may be classified also according to the presence or absence of a maternal (decidual) component. Examples of deciduate placentas are those of man and the guinea pig. Adeciduate placentas are common to such animals as the ungulates and carnivores.

HISTOLOGY. The Grosser classification (16) retains its limited value in histological categorization of placentas. It has, however, proved an increasingly inadequate means of predicting placental function. The shortcomings of the Grosser classification include its failure to account for anatomic variation within the placenta, changes accompanying placental aging, and accessory placental organs. Its basic deficiency, however, is the implication that a reduction in the number of layers in the placental membrane is necessarily equivalent to increased placental efficiency. Although the transfer of substances that cross the placenta by simple diffusion is likely to be influenced by the thickness of the barrier, the Grosser scheme fails to take account of the physiological activity of the placental membranes, particularly with regard to enzymatic facilitation of transport, pinocytosis, and cytopempsis.

The minimal histological barrier in Grosser's original scheme comprised three fetal components: trophoblast, connective tissue, and endothelium. In the hemochorial placenta the trophoblast is exposed directly to the maternal blood. The persistence of maternal endothelium adds a fourth layer to form the endotheliochorial placenta. If, in addition, endometrial connective tissue remains, the postulated syndesmochorial placenta would result. When the endometrial epithelium enters into formation of a six-layered membrane, the epitheliochorial condition prevails. On the basis of knowledge gained through electron microscopy, this classification has been refined. The endotheliochorial placenta is much more likely to be "vasochorial," since the maternal capillaries must be supported by some form of connective tissue. It is most unlikely, however, that this supporting tissue is a remnant of the original endometrium. It is more likely a product of the trophoblast or perhaps a manifestation of the reaction of trophoblast to endometrium. In the cat, for example, maternal endometrial stromal cells persist to form an essentially syndesmochorial condition (45). Similar cells have recently been described in the dog in our laboratory. The classic syndesmochorial condition, as originally described in the sheep, goat, and cow, according to electron-microscopic observations, represents more nearly an epitheliochorial condition, since persistent remnants of maternal uterine epithelia have been found. The classic syndesmochorial condition, moreover, is unlikely to occur in the definitive placenta except in limited areas, for there are no known species in which the main chorioallantoic mass is of this histological type.

The typical epitheliochorial placenta is found among Perissodactyla, Artiodactyla, Pholidota, Cetacea, Talpidae, and among the primates, Lemuridae and Lorisidae. The vasochorial placenta with varying contributions of endometrial stromal cells is found typically among the Carnivora. Recent reexamination of the hyena's placenta in this laboratory suggests that it too may be endotheliochorial rather than hemochorial, as previously reported (42). The endotheliochorial or vasochorial condition is found also among members of the Bradypodidae, Soricidae, Chiroptera, Tubulidentata, and Proboscidea.

The hemochorial condition is subdivided into labyrinthine and villous types. A hemochorial labyrinth is found among members of the Insectivora, Chiroptera, Hyracoidea, Tarsiidae, Rodentia, and Lagomorpha. The hemochorial villous condition is found among the higher primates, Edentata, Insectivora, and certain isolated members of other groups.

The number of layers in the placenta fails, however, to provide an accurate index even of the ease of diffusion. For example, capillaries may indent both trophoblast and endometrium in an almost intraepithelial location. Thus without changing the number of cellular layers the thickness of the membranes is significantly reduced. Mossman (27) originally suggested that even the trophoblast may disappear from the mature placentas of certain rodents and lagomorphs. On the basis of ultrastructural evidence, however, it is now agreed that this postulated hemoendothelial condition is actually hemochorial (28, 42). In all placentas thus far subjected to electron microscopy, at least one layer of trophoblast has been shown to persist throughout gestation (6, 11, 42). The immunologic significance of this persistent trophoblast is discussed later in this chapter.

Rigid histological classifications neglect transitions within the same placenta and fundamental differences in origin and function of numerous placental specializations that appear superficially homologous or analogous. The human chorion laeve is perhaps analogous, but certainly not homologous, with the true chorion of the rabbit. Another example is the carnivore's placental hematoma, which may superficially resemble the true hemochorial condition. In the placental hematoma, however, stagnant blood extravasates between the chorion and the endometrial surface. This structure is histotrophic—it provides nutrition for the trophoblast from sources other than circulating blood. In contrast, the hemochorial placenta of man represents a true hemotrophic relation, since the nutrition is derived from circulating blood.

The Hemochorial Condition

In a hemochorial labyrinth the trophoblast forms lamellae between the blood-filled spaces. In the villous placenta, such as that of man, there is an initial rupture of the maternal vessels by the trophoblast with escape of blood to form large sinusoids with trabeculae across the blood-filled spaces (17, 34). Wynn (42) illustrated the villous condition in a variety of taxonomically unrelated animals and confirmed the presence of numerous transitions from villous to labyrinthine forms, as seen particularly in the placentas of some New World monkeys. In the human placenta the villi are essentially free; the apparent intervillous connections are formed not by syncytiotrophoblast but by fibrinous adhesions resulting from organization of minute hematomas. The labyrinthine condition is not different fundamentally; in the squirrel monkey, for example, the breakdown of syncytium converts the trabeculae in the affected areas to villi. In man there is no evidence of ontogenetic recapitulation of postulated phylogenetic development. Because the human placenta achieves a hemochorial status long before fetal vessels and mesenchyme appear—before the formation of the definitive placenta—there are no recognized intermediate stages of development. The varieties of placentation among the anthropoids may be related to the differential activity of the ectoplacental trophoblast. In the platyrrhine (New World) monkeys, such as *Saimiri* and *Leontocebus*, there is less freedom of individual villi as a result of the initially broad attachment to the endometrium, but early and massive proliferation of trophoblast occurs. In the catarrhine (Old World) monkeys, such as

the macaque (38) and baboon (46), trophoblastic penetration is earlier and more extensive. Among anthropoids the most highly invasive trophoblast occurs in the early human blastocyst (21, 22) with the result that the chorionic villi lie free in the intervillous space in contact with maternal blood almost as soon as they are formed. The hemochorial condition appears to result from extensive erosion of maternal vessels associated with suppression of growth of maternal capillaries.

Comparative Electron Microscopy

A major result of the ultrastructural studies of a variety of placental forms has been the provision of data indicative of functional adaptations of each of the layers of the placental membrane, especially the trophoblast. Density of the trophoblastic nuclei, as noted with light microscopy, is explained by the high content of deoxyribonucleoprotein particles. Cytoplasmic basophilia of the physiologically active forms of trophoblast is correlated with the abundant granular endoplasmic reticulum. Deposits of glycoprotein and lipid granules are related, respectively, to the histochemicaly detected periodic acid-Schiff (PAS)-positive and sudanophilic materials.

Secretory cells are characterized by a well-developed system of organelles and, in many cases, by discrete granules or droplets. Since secretion is an energy-demanding process, a common feature of secretory cells is abundance of mitochondria. Active trophoblastic cells are rich in mitochondria, which generally are rod shaped or ovoid with transverse parallel cristae. Tubular cristae, however, are occasionally encountered in connection with placental steroidogenesis.

Rough-surfaced endoplasmic reticulum is associated with protein synthesis. According to Björkman (6), it is extensively developed not only in trophoblast, but also in uterine epithelial cells in swine, in the cryptal syncytium of sheep, and in maternal endothelium of many endotheliochorial placentas.

Decidual cells, although often containing sparse organelles, may in certain species and certain areas develop an extensive endoplasmic reticulum. Such examples are the so-called decidual giant cells of the carnivores, the basal decidua of the rabbit, and the decidual cells in the basal plates of guinea pig and man (40), where they may approach in ultrastructural complexity the trophoblastic giant cells. Prominent smooth-surfaced endoplasmic reticulum is characteristic of cells that produce substances other then proteins, such as steroids.

In general the active secretory forms of trophoblast contain well-developed, rough-surfaced endoplasmic reticulum, whereas elements such as Langhans' cells, which serve basically as reserve or stem trophoblastic cells, contain relatively sparse endoplasmic reticulum but numerous polyribosomes. The Golgi apparatus, which is believed to be the site of formation of secretory granules, is best developed in tissues that are most active in the formation of secretory products. Such tissues include human syncytiotrophoblast, trophoblastic giant cells in rodents and ruminants, and maternal endothelium in the typical endotheliochorial labyrinth. All these tissues have well-developed Golgi membranes and vesicles.

The so-called trophoblastic brush border appears under the electron microscope as a border of inconstant microvilli. Convolutions of plasma membranes and formation of pinocytotic vesicles and vacuoles are related to the transport of water and ions. Some of the largest vacuoles, however, which can be detected with the light microscope, represent dilated cisternae of endoplasmic reticulum. In well-preserved tissues all components of the placental membrane can be shown to contribute to a virtually continuous system of channels from the free trophoblastic surface through the syncytioplasm, basal laminae, and fetal capillary; thus a direct route for rapid transport of products of absorption and secretion is provided.

A notable feature of some placental epithelia is the system of complexly folded basal plasma membranes. This specialization is most prominent in epithelia noted for transport of water, such as the proximal and distal convoluted tubules of the kidney and choroid plexus.

Micropinocytosis is considered an important activity of capillary endothelium, as well as of trophoblast. The term *pinocytosis* refers to the incorporation of fluid by the cell for its own use, whereas the term *cytopempsis* applies more accurately to the transport of vesicles and their contents across the cell. Cytopempsis may be difficult to distinguish from pinocytosis, although the occurrence of multivesicular bodies, which may possibly result from the collection of micropinocytotic vesicles, may be an indication of absorption (6).

Enders (11) recently suggested an anatomical classification of hemochorial placentas based on the number of layers of trophoblast as described by electron microscopy. In the labyrinthine placentas of guinea pig and chipmunk, for example, a single complete layer of syncytial trophoblast (the hemomonochorial condition) is found. In other rodents, such as *Zapus hudsonicus* (the jumping mouse), the hemomonochorial membrane comprises exclusively giant cells rather than a true syncytium (28). In the villous hemomonochorial category are the placentas of man and macaque, as well as the taxonomically unrelated armadillo (11, 42). In the hemomonochorial membrane in which only the syncytial layer is continuous, as in the guinea pig's labyrinth or in the mature human villus, individual cytotrophoblastic elements are occasionally found and presumably represent cells that give rise to the syncytium, as described later in this chapter. In the armadillo the syncytium arises from caps of cytotrophoblast at the tips of the growing villi, for a layer of Langhans' cells is absent. In the syncytiotrophoblast of the armadillo, the complexity of the microvilli and the apparent polarity of the organelles are more pronounced than in other hemochorial forms thus far studied ultrastructurally.

The true rabbit (*Oryctolagus cuniculus*) and the cottontail rabbit (*Sylvilagus floridanus*) have hemodichorial membranes (11, 28) in which the outer layer is syncytial and the inner layer basically cellular (Fig. 1). The membrane

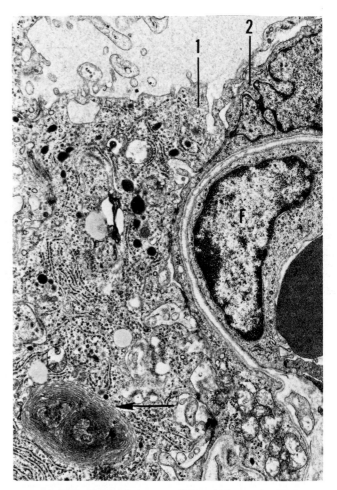

FIG. 1. Hemodichorial placenta of the rabbit at term. Note two-layered trophoblast (*1, 2*), fetal capillary (*F*), and membranous whorl (*arrow*) characteristic of this species. × 11,500.

may become so thin focally that two layers cannot be resolved with the light microscope. At times, even the entire trophoblastic covering appears absent, although normally it is always detectable with the electron microscope.

In several species the three-layered trophoblast forms a hemotrichorial membrane, as in the laboratory rat and mouse, the hamster (Fig. 2), the deer mouse (*Peromyscus maniculatus*), and the meadow mouse or common vole (*Microtus pennsylvanicus*) (11, 28). In these placentas the outer layer of trophoblast is cellular, whereas the inner two layers form either a true syncytium or a series of imbricated pseudosyncytial masses. The layer of trophoblast nearest the maternal blood is rich in granular endoplasmic reticulum, whereas the inner two layers are usually less well differentiated.

In the placenta of the hyena, as well as in typical endotheliochorial forms (6, 45), the base (fetal side) of the syncytium forms podocytic processes that resemble those of the visceral epithelium of Bowman's capsule (Fig. 3). The free surface (maternal side) is thrown up into blunt microvilli, which are generally less well developed than those in the hemochorial forms.

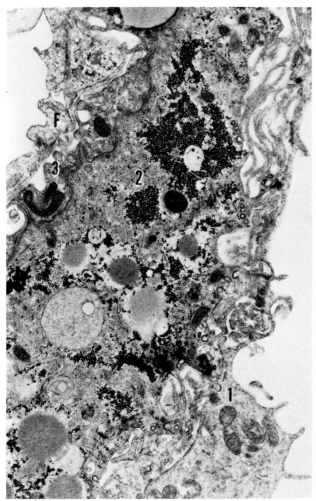

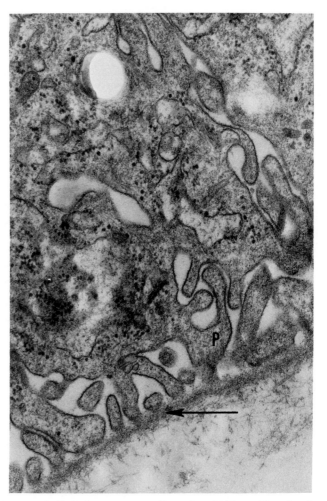

FIG. 2. Hemotrichorial placenta of the hamster at term. Three-layered trophoblast (*1, 2, 3*) and fetal capillary endothelium (*F*) are shown. × 13,600.

FIG. 3. Cat's placenta at term. Base of trophoblast with podocytic specializations (*P*) and basal lamina (*arrow*) are shown. × 46,200.

Ultrastructural examination of the less intimate placental membranes has consistently revealed the epitheliochorial, rather than the syndesmochorial, condition. Electron-microscopic studies of the horse, pig, and rhinoceros and histological examination of the camel, dromedary, and llama leave little doubt that the placenta in these animals is epitheliochorial (42). The classification of placentas of other ruminants, however, remained somewhat controversial until the demonstration of microvillous interdigitations between trophoblast and cryptal epithelium in the placentome (Fig. 4). Björkman (5) has shown that the placentas of cow and even sheep, formerly considered prototypical syndesmochorial organs, were actually epitheliochorial.

The equine placenta represents the typical epitheliochorial condition with its six-layered thick membrane. Both trophoblast and endometrial epithelium are complete, and the capillaries only occasionally abut the basal surfaces of the epithelia. Other epitheliochorial placentas have thinner membranes. The porcine placenta, often considered one of the most primitive in Grosser's classifi-

cation, becomes a considerably reduced barrier toward midgestation as a result of intraepithelial capillaries on both sides. Thus fetal and maternal blood streams are separated only by endothelia and thin layers of cytoplasm from trophoblast and endometrial epithelium. According to Björkman (6), intraepithelial capillaries also occur in ruminants, although to a lesser extent.

In the bovine placentome the cryptal layer is distinctly cellular. Among the Cervidae, both cellular and syncytial cryptal epithelia have been described. According to Björkman (5), the cryptal lining in the ovine placentome is mainly syncytial. In the bovine cryptal layers the cuboidal cells rest on a thick and even basal lamina. In the placental crypt of the sheep the contact between the trophoblast and the stroma is irregular; cytoplasmic processes penetrate the fibrous layers of the stroma and establish contact with fibroblasts and endothelium of the maternal capillaries. The fetal mesenchyme in these thick membranes is circumvented by intraepithelial capillaries, and maternal connective tissue is bypassed by the direct contact between maternal capillaries and cryptal syncytium. As mentioned in the discussion of the Grosser classification, the number of layers in the placental mem-

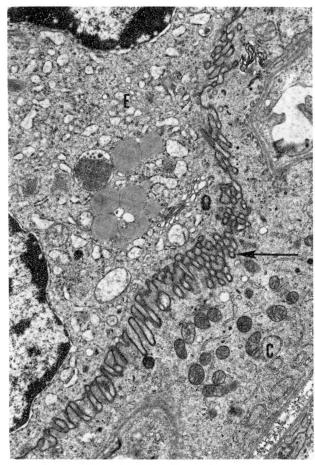

FIG. 4. Placenta of sheep at term. Chorionic (C) and endometrial (E) epithelia and their interdigitating plasma membranes (arrow) are shown. × 13,600.

brane in such cases fails to indicate the true intimacy of the placental membrane.

The "barrier," furthermore, is influenced not only by the number of layers and their permeabilities, but also by the spatial relations of the cells within each layer. The fetal tissue immediately adjacent to maternal tissue or blood forms a continuous layer, except for the external layer of trophoblast in the hemotrichorial placenta. If this tissue is cellular, the apical portions of the cells are joined by tight junctions. Extracellular spaces between the basal lamina and the trophoblast occur in many endotheliochorial and hemochorial placentas. Similar spaces may be found on the maternal side, as in the porcine placenta, but they are always sealed distally by tight intercellular junctions. Although such spaces may reduce the barrier to some extent, substances passing along this route must traverse the plasma membranes and cytoplasm because of the tight junctions.

HUMAN PLACENTATION

Gross Anatomy

At the completion of its morphogenesis, the human placenta is a hemochorial villous, discoidal, deciduate

organ. At term, its average diameter normally ranges between 15 and 20 cm, and its thickness is approximately 3 cm. Its normal weight is about 500 g with a volume of approximately 500 ml, comprising about 350 ml of fetal villi and 150 ml of maternal blood. Aherne & Dunnill (1) reported the average volume of the normal placenta to be 488 ml, with a range of 391–723 ml. Estimates of the surface area presented by the villi have ranged between 4 and 14 m², an area corresponding roughly to the total absorptive surface of the adult intestinal tract. Aherne & Dunnill (1) calculated the villous area by planimetry to be 11.0 ± 1.3 m². Viewed from the uterine aspect the placenta appears to be divided by grooves into between 15 and 20 maternal cotyledons, which are covered by the decidua basalis. The fetal cotyledons, which are valid circulatory units, comprise a major stem villus and its branches, which project into the intervillous space. Because of repeated subdivisions the villi are densest near the decidua and least concentrated toward the chorionic plate. The fetal surface of the placenta is not subdivided but is covered completely by the vascularized mesoderm of the chorion, through which course branches and tributaries of large umbilical vessels. The amnion is closely applied to the chorion and is often fused with it, especially at the placental margin.

Histology

The human placental membrane comprises three layers: trophoblast, connective tissue, and capillary endothelium. The syncytial trophoblast, which is in contact with maternal blood, is relatively thick in early placental development but thins progressively throughout gestation. Toward the end of the first trimester, the Langhans' cells, or villous cytotrophoblast, begin to decrease in prominence, although they persist in reduced numbers throughout gestation. The cytotrophoblast, as described later in this chapter, remains the source of all syncytium throughout gestation. In pathological states in which there is greater formation of new syncytium, perhaps as a homeostatic response to a stress, such as hypoxia, the Langhans' cells assume greater prominence (3).

The total thickness of the placental membrane may decrease from 0.025 to 0.002 mm. During maturation the villus may be converted from a thick structure with an almost uninterrupted layer of cytotrophoblast to an extremely thin membrane that separates fetal and maternal blood streams at term. In normal placental development, however, at least syncytiotrophoblast and fetal capillary endothelium are consistently present.

As the placenta ages, its terminal villi form increasingly numerous subdivisions. The more obvious histological changes that are consistent with increased efficiency of transfer include an increase in the ratio of villous surface to volume, a decrease in thickness of the syncytium, discontinuity of the Langhans' layer, and reduction in the proportion of villous connective tissue relative to the trophoblast. In the villi of the early placenta, fibrocytes with branching processes are separated by abundant, loose intercellular matrix. The core of the mature villus comprises a denser stroma with closely packed spindly cells. The villous capillaries, moreover, increase in number and progressively approach the surface. During placental maturation the so-called Hofbauer cells are also markedly reduced in number. The origin and significance of these rounded cells with vesicular, often eccentric, nuclei and granular or vacuolated cytoplasm have been studied by Wynn (39) and more recently by Enders & King (12).

Whereas the apparent conversion of the terminal villi to delicate sacs virtually filled with thin-walled vessels may lead to increased efficiency of transfer, not all changes characteristic of placental aging may be so directed. Thickening of the basement membranes of endothelium and trophoblast, obliteration of fetal and maternal vessels, and deposition of fibrinoid in the chorionic and basal plates, septa, and intervillous space appear incompatible with more efficient placental function. Such changes, furthermore, may be initiated as early as the first trimester. Syncytial clumps were formerly considered additional evidence of placental aging, but Hamilton & Boyd (18), as well as Wynn (41), have recently shown that they are not necessarily associated with trophoblastic degeneration. Details of the histology and histochemistry of the human placenta are provided in the classic papers from Wislocki's laboratory (35, 36).

Ultrastructure

METABOLIC ADAPTATIONS. The syncytiotrophoblast, the single most active and variable component of the human placenta, has been shown by electron microscopy to be a true syncytium, which may be constantly reoriented about the terminal villi. Formation of syncytial clumps at one pole of the villus may be associated with extreme attenuation of the trophoblast to form epithelial plaques, or maximal reduction in thickness of the placental membrane, at the other pole.

The ribonucleoprotein particles associated with the extensive ergastoplasm of the syncytium and the numerous free ribosomes create the basophilia noted in light microscopy; distension of channels of endoplasmic reticulum creates the vesicular syncytioplasm observed by conventional histological methods (Fig. 5). The free surface of the syncytium is characterized by a microvillous border associated with pinocytotic vesicles and vacuoles. The plasma membranes abutting the basal lamina are often complexly convoluted, occasionally forming podocytic processes comparable to those of the renal glomeruli and tubules. Typical Langhans' cells, however, are ultrastructurally simple with large nuclei, prominent nucleoli, large mitochondria, and a few Golgi bodies. The cytoplasm is studded with numerous free ribosomes but is relatively devoid of well-developed endoplasmic reticulum. These ultrastructural features are common to embryonic and neoplastic cells, the primary function of which is growth and differentiation rather than elaboration of specialized endocrine or exocrine products (Fig. 6).

The normal chorionic villus is completely covered by syncytial trophoblast, which rests in part on a basal lam-

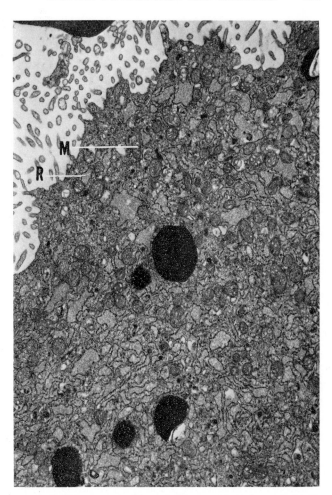

FIG. 5. Human syncytial trophoblast at 12 weeks packed with numerous mitochondria (*M*) and dilated channels of endoplasmic reticulum (*R*). × 11,500.

ina and in part on the incomplete layer of Langhans' cells. Although the Langhans' layer, which is more or less continuous in the early villus (33, 42), usually becomes attenuated or interrupted during placental maturation, Langhans' cells may be identified in the human placenta throughout gestation (7, 30, 37, 42). Secretory granules, often bounded by membranes, are commonly found in the syncytium but only rarely in typical Langhans' cells. The large mitochondria that are located between the folds of membranes are presumably related to the supply of energy for transfer against a gradient. Vacuoles and vesicles that extend throughout the trophoblast may communicate with channels of endoplasmic reticulum to form a virtually continuous conduit from maternal surface of the trophoblast through fetal capillary endothelium. Pinocytosis, furthermore, may originate in the capillary in the direction of fetus or placenta to intervillous space, in accordance with the known secretory functions of the fetoplacental unit (41). According to Fawcett (13), after pinocytosis a compensatory synthesis of plasma membranes may occur.

In classic pinocytosis, outfoldings of the plasma membrane enclose relatively large globules of fluid. In micropinocytosis of the type associated with microvilli, invagi-

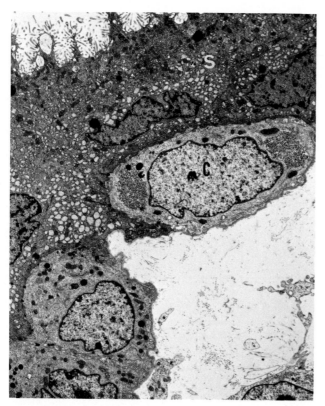

FIG. 6. Human villus at 6 weeks. Dense syncytium (S) and ultrastructurally simple cytotrophoblast (C) are shown. × 11,500.

nations of the plasma membrane effect transfer of fluid-filled microvesicles across the capillary wall at a rate adequate at least for metabolism of the cell itself. Such stable differentiations as striated borders are related principally to selective absorption, whereas unstable microvilli may be associated with both absorption and secretion. Minor ultrastructural differences in the trilaminar unit membrane may explain significant differences in placental absorption, secretion, and transfer against a gradient in both directions.

In a correlative cytochemical study, Hempel & Geyer (19) found that alkaline phosphatase was most prominently detected on the microvilli and remaining apical plasma membrane of the syncytial trophoblast. The reaction for the enzyme was weaker in the intracytoplasmic vesicles and basal plasmalemma. The reaction was positive also in the plasma membranes of the cytotrophoblast and in vesicles related to cytopempsis in the fetal capillary endothelial cells.

During synthesis, the endoplasmic reticulum may be distended with products of varying electron density. Precursors that are synthesized in the endoplasmic reticulum are subsequently assembled into secretory granules in the Golgi complexes. Mitochondria and Golgi complexes, though numerous, may be difficult to detect in the electron-dense syncytioplasm. The smooth-surfaced endoplasmic reticulum, which functions in segregation and transport of cellular products other than proteins, also is well developed in the active syncytium. Lysosomes, which contain such hydrolytic enzymes as acid phosphatase, are

numerous in the syncytium but not in the cytotrophoblast. Many granules in the syncytiotrophoblast are limited by single membranes and appear proteinaceous, whereas certain intensely osmiophilic droplets unlimited by membranes are very likely lipids, including steroids. In some series of vacuoles there is a progressive decrease in density of contents as the distance from the free syncytial surface increases, a picture compatible with the gradual incorporation of metabolites obtained through absorption from the intervillous space. Other granules appear to maintain their membranes until they are incorporated into a promontory of syncytium from which they are discharged into the intervillous space, as in apocrine or merocrine secretion.

Transfer may be facilitated by the plasmodial activity of the syncytium, which minimizes the thickness of the membrane in certain areas. Although classic pinocytosis may achieve the incorporation of sizable droplets of fluid by the plasma membranes and their transfer across trophoblast and endothelium, micropinocytosis, accompanied by submicroscopic vesiculation of the plasma membrane, may be more selective. The demonstration, particularly in glutaraldehyde-fixed material, of antennulae microvillares on the syncytiotrophoblast has added another element of selectivity to the process of micropinocytosis that perhaps entails the exclusion of certain classes of proteins from the cell. Mesenchymal cells, too, may adjust their rates of synthesis and transfer to demand and thus provide an additional means of transport of metabolites. Electron microscopy has amply demonstrated the participation of all placental elements in greatly diversified but finely coordinated functions that serve to maintain fetal homeostasis, despite altering physiological conditions.

Ancillary structural adaptations, detected by electron microscopy, include gradual decrease in the mass of cytotrophoblast and possibly attenuation of basal laminae, at least of the endothelium. At all times, however, the normal minimal histological barrier comprises trophoblast, fetal capillary, and their basal laminae. The persistence of trophoblast is probably of prime significance in maintaining the immunologically crucial buffer zone, as discussed later in this chapter.

Placental transfer, even by diffusion, depends on factors other than the thickness and area of the membrane. Other important variables are the concentrations of the substance in fetal and maternal bloods, the rate of maternal blood flow through the intervillous space, and the amount of substance metabolized by the placenta during transfer. Ultrastructure consequently reflects only a few of the variables in transfer. The hazards of sampling, inherent in the interpretation of fine structure in general, are of even greater significance in the study of the placenta, which exhibits enormous structural variations with age and circulatory relations. The differences are often striking not only from chorionic to basal plate and from cotyledon to cotyledon, but even from one villus to another or within the same terminal villus. Quantitation, in physiologically significant terms, of

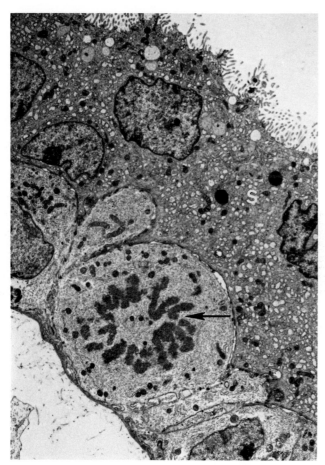

FIG. 7. Human villus at 6 weeks. Mitotic figure (*arrow*) in cytotrophoblast (Langhans' cell), which presumably gives rise to syncytium (*S*), is shown. × 4,040.

such highly variable ultrastructural features as the length, width, and number of microvilli is thus likely to be quite midleading.

ORIGIN OF THE SYNCYTIUM. Elucidation of the mechanism of syncytial growth requires resolution of the discrepancy between the increase in number of nuclei in the syncytiotrophoblast and the apparent absence of intrinsic nuclear replication. Mitotic figures, though frequently observed in the cytotrophoblast, are not found in the syncytium (Fig. 7). To distinguish amitotic nuclear proliferation within the syncytium from cytotrophoblastic origin of the syncytiotrophoblast, Galton (15) employed microspectrophotometry based on the measurement of nuclear deoxyribonucleic acid (DNA). He noted a bimodal distribution of DNA in the syncytium at a time of rapid placental growth, whereas the high proportion of cytotrophoblastic nuclei contained DNA in excess of the diploid amount, a confluence of events reflecting synthesis of nucleic acid in interphase nuclei preparatory to division. Galton's observations led to the suggestion that the rapid accumulation of nuclei in the syncytium is explained by cellular proliferation within the cytotrophoblast followed by coalescence of daughter cells in the syncytium. Evidence of another kind was provided by Richart (31), who noted

early incorporation of tritiated thymidine by cytotrophoblast, but not by syncytium, in placental culture. Midgley et al. (26) extended the idea by study of the rhesus monkey in vivo. They found that, although tritiated thymidine appeared at first only in cytotrophoblastic nuclei, the label could be detected later in syncytium also. These findings indicated that syncytiotrophoblast is derived from cellular elements and is itself a mitotic end stage. Subsequent studies of the same problem in several laboratories supported the conclusion that newly formed syncytium takes up the label that was originally confined to cellular trophoblast.

The electron-microscopic corroboration of the derivation of the syncytium from the cytotrophoblast has been provided by the demonstration of morphologically transitional cells in the normal placentas of man and monkey and in neoplastic human trophoblast (29, 33, 42). The absence of intratrophoblastic basement membranes separating syncytium from Langhans' cells, as suspected by light microscopists, has been confirmed. The typical Langhans' cell has a large nucleus with a prominent nucleolus, occasional large mitochondria, and few Golgi bodies. The cytoplasm is studded with numerous free ribosomes but is relatively devoid of smooth and rough endoplasmic reticulum. Such an ultrastructural pattern is common to many poorly differentiated tumors and is characteristic of those cells the primary function of which is growth and differentiation, rather than elaboration of specialized exocrine or endocrine products. In the transitional, or intermediate, cells, the nucleocytoplasmic ratio decreases and the intranuclear deoxyribonucleoprotein (DNP) granules become more numerous and less evenly distributed, whereas within the cytoplasm both smooth and rough forms of endoplasmic reticulum increase (Fig. 8). Mature syncytial trophoblast characteristically has well-developed ergastoplasm and Golgi bodies, the organelles necessary for production of protein. Both nuclear and cytoplasmic transitions occur as cytotrophoblast differentiates into syncytium, the ultrastructurally mature form of trophoblast. Residual plasma membranes with attached desmosomes in well-fixed syncytium provide additional evidence of incorporation of the cytotrophoblast into syncytium. The demonstration of well-preserved organelles in areas between the membranes decreases the likelihood of artifact and suggests that plasma membranes gradually disappear as syncytium evolves from cellular trophoblast, to which it may remain attached by desmosomes.

The significance of these findings lies in the capacity of the placenta to form new syncytiotrophoblast throughout its life from the cellular reserve elements. In conditions of stress, such as hypoxia, new syncytium may form more rapidly to meet the needs of the fetus. The evidence bearing on the cytotrophoblastic contribution to the syncytium has recently been summarized by Boyd & Hamilton (7, 8).

NONVILLOUS TROPHOBLAST. Although most attention has been directed to the two forms of villous trophoblast, Langhans' cells and syncytium, other regions of the pla-

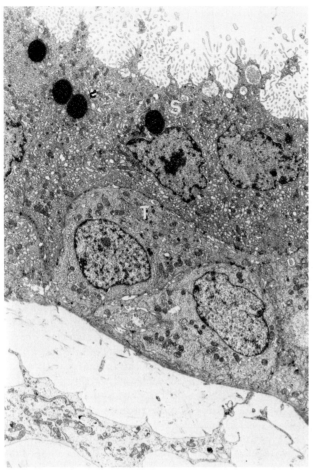

FIG. 8. Human villus at 9 weeks. Well-differentiated syncytio-trophoblast (*S*) and transitional cell (*T*) of intermediate ultra-structural complexity are shown. × 4,040.

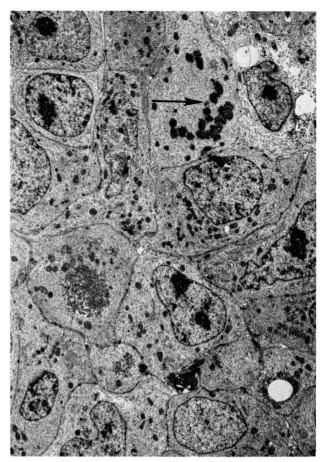

FIG. 9. Human cell column at 6 weeks. Cytotrophoblast in various stages of differentiation is shown. *Arrow* indicates a mitotic figure. × 4,040.

centa contain specialized cells that may retain endocrine or immunologic functions throughout pregnancy.

The cytotrophoblast of the chorionic wall proliferates into the syncytial trabeculae and converts them to primary villi. Chorionic mesoderm then invades the villi or differentiates in situ with them: thus the primary villi are converted to secondary villi. The appearance within the mesodermal cores of embryonic blood vessels gradually transforms the secondary villi into tertiary villi. The extremities of these villi retain a thin covering of syncytium and a core of cytotrophoblast and thus form so-called cell columns. Proliferation of the cells of these columns results in growth and peripheral extension of the villi. According to Boyd & Hamilton (8), continuation of the process leads to penetration by the cells of each column into the peripheral syncytium. These cytotrophoblastic elements then protrude into the junctional zone between the decidua and syncytium, where fusion of the lateral proliferations from the cell columns of the adjacent villi leads to formation of the cytotrophoblastic shell. As a result of these changes, each persisting villus is attached at its proximal end to the chorionic plate and at its distal extremity to the cytotrophoblastic shell.

The primitive cytotrophoblast forms all trophoblastic derivatives, cellular and syncytial. The villous cytotrophoblast (Langhans' layer) is continuous with the cytotrophoblast of the chorionic plate, which in turn merges into that of the chorion laeve. Elements of the cytotrophoblastic shell later become part of the boundary zone at the basal plate and contribute to the placental septa and probably to the cell islands (40).

Ultrastructurally these cytotrophoblastic variants are more complex than Langhans' cells. Like the intermediate cells in the villi, they may approach or equal the mature syncytial trophoblast in ultrastructural complexity (Fig. 9). The specialized cytotrophoblast of the basal plate, cell islands, and septa may be difficult to distinguish, even ultrastructurally, from the complex decidual elements with which they may be intimately related in those areas.

Specialized syncytial areas that require further study include, in the terminology of Hamilton & Boyd (18), syncytial sprouts, stromal trophoblastic buds, syncytial knots, multinuclear giant cells, syncytiotrophoblast of the chorion laeve, and the epithelial plaques described earlier in this chapter. In regions where the fetal capillary is very close to the overlying trophoblast, the two basal laminae may be so intimately related as to appear confluent. These regions form so-called vasculosyncytial membranes, or junctions, the minimal anatomical separation between intervillous space and fetal blood.

THE VILLOUS MESENCHYME. The villous core, which comprises fetal capillaries, fibroblasts, Hofbauer cells, and other mesenchymal elements, has been less extensively studied by electron microscopy than has the trophoblast. Ultrastructural alterations in these elements, however, may affect placental transfer and metabolism significantly. During placental development, the lumen of the capillary may widen and the endothelial lining may thin to adapt to increased efficiency of transfer. Fenestrations in the endothelium, moreover, have been shown to represent not pores but sites for active exchange. To minimize the histological barrier, the pericytes surrounding the capillaries and the endothelial basal lamina may thin or disappear, and outpouchings of the endothelium toward the trophoblastic basal lamina may bring the capillary and trophoblast virtually into contact. On the luminal side of the capillary, large projections may be found, particularly near the junction of two endothelial cells. These structures are associated with classic pinocytosis. Micropinocytotic vacuoles are also prominent elsewhere near the capillary endothelial surface to assist in more selective transfer. This micropinocytosis may be important in meeting metabolic requirements of the placenta itself. Another possible ultrastructural adaptation to the needs of the placenta is the development of a variety of mesenchymal cellular vacuoles, which may be vehicles of transport for metabolism of the villus. An additional feature that may reflect autonomous regulation of placental function is the abundance of endothelial tonofilaments, which may control the state of contraction of the capillary in the absence of a muscular coat or an intrinsic nerve supply (33).

The origin and function of the Hofbauer cells continue to generate speculation. Wynn (39) studied their sex chromatin, histochemistry, and ultrastructure in an attempt to ascertain their immunologic and metabolic significance, if any, in human placentation. Hofbauer cells are characterized by vacuolar cytoplasm, scant endoplasmic reticulum, and relative paucity of other organelles (Fig. 10). The cells may be distinguished by both histochemistry and electron microscopy from typical fibroblasts and plasma cells, although degenerating fibroblasts and Hofbauer cells may be indistinguishable. It is, however, most unlikely that the rare plasma cells in the placenta give rise to the numerous Hofbauer cells. The relation of fibrocytes to Hofbauer cells is complicated by the finding of primitive mesenchymal elements that may differentiate in either direction and by the common vacuoles and irregular outlines of older fibrocytes, which make them quite similar to Hofbauer cells.

Enders & King (12) recently examined human placentas at various stages of gestation and showed that the Hofbauer cells are ultrastructurally similar to ordinary macrophages except for unusually large cytoplasmic

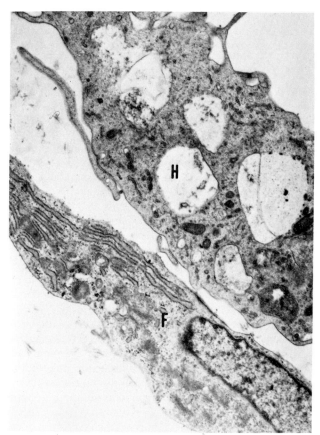

FIG. 10. Human placenta at term. Hofbauer cell (H) and fibrocyte (F) within core of villus are shown. × 9,190.

flanges and inclusion vacuoles. They believe that the vacuoles result from macropinocytosis. In addition, these investigators found micropinocytotic vesicles coated with a layer of moderately dense filamentous material and presumably related to uptake of protein. The present consensus is that the typical Hofbauer cell is most likely a macrophage with an unusual capacity for ingestion of fluid.

IMMUNOLOGIC CONSIDERATIONS. A single satisfactory explanation for the retention of the placental homograft remains to be provided. A theory based on antigenic immunity must be discarded in light of Billingham's demonstration that transplantation antigens appear very early in life (4). The second explanation, based on diminished immunologic reactivity of the mother during pregnancy, provides only an ancillary factor in the prevention of the development of maternal isoimmunization during pregnancy in a few species. If immunologic privilege provided by the uterus were the only factor, human ectopic pregnancies could never survive. Since transplantation immunity can be evoked and expressed in the uterus as elsewhere, the survival of the homograft must be related to a peculiarity of the conceptus rather than the uterus. The fourth explanation involves an effective barrier between the fetus and the mother. Lanman et al. (24) have provided indirect support for the last hypothesis in their experiments in which fertilized rabbit ova were transferred to a recipient's uterus. Neither prior exposure of the foster mother to skin grafts from the parents nor re-exposure to homografts from these donors at the time of egg transfer or at midgestation adversely affected the pregnancy. The only reasonable explanation for the survival of the homograft thus appears to be a fairly complete anatomic separation of maternal and fetal circulations.

Comparative electron microscopy of the placenta has supported the concept of the prime role of the trophoblast in maintaining the immunologic barrier (43, 44). In all placentas examined with the electron microscope, at least one layer of trophoblast persists throughout gestation (42). If the trophoblast lacks or fails to express histocompatibility antigens, an immunologic barrier would be created. The suggestion by Kirby et al. (23) that an extracellular peritrophoblastic deposit, rather than a relative lack of histocompatibility antigens in the trophoblast, was the basis of the barrier rekindled interest in so-called fibrinoids as a general phenomenon of mammalian placentation. I have employed the term *fibrinoid*, however, in the restricted conventional sense of the histopathologist to refer to a group of substances recognized with the light microscope (43). Although fibrinoids are not demonstrable in all mammalian placentas, a submicroscopic glycocalyx may be found with the aid of the electron microscope on most trophoblastic plasma membranes (44). It is still not clear, however, to what extent these extracellular polysaccharides, which often form incomplete coverings, serve as mechanical barriers to the passage of transplantation antigens from fetus to mother. The interesting hypothesis of Currie & Bagshawe (9) holds that pericellular sialomucins present a chemical barrier to immunologically competent cells. They reported that maternal lymphocytes respond in vitro to trophoblast as they do to other allogeneic tissues and suggested originally that the trophoblast escapes attack in vivo by electrochemical repulsion of negatively charged maternal lymphocytes, since the sialomucin confers a high electronegative surface charge. It now seems more likely that the sialic acid acts by steric hindrance to prevent contact with underlying antigenic groups. More recently, Currie et al. (10) showed that attacking the mucopolysaccharide coat with neuraminidase, which disrupts the sialomucin, results in the ability of the treated trophoblastic cells to express histocompatibility antigens on transplantation.

The deposition of fibrinoids and related noncellular components at the surfaces of contiguous fetal and maternal tissues could theoretically inhibit the immune response. A second important factor may be the passage of fetal blood or trophoblastic sprouts into the maternal circulation, thereby saturating the maternal antibody-producing system. A third factor, at least in certain species, could be relative deficiency of endometrial lymphatics, which theoretically confers a degree of immunologic protection to the placenta in those animals.

Ultrastructural examination of the placenta has eluci-

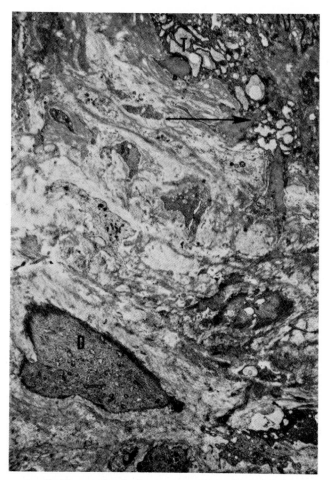

FIG. 11. Human basal plate at term. Decidua (*D*) with pericellular capsule and degenerating trophoblast (*T*) surrounded by fibrinoid (*arrow*) are shown. × 4,200.

dated several immunologic factors (44). Because the highly invasive trophoblast of the guinea pig is purely syncytial but that of the mouse is cellular, syncytial transformation is not prerequisite to immunologic protection. In many hemochorial placentas the pericellular decidual capsules may provide some protection through formation of mechanical barriers, but these materials are not found in placentas of all types or in ectopic human pregnancies. In the floor of the human placenta, for example, ultrastructurally well-preserved trophoblast and decidua are rarely in direct contact but remain separated by regressing tissues of fetal and maternal origins, by fibrinoid, or by both (40). This fibrinoid may arise from degeneration of decidual or trophoblastic cytoplasm or through transformation of the ground substance surrounding these cells (Fig. 11). In the human basal plate the apparently viable giant cells are essentially syncytiotrophoblastic and represent either derivatives of the peripheral syncytium or results of differentiation in situ of cytotrophoblast. Studies by Kirby et al. (23) indicated that the fibrinoid in the mouse placenta was of trophoblastic origin, whereas ultra-

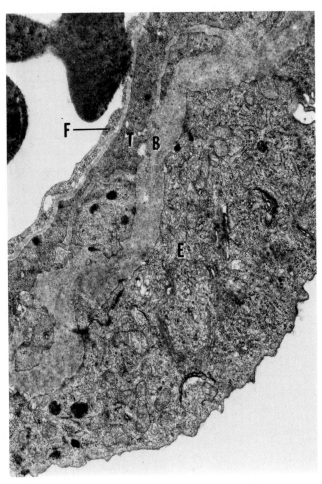

FIG. 12. Placental lamella of dog at term. Thick maternal endothelium (*E*), stout basal lamina (*B*), trophoblast (*T*), and fetal endothelium (*F*) are shown. × 13,600.

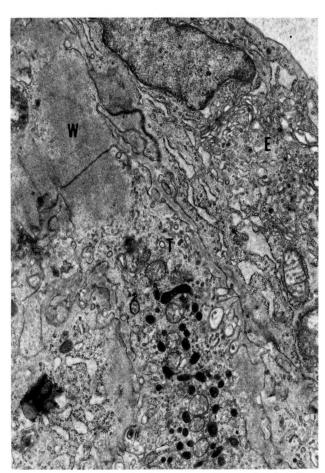

FIG. 13. Placental lamella of cat at term. Maternal endothelium (*E*) and trophoblast (*T*) with its terminal web (*W*) are shown. × 13,600.

structural examination of the human basal plate by Wynn (40) suggested that there is a contribution by decidua also. Fibrinoids and similar acellular barriers have been described in the decidual capsule and between the decidua and fetal giant cells of the rat's placenta, as well as in the guinea pig's junctional zone. Wimsatt (34) has identified in the placentas of certain Chiroptera an interstitial membrane morphologically similar to fibrinoid, as is the hypertrophic basal lamina of the maternal endothelium in placentas of many carnivores (Fig. 12). In the cat's placenta, for example, the terminal web of the trophoblast (Fig. 13) may be mistaken for extracellular "basement membrane-like" material (45). Although histologically demonstrable fibrinoids are absent from the epitheliochorial placentas of the sow, cow, mare, and sheep, mucopolysaccharides may be found by electron microscopy on the interdigitating microvilli of chorionic and endometrial epithelia.

On the one hand, the fibrinoids that are recognized by conventional histochemical techniques appear to reflect the cellular interplay of trophoblast and endometrium. On the other hand, the ultrastructurally demonstrable

sialomucins, which correspond to the widely distributed glycocalyces of plasma membranes in general, may play an important role as antigenic barriers. If the glycocalyx is crucial to the immunologic protection of the trophoblast, it probably owes this effect to anatomical, rather than chemical, factors in that the trophoblast, in contrast to other tissues, may be covered on all sides by sialomucins in areas in which antigenically mature fetal tissues and immunologically competent maternal cells are in contact. The problem deserves further study by ultracytochemical techniques. Finally it is significant that, in every placenta examined by electron microscopy, at least one layer of trophoblast persists essentially throughout gestation. The conclusion that immunologic protection of the placental homograft is provided, at least in part, by the trophoblast and the pericellular sialomucins on its plasma membranes therefore seems reasonable.

PLACENTAL ENDOCRINOLOGY

Ultrastructure of Endocrine Cells

Although the principal ultrastructural adaptations to

formation of steroid and peptide hormones apply to the placenta, as well as to other endocrine organs, special features unique to a tissue that produces both types require further comment. The following description of protein synthesis is based on the recent review by Fawcett and co-workers (14).

Information encoded in the DNA of the nuclear chromatin is carried to the cytoplasm in the form of messenger RNA, which is thought to leave the nucleus through pores in the nuclear envelope. In the cytoplasm, varying numbers of ribosomes become associated with each molecule of messenger RNA to form the linear arrays of 150-A particles recognized in electron micrographs as polysomes. In tissues like the trophoblast that synthesize protein for export, the polysomes are usually associated with the outer surface of the membranes of rough-surfaced endoplasmic reticulum. The ribosomes adhere to the endoplasmic reticulum with their larger subunit adjacent to its limiting membrane. The growing polypeptide chains penetrate the underlying membrane and are released into the lumen of the endoplasmic reticulum. The protein is then channeled through the tubules and cisternae of the endoplasmic reticulum to the Golgi region, where it is transferred in many small, smooth-surfaced vesicles that bud off from the ends of the cisternae of the endoplasmic reticulum. In the Golgi complex the product is formed into membrane-bound granules. The secretory product is later released by a process in which the membrane of the droplet coalesces with that of the cell surface in a fashion that permits discharge of the secretion without breaching the cell membrane.

Stimulation of a particular cell is attended by marked increase in the endoplasmic reticulum and enlargement of the Golgi complex. In many endocrine organs, and presumably in the trophoblast as well, certain granules not released or needed, as well as excess membranes and ribosomes of the endoplasmic reticulum, may be incorporated into autophagic vacuoles and digested by lysosomal enzymes. Lysosomes with cytochemically demonstrable acid phosphatase are numerous in syncytiotrophoblast.

Release of a hormone, according to Fawcett and co-workers (14), involves movement of membrane-bound dense granules to the cell surface followed by a fusion of their limiting membrane with the plasma membrane. Because intermediate stages of extrusion of granules are rare, it is assumed that fusion of the secretory vesicles with the cell membrane is rapid and that solubilization of the extruded granule is almost immediate. The bulk of ultrastructural evidence favors a process involving coalescence of membrane-limited vesicles, with the cell membrane extruding intact secretory granules that undergo dissolution extracellularly (14). At high rates of secretion the cell product may not be concentrated into granules before release, but the same mode of discharge is believed to apply to the pale vesicles, the contents of which may be fluid under these conditions. In the

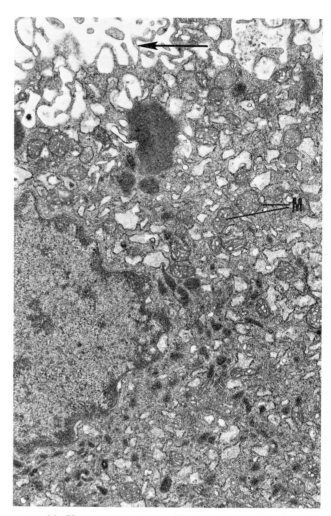

FIG. 14. Human syncytiotrophoblast at 8–9 weeks. Complex microvilli (*arrow*) and mitochondria (*M*) with tubular cristae are shown. × 13,600.

placenta the hormones are released into the maternal blood (intervillous space) rather than the fetal capillaries.

The ultrastructural features of typical steroid-producing cells, such as those of testis, ovary, and adrenal, differ from those of protein-secreting cells. The organelles associated with protein synthesis are relatively inconspicuous in steroid cells, and there are no demonstrable granules or vacuoles of stored secretory product. The most distinctive ultrastructural features of steroid-secreting cells are an extensive smooth-surfaced endoplasmic reticulum, very prominent Golgi complexes, mitochondria of highly variable size and often of unusual internal structure, numerous lysosomes and accumulations of lipochrome pigment, and lipid droplets. In steroid cells there may be a large juxtanuclear Golgi complex without a clearly defined boundary between the Golgi tubules and the smooth endoplasmic reticulum. In protein-secreting cells, however, the two organelles are believed to be morphologically distinct but functionally interrelated by way of small vesicles that arise from the granular endoplasmic reticulum and migrate to the

Golgi complex, where they coalesce with the membranes of its outermost cisternae (14). The mitochondrial cristae of steroid-secreting cells are thought to be tubular extensions of the inner membrane rather than flat folds or lamellae. In the placenta the steroid cells usually have conventional, rather than tubular, cristae, although in first trimester trophoblast both varieties are observed (Fig. 14). Throughout placental development, membrane-limited dense bodies of diverse internal structure, usually interpreted as representing various stages in transition from lysosomes to lipofuscin pigment, are found. These bodies may be spherical with a homogeneous, finely granular content of moderate density, or they may have extremely dense osmiophilic granules of varying size and shape scattered throughout the less dense granular matrix. According to Fawcett and coworkers (14), these irregular, heterogeneous structures are often regarded as lipofuscin pigment and represent accumulated undigestible residues of autophagic activity.

Lipid droplets often appear black after fixation in osmium tetroxide and pale gray after fixation in glutaraldehyde. The agranular endoplasmic reticulum in the trophoblast may be difficult to distinguish in the electron-dense syncytium but may comprise randomly oriented tubules or concentric systems of fenestrated cisternae. The number of lipid droplets tends to be low when steroid secretion is maximal. Steroid-secreting cells, however, show no recognizable accumulations of secretory materials in the Golgi complex or elsewhere, nor can morphological evidence of release of hormones be detected at the cell surface.

Because the human syncytiotrophoblast is believed to produce both peptide and steroid hormones, all the ultrastructural specializations just described may be found in that tissue. In the remainder of this chapter, the evidence for the assumption that the endocrinologically active tissue of the human placenta is the syncytiotrophoblast, with possible small contributions from other well-differentiated specialized forms of trophoblast, is presented.

Origin of Human Placental Hormones

In their classic histological description of the human placenta, Wislocki & Bennett (35) attributed to the syncytium the production of the steroids, estrogen and progesterone, which were considered the basis for the phenylhydrazone reaction demonstrated histochemically. Positive staining of the Langhans' cells with the periodic acid-Schiff reagent was considered suggestive of localization of chorionic gonadotrophin, which was known to be a glycoprotein, in the cellular trophoblast. Their suggestion was supported by circumstantial evidence of the association of high levels of chorionic gonadotrophin with clinical situations in which there are increased numbers of Langhans' cells, such as early pregnancy, chorionic neoplasia, and plural gestations.

Nevertheless, to students of placental ultrastructure the simplicity of the villous cytotrophoblast was inconsistent with that of other tissues known to produce proteins, as previously described. In the syncytium were found all the subcellular organelles required for this function, especially abundant rough-surfaced endoplasmic reticulum, Golgi complexes, and numerous mitochondria, which provide the enzymes. Immunofluorescent localization of chorionic gonadotrophin in both normal (25) and neoplastic (29) trophoblast has supported the concept that both steroids and proteins are produced by the syncytium. Furthermore, many so-called cytotrophoblastic cells that appear to localize chorionic gonadotrophin under the light microscope are ultrastructurally transitional, a phenomenon suggesting simultaneous maturation of endocrine activity during morphological evolution of Langhans' cells to syncytium. Human chorionic somatomammotrophin (placental lactogen) similarly has been localized in syncytiotrophoblast but not in Langhans' cells (32). It is reasonable to predict that the third postulated protein hormone of the placenta, chorionic thyrotrophin, will also be localized to the syncytiotrophoblast. The syncytium may thus be regarded as the endocrinologically and morphologically mature form of trophoblast, whereas the Langhans' cells are reserve, or stem, elements, the main function of which is to form new syncytium. The temporal coexistence of maximal cytotrophoblastic proliferation with high titers of chorionic gonadotrophin in urine and serum has often been quoted. The lower titers of the hormone late in gestation, however, may reflect decrease not in mass of cytotrophoblast but in production by the multifunctional syncytium.

Although there is impressive evidence from several laboratories that the placental syncytium is the source of these protein hormones, the anatomical localization of a hormone cannot necessarily be equated with its origin at a particular site. In simplest terms, the more complex the trophoblast, the more capable it is of producing hormones. As Langhans' cells differentiate ultrastructurally, their endocrine potential increases simultaneously. Although the typical Langhans' cell in the mature chorionic villus is an unlikely source of protein hormones, transitional villous trophoblast and ultrastructurally complex forms of cytotrophoblast elsewhere in the normal placenta and in chorionic neoplasms may be endocrinologically active.

Although there has never been serious doubt that the syncytium produces the steroid hormones, correlation of blood levels of hormonal steroids with ultrastructural identification of lipid is impractical. For example, lack of increase in syncytial lipid granules, despite elevated blood levels of steroidal hormones, may well reflect increased excretion by the syncytium rather than decreased production.

In conclusion the syncytium appears to be the differentiated form of trophoblast, capable of synthesis of steroids and peptides, and primarily responsible for the production of all placental hormones.

REFERENCES

1. AHERNE, W., AND M. S. DUNNILL. Morphometry of the human placenta. *Brit. Med. Bull.* 22: 5–8, 1966.
2. AMOROSO, E. C. Placentation. In: *Marshall's Physiology of Reproduction*, edited by A. S. Parkes. London: Longmans, 1952, vol. II, p. 127–311.
3. BENIRSCHKE, K., AND S. G. DRISCOLL. *The Pathology of the Human Placenta.* New York: Springer-Verlag, 1967.
4. BILLINGHAM, R. E. Transplantation immunity and the maternal-fetal relation. *New Engl. J. Med.* 270: 667–672; 720–725, 1964.
5. BJÖRKMAN, N. Fine structure of the ovine placentome. *J. Anat.* 99: 283–297, 1965.
6. BJÖRKMAN, N. Contributions of electron microscopy in elucidating placental structure and function. *Intern. Rev. Gen. Exptl. Zool.* 3: 309–371, 1968.
7. BOYD, J. D., AND W. J. HAMILTON. Development and structure of the human placenta from the end of the 3rd month of gestation. *J. Obstet. Gynaecol. Brit. Commonwealth* 74: 161–226, 1967.
8. BOYD, J. D., AND W. J. HAMILTON. *The Human Placenta.* Cambridge, England: Heffer, 1970.
9. CURRIE, G. A., AND K. D. BAGSHAWE. The masking of antigens of trophoblast and cancer cells. *Lancet* 1: 708–710, 1967.
10. CURRIE, G. A., W. VAN DOORNINCK, AND K. D. BAGSHAWE. Effect of neuraminidase on the immunogenicity of early mouse trophoblast. *Nature* 219: 191–192, 1968.
11. ENDERS, A. C. A comparative study of the fine structure of the trophoblast in several hemochorial placentas. *Am. J. Anat.* 116: 29–67, 1965.
12. ENDERS, A. C., AND B. F. KING. The cytology of Hofbauer cells. *Anat. Record* 167: 231–252, 1970.
13. FAWCETT, D. W. Surface specializations of absorbing cells. *J. Histochem. Cytochem.* 13: 75–91, 1965.
14. FAWCETT, D. W., J. A. LONG, AND A. L. JONES. The ultrastructure of endocrine glands. *Recent Progr. Hormone Res.* 25: 315–380, 1969.
15. GALTON, M. DNA content of placental nuclei. *J. Cell Biol.* 13: 183–191, 1962.
16. GROSSER, O. *Frühentwicklung, Eihautbildung und Placentation des Menschen und der Säugetiere.* Berlin: Springer, 1927.
17. HAMILTON, W. J., AND J. D. BOYD. Development of the human placenta in the first three months of gestation. *J. Anat.* 94: 297–328, 1960.
18. HAMILTON, W. J., AND J. D. BOYD. Specializations of the syncytium of the human chorion. *Brit. Med. J.* 1: 1501–1506, 1966.
19. HEMPEL, E., AND G. GEYER. Submikroskopische Verteilung der alkalischen Phosphatase in der menschlichen Placenta. *Acta Histochem.* 34: 138–147, 1969.
20. HERTIG, A. T. Angiogenesis in the early human chorion and in the primary placenta of the macaque monkey. *Contrib. Embryol. Carnegie Inst. Wash.* 25: 38–82, 1935.
21. HERTIG, A. T., AND J. ROCK. Two human ova of the pre-villous stage, having an ovulation age of about eleven and twelve days respectively. *Contrib. Embryol. Carnegie Inst. Wash.* 29: 127–156, 1941.
22. HERTIG, A. T., AND J. ROCK. Two human ova of the pre-villous stage, having a developmental age of about seven and nine days respectively. *Contrib. Embryol. Carnegie Inst. Wash.* 31: 65–84, 1945.
23. KIRBY, D. R. S., W. D. BILLINGTON, S. BRADBURY, AND D. J. GOLDSTEIN. Antigen barrier of the mouse placenta. *Nature* 204: 548–549, 1964.
24. LANMAN, J. T., J. DINERSTEIN, AND S. FIKRIG. Homograft immunity in pregnancy: lack of harm to fetus from sensitization of mother. *Ann. NY Acad. Sci.* 99: 706–710, 1962.
25. MIDGLEY, A. R., JR., AND G. B. PIERCE, JR. Immunohistochemical localization of human chorionic gonadotropin. *J. Exptl. Med.* 115: 289–294, 1962.
26. MIDGLEY, A. R., JR., G. B. PIERCE, JR., G. A. DENEAU, AND J. R. S. GOSLING. Morphogenesis of syncytiotrophoblast in vivo: an autoradiographic demonstration. *Science* 141: 349–350, 1963.
27. MOSSMAN, H. W. Comparative morphogenesis of the fetal membranes and accessory uterine structures. *Contrib. Embryol. Carnegie Inst. Wash.* 26: 129–246, 1937.
28. MOSSMAN, H. W. Comparative biology of the placenta and fetal membranes. In: *Fetal Homeostasis*, edited by R. M. Wynn. New York: NY Acad. Sci., 1967, vol. II, p. 13–97.
29. PIERCE, G. B., JR., AND A. R. MIDGLEY, JR. The origin and function of human syncytiotrophoblastic giant cells. *Am. J. Pathol.* 43: 153–173, 1963.
30. RHODIN, J. A. G., AND J. TERZAKIS. The ultrastructure of the human full-term placenta. *J. Ultrastruct. Res.* 6: 88–106, 1962.
31. RICHART, R. Studies of placental morphogenesis. I. Radioautographic studies of human placenta utilizing tritiated thymidine. *Proc. Soc. Exptl. Biol. Med.* 106: 829–831, 1961.
32. SCIARRA, J. J., S. L. KAPLAN, AND M. M. GRUMBACH. Localization of anti-human growth hormone serum within the human placenta: evidence for a human chorionic "growth-hormone-prolactin." *Nature* 199: 1005–1006, 1963.
33. TERZAKIS, J. A. The ultrastructure of normal human first trimester placenta. *J. Ultrastruct. Res.* 9: 268–284, 1963.
34. WIMSATT, W. A. Some aspects of the comparative anatomy of the mammalian placenta. *Am. J. Obstet. Gynecol.* 84: 1568–1594, 1962.
35. WISLOCKI, G. B., AND H. S. BENNETT. Histology and cytology of the human and monkey placenta, with special reference to the trophoblast. *Am. J. Anat.* 73: 335–449, 1943.
36. WISLOCKI, G. B., AND E. W. DEMPSEY. The chemical histology of the human placenta and decidua with reference to mucoproteins, glycogen, lipins, and acid phosphatase. *Am. J. Anat.* 83: 1–41, 1948.
37. WISLOCKI, G. B., AND E. W. DEMPSEY. Electron microscopy of the human placenta. *Anat. Record* 123: 133–167, 1955.
38. WISLOCKI, G. B., AND G. L. STREETER. On the placentation of the macaque (*Macaca mulatta*), from the time of implantation until the formation of the definitive placenta. *Contrib. Embryol. Carnegie Inst. Wash.* 27: 1–66, 1938.
39. WYNN, R. M. Derivation and ultrastructure of the so-called Hofbauer cell. *Am. J. Obstet. Gynecol.* 97: 235–248, 1967.
40. WYNN, R. M. Fetomaternal cellular relations in the human basal plate: an ultrastructural study of the placenta. *Am. J. Obstet. Gynecol.* 97: 832–851, 1967.
41. WYNN, R. M. The interpretation of placental ultrastructure. In: *Advances in Obstetrics and Gynecology*, edited by S. L. Marcus and C. C. Marcus. Baltimore: Williams & Wilkins, 1967, vol. I, p. 21–37.
42. WYNN, R. M. Morphology of the placenta. In: *Biology of Gestation*, edited by N. S. Assali. New York: Acad. Press, 1968, vol. I, p. 93–184.
43. WYNN, R. M. Noncellular components of the placenta. *Am. J. Obstet. Gynecol.* 103: 723–739, 1969.
44. WYNN, R. M. Immunological implications of comparative placental ultrastructure. In: *Blastocyst Biology*, edited by R. J. Blandau. Chicago: Univ. of Chicago Press, 1971, chapt. 29, p. 495–514.
45. WYNN, R. M., AND N. BJÖRKMAN. Ultrastructure of the feline placental membrane. *Am. J. Obstet. Gynecol.* 102: 34–43, 1968.
46. WYNN, R. M., M. PANIGEL, AND A. H. MACLENNAN. Fine structure of the placenta and fetal membranes of the baboon. *Am. J. Obstet. Gynecol.* 109: 638–648, 1971.

CHAPTER 43

Passage of hormones through the placenta

JOHN B. JOSIMOVICH | *University of Pittsburgh School of Medicine, Department of Obstetrics and Gynecology, Pittsburgh, Pennsylvania*

CHAPTER CONTENTS

OVER FORTY YEARS AGO, discovery of endocrine feedback systems operating within the fetus prompted the French physiologist M. Aron (2) to predict that the fetal *milieu intérieur* must enjoy a high degree of protection from maternal endocrine influences. The relationship between the fetal endocrine environment and hormones passing from the mother has been recently reviewed in detail by MacNaughton (75). Earlier reviews also give details of transfer of certain hormones (45, 115). The study of transplacental passage of hormones between mother and conceptus originated in morphological studies of the fetus after removal of endocrine organs or after administration of hormone to the mother. Physiologists and clinicians have given renewed attention to the problem because of the availability of the radioisotopically labeled hormones. Fully quantitative studies of the nature of hormone passage are usually limited by ignorance of the rates of hormone metabolism in fetal and maternal compartments, by lack of simultaneous measurements of fetal and maternal blood flow to the placenta, and by failure in producing a steady state of hormone concentration in the injected compartment, such as can be achieved by an infusion. The importance of these factors was emphasized by Plentl (95). Furthermore researchers rarely know whether the radioactively labeled hormone was isolated from the transplacental compartment in the same form in which it was injected, or whether detected, labeled material still possesses any biological activity. Despite these deficiencies, a summary of the state of knowledge thus far achieved is attempted in this chapter.

PANCREATIC HORMONES: INSULIN AND GLUCAGON

Transplacental passage of insulin from fetus to mother was suggested by the abeyance of severe hyperglycemia and ketosis in the bitch when pancreatectomy was performed within 4–6 weeks of the end of pregnancy (2, 12–14, 26). Aron and co-workers (4) confirmed these findings in pregnant cats and dogs. It was thought that the hyperplasia of the fetal islets of Langerhans brought about by maternal hyperglycemia already observed in offspring of human diabetics (31) could result in a salutary wave of fetal insulin protecting the pancreatectomized mother from diabetic crisis. Grillo & Cunningham (42) more recently proved by immunoassay that, indeed, plasma insulin remains in the normal, "nonpancreatectomized," range during pregnancy, which proves that fetal insulin protects the mother. Several workers employing goats, bitches, rabbits, or rats found that insulin administration to fetus or mother resulted in diaplacental hypoglycemia (22, 88, 90, 101, 102, 108, 116). Schlossmann (108) suspected that the observed effects of insulin injection were due more to transplacental equilibration of glucose than to passage of insulin. Knobil & Josimovich (63) found that insulin in doses incapable of causing maternal hypoglycemia, when injected directly into the uterine artery supplying one gravid uterine horn of the pregnant rat, caused hypoglycemia within the fetuses lying in that horn. This response was not detected in the conceptuses lying in the opposite horn. Despite these findings, which encouraged the hypothesis of placental passage of insulin, no evidence of insulin passage from fetus to mother was found by Davies & Lacy (27) in the rabbit or in the reverse direction by van Kessel and colleagues (61) in the rhesus monkey.

Clearly the hypothesis of Aron, that maternal insulin secretion should not interfere with fetal insulin signals, has been vindicated by studies of endogenous insulin, such as those carried out by Little and colleagues (71) in the rhesus monkey. The advent of ^{131}I-labeling of insulin and of radioimmunoassays for detecting endogenous insulin provided tools permitting closer examination of whether insulin could cross from mother to fetus. Using

[131]I-labeled insulin, Goodner & Freinkel (40) found no evidence of passage of the trace in the rat. In the rhesus monkey and man, very small amounts were, however, identified in the plasma across the placenta from the site of administration, after single maternal or fetal injections or after brief infusions (10, 39, 57, 80). Careful review of the data suggests that the protection of fetal insulin homeostatic signals from maternal "noise" may be less attributable to a placental barrier to insulin passage than to avid degradation of insulin by the fetus. This concept is supported by the mathematical formulations of Gitlin and colleagues (39). Josimovich & Knobil (57), who injected ^{131}I-labeled insulin into rhesus monkeys, showed a significant umbilical arterial-venous difference in labeled insulin, with higher concentrations of insulin in the vein. Larger amounts of insulin degradation products were found in the umbilical artery than in the vein. These data combined with the knowledge of optimal umbilical plasma flow in the rhesus monkey (8) suggest that the monkey fetus can clear as much as 225 microunits insulin per minute. Thus fetal degradation may at least in part account for the ability of the fetus to rid itself of "background noise." The ready transfer of ^{131}I-labeled insulin from fetal to maternal side, when the human placenta is mounted in a special chamber (60), agrees with the interpretation of a rather unrestricted passage claimed by Gitlin. The greater barrier to passage from the maternal to fetal compartment found in vitro might have reflected disruption of the maternal intervillous vascular spaces in this artificial preparation. All claims that insulin can traverse the placenta must be evaluated after the health of the mother, placenta, and fetus has been determined, since severe uterine contractions or anoxia, or both, have been shown to increase the amount of transfer detected (54).

In contrast to the difficulty in demonstrating the passage of insulin, Chez and co-workers (15) have demonstrated the bidirectional transfer of ^{131}I-labeled preparations of glucagon in the rhesus monkey. Their data showed that the rate of fetal degradation of glucagon, which had entered from the maternal circulation, was slow enough to prevent lowering of fetal concentrations over a 1-hr period. This finding suggests that the fetus might be much more influenced by maternal glucagon than by insulin, a finding supported by the rise in fetal plasma insulin detected by the same workers after glucagon injection into the mother.

PITUITARY HORMONES

Considerable evidence exists on the degree of placental passage of anterior pituitary hormones. Less information is available on the products of the pars intermedia or pars nervosa, other than that the placenta is rich in oxytocinase (11), which apparently limits passage of oxytocin from mother to fetus, at least in the ewe (86). Kotásek and colleagues (65) found evidence for greater passage of oxytocin in the second trimester of human pregnancy.

High concentrations, but not normal, physiological amounts, of acutely injected adrenocorticotrophic hormone (ACTH) can apparently stimulate ascorbic acid and cholesterol depletion in the fetal adrenals, as was first shown by Jones and co-workers (53) in the rat. Knobil & Briggs (62) showed, furthermore, that the enlargement of fetal adrenals following maternal adrenalectomy (51, 52, 121) could be abolished by maternal hypophysectomy. Lanman (66) gave indirect evidence for passage of ACTH in man.

Conflicting results cloud the issue of whether thyrotrophic hormone (TSH) can cross from mother guinea pig to her offspring—Döderlein (30) and Theresà (119) detected morphological effects in the fetal thyroid after administration of rather large doses of TSH to the mothers, whereas Aron (3), Grumbrecht & Loeser (44), and Schittenhelm & Eisler (107) were unable to find such alterations. Peterson & Young (93) could find no effect on fetal thyroid morphology of TSH administered to pregnant guinea pigs that had undergone previous thyroidectomy. Knobil (63), furthermore, found no effect of maternal thyroidectomy on fetal thyroid weight in the rat. He concluded that even the high levels of TSH in the mother's circulation could not affect fetal thyroid physiology. Studies in man have shown, however, that an exophthalmic factor associated with thyrotoxicosis could cross the placenta and cause exophthalmos in the fetus. The fetal exophthalmos regresses soon after delivery (111). Elsas and colleagues (32) and McKenzie (76) found that transplacental passage of long-acting thyroid stimulator (LATS) from the mother is a cause of neonatal thyrotoxicosis.

Pituitary growth hormone labeled with ^{131}I could not be detected in plasma across the placenta in the rabbit (67), in the rhesus monkey when experiments of both fetal and maternal injection were carried out (15), or in man (38, 68).

The pituitary gonadotrophins, follicle-stimulating hormone (FSH) and luteinizing hormone (LH, ICSH), have not been studied to any extent for their ability to traverse the placenta. The difficulty in immunologically or biologically distinguishing LH from the chorionic gonadotrophin (HCG) present in both fetal and maternal circulations has prevented studies of LH passage. Midgely & Jaffe (78) have recently been able to distinguish between the two and have found that fetal serum gonadotrophins consist almost entirely of HCG. Corey (21) did not detect effects of pituitary extracts administered to rat fetuses late in pregnancy; this suggests that testing transplacental passage of LH in this species would be difficult.

Only one group of workers has been able to detect FSH during human pregnancy (33). The greater concentrations of this hormone found in the maternal circulation at term in this one study suggests that some restriction of passage exists or that there is a more rapid rate of catabolism of FSH within the fetus.

PLACENTAL PEPTIDE HORMONES

Faiman and co-workers (33) have shown that umbilical cord serum, when compared to human maternal serum, contains only about 10% as much HCG or fetal pituitary LH. The rapid decrease in concentrations found in the newborn suggested that most of the material measured was HCG. Midgely & Jaffe (78) found 570–800 times as much HCG in the maternal as in the fetal circulation at term. In their in vitro studies of the human placenta, Zardini and co-workers (123) detected fetal circulation perfusate concentrations of less than 1% the concentration artificially produced in the maternal bath, which again suggests little passage of this hormone across the trophoblastic barrier.

Human placental lactogen (HPL, chorionic somatomammotrophin) has been detected in the fetus in concentrations varying from 0.3 to 1.0% of that found in the maternal circulation; this finding discourages the hope that this chorionic hormone could enter the fetal circulation in amounts sufficient to affect fetal metabolism (7, 55, 58).

Little data exists on the fetal-to-maternal plasma concentration ratio present for rat chorionic mammotrophin (98) or for the maternal decidual gonadotrophin found in the Equinidae (e.g., pregnant mares' serum gonadotrophin in the horse) (16).

PARATHYROID HORMONE AND THYROCALCITONIN

Direct measurement of the ability of parathyroid hormone to cross the placenta is awaited with interest, since previous studies failed to give definitive interpretation. Hoskins & Snyder (49) could not find alterations in maternal serum calcium concentrations after injection of the hormone into the fetuses of pregnant bitches. However, as Ludwig (73), among other clinicians, noted, neonatal tetany in the offspring of mothers suffering from hyperparathyroidism, which could be presumed to be a consequence of excessive maternal storing of calcium, does not rule out passage of the hormone.

Garel and colleagues (36) could find no transplacental passage of ^{125}I-labeled thyrocalcitonin in the rat.

THYROXINE AND TRIIODOTHYRONINE

Courrier & Aron (23) were the first to inquire as to whether thyroid hormone could cross the placental barrier. They concluded that it could not, since they found that allegedly massive amounts of beef or pork thyroid in the diets of pregnant bitches and guinea pigs failed to affect fetal thyroid morphology, whereas it caused morphological signs of colloid follicle inactivity in the mothers. Grumbrecht & Loeser (44) found that daily administration of 0.5 mg thyroxine to pregnant rats gave morphological evidence of fetal gland suppression.

This dosage was in fact toxic enough to cause fetal death. Therésà (119) confirmed these findings in the rat but paradoxically found stimulation of fetal thyroids when thyroxine was given to pregnant guinea pigs. Peterson & Young (93), however, showed that thyroxine administered to pregnant guinea pigs could suppress fetal goiters caused by propylthiouracil (PTU) administered to the mothers. Knobil & Josimovich (63) confirmed this experiment by finding that a normal thyroid-replacement dose of thyroxine could completely inhibit fetal goitrogenesis in the rat caused by PTU in the maternal diet. Hamburgh and colleagues (46) obtained similar findings, albeit larger doses of thyroxine were required. Since the passage of TSH does not appear to occur in this species (63) but that of uracil and its derivatives does occur (103), apparently enough thyroxine could cross to suppress the fetal pituitary-thyroid axis. Because Dempsey & Astwood (28) had originally shown that thyroxine suppression of PTU-induced goitrogenesis depends on the environmental temperature of the rat, transplacental passage of relatively small quantities of thyroxine might be needed to suppress the fetal pituitary, since the fetus is maintained at maternal body temperature.

Grumbach & Werner (43) were the first to use ^{131}I-labeled thyroxine to test the permeability of the placental barrier to this hormone. Injections of trace into pregnant human females, 10 min to 169 hr before delivery, resulted in concentrations in umbilical cord sera only a fraction of that present in the maternal circulation, which suggested a barrier to passage. These findings were confirmed by Kearns & Hutson (59) after oral administration of the labeled hormones. Similar results were obtained in sheep, guinea pigs, rabbits, rats, and in the rhesus monkey (35, 46, 48, 50, 83, 87, 94, 100, 112). London and colleagues (72) found slight passage of trace from mother to fetus when the umbilical vessels of the guinea pig fetus were attached to an extracorporeal perfusion system, whereas little could be detected in the mother after injection into the fetal circulation. It is of interest that, when Contopoulos and colleagues (19) injected labeled thyroxine into five different species, they found none up to 4 hr later in the pig or sheep fetus, increasing amounts after 1 hr in the ferret fetus, and larger amounts of the labeled hormone as early as 5 min after injection in the conceptuses of the guinea pig and rat. Kock and co-workers (64) demonstrated restriction in passage of labeled thyroxine in the rhesus monkey. Josimovich, Ingbar, and Knobil [(56); unpublished observations] found that, when ^{131}I-labeled thyroxine was injected into pregnant rhesus monkeys in late pregnancy, labeled hormone was detected in the fetal circulation with no significant difference in concentration between umbilical venous and arterial plasma. An equilibrium was reached sometime between 4 and 20 hr after maternal injection, such that the disappearance rates from catabolism in both mother and fetus became equivalent, as shown in Figure 1. Fetal blood samples drawn repeatedly from indwelling catheters in the inter-

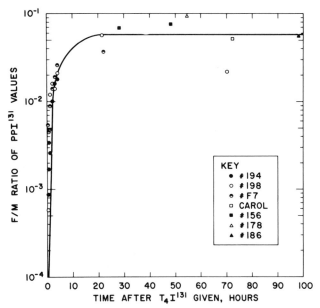

FIG. 1. Fetal-to-maternal (*F/M*) ratio of plasma TCA precipitable [131]I (*PPI*[131]) over a 4-day period in several rhesus monkeys, 120–141 days of gestation; 0.2 μg/kg of 50 μCi/μg carrier-free ^{131}I-labeled thyroxine given intravenously to the mothers. Maternal blood samples were drawn from a saphenous vein. Fetal samples were drawn from indwelling interplacental vein catheters (to sample umbilical venous blood). Key indicates the individual monkeys studied. The F:M PPI[131] ratio achieved a plateau of 0.06 between 4 and 20 hr after maternal injection.

placental veins and maternal samples drawn from the saphenous vein in the eight monkeys revealed the maintenance of a 20:1 ratio of maternal-to-fetal plasma TCA (trichloroacetic acid)-precipitable [131]I (PPI[131]) concentrations. Such a ratio could be accounted for only if a mechanism that resulted in more rapid transport toward the mother than passage toward the fetus existed, as was also concluded from similar experiments by Kock and colleagues (64). Differential rates of metabolism in the two circulations could not explain this equilibrium, nor could simple diffusion. Osorio & Myant (89) studied the kinetics of diffusion of ^{131}I-labeled thyroxine through a cellophane barrier. They found that a 1:1 concentration equilibrium would be slowly approached at a rate with a half-time of 13 hr. If human serum containing thyroxine-binding globulin (TBG) were placed on one side, the equilibrium, approached gradually, would favor the side containing the protein. The ratio of maternal-to-fetal plasma thyroxine-binding affinity per milliliter has been repeatedly found to differ from 1.0 (84), but this cannot account for the approximately 20:1 ratio of maternal-to-fetal ^{131}I-labeled thyroxine concentrations found in the rhesus monkey. Thus the placenta may possess properties favoring fetal-to-maternal passage, which adds to the effect of the differences in diaplacental thyroxine-binding protein affinities. Fisher and colleagues (35) based a similar conclusion on unlabeled thyroxine loading experiments in man.

Triiodothyronine labeled with ^{131}I was first noted to pass the placenta to the fetus in the rat (85) and guinea

pig (72, 74), although fetal concentrations lower than that found after labeled thyroxine administration were achieved. London and co-workers (72) could find no transfer into the mothers after administration into the fetal extracorporeal circulation in the guinea pig. Postel (96) found that large doses of triiodothyronine administered to pregnant guinea pigs failed to inhibit perchlorate-induced fetal goiters. Knobil & Josimovich (63) found that triiodothyronine had only one-half the effectiveness of thyroxine in suppressing PTU-induced fetal goitrogenesis. Raiti and colleagues (97) found that moderate depression of fetal human plasma thyroxine could be obtained when moderately large doses of triiodothyronine were given daily to the mother and usually only if the concentration of her own plasma thyroxine was markedly depressed. There was little correlation in their study between evidence of fetal transfer of triiodothyronine and maternal-to-fetal TBG ratios. The studies of Grumbach & Werner (43) and of Kearns & Hutson (59) did not agree with these other studies in that the two groups found higher concentrations of the labeled hormone in the umbilical cord sera after administration to the mother than when a comparable dose of labeled thyroxine had been given. Quite the opposite findings were suggested in the study of Schultz and colleagues (109), in which labeled triiodothyronine was given to either rhesus monkey fetus or mother and then chromatographically identified in plasma. They achieved little passage of trace from mother to fetus but greater transfer from fetus to mother. Thus, with the exception of the studies of Grumbach and of Kearns, triiodothyronine appears to cross the placenta to the fetus less readily than does thyroxine.

ADRENAL CORTICAL AND MEDULLARY HORMONES

The fetal pituitary-adrenal axis can apparently respond to external stimuli; this indicates a certain degree of passage of maternal corticosteroids or their metabolites. The finding by Rogoff & Stewart (99) that the pregnant bitch survives adrenalectomy much longer than does the nonpregnant animal was confirmed in the rat, cat, and man (18, 34, 104, 120). Corey (20) found that, after adrenalectomy, pregnant cats survived no longer than did nonpregnant cats. The findings of the majority of these workers suggested that fetal adrenal hormones were passing to the mother. The need for such a process has been called into question, however, by the finding that increased concentrations of corticosteroid-binding globulins (CBG) occur during pregnancy. Greater affinity for this steroid increases total maternal plasma corticosteroids in most species (105) and slows the rate of degradation of the steroid (17, 117). Such a greater retention of corticosteroids in the maternal circulation, however, only enhances the protective effect of steroids that must reach the hypocorticoid mother from the placenta or fetus, or both. Progesterone (or its metabolites) was found to have protective effects in hypocorticoid animals, specifically the rat, perhaps because of its sodium-retaining properties (37, 41, 77, 110). Indirect evidence that corticosteroids may pass from mother to fetus was first described by Courrier and his co-workers (24, 25) who found that cortisone administered to mother rats or rabbits resulted in a diminution of size and lessened histological evidence of secretory activity of the fetal adrenal cortices. Bashore and colleagues (5) injected ^{14}C-labeled cortisol into pregnant rhesus monkeys and after 30 min obtained similar concentrations in extracts of fetal and maternal plasma believed to contain unaltered hormone. Migeon and co-workers (79) demonstrated that ^{14}C-labeled cortisol injected into nonpregnant human beings achieved fetal concentrations about one-third that level attained in the maternal circulation. These studies were confirmed by Abramovich & Wade (1). As Peterson (92) pointed out in his review, the maternal-to-fetal ratio for endogenous cortisol is 3 : 1 and cannot be explained by diaplacental differences in plasma cortisol-binding affinity: the affinity of fetal and that of maternal plasma are indistinguishable, even though the concentration of CBG is greater in the maternal bloodstream. Another interpretation of the lower fetal plasma corticosteroid concentrations was afforded by the studies of Leyssac (70). He found that hydrocortisone infusion into pregnant women resulted in a similar concentration in umbilical venous plasma and that the fetal cardiac plasma levels were considerably lower, presumably as a result of fetal hepatic metabolism of the steroid. These studies lead to the conclusion that fetal catabolism, not a placental barrier, maintains lower fetal corticosteroid levels.

Bayard and co-workers (6) found that in contrast to cortisol, administration of ^{14}C-labeled aldosterone in pregnant women resulted in fetal plasma concentrations averaging 73% of that present in the maternal circulation (range 40–123%), which suggested either less of a placental barrier for this corticosteroid or a slower fetal rate of degradation.

Little direct information exists on the transplacental passage of adrenal medullary hormones. Sandler and colleagues (106) injected ^{14}C-labeled DL-noradrenaline into pregnant women and found fetal umbilical cord serum or heart serum values 0.6–18% of that present in the maternal serum 2–5 min after maternal injection. Since the D isomer might pass less well, the L isomer of the hormone might have achieved higher levels in the fetal circulation than that measured for the DL mixture.

PROGESTERONE, ANDROGENS, AND ESTROGENS

The intricate patterns of interconversion and exchange of steroids and their conjugates between fetus, amniotic fluid, placenta, and mother have been delineated by many workers. Diczfalusy (29), Solomon & Friesen (115), and Siiteri & MacDonald (113) have written the most extensive reviews on this subject. Because proges-

terone and estrogen originate in the human placenta at midpregnancy, the large quantities secreted would tend to dwarf in importance the passage of smaller amounts of hormones between mother and offspring.

Harbert and colleagues (47) measured progesterone concentrations in umbilical arterial and venous plasma and in maternal serum plasma. From their calculations they concluded that about one-third of placental progesterone is metabolized by the fetus and the rest by the mother. They noted that "The observed concentration differences of progesterone across the placental membranes is determined primarily by rate of secretion, with blood flow, extent of mixing, pool size, and protein-binding in mother and fetus being contributing factors." The mother converts approximately one-half of the total progesterone to pregnanediol glucuronide, whereas the fetus metabolizes the hormones into a number of new steroids, including 20α-dihydroprogesterone sulfate (47, 115). Unfortunately, data are sparse on the amount of progesterone passing from mother to fetus in most mammals in whom the hormone is produced by the maternal ovary rather than by the placenta.

The ability of androgens to traverse the placenta to the fetus and exert effects is undoubtedly due to the presence or absence of aromatizing enzymes in the placenta. In the rat, various doses of testosterone propionate administered to the mother were found to masculinize the external genitalia or to delay vaginal opening after birth in the female offspring (114, 118). In man, the presence of aromatizing enzymes causes avid consumption of dehydroepiandrosterone and its sulfate conjugates (9), and thus little passage of unaltered androgen from the mother to the fetus is allowed. That concentrations of such androgens as Δ⁴-androstenedione and testosterone are two-thirds lower in umbilical venous plasma than in the maternal circulation (81) remains unexplained. The well-known, ready interconversion between these two steroids added to the greater concentration of testosterone-binding globulin in the maternal circulation (91) might account for an equilibrium favoring higher concentrations of the two steroids in the mother. Wilkins (122) has described the adverse effect of genital masculinization in fetal females apparently caused by administration of certain synthetic progestins possessing androgenic activity. It can only be presumed that the lack of placental metabolism of these synthetic compounds was responsible for the damage to the offspring.

The human placenta produces estrogens in large quantities from neutral steroid precursors from mother and fetus. Levitz (69) reviewed work he and his collaborators carried out in the guinea pig on the passage of radioactively labeled estrogens, both conjugated and unconjugated, between various compartments. He estimated that 35% of the free, and 2% of the conjugated, estrogen could be transferred from the fetal circulation to the mother in each circulatory cycle. He found that sulfates were transmitted twice as readily as was glucuronide, perhaps because of the action of placental aryl sulfatase. In the human being, also, the rate of passage of estrogens would appear to be greater from fetus to mother than in the opposite direction (29).

SUMMARY

The relative freedom of the fetus from direct maternal endocrine influence results from a combination of mechanisms that may vary among species and at different times during an individual gestation. These mechanisms are fetal metabolism (e.g., insulin, progesterone), different hormone-binding affinities of maternal and fetal plasma (e.g., thyroxine, testosterone), unidirectional or bidirectional placental hindrance (e.g., growth hormone, thyroid hormones), and placental metabolism (e.g., dehydroepiandrosterone). Assessment of the individual contributions of these four mechanisms, as well as differentiation of further mechanisms of placental transport, await steady-state kinetic analyses not yet available.

REFERENCES

1. Abramovich, D. R., and A. P. Wade. Transplacental passage of steroids: the presence of corticosteroids in amniotic fluid. *J. Obstet. Gynaecol. Brit. Commonwealth* 76: 610–614, 1969.
2. Aron, M. Sur le passage de l'insuline à travers le placenta. *Compt. Rend. Soc. Biol.* 100: 844–845, 1929.
3. Aron, M. Sur l'imperméabilité du placenta à la substance préhypophysaire active sur la glande thyröide. *Compt. Rend. Soc. Biol.* 103: 151–152, 1930.
4. Aron, M., E. Stulz, and R. Simon. Fonctionnement du pancréas foetal après ablation du pancréas maternel. *Compt. Rend. Soc. Biol.* 89: 571–573, 1923.
5. Bashore, R. A., F. Smith, and E. M. Gold. Placental transfer and metabolism of 4-^{14}C-cortisol in the pregnant monkey. *Nature* 228: 774–776, 1970.
6. Bayard, F., I. G. Ances, A. J. Tapper, V. V. Weldon, A. Kowarski, and C. J. Migeon. Transplacental passage and fetal secretion of aldosterone. *J. Clin. Invest.* 49: 1389–1393, 1970.
7. Beck, P., M. L. Parker, and W. H. Daughaday. Radioimmunologic measurement of human placental lactogen in plasma by a double antibody method during normal and diabetic pregnancies. *J. Clin. Endocrinol.* 25: 1457–1462, 1965.
8. Behrman, R. E., E. N. Peterson, and C. W. de Lannoy. The supply of O_2 to the primate fetus with two different O_2 tensions and anesthetics. *Respiration Physiol.* 6: 271–283, 1969.
9. Bolté, E., S. Mancuso, G. Eriksson, N. Wiqvist, and E. Diczfalusy. Studies on the aromatisation of neutral steroids in pregnant women. 2. Aromatisation of dehydroepiandrosterone sulphate administered simultaneously into a uterine artery. *Acta Endocrinol.* 45: 560–575, 1964.
10. Buse, M. G., W. J. Roberts, and J. Buse. The role of the human placenta in the transfer and metabolism of insulin. *J. Clin. Invest.* 41: 29–41, 1962.
11. Caldeyro-Barcia, R., S. Melander, and J. A. Coch. Neurohypophyseal hormones. In: *Endocrinology of Pregnancy*, edited by F. Fuchs and A. Klopper. New York: Harper & Row, 1971, p. 235–285.
12. Carlson, A. J., and H. M. Drennan. The control of pancreatic diabetes in pregnancy by the passage of the internal secretion of the pancreas of the fetus to the blood of the mother. *Am. J. Physiol.* 28: 391–395, 1911.
13. Carlson, A. J., and H. Ginsburg. The influence of pregnancy on the hyperglycemia of pancreatic diabetes. *Am. J. Physiol.* 36: 217–221, 1914.
14. Carlson, A. J., J. S. Orr, and W. S. Jones. The absence of sugar in the urine after pancreatectomy in pregnant bitches near term. *J. Biol. Chem.* 17: 19–22, 1914.
15. Chez, R. A., D. H. Mintz, E. O. Horger, iii, and D. L. Hutchinson. Factors affecting the response to insulin in the normal subhuman pregnant primate. *J. Clin. Invest.* 49: 1517–1527, 1970.
16. Clegg, M. T., J. M. Boda, and H. H. Cole. The endometrial cups and allantochorionic pouches in the mare with emphasis on the source of equine gonadotrophin. *Endocrinology* 54: 448–463, 1954.

17. Cohen, M., M. Stiffel, W. J. Reddy, and J. C. Laidlaw. The secretion and disposition of cortisol during pregnancy. *J. Clin. Endocrinol.* 18: 1076–1092, 1958.
18. Collings, W. D. Effect of experimentally induced pseudopregnancy upon survival of adrenalectomized cats. *Endocrinology* 28: 75–82, 1941.
19. Contopoulos, A. N., M. Ryan, C. R. Contopoulos, and E. C. Amoroso. Transplancental passage of thyroxine and iodine^{131} in the sow, ewe, ferret, guinea-pig and rat (Abstract). *Proc. Zool. Soc. London* 42: 699, 1964.
20. Corey, E. L. A study of the survival period in the pregnant and lactating cat following bilateral adrenal extirpation. *Physiol. Zool.* 1: 147–152, 1928.
21. Corey, E. L. Fetal and early postnatal responses of rat gonads to pituitary injections. *Physiol. Zool.* 3: 379–391, 1930.
22. Corey, E. L. Placental permeability to insulin in the albino rat. *Physiol. Zool.* 5: 36, 1932.
23. Courrier, R., and M. Aron. Sur le passage de l'hormone thyröidienne de la mère au foetus à travers le placenta. *Compt. Rend. Soc. Biol.* 100: 839, 1929.
24. Courrier, R., and A. Colonge. Endocrinologie—cortisone et gestation chez la lapine. *Compt. Rend.* 232: 1164–1166, 1951.
25. Courrier, R., A. Colonge, and M. Baclesse. Action de la cortisone administrée à la mère sur la surrenale du foetus du rat. *Compt. Rend.* 233: 333–336, 1951.
26. Cuthbert, F. P., A. C. Ivy, B. L. Isaacs, and J. Gray. The relation of pregnancy and lactation to extirpation diabetes in the dog. *Am. J. Physiol.* 115: 480–486, 1936.
27. Davies, J., and P. E. Lacy. Observations on the failure of insulin to pass from the fetus to the mother in the rabbit. *Am. J. Obstet. Gynecol.* 74: 514–517, 1957.
28. Dempsey, E. W., and E. B. Astwood. Determination of the rate of thyroid hormone secretion at various environmental temperatures. *Endocrinology* 32: 509–518, 1943.
29. Diczfalusy, E., and S. Mancuso. Oestrogen metabolism in pregnancy. In: *Foetus and Placenta*, edited by A. Klopper and E. Diczfalusy. Oxford: Blackwell, 1969, chapt. 5, p. 191–248.
30. Döderlein, G. Weitere experimentelle Untersuchungen über die Wirkung des thyreotropes Hormons des Hypophysenvorderlappens. *Arch. Gynaekol.* 155: 22–35, 1934.
31. Dubreuil, G., and Anderodias. Îlots de Langerhans géants chez un nouveau-né issu de mère glycosurique. *Compt. Rend. Soc. Biol.* 83: 1490–1493, 1920.
32. Elsas, L. J., R. Whittemore, and G. N. Burrow. Maternal and neonatal Graves' disease. *J. Am. Med. Assoc.* 200: 250–252, 1967.
33. Faiman, C., R. J. Ryan, S. J. Zwirek, and M. E. Rubin. Serum FSH and HCG during human pregnancy and puerperium. *J. Clin. Endocrinol.* 28: 1323–1329, 1968.
34. Firor, W. N., and A. Grollman. Studies on the adrenal. i. Adrenalectomy in mammals with particular reference to the white rat (*Mus norvegicus*). *Am. J. Physiol.* 103: 686–698, 1933.
35. Fisher, D. A., H. Lehrman, and C. Lackey. Placental transport of thyroxine. *J. Clin. Endocrinol.* 24: 393–400, 1964.

36. GAREL, J. M., G. MILHAUD, AND P. SIZONENKA. Thyrocalcitonine et barrière placentaire chez le rat. *Compt. Rend.* 269: 1785–1787, 1969.

37. GAUNT, R., AND H. W. HAYS. Role of progesterone and other hormones on survival of pseudopregnant adrenalectomized ferrets. *Am. J. Physiol.* 124: 767–773, 1938.

38. GITLIN, D., J. KUMATE, AND C. MORALES. Metabolism and maternofetal transfer of human growth hormone in the pregnant woman at term. *J. Clin. Endocrinol.* 25: 1599–1608, 1965.

39. GITLIN, D., J. KUMATE, AND C. MORALES. On the transport of insulin across the human placenta. *Pediatrics* 35: 65–69, 1965.

40. GOODNER, C. J., AND N. FREINKEL. Carbohydrate metabolism in pregnancy. IV. Studies on the permeability of the rat placenta to I^{131} insulin. *Diabetes* 10: 383–392, 1961.

41. GREENE, R. R., J. A. WELLS, AND A. C. IVY. Progesterone will maintain adrenalectomized rats. *Proc. Soc. Exptl. Biol. Med.* 40: 83–86, 1939.

42. GRILLO, T. A. I., AND J. G. CUNNINGHAM. Serum insulin in totally pancreatectomized dogs. *J. Endocrinol.* 39: 307–308, 1967.

43. GRUMBACH, M. M., AND S. C. WERNER. Transfer of thyroid hormone across the human placenta at term. *J. Clin. Endocrinol.* 16: 1392–1395, 1956.

44. GRUMBRECHT, P., AND A. LOESER. Fruchttod durch thyreotropes Hormon der Hypophyse. *Klin. Wochschr.* 17: 233–235, 1938.

45. HAGERMAN, D. D., AND C. A. VILLEE. Transport functions of the placenta. *Physiol. Rev.* 40: 313–330, 1960.

46. HAMBURGH, M., E. SOBEL, R. KOBLIN, AND A. RINESTONE. Passage of thyroid hormone across the placenta in intact and hypophysectomized rats. *Anat. Record* 144: 219–227, 1962.

47. HARBERT, G. M., H. S. McGAUGHEY, W. A. SCOGGINS, AND W. N. THORNTON. Concentration of progesterone in newborn and maternal circulation at delivery. *Obstet. Gynecol.* 23: 413–426, 1964.

48. HIRVONEN, L., AND H. LYBECK. On the permeability of guinea pig placenta for thyroxine. *Acta Physiol. Scand.* 36: 17–22, 1956.

49. HOSKINS, F. M., AND F. F. SNYDER. Calcium content of maternal and foetal blood serum following injection of parathyroid extract in foetuses *in utero*. *Proc. Soc. Exptl. Biol. Med.* 25: 264–266, 1928.

50. HOSKINS, L. C., P. P. VAN ARSDELL, JR., AND R. H. WILLIAMS. Placental transmission and mammary gland secretion of thyroxine in the rat. *Am. J. Physiol.* 193: 509–512, 1958.

51. HOUSSAY, B. A. Accion de la insuficiencia suprarenal durante la preñez sobre la madre y hijo. *Rev. Soc. Arg. Biol.* 21: 316–331, 1945.

52. INGLE, D. J., AND G. T. FISHER. Effect of adrenalectomy during gestation on the size of the adrenal glands of newborn rats. *Proc. Soc. Exptl. Biol. Med.* 34: 149–150, 1938.

53. JONES, J. M., C. W. LLOYD, AND T. C. WYATT. A study of the interrelationships of maternal and fetal adrenal glands. *Endocrinology* 53: 182–191, 1953.

54. JOSIMOVICH, J. B. The role of the placenta in the synthesis and metabolism of proteins. In: *Diagnosis and Treatment of Fetal Disorders*, edited by K. Adamsons. New York: Springer-Verlag, 1968, p. 102–112.

55. JOSIMOVICH, J. B. Placental lactogenic hormone. In: *Endocrinology of Pregnancy*, edited by F. Fuchs and A. Klopper. New York: Harper & Row, 1971, p. 184–196.

56. JOSIMOVICH, J. B., S. H. INGBAR, AND E. KNOBIL. Transplacental passage of I^{131}-thyroxine in the rhesus monkey. In: *Transcript of Third Rochester Trophoblast Conference*, edited by C. J. Lund and H. A. Thiede. New York: Univ. of Rochester, 1965, p. 178–195.

57. JOSIMOVICH, J. B., AND E. KNOBIL. Placental transfer of I^{131}-insulin in the rhesus monkey. *Am. J. Physiol.* 200: 471–476, 1961.

58. KAPLAN, S. L., AND M. M. GRUMBACH. Serum chorionic "growth hormone-prolactin" and serum pituitary growth hormone in mother and fetus at term. *J. Clin. Endocrinol.* 25: 1370–1374, 1965.

59. KEARNS, J. E., AND W. HUTSON. Tagged isomers and analogues of thyroxine (their transmission across the placenta and other studies). *J. Nucl. Med.* 4: 453–461, 1961.

60. KELLER, J. M., AND J. S. KROHMER. Insulin transfer in the isolated human placenta. *Obstet. Gynecol.* 32: 77–80, 1968.

61. KESSEL, H. I. A. M. VAN, L. A. M. STOLTE, J. E. SEELEN, AND R. J. J. L. KNIPSCHEER. Placental permeability for insulin (Abstract). *Acta Physiol. Pharmacol. Neerl.* 12: 167, 1963.

62. KNOBIL, E., AND F. N. BRIGGS. Fetal-maternal interrelationships; hypophyseal-adrenal system. *Endocrinology* 57: 147–152, 1955.

63. KNOBIL, E., AND J. B. JOSIMOVICH. Placental transfer of thyrotropic hormone, thyroxine, triiodothyronine, and insulin in the rat. *Ann. NY Acad. Sci.* 75: 895–904, 1959.

64. KOCK, H. C., W. REICHERT, L. STOLTE, H. VAN KESSEL, AND J. SEELEN. Placental thyroxine transfer and foetal thyroxine utilization. *Acta Physiol. Pharmacol. Neerl.* 13: 363–375, 1965.

65. KOTÁSEK, A., I. V. PLIŠKA, I. KREJČÍ, T. BARTH, AND M. BŘEŠTÁK. Pokus o sledování placentární bariéry pro oxytocin ve druhém trimestru těhotenství. *Česk. Gynekol.* 35: 85–86, 1970.

66. LANMAN, J. T. Adrenal function in premature infants. II. ACTH-treated infants and infants born of toxemic mothers. *Pediatrics* 12: 62–71, 1953.

67. LARON, Z., S. MANNHEIMER, AND S. GUTTMANN. Lack of transplacental passage of growth hormone in rabbits. *Experientia* 22: 831–832, 1966.

68. LARON, Z., A. PERTZELAN, S. MANNHEIMER, J. GOLDMAN, AND S. GUTTMANN. Lack of placental transfer of human growth hormone. *Acta Endocrinol.* 53: 687–692, 1966.

69. LEVITZ, M. Conjugation and transfer of fetal-placental steroid hormones. *J. Clin. Endocrinol.* 26: 773–777, 1966.

70. LEYSSAC, P. Hydrocortisone in foetal plasma following intravenous administration of hydrocortisone to the mother. *Acta Obstet. Gynecol. Scand.* 40: 181–186, 1961.

71. LITTLE, W. A., D. NASSER, AND W. N. SPELLACY. Carbohydrate metabolism in the primate fetus. *Am. J. Obstet. Gynecol.* 109: 732–743, 1971.

72. LONDON, W. T., W. L. MONEY, AND R. W. RAWSON. Placental transport of I^{131}-labeled thyroxine and triiodothyronine in the guinea pig. *Endocrinology* 73: 205–209, 1963.

73. LUDWIG, G. D. Hyperparathyroidism in relation to pregnancy. *New Engl. J. Med.* 267: 637–642, 1962.

74. LYBECK, H. On the permeability of guinea pig placenta for triiodothyronine in late pregnancy. *Proc. Congr. Intern. Physiol., 20th, Bruxelles, July, 1956*, p. 566–567.

75. MacNAUGHTON, M. C. Endocrinology of the foetus. In: *Foetus and Placenta*, edited by A. Klopper and E. Diczfalusy. Oxford: Blackwell, 1969, p. 557–602.

76. McKENZIE, J. M. Neonatal Graves' disease. *J. Clin. Endocrinol.* 24: 660–668, 1964.

77. McKEOWN, T., AND W. R. SPURRELL. The results of adrenalectomy in the pregnant rat. *J. Physiol., London* 98: 255–262, 1940.

78. MIDGELY, A. B., JR., AND R. B. JAFFE. Gel filtration radioimmunoassay to distinguish human chorionic gonadotrophin from luteinizing hormone. *Nature* 213: 733, 1967.

79. MIGEON, C. J., J. BERTRAND, AND P. E. WALL. Physiological disposition of 4-C-14 cortisol during late pregnancy. *J. Clin. Invest.* 36: 1350–1362, 1957.

80. MINTZ, D. H., R. A. CHEZ, AND E. O. HORGER, III. Fetal insulin and growth hormone metabolism in the subhuman primate. *J. Clin. Invest.* 48: 176–186, 1969.

81. MIZUNO, M., J. LOBOTSKY, C. W. LLOYD, T. KOBAYASHI, AND Y. MURASAWA. Plasma androstenedione and testosterone during pregnancy and in the newborn. *J. Clin. Endocrinol.* 28: 1133–1142, 1968.

82. MYANT, N. B. Passage of thyroxine and tri-iodothyronine from mother to fetus in pregnant women. *Clin. Sci.* 17: 75–79, 1958.

83. MYANT, N. B. The passage of thyroxine and triiodothyronine from mother to foetus in pregnant rabbits, with a note on the concentration of protein-bound iodine in foetal serum. *J. Physiol., London* 142: 329–342, 1958.

84. MYANT, N. B., AND C. OSORIO. Serum proteins, including thyroxine-binding proteins in maternal and foetal rabbits. *J. Physiol., London* 146: 344–357, 1960.

85. NATAF, B., M. SFEZ, R. MICHEL, AND J. ROCHE. Sur la perméabilité du placenta à la L-3:5:3' triiodothyronine. *Compt. Rend. Soc. Biol.* 150: 1088–1090, 1956.

86. NODDLE, B. A. Transfer of oxytocin from the maternal to the foetal circulation in the ewe. *Nature* 203: 414, 1964.

87. NOUMURA, T. Development of the hypophyseal-thyroidal system in the rat embryo and its relation to the maternal system. *Japan. J. Zool.* 12: 301–318, 1959.

88. ÖLOW, J. Über den Übergang von Insulin aus dem Fötus in die Mutter. *Biochem. Z.* 217: 475, 1930.

89. OSORIO, C., AND N. B. MYANT. The passage of thyroid hormone from mother to foetus and its relation to foetal development. *Brit. Med. Bull.* 16: 159–164, 1960.

90. PACK, G. T., AND D. BARBER. The placental transmission of insulin from fetus to mother (Abstract). *Am. J. Physiol.* 90: 466, 1929.

91. PEARLMAN, W. H., O. CRÉPY, AND M. MURPHY. Testosterone-binding levels in the serum during the normal menstrual cycle, pregnancy, and the post-partum period. *J. Clin. Endocrinol.* 27: 1012–1018, 1967.

92. PETERSON, R. E. Cortisol. In: *Endocrinology of Pregnancy*, edited by F. Fuchs and A. Klopper. New York: Harper & Row, 1971, p. 155–166.

93. PETERSON, R. R., AND W. C. YOUNG. The problem of placental permeability for thyrotrophin, propylthiouracil, and thyroxine in the guinea pig. *Endocrinology* 50: 218–225, 1952.

94. PICKERING, D. L. Maternal thyroid hormone in the developing fetus. *Am. J. Diseases Children* 107: 567–573, 1964.

95. PLENTL, A. A. The dynamics of amniotic fluid. *Ann. NY Acad. Sci.* 75: 746–761, 1959.

96. POSTEL, S. Placental transfer of perchlorate and triiodothyronine in the guinea pig. *Endocrinology* 60: 53–66, 1957.

97. RAITI, S., G. R. HOLZMAN, R. L. SCOTT, AND R. M. BLIZZARD. Evidence for the placental transfer of tri-iodothyronine in human beings. *New Engl. J. Med.* 277: 456–459, 1967.

98. RAY, E. W., S. C. AVERILL, W. R. LYONS, AND R. E. JOHNSON. Rat placental hormone activities corresponding to those of pituitary mammotropin. *Endocrinology* 56: 354–373, 1955.

99. ROGOFF, J. M., AND G. N. STEWART. Studies on adrenal insufficiency. III. The influence of pregnancy upon the survival period in adrenalectomized dogs. *Am. J. Physiol.* 103: 686–698, 1933.

100. ROY, S. K., AND Y, KOBAYASHI. Placental transfer of l-thyroxine and triiodo-l-thyronine in rats during late pregnancy. *Proc. Soc. Exptl. Biol. Med.* 110: 699–701, 1962.

101. RUGGERI, E., R. RIZZU, AND A. PECILE. Sul passagio transplacentare dell'insulina. *Minerva Ginecol.* 6: 72–73, 1954.

102. RUPP, H. Die Durchlässigkeit der Placenta und Eihaüte für Antigene, Antikörper und Inkrete. *Arch. Gynaekol.* 143: 80–145, 1930.

103. SABBAGHA, R. E., AND T. T. HAYASHI. Transfer of ¹⁴C-thiouracil during pregnancy. *Am. J. Obstet. Gynecol.* 103: 121–127, 1969.

104. SAMUELS, L. T., G. T. EVANS, AND J. L. MCKELVEY. Ovarian

and placental function in Addison's disease. *Endocrinology* 32: 422–428, 1943.

105. SANDBERG, A., AND W. R. SLAUNWHITE. Transcortin: a corticosteroid-binding protein of plasma. II. Levels in various conditions and the effects of estrogens. *J. Clin. Invest.* 38: 1290–1297, 1959.

106. SANDLER, M., C. R. J. RUTHVEN, S. F. CONTRACTOR, C. WOOD, R. T. BOOTH, AND J. H. M. PINKERTON. Transmission of noradrenaline across the human placenta. *Nature* 197: 598, 1963.

107. SCHITTENHELM, A., AND B. EISLER. Übertragung des thyrotropes Hormons durch die Placenta und die Milch. *Z. Ges. Exptl. Med.* 95: 124–125, 1935.

108. SCHLOSSMANN, H. Beitrage zur Biologie der Plazenta. II. Mitteilung: ist die Plazenta für Insulin durchlässig? *Arch. Exptl. Pathol. Pharmacol.* 159: 213–222, 1931.

109. SCHULTZ, M. A., J. B. FORSANDER, R. A. CHEZ, AND D. L. HUTCHINSON. The bidirectional placental transfer of I¹³¹ 3:5:3' triiodothyronine in the rhesus monkey. *Pediatrics* 35: 743–752, 1965.

110. SCHWABE, E., AND F. C. EMERY. Progesterone in adrenalectomized rats. *Proc. Soc. Exptl. Biol. Med.* 40: 383–385, 1939.

111. SCHWARZ, G. Ein Fall von diaplacentar Übertragen Exophthalmus. *Acta Endocrinol.* 30: 616–620, 1959.

112. SHEPPARD, R. H., V. M. TURNER, AND W. M. PAUL. A study of transplacental transfer of thyroid hormone in sheep. *J. Clin. Invest.* 37: 931, 1958.

113. SIITERI, P. K., AND P. C. MACDONALD. Placental estrogen biosynthesis during human pregnancy. *J. Clin. Endocrinol.* 26: 751–761, 1966.

114. SMITH, W. N. ADAMS. Transplacental influence of androgen upon ovulatory mechanisms in the rat. *J. Endocrinol.* 48: 477–478, 1970.

115. SOLOMON, S., AND H. G. FRIESEN. Endocrine relations between mother and fetus. *Ann. Rev. Med.* 19: 399–430, 1968.

116. SPOTO, P. Diabete e gravidanza. Passagio transplacentare dell'insulina. *Minerva Ginecol.* 6: 61, 1954.

117. STEINBECK, A. W. The adrenal cortex and its reproductive functions. In: *Human Reproductive Physiology*, edited by H. M. Carey. Washington, D.C.: Butterworths, 1963, chapt. 9, p. 122–154.

118. SWANSON, H. E., AND J. J. VAN DER WERFF TEN BOSCH. The "early-androgen" syndrome; differences in response to pre-natal and post-natal administration of various doses of testosterone proprinate in female and male rats. *Acta Endocrinol.* 47: 37–50, 1964.

119. THERÉSÀ, S. De la perméabilité du placenta aux hormones thyröide et thyréotrope. *Bull. Biol. Med. Exptl. USSR* 7: 544–548, 1939.

120. THORN, G. W. *The Diagnosis and Treatment of Adrenal Insufficiency*. Springfield, Ill.: Thomas, 1949.

121. WALAAS, E., AND O. WALAAS. Studies on the compensatory hypertrophy of the fetal adrenal glands in the albino rat, produced by adrenalectomy during pregnancy. *Acta Pathol. Microbiol. Scand.* 21: 640–672, 1944.

122. WILKINS, L. Masculinization of the female fetus due to use of orally given progestins. *J. Am. Med. Assoc.* 172: 1028–1032, 1960.

123. ZARDINI, L., P. G. CROSIGNANI, F. POLVANI, AND M. PANIGEL. (Abstract). 35ᵉ Reunion de l'Association des Physiologistes, Milan, June, 1967.

CHAPTER 44

Steroid hormones in mammalian pregnancy

KENNETH J. RYAN | *Department of Obstetrics and Gynecology, Harvard Medical School, and Boston Hospital for Women, Boston, Massachusetts*

CHAPTER CONTENTS

MAMMALIAN PREGNANCY characteristically involves the processes of placentation, intrauterine development, viviparity, and postpartum lactation, which depend in large measure on the specific actions of estrogenic and progestational hormones. These steroids are synthesized during gestation by the maternal ovaries or fetal placenta, or both, in all mammals, although the quantity, distribution, and metabolism of hormones may vary widely among animal species (13).

Although pregnancy begins for the fetus at the time of fertilization, it begins for the mother only when the presence of the blastocyst is recognized by the maternal organism and ovarian cyclicity is replaced by "pregnancy-specific" endocrine mechanisms. The cues to the mother initiated by the blastocyst may be altered uterine metabolism and/or secretion of a gonadotrophin, which independently or in concert transform the corpus luteum of the cycle into the corpus luteum of pregnancy with a lengthened life-span and augmented steroid production (32). In animals with short gestation periods (20–60 days), this prolongation of the function of the corpus luteum suffices to provide all the extra steroid hormones needed for the successful completion of pregnancy. In animals with longer gestation periods, the placenta assumes varying degrees of steroid-producing activity and replaces ovarian function completely or in part (7). The fetus, long considered a nonparticipant in the endocrinology of pregnancy, has been implicated along with the placenta in the active biosynthesis and metabolism of steroid hormones, especially in mammals with long

gestation periods (14). In addition the maternal and fetal adrenal glands appear to have reproductive, as well as homeostatic, functions in the endocrine control of pregnancy (9).

More is known about reproductive endocrinology in man than in most mammalian species. This can undoubtedly be accounted for by the ready access to human material (maternal blood and urine, placenta, amniotic fluid, and fetus) in which the levels of hormones are high and tissue enzymes active. Much of the classic literature on endocrine function of animals during pregnancy antedates the human studies and, although extremely valuable, is often simply descriptive and involves the effects of oophorectomy on the course of gestation (7, 23). Measurement of steroid hormones in laboratory and domestic animals has often been by relatively nonspecific bioassays or by chemical assays too insensitive for the low levels of hormones found in the body fluids and tissues of many of these species (23). Application of radioimmunoassay, competitive protein binding, and refined chemical techniques for assay of steroids; introduction of experimental fetal surgery; and extension of detailed placental biochemistry studies to animals are all providing exciting, new comparative data. It should now at least be possible to formulate hypotheses for the endocrine control of pregnancy in a wide spectrum of mammalian species and to test them experimentally.

THE CORPUS LUTEUM

It is almost axiomatic that the corpus luteum is the primary endocrine unit of mammalian pregnancy, for, without its steroid production, most gestations could never start, and, without its continued function, many could never be maintained. The role of the corpus luteum in reproduction was defined in the early 1900s when its essential role for pregnancy and deciduoma formation was established through study of the effects of its surgical removal (7). The abortion or endocrine deficiency produced by corpus luteum extirpation could be reversed by luteal extracts from which progesterone was ultimately isolated and characterized.

Progesterone has since been identified or its presence indicated in practically every mammalian corpus luteum (the elephant is a notable exception) in which it has been sought (29, 32), and the steroid is secreted at higher than peripheral levels in venous effluent from ovaries bearing corpora lutea (20). The following generalization may thus be offered: progesterone is necessary for the commencement and maintenance of pregnancy in all mammals, and its primary origin is the corpus luteum, which, as is discussed below, may or may not be replaced by a placental source later in gestation.

However, variations within this theme indicate diversity among mammalian species. In some species, such as the human being, in which a single offspring is most common, the follicle from which the ovum and ultimately the blastocyst are derived becomes the definitive steroid-secreting corpus luteum. In animals with multiple ovulations and offspring, a correspondingly greater number of corpora are formed, even to the point that many more functional corpora than blastocysts are present. In the horse and elephant, additional luteal function is provided by subsequent ovulations and successive crops of corpora lutea during pregnancy. In Macroscelididae (shrew) and Tenrecidae (hedgehog), the corpus luteum appears to form before release of the ovum. In the guinea pig and armadillo, implantation of the blastocyst may occur, even if the ovaries are removed, which leaves no obvious source for the continued production of progesterone and an unexplained exception to the generalizations on the need for the corpus luteum and its hormones in early pregnancy. Within these minor variations, the concept of the need for corpus luteum function and progesterone in mammalian gestation is firmly established (32).

Although the relationship of progesterone to the corpus luteum is quite secure, the need for and source of estrogens in mammalian pregnancy are less readily defined. In most species where oophorectomy interrupts pregnancy, administration of carefully adjusted ratios of estrogen and progesterone provide the most successful replacement therapy and reversal of the endocrine deficiency (13, 22a). In several species (rabbit, mouse) only progesterone replacement is essential. In these same species no convincing evidence exists for a placental or other extraovarian source of estrogen. It may therefore be possible for pregnancy to proceed in the absence of estrogens, especially in animals with short gestation periods. In all animals with long gestation periods, enzymatic studies (1, 2, 5, 6) and extraction of tissues provide conclusive evidence that the placenta is the extraovarian source for estrogen production after oophorectomy.

Animal corpora lutea also differ in their capacity to synthesize estrogens de novo. Whereas luteal tissue from many mammals can convert androgens to estrogens, only human corpora have thus far been demonstrated to efficiently convert acetate and C_{21} compounds like progestrone to estrogens; this demonstrates the presence of a complete biosynthetic pathway (27). In most other species, follicles and not the corpora lutea probably pro-vide the ovarian estrogens of the cycle and of pregnancy. Placental estrogens appear to be present only in animals with long gestation periods.

The broad comparative basis for the role of the corpus luteum, progesterone, and estrogens in mammalian pregnancy has thus been established by oophorectomy and replacement studies, which are summarized in Tables 1 and 2. Animals can be divided into those that do and those that do not maintain gestation after ovarian or corpora lutea removal and those with a gestation period equal to or longer than pseudopregnancy. In general, animals that do abort or resorb their fetuses have a short gestation period (12–63 days), their corpora do not regress, neither progesterone nor estrogen can be isolated from their placentas, the progesterone level is higher in ovarian veins than in peripheral or uterine veins, and their placentas are devoid of significant enzymatic activity for steroid formation (7, 25). Abortion can be prevented by progesterone or estrogen and progesterone replacement. The abortion-inducing effect is not an all-or-none phenomenon and is clearly related to the time of gestation at which oophorectomy is performed, and the ratio of fetal to placental mass. Oophorectomy in the rat can be tolerated without loss of pregnancy if it is performed close to term or if most of the fetuses are removed and the placentas are left in situ. These appear to be extreme conditions that do not reflect major controlling factors under usual physiological conditions.

In the animals that abort after oophorectomy but have a prolonged pregnancy, placental production of estrogen still occurs (25).

TABLE 1. *Steroid Hormones in Mammals that Abort After Oophorectomy*

Species	Gestation Length, days	Placental Progesterone	Placental Estrogen	In Vitro Placental Aromatization
Opossum	12.5			
Hamster	16–19			
Mouse	20		None	
Rat	21	None	None	None
Rabbit	30–32	None		None
Dog	58–63	None	None	None
Sow	112–115	None	Present	Present
Goat	151	None	Present	Present

TABLE 2. *Steroid Hormones in Mammals that Do Not Abort After Oophorectomy*

Species	Gestation Length, days	Placental Progesterone	Placental Estrogen	In Vitro Placental Aromatization
Cat	63			
Guinea pig	68	Present		None
Sheep	144	Present	Present	Present
Macaque	165	Present	Present	Present
Human	267	Present	Present	Present
Cow	280	Present	Present	Present
Horse	330	Present	Present	Present

Some mammals will maintain pregnancy after oophorectomy if it is performed after a certain time period, which is usually early in gestation. The cat, cow, and horse, however, will tolerate oophorectomy only past the midpoint in gestation; this suggests a delayed onset in the production of sufficient placental steroid hormones (7).

In general, animals that do not abort after oophorectomy have a longer gestation period and have placental production of progesterone (Fig. 1) and estrogens with continued high levels of steroid secretion, even in the absence of the maternal ovaries. The guinea pig, with a short gestation period and placental production of progesterone, cannot synthesize estrogens from a placental source (2) and is an exception in this, as in other, aspects of reproduction.

Although it should be obvious, it is worth emphasizing that, once the placenta provides steroid hormones in addition to its more fundamental transfer function, the need for estrogens and progesterone in the continued maintenance of pregnancy can no longer be defined by simple extirpation studies. The role of estrogens and progesterone in animals with long gestation periods and placental steroid production may only be conclusively defined sometime in the future by specific antibodies that can interfere with hormone function without grossly disrupting placental nutritional and transfer activities.

The transition from dependence on the corpus luteum to placental steroid production has been most graphically demonstrated for progesterone by a sampling of peripheral sera as pregnancy progresses in the human being (Fig. 2) and for estrogen by assay of urinary excretion in the pregnant sow (Fig. 3). In each instance a dip and a subsequent rise in hormone secretion occur at the time one hormone source is believed to take over from the other.

Thus far the presence of placental progesterone pro-

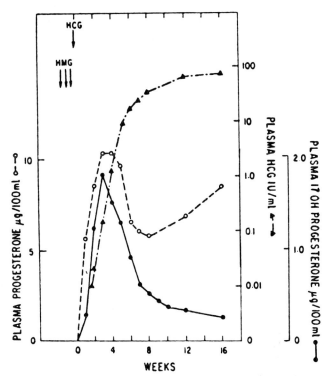

FIG. 2. Progesterone, 17-hydroxyprogesterone (*17 OH progesterone*), and chorionic gonadotrophin (*HCG*) plasma levels in early pregnancy of the human being. Note the dip of progesterone (*open circles*) and subsequent rise at 8 weeks, which suggests a transition from a corpus luteum to a placental source. The 17-hydroxyprogesterone is believed to be due only to corpus luteum secretion and falls at the time of the dip without a subsequent rise. *HMG*, human menopausal gonadotrophin. [From Yoshimi et al. (34).]

duction correlates with the ability of the animal to withstand oophorectomy without aborting, whereas the presence of placental estrogen production correlates best with gestation periods longer than pseudopregnancy and is unrelated to the effects of oophorectomy on the animal.

PLACENTAL PRODUCTION OF STEROID HORMONES

Progesterone and estrogens have been isolated from the placentas of many mammalian species and correlated with their dependence on the presence of ovaries for maintenance of pregnancy and gestation length, but such studies offer, at best, only indirect evidence of secretory activity (7, 23). In the human being, progesterone, estradiol-17β, and estriol have been recovered in highest concentration in effluent blood draining the placenta; this provides more substantive proof of hormone production. Until similar information is provided from other animal sources, our conclusions on placental endocrine function must be largely inferential. It has also been demonstrated that, in several cases after oophorectomy, urinary and/or blood steroid concentrations remain elevated but decline after delivery; such observations further implicate the placenta [(36); see Fig. 1].

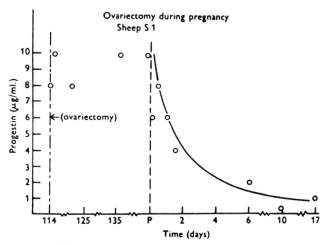

FIG. 1. Effect of ovariectomy on progestin levels in the pregnant ewe as measured by bioassay. Days after fertilization to parturition (*P*) are indicated on the *left*; days after parturition on the *right*. Note absence of abortion or a drop in blood levels after castration. [From Zarrow (36).]

In our own laboratory, we have systematically studied the enzymatic capacity of placental tissue to synthesize steroids in vitro. Such studies may provide a broad overview of the potential for placental endocrine function and provide the basis for the in vivo measurements that are still clearly needed (1–6, 31).

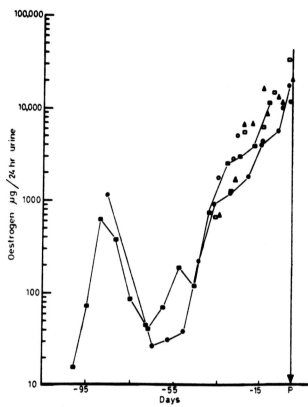

FIG. 3. Daily estrogen excretion by 6 pregnant sows. Note dip and subsequent rise at about 65 days before parturition (P). [From Raeside (24).]

Diverse studies in the human being, in which both in vitro and in vivo techniques were used, have indicated that the placenta is an incomplete endocrine organ. Steroids are not synthesized readily from acetate in the placenta, as in other endocrine tissues; rather, the human placenta converts preformed steroid precursors that reach it via the blood stream—maternal cholesterol or pregnenolone for progesterone production, and fetal androgens for estrogen synthesis [Fig. 4; (14)].

Progesterone Synthesis by the Placenta

In the human being, labeled blood-borne cholesterol is converted to progesterone, and the distribution of isotopic label indicates a preferential use of cholesterol over other possible precursors for progesterone synthesis (17). The enzyme systems have been localized in the mitochondria and microsomes of the placental cell, and in vitro conversion is readily demonstrable (25). Pregnenolone, the steroid intermediate between cholesterol and progesterone, is present in high concentration in both maternal and fetal blood and can also be converted in vivo and in vitro to progesterone. Subsequently pregnenolone conversion to progesterone has been demonstrated in a wide variety of animal placentas (1, 3–5), but caution in interpretation is necessary, since even tissue from the rat (31) and rabbit (21) that can produce little or no placental progesterone can carry out this reaction. Comparative studies of placental capacity to convert acetate or cholesterol to progesterone are not yet available but are clearly needed.

Placental Metabolism of Progesterone

In sharp contrast to that of the human being, the placentas of most animals and subhuman primates that have been studied extensively metabolize progesterone

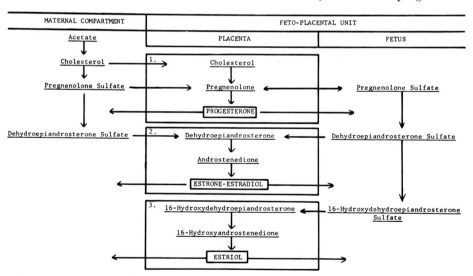

FIG. 4. Diagrammatic representation of steroid synthesis by the placenta in the human being. Compartmentalization and discontinuity in the formation of progesterone, estradiol, and estriol from either maternal or fetal precursors are demonstrated. The pathways under *1.* from pregnenolone to progesterone and under *2.* from dehydroepiandrosterone to estrone-estradiol have been demonstrated in a wide range of animal species. [From Ryan (25).]

TABLE 3. *Progesterone Metabolism in Vitro by Mammalian Placentas*

Metabolites	Species
5β-Pregnanediols, 5β-pregnanalones	Cow, sheep
5α-Pregnanediols, 5α-pregnanalones, 5α-pregnanediones	Rat, horse, macaque, baboon, squirrel monkey, orangutan
6β-Hydroxyprogesterone	Human, baboon, rhesus, squirrel monkey, orangutan

to a wide variety of biologically less active steroids (1, 3–5, 31). Some species differences exist in the stereospecificity of ring A reduction and the spectrum of metabolites produced, but the compounds formed by the placenta in vitro are similar to the urinary metabolites isolated from the same species (Table 3). Since progesterone secretion and blood levels are a consequence of the balance between production and degradation, placental metabolism may have physiological significance. For example, near term, in the horse and macaque, in which placental progesterone metabolism is extensive, blood levels are much lower than they are in the human being (29). Other factors that might influence blood levels of steroids are considered below.

PLACENTAL ESTROGEN SYNTHESIS
AND THE FETOPLACENTAL UNIT

As for placental progesterone formation where de novo synthesis does not take place, estrogens are synthesized by the human placenta not from acetate but from preformed C_{19} steroidal precursors of adrenal origin. A major contribution of the fetal adrenal to the secretion of these precursors has been established by demonstration of a drop in maternal estrogen excretion if the fetus dies, if the fetus has no adrenal (as in anencephaly), or if the adrenal is inhibited by exogenous corticoids. Although the human placenta alone cannot synthesize estrogens from acetate or C_{21} steroid precursors in vitro, a combination of the placenta and fetal adrenal can accomplish such a conversion (14). In vivo studies with labeled steroids or perfusion of an intact fetoplacental unit have indicated that dehydroepiandrosterone sulfate and 16α-hydroxydehydroepiandrosterone sulfate of human fetal adrenal origin are the immediate precursors of placental estrone-estradiol and estriol, respectively (see Fig. 4). These precursors are present in fetal blood in high concentration and perfuse the placenta where conversion can take place (14).

Extensive studies with placentas of many mammalian species reveal that, like that of the human being, none of the specimens tested have the capacity to convert C_{21} steroids (pregnenolone or progesterone) to estrogens (1, 2). The incomplete endocrine activity of the placenta is a general phenomenon not restricted to man. However, animals with short gestation periods (e.g., rat, rabbit, and

guinea pig) do not have the capacity for placental estrogen synthesis in vitro, and estrogens have not been detected in their placentas (2, 31). All tested animals with a long gestation period can aromatize C_{19} androgens to estrogens in a manner quite analogous to that of the human being (Table 4), and estrogens have been isolated from their placental tissue (2, 4, 23). The immediate precursors tested for in vitro conversion were dehydroepiandrosterone and androstenedione, and the latter compound has been produced by the fetal adrenals of porcine (K. J. Ryan, unpublished observations) and ovine (12) species in vitro.

Since the sow and sheep can continue to secrete estrogens after oophorectomy and their placentas can convert only androgens to these phenolic steroids, it is assumed that the precursor source for this continued estrogen output is either the maternal or fetal adrenals.

When tested specifically, the macaque, pig (K. J. Ryan, unpublished observations), and sheep have the requisite combination of enzymes in their fetal adrenals and placentas to effect synthesis of estrogens when the two tissues are incubated together but not alone (12). A significant maternal adrenal source for the estrogen precursors has been ruled out in the human being but not in these or other species (Table 5).

The possible physiological significance of the fetoplacental unit in estrogen biosynthesis is that the level of estrogen produced depends on a precursor that increases in amount as the fetus grows whereas progesterone formation depends on a relatively unrestricted maternal precursor, cholesterol. Hence the ratios of the two steroids can and do change as the fetus grows and the pregnancy progresses.

TABLE 4. *Estrogens Formed by Mammalian Placentas from Dehydroepiandrosterone or Androstenedione in Vitro*

Species	Estrogens Formed
Human, marmoset, squirrel monkey, rhesus monkey, Iris monkey, baboon, chimpanzee, orangutan	Estradiol-17β, estrone
Horse, sow	Estradiol-17β, estrone
Cow, sheep, goat	Estradiol-17β, estradiol-17α, estrone
Guinea pig, rat, dog, rabbit	None

TABLE 5. *Estrogen Synthesis from Pregnenolone in Vitro by Combinations of Fetal or Maternal Adrenals and Placentas from Sheep, Macaque, and Pig*

Tissue	Estrogen Formation
Maternal adrenal alone	
Maternal adrenal plus placenta	+
Placenta alone	
Fetal adrenal plus placenta	+
Fetal adrenal alone	

PLACENTAL ESTROGEN METABOLISM

As with placental progesterone metabolism, species differ in the types of estrogens formed and in their subsequent conversions. Although estrone and estradiol-17β are formed by all placentas tested, estradiol-17α is also seen, but only in the cow, goat, and sheep (see Table 4). Estriol is limited predominantly to the human being and other primates, and it has not been isolated from the urine or placentas of other species in significant quantities. The ring B unsaturated estrogens, equilin and equilenin, are found mainly in the equine species, and the pathway for their formation is not completely understood. Some type of fetoplacental interaction appears likely for synthesis of this type of estrogen as well. The physiological significance of these species differences in steroid metabolism is not apparent but could influence the levels of active hormones in blood.

STEROID DYNAMICS AND BINDING
IN SERUM AND TISSUE

The levels of steroid hormones in serum generally rise progressively during pregnancy and decline precipitously just before or after parturition (Fig. 5). However, many variations on this general scheme bear scrutiny. As stated earlier, there may be a diphasic curve with a dip during the transition from corpus luteum production to placental production of steroids (see Figs. 2 and 3). In some cases, a metabolite, such as 20α-hydroxypregn-4-en-3-one in the rat or rabbit [Fig. 6; (10, 16, 18, 33)], estriol in the human being, estradiol-17α in the cow, and equilin in the horse, may rise dramatically and dominate the steroid metabolic pattern. In some species, serum levels of hormones during much of pregnancy may be extremely low, as is that of progesterone in the rhesus

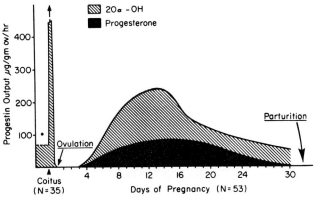

FIG. 6. Production of progesterone and 20α-hydroxypregn-4-en-3-one (20α-OH) by the rabbit ovary from coitus to parturition. [From Hilliard et al. (18).]

monkey and horse (29). In some species (rabbit, rat) serum progesterone may decline and/or estrogens rise before the onset of parturition (10, 16, 18, 33, 35) or may not (ewe, human being) [(8, 22); see Fig. 5]. If the fetus dies, estrogens will decline in the human being and may also decline in other species not yet tested. The possible physiological significance of such changes lies in the assumption that these specific hormones are somehow important to the endocrine control of pregnancy both in the maintenance of gestation and the initiation of parturition. In spite of this, no clear-cut pattern applicable to all species is apparent. For example, progesterone can maintain pregnancy in oophorectomized rats, whereas a major metabolite, 20α-hydroxypregn-4-en-3-one, cannot (30). The relative amounts present could be important, but this varies among species. If progesterone maintains pregnancy, one would expect a fall to initiate and precede its termination, and, if progesterone is so important, it should be elevated in the serum of all animals.

Fecal excretion of steroid metabolites may be as high as or higher than urinary values in certain animals and must be considered in the total evaluation of hormone metabolism.

Possible resolution of the discrepancies among past hypotheses, predicted events, and experimental findings may lie in the observations that progesterone and estrogens can be bound to proteins in both sera and tissues and total blood or uterine levels may not reflect that amount of hormone available in either bound or free form for biological effect.

Species do vary in the amount of specific proteins present in the serum to bind hormones. For example the concentration in serum of corticosterone-binding globulin (CBG), which binds progesterone, is high in the human being, in which total progesterone concentrations in blood, are high, and absent or low in many other species, in which levels of progesterone in blood are much lower (28). If only the free steroid were active, the elevated total of bound and unbound steroid concentration in the blood would not indicate the amount of free steroid actually present and necessary for a given level of activity. If the active hormone is bound to the uterus, the

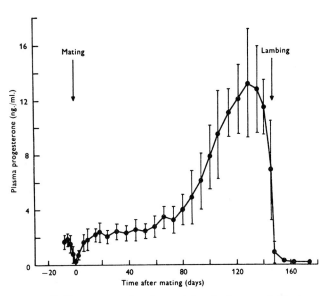

FIG. 5. Progesterone in the peripheral plasma of 14 sheep throughout pregnancy. [From Bassett et al. (8).]

concentration of steroids in the blood may be unimportant and even misleading with regard to effects on the myometrium.

ROLE OF THE FETUS IN ENDOCRINE
CONTROL OF PREGNANCY

Even before knowledge of the fetoplacental unit existed, there was an extensive amount of literature on the influence of fetal genetic factors in pregnancy duration. More recently, syndromes have been described in dairy cattle where specific autosomal recessive fetal genotypes can be associated with fetal pituitary and adrenal defects and a prolongation of the pregnancy (19). Experimental removal of the fetal adrenals or their pituitary support can result in lengthening of gestation (15). In the ovine and bovine species, corticoids administered to the fetus but not the mother can initiate labor whether the fetus is intact or adrenalectomized. There is also evidence in the sheep of a rapid rise in fetal but not maternal serum corticoids just before the onset of parturition [Fig. 7; (9)]. Even in the human being, the presence of a fetus with hypoplastic adrenals (anencephaly) is associated with prolonged gestation if no other complication, such as hydramnios, exists. There is thus a clear indication of fetal endocrine effects on gestation length.

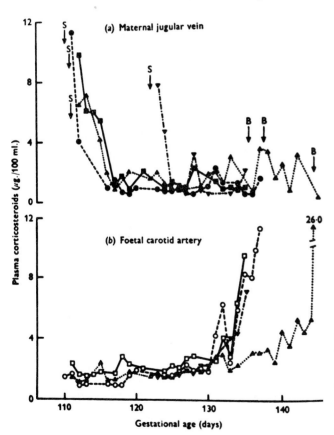

FIG. 7. Plasma corticosteroid concentrations of 4 pregnant ewes and their chronically cannulated lamb fetuses in utero. S, day of surgery; B, day of birth. [From Bassett & Thorburn (9).]

In addition to the adrenal cortical effects noted above, there are less well-defined studies revealing an influence of estrogens on the acceleration of labor readiness or actual induction of increased uterine contractility. Since the fetus is intimately concerned with providing estrogen precursors, another possible connection between fetal endocrine activity and pregnancy control could be inferred (26).

HYPOTHESES FOR STEROID HORMONE CONTROL
OF MAMMALIAN PREGNANCY

From the comparative data on steroid hormone metabolism, the natural and experimental studies of fetal endocrine effects on pregnancy length, and the knowledge of steroid binding in serum and tissues, hypotheses for the role of steroid hormone control of mammalian pregnancy may be advanced for future experimental testing. There is abundant evidence that the myometrium can accommodate the expanding volume of a growing fetus and remain relatively quiescent during most of pregnancy. As the gestation progresses, the myometrium either gradually or abruptly (depending on species) becomes more active and responds with greater sensitivity to various stimulatory agents, such as oxytocin. The pattern of myometrial contractility is believed to be primarily under the influence of progesterone, and hence an absolute or relative drop in its concentration or biological effectiveness would seem to be the most logical basis for the onset of labor readiness (11). Labor itself could be induced by any number of stimuli once the muscle becomes sufficiently sensitive. It is possible that the genesis of muscle sensitivity or labor readiness varies in different animal species.

The factors that might alter progesterone effectiveness could include a critical uterine volume or rate of change in volume, oxytocin, prostaglandin, nervous stimuli, catecholamines, estrogens, or other as yet unknown factors.

The effects of fetal cortisol in inducing labor may be a direct antagonism of progesterone effect on myometrium, displacement of progesterone from protein receptors, stimulation of the synthesis of other agents, such as lecithin or prostaglandin, that cause myometrial contractility, or effects on progesterone synthesis or metabolism.

The effects of estrogen on myometrial contractility could be a direct antagonism of progesterone action (for which there is some preliminary evidence) by displacement of progesterone from protein receptors or interference with progesterone synthesis or degradation.

These, as well as other possibilities, are now being actively investigated. However, measurements of progesterone concentrations in blood or uterus have not thus far provided insight into the genesis of labor or the physiological roles of steroids during pregnancy.

SUMMARY

The dynamics and roles of steroid hormones in mammalian pregnancy may be summarized as follows:

1. Estrogens and progesterone are required for the initiation and maintenance of pregnancy in almost all mammals, with the exceptions that a rare species may implant in the absence of an obvious source of hormones (guinea pig and armadillo) or that pregnancy may be maintained with progesterone alone. In most species that abort after oophorectomy, replacement of the proper absolute and relative amounts of estrogen and progesterone provides the best results.

2. If pregnancy is longer than the luteal phase of the cycle, new endocrine-specific mechanisms are required to continue the production of estrogens and progesterone. If pregnancy is as long as pseudopregnancy, an augmented corpus luteum life will usually suffice for this purpose. If pregnancy is much longer, placental endocrine function to produce estrogen and/or progesterone is required.

3. No mammalian placenta has been shown capable of converting C_{21} steroids, such as progesterone or pregnenolone, to androgens or estrogens. Hence, all placentas are incomplete endocrine organs that cannot synthesize estrogens de novo. Progesterone itself is formed largely from blood-borne cholesterol in the human being.

4. All tested animals with long gestation periods have a placental aromatizing system that converts androgens to estrogens. The fetal adrenal is the source of the androgen precursor in the human being and may be in other species as well.

5. Fetal genetic factors influence pregnancy length and may do so via endocrine mechanisms, such as the amounts of fetal adrenal cortisol or of estrogen precursors.

6. Hypotheses on the steroid control of pregnancy may be formulated on the basis of current knowledge, which should guide experimental study and hopefully provide better understanding of the endocrine physiology of reproduction.

REFERENCES

1. AINSWORTH, L., M. DAENEN, AND K. J. RYAN. Steroid hormone transformations by endocrine organs from pregnant mammals. IV. Biosynthesis and metabolism of estrogens and progesterone by primate placental preparations in vitro. *Endocrinology* 84: 1421–1429, 1969.
2. AINSWORTH, L., AND K. J. RYAN. Steroid hormone transformations by endocrine organs from pregnant mammals. I. Estrogen biosynthesis by mammalian placental preparations in vitro. *Endocrinology* 79: 875–883, 1966.
3. AINSWORTH, L., AND K. J. RYAN. Steroid hormone transformations by endocrine organs from pregnant mammals. II. Formation and metabolism of progesterone by bovine and sheep placental preparations in vitro. *Endocrinology* 81: 1349–1356, 1967.
4. AINSWORTH, L., AND K. J. RYAN. Steroid hormone transformations by endocrine organs from pregnant mammals. III. Biosynthesis and metabolism of progesterone by the mare placenta in vitro. *Endocrinology* 84: 91–97, 1969.
5. AINSWORTH, L., AND K. J. RYAN. Steroid hormone transformations by endocrine organs from pregnant mammals. V. The biosynthesis and metabolism of progesterone and estrogens by orangutan placental tissue in vitro. *Steroids* 14: 301–314, 1969.
6. AINSWORTH, L., AND K. J. RYAN. Steroid hormone transformations by endocrine organs from pregnant mammals. VI. The conversion of Δ^4-androstene-3,17-dione to estrogens by goat placental preparations in vitro. *Steroids* 16: 553–559, 1970.
7. AMOROSO, E. C., AND C. A. FINN. Ovarian activity during gestation, ovum transport and implantation. In: *The Ovary*, edited by S. Zuckerman. New York: Acad. Press, 1962, vol. 1, p. 451–537.
8. BASSETT, J. M., T. J. OXBORROW, I. D. SMITH, AND G. D. THORBURN. The concentration of progesterone in the peripheral plasma of the pregnant ewe. *J. Endocrinol.* 45: 449–457, 1969.
9. BASSETT, J. M., AND G. D. THORBURN. Foetal plasma corticosteroids and the initiation of parturition in sheep. *J. Endocrinol.* 44: 285–286, 1969.
10. CHATTERTON, R. T., JR., G. J. MACDONALD, AND R. O. GREEP. Biosynthesis of progesterone and 20α-hydroxypregn-4-en-3-one by the rat ovary during the estrous cycle and early pregnancy. *Endocrinology* 83: 1–10, 1968.

11. CSAPO, A. I., AND C. WOOD. The endocrine control of the initiation of labour in the human. In: *Recent Advances in Endocrinology*, edited by V. H. T. James. Boston: Little, Brown, 1968, p. 207–239.
12. DAVIES, I. J., K. J. RYAN, AND Z. PETRO. Estrogen synthesis by adrenal-placental tissues of the sheep and the Iris monkey in vitro. *Endocrinology* 86: 1457–1459, 1970.
13. DEANESLY, R. The endocrinology of pregnancy and foetal life. In: *Marshall's Physiology of Reproduction*, edited by A. S. Parkes. Boston: Little, Brown, 1966, vol. 3, p. 891–1063.
14. DICZFALUSY, E. Steroid metabolism in the foeto-placental unit. In: *The Foeto-Placental Unit*, edited by A. Pecile and C. Finzi. Amsterdam: Excerpta Medica Foundation, 1969, p. 65–109.
15. DROST, M., AND L. W. HOLM. Prolonged gestation in ewes after foetal adrenalectomy. *J. Endocrinol.* 40: 293–296, 1968.
16. HASHIMOTO, I., D. M. HENDRICKS, L. L. ANDERSON, AND R. M. MELAMPY. Progesterone and pregn-4-en-20α-ol-3-one in ovarian venous blood during various reproductive states in the rat. *Endocrinology* 82: 333–341, 1968.
17. HELLIG, H., Y. LEFEBVRE, D. GATTERLAN, AND E. BOLTE. Placental progesterone synthesis in the human. In: *The Foeto-Placental Unit*, edited by A. Pecile and C. Finzi. Amsterdam: Excerpta Medica Foundation, 1969, p. 152–161.
18. HILLIARD, J., H. G. SPIES, AND C. H. SAWYER. Cholesterol storage and progestin secretion during pregnancy and pseudopregnancy in the rabbit. *Endocrinology* 82: 157–165, 1968.
19. HOLM, L. W. Prolonged pregnancy. In: *Advances in Veterinary Science*, edited by C. A. Brandly and C. Cornelius. New York: Acad. Press, 1967, vol. 11, p. 159–205.
20. LINZELL, J. L., AND R. B. HEAP. A comparison of progesterone metabolism in the pregnant sheep and goat: sources of production and an estimation of uptake by some target organs. *J. Endocrinol.* 41: 433–438, 1968.
21. MATSUMOTO, K., G. YAMANE, H. ENDO, K. KOTOH, AND K. OKANO. Conversion of pregnenolone to progesterone by rabbit placenta in vitro. *Acta Endocrinol.* 61: 577–584, 1969.
22. MELLIN, T. N., R. E. ERB, AND V. L. ESTERGREEN, JR. Urinary excretion of estrogen by the bovine before and after parturition. *J. Animal Sci.* 25: 955–961, 1966.
22a. MEYER, R. K., R. C. WOLF, AND M. ARSLAN. Implantation

and maintenance of pregnancy in progesterone-treated ovariectomized monkeys. *Recent Advan. Primatol.* 2: 30–35, 1969.
23. NEWTON, W. H. Hormones and the placenta. *Physiol. Rev.* 18: 419–446, 1938.
24. RAESIDE, J. I. Urinary oestrogen excretion in the pig during pregnancy and parturition. *J. Reprod. Fertility* 6: 427–431, 1963.
25. RYAN, K. J. Theoretical basis for endocrine control of gestation—a comparative approach. In: *The Foeto-Placental Unit,* edited by A. Pecile and C. Finzi. Amsterdam: Excerpta Medica Foundation, 1969, p. 120–131.
26. RYAN, K. J. Endocrine control of gestational length. *Am. J. Obstet. Gynecol.* 109: 299–306, 1971.
27. SAVARD, K., J. M. MARSH, AND B. F. RICE. Gonadotropins and ovarian steroidogenesis. *Recent Progr. Hormone Res.* 21: 285–356, 1965.
28. SEAL, U. S., AND R. P. DOE. Vertebrate distribution of corticosteroid-binding globulin and some endocrine effects on concentration. *Steroids* 5: 827–841, 1965.
29. SHORT, R. V. Progesterone. In: *Hormones in Blood,* edited by C. H. Gray and A. L. Bacharach. New York: Acad. Press, 1961, p. 379–437.
30. TALWALKER, P. K., C. KRAHENBUHL, AND P. A. DESAULLES. Maintenance of pregnancy in spayed rats with 20α-hydroxypregn-4-ene-3-one and 20β-hydroxypregn-4-ene-3-one. *Nature* 209: 86–87, 1966.
31. TOWNSEND, L., AND K. J. RYAN. In vitro metabolism of pregnenolone-7α-^{3}H, progesterone-4-^{14}C and androstenedione-4-^{14}C by rat placental tissue. *Endocrinology* 87: 151–155, 1970.
32. VAN TIENHOVEN, A. The ovary. In: *Reproductive Physiology of Vertebrates.* Philadelphia: Saunders, 1968, p. 104–159.
33. WIEST, W. G. Progesterone and 20α-hydroxypregn-4-en-3-one in plasma, ovaries and uteri during pregnancy in the rat. *Endocrinology* 87: 43–48, 1970.
34. YOSHIMI, T., C. A. STROTT, J. R. MARSHALL, AND M. B. LIPSETT. Corpus luteum function in early pregnancy. *J. Clin. Endocrinol. Metab.* 29: 225–230, 1969.
35. YOSHINAGA, K., R. A. HAWKINS, AND J. R. STOCKER. Estrogen secretion by the rat ovary in vivo during the estrous cycle and pregnancy *Endocrinology* 85: 103–112, 1969.
36. ZARROW, M. X. Gestation. In: *Sex and Internal Secretions,* edited by W. C. Young. Baltimore: Williams & Wilkins, 1961, vol. 2, p. 958–1031.

CHAPTER 45

Placental protein and polypeptide hormones

HENRY G. FRIESEN | *Royal Victoria Hospital, Montreal, Canada*

CHAPTER CONTENTS

THE PLACENTA is a remarkable endocrine organ because of the diversity of hormones it secretes or metabolizes. In addition to its central role in steroidogenesis as part of the fetoplacental unit, it is also the source of several protein and polypeptide hormones. The total number of hormones recognized as secreted by the placenta has fluctuated since human chorionic gonadotrophin (HCG) was first identified as a placental hormone. Initially the criteria for the existence of a new placental hormone were not very rigorous and frequently depended on nothing more than the demonstration of a particular biological effect following the administration of a placental extract. Because HCG was closely related to pituitary luteinizing hormone (LH), an extensive search was made to determine whether placental extracts contained other pituitary-like hormones, and claims that the placenta contains ACTH, melanocyte-stimulating hormone (MSH), vasopressin, growth hormone, prolactin, and lipid-metabolizing hormones have been made. Diczfalusy & Troen (24) have reviewed these reports critically and conclude that the evidence for other placental protein hormones is not convincing. However, after the discovery of human placental lactogen (HPL) by Josimovich & MacLaren (65), interest in the placenta as an endocrine gland was renewed. An additional impetus to research on placental protein and polypeptide hormones has come from ad-

vances in protein chemistry in the past two decades, which have provided vastly improved methods of purification and analysis of proteins; such improved methods have greatly facilitated studies on the isolation, chemistry, and measurement of the blood concentrations of hormones under different physiological and pathological conditions. The amino acid sequence of the two placental protein hormones is under investigation. Radioimmunoassays of placental hormones have almost replaced bioassays and have permitted the measurement of levels of hormones in circulating blood under many experimental conditions. Consequently a search for control mechanisms regulating the synthesis and secretion of the different placental hormones can now be undertaken with some prospect of success. Immunologic techniques also have been very helpful in identifying the type of placental cell responsible for the synthesis and secretion of the different placental hormones.

In this chapter an attempt is made to review highlights of the chemistry and physiology of several placental hormones. Attention has been focused particularly on the placental lactogens and luteotrophins, an area of particular current interest, and I have tried to clarify the rather confusing and sometimes contradictory evidence for the existence of placental thyroid-stimulating hormones.

No attempt is made in this chapter to provide an exhaustive literature review of the subject of placental protein and polypeptide hormones [for more detailed accounts of some of the areas covered, see reviews (11, 13, 24)]. Pregnant mares' serum gonadotrophin (PMSG), which appears in the pregnant mare and some other perissodactyls, is derived from highly specialized excrescences of the fertile uterine horn (endometrial cups) and, in the strict sense therefore, PMSG is not of placental origin and is not considered further in this chapter. Several thoughtful reviews of the chemistry and secretion of this hormone are available (77, 98).

HUMAN CHORIONIC GONADOTROPHIN

The discovery of human chorionic gonadotrophin (HCG) is traditionally attributed to Aschheim & Zondek (3), who in 1927 showed that blood and urine of pregnant women contained a principle that caused ovarian growth and corpus luteum formation in immature mice. The biological effects of placental extracts actually were described earlier by Aschner (4), who observed in 1913 that water-soluble placental extracts produced ovarian hyperemia and vaginal estrus in guinea pigs. Not until 1938 was the production of HCG by placental cells in tissue culture demonstrated, and this report removed any lingering doubt about the source of HCG in pregnancy (40). During subsequent years considerable information has accumulated regarding the purification, chemistry, secretion, and metabolism of this hormone. The first two topics have been considered by Morgan and coauthors in this *Handbook*; therefore only the site of production of HCG, its biological effects, and its secretion in pregnancy and trophoblastic disease are reviewed in this chapter.

Cell of Origin

The initial suggestion that the cytotrophoblast synthesized and secreted HCG was based on studies that demonstrated a good correlation between the early increase in HCG concentrations and the relative frequency of Langhans' cells in placental tissue early in pregnancy (117). As HCG concentrations decreased in the second trimester, the number of cytotrophoblast cells fell and the number of syncytiotrophoblast cells increased. Moreover histochemical studies of placental tissue showed that the cytotrophoblast was rich in glycoproteins, and, because HCG is a glycoprotein, Weber (130) suggested that it might be secreted by the cytotrophoblast. These deductions proved to be in error when Midgley & Pierce (84), using the more direct immunofluorescence techniques, showed that antiserum to HCG localized in the syncytiotrophoblast; the next year Leznoff & Davis (72), using the indirect immunofluorescence method, confirmed these observations. Electron-microscopic studies have shown that the syncytiotrophoblast, in contrast to the cytotrophoblast, has a well-developed endoplasmic reticulum. Ultrastructural localization of HCG in human term placentas by immunocytochemical methods has indicated that HCG is found principally on the maternal surface of the apical membrane and in the cisternae of the rough endoplasmic reticulum of the syncytiotrophoblast (25). Human chorionic gonadotrophin was not found in the cytotrophoblast. These observations suggest that the hormone may be transported directly from the ergastoplasmic cisternae of the syncytiotrophoblast into the maternal blood. Previous ultrastructural observations on the human placenta suggested that the merocrine mechanism of secretion also prevails in the syncytiotrophoblast. After synthesis in the ergastoplasm, HCG passes through the Golgi system for packaging in cytoplasmic granules. The latter are secreted into the lumen of the overlying maternal vessel. Because the more definitive studies with ultrastructural localization fail to demonstrate the presence of HCG in the Golgi, lamellae, vesicles, and cytoplasmic granules, whether HCG export requires Golgi mediation is doubt-

ful. More recently, Patillo et al. (93) have shown that a special type of cell with the morphological characteristics of the cytotrophoblast also may secrete HCG. This cell line, which has been maintained in tissue culture for many years, originally was established by incubating tumor tissue from a patient with a choriocarcinoma. Despite the fact that the cells resemble the cytotrophoblast or a transitional cell type between it and the syncytiotrophoblast, they have retained the capacity to synthesize and secrete HCG, but normally it is the syncytiotrophoblast that secretes HCG.

Assays

BIOASSAY. Two broad categories of bioassays have been developed for the detection of HCG: in the first type the end point is a qualitative response, such as ovarian hyperemia in the immature rat or expulsion of spermatozoa in frogs; in the second type of assay, which is more commonly used for research purposes, a graded response is observed. In general it consists of measuring one of the following: ovarian, uterine, prostatic, or seminal vesicle weight of intact, immature rats or hypophysectomized rats. The different assays employed do not always give identical results and may not measure the same activities. The biological activity of HCG therefore is not always easy to define, and hormonal polymorphism and polymerization, as well as the synergistic or inhibitory effects of physiological fluids, may all modify the biological activity of different preparations. Indeed, Hamashige et al. (48) have isolated three electrophoretically distinct components from HCG preparations; each of the components produces characteristic biological responses on the gonads, on steroidogenesis, and on spermatogenesis in hypophysectomized rats. These findings are best explained if HCG contains a multiplicity of sites of biological activity. The design and characteristics of the various assay procedures are evaluated in several excellent reviews. The problems of specificity, reproducibility, and sensitivity of the different bioassays and seasonal variation in the test animals are considered in detail (13, 23, 75). An international reference standard proposed by the National Institute for Medical Research, Mill Hill, is available, and all results should be expressed in terms of this reference preparation. The international unit of HCG is defined as the activity contained in 1.279 μg of the second international standard.

IMMUNOASSAY. In more recent studies immunoassay techniques for the measurement of HCG largely have replaced bioassay methods (14) because the former are simpler, more rapid, less expensive, and usually more sensitive. One of the major problems encountered when using immunoassays for measuring HCG is that of specificity. Most of the HCG preparations used for generating antisera are impure. In addition, although there may be homogeneity of the polypeptide backbone of the molecule, heterogeneity of the carbohydrate moieties of the molecule may well be present, and currently no methods are available to rule out this possibility. These sugar moieties probably are important for biological activity because limited desialylation by neuraminidase can alter the biological activity of HCG without seriously affecting its immunologic potency (127). This phenomenon may account for the discrepancies that have been reported between estimates of potency for HCG preparations when bio- and immunoassays have been used for the same samples (132). In addition to the possible heterogeneity of the carbohydrate moieties and variable sialic acid content of HCG preparations, other placental and urinary glycoproteins frequently contaminate HCG preparations that are derived from urine extracts. Antibodies directed against these impurities can be eliminated by immunoabsorption with urinary concentrates from children or males, and thus a specific antiserum to HCG is obtained. Antisera to HCG invariably crossreact with pituitary LH; this cross reaction occurs because of the chemical homology that exists between the two hormones. In view of the common subunit shared by thyrotrophin (TSH) and LH (95, 97), it is not surprising that some antisera to HCG also cross-react with TSH (18).

Concentration in Tissue, Blood, and Urine

The concentration of HCG in placental tissue at various periods of pregnancy has been studied by Diczfalusy (23) and Loraine & Matthew (76). Maximal concentrations were found in placental tissue in the second and third month (100–500 IU/g wet wt); thereafter the concentration fell to 10–20 IU/g wet wt at term. If one assumes "pure" HCG preparations to have a potency of 20,000 IU/mg, 1 kg of placental tissue would yield only 1 mg of HCG. Because of the low HCG concentrations in the tissues of term placentas, urine collected early in pregnancy has been the principal source of material for further purification of HCG. The heterogeneity of the most highly purified HCG preparations upon gel electrophoresis may result from the fact that HCG is purified from large pools of urine collected in pregnancy, and furthermore some of the products purified undoubtedly are metabolites of HCG. With the greater frequency of abortions performed in the first trimester of pregnancy, it should be possible to obtain sufficient placental tissue early in pregnancy, when the HCG concentration is sufficiently great to make the purification of placental HCG feasible. Such a study might demonstrate physical and chemical differences between urinary and placental HCG.

The measurement of HCG in both blood and urine throughout pregnancy has been reported in many studies using bioassays or immunoassays (11, 13, 128). A rapid increase in urine and serum concentrations of HCG follows the onset of pregnancy, with maximum levels occurring at about 60 days. Because this hormone can be measured in urine within a few days of implantation, its detection forms the basis of most pregnancy tests. The mean concentrations of maternal serum HCG

between days 60 and 80 range from 50 to 100 IU/ml, decrease to a mean of 10 to 20 IU/ml, and usually increase slightly again at the end of pregnancy. The concentration of HCG in fetal blood is one-tenth that of the maternal level, which suggests that placental transfer of HCG to the fetus is minimal (26). The disappearance rates for both LH and HCG appear to follow a double exponential curve—the initial disappearance of LH is rapid, with a half-time disappearance rate ($t_{1/2}$) of 21 min compared to a $t_{1/2}$ of 11 hr for HCG. In the second phase, LH has a $t_{1/2}$ of 4 hr and HCG a $t_{1/2}$ of 23 hr (134). This difference in the rate of metabolism of the two hormones is of some practical importance when HCG preparations are used therapeutically in an attempt to induce ovulation in women. A single injection at the midpoint of the cycle is usually adequate, whereas LH, because of its shorter biological half-life, may have to be administered more frequently to be effective.

In subhuman primates, chorionic gonadotrophin (MCG) is also found in the urine in pregnancy. Tullner (119) has defined the temporal patterns of MCG excretion in the urine of rhesus monkey, stump tail monkey, and baboon. Only slight variations in the duration of production of MCG were noted, although the amounts excreted varied somewhat among the species studied. In the rhesus monkey, chorionic gonadotrophin was detected in the urine only until day 36. In the baboon a rapid rise in serum gonadotrophin was observed at days 18–20, concentrations reaching 26 IU/ml at 22 days and then falling rapidly. In the gorilla the pattern was more similar to that seen in the human female—MCG persisted throughout pregnancy. Antisera to HCG crossreacted with MCG, but the degree of cross reaction was minimal, and most antisera did not cross-react.

The serum concentration of HCG has been measured in a large number of patients in whom pregnancy was associated with a variety of abnormalities, including diabetes, toxemia of pregnancy, Rh-isoimmunization, and multiple pregnancies (13). Although a great deal of interesting data has been accumulated, most has not been helpful in the clinical management of the complications of pregnancy. However, Brody & Carlstrom (14) studied patients with clinical evidence of threatened abortion and found that abnormally low HCG levels invariably were found when pregnancy ended with a complete abortion. In addition HCG determinations are of great value in following patients with choriocarcinoma; rising concentrations following surgery and chemotherapy provide reliable evidence of recurrence of the malignancy (60). Of considerable theoretical interest is the report that HCG concentrations in women with a male fetus are lower than in women with a female fetus (13), an observation raising the possibility that the sex of the fetus in some way modifies HCG synthesis and secretion.

Physiological Role

The physiological role of HCG generally is stated to be the maintenance of the corpus luteum early in pregnancy. As a result of the appearance of HCG, ovarian function continues in an uninterrupted fashion until the conceptus has developed to a point where it becomes autonomous. Indeed studies in man (16) and monkeys (59) have demonstrated that the administration of HCG prolongs the life-span of the corpus luteum. However, the continued secretion of HCG throughout pregnancy, when the corpus luteum is no longer necessary for the maintenance of pregnancy, remains puzzling.

Perhaps the best evidence that a placental gonadotrophin, presumably MCG, is the hormone maintaining the corpus luteum is derived from studies of Neill et al. (87). They measured circulating progesterone concentrations as an index of corpus luteum function during the normal menstrual cycle, as well as in pregnancy, in rhesus monkeys. In fertile cycles there is a short-lived increase in the concentration of plasma progesterone at days 22–24 (days 9–11 of pregnancy) at a time when the concentration of plasma progesterone is falling in nonfertile cycles. The reversal of the decline may be interpreted as a "rescue" of the corpus luteum by a gonadotrophic stimulus. The rise in plasma progesterone concentration in early pregnancy also exceeds that found in nonfertile cycles and coincides with the implantation of the blastocyst and the early formation of the syncytiotrophoblast. Since this structure is the source of chorionic gonadotrophin in man and monkey, it probably is the source of the gonadotrophic stimulus. This supposition requires confirmation by direct specific measurement of serum chorionic gonadotrophin at this early period of pregnancy. In rhesus monkeys MCG has been detected in urine as early as day 12 of pregnancy (118) and presumably, if more sensitive methods for detection were available, would be found in the serum even earlier. In the monkey, plasma progesterone levels do not remain elevated and in fact fall when chorionic gonadotrophin excretion is increasing. The corpus luteum appears to become refractory to continued stimulation, and indeed this has been demonstrated by Neill (personal communication), who showed that the corpus luteum failed to continue secreting progesterone when HCG was injected in increasing amounts in the second half of the cycle. The pattern of progesterone secretion paralleled that found in early pregnancy (88). The nature of the refractoriness of the corpus luteum to HCG is not clear, but one possibility is that the precursors for progesterone, probably cholesterol, are depleted by HCG. Hilliard et al. (58) have reported that progestin secretion by the rabbit interstitium is stimulated initially by LH but becomes relatively unresponsive to exogenous LH and that the length and extent of refractoriness were more pronounced as the initial dose of gonadotrophin was increased.

In human beings, as in monkeys, progesterone, 17α-hydroxyprogesterone, and HCG concentrations all increase early in pregnancy (134). The highest concentration of progesterone and 17α-hydroxyprogesterone occurs 3–4 weeks after ovulation, and by 6–8 weeks plasma progesterone concentration reaches a nadir, which is

followed by a secondary increase. The first peak is presumed to reflect the secretion of progesterone by the corpus luteum, whereas the second peak is due to placental secretion. To define the luteal and placental contributions to circulating progesterone, plasma levels of 17α-hydroxyprogesterone (17α-OHP) were measured concurrently. Since the placenta is incapable of 17α-hydroxylation, levels of 17α-hydroxyprogesterone provide an index of ovarian contribution. The curves for concentration of plasma progesterone and 17α-OHP begin to diverge at the eighth week of pregnancy when the placenta becomes the major contributor to the progesterone pool. Strott et al. (114) have shown that HCG injections enhance the production of progesterone and 17α-OHP in patients with inadequate or normal luteal function. In another study the administration of HCG extended the life-span of the nongravid corpus luteum to a maximum of 9 days (49), whereas the gravid corpus luteum functions considerably longer (53, 134). Human chorionic gonadotrophin may act synergistically with human prolactin or human placental lactogen, or both, to prolong the life-span of the corpus luteum beyond that resulting from the administration of HCG alone; in preliminary studies we have found increased concentrations of prolactin early in pregnancy (6). The reason luteal function wanes, despite increased HCG and prolactin levels, remains to be elucidated, as does the luteal function of HCG after the first trimester.

The possibility that the ovary is the primary target tissue for HCG is suggested by a study in which, after ^{131}I-labeled HCG was injected into rats, ovarian tissue-to-blood ratios of HCG reach values as high as 5 (70). A new method of labeling HCG with ^{3}H has shown that the labeled hormone is concentrated by the ovary of a pseudopregnant rat (126). During the luteal phase of the menstrual cycle LH also is extracted by the ovary, whereas follicle-stimulating hormone (FSH) is not (74). Presumably a similar ovarian extraction of HCG occurs in pregnancy. In animals the administration of HCG consistently causes hypertrophy and luteinization of interstitial and theca cells, but the precise mechanism of action of HCG and LH in stimulating steroidogenesis by the ovary is not fully understood (53).

Whether HCG, in addition to its LH-like activity, has some FSH-like activity is controversial (21). The most convincing evidence against any FSH activity in HCG has been obtained from experiments in which 1,000–5,000 IU of HCG derived from tissue culture media of a choriocarcinoma cell line was administered to hypophysectomized rats (93). Uterine or ovarian weight did not increase but, if 1 unit of FSH was injected together with the HCG, a marked response was observed. In addition to its action on the ovary, a number of investigators have suggested that HCG may influence steroidogenesis by the placenta or may have an effect on the fetus (15), but no concrete evidence that HCG has an important effect on either exists. In summary, although many biological effects of HCG have been demonstrated in a variety of animals that normally do not secrete HCG, a clearer understanding of its physiological role early in pregnancy is beginning to emerge, but no valid hypothesis of its subsequent function in pregnancy is available.

HUMAN PLACENTAL LACTOGEN

During the past decade a major impetus to the study of placental protein and polypeptide hormones was provided by Josimovich & MacLaren (65), who discovered that crude placental extracts cross-react with antisera to human growth hormone (HGH). Their search for a human placental luteotrophin was based in part on earlier reports of the presence of a placental luteotrophin in the rat (5). The immunologic cross reaction between antisera to HGH and a human placental extract soon was confirmed (67), and the existence of a new placental hormone was firmly established. Several different names have been assigned to this hormone: placental lactogen, chorionic growth hormone prolactin (CGP), purified placental protein (PPH), and finally human chorionic somatomammotrophin (HCS). The confusing number of terms were introduced when different investigators wished to emphasize one or another of the biological activities of the hormone or, not being certain of the physiological role for the hormone, preferred to assign a noncommittal designation.

Purification and Chemistry

Several methods for the purification of HPL have been described in which fresh placentas were the tissue source (32, 65). In a second method of purification, a side fraction obtained during the purification of gamma globulin from placental extracts was used as the starting material (28, 33). The latter approach has the great advantage that very large amounts of HPL can be obtained, amounts that have made clinical studies of HPL feasible and have permitted many investigators to develop radioimmunoassays for the measurement of HPL in a variety of clinical conditions. Unfortunately, because no international reference preparation is available, comparison of results from different laboratories has not always been easy. However, the lack of an appropriate reference standard has now been partially rectified since the National Institutes of Health, Endocrine Study Section, has made available a reference preparation for all investigators interested in studies of HPL.

Human placental lactogen is a single-chain polypeptide similar to HGH in molecular weight, amino acid composition, and amino acid sequence (2, 32, 91). Like HGH, HPL has 188 or 190 amino acids with two intrachain disulfide bonds in similar locations; the smaller bond occurs near the carboxy terminus, and the larger one is closer to the center of the molecule (109, 110). Sherwood has shown that 12 of 20 tryptic peptides of HGH and HPL have an identical amino acid composition or, at most, conservative replacements of individual amino acids within the peptide sequence. At a work-

shop on prolactin held in January, 1971, at the National Institutes of Health, Niall, Li, and Sherwood each reported on the amino acid sequence of HPL. The comparison of the sequence of HGH and HPL was most interesting and demonstrated major degrees of homology. The COOH-terminal amino acid of both HPL and HGH is phenylalanine (19), and the NH₂-terminal amino acids of HPL and HGH are valine and phenylalanine, respectively. Both molecules have a single tryptophan residue, which in the HGH molecule was reported to be at position 25 (73) and in the HPL molecule at position 85 (91). Niall (90), upon reexamining the amino acid sequence of HGH and HPL, discovered an error in the original amino acid sequence of HGH. Niall's studies were prompted because marked resemblances between HGH and HPL were noted for the first 15 residues and from residue 32 onward, but the intermediate sequences of HGH and HPL showed little similarity. The intermediate sequence is reported to contain tryptophan at position 25, but with successive Edman degradation Niall identified phenylalanine, and not tryptophan, at position 25. Circumstantial evidence suggested that the position of the residue containing tryptophan should be reassigned so that tryptophan is located at position 85; this results in a very close structural homology between HGH and HPL (Fig. 1). Sequence comparisons show that 80% of the amino acids in corresponding positions are identical amino acid pairs or are related through highly favored codon substitutions. Preliminary results for the rest of the HPL molecule indicate that this degree of similarity is seen throughout the whole polypeptide chain and is not confined to part of the molecule.

Homologies between the two human hormones and ovine prolactin are also evident though less striking (91). One of the most remarkable findings in this study was the evidence for internal homology within the HPL molecule (91). Apparently four peptides, approximately

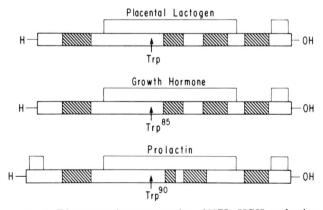

FIG. 1. Diagrammatic representation of HPL, HGH, and ovine prolactin molecules. *Cross-hatched* regions of each polypeptide chain represent internally homologous sequences in each molecule. Apart from internal homologies within each molecule, the 3 hormones exhibit considerable homology to one another, as indicated here by similar location of disulfide bridges (*narrow lines*) and tryptophan (*Trp*) residues at position 85 in HPL and HGH and at position 90 in ovine prolactin. [From Niall et al. (91).]

20 amino acid residues in length, were homologous. Both HGH and ovine prolactin possess a similar internal homology. These findings are consistent with the hypothesis that the three hormones may have arisen from a shorter primordial peptide of perhaps 25–50 amino acids through successive tandem duplication of the original structural cistron. The resulting primitive polypeptide may have more closely resembled prolactin, since this hormone is found throughout the vertebrates, whereas growth hormone and placental lactogen probably evolved at a later stage.

Biological Effects

Although many biological effects have been well documented after the administration of HPL, no primary action of the hormone has been defined. The hormone produces somatotrophic, lactogenic, and a number of miscellaneous effects.

The growth-promoting effect of placental lactogen has been demonstrated in hypophysectomized rats (28) and in hypopituitary dwarfs (43). However, the amount of hormone required to produce an unequivocal effect is very large when compared with the amount of growth hormone required to produce a similar response. For example, in the studies of Florini et al. (28), daily injections of 1.0 mg/day produced minimal body weight gain, whereas, in hypophysectomized rats, 10 μg/day of growth hormone produced an equivalent response. Breuer (12) also showed that the dimer of HPL is active, whereas the monomer of HPL is less active. At least two reports demonstrated a growth-hormone-like effect in the tibia assay (33, 67), although other investigators have been unable to confirm this finding (28, 66). Josimovich (64) showed that, when doses of placental lactogen that alone failed to stimulate growth were administered together with minimally effective doses of growth hormone, the effect of the latter was augmented greatly. Uptake of radioactive sulfate by rib cartilage, another test for somatotrophic activity, was also stimulated by placental lactogen (67). When hypophysectomized rats are treated with growth hormone, a synchronous wave of DNA synthesis occurs 48 hr later in a number of tissues, including the rat costal cartilage and adipose tissue; HPL produces a similar effect but is much less potent than HGH (85). Moreover, Breuer (12) showed that the HPL monomer produces a similar but smaller effect than the dimer, a point worth noting in view of a recent suggestion that only the monomer of HPL has somatotrophic activity, whereas the dimer does not.

The stimulation of growth in hypopituitary patients after injections of HPL has been reported by Grumbach et al. (43). The metabolic changes they observed were qualitatively similar to those that accompany the administration of HGH, namely, nitrogen retention, increase in serum free fatty acids, increase in hydroxyproline excretion, and hypercalciuria. Unfortunately, because of a lack of HPL, it has not been possible to du-

plicate these studies. However, in short-term metabolic balance studies, Schultz & Blizzard (104) were unable to demonstrate any nitrogen retention with equivalent amounts of HPL. It would be desirable to obtain additional studies of the effectiveness of HPL on growth in hypopituitary patients, but one of the difficulties with studies of this kind is that as much as 400–1,000 mg of HPL per day must be administered to achieve serum concentrations comparable to those found in pregnancy. If the administration of lesser amounts does not produce a significant clinical response, namely, an increase in growth, one cannot draw any conclusion about the physiological role of HPL as a growth-promoting agent. By comparison, 2 mg of HGH administered three times a week produces a very satisfactory increase in growth in hypopituitary dwarfs. In view of the large amounts of HPL that would be required for these clinical studies and the limited supply available, these studies unfortunately may never be carried out.

The biological effects following the administration of HPL to nonpregnant animals or patients suggest that some of the metabolic changes occurring in pregnancy may be mediated by HPL. Some of the changes attributed to HPL include the rise in concentration of plasma free fatty acids and increased mobilization of fat stores; the lack of sensitivity to endogenous and exogenous insulin accompanied by elevated circulating insulin levels in response to a glucose load; and the islet cell hyperplasia observed in pregnancy. Grumbach et al. (42) reported a rise in free fatty acids in hypopituitary subjects after the administration of HPL, and Turtle et al. (124) demonstrated a direct effect of HPL on lipolysis in vitro. When physiological amounts of HPL were infused into normal subjects for a 12-hr period, glucose tolerance was impaired, despite increased concentrations of plasma insulin (9). Moreover, HPL given to diabetics produced frank ketosis and hyperglycemia (101). Finally the synthesis and secretion of insulin in vitro by pancreatic islet tissue from hypophysectomized rats were greatly enhanced by pretreating the animals with HPL (78, 79). Although everyone would like to ascribe many of the metabolic changes that occur in pregnancy to a single hormone, such as HPL, caution must be exercised. The data presented by Beck (8), for example, clearly demonstrate that a complex interaction between HPL and progesterone may affect insulin production by islet cells, as well as peripheral tissue sensitivity to insulin. In addition, other hormonal changes that occur in pregnancy also may modify the handling of a glucose load or the secretion of insulin.

Grumbach et al. (43) formulated a hypothesis for the metabolic role of HPL in pregnancy. Human placental lactogen is secreted principally into the mother's circulation from which it is transported throughout the body; it stimulates lipolysis, and this leads to an increase in serum free fatty acids. The elevated levels of free fatty acids furnish energy for maternal metabolism, and in addition the increase in intracellular free fatty acids in adipose tissue inhibits glucose utilization; therefore the role of HPL is a glucose-sparing one. Through its anabolic and anticatabolic effect on protein metabolism and in concert with insulin, HPL probably conserves protein and ensures the greater availability of a steady flow of amino acids from mother to fetus in the fed state.

In pregnancy, with fasting or prolonged starvation, hypoglycemia of greater severity develops more rapidly than in the nonpregnant state, and an absolute hypoinsulinemia develops. This, in turn, either alone or with contrainsulin factors, such as HPL, may result in greater lipid mobilization leading to a relatively greater degree of ketonemia than in the nonpregnant state. The importance of HPL in mediating the metabolic changes that accompany food deprivation is strongly suggested, because, when pregnant patients were fasted for extended periods, the concentration of serum HPL increased by 30% (125). This observation provides the first direct evidence that HPL secretion may be regulated by metabolic factors accompanying food deprivation.

The second major biological action of HPL is on the mammary gland. Josimovich & MacLaren (65) first reported the increased development of the pigeon crop sac mucosa when HPL was injected locally. In other studies (29, 33) potency estimates of 1–4 IU/mg have been obtained by the pigeon crop sac assay. However, in the rabbit, HPL stimulates breast development to an even greater extent (34); estimates of potency are equal to the best preparations of ovine prolactin, namely, 25 IU/mg (30). Human placental lactogen resembles HGH in its limited ability to stimulate the pigeon crop sac and in its high lactogenic potency in the rabbit. Turkington & Topper (123) have shown that HPL in the presence of insulin and hydrocortisone causes histological development of alveoli and stimulates casein synthesis in organ culture of mouse mammary gland, the minimal effective dose being well within the physiological range of HPL in pregnancy.

The mechanism of action of HPL or prolactin on mammary gland explants has been studied extensively by Turkington (120, 122). He has shown that prolactin exerts its action primarily via a membrane effect, and presumably the same is true for HPL (123). Apparently HPL actively stimulates the mammary gland, and, although the effects are primarily lactogenic, rather than mammotrophic, they suggest an important role for HPL in the development of the mammary gland during pregnancy. The influence of the pituitary on mammary gland growth and function during pregnancy in human beings is not entirely clear because of the difficulty encountered in separating growth hormone from prolactin in primates (36). However, the two hormones have been separated by affinity chromatography in which antibodies to placental lactogen were used to adsorb growth hormone from pituitary preparations containing prolactin (45). As a result, a radioimmunoassay for human and monkey pituitary prolactin has been developed in our laboratory in which HGH and HPL failed to cross-react to any significant degree (46). For the first time with a modification of this assay it has been possible to explore

the role of pituitary prolactin in pregnancy and during lactation (47). We have observed that the concentration of human prolactin increases progressively throughout pregnancy from 20 ng/ml in the first trimester to 50–500 ng/ml at term. During the immediate postpartum period, the concentration of prolactin actually falls, but with breast feeding very rapid and striking increases in serum prolactin concentration were observed (61). The increase in serum prolactin noted during pregnancy raises interesting questions: Why should two mammotrophic hormones be secreted in pregnancy in such high concentrations? And, more specifically, what is the effect of each hormone on mammary development in pregnancy?

The luteotrophic action of HPL in the rat first was reported by Josimovich & MacLaren (65) and subsequently was confirmed by other investigators (33). Whether this effect is of physiological importance in primates is doubtful, since in primates prolactin itself may not be of great importance as a luteotrophic hormone. In addition to the three well-documented effects described above, placental lactogen stimulates erythropoiesis (63) and aldosterone excretion in urine (83).

Many sites of action for HPL have been suggested, but the precise physiological role of HPL in pregnancy is by no means settled. This is partly because it is impossible to use one of the classic approaches of endocrinology, namely, observing the physiological changes produced during pregnancy after the elimination of HPL.

Synthesis and Secretion

Immunofluorescence localization studies have shown that HPL is confined to the syncytiotrophoblast (7, 105). Human placental lactogen was identified in all normal placental tissues studied, in specimens ranging from 12-day embryos to full-term placentas. The cytoplasm of the syncytiotrophoblast, including syncytial knots, was brightly stained, whereas the nuclei, the cytotrophoblast, and the stroma of the villi were always unstained (7). Kaplan & Grumbach (68) were among the first to measure serum HPL throughout pregnancy and in the immediate postpartum period. Concentrations of HPL rose progressively to a mean of 5 μg/ml at term, whereas in the fetus the HPL concentration was very low (less than 33 ng/ml). In subsequent studies (43) they calculated that the half-time disappearance of HPL was 12.9 min in the first phase and 42 min in the second phase. From the volume of distribution (10 liters) and half-life of HPL in the mother it was possible to calculate that the production of HPL averaged 1 g/day (69). With this remarkably high daily production rate we believed that it should be possible to study the synthesis of HPL in vitro as a model substance for studying the synthesis of placental proteins (37). In these and subsequent studies (115, 116), we were able to confirm the high rate of placental lactogen synthesis relative to other proteins synthesized by the placenta. Indeed, in some in vitro studies, as much as 60% of the newly synthesized radio-active proteins was placental lactogen, but on the average about 10% of the newly synthesized proteins released into the media was placental lactogen. In vitro we were able to identify the synthesis of two species of HPL of widely differing molecular weights. The component of greater molecular weight predominated in the tissue, especially with more extended incubation periods, whereas the species of lesser molecular weight was the only component released into the medium initially. The relationship of the two immunologic species of HPL to each other is not clear; there may be a precursor-product relationship between the two—that is, the component of greater molecular weight may be converted into the component of lesser molecular weight.

A correlation between placental weight and serum HPL concentrations has been found in some studies (106, 108) but not in others (99). These findings suggest that placental mass in some way controls HPL secretion. Unfortunately this hypothesis does not elucidate the exact mechanism by which the syncytiotrophoblast regulates the synthesis and secretion of HPL. In our studies on placental lactogen synthesis in vitro we observed very wide variations in the rate of HPL synthesis compared to protein synthesis; the marked variations were noted occasionally even among different fragments from the same placenta. If the studies in vitro have any relevance to the control of HPL synthesis in vivo, one may well speculate about the mechanisms that may exist intracellularly for the regulation of HPL synthesis. In addition, extracellular factors that influence the secretion of HPL may operate. Unfortunately we have almost no knowledge of any homeostatic mechanisms that regulate the endocrine function of the placenta. The first evidence of this homeostatic mechanism may be inferred from the preliminary observations of Tyson—with prolonged fasting, HPL concentrations increased by 30% (125).

Because of the high concentration of serum HPL and its short half-life, it appeared likely that measurements of serum HPL might provide a useful index of placental function and might indicate those patients with a high risk of fetal death during pregnancy. Serum HPL concentrations have been measured in a large number of patients throughout pregnancy in an attempt to correlate HPL concentrations with different clinical conditions (99, 102, 108, 112). A wide range of normal values usually is observed at all stages of gestation. Apparently some patients with diabetes mellitus, but by no means all, and with Rh-isoimmunization have a modest increase in serum HPL. The increased HPL concentrations in diabetes, however, probably have no great clinical significance and certainly do not account for the increased insulin requirements during pregnancy. Mothers who deliver "small for date" babies tend to have lower concentrations of serum HPL than do other mothers. In a study carried out by Spellacy (113), serum HPL concentrations from the 30th week onward were monitored. Any serum HPL concentrations less than 4 μg/ml were said to fall into the fetal danger zone.

Analysis of the data was focused on 21 women who eventually delivered stillborn infants. There were three patients with rhesus factor sensitization, and all HPL concentrations were above the fetal danger zone. Among five diabetic patients only one patient with complicating hypertension had a low HPL concentration. In 13 patients with hypertension who delivered stillborn infants, all HPL values were low. In such patients serial estimations of HPL might be of predictive value. If serum HPL concentrations fall in patients with hypertension to below 4 μg/ml, the risk of fetal death is very high. The usefulness of HPL determinations as a clinical tool requires additional critical analysis: first, HPL concentrations in high-risk pregnancies that have a successful outcome must be carefully defined; second, when fetal death occurs, HPL concentrations must be carefully scrutinized; and finally, evidence demonstrating that induction of labor or Caesarian section in a patient in whom concentration of HPL is low results in a significant lowering of perinatal mortality must be obtained. Only then can it be said that HPL is a helpful clinical tool in the management of the high-risk pregnant patient.

In another study in which 13 patients with threatened abortion were investigated, serum HPL concentrations also seemed to be helpful in predicting whether or not the conceptus would be retained (39). In eight patients in whom the threatened abortion progressed to a complete spontaneous abortion, serum HPL concentrations were either undetectable or low, whereas in the five patients in whom pregnancy continued and progressed favorably, HPL concentrations increased normally. This report suggests that in the early stages of pregnancy placental dysfunction may be one of the principal causes of abortion, whereas in the later stages of pregnancy placental dysfunction may less frequently be the primary cause of fetal distress.

Human placental lactogen has been detected in a number of patients with neoplastic trophoblastic disease (100). In addition Weintraub & Rosen (131) have reported the ectopic production of HPL by nontrophoblastic cancers in 11 of 128 patients. With more sensitive methods, such as affinity chromatography, they were able to increase the incidence of positive tests. Suitable screening test procedures to examine patients who have a high risk of developing neoplastic disease for the presence of these placental and other ectopic hormones may be developed. Study of HPL and other embryonic proteins may not only prove useful in the diagnosis and management of cancer, but may also provide insight into regulatory mechanisms in the normal and neoplastic cell.

MONKEY PLACENTAL LACTOGEN

Purification and Chemistry

Monkey placentas also contain a substance that reacts with antisera to HGH and HPL (66, 67). This cross-

TABLE 1. *Concentration of MPL, HPL, and HCG in Placental Extracts and 24-Hr Incubation Media*

Hormone	Tissue Placental Extract, μg/g dry wt	Medium Placental Extract, μg/g dry wt
MPL	330	190
HPL	3,000	3,500
HCG*	12	12

Incubation studies were performed as described previously (115) in Krebs-Ringer bicarbonate buffer.   * The concentration of HCG is expressed in terms of human luteinizing hormone standard (potency of 4 NIH-LH units/mg).

reacting substance was purified by Grant et al. (41) and by Shome & Friesen (111). We compared the chemistry of monkey placental lactogen (MPL) with that of HPL and HGH. The yield of placental lactogen from placentas of monkeys was considerably less than that from placentas of human beings (Table 1). Upon purification, two components that cross-reacted with antisera to HGH were recognized. From 10 to 15 mg of MPL-2 was obtained per kilogram of frozen placental tissue, whereas about one-half that amount of MPL-1 was obtained. The molecular weights of MPL-2 and MPL-1 are very similar, but the electrophoretic mobility of MPL-2 on acrylamide gel electrophoresis is considerably greater than that of MPL-1. The mobilities of several hormones relative to the tracking dye were 0.8 for MPL-2, 0.72 for HPL, 0.58 for HGH, and 0.52 for MPL-1. There was a striking similarity in the amino acid composition of the four preparations. Monkey placental lactogen-2 and MPL-1 contain four half-cystine residues, which suggests that, like HPL and HGH, MPL has two disulfide bonds. The total number of amino acids and the distribution of polar and nonpolar amino acids in MPL were very similar to those in HGH. The major difference was in the content of the histidine, tyrosine, and tryptophan residues. Monkey placental lactogen-2 contained the highest number of histidine residues and was followed by HPL and MPL-1 and HGH. Although HGH and HPL contain only one residue each of tryptophan, MPL-2 contains two residues of this amino acid. The tyrosine content of MPL-2 is half that of HGH, and HPL and MPL-1 have an intermediate value. Peptide maps of MPL-1 and MPL-2 were compared with similar maps of HGH and HPL. A greater number of tryptic peptides appear to be common between HPL and HGH than between MPL and HGH.

In a limited number of studies on the somatotrophic activity of MPL, MPL appeared to have a greater growth-promoting potency than did HPL. Biosynthesis of MPL has been studied after the infusion of radioactive amino acids into the uterine artery or directly into the placenta in vivo, after which placental tissue fragments were incubated in vitro (35). Two major radioactive protein peaks were apparent, one of which appeared to correspond to MPL-2. The electrophoretic mobility of the second component, which remained unidentified in the earlier studies, coincides with that of MPL-1; this

suggests that both forms of placental lactogen are synthesized in vivo.

From the studies on the immunochemistry of MPL, HPL, and HGH it is clear that MPL cross-reacts to a greater extent with antisera to HGH than does HPL (10). The cross reaction of placental extracts in a number of nonhuman primates has been studied by using a radioimmunoassay for MPL. Extracts from all species studied, including the chimpanzee, African green monkey, squirrel monkey, and macaque species, cross-reacted equally.

Secretion

During pregnancy it is difficult if not impossible to subject patients to a variety of experimental conditions in order to explore factors that might influence HPL synthesis and secretion. Hence we developed methods to measure MPL and to study the factors regulating its secretion throughout pregnancy. The synthesis and secretion of MPL and HPL indeed proved very similar; the concentrations of placental lactogen increased throughout pregnancy to reach a mean concentration of 6 μg/ml, whereas umbilical vein MPL was less than 50 ng/ml. After delivery, maternal MPL concentrations decreased rapidly with a half-time disappearance rate of 20 min (10).

The fetus was removed surgically through a hysterectomy incision, with care taken not to interfere with the placenta, to examine directly whether measurement of MPL concentrations might provide a useful index of the status of the fetus. Concentrations of MPL decreased only modestly to values that were 75% of the preoperative level. It appeared to us therefore that less drastic changes of fetal well-being would probably not produce a more profound diminution of MPL concentrations. From these studies we would conclude that serum MPL and probably HPL are not likely to be a very useful index of fetal jeopardy. After ligation of the interplacental vessels, which pass between the primary and secondary placental disks, a marked diminution of the perfusion of the secondary placental disk by fetal blood occurs; yet this was accompanied by only a very minor change in MPL concentrations, which suggested that fetal perfusion of placental tissue is not a critical factor in the regulation of placental lactogen secretion. After an incision in the central portion of the secondary placental disk, an abruptio placenta was induced manually by separating the central portion of the placenta without disturbing the fetus or the primary disk. Serum MPL concentrations under these experimental conditions decreased promptly and stabilized at a concentration that was about 50% of the initial preoperative concentrations; this suggested that the primary and secondary placentas secrete almost equal amounts of MPL. These studies were of short duration, so we were unable to determine whether the remaining placental disk would be able to increase the amount of MPL secreted and thus to raise the serum MPL concentrations to preoperative levels. When the fetus was removed but the placenta was retained for 1–7 weeks after removal, the expected increase in placental lactogen that occurs as pregnancy progresses failed to develop. Thus, even though the fetus does not exert an acute control over MPL secretion, it may do so secondarily by stimulating placental growth and hence MPL secretion. In a limited number of studies in which the uterine blood flow and the maternal placental perfusion were reduced by partially clamping the maternal aorta, there was an immediate fall in the serum MPL concentration proportional to the decrease in uterine blood flow. Hence the latter appears to be an important determinant in maintaining serum MPL concentrations.

Studies by Chez et al. (20) have shown that sustained maternal or fetal hypoglycemia has no effect on MPL concentrations. However, neonatal plasma growth hormone levels increase in response to hypoglycemia. This pattern is similar to that seen in human beings where neither sustained hyperglycemia nor hypoglycemia causes any systematic change in maternal HPL levels (100).

We believe that a better understanding of the factors controlling MPL and HPL synthesis and secretion will be obtained and that this knowledge undoubtedly will be of value in defining the role of HPL in pregnancy.

RAT PLACENTAL LUTEOTROPHIN

Studies by Selye et al. (107) and Newton & Beck (89) clearly showed that the placenta functioned as an important endocrine gland in the maintenance of pregnancy in the rat and mouse. Pencharz & Long (94) were perhaps the first to demonstrate that pregnancy in rats would continue despite hypophysectomy, provided it was carried out during the second half of pregnancy. The 12th day was critical, because pituitary ablation earlier than this day resulted in the termination of pregnancy. Utilizing the deciduoma reaction, Astwood & Greep (5) demonstrated that the life-span of corpora lutea could be maintained and extended beyond the usual 12 days by injections of rat placental extracts from days 8 to 16. The luteotrophic activity of the extracts seemed to reside in the fetal portion of the placenta, with the highest activity found in placental extracts obtained on day 12 of pregnancy by Averill and co-workers (6, 96). These studies have been amplified and extended by Matthies and associates (80–82), who demonstrated that a hormone possessing luteotrophic and mammotrophic activity is present in trophoblastic elements of the rat placenta and in maternal peripheral blood. The luteotrophic activity present in one 12-day "fetal placenta" or in 0.1 ml of serum from the 12-day pregnant rat is approximately equivalent to 50 μg of ovine prolactin. Matthies suggested that the hormone might properly be termed *rat chorionic mammotrophin*. The highest concentration of this hormone in maternal serum occurs on the 12th day, and it is not present thereafter, as judged by the relatively crude bioassay

method used. In attempting to assign a role for this hormone in normal pregnancy it is important to recall that pseudopregnancy in the rat is usually of 12 days duration. Therefore it would seem to be of considerable advantage to have an extrahypophysial source of luteotrophin to ensure the maintenance of the corpus luteum. An increase in luteal volume is seen between days 11 and 16 of pregnancy, with a particularly rapid growth of the corpus luteum between days 11 and 12 (129). The change in volume in this 24-hr period exceeds 50% and is coincident with the putative release of placental luteotrophin. The maternal placenta surgically separated from the fetal placenta was unable to maintain either the diestrous period of pregnancy or the growth of the corpus luteum—evidence that the fetal placenta was the probable source of the luteotrophic hormone. If the luteal cells are deprived of trophic hormone for 48 hr or more, both prolactin and rat chorionic mammotrophin can have an opposite effect, that is, they will hasten luteolysis (82).

In addition to acting as a luteotrophic hormone, this placental hormone enhances breast development. In the rat the mammary gland on day 12 of pregnancy is more highly developed than that found on day 12 of pseudopregnancy, and the administration of placental extracts causes alveolar development and lactational responses.

Preliminary studies with gel filtration indicate that chorionic mammotrophin behaves as a protein with a molecular weight greater than 30,000. Purification and characterization of this protein and immunoassay methods for measuring the levels of circulating hormone in pregnancy need to be developed.

In addition to luteotrophic and mammotrophic activity in rat placentas, evidence of growth-hormone-like activity in the plasma of pregnant rats exists (22). The somatotrophic effect in pregnant rat plasma was still evident after hypophysectomy. Matthies (80) was not able to demonstrate any somatotrophic activity by the tibia assay with placental extracts that contained mammotrophic activity. More recent studies in which concentrations of serum prolactin (1) and growth hormone (103) were studied by radioimmunoassay throughout pregnancy failed to show any progressive increase in the concentration of either hormone. Therefore, in the rat, unlike the human being, a placental hormone immunologically related to a pituitary hormone apparently is not secreted during pregnancy. However, Ito & Martin (62) detected a growth-hormone-like substance in the serum of pregnant rats. They used a radioimmunoassay for growth hormone that differed from the method used by most other investigators in that the source of the antigen was growth hormone extracted from a somatomammotrophic pituitary tumor. No studies to determine whether rat placental extracts contained this cross-reacting substance were carried out. A report that rat placental extracts from several other species, including the rat, cross-react in an immunoassay for HPL has not been confirmed (44).

It is difficult to implicate rat chorionic mammo-trophin as the hormone that mediates the metabolic changes occurring in the rat during pregnancy. These changes, which have been well documented by Freinkel et al. (31), are very similar to some of the metabolic changes of human pregnancy. There is a decreased carbohydrate tolerance with lack of insulin sensitivity (71), despite increased circulating concentrations of insulin (54), which progresses as pregnancy advances. One question remains unanswered—which humoral factors, if any, mediate these changes. If a placental hormone causes the changes in metabolism, its con-centration should rise progressively throughout preg-nancy, and this consideration would exclude chorionic mammotrophin, which reaches a maximum concentra-tion on day 12. Therefore a search for a rat placental hormone that might mediate the metabolic changes of pregnancy seems warranted.

HUMAN CHORIONIC THYROTROPHINS

Because goiters develop in the mother not infre-quently during pregnancy it has been suggested that thyroid enlargement may be related to an iodine de-ficiency that is unmasked by the increased iodine re-quirements of pregnancy. A second explanation has been offered—that the concentration of a thyroid stimulator increases in pregnancy and that the source of this hormone is the placenta. The initial evidence for this hypothesis was indirect and was based on the ob-servation that the protein-bound iodine (PBI) and thyroidal iodine uptake were elevated in one patient with choriocarcinoma (86). Clinical manifestations of hyperthyroidism were minimal, and the abnormal thyroid function returned to normal with effective chemotherapy of the tumor. Odell et al. (92) described seven patients with metastatic trophoblastic disease who also had an increased plasma concentration of PBI and thyroidal iodine uptake. These patients were clinically euthyroid and had minimal thyroid enlarge-ment. In some of these patients increased quantities of TSH were detected by bioassay in the plasma or in tumor extracts. Elevated concentrations of immuno-reactive TSH in plasma were not found. After treatment of the malignancy with chemotherapeutic agents, thyroid function returned to normal as evidence of the metastatic disease disappeared. Subsequently, in normal human placental tissue, Hennen (50) reported the presence of a thyrotrophin-like material, which he called human chorionic thyroid-stimulating factor. He noted a rather close, but not identical, relationship between human pituitary thyrotrophin and the pla-cental thyroid-stimulating factor.

After the demonstration of a TSH-like factor in normal placental tissue, one report suggested that, in some preg-nancies associated with a hydatidiform mole, TSH con-centrations in plasma measured by bioassay were ele-vated (38). Although no serial observations were made in

individual patients by Hennen et al. (52), they reported that the mean TSH concentrations in the first trimester of pregnancy were higher than in the third and suggested that the placenta was the source of the thyroid stimulator. The work of both Hershman and co-workers (55–57) and Hennen and associates (51, 52) on the purification of placental thyrotrophins has helped to resolve some of the contradictory results apparent in reports from different investigators on the biological activity and immunologic relationships of placental thyroid stimulators. One of the principal difficulties encountered in attempts at purifica-tion has been the low and variable concentration of thyrotrophin in placental extracts. Although the concen-tration of TSH in placental tissue is low, the total amount per placenta approaches the total pituitary content of TSH, that is, 113–2,200 milliunits. The major component of placental thyrotrophin has the same elution volume as pituitary TSH after gel filtration, and in the McKenzie mouse bioassay the temporal responses of human pla-cental thyrotrophin and beef pituitary thyrotrophin were similar. The potency of the best preparations that have been obtained is 1/10th to 1/20th that of pituitary TSH. Antibodies to human and beef TSH neutralize the bio-logical activity of placental TSH. In a radioimmuno-assay for beef TSH, placental TSH cross-reacts com-pletely, but the latter reacts only very weakly in an immunoassay for human TSH. In one pregnant patient studied by Hennen et al. (52), the serum thyrotrophic activity had the same immunologic specificity as pla-cental thyrotrophin, rather than pituitary thyrotrophin; this provides direct evidence that the source of the ele-vated concentration of plasma thyrotrophin in that pa-tient was the placenta.

In addition to a placental thyrotrophin that is im-munologically related to beef TSH and is also similar in size to beef TSH, there appears to be a second thyroid stimulator in normal placental tissue, which, however, is more readily demonstrable in patients with hydatidiform moles. Hershman et al. (55) have shown that the mo-lecular weight of this factor is similar to that of albumin, that it is not neutralized by antibodies to bovine or human TSH, and that it does not cross-react in the radioimmunoassay for bovine or human TSH. In the McKenzie bioassay the dose-response curve of this frac-tion is more prolonged than that of pituitary TSH. Furthermore the thyroid-stimulating activity in com-mercial preparations of HCG (17) has the same elution volume as molar thyrotrophin, and immunologically it does not cross-react with antisera to bovine or human TSH. This finding strongly suggests that under normal circumstances the larger molecular weight thyroid stimu-lator is secreted and excreted in the urine along with HCG. It is also probable that the concentration of this substance, like that of HCG, is maximal early in preg-nancy. The physiological significance of these thyroid stimulators will be defined more fully as methods for measuring each component in pregnancy are developed. Since the amino acid sequence of one of the two subunits of LH is identical to that of one of the two subunits of

TSH (95), placental thyrotrophin of high molecular weight may be closely related to HCG, whereas placental thyrotrophin of lower molecular weight may be more closely related to pituitary TSH and LH.

Hershman et al. (56) found small but significant amounts of bioassayable thyroid-stimulating activity in guinea-pig placentas but failed to detect any in rat placentas at various stages of gestation or in several porcine placentas. No search for a thyroid stimulator has been made in nonhuman primates.

CONCLUSION

In this chapter I have reviewed the evidence for the existence and cellular origin of several placental protein and polypeptide hormones. Important recent developments received special emphasis. Great progress has been made in elucidating the structure of HCG and HPL. It is very likely that even before the publication of this chapter the complete amino acid sequence of HCG and HPL will be reported. This achievement will probably be followed by exciting studies of the structure-function relationships of the two hormones, which will lead to a better understanding of the structural requirements for growth-promoting activity. This new information may enable chemists to modify HPL and thus enhance somatotrophic activity to a point where it may be a useful therapeutic agent in growth disorders, a prospect that should be especially gratifying to those who have been studying the chemistry of placental lactogen and growth hormone.

The evidence for a rat placental luteotrophin is still based on evidence derived from experiments with crude placental extracts. Purification must be achieved if our understanding of its role in pregnancy is to be advanced. If rat placental luteotrophin were isolated, specific immunoassays would permit more reliable measurements of its concentration throughout pregnancy. A similar consideration applies to chorionic thyroid stimulators, although the problems to be faced in isolating the two hormones are very different. With rat placental luteotrophin the tissue source is limiting, whereas with human chorionic thyrotrophins there is an abundance of fresh placental tissue, but the concentration of the hormone in the tissue is trivial. The introduction of radioimmunoassay techniques for measuring circulating hormones has generated voluminous data on hormone concentrations in pregnancy, but the clinical usefulness of most of these measurements remains to be proved. From the physiologist's point of view, it is disheartening to discover that no mechanisms for the control of placental protein and polypeptide hormone secretion have been elucidated, despite the many measurements of hormone concentrations that have been made in pregnancy. Although many biological effects have been documented after the administration of crude placental extracts or highly purified placental hormones, the precise mechanism of action of any placental hormone has not been clarified. Moreover, a number of physiological roles have been postulated for each of the placental hormones, but the role and mechanism of action of each one throughout pregnancy cannot be stated with certainty.

REFERENCES

1. AMENOMORI, Y., C. L. CHEN, AND J. MEITES. Serum prolactin levels in rats during different reproductive states. *Endocrinology* 86: 506–510, 1970.
2. ANDREWS, P. Molecular weight of human placental lactogen investigated by gel filtration. *Biochem. J.* 111: 799–800, 1969.
3. ASCHHEIM, S., AND B. ZONDEK. Hypophysen Vorderlappenhormon und Ovarial-Hormon im Harn von Schwangeren. *Klin. Wochschr.* 6: 1322, 1927.
4. ASCHNER, B. Ueber brunstartige Erscheinungen (Hyperämine und Hämorrhagie am weiblichern Genitale) nach subkutaner Injektion von Ovarial oder Placentarextract. *Arch. Gynaekol.* 99: 534–540, 1913.
5. ASTWOOD, E. B., AND R. O. GREEP. A corpus luteum stimulating substance in the rat placenta. *Proc. Soc. Exptl. Biol. Med.* 38: 713–716, 1938.
6. AVERILL, S. C., E. W. RAY, AND W. R. LYONS. Maintenance of pregnancy in hypophysectomized rats with placental implants. *Proc. Soc. Exptl. Biol. Med.* 75: 3–6, 1950.
7. BECK, J. S., AND A. R. CURRIE. Immunofluorescence localization of growth hormone in the human pituitary gland and of a related antigen in the syncytiotrophoblast. *Vitamins Hormones* 25: 89–121, 1967.
8. BECK, P. Reversal of progesterone enhanced insulin production by human chorionic somatomammotropin. *Endocrinology* 87: 311–315, 1970.
9. BECK, P., AND W. H. DAUGHADAY. Human placental lactogen: studies of its acute metabolic effects and disposition in normal man. *J. Clin. Invest.* 46: 103–110, 1967.
10. BELANGER, C., B. SHOME, R. MYERS, AND H. FRIESEN. Studies

of the secretion of monkey placental lactogen. *J. Clin. Invest* 50: 2660–2667, 1971.
11. BORTH, R. *Chorionic Gonadotropin in Endocrinology of Pregnancy*, edited by F. Fuchs and A. Klopper. New York: Harper & Row, 1971, p. 16–31.
12. BREUER, C. B. Stimulation of DNA synthesis in cartilage of hypophysectomized rats by native and modified placental lactogen and anabolic hormones. *Endocrinology* 85: 989–999, 1969.
13. BRODY, S. Protein hormones and hormonal peptides from the placenta. In: *Fetus and Placenta*, edited by A. Klopper and E. Diczfalusy. London: Blackwell, 1969, p. 299–411.
14. BRODY, S., AND G. CARLSTROM. Immunoassay of human chorionic gonadotrophin in normal and pathological pregnancy. *J. Clin. Endocrinol.* 22: 564–574, 1962.
15. BRODY, S., AND G. CARLSTROM. Immunoassay of human chorionic gonadotrophin: methodological and clinical aspects. *Acta Endocrinol. Suppl.* 67: 19–20, 1962.
16. BROWNE, J. S. L., AND E. H. VENNING. The effect of intramuscular injection of gonadotropic substances on the corpus luteum phase of the human. *Am. J. Physiol.* 123: 26, 1938.
17. BURGER, A. Studies on a thyroid stimulating factor in urinary chorionic gonadotrophin preparation. *Acta Endocrinol.* 55: 587, 1967.
18. BURR, I. M., P. C. SIZONENKO, S. L. KAPLAN, AND M. M. GRUMBACH. Observations on the binding of human TSH by antisera to human chorionic gonadotrophin. *J. Clin. Endocrinol.* 29: 691–694, 1969.
19. CATT, K. J., B. MOFFAT, AND H. D. NIALL. Human growth

hormone and placental lactogen: structural similarity. *Science* 157: 321, 1967.

20. CHEZ, R. A., D. H. MINTZ, E. O. HORGER, AND D. L. HUTCHISON. Factors affecting the response to insulin in the normal subhuman pregnant primate. *J. Clin. Invest.* 49: 1512–1527, 1970.

21. COLE, H. H., AND M. BIGELOW. Follicle stimulation as an intrinsic property of human chorionic gonadotropin. *Anat. Record* 157: 19–25, 1966.

22. CONTOPOULOS, A. N., AND M. E. SIMPSON. Increased growth promoting substance in the plasma of pregnant rats. *Endocrinology* 61: 765–773, 1957.

23. DICZFALUSY, E. Estimation of human chorionic gonadotrophin in the human placenta. *Acta Endocrinol. Suppl.* 12: 9–81, 1953.

24. DICZFALUSY, E., AND P. TROEN. Endocrine functions of the placenta. *Vitamins Hormones* 19: 229–311, 1961.

25. DRESKIN, R. B., S. S. SPICER, AND W. B. GREEN. Ultrastructural localization of chorionic gonadotropin in human term placenta. *J. Histochem. Cytochem.* 18: 862–874, 1970.

26. FAIMAN, C., R. J. RYAN, S. I. ZWIREK, AND M. E. RUBIN. Serum FSH and HCG during pregnancy and the puerperium. *J. Clin. Endocrinol.* 28: 1323–1329, 1968.

27. FELIG, P., AND V. LYNCH. Starvation in human pregnancy: hypoglycemia, hypoinsulinemia, and hyperketonemia. *Science* 170: 990–992, 1970.

28. FLORINI, J. R., G. TONELLI, C. B. BREUER, J. CAPPALA, I. RINGLER, AND P. H. BELL. Characterization and biological effects of purified placental protein (PPH). *Endocrinology* 79: 692–708, 1966.

29. FORSYTHE, I. A. Lactogenic and pigeon crop-stimulating activities of a human placental lactogen preparation. *J. Endocrinol.* 37: xxxv–xxxvii, 1967.

30. FORSYTHE, I. A., AND S. J. FOLLEY. Prolactin and growth hormone in man and other mammals. In: *Ovo-Implantation, Human Gonadotropins and Prolactin*, edited by P. O. Hubinot. New York: Karger, 1970, p. 266–278.

31. FREINKEL, N., E. HERRERA, R. H. KNOPP, AND H. J. RUDER. Metabolic realignments in late pregnancy. *Advan. Metab. Disorders Suppl.* 1, 1970.

32. FRIESEN, H. Purification of a placental factor with immunological and chemical similarity to human growth hormone. *Endocrinology* 76: 369–381, 1965.

33. FRIESEN, H. Further purification and characterization of a placental protein with immunological similarity to human growth hormone. *Nature* 208: 1214–1215, 1965.

34. FRIESEN, H. Lactation induced by human placental lactogen and cortisone acetate in rabbits. *Endocrinology* 79: 212–215, 1966.

35. FRIESEN, H. Biosynthesis of placental proteins and placental lactogen. *Endocrinology* 83: 744–753, 1968.

36. FRIESEN, H., H. GUYDA, AND J. HARDY. Biosynthesis of human growth hormone and prolactin. *J. Clin. Endocrinol.* 31: 611–624, 1970.

37. FRIESEN, H., S. SUWA, AND P. PARE. Synthesis and secretion of human placental lactogen and other proteins by placenta. *Recent Progr. Hormone Res.* 25: 161–205, 1969.

38. GALTON, V. A. Abnormalities of thyroid hormone economy in patients with hydatidiform mole. *Program Ann. Meeting Am. Thyroid Assoc., Rome, Italy*, 1965, p. 35.

39. GENAZZONI, A. R., M. L. AUBERT, M. CASOLI, P. FIARRETTI, AND J. P. FELBER. Use of human placental lactogen radioimmunoassay to predict outcome in cases of threatened abortion. *Lancet* 2: 1385–1387, 1969.

40. GEY, G. O., G. E. SEEGAR, AND L. M. HELLMAN. The production of a gonadotrophic substance (prolan) by placental cells in tissue culture. *Science* 88: 306–307, 1938.

41. GRANT, D. B., S. L. KAPLAN, AND M. M. GRUMBACH. Studies on a monkey placental protein with immunochemical similarity of human growth hormone and human chorionic somatomammotropin. *Acta Endocrinol.* 63: 730–746, 1970.

42. GRUMBACH, M. M., S. L. KAPLAN, C. L. ABRAMS, J. J. BELL,

AND F. A. CONTE. Plasma free fatty acid response to the administration of chorionic growth hormone prolactin. *J. Clin. Endocrinol. Metab.* 26: 478–482, 1966.

43. GRUMBACH, M. M., S. L. KAPLAN, J. J. SCIARRA, AND I. M. BURR. Chorionic growth hormone prolactin (CCP). Secretion disposition biologic activity in man and postulated function as the "growth hormone" of the second half of pregnancy. *Ann. NY Acad. Sci.* 148: 501–531, 1968.

44. GUSDON, J. P., N. H. LEAKE, A. H. VAN DYKE, AND W. ATKINS. Immunochemical comparison of human placental lactogen and placental proteins from other species. *Am. J. Obstet. Gynecol.* 107: 441–444, 1970.

45. GUYDA, H., AND H. FRIESEN. The separation of monkey prolactin from monkey growth hormone by affinity chromatography. *Biochem. Biophys. Res. Commun.* 43: 1068–1075, 1971.

46. GUYDA, H., P. HWANG, AND H. FRIESEN. Immunological evidence for monkey and human prolactin (MPL and HPr). *J. Clin. Endocrinol. Metab.* 32: 120–123, 1971.

47. GUYDA, H., P. HWANG, AND H. FRIESEN. Biosynthesis of human growth hormone (HGH) and prolactin (HPr) (Abstract). *Clin. Res.* 19: 374, 1971.

48. HAMASHIGE, S., J. D. ALEXANDER, E. V. ABRAVANEL, AND M. A. ASTOR. New evidence demonstrating the multivalent nature of human chorionic gonadotropin. *Fertility Sterility* 22: 26–38, 1971.

49. HANSON, F. W., J. E. POWELL, AND V. C. STEVENS. Effects of HCG and human pituitary LH on steroid secretion and functional life of the human corpus luteum. *J. Clin. Endocrinol.* 32: 211–215, 1971.

50. HENNEN, G. Detection and study of a human chorionic-thyroid-stimulating factor. *Arch. Intern. Biochem.* 73: 689–695, 1965.

51. HENNEN, G., AND J. G. PIERCE. Further characterization of the human chorionic thyroid-stimulating factor. In: *Protein and Polypeptide Hormones (HCTSF)*, edited by M. Margoulies. Amsterdam: Excerpta Medica Foundation, 1969, p. 511–516.

52. HENNEN, G., J. G. PIERCE, AND P. FREYCHET. Human chorionic thyrotropin: further characterization and study of its secretion during pregnancy. *J. Clin. Endocrinol.* 29: 581–594, 1969.

53. HENZL, M. R., AND E. J. SEGRE. Physiology of human menstrual cycle and early pregnancy: a review of recent investigations. *Contraception* 1: 315–338, 1970.

54. HERRERA, E., R. H. KNOPP, AND N. FREINKEL. Carbohydrate metabolism in pregnancy. VI. Plasma levels, insulin, liver composition, and nitrogen metabolism during late gestation in the fed and fasted rat. *J. Clin. Invest.* 48: 2260–2272, 1969.

55. HERSHMAN, J. M., H. P. HIGGINS, AND W. R. STARNES. Differences between thyroid stimulator in hydatidiform mole and human chorionic thyrotropin. *Metabolism* 19: 735–744, 1970.

56. HERSHMAN, J. M., AND W. R. STARNES. Extraction and characterization of a thyrotropic material from the human placenta. *J. Clin. Invest.* 48: 923–929, 1969.

57. HERSHMAN, J. M., AND W. R. STARNES. Placental content and characterization of human chorionic thyrotropin. *J. Clin. Endocrinol.* 32: 52–58, 1971.

58. HILLIARD, J., H. G. SPIES, L. LUCAS, AND C. H. SAWYER. Effect of prolactin on progestin release and cholesterol storage by rabbit ovarian interstitium. *Endocrinology* 82: 122–131, 1968.

59. HISAW, F. L. The placental gonadotropin and luteal function in monkeys [*Macaca mulatta*]. *Yale J. Biol. Med.* 17: 119–137, 1944.

60. HOBSON, B. M. The excretion of chorionic gonadotrophin by women with chorioadenoma and choriocarcinoma. *J. Obstet. Gynaecol. Brit. Empire* 66: 282–287, 1959.

61. HWANG, P., H. FRIESEN, AND H. GUYDA. A radioimmunoassay for human prolactin. *Proc. Natl. Acad. Sci. US* 68: 1902–1906, 1971.

62. ITO, A., AND J. M. MARTIN. Prolactin (PL) and growth hor-

mone levels in rat serum. *Endocrine Soc. Meeting, 52nd, St. Louis, 1970, Abstr. 177.*

63. JEPSON, J., AND H. FRIESEN. The mechanism of action of human placental lactogen on erythropoiesis. *Brit. J. Haematol.* 15: 465–471, 1968.

64. JOSIMOVICH, J. B. Potentiation of somatotrophic and diabetogenic effects of growth hormone by human placental lactogen (HPL). *Endocrinology* 78: 707–714, 1966.

65. JOSIMOVICH, J. B., AND J. A. MACLAREN. Presence in the human placenta and term serum of a highly lactogenic substance immunologically related to pituitary growth hormone. *Endocrinology* 71: 209–220, 1962.

66. JOSIMOVICH, J. B., AND D. H. MINTZ. Biological and immunochemical studies on human placental lactogen. *Ann. NY Acad. Sci.* 148: 488–500, 1968.

67. KAPLAN, S. L., AND M. M. GRUMBACH. Studies of a human and simian placental hormone with growth hormone-like and prolactin-like activities. *J. Clin. Endocrinol.* 24: 80–100, 1964.

68. KAPLAN, S. L., AND M. M. GRUMBACH. Serum chorionic growth hormone prolactin and serum pituitary growth hormone in mother and fetus at term. *J. Clin. Endocrinol.* 25: 1370–1374, 1965.

69. KAPLAN, S. L., E. GURPIDE, J. J. SCIARRA, AND M. M. GRUMBACH. Metabolic clearance rate and production rate of chorionic growth hormone prolactin in late pregnancy. *J. Clin. Endocrinol.* 28: 1450–1460, 1968.

70. KAZETO, S., AND M. W. HRESHCHYSHN. Tissue distribution of human chorionic gonadotropin. *Am. J. Obstet. Gynecol.* 106: 1229–1234, 1970.

71. KNOPP, R. H., H. J. RUDER, E. HERRERA, AND N. FREINKEL. Carbohydrate metabolism in pregnancy. VII. Insulin tolerance during late pregnancy in the fed and fasted rat. *Acta Endocrinol.* 65: 352–360, 1970.

72. LEZNOFF, A., AND B. A. DAVIS. The cytological localization of human chorionic gonadotropin. *Can. J. Biochem.* 41: 2517–2521, 1963.

73. LI, C. H., W. K. LIU, AND J. S. DIXON. Human pituitary growth hormone. XII. The amino acid sequence of the hormone. *J. Am. Chem. Soc.* 88: 2050–2051, 1966.

74. LLERENA, L. A., A. GUEVARA, J. LOBOTSKY, C. W. LLOYD, J. WEISZ, M. PUPKIN, J. ZANARTA, AND J. PUGA. Concentration of luteinizing and follicle-stimulating hormones in peripheral and ovarian venous plasma. *J. Clin. Endocrinol.* 29: 1083–1090, 1969.

75. LORAINE, J. A., AND E. T. BELL (editors). *Recent Research on Gonadotrophic Hormones.* Edinburgh: Livingstone, 1966.

76. LORAINE, J. A., AND G. D. MATTHEW. The placental concentration of chorionic gonadotrophin in normal and abnormal pregnancy. *J. Obstet. Gynaecol. Brit. Empire* 60: 640–649, 1953.

77. LUNENFELD, B., AND A. ESHKOL. Immunology of follicle stimulating and luteinizing hormone. *Vitamins Hormones* 27: 131–198, 1969.

78. MALAISSE, W. J., F. MALAISSE LAGAE, C. PICARD, AND J. FLAMENT DURAND. Effects of pregnancy and chorionic growth hormone upon insulin secretion. *Endocrinology* 84: 41–44, 1969.

79. MARTIN, J. M., AND H. FRIESEN. Effect of human placental lactogen on the isolated islets of Langerhans in vitro. *Endocrinology* 84: 619–621, 1969.

80. MATTHIES, D. L. Studies of the luteotropic and mammotropic factor found in trophoblast and maternal peripheral blood of the rat at mid-pregnancy. *Anat. Record* 159: 55–68, 1967.

81. MATTHIES, D. L., AND W. R. LYONS. Luteotrophic and luteolytic activities in rat chorionic mammotrophin. *Anat. Record* 166: 346, 1970.

82. MATTHIES, D. L., AND W. R. LYONS. Luteotropic and luteolytic effects of rat chorionic mammotropin. *Proc. Soc. Exptl. Biol. Med.* 136: 520–523, 1971.

83. MELBY, J. C., S. L. DALE, T. E. WILSON, AND A. S. NICHOLS. Stimulation of aldosterone secretion by human placental lactogen. *Clin. Res.* 14: 283, 1966.

84. MIDGLEY, A. R., AND G. B. PIERCE. Immunohistochemical

85. MURAKAWA, S., AND M. S. RABEN. Effect of growth hormone and placental lactogen on DNA synthesis in rat costal cartilage and adipose tissue. *Endocrinology* 83: 645–650, 1968.

86. MYERS, W. P. L. An analysis of medical problems in cancer. *Med. Clin. N. Am.* 45: 563–583, 1961.

87. NEILL, J. D., E. D. B. JOHANSSON, AND E. KNOBIL. Patterns of circulating progesterone concentrations during the fertile menstrual cycle and the remainder of gestation in the rhesus monkey. *Endocrinology* 84: 45–48, 1969.

88. NEILL, J. D., AND E. KNOBIL. On the nature of the initial lutiotropic stimulus of pregnancy in the rhesus monkey. *Endocrinology* 90: 34–38, 1971.

89. NEWTON, W. H., AND N. BECK. Placental activity in mouse in absence of pituitary gland. *J. Endocrinol.* 1: 65–75, 1939.

90. NIALL, H. D. A revised primary structure for human growth hormone. *Nature* 230: 90–91, 1971.

91. NIALL, H. D., M. L. HOGAN, R. SAUER, I. Y. ROSENBLUM, AND F. C. GREENWOOD. Pituitary and placental lactogenic and growth hormones: evolution from a primordial gene reduplication. *Proc. Natl. Acad. Sci. US* 68: 866–869, 1971.

92. ODELL, W. D., R. W. BATES, R. RIVLIN, M. B. LIPSETT, AND R. HERTZ. Increased thyroid function without clinical hyperthyroidism in patients with choriocarcinoma. *J. Clin. Endocrinol.* 23: 658–664, 1963.

93. PATILLO, R. A., G. O. GEY, E. DELFS, W. Y. HUANG, L. HAUSE, J. GARANCIS, M. KNOTH, J. AMATRUDA, J. BERTINO, H. G. FRIESEN, AND R. F. MATTINGLY. The hormone-synthesizing trophoblastic cell in vitro: a model for cancer research and placental hormone synthesis. *Ann. NY Acad. Sci.* 172: 288–298, 1971.

94. PENCHARZ, R. I., AND J. A. LONG. Hypophysectomy in the pregnant rat. *Am. J. Anat.* 53: 117–139, 1933.

95. PIERCE, J. G., T. LIAO, S. M. HOWARD, B. SHOME, AND J. S. CORNELL. Studies on structure of thyrotropin: its relationship to luteinizing hormone. *Recent Progr. Hormone Res.* 27: 165–212, 1971.

96. RAY, E. W., S. C. AVERILL, W. R. LYONS, AND R. E. JOHNSON. Rat placental hormone activities corresponding to those of pituitary mammotropin. *Endocrinology* 56: 359–373, 1965.

97. REICHERT, L. W., JR., A. R. MIDGELY, G. D. NISWENDER, AND D. N. WARD. Formation of a hybrid molecule from subunits of bovine and human luteinizing hormone. *Endocrinology* 87: 534–541, 1970.

98. ROWLANDS, I. W. Level of gonadotropins in tissues and fluids with emphasis on domestic animals. In: *Gonadotropins: Their Chemical and Biological Properties and Secretory Control*, edited by H. H. Cole. San Francisco: W. H. Freeman, 1964, p. 74–112.

99. SAMAAN, N., H. S. GALLAGHER, W. A. MCROBERTS, AND A. M. FARRIS, JR. Serial estimation of human placental lactogen (HPL), estriol, and pregnanediol in pregnancy correlated with whole organ section of placenta. *Am. J. Obstet. Gynecol.* 109: 53–73, 1971.

100. SAMAAN, N., S. C. C. YEN, H. FRIESEN, AND O. H. PEARSON. Serum placental lactogen levels during pregnancy and in trophoblastic disease. *J. Clin. Endocrinol.* 26: 1303–1308, 1966.

101. SAMAAN, N., S. C. C. YEN, D. GONZALEZ, AND O. H. PEARSON. Metabolic effects of placental lactogen (HPL) in man. *J. Clin. Endocrinol.* 28: 485–495, 1968.

102. SAXENA, B. N., K. EMERSON, JR., AND H. A. SELENKOW. Serum placental lactogen (HPL) levels as an index of placental function. *New Engl. J. Med.* 281: 225–231, 1969.

103. SCHALCH, D. S., AND S. REICHLIN. Stress and growth hormone release. In: *Growth Hormone*, edited by A. Pecile and E. E. Müller. Amsterdam: Excerpta Medica Foundation, 1968, p. 211–225.

104. SCHULTZ, R. B., AND R. M. BLIZZARD. A comparison of human placental lactogen (HPL) and human growth hormone (HGH) in hypopituitary patients. *J. Clin. Endocrinol.* 26: 921–924, 1966.

105. SCIARRA, J. J., S. L. KAPLAN, AND M. M. GRUMBACH. Lo-

localization of human chorionic gonadotropin. *J. Exptl. Med.* 115: 289–294, 1962.

calization of anti-human growth hormone serum within placenta: evidence for a human chorionic growth hormone prolactin. *Nature* 199: 1005–1006, 1963.

106. SCIARRA, J. J., L. M. SHERWOOD, A. A. VARMA, AND W. LUNDBERG. Human placental lactogen (HPL) and placental weight. *Am. J. Obstet. Gynecol.* 101: 413–416, 1968.

107. SELYE, H., J. B. COLLIP, AND D. L. THOMPSON. Effect of hypophysectomy upon pregnancy and lactation. *Proc. Soc. Exptl. Biol. Med.* 30: 589–590, 1933.

108. SEPPALA, M., AND E. RUOSLAHTI. Serum concentration of human placental lactogenic hormone (HPL) in pregnancy complications. *Acta Obstet. Gynecol. Scand.* 49: 143–147, 1970.

109. SHERWOOD, L. M. Similarities of the chemical structure of human placental lactogen and pituitary growth hormone. *Proc. Natl. Acad. Sci. US* 58: 2307–2314, 1967.

110. SHERWOOD, L. M., AND S. HANDWERGER. Correlations between structure and function of human placental lactogen and human growth hormone. In: *Fifth Rochester Trophoblast Conference*, edited by C. Lund and J. W. Choate. Rochester: Rochester Univ. Press, 1969, p. 230–255.

111. SHOME, B., AND H. FRIESEN. Purification and characterization of monkey placental lactogen. *Endocrinology* 89: 631–641, 1971.

112. SINGER, W., P. DESJARDINS, AND H. FRIESEN. Human placental lactogen: an index of placental function. *Obstet. Gynecol.* 36: 222–232, 1970.

113. SPELLACY, W., E. TEOH, W. BUHI, S. BIRK, AND S. McCREARY. Value of human chorionic somatomammotropin in managing high-risk pregnancies. *Am. J. Obstet. Gynecol.* 109: 588–598, 1971.

114. STROTT, C. S., T. YOSHIMI, G. T. ROSS, AND M. B. LIPSETT. Ovarian physiology: relationship between plasma LH and steroidogenesis by the follicle and corpus luteum; effect of HCG. *J. Clin. Endocrinol.* 29: 1157–1167, 1969.

115. SUWA, S., AND H. FRIESEN. Biosynthesis of human placental proteins and human placental lactogen (HPL) in vitro. I. Identification of ^{3}H-labeled HPL. *Endocrinology* 85: 1028–1036, 1969.

116. SUWA, S., AND H. FRIESEN. Biosynthesis of human placental proteins and human placental lactogen (HPL) in vitro. II. Dynamic studies of normal term placentas. *Endocrinology* 85: 1037–1045, 1969.

117. TENNEY, B., AND F. PARKER. Some observations of the gonadotrophic hormone of pregnancy. *Endocrinology* 21: 687–688, 1937.

118. TULLNER, W. W. Urinary chorionic gonadotropin excretion in the monkey (*Macaca mulatta*)—early phase. *Endocrinology* 82: 874–875, 1968.

119. TULLNER, W. Comparative studies of chorionic gonadotropin and estrogens in urine and serum of subhuman primates during pregnancy. In: *Fifth Rochester Trophoblast Conference*, edited by C. Lund and J. W. Choate. Rochester: Rochester Univ. Press, 1969, p. 363–377.

120. TURKINGTON, R. W. Hormonal regulation of transfer ribonucleic acid and transfer ribonucleic acid-methylating enzymes during development of the mouse mammary gland. *J. Biol. Chem.* 244: 5140–5148, 1969.

121. TURKINGTON, R. W. Stimulation of RNA synthesis in isolated mammary cells by insulin and prolactin bound to sepharose. *Biochem. Biophys. Res. Commun.* 41: 1362–1367, 1970.

122. TURKINGTON, R. W., AND M. RIDDLE. Hormone dependent phosphorylation of nuclear proteins during mammary glands differentiation in vitro. *J. Biol. Chem.* 244: 6040–6046, 1969.

123. TURKINGTON, R. W., AND Y. J. TOPPER. Stimulation of casein synthesis and histological development of mammary gland by human placental lactogen in vitro. *Endocrinology* 79: 175–181, 1966.

124. TURTLE, J. R., P. BECK, AND W. H. DAUGHADAY. Purification of human placental lactogen. *Endocrinology* 79: 187–190, 1966.

125. TYSON, J., K. L. AUSTIN, AND J. W. FARINHOLT. Prolonged nutritional deprivation in normal pregnancy: changes in human chorionic somatomammotropin and growth hormone secretion. *Am. J. Obstet. Gynecol.* 109: 1080–1082, 1971.

126. VAITUKAITES, J., J. HAMMOND, G. ROSS, J. HICKMAN, and G. ASHWELL. A new method of labeling human chorionic gonadotropin for physiologic studies. *J. Clin. Endocrinol.* 32: 290–293, 1971.

127. VAN HALL, E. U., J. L. VAITUKAITES, G. T. ROSS, J. W. HICKMAN, AND G. ASHWELL. Immunological and biological activity of HCG following progressive desialylation. *Endocrinology* 88: 456–464, 1971.

128. VARMA, K., L. LARRAGA, AND H. A. SELENKOW. Radioimmunoassay of serum human chorionic gonadotropin during normal pregnancy. *Obstet. Gynecol.* 37: 10–18, 1971.

129. WAYNFORTH, H. B. Changes in the volume of rat corpus luteum during pregnancy and after surgical interference with the uterus and the placenta. *Acta Endocrinol.* 66: 296–302, 1971.

130. WEBER, J. Histochemical studies of the production of gonadotrophin in the placenta and fetal membranes. *Acta Obstet. Gynecol. Scand. Suppl.* 42: 6–82, 1963.

131. WEINTRAUB, B. D., AND S. W. ROSEN. Ectopic production of human chorionic somatomammotropin by non-trophoblastic cancers. *J. Clin. Endocrinol.* 32: 94–101, 1971.

132. WILDE, C. E. The correlation between immunological and biological estimation of HCG in body fluids. *Acta Endocrinol. Suppl.* 142: 360–377, 1969.

133. YEN, S. C. C., O. LLERENA, AND O. H. PEARSON. Disappearance rates of endogenous luteinizing hormone and chorionic gonadotropin in man. *J. Clin. Endocrinol.* 28: 1763–1767, 1968.

134. YOSHIMI, T., C. A. STROTT, J. R. MARSHALL, AND M. B. LIPSETT. Corpus luteum function in early pregnancy. *J. Clin. Endocrinol.* 29: 225–230, 1969.

CHAPTER 46

Chemistry of human chorionic gonadotrophin

F. J. MORGAN

S. KAMMERMAN

R. E. CANFIELD

Department of Medicine, College of Physicians and Surgeons, Columbia University, New York, New York

HUMAN CHORIONIC GONADOTROPHIN (HCG) was discovered as a gonadotrophic principle in the urine and serum of pregnant women by Aschheim & Zondek (3) in 1927. Although these workers believed that it was formed in the anterior pituitary, later investigations, reviewed by Diczfalusy & Troen (19), clearly showed that its origin was the chorionic tissue of the placenta. The role of HCG appears to be the maintenance of the progestin production of the corpus luteum in early pregnancy. Levels of biologically active HCG in the urine rise to a maximum during the first 10–12 weeks of pregnancy and decline thereafter.

The study of the chemistry of HCG has been neglected until recently in comparison with the efforts devoted to the trophic hormones of the pituitary. This is understandable in view of the central place of the pituitary gland in endocrine physiology and the tendency to consider pregnancy a disturbance of the steady state. The difficulties encountered in obtaining preparations of HCG that were demonstrably pure by classic bio-chemical and immunochemical criteria compounded this trend.

However, HCG does possess several features that make its study attractive to the biological chemist. In contrast to the pituitary hormones, the crude material is available fairly readily in almost unlimited quantities. It is derived from a human source, which is of importance in view of the species variation observed with many of the polypeptide hormones. Its similarity to luteinizing hormone (LH) with regard to biological activity and immunologic reactivity (23, 95) suggests that it may provide an important model for the investigation of the structural features necessary for gonadotrophic activity. The clear findings of significant structural relationships among the pituitary trophic hormones themselves, both gonadotrophic and thyrotrophic (76), extend its potential as a model even further. Each member of this group of hormones is composed of two dissimilar, noncovalently bound glycoprotein subunits. One subunit, the α subunit, has an identical or very similar amino acid sequence in all the studied hormones; the other subunit, the β subunit, differs between the hormones and confers the unique biological activity on the hormone.

This chapter is limited in scope to the chemistry of human chorionic gonadotrophin. Historical development of the field is not stressed because this approach has been covered in the past (24, 69, 70). Rather, attention is focused on more recent studies, and emphasis is placed on those performed with potent preparations of HCG. Many earlier studies in which contradictory or unclear results were obtained involved the use of cruder preparations, and the influence of the impurities present in those materials is difficult to interpret. The majority of studies have been performed on HCG extracted from the urine of women in the first trimester of normal pregnancy, and the discussion usually refers to such preparations. Human gonadotrophin of chorionic origin can also be obtained directly from normal placentas, from hydatidiform moles, and from patients with tropho-blastic malignancies. Mention of these preparations is made when it is appropriate. The subject of HCG assay, both biological and immunologic, is not mentioned except when pertinent, because it has been well reviewed elsewhere (54, 94), as has the immunochemistry of HCG (57).

PREPARATION AND PROPERTIES OF HUMAN CHORIONIC GONADOTROPHIN

Preparation

Early methods for the purification of HCG have been reviewed in several publications (24, 54, 70); their major purpose was to obtain preparations suitable for the physiological studies. In essence, these methods involved the formation of a crude urinary concentrate, which was followed by partial purification in which alcohol precipitation and selective denaturation of contaminating proteins were used. A potency of up to 6,000–8,000 IU/mg was achieved in these preparations. A crystalline preparation of HCG has also been reported (18), but this interesting finding has not been repeated. Recent techniques designed to provide HCG for chemical studies incorporate the best features of those procedures, combined with column chromatography on ion exchangers and molecular sieves. The purification of HCG from urine follows the general scheme: *a*) formation of a crude urinary extract by a selective adsorption and desorption process in which a technical adsorbent, usually benzoic acid (46) or permutit (47), is used; *b*) purification of the crude extract either by ethanol fractionation or batch adsorption to an ion exchanger; and *c*) a final purification procedure involving gel filtration and ion-exchange chromatography of the active product. At present no one method appears to offer distinct advantages. Van Hell et al. (89) obtained HCG with a biological activity of 14,400 IU/mg from crude urinary material by ethanol fractionation, CM-Sephadex chromatography, and gel filtration on Sephadex G-100. Bahl (7) employed chromatography on DEAE-Sephadex and Sephadex G-100 to prepare a product that assayed at 12,000 IU/mg. The preparation of Mori (67) obtained by chromatography on Sephadex G-100 and DEAE-cellulose assayed at 12,000 IU/mg. Bell et al. (11) employed ethanol precipitation, DEAE-Sephadex chromatography, and gel filtration on Bio-Gel P-60. This method, originally used in the authors' laboratory, has undergone some revision in details to improve yields and permit large-scale preparation. The method as presently used has been described in detail elsewhere (14, 17). The final product assays at 13,000–15,000 IU/mg when bioassayed by the rat ventral prostate weight method (32, 58) with the second international standard for HCG used as a reference preparation.

TABLE 1. *Amino Acid Composition of HCG*

Amino Acid	Goverde et al., 1968	Bahl, 1969	Bell et al., 1969	Mori, 1970	Average
Alanine	6.1	5.4	5.8	5.6	5.7
Arginine	6.4	6.6	6.5	6.7	6.6
Aspartic acid	7.7	7.4	8.4	8.4	8.0
Cystine (half)	6.3	8.6	7.6	8.6	7.8
Glutamic acid	7.8	7.9	8.6	7.2	7.9
Glycine	6.0	5.3	6.0	5.2	5.6
Histidine	2.2	1.8	1.8	1.7	1.9
Isoleucine	2.7	2.4	2.6	2.4	2.5
Leucine	6.7	6.4	6.7	6.6	6.6
Lysine	4.4	4.4	4.3	4.3	4.4
Methionine	1.9	1.7	0.7	1.2	1.4
Phenylalanine	3.1	2.4	2.6	2.9	2.8
Proline	11.9	12.2	12.6	12.1	12.2
Serine	8.5	9.5	8.4	9.2	8.9
Threonine	7.7	7.3	7.5	7.2	7.6
Tyrosine	3.4	2.6	2.7	3.4	3.0
Valine	7.1	7.9	7.3	7.3	7.4
Estimated biological potency (IU/mg)	18,800	12,000	13,300	12,800	

Residues per 100 amino acids. Some of the original data have been recalculated to permit this comparison. Quantitative estimates of tryptophan were not made by all authors. There appears to be no tryptophan in the HCG molecule (9).

Standards

The second international standard for HCG was established in 1965 (10); a partially purified preparation, it has a potency for each ampoule of 5,300 IU. Biological and immunologic potencies are numerically equal in this preparation, although this ratio does not necessarily persist in other preparations.

Chemical Composition

Early work suggested that HCG was a glycoprotein (33–35), but until highly potent preparations of HCG were available, meaningful analysis of the amino acid and carbohydrate constituents was not possible.

The amino acid composition and the potencies of four different preparations of HCG are given in Table 1; the results have been expressed as the number of each amino acid residue per 100 residues, so that comparisons can be made regardless of different assumptions by the authors about the molecular weight of the molecule. The results from the four laboratories are in very good agreement and indicate that the protein component is being purified to the same extent. The average of these results is the best available estimate of amino acid composition for HCG. There is a particularly high content of proline and cystine. The carbohydrate content of the molecule in preparations of high potency is about 30%. Got and his co-workers (30) showed that HCG contained mannose, galactose, fucose, glucosamine, galactosamine, and sialic acid. Quantitative estimations of the various sugar components are given in Table 2. The sugar

TABLE 2. *Carbohydrate Composition of HCG*

Carbohydrate	Got, 1960	Goverde et al., 1968	Bahl, 1969	Mori, 1970
Galactose	4.9	3.9	5.3	5.0
Mannose	4.9	2.9	5.3	4.8
Fucose	1.2	0.6	0.6	0.6
N-Acetylglucosamine	7.0	7.3	8.9	8.8
N-Acetylgalactosamine	1.7	1.8	2.1	1.8
Sialic acid	8.5	8.2	9.0	8.4
Total	28.2	24.7	31.2	29.4

Values expressed as g/100 g. Some of the original data have been recalculated to permit this comparison.

estimates represent the average composition of the total population of HCG molecules. The hormone has a high content of sialic acid. A high content of proline and cystine, together with a significant, though lesser, carbohydrate component, is also a feature of luteinizing hormone (91, 92).

Some discrepancies regarding the assessment of purity of these highly potent preparations of HCG remain. The preparations of Got and co-workers (28–30) and of Bahl (7) migrate as a single species on ultracentrifugation and electrophoresis. However, another preparation of similar potency, although it is a single band electrophoretically, was said to show two peaks on ultracentrifugation (56). The final preparation of Bell et al. (11), although homogeneous by ultracentrifugation, stains as a broad band after polyacrylamide disc gel electrophoresis. Van Hell and his colleagues (89) report that their most potent preparation has three bands on electrophoresis, whereas preparations of lesser potency migrate as a single band. In their studies, Goverde et al. (31) and Schurrs et al. (83) noted a significant correlation between increasing sialic acid content and increasing biological potency of the purified fractions. They also noted a tendency for the ratio of immunologic to biological activity to decrease with increasing degrees of purification. Although their most potent preparations reached a biological activity of 18,000 IU/mg, immunologic activity did not rise above 5,000 IU/mg. These authors suggest tentatively that the immunochemically important determinants may remain intact in a biologically inactive molecule. Mori (67) showed that the carbohydrate moiety, essential for biological activity in vivo, was not involved in the antigenic structure. The studies of Bell et al. (11, 15) on the fractions in the hormonally active peak obtained from DEAE-Sephadex confirm and extend this concept. In these studies, fractions of increasingly acidic nature (i.e., in increasing order of elution from DEAE-Sephadex) were shown to have a higher sialic acid content, although the amino acid composition of all these fractions was essentially the same. The biological importance of the sialic acid content is discussed in the section on desialylation.

From a chemical standpoint, the discussion of the homogeneity of HCG preparations has been somewhat

confusing. The general problem with regard to glycoproteins has been discussed by Gibbons (26). Homogeneity is generally inferred from the absence of heterogeneity by some criterion; the more criteria used, the more convincing the demonstration. Preparations lacking heterogeneity by one set of criteria may be heterogeneous by another set. The nature of the variability within the population of HCG molecules has not been clearly described, except for the differences in sialic acid noted above. Spiro (84) has reviewed the current knowledge of the biosynthesis of glycoprotein molecules. One should expect a degree of polydispersity in glycoprotein molecules (such as HCG) where biosynthesis of part of the molecule, the carbohydrate portion, takes place after the completion of polypeptide synthesis and may not always be complete. The addition of the carbohydrate portion is accomplished by a series of specific glycosyltransferases, which introduce the sugar residues into the polypeptide chain (84). Degradation in vivo or during the purification is also possible. The presence of subfractions in a preparation is an inherent property of polydisperse preparations and does not necessarily imply heterogeneity. Even the finding of discrete bands on electrophoresis, provided the distribution is not obviously polymodal, is not necessarily evidence of heterogeneity. Thus it seems reasonable to conclude that preparations such as those described in Table 1 are polydisperse, that is, contain a population of closely related molecules with identical or nearly identical polypeptide chains but with some variation in the carbohydrate substituents.

Other doubts about the biological purity of HCG arise from the presence in many HCG preparations of other hormonal activities, especially follicle-stimulating and thyrotrophic activity. There are four possibilities: *1*) they represent contaminating pituitary hormones; *2*) they are proteins originating from another endocrine organ, presumably the placenta; *3*) they are hybrid molecules formed with subunits of other gonadotrophins; or *4*) HCG possesses inherent follicle-stimulating hormone (FSH)-like and thyrotrophic hormone (TSH)-like activity. From the point of view of the chemistry of HCG, it is important to distinguish the last possibility from the others. Preparations of HCG are known to possess FSH-like activity (43, 81). However, it seems likely that the FSH activity resides in a molecule different from HCG. There is evidence that some antisera can selectively neutralize the FSH-like activity while they leave the HCG unchanged, and the separation of HCG molecules from the FSH-like activity has been reported (74). The nature of the FSH-like material is still unclear. The thyrotrophic principle found in crude preparations of HCG (13) has not been clearly identified. Studies on the thyrotrophin extracted from placental tissue and from hydatidiform moles have appeared, but the nature of this hormone is not yet clear (40, 41). It has also been reported (36–38) that different biological activities of HCG, such as gonadal response, steroidogenesis, and spermatogenesis, can be separated by chromatographic means, but a structural basis for these findings is not yet established. This area is still one of uncertainty, but the increasing evidence supports the concept that the placenta produces other trophic hormones in addition to HCG.

Immunologic criteria have also provided evidence of impurities in preparations of HCG. Wilde & Bagshawe (96) have demonstrated a second antigenic component (trophoblastic antigen unidentified, TAU) in partly purified HCG from the urine of pregnant women and from women with trophoblastic tumors. It is seen on immunoelectrophoresis as a characteristic cathodal spur, partially reacting with the main antigen. This antigen possesses no biological activity by the methods employed and seems identical with antigen 6 of Hamashige et al. (36, 37). The main HCG band is associated with all the biological activity and much of the immunologic activity. The chemical nature of TAU is uncertain. It may represent degraded HCG or an excess of the α or β subunit, which are known to react partially with antibodies to HCG (17).

Physicochemical Properties

Experimental determination of the molecular weight of native HCG has given varying values. Ultracentrifugation studies on the preparations reported in Table 1 gave figures of 62,000 (89), 47,000 (7), 46,000 (11), and 37,700 (67). Other estimates of molecular weight by ultracentrifugation range from 30,000 (28) to 100,000 (55). The method of light scattering gave a value of 30,000 (28). Nydick et al. (71) used radiation inactivation of biological activity and also arrived at a molecular weight of 30,000. Blobel et al. (12) found that the molecular weight rose from 29,000 to 57,000 when calcium ions were removed by dialysis against EDTA. Calculations from gel filtration data have given figures of 59,000 (7) and 83,000 (20); this method, which is really a measure of molecular dimensions, is known to give falsely high values for glycoproteins with appreciable carbohydrate content (2). It has been reported that HCG possesses 2 moles of NH_2-terminal amino acid per 46,000 g of HCG (64).

The difficulty in obtaining accurate molecular weights of glycoproteins by physicochemical methods, such as ultracentrifugation, is due largely to the dimensional asymmetry and high molecular charge density of the molecules. The methods are in principle applicable to glycoprotein molecules, but greater difficulties exist in obtaining meaningful extrapolation in order to eliminate the effects caused by the concentration of the glycoprotein or the nature of the medium used for the measurements. It should also be remembered that the figure for molecular weight of a polydisperse population will be an average molecular weight (26). The value obtained by gel filtration certainly provides an upper level of the molecular weight range, and most of the other physicochemical measurements of molecular weight fall into the

TABLE 3. *Physicochemical Characteristics of Human Chorionic Gonadotrophin*

Property	Value	Ref.
Sedimentation coefficient, $S_{20,w}$ (S)	2.7	28
	2.89	7
	3.07	67
Diffusion constant, D_{20} ($cm^2\ sec^{-1}$)	8.2×10^{-7}	28
Partial specific volume, ml/g	0.727	28
Isoelectric point, pH	2.95	28
Extinction coefficient, $E_{1\ cm}^{1\ mg/ml}$ at 278 nm	0.425	28
	0.388	7
Frictional ratio, f:fo	1.28	28

broad range of 30,000–50,000. A calculation of the molecular weight, based on the carbohydrate content and the linear amino acid sequence described in a succeeding section, gives a molecular weight of approximately 36,000; this figure is probably more accurate than those measured experimentally on the intact molecule. Experimental values for other physical constants of HCG are given in Table 3.

Subunit Structure

Human chorionic gonadotrophin possesses two nonidentical subunits (15, 64, 85). Electrophoresis of *S*-carboxymethyl-HCG in polyacrylamide gels at pH 9.3 gave two distinct bands (Fig. 1). The bands differed significantly in amino acid composition; the average was very close to that of the native hormone. Furthermore, peptide maps of the tryptic digest of each band showed many differences (15, 17).

The subunits can be prepared from native HCG by dissociation in acidified 10 M urea solution at 40 C for 1 hr, followed by chromatography on DEAE-Sephadex in urea-containing buffers (64). The subunits prepared in this fashion have the same amino acid compositions as those of the carboxymethylated subunits. Although each native subunit stains as several bands on polyacrylamide disc gel electrophoresis, when individually reduced and carboxymethylated they become indistinguishable electrophoretically from the subunits prepared directly from *S*-carboxymethyl-HCG. The subunits have been designated α and β; the α subunit is eluted first from the DEAE-Sephadex column (64). Another analysis of HCG subunits prepared in a somewhat different manner (85) showed that, as well as the amino acid composition, the carbohydrate of each subunit varied significantly. The β subunit contained twice as much carbohydrate and sialic acid as the α subunit. Electrophoresis of native HCG in sodium dodecyl sulfate-containing polyacrylamide gels [a technique used for determination of the molecular weight of protein molecules and their subunits (93)] resulted in the appearance of two bands that corresponded to the subunits isolated after urea dissociation (64). Therefore HCG possesses two nonidentical subunits that differ in amino acid composition, carbohydrate composition, and molecular size. Since the subunits can

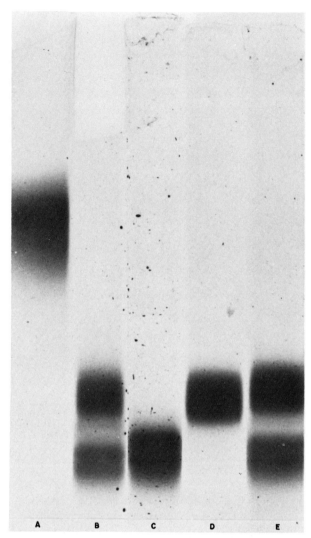

FIG. 1. Analytical polyacrylamide disc gel electrophoresis of native HCG and S-carboxymethyl-HCG at pH 9.3. *A*: native HCG. *B*: S-carboxymethyl-HCG. *C*: the faster migrating band (S-carboxymethyl-HCG-α) isolated from a preparative electrophoresis. *D*: the slower migrating band (S-carboxymethyl-HCG-β) isolated from a preparative electrophoresis. *E*: mixture of equal parts of S-carboxymethyl-HCG-α and S-carboxymethyl-HCG-β obtained from preparative electrophoresis. Anode is located at the bottom. [From Morgan & Canfield (64).]

be dissociated by urea, they are not held together by disulfide bridges.

Estimation of the molecular weight of the subunits is beset by the same problems that exist for the HCG molecule itself. Sodium dodecylsulfate-polyacrylamide disc gel electrophoresis gives figures of 18,000 and 29,000 for the molecular weight of the α and β subunits, respectively, whereas gel filtration techniques give values of 25,000 and 40,000 (64). These latter figures are certainly overestimates and possibly also exaggerate the actual differences between the subunits.

The isolated α and β subunits can reassociate on incubation in 0.01 M phosphate buffer at pH 7.0 at room temperature to reform the native molecule (64). After

reassociation the polyacrylamide disc gel electrophoresis pattern (64) and the elution position on gel filtration (17) are indistinguishable from those of native hormone. Preparations of HCG subunits prepared by urea dissociation and ion-exchange chromatography commonly contain up to 2% of the initial biological activity of 13,000–15,000 IU/mg, which the parent HCG possesses. The product formed after incubation of the mixture of the α and β subunits assays at about 9,000 IU/mg (64). This indicates a remarkable degree of restoration of activity. It is probable that neither subunit possesses any intrinsic activity in conventional bioassay systems. Antibody capable of combining with native HCG, but not with HCG-β subunit, can neutralize the low biological activity in β subunit preparations (77), and it seems that the activity must represent contamination with native HCG.

The HCG-α subunit can also recombine with bovine luteinizing hormone (LH) β subunit to yield gonadotrophic activity and, more significantly, with bovine TSH-β subunit to give a product with thyroid-stimulating activity (75), which indicates the close structural similarity among the α subunits of these hormones whose specificity appears to be determined by the nature of the β subunit.

Primary Structure of the Subunits

The amino acid sequences of the α and β subunits are shown in Figures 2 and 3. The HCG-α subunit has 92 amino acid residues and two sites of attachment of complex carbohydrate chains, at asparagine residues 52 and 78. The HCG-β subunit has 139 amino acid residues; there are two sites of attachment of complex carbohydrate chains, at asparagine residues 13 and 28; in addition there are three sites of attachment of small oligosaccharide chains, at serine residues 118, 121, and 123.

The amino acid sequence of the HCG-α sequence shows marked homology with the α subunit of ovine and bovine LH and TSH, which are themselves identical. The half-cystine residues are equal in number and in similar positions, which indicates that the disulfide bridges in all the molecules are probably identical, although which cysteine residues are paired has not been determined. There appears to be a deletion of four residues at the NH2-terminus of the HCG-α subunit when the sequences are aligned to demonstrate maximum homology. In addition some HCG-α subunit molecules appear to be lacking two or three residues from the NH2-terminus of the major species present; this leads to a degree of NH2-terminal heterogeneity (17a). A partial NH2-terminal sequence for human LH-α subunit is identical with HCG-α in this region, except for the deletion of three NH2-terminal residues in human LH-α (42). The HCG-β subunit bears a marked, though less striking, resemblance to the β subunit of ovine LH and bovine TSH. It possesses more sites of carbohydrate attachment and has additional residues at the carboxy terminus of the molecule, which are not seen in the ovine LH-β.

FIG. 2. Proposed amino acid sequence of HCG-α subunit [[9]; F. J. Morgan and R. E. Canfield, unpublished observations]. Amino acid sequences of ovine LH-α (53, 72) and bovine TSH-α (51) are shown for comparison; LH and TSH are thought to have identical amino acid sequences for the α subunits, although the assignment of amides is incomplete (76). The alignment is based on the position of the half-cystine residues, which have identical distributions. *Numbers* refer to HCG-α sequence.

FIG. 2 — amino acid sequences (rows: HCG-α and LH/TSH-α)

Positions 1–32:

1				5					10					15					20					25					30		
Ala	Pro	Asp	Val	Gln	Asp	Cys	Pro	Glu	Cys	Thr	Leu	Gln	Glu	Asn(CHO)	Pro	Phe	Phe	Ser	Gln	Pro	Gly	Ala	Pro	Ile	Leu	Gln	Cys	Met	Gly	Cys	Cys
Glu	Pro	Gly	Met	Glx	Gly	Cys	Pro	Glx	Cys	Thr	Leu	Glx	Asn	Asn(CHO)	Phe	Phe	Ser	Ser	Lys	Pro	Asx	Ala	Pro	Ile	Tyr	Gln	Cys	Met	Gly	Cys	Cys

Positions 35–66:

35				40					45					50					55					60					65		
Ser	Arg	Ala	Tyr	Thr	Pro	Leu	Arg	Ser	Lys	Lys	Thr	Met	Leu	Val	Gln	Lys	Asn(CHO)	Thr	Ser	Glu	Ser	Thr	Cys	Cys	Val	Ala	Lys	Ser	Tyr	Asn	Arg
Ser	Arg	Ala	Tyr	Thr	Pro	Ala	Arg	Ser	Lys	Lys	Thr	Met	Leu	Val	Gln	Lys	Asn(CHO)	Thr	Ser	Glx	Ser	Thr	Cys	Cys	Val	Ala	Lys	Ala	Phe	Thr	Lys

Positions 70–92:

70				75					80					85					90		
Val	Thr	Val	Met	Gly	Gly	Phe	Lys	Val	Glu	Asn(CHO)	His	Thr	Ala	Cys	His	Cys	Ser	Thr	Cys	Tyr	Tyr
Val	Thr	Val	Met	Gly	Asn	Gly	Asn	Val	Glx	Asn(CHO)	His	Thr	Glu	Cys	His	Cys	Ser	Thr	Cys	Tyr	Tyr

…His/His Lys/Lys Tyr/Tyr Ser OH/Ser OH

FIG. 3. Proposed amino acid sequence of HCG-β subunit (9). Amino acid sequences of ovine and bovine LH-β (52, 59, 60) and of bovine TSH-β (51) are shown for comparison. Amide assignments are incomplete. In order to demonstrate similarities, alignment has been made on the basis of half-cystine positions. Although the nature of the blocking group has not been determined (52, 59), LH-β does not appear to have a free α-amino group. *Numbers* refer to HCG-β sequence. Some details of this proposal have been questioned (Morgan, F. J., et al., *FEBS Letters* 31: 101, 1973).

FIG. 3 — amino acid sequences (rows: HCG-β, LH-β, TSH-β)

Positions 1–29:

1				5					10					15					20					25				
Ser	Lys	Glx	Pro	Leu	Arg	Pro	Arg	Cys	Arg	Pro	Ile	Asn(CHO)	Ala	Thr	Leu	Ala	Val	Glx	Lys	Glx	Gly	Cys	Pro	Val	Cys	Ile	Thr	Val
Ser	Arg	Gly	Pro	Leu	Arg	Pro	Leu	Cys	Arg	Pro	Ile	Asn(CHO)	Ala	Thr	Leu	Ala	Ala	Glu	Lys	Glu	Ala	Cys	Pro	Val	Cys	Ile	Thr	Val
							Phe	Cys		Pro	Thr	Glu	Tyr	Met	Met	His	Val	Glu	Arg	Lys	Glu	Cys	Ala	Tyr	Cys	Leu	Thr	Ile

Positions 30–58:

30				35					40					45					50					55				
Thr	Ile	Cys	Ala	Gly	Tyr	Cys	Pro	Thr	Met	Thr	Arg	Val	Leu	Glx	Gly	Val	Leu	Pro	Ala	Leu	Pro	Gln	Val	Val	Cys	Asn(CHO)	Tyr	Arg
Thr	Ile	Cys	Ala	Gly	Tyr	Cys	Pro	Ser	Met	Lys	Arg	Val	Leu	Pro	Val	Ile	Leu	Pro	Pro	Met	Pro	Gln	Arg	Val	Cys	Asn(CHO)	Tyr	Arg
Thr	Val	Cys	Ala	Gly	Tyr	Cys	Pro	Thr	Met	Thr	Arg	Val	Leu	Asx	Val	Tyr	Leu	Pro	Leu	Leu	Gln	His	Asp	Val	Cys	Ile	Tyr	Arg

Positions 60–87:

60				65					70					75					80					85		
Asx	Val	Arg	Phe	Glx	Ser	Ile	Arg	Leu	Pro	Gly	Cys	Pro	Arg	Gly	Val	Asx	Pro	Val	Val	Ser	Tyr	Ala	Val	Ala	Leu	Ser	Cys
Glu	Val	Arg	Phe	Ala	Ser	Val	Arg	Leu	Pro	Gly	Cys	Pro	Arg	Gly	Met	Val	Pro	Met	Val	Ser	Phe	Ala	Val	Ala	Leu	Ser	Cys
Asp	Val	Arg	Tyr	Gly	Val	Ala	Glu	Ile	Pro	Gly	Cys	Pro	Arg	His	Val	Thr	Pro	Tyr	Phe	Ser	Tyr	His	Ile	Leu	Ala	Ile	Cys

Positions 90–120:

90				95					100					105					110					115					120
Gly	Gly	Pro	Lys	Asx	His	Pro	Leu	Thr	Cys	Asx	Asx	Pro	Arg	Phe	Glx	Asx	Ser	Ser	Ser	Ser	Lys	Ala	Pro	Pro	Pro	Ser(CHO)	Leu	Pro	Ser	Pro
Gly	Gly	Cys	Lys	His	Leu	Ser	Thr	Ala	Cys	Asp	Gly	Gly	Arg	Thr	Glx	Ala	Lys	Ser	His	Leu	Ala	His	Pro	Leu	Pro	Ser(CHO)	Ile	Asp	Leu OH	
Gly	Gly	Cys	Lys	Pro	Gly	Ile	Asp	Thr	Cys	Asx	Thr	Ser	Tyr	Ile	Lys	Ser	Cys	Lys	Ala	Asn	Tyr	Ser	Lys	Tyr	Met OH					

HCG-β (125–145): …Arg-Ser(CHO)-Arg-Leu-Pro-Gly-Pro-Ser-Asx-Thr-Pro-Ile-Leu-Pro-Glx-Ser-Leu-Pro OH

The structure of the carbohydrate portion of HCG has been determined from an analysis of two glycopeptides purified from a tryptic digest of carboxyamidomethylated desialyzed HCG (8). The sequence of monosaccharides in the carbohydrate chain was determined by stepwise degradation of the sugars from the non-reducing ends with specific enzymes. The following monosaccharide sequence was determined: N-acetylneuraminic acid (or fucose) → galactose → N-acetylglucosamine → mannose. The carbohydrate units of the glycopeptides were each composed of several of these chains, and the whole unit was linked to the polypeptide chain by an N-acetylglucosaminyl-β asparaginyl linkage. This type of chain is found twice in both the α and β subunits; it has also been found in other glycoproteins (84). In addition, three small oligosaccharide chains, N-acetylneuraminic acid → galactose → N-acetylgalactosamine, linked to the polypeptide chain by N-acetylgalactosaminyl-serine linkages were detected. The galactosamine-containing units reside in the β chain only; the α chain contains no appreciable galactosamine (85).

Placental HCG

The relationship between placental and urinary HCG merits further study. Various modifications of the basic structure may occur on secretion of the molecule, by proteolysis in the plasma or urine, and by degradation during purification. Kikutani (48) has isolated a gonadotrophic material from first trimester chorionic villi by benzoic acid adsorption of a dilute ammonia extract followed by fractional ethanol precipitation. The material, a glycoprotein with 20% sugar, was studied by electrophoresis and ultracentrifugation and was said to have a high purity. The NH_2-terminal amino acid was reported to be valine, and the COOH-terminal amino acid, leucine. Other authors have used parallel purification methods to prepare HCG from both first trimester placental tissue and urine (4, 6). The behavior of both preparations is very similar, as is the amino acid composition of the final product. However, gonadotrophin extracts from term placentas has been reported to differ biologically from urinary HCG (49).

Choriocarcinoma HCG

Whether HCG prepared from the urine of patients with choriocarcinoma or hydatidiform mole is the same as pregnancy HCG has concerned some investigators (62, 79, 82). The immunologic properties are similar (50). Reisfield and his colleagues (79, 80) reported that the electrophoretic mobility of choriocarcinoma HCG differed from that of pregnancy HCG, but this was not confirmed by Wilde & Bagshawe (96) with their preparation of choriocarcinoma HCG. Moreover, since bands of different electrophoretic mobility are found within purified preparations of pregnancy HCG (89), differences between preparations by this criterion may not be significant. Differences in chromatographic behavior

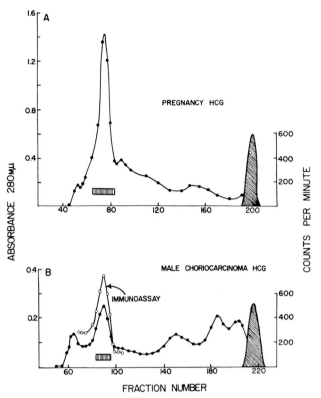

FIG. 4. Gel filtration of HCG preparations on Bio-Gel P-150. *A*: elution pattern for a sample of pregnancy HCG. *B*: elution pattern for a sample of HCG prepared from a pool of urine obtained from male patients with choriocarcinoma. Column size, 180 × 2.5 cm; elution buffer, 0.05 M sodium phosphate; pH 5.0; fraction size, 3.7 ml. Radioactive glucose was added as a marker and is represented by the *shaded area*. [From Canfield et al. (15).]

have also been noted (62). Hamburger (39) has pointed out that choriocarcinoma HCG has the same characteristic effect on uterine and ovarian weight increase that pregnancy HCG does. Canfield et al. (15) purified HCG from pooled male choriocarcinoma urine and showed that it behaved very similarly to pregnancy HCG during the purification process (Fig. 4) and that the final product gave the same polyacrylamide disc gel pattern as did pregnancy HCG. Amino acid composition of the product agreed very well with that of pregnancy HCG (Table 4). Human chorionic gonadotrophin from the urine of a single female with choriocarcinoma had similar properties, and the purified product assayed at 15,000 IU/mg (17). It seems that urinary HCG from choriocarcinoma patients is similar to first trimester pregnancy HCG, at least in the polypeptide components. The carbohydrate content of some preparations of HCG from choriocarcinomas has been shown to be higher than that of placental HCG (5).

MODIFICATION OF HUMAN
CHORIONIC GONADOTROPHIN

Modification of the structure of HCG can affect its activity in a way that provides insight into the structural

TABLE 4. *Amino Acid Composition of Male Choriocarcinoma HCG*

Amino Acid	#86	#89	#92	Average
Alanine	5.2	5.2	5.3	5.2
Arginine	6.9	6.9	6.5	6.8
Aspartic acid	7.4	7.2	7.6	7.4
Cystine (half)	8.6	8.2	8.5	8.4
Glutamic acid	8.2	8.0	8.0	8.1
Glycine	4.6	4.6	4.7	4.6
Histidine	2.0	1.8	1.8	1.9
Isoleucine	2.6	2.7	2.6	2.6
Leucine	6.4	6.5	6.6	6.5
Lysine	4.9	4.9	4.7	4.8
Methionine	1.7	1.6	1.9	1.7
Phenylalanine	2.5	2.6	2.5	2.5
Proline	12.7	13.6	12.7	13.0
Serine	8.6	8.3	8.6	8.5
Threonine	7.5	7.4	7.6	7.5
Tyrosine	2.7	2.8	2.7	2.7
Valine	7.6	7.7	7.7	7.7

Residues per 100 amino acids. No corrections have been made for destruction during acid hydrolysis. Tryptophan analyses were not performed. Numbers (86, 89, 92) refer to fractions in the lower part of Fig. 4. [From Canfield et al. (15).]

features necessary for gonadotrophic activity. It is now realized that the response in an in vivo bioassay is modified by such factors as rate of adsorption, plasma half-life, and the nature of the response measured. It is possible that substances inactive in an in vivo bioassay system will be active when presented directly to the target tissue in an in vitro assay where the modifying factors have been removed.

Desialylation

Sialic acid may be selectively hydrolyzed from HCG by treatment with dilute mineral acid under mild conditions (e.g., 0.1 M H_2SO_4 at 80 C for 1 hr) or by treatment with the enzyme, neuraminidase (E.C.3.2.1.18), which specifically removes sialic acid residues from glycoproteins and, often, complex carbohydrates. The acid treatment results in complete loss of sialic acid residues from HCG (8, 67). When enzyme is used, the degree of sialic acid loss depends on the amount of enzyme used and the length of incubation (88). Both treatments result in no loss of other monosaccharides or of amino acids from HCG (8, 67).

Loss of sialic acid has been reported to reduce markedly biological activity. The effect of progressive loss of sialic acid on the in vivo activity of HCG has been elegantly studied by Van Hall et al. (88). Preparations of HCG containing decreasing amounts of sialic acid were studied by radioimmunoassay and by bioassay in both the ovarian ascorbic acid depletion (OAAD) assay and the rat ventral prostate weight (VPW) assay. The latter bioassay is a measure of chronic response in a target organ, whereas the former is a measure of a more acute biochemical process. Desialylation did not affect the immunologic activity of HCG, a result that was in agreement with earlier findings (Fig. 5). Progressive desialyla-

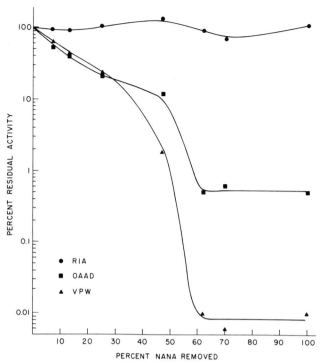

FIG. 5. Effect of progressive desialylation on immunologic and biological activity of HCG. *RIA,* radioimmunoassay; *OAAD,* ovarian ascorbic acid depletion assay; *VPW,* ventral prostate weight assay; *NANA,* N-acetylneuraminic acid. The starting material had a potency of close to 12,000 IU/mg (VPW assay). [From Van Hall et al. (88).]

tion up to 62% resulted in a marked, but not complete, loss of biological activity in both bioassays; further removal of sialic acid from 62% to 100% did not remove this residual biological activity as measured by the two bioassays. There was an equal and parallel loss of biological activity during removal of the initial 25% of the sialic acid, but, between 25% and 62% loss, the fall in activity as measured in the VPW assay was much more pronounced than that measured in the OAAD assay. The residual level as measured by the VPW assay was therefore much lower than that measured by the OAAD assay—the index of discrimination (OAAD/VPW) was about 50.

The preparations of LH from various species that have shorter half-lives in the test animal have been shown to possess relatively higher potencies in the OAAD assay with respect to the VPW assay than have those with longer half-lives (73). Furthermore, there seems to be a direct relationship between sialic acid content and plasma half-life in many proteins (63). Van Hall et al. (88) interpret their findings as suggesting that progressive desialylation, by reducing the plasma half-life of HCG, results in a reduction of biological activity, which is more pronounced when measured by a chronic response than by an acute response. The interpretation that loss of biological activity merely represents lessened half-life is supported by clear evidence that asialo HCG competes at least equally with native HCG for binding to target tissues in vitro (21, 44, 86) and can be shown to be metabolically active in such systems (21).

Physiochemical measurements show that asialo HCG is less stable to perturbation than is native HCG (68).

Oxidation

Treatment with periodate has been reported to cause considerable loss of the biological activity of HCG (25). It is known that bound N-acetylneuraminic acid consumes two moles of periodate with the formation of one mole of formic acid, one mole of formaldehyde, and a seven-carbon fragment (45). Advantage of this reaction was taken to label HCG of moderate potency (9,000 IU/mg) by reducing periodate-treated HCG with tritiated potassium borohydride (87). The periodate-treated HCG lost over half its activity; the biological activity was, however, restored to 80% of the original activity after the borohydride reduction. This provides an elegant means of labeling HCG with minimal potential disturbance to the tertiary structure of the molecule.

Iodination

Iodination is an important reaction, for it is frequently used to label protein for physiological studies or as a tracer for radioimmunoassays. It is possible to iodinate HCG to a level of approximately one iodine atom per mole and retain most of the biological activity (57, 61). When HCG is labeled by the chloramine-T method, more than 90% of the radioactivity is located on the α subunit (66).

Alanylation

Eshkol (22) has reported the introduction of an average of 1.6 and 2.7 alanine residues into HCG by reaction with the N-carboxyanhydride of alanine-^{3}H. Activity was retained almost fully with the smaller degree of substitution.

Urea Treatment

Treatment with urea at 1–8 M concentrations was reported to inactivate HCG (90); this inactivation was thought to result in part from carbamylation by cyanate. However, the regaining of a large percentage of the original activity when the subunits, prepared by dissociation in 10 M urea, are incubated together suggests that urea treatment does not necessarily produce any significant irreversible damage (64). Exposure to cyanate

is reduced by the use of deionized urea, maintenance of acid conditions when possible, and minimization of the duration of exposure to urea solution. A possible explanation for some of the earlier findings is the formation of dissociated subunits that have little biological activity.

Proteolytic Enzyme Digestion

Biological activity is partially or completely lost on exposure to trypsin and chymotrypsin (1, 27, 67, 78). However, experiments were carried out without the present knowledge of the structure of HCG, and a re-examination of the effects of various enzymes on HCG and its subunits, together with careful characterization of the split products and their activity, would seem to be warranted.

CONCLUSION

The main structural features of HCG—amino acid and carbohydrate composition, subunit structure, and linear amino acid sequences—have now been determined. It is clear that in all these respects HCG is very closely related to the pituitary glycoprotein trophic hormones and probably also to the other placental glycoprotein hormones about which much less detail is known. The simplification provided by the recognition of the subunit structure and the ability to prepare individual subunits have provided solutions to many features, such as purity and size, which were experimental problems in earlier work on the intact molecule.

The aim of structural studies of HCG is to arrive at some understanding of its action in terms of the three-dimensional structure of the hormone and its receptor site. It is evident that, although much progress has been made in the understanding of the structure of HCG, this goal is still somewhat distant. The heterogeneous nature of the carbohydrate portion of the molecule and the difficulty in obtaining preparations suitable for X-ray crystallographic analysis combine to make the determination of the total structure a very complex problem. However, now that pure preparations of the hormone are available and a broad understanding of the structure is possible, much important information can be expected to result from a careful study of specific chemical and enzymatic modifications of the hormone and its individual subunits.

REFERENCES

1. ABRAMOWITZ, A., AND F. L. HISAW. The effects of proteolytic enzymes on purified gonadotropic hormones. *Endocrinology* 25: 633–637, 1939.
2. ANDREWS, P. Estimation of molecular size and molecular weights of biological compounds by gel filtration. In: *Methods of Biochemical Analysis*, edited by D. Glick. New York: Interscience, 1970, vol. 18, p. 1–53.
3. ASCHHEIM, S., AND B. ZONDEK. Hypophysen vorderlappen Hormon und Ovarialhormon im Harn von Schwangeren. *Klin. Wochschr.* 6: 1322, 1927.
4. ASHITAKA, Y. Studies on the biochemical properties of highly purified human chorionic gonadotropin extracted from chorionic tissue. *Acta Obstet. Gynecol. Japon.* 17: 124–135, 1970.
5. ASHITAKA, Y., M. MOCHIZUKI, AND S. TOJO. Purification and properties of chorionic gonadotropin from the trophoblastic tissue of hydatidiform mole. *Endocrinology* 90: 609–617, 1972.

6. ASHITAKA, Y., Y. TOKURA, M. TANE, M. MOCHIZUKI, AND S. TOJO. Studies on the biochemical properties of highly purified HCG. *Endocrinology* 87: 233–244, 1970.

7. BAHL, O. P. Human chorionic gonadotropin. I. Purification and physicochemical properties. *J. Biol. Chem.* 244: 567–574, 1969.

8. BAHL, O. P. Human chorionic gonadotropin. II. Nature of the carbohydrate units. *J. Biol. Chem.* 244: 575–583, 1969.

9. BAHL, O. P., R. B. CARLSEN, R. BELLISARIO, AND N. SWAMINATHAN. Human chorionic gonadotropin: amino acid sequence of the alpha and beta subunits. *Biochem. Biophys. Res. Commun.* 48: 416–422, 1972.

10. BANGHAM, D. R., AND B. GRAB. The second international standard for chorionic gonadotrophins. *Bull. World Health Organ.* 31: 111–125, 1964.

11. BELL, J. J., R. E. CANFIELD, AND J. J. SCIARRA. Purification and characterization of human chorionic gonadotropin. *Endocrinology* 84: 298–307, 1969.

12. BLOBEL, R., H. UHLIG, AND G. SCHUMACHER. Biochemical studies with human chorionic gonadotrophin (HCG). *Acta Endocrinol. Suppl.* 67: 72, 1962.

13. BURGER, A. Further studies on a thyroid stimulating factor in crude chorionic gonadotrophin preparations and in urine. *Acta Endocrinol.* 55: 600–610, 1967.

14. CANFIELD, R. E., AND F. J. MORGAN. Purification and biochemical characterization of human chorionic gonadotropin. In: *Methods in Investigative and Diagnostic Endocrinology*, edited by S. A. Berson. Amsterdam: North-Holland. In press.

15. CANFIELD, R. E., G. M. AGOSTO, AND J. J. BELL. Studies of the chemistry of human chorionic gonadotropin. In: *Gonadotropins and Ovarian Development*, edited by W. R. Butt, A. C. Crooke, and M. Ryle. Edinburgh: Livingstone, 1970, p. 161–170.

16. CANFIELD, R. E., AND J. J. BELL. Preliminary studies of the structure of human chorionic gonadotropin. In: *Progress in Endocrinology*, edited by C. Gaul. Amsterdam: Excerpta Medica Foundation, 1968, p. 402–406.

17. CANFIELD, R. E., F. J. MORGAN, S. KAMMERMAN, J. J. BELL, AND G. M. AGOSTO. Studies of human chorionic gonadotropin. *Recent Progr. Hormone Res.* 27: 121–164, 1971.

17a.CANFIELD, R. E., F. J. MORGAN, S. KAMMERMAN, AND G. T. ROSS. Studies on the structure and recombination of the subunits of human chorionic gonadotropin. In: *Structure-Activity Relationships of Protein and Polypeptide Hormones, Part II*, edited by M. Margoulies and F. C. Greenwood. Amsterdam: Excerpta Medica Foundation, 1973, p. 337–339.

18. CLAESSON, L., B. HOGBERG, T. ROSENBERG, AND A. WESTMAN. Crystalline human chorionic gonadotrophin and its biological action. *Acta Endocrinol.* 1: 1–18, 1948.

19. DICZFALUSY, E., AND P. TROEN. Endocrine functions of the human placenta. *Vitamins Hormones* 19: 229–311, 1961.

20. DONINI, P., I. PUZZUOLI, D. D'ALESSIO, G. BERGESI, AND S. DONINI. Purification and properties of urinary follicle-stimulating and luteinizing hormones. In: *Gonadotropins 1968*, edited by E. Rosemberg. Los Altos: Geron-X, 1968, p. 37–39.

21. DUFAU, M. L., K. J. CATT, AND T. TSURUHARA. Retention of *in vitro* biological activities by desialylated human luteinizing hormone and chorionic gonadotropin. *Biochem. Biophys. Res. Commun.* 44: 1022–1029, 1971.

22. ESHKOL, A. Labelling of antigens by various isotopes. In: *Karolinska Symposium on Research Methods in Reproductive Endocrinology. First Symposium: Immunoassay of Gonadotropins*, edited by E. Diczfalusy. Stockholm: Karolinska Institute, 1969, p. 145–159.

23. FRANCHIMONT, P. A study of the cross-reaction between human chorionic and pituitary luteinizing hormones (HCG and HLH). *European J. Clin. Invest.* 1: 65–68, 1970.

24. GESCHWIND, I. I. The chemistry and immunology of gonadotropins. In: *Gonadotrophins—Their Chemical and Biological Properties and Secretory Control*, edited by H. H. Cole. San Francisco: Freeman, 1964, p. 1–34.

25. GESCHWIND, I. I., AND C. H. LI. The reaction of several

protein hormones with periodate. *Endocrinology* 63: 449–459, 1958.

26. GIBBONS, R. A. Physico-chemical methods for the determination of the purity, molecular size and shape of glycoproteins. In: *Glycoproteins*, edited by A. Gottschalk. Amsterdam: Elsevier, 1966, p. 29–95.

27. GOT, R. Récentes acquisitions sur la gonadotropine choriale humaine. *Pathol. Biol.* 8: 1583–1592, 1960.

28. GOT, R., AND R. BOURRILLON. Nouvelles données physiques sur la gonadotropine choriale humaine. *Biochim. Biophys. Acta* 39: 241–247, 1960.

29. GOT, R., AND R. BOURRILLON. Critères de pureté de la gonadotropine choriale humaine. *Bull. Soc. Chim. Biol.* 42: 31–39, 1965.

30. GOT, R., R. BOURRILLON, AND J. MICHON. Les constituants glucidiques de la gonadotropine choriale humaine. *Bull. Soc. Chim. Biol.* 42: 41–49, 1960.

31. GOVERDE, B. C., F. J. N. VEENKAMP, AND J. D. H. HOMAN. Studies on human chorionic gonadotrophin. *Acta Endocrinol.* 59: 105–119, 1968.

32. GREEP, R. O., H. B. VAN DYKE, AND B. F. CHOW. Use of anterior lobe of prostate gland in the assay of metakentrin. *Proc. Soc. Exptl. Biol. Med.* 46: 644–649, 1941.

33. GURIN, S., C. BACHMAN, AND D. W. WILSON. The gonadotropic hormone of urine of pregnancy. I. A simple method of extraction and purification. *J. Biol. Chem.* 128: 525–536, 1939.

34. GURIN, S., C. BACHMAN, AND D. W. WILSON. The gonadotropic hormone of urine of pregnancy. II. Chemical studies of preparations having high biological activity. *J. Biol. Chem.* 133: 467–477, 1940.

35. GURIN, S., C. BACHMAN, AND D. W. WILSON. The gonadotropic hormone of urine of pregnancy. III. Evidence of purity obtained by studies of electrophoresis and sedimentation. *J. Biol. Chem.* 133: 477–484, 1940.

36. HAMASHIGE, S., J. D. ALEXANDER, E. W. ABRAVANEL, AND M. A. ASTOR. New evidence demonstrating the multivalent nature of human chorionic gonadotropin. *Fertility Sterility* 22: 26–38, 1971.

37. HAMASHIGE, S., AND M. A. ASTOR. New observations on the gonadotropic action of human chorionic gonadotropin derived by study of chromatographic fractions. *Fertility Sterility* 20: 1029–1038, 1969.

38. HAMASHIGE, S., M. A. ASTOR, E. R. ARQUILLA, AND D. H. VAN THIEL. Human chorionic gonadotropin: a hormone complex. *J. Clin. Endocrinol. Metab.* 27: 1690–1704, 1967.

39. HAMBURGER, C. Discussion. In: *Gonadotropins*, edited by G. E. W. Wolstenholme and J. Knight. Boston: Little, Brown, 1965, p. 56.

40. HENNEN, G., J. G. PIERCE, AND P. FREYCHET. Human chorionic thyrotropin: further characterization and study of its secretion during pregnancy. *J. Clin. Endocrinol. Metab.* 29: 581–594, 1969.

41. HERSHMAN, J. M., H. P. HIGGINS, AND W. R. STARNES. Differences between thyroid stimulator in hydatidiform mole and human chorionic thyrotropin. *Metabolism* 19: 735–744, 1970.

42. INAGAMI, T., K. MURAKAMI, D. PUETT, A. S. HARTREE, AND A. NUREDDIN. N-terminal amino acid sequence of the alpha-subunit of human pituitary luteinizing hormone. *Biochem. J.* 126: 441–442, 1972.

43. ISERSKY, C., B. LUNENFELD, AND M. C. SHELESNYAK. Immunologic studies on gonadotropins. II. Biological assessment of the antigenic nature of the follicle-stimulating principle in human chorionic gonadotropin preparations. *J. Clin. Endocrinol. Metab.* 23: 54–58, 1963.

44. KAMMERMAN, S., R. E. CANFIELD, J. KOLENA, AND C. P. CHANNING. The binding of iodinated hCG to porcine granulosa cells. *Endocrinology* 91: 65–74, 1972.

45. KARKAS, J. D., AND E. CHARGAFF. Studies on the stability of simple derivatives of sialic acid. *J. Biol. Chem.* 239: 949–957, 1964.

46. KATZMAN, P. A., AND E. A. DOISY. Preparation of extracts of

the anterior pituitary-like substance of urine of pregnancy. *J. Biol. Chem.* 98: 739–754, 1932.

47. KATZMAN, P. A., M. GODFRID, C. K. CAIN, AND E. A. DOISY. The preparation of chorionic gonadotropin by chromatographic absorption. *J. Biol. Chem.* 148: 501–507, 1943.

48. KIKUTANI, M. The chemical studies on placental chorionic gonadotropin hormone. I. On extraction, purification, and the sugar of principle of Mainini reaction. *J. Pharm. Soc. Japan* 77: 370–375, 1957.

49. KOIDE, S. S. Isolation of gonadotropin from human term placenta. *Proc. Soc. Exptl. Biol. Med.* 132: 1137–1139, 1969.

50. LEWIS, J., JR., S. DRAY, S. GENUTY, AND H. S. SCHWARTZ. Demonstration of immunological similarities of human pregnancy gonadotropin and choriocarcinoma gonadotropin with antisera prepared in rabbits and monkeys. *J. Clin. Endocrinol. Metab.* 24: 197–204, 1964.

51. LIAO, T.-H., AND J. G. PIERCE. The primary structure of bovine thyrotropin. *J. Biol. Chem.* 246: 850–865, 1971.

52. LIU, W.-K., H. S. NAHM, C. M. SWEENEY, G. N. HOLCOMB, AND D. N. WARD. The primary structure of ovine luteinizing hormone. II. The amino acid sequence of the reduced, S-carboxymethylated A-subunit (LH-beta). *J. Biol. Chem.* 247: 4365–4381, 1972.

53. LIU, W.-K., H. S. NAHM, C. M. SWEENEY, W. M. LAMKIN, H. N. BAKER, AND D. N. WARD. The primary structure of ovine luteinizing hormone. I. The amino acid sequence of the reduced and S-aminoethylated S-subunit (LH-alpha). *J. Biol. Chem.* 247: 4351–4364, 1972.

54. LORAINE, J. A. Human chorionic gonadotropin. In: *Hormones in Blood*, edited by C. H. Gray and A. L. Bacharach. London: Acad. Press, 1967, p. 313–332.

55. LUNDGREN, H. P., S. GURIN, C. BACHMAN, AND D. W. WILSON. The gonadotropic hormone of urine of pregnancy. IV. *J. Biol. Chem.* 142: 367–370, 1942.

56. LUNENFELD, B. Discussion. In: *Gonadotropins*, edited by G. E. W. Wolstenholme and J. Knight. Boston: Little, Brown, 1965, p. 60.

57. LUNENFELD, B., AND A. ESHKOL. Immunology of human chorionic gonadotropin (HCG). *Vitamins Hormones* 25: 137–190, 1967.

58. McARTHUR, J. W. The identification of pituitary interstitial cell stimulating hormone in human urine. *Endocrinology* 50: 304–310, 1952.

59. MAGHUIN-ROGISTER, G., AND A. DOCKIER. The amino acid sequence of the bovine luteinizing hormone beta subunit. *FEBS Letters* 19: 209–213, 1972.

60. MAGHUIN-ROGISTER, G., AND G. HENNEN. Porcine luteinizing hormone. The amino acid sequence of the beta subunit. *FEBS Letters* 23: 225–229, 1972.

61. MIDGLEY, A. R., JR. Radioimmunoassay: a method for human chorionic gonadotropin and human luteinizing hormone. *Endocrinology* 79: 10–18, 1966.

62. MOCHIZUKI, N., Y. ASHITAKA, Y. TOKURA, AND S. TOJO. Comparative study on the biochemical character of HCGs from trophoblastic tumor and normal pregnancy. *Folia Endocrinol. Japon.* 44: 482–485, 1968.

63. MORELL, A. G., G. GREGORIADIS, I. H. SCHEINBERG, J. HICKMAN, AND G. ASHWELL. The role of sialic acid in determining the survival of glycoproteins in the circulation. *J. Biol. Chem.* 246: 1461–1467, 1971.

64. MORGAN, F. J., AND R. E. CANFIELD. Nature of the subunits of human chorionic gonadotropin. *Endocrinology* 88: 1045–1053, 1971.

66. MORGAN, F. J., S. KAMMERMAN, AND R. E. CANFIELD. Studies on the structure and activity of hCG. In: *Gonadotropins*, edited by B. B. Saxena, C. G. Beling, and H. M. Gandy. New York: Interscience, 1972, p. 211–215.

67. MORI, K. F. Antigenic structure of human gonadotropins: importance of protein moiety to the antigenic structure of human chorionic gonadotropin. *Endocrinology* 86: 97–106, 1970.

68. MORI, K. F., AND T. R. HOLLANDS. Physicochemical char-

acterization of native and asialo human chorionic gonadotropin. *J. Biol. Chem.* 246: 7223–7229, 1971.

69. MORRIS, C. J. O. R. Chemistry of the gonadotropins. *Brit. Med. Bull.* 11: 101–104, 1955.

70. MORRIS, C. J. O. R. Chemistry of gonadotrophins. In: *Marshall's Physiology of Reproduction*, edited by A. S. Parkes. London: Longmans, 1966, vol. III, p. 379–411.

71. NYDICK, M., R. J. BERRY, AND W. D. ODELL. Molecular weight of human chorionic gonadotropin as estimated by means of radiation inactivation of biologic activity. *J. Clin Endocrinol. Metab.* 24: 1049–1054, 1964.

72. PAPKOFF, H., M. R. SAIRAM, AND C. H. LI. Amino acid sequence of the subunits of ovine pituitary interstitial cell-stimulating hormone. *J. Am. Chem. Soc.* 93: 1531–1532, 1971.

73. PARLOW, A. F. Comparative bioassay of luteinizing hormones by three methods. In: *Gonadotropins 1968*, edited by E. Rosemberg. Los Altos: Geron-X, 1968, p. 59–65.

74. PETRUSZ, P. Biological and immunological characterization of gonadotrophic profiles. In: *Karolinska Symposium on Research Methods in Reproductive Endocrinology. First Symposium: Immunoassay of Gonadotropins*, edited by E. Diczfalusy. Stockholm: Karolinska Institute, 1969, p. 77–91.

75. PIERCE, J. G., O. P. BAHL, J. S. CORNELL, AND N. SWAMINATHAN. Biologically active hormones prepared by recombination of the alpha chain of human chorionic gonadotropin and the hormone-specific chain of bovine thyrotropin or of bovine luteinizing hormone. *J. Biol. Chem.* 246: 2321–2324, 1971.

76. PIERCE, J. G., T.-H. LIAO, R. B. CARLSEN, AND T. REIMO. Comparisons between the α chain of bovine thyrotropin and the C1 chain of luteinizing hormone. *J. Biol. Chem.* 246: 866–872, 1971.

77. RAYFORD, P. L., J. L. VAITKUKAITIS, G. T. ROSS, F. J. MORGAN, AND R. E. CANFIELD. Use of specific antisera to characterize biologic activity of hCG beta subunit preparations. *Endocrinology* 91: 144–146, 1972.

78. REICHERT, L. E. Differential effect of chymotryptic digestion on the biological activity of pituitary, serum and urinary gonadotropins. *Endocrinology* 84: 9–13, 1969.

79. REISFELD, R. A., D. M. BERGENSTAL, AND R. HERTZ. Distribution of gonadotropic hormone activity in the serum proteins of normal pregnant women and patients with trophoblastic tumors. *Arch. Biochem. Biophsy.* 81: 456–463, 1959.

80. REISFELD, R. A., AND R. HERTZ. Purification of chorionic gonadotropin from the urine of patients with trophoblastic tumors. *Biochim. Biophys. Acta* 43: 540–543, 1960.

81. ROBYN, C., P. PETRUSZ, AND E. DICZFALUSY. Follicle stimulating hormone-like activity in human chorionic gonadotropin preparations. *Acta Endocrinol.* 60: 137–156, 1969.

82. SCHWARTZ, H. S., AND N. MANTEL. Evidence for a variant of gonadotropin in choriocarcinoma. *Cancer Res.* 23: 1724–1734, 1963.

83. SCHURRS, A. H. W. M., E. de JAGER, AND J. D. H. HOMAN. Studies on human chorionic gonadotrophin. III. Immunochemical characterization. *Acta Endocrinol.* 59: 120–138, 1968.

84. SPIRO, R. G. Glycoproteins: their biochemistry, biology and role in human disease. *New Engl. J. Med.* 281: 991–1001; 1043–1056, 1969.

85. SWAMINATHAN, N., AND O. P. BAHL. Dissociation and recombination of the subunits of human chorionic gonadotropin. *Biochem. Biophys. Res. Commun.* 40: 422–427, 1970.

86. TSURUHARA, T., M. L. DUFAU, J. HICKMAN, AND K. J. CATT. Biological properties of hCG after removal of terminal sialic acid and galactose residues. *Endocrinology* 91: 296–301, 1972.

87. VAITUKAITIS, J., J. HAMMOND, G. ROSS, J. HICKMAN, AND G. ASHWELL. A new method of labeling human chorionic gonadotropin for physiologic studies. *J. Clin. Endocrinol. Metab.* 32: 290–293, 1971.

88. VAN HALL, E. V., J. L. VAITUKAITIS, G. T. ROSS, J. W. HICKMAN, AND G. ASHWELL. Immunological and biological activity of HCG following progressive desialylation. *Endocrinology* 88: 456–464, 1971.

89. VAN HELL, H., R. MATTHIJSEN, AND J. D. H. HOMAN. Studies

on human chorionic gonadotrophin. I. Purification and some physico-chemical properties. *Acta Endocrinol.* 59: 89–104, 1968.

90. VISUTAKUL, P., E. T. BELL, J. A. LORAINE, AND R. B. FISHER. The effect of urea on the biological activity of gonadotrophins of placental, endometrial and urinary origin. *J. Endocrinol.* 36: 23–28, 1966.

91. WALBORG, E. F., AND D. N. WARD. The carbohydrate components of ovine luteinizing hormone. *Biochim. Biophys. Acta* 78: 304–312, 1963.

92. WARD, D. N., E. F. WALBORG, AND M. ADAMS-MAYNE. Amino acid composition and electrophoretic properties of ovine luteinizing hormone. *Biochim. Biophys. Acta* 50: 224–232, 1961.

93. WEBER, K., AND M. OSBORN. The reliability of molecular weight determinations by dodecyl sulfate-polyacrylamide gel electrophoresis. *J. Biol. Chem.* 244: 4406–4412, 1969.

94. WIDE, L. An immunological method for the assay of human chorionic gonadotropin. *Acta Endocrinol. Suppl.* 70: 1–111, 1962.

95. WIDE, L., P. ROOS, AND C. GEMZELL. Immunological determination of human pituitary luteinizing hormone (LH). *Acta Endocrinol.* 37: 445–449, 1961.

96. WILDE, C. E., AND K. D. BAGSHAWE. The purification of chorionic gonadotropin. In: *Gonadotropins*, edited by G. E. W. Wolstenholme and J. Knight. Boston: Little, Brown, 1965, p. 46–55.

CHAPTER 47

Placental vasculature and circulation

ELIZABETH M. RAMSEY | *Carnegie Institution of Washington, Department of Embryology, Baltimore, Maryland*

CHAPTER CONTENTS

THE CONCEPT of the placental barrier, which was an article of faith to a previous generation, has undergone substantial modification in the light of recent research (30). No longer can the transfer of substances between mother and fetus be regarded as a simple diffusion of crystalloids and dissolved gases, nor can the postulate be accepted that the fewer the tissue layers between maternal and fetal blood, the more efficient the transfer. The very term *placental barrier* is now more appropriately replaced by *placental membrane*, though, since familiar expressions die hard, barrier will doubtless still be used and is acceptable if the limitations of the barrier action are kept clearly in mind.

Basic to a consideration of the newer concepts of placental transfer is an understanding of current opinion regarding uteroplacental and fetoplacental vasculature and circulation, for here, too, recent research has been active with resultant modifications of older ideas and introduction of new ones.

Knowledge of placental vasculature and circulation in primates is based in large part on studies in subhuman primates, especially the rhesus monkey. It has been repeatedly shown that reproduction in rhesus is so similar to that in man, both anatomically and physiologically, that this animal can be used as an experimental model for reproductive studies. In the following discussion, instances of important species difference are noted, but otherwise all statements refer to primates in general, as checked by workers using rhesus, baboon (32, 33), and human subjects.

UTEROPLACENTAL CIRCULATION

Vascular Anatomy

ARTERIAL. The uterine arteries are the major source of the arterial blood supply to the uterus, though anastomotic branches from the ovarian arteries contribute a small and variable proportion of the blood. After proceeding on an oblique course directly into the middle layer of the myometrium, the main afferent stems break up into an arcuate wreath, which sends small branches back into the outer muscle layers and forward into the inner layers to provide mural nutrition (21, 22, 41). The endometrium is supplied by larger branches of the arcuate arteries, the radial arteries, which pass at right angles across the inner muscularis, traverse the myoendometrial junction, and continue toward the uterine lumen (Fig. 1). It has been customary to limit the term *radial artery* to the myometrial segment of the vessel and to call the endometrial segment the spiral artery, but, as will be shown below, the histological character of the walls of the myometrial and endometrial segments is basically so similar that the spiral artery is properly to be regarded as a prolongation of the radial. Indeed use of the unmodified term *spiral artery* is fraught with some danger, since many uterine arteries pursue a convoluted course (e.g., those composing the arcuate wreath), and confusion arises unless *endometrial spiral* is clearly specified.

Shortly after it crosses the myoendometrial junction, the endometrial spiral artery gives off branches that ramify in the deepest layer of the endometrium; these are known as the *basal arteries* (8, 9, 17, 36). They nourish this basal layer and, their course being restricted to it, are not involved in the menstrual slough. The basal arteries are essentially muscular with little or no elastic tissue, and their constitution remains unaltered throughout the menstrual cycle and in pregnancy. They have traditionally been considered of an entirely different nature from the spiral arteries, though Markee (36), in his exhaustive study of intraocular endometrial transplants on which so much of our information about endometrial vasculature is based, described occasional transformation of basal arteries into spiral ones. The question thus remains open as to whether the basal arteries are fundamentally different and incapable of the sort of response

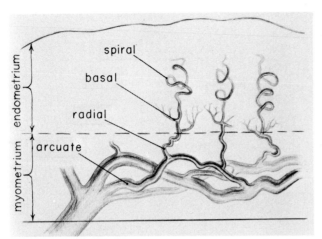

FIG. 1. Schematic representation of uterine arteries. [From Okkels & Engle (41).]

to hormonal stimuli the spirals exhibit or are merely branches that supply an area of the mucosa in which no hormonal involvement occurs, vide the lack of cyclic change in stroma and glands of the basalis.

At the beginning of a menstrual cycle, when the slough terminating the previous cycle has been completed and regeneration of the mucosa is just commencing, many of the endometrial spiral arteries have been reduced to short stumps. From their tips, capillary sprouts promptly arise and form a subepithelial plexus. The capillary connections between arteries and plexus elongate pari pasu with the regrowth of the mucosal stroma and glands (Fig. 2). Media and adventitia gradually form around them and create the impression that the arteries "grow toward the surface epithelium," though in truth it is the endothelial tube that grows and subsequently is transformed into a three-layered channel. Elongation of the arteries by this process continues unabated throughout the luteal phase of the cycle and indeed, if pregnancy occurs, will continue until formation of the definitive placenta is completed. The lengthening of the arteries becomes more rapid than the increase in diameter of the endometrium, so that the vessels must coil to accommodate themselves to the restricted space in which they course. This is believed to cause decrease in the rate of blood flow (8, 9).

If pregnancy occurs, the fertilized ovum implants at a time when the endometrium and its vessels have attained maximum growth and development. Subsequently the endometrium is eroded by trophoblast and compressed by growth of the overlying conceptus, so that back and forth and lateral looping of the vessels must be added to the coiling [Fig. 3; (43)]. At midpregnancy, when stretching replaces growth of uterine parts as the predominant element in uterine enlargement (54), the coils of the arteries are paid out. This is a more conspicuous feature in the monkey than in man, as may be seen in Figure 3, perhaps because the myometrium of the monkey is thinner than that of man with respect to the thickness of the placenta.

The sensitivity of endometrial spiral arteries to hormonal stimuli is manifested both by the exuberant growth noted above and by the development of transient vasoconstrictions that initiate ischemia. The ischemia in turn produces the necrosis that leads to menstrual bleeding and slough (8, 9). Two important features of the vasoconstriction merit special attention because of the role it plays in certain vascular phenomena of pregnancy. First, the constriction occurs deep in the vessels, just above or just below the myoendometrial junction (see Fig. 2B); and second, it is not of uniform or simultaneous occurrence, some vessels becoming narrowed or occluded at one time and others at another. Thus the menstrual slough is in fact a somewhat spotty affair, and by no means is all the endometrium shed (8, 9, 36).

At its origin from the arcuate artery, the wall of the radial endometrial spiral artery has the typical histological constitution of a distributing artery. This composition continues through the basal portion of the endometrium. Then, as the artery traverses the functionalis, the formation of media and adventitia around the endothelial tubes becomes less and less complete, until the stout elastic lamellae separating endothelium and media in the deeper segments appear only as a loose

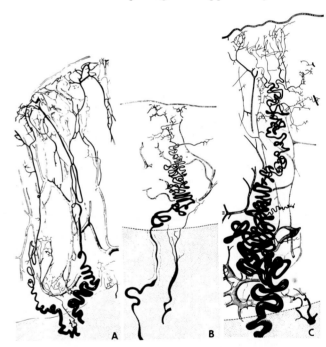

FIG. 2. Camera lucida drawings of vascular beds at various stages of the menstrual cycle in the rhesus monkey. Myometrium is *stippled*. × 30. *A*: 12th day of cycle. Mature ovarian follicle present. Note elongated capillaries extending from tips of spiral arteries to subepithelial plexus beneath endometrial surface. *B*: 15 hr after ovulation. Coiling of spiral artery increased and closer approximation of artery to endometrial surface. Marked constriction of radial artery in myometrium close to myoendometrial junction. Decrease in endometrial diameter is a transitory phenomenon characteristic of the hours immediately pre- and postovulation. *C*: 27th day of menstrual cycle. Mature corpus luteum present. Markedly increased coiling of spiral artery. Still closer approximation of artery to endometrial surface. [From Bartelmez (9).]

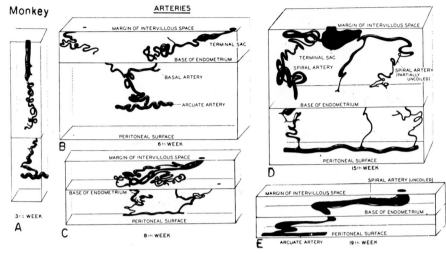

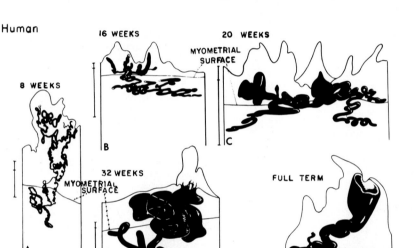

FIG. 3. Diagrammatic representations of the course and configuration of the uteroplacental arteries in the rhesus monkey and man at comparable stages of gestation. [Monkey diagrams drawn by the late James F. Didusch, human diagrams by Frank B. Price; from Ramsey & Harris (50).]

fibrillar network and the scattered fibrils in the media and adventitia disappear altogether (29). Recent studies suggest that the elastic tissue persists further in monkeys (midfunctionalis) than it does in man (midbasalis) (50).

The effect of pregnancy on the structure of the arterial walls is as marked as it is on their gross configuration. In the early stages of implantation, as the trophoblast penetrates the endometrium, it first encounters the elements of the subepithelial capillary network, as described in a monograph by Boyd & Hamilton (14), which is a definitive and invaluable guide to all aspects of primate placental structure and function, including vasculature and circulation. In some instances, these channels resist erosion and the trophoblast flows around and engulfs them; in others the trophoblast breaches ("taps") the capillary walls (29). As the result of these two mechanisms, maternal blood under very low pressure enters the lacunae of the trophoblastic shell. As the trophoblast penetrates further, it causes disintegration of arterial walls with resultant extravasation into the stroma and into the lumina of glands. More importantly, connection between uterine arteries and trophoblastic lacunae is

effected during the second week following implantation, at the time when chorionic villi are beginning to form. Thereafter the lacunar system may be designated the intervillous space (IVS), and gradually true uteroplacental circulation is set up. The blood entering the IVS is under the vis a tergo of maternal arterial pressure. This pressure is somewhat reduced from the systemic level by arterial coiling (as described above) but even so is higher than that existing in the intervillous space.

The trophoblast not only breaches arterial walls, it also replaces them. In a manner that has been compared to candle grease running down the lumen of a tube, cytotrophoblast first accumulates within arterial lumina (Fig. 4) and then comes to replace the media (28, 29). The process commences during the first two weeks after conception in the monkey and baboon, but a little later in man. It may be postulated that by removing the muscle layers this process further weakens the walls of spiral arteries, which already are deficient in elastic tissue. The impact of maternal blood pressure in these weakened segments produces the terminal dilatations that characterize the arteries' gross morphology

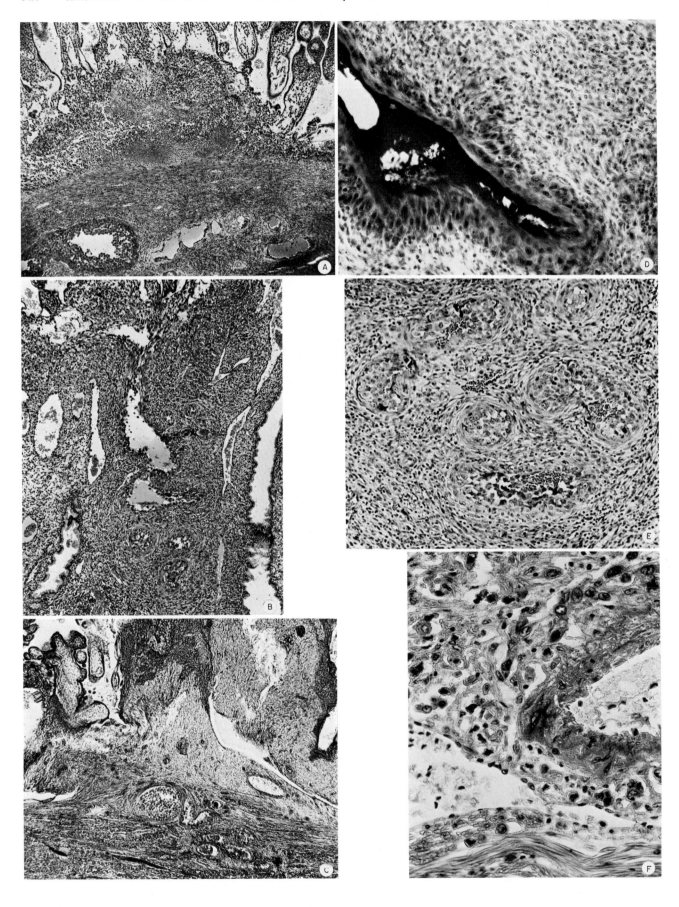

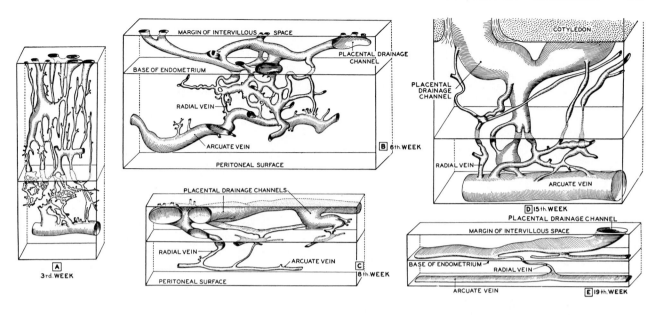

FIG. 5. Diagrammatic representations of the course and configuration of uteroplacental veins in the rhesus monkey. [Drawn by the late James F. Didusch; from Ramsey (44).]

(see Fig. 3). The increased uterine arterial blood volume effected by this mechanism provides for the increasing requirements of the growing placenta. In man, the invasion of arterial walls proceeds from without, as well as from within, since trophoblastic elements invade the endometrium extensively (see Fig. 4). In monkey and baboon there is no stromal invasion by trophoblast, and replacement of arterial walls is exclusively from the lumen (see Fig. 4A, B, D, E). The depth of the penetration and the fate of the penetrating cells are as yet undetermined, but it is clear that the walls of the radial segment of the arteries remain physiologically intact, for the intermittent vasoconstrictions noted during the menstrual cycle continue throughout pregnancy, as demonstrated by radioangiography [Fig. 6; (37, 48)].

VENOUS. The venous drainage of the nonpregnant uterus is accomplished via a grid of long vertical channels and shorter horizontal limbs with dilatations at intersection points known as "venous lakes." The vertical channels follow the course of the endometrial glands rather closely (18). The venous lakes fluctuate in size and appear to cushion changes in uterine blood volume and flow rate. The ovarian veins participate in the drainage of the uterus. They play a more dominant role in monkeys than in man.

In pregnancy the veins have a subsidiary and essentially passive role (44). That the trophoblast does not invade or replace the walls of veins is a striking fact for which no explanation is yet apparent. Only rarely is as much as a single cytotrophoblastic cell encountered in the lumen of a vein—except in later pregnancy, when, as is well known, whole villi may be swept into uterine veins and thence into the systemic circulation. The only changes that do occur in veins during pregnancy are the result of external pressure by virtue of which many channels are obliterated and the number of exits from the intervillous space is correspondingly curtailed. The remaining veins become distended by the increasing quantity of blood entering them from the intervillous space (Fig. 5). Orifices of exit from the placenta are present in all regions of the placental base, centrally, as well as at the margin. There is no discrete "sinus" in the sense of Spanner (56), though large veins often do drain the margin, and there is always a major wreath of veins within the endometrium at the epiplacental angle [Fig. 7; (45)].

Whether arteriovenous anastomoses occur is still unsettled. The preponderance of current opinion is that they do not (8). They have been carefully looked for in radioangiographic studies but have never been found.

FIG. 4. Microscopic sections showing intraarterial trophoblastic penetration. A and D: rhesus; B and E: baboon; C and F: man. A–C show cytrophoblast in arterial lumina; D–F show, in addition, replacement of vessel wall to varying degrees. Note also in the human specimens the trophoblastic invasion of endometrial stroma. A: monkey C477, 29th day of pregnancy; section 1–2. × 41. B: baboon A65–177, 18th day of pregnancy; section 38–2–1. × 41. C: man, Carnegie 9051, 14th week of pregnancy; section 27. × 34. D: monkey C629, 53rd day of pregnancy; section 10. × 150. E: baboon A65–177, 18th day of pregnancy; section 36–2–4. × 150. F: man, Carnegie 10118, 15th week of pregnancy; section 1. × 300. [B and E, courtesy of M. L. Houston, University of Texas Dental School, San Antonio, Texas; C and F from Harris & Ramsey (29).]

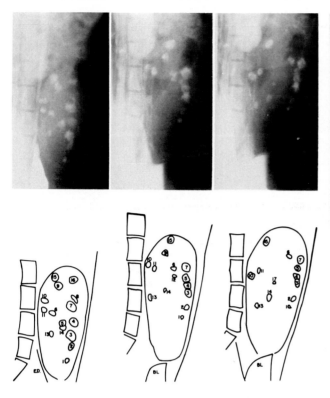

FIG. 6. Photographs of lateral radiograms of the pregnant monkey uterus taken 6 sec after intrafemoral injection of a radiopaque medium, together with tracings identifying the different arterial entries to the intervillous space. All injections made during uterine relaxation. *BL*, bladder; *ED*, extravasated contrast medium. Monkey 64/95, 92 days pregnant. [From Martin et al. (37).]

Hemodynamics

ARTERIAL. Use of the rhesus monkey as a model for primate reproduction is even more imperative in physiological than in anatomic studies, since the necessary in vivo techniques of physiological investigation are often unsuitable for use in clinical patients. Studies in monkeys by various investigators, radioangiographic studies in particular, have confirmed the hypothesis originally formulated on the basis of anatomical studies. This states that in pregnancy maternal blood entering the intervillous space under the vis a tergo of maternal systemic blood pressure is driven toward the chorionic plate in discrete fountainlike streams or "spurts" (Borell's "jets") [(12, 13); Fig. 8]. The pressure in the afferent streams tends to sweep aside those chorionic villi around the orifice of entry that are free-floating, that is, not anchored to the basal plate. There is little lateral dispersion of the incoming blood until the pressure and momentum of the stream decrease (47). Meanwhile the arterial blood bathes the chorionic villi, and exchange with fetal blood takes place. Further incoming arterial blood forces the blood already present in the intervillous space into the endometrial veins through orifices of exit

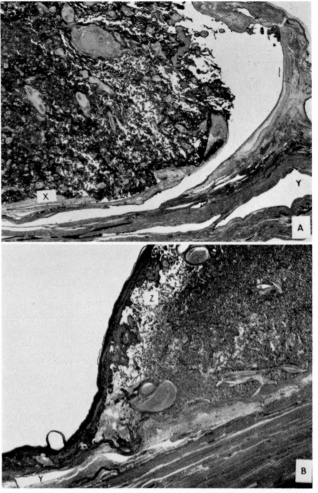

FIG. 7. Photomicrographs of the margin of the attached human placenta. *A*: a region where there is dilatation of the periphery of the intervillous space, a "marginal lake" drained by a wide villous channel. A slender vein (*x*) with an oblique course drains the marginal lake indirectly. At *y* is a part of the characteristic venous wreath at the epiplacental angle. Carnegie 9033, term; slide D50. × 7.5. *B*: a region where no marginal lake is present; *y*, as above; *z*, the subchorial lake. Carnegie 9158, 28th week of pregnancy; slide B25. × 6. [From Ramsey(45).]

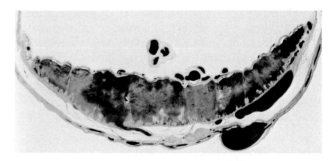

FIG. 8. Cross section of monkey placenta in situ. At *left*, a portion of an endometrial artery traversing uterine wall to its point of entry into intervillous space. The blood in the vessels spurts, under head of maternal pressure, toward chorionic plate with little lateral diffusion. Monkey C750, 123rd day of pregnancy. × 0.9. [From Ramsey (46).]

in the placental base (Fig. 9). In still radiograms taken in rapid succession and in cineradiographic films, it is possible to trace the course of a radiopaque medium through the placenta in just this fashion (Fig. 10).

Myometrial contractions throughout pregnancy and in labor alter the basic circulatory pattern: strong contractions completely prevent inflow of blood to the intervillous space, and lesser contractions diminish it. This effect may be demonstrated by counting the spiral arteries that discharge their contents into the intervillous space and noting the decrease in their number (Fig. 11). This action is quite separate and distinct from the independent contractility of individual spiral arteries during uterine relaxation (see Fig. 6). The independent contractility reflects the continuing vasoconstrictive activity of these arteries, which was already manifested in the menstrual cycle (see section *Vascular Anatomy*, ARTERIAL). We have no evidence that, under normal circumstances, these episodes of vasoconstriction during pregnancy are sufficiently prolonged to occasion ischemia or regressive changes in the tissues supplied.

VENOUS. During myometrial contractions, venous drainage is also affected. This is not in accordance with the old concept that "the intervillous space is squeezed like a sponge." Rather, blood is trapped in the space. This results from closure of the thin-walled drainage channels by the contraction of the uterine muscles. At the onset of a contraction some blood is milked into the systemic circulation from the uterine mural channels, as evidenced by the blood flow studies of Hendricks (31).

FETAL PLACENTAL CIRCULATION

The chorionic villi, which form the scaffold in which the fetal blood vessels run, resemble inverted trees rooted in the chorionic plate and depending into the intervillous space. The larger villous trunks occur toward the center of each cotyledon (see below), and the next divisions or stem villi spread out toward the placental margin. Branches of stem villi interdigitate to form the fetal cotyledons (Fig. 12), which correspond roughly to the more or less distinct lobulations seen on the maternal surface of the delivered placenta (maternal cotyledons) (Fig. 13). There is no structural connection between the villi in adjacent cotyledons, and the circulations have been shown to be completely independent, in contrast to Stieve's concept of a placental "network" (57). Human placentas have fewer stem villi than do rhesus placentas, and human stems are larger and less immediately broken down into complex branches. Thus the main stem villi of the macaque correspond to the secondary branches of the human villous stem. An explanation of this variation may perhaps be found in the deeper penetration of the trophoblast in human interstitial implantation, as compared with the condition in the monkey in which implantation is superficial and trophoblastic invasion far less pronounced. As a result, the branching of main stem villi, which occurs within the chorionic plate in the macaque, has been "pulled down" into the intervillous space in man (38).

The fetal blood vessels of the placenta exactly follow the treelike subdivisions of the chorionic villi. As soon as the umbilical arteries containing fetal venous blood

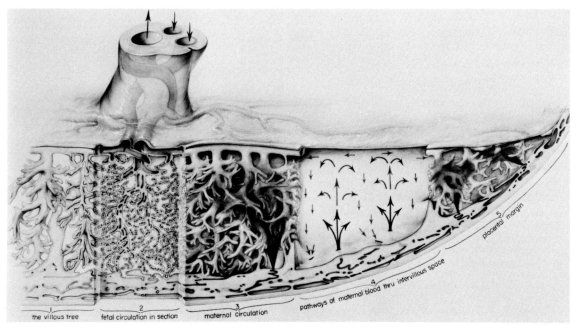

FIG. 9. Composite drawing of the primate placenta showing its structure and circulation. [Drawing by Ranice Davis Crosby; courtesy of the Carnegie Institution of Washington.]

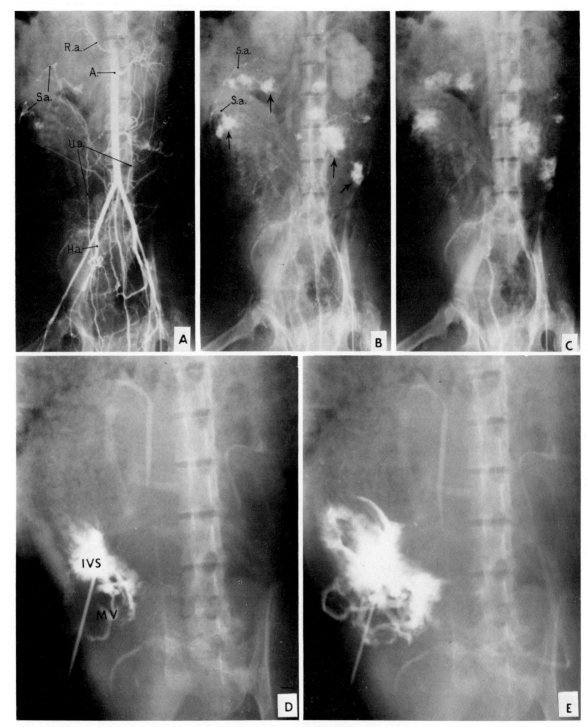

FIG. 10. Photographs of X-rays made after injection with a radiopaque medium. In *A–C* injection was made into a femoral artery, in *D* and *E*, directly into the intervillous space. *A–C* were made at 2, 3, and 7.5 sec, respectively, after injection of the contrast material and show its progress through systemic and uterine arteries into the intervillous space of the placenta. *R.a.*, renal artery; *A*, aorta; *U.a.*, uterine artery; *H.a.*, hypogastric artery; *S.a.*, endometrial spiral artery; *arrow*, "spurts" into the intervillous space. Monkey 60–14, 100th day of pregnancy. *D* and *E* were made 2 and 20 sec, respectively, after injection and show passage of the contrast material from the intervillous space into the venous channels of the uterine wall. *IVS*, pool of contrast material in intervillous space; *MV*, mural veins. Monkey 62–26, 124th day of pregnancy. [*A–C* from Ramsey et al. (49); *D* and *E* from Ramsey et al. (52).]

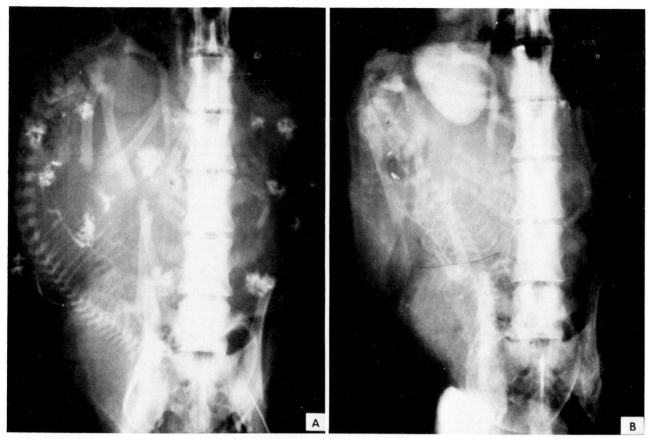

FIG. 11. Photographs of radiograms made 8 sec after injection of radiopaque medium into maternal femoral artery. *A:* during uterine relaxation; *B:* during a strong uterine contraction. Note absence of contrast medium in the intervillous space in *B.* Monkey 62–30, 141st day of pregnancy. [From Ramsey et al. (48).]

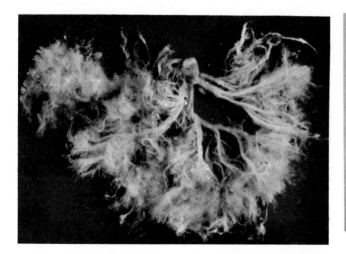

FIG. 12. A main stem villus isolated from a human placenta after partial trypsin digestion. × 0.8. [From Martin & Ramsey (38).]

FIG. 13. Maternal surface of placenta from a pregnancy in 21st week. Note lobulations that correspond to cotyledons. Tissue photographed in fresh state; no digestion or fixation. Carnegie 10137.

reach the fetal surface of the placental disk, they break up into numerous branches that penetrate the chorionic plate and travel between amnion and chorion toward the periphery of the disk (38, 58). Central insertion of the cord and its vessels is generally considered modal, although eccentric insertion is fully compatible with a

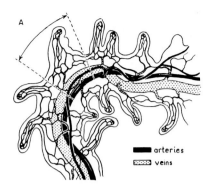

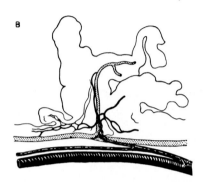

Superficial capillary network

Paravascular network

FIG. 14. Schematic representations of the course of fetal blood vessels in the chorionic villi of the human placenta. In *A*, the vasculature is shown as it would appear if the paravascular network were dissected away. The points at which the network attaches to the stem vessels are indicated by *dashed lines*. [From Bøe (11).]

normal course of pregnancy. Branches of the first divisions of the umbilical arteries penetrate the chorion at a sharp angle to enter the villous trunks. The arteries travel down the trunks and subdivide, as do the villi themselves. They lose caliber and wall structure in typical fashion as they proceed into the finer and finer ramifications of the cotyledons and eventually persist as capillaries in the terminal villous twigs. The venules draining the capillary plexus retrace the course of the arterioles and arteries until they return the now arterial blood to the fetus via the single umbilical vein.

The course of the capillaries in the terminal villi is more complicated than that of the villi, which is a simple arborization. As has been shown by Bøe [(11); Fig. 14], the vasculature is well adapted to cope with physiological demands and pathological emergencies, for the simple superficial capillary bed is supplemented by a paravascular network providing extravillous shunts that may bypass nonfunctioning villi. It is an important attribute of the terminal villi that they form new villous twigs throughout pregnancy by continued budding of syncytium (Fig. 15). These new terminal villi are vascularized by sprouts arising from capillaries already existing in older villi. The capillaries approach the surface of the villi more closely as pregnancy advances

until, at term, syncytiotrophoblast alone covers them and in many places is stretched so thin as to be almost invisible by light microscopy. Reference is made to the comprehensive and intensive electron-microscopic studies of Ralph Wynn, which he summarizes in an earlier chapter in this volume of the *Handbook*.

It may be useful to emphasize that the syncytiotrophoblast that forms the outer border of the villi is, looked at in another way, the lining of the channels between villi to which the descriptive designation "inter-villous space" is applied. Syncytiotrophoblast also composes the placental surface of the chorionic plate and the floor of the placenta at its junction with maternal tissue.

MATERNAL FETAL VASCULAR RELATIONSHIPS

Anatomy and Physiology

The relationship of maternal and fetal placental vasculature at the macroscopic level is readily apparent from the photographs of acrylic casts made in the Carnegie Laboratory (Fig. 16). Liquid, white plastic had

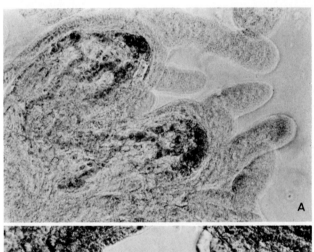

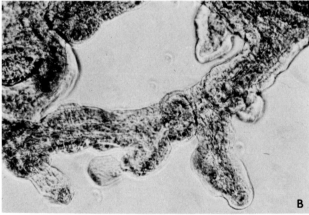

FIG. 15. Photographs of fresh human chorionic villi visualized by phase contrast microscopy. *A*, at 8 weeks; *B*, at 38 weeks. Note abundant syncytial buds in *A* and a great reduction in number and size of buds in *B*. Capillaries are closer to the surface of the villi in *B*. (Courtesy of H. R. Misenhimer, Rush Medical College, Chicago, Illinois.)

tions), demonstrate the same gross relationship of spiral artery entries and cotyledons as that shown by the casts [Fig. 17; (51)].

Understanding of the interaction of maternal and fetal circulations at the microscopic level has presented investigators with some difficulty. The placentas of lower

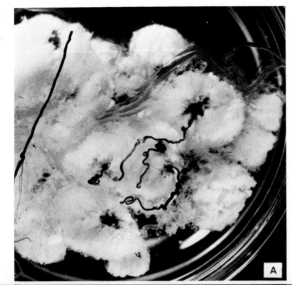

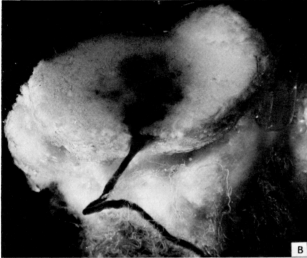

FIG. 16. *A*: acrylic cast of fetal vessels within placental villi (*white*) and of maternal uteroplacental arteries (*black*). Monkey 7B, 159th day of pregnancy. × 0.8. *B*: cross section of a single cotyledon of a similar acrylic cast. Section made at the point of entry of an endometrial spiral artery. Monkey 66–95, 136th day of pregnancy. × 1.6. [From Martin & Ramsey (38).]

been injected into the fetal vessels of monkeys via an umbilical artery and red plastic into the maternal aorta, whence it penetrated the uterine arteries and finally entered the intervillous space. The injections were made in anesthetized animals in vivo; the fetal and maternal systemic blood pressure, respectively, supplied the propulsive force. All parenchymal tissue was digested after the plastic had hardened (38). The results shown are in accord with those of Panigel (42), Arts (5), Romney & Reid (55), Boyd & Hamilton (14), Crawford (16), Wilkin (58), Freese (24), and Freese et al. (25), among others who carried out similar injections. In the four latter investigations large central cavities in the fetal cotyledons not duplicated in the other work were seen. Radioangiographic studies, employing double injections of opaque material (into maternal and fetal circula-

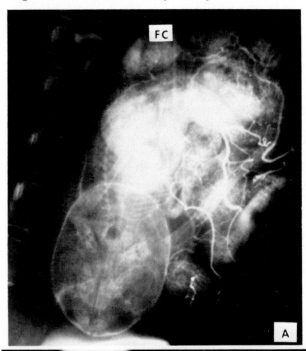

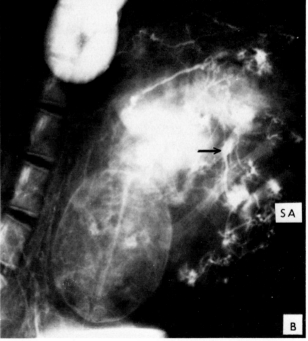

FIG. 17. Radiograms made during a combined fetal and maternal injection study. *A*: taken 3 sec after injection of contrast medium into the fetal circulation; *B*: taken 2 sec after immediately subsequent maternal injection. *FC*, fetal cotyledon; *SA*, endometrial spiral artery; *arrow*, "spurts" into the intervillous space. Monkey 65–80, 152nd day of pregnancy. [From Ramsey et al. (51).]

animals, particularly the labyrinthine types, had been quite thoroughly worked out before primate placentas came under investigation (4). Sir Joseph Barcroft, who did the classic work on the sheep's placenta, established that, in this species, blood in maternal and fetal capillaries flows in opposite directions, as illustrated in Figure 18 (7). In this countercurrent type of flow, venous fetal blood makes its first contact with maternal blood which is also in the venous state and gradually encounters increasingly oxygenated maternal blood until equilibrium is established between the two. Countercurrent flow was subsequently shown by Noer (40), in an artificial placental model, to be the most efficient method for exchange of diffusible substances. For many years the attempt was made to force the hemochorial, villous placenta into this pattern. With increasing information, particularly that derived from study of primate placentas, it has become apparent that intervillous space flow is not orderly, as is the flow in a labyrinth with clearly demarcated channels and well-observed traffic regulation. In Figure 9, column 4, is shown how diverse, in fact, are the pathways by which maternal blood permeates the intervillous space. It is clear that, although any given villus or cluster of villi may be bathed on all sides by arterial blood from an entering spurt, its immediate neighbor may be in the path of venous blood converging on a venous exit, and within the villus both the venous and arterial ends of the capillary bed are surrounded by maternal blood of identical composition. The anatomical finding is confirmed by the blood chemistry studies of Bartels and associates (10) who illustrate what they call multivillous flow, as shown in their diagram reproduced

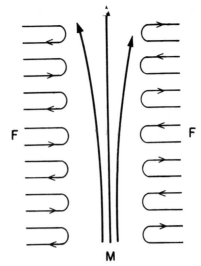

FIG. 19. Schematic diagram of a single blood flow unit in the multivillous human placenta. The same stream of maternal blood passes many villous capillaries. *M*, maternal; *F*, fetal. [From Bartels et al. (10).]

in Figure 19. The great complexity and nonhomogeneity of the intervillous space that is brought about by these arrangements has been further demonstrated in studies of the pH and oxygen and carbon dioxide content of various regions of the space (6, 26). In addition, recent work with injected microspheres (35) and studies of the ratio of diffusion of oxygen and carbon monoxide (34) point to the possibility of uneven distribution of bloodstreams and even a shunting of blood away from functional exchange sites. Although much of the microsphere work and many of the blood gas studies have been done in subprimate animals, the information is highly suggestive for all placental forms.

Placentometry

Determination of the total chorionic surface in the placenta is a matter of practical importance, since this represents the potential area for maternal-fetal exchange. Numerous attempts have been made to measure this area by planimetry (15, 19, 20, 59), nuclear counts (53), and more recently by the methods of mean linear intercepts (1, 2, 59) and grid of equidistant points (1, 2). Each of the methods has individual difficulties; all share the disadvantage that they are performed after fixation and embedding and must be based on sample blocks whose representativeness is always open to question. Furthermore, absolute and relative values change as pregnancy advances (1, 59). Only values obtained at similar gestational age should be compared. (Values quoted below are all for term placentas.) The values obtained by Dodds (20) and Rech (53), based on study of single cases, lay between 6.4 and 7 m². Those of the other workers cited fall between 11 and 14 m². The recent investigations of Aherne & Dunnill (1, 2) were particularly thorough and detailed, as may be seen from the chart in Table 1. Only Aladjem (3) has studied fresh, unfixed tissue by employ-

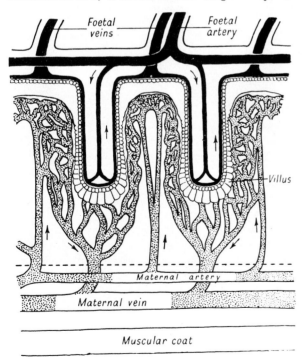

FIG. 18. Arrangement of blood vessels in the sheep placenta; classic counterflow of maternal and fetal blood is illustrated. [From Amoroso (4).]

TABLE 1. *Summary of Placental Morphometry in Normal Pregnancy*

Morphometric Factor	Normal Value	Standard Deviation
Placental volume	488 ml	99
Nonparenchyma	20.8%	3.6
Volume proportions of parenchyma		
Intervillous space	35.8%	3.2
Chorionic villi	57.9%	5.7
Fibrin	4.3%	2.1
Villous surface area	11 m²	1.3
Capillary surface area	12.2 m²	1.5
Mean capillary volume	45 ml	
Proportion of villi occupied by tropho-blast	25.3%	1.9
Minimum thickness of placental membrane (electron-microscopic measurements)	3.5 μ	

Mean values of 10 cases at 39–40 weeks of gestation. [Adapted from Aherne & Dunnill (1, 2).]

ing phase contrast microscopy. However, he too has had to be content with samples. His value for total capillary surface area is somewhat lower than that of Aherne & Dunnill (1, 2)—that is, 75% of villous surface area. This figure and that for the diameter of the placental membrane are the crucial ones for considerations of diffusion, as pointed out by Mossman (39). Aherne & Dunnill's (1, 2) value for the latter, 3.5 μ, is midway between those of Wilkin and Wulf (59, 60), 2 and 5.5 μ, respectively, and is in close agreement with that found in Wynn's studies (61), which confirm this range. All authors note the variable thickness of the membranes from place to place. Such variability renders extremely difficult the establishment of a single figure suitable for use in a diffusion equation. Aherne & Dunnill (1, 2) cite the additional complication that the membrane itself is metabolically active and therefore can add to and subtract from transfer gradient values.

The Placental Barrier

The variability in thickness of the placental membrane is one of the factors that has brought the validity

of the Grosser theory (27) into question (Fig. 20). In all fairness it should be stated that Grosser was far less dogmatic in enunciation of his theory and far less insistent on its direct and universal physiological application than were some of his disciples. Nevertheless it is the more rigid interpretation of the theory that is now associated with "The Grosser Classification" and to which exception must be taken on several points: *a)* not all regions of the placenta of any given animal show identical constitution with respect to Grosser's six layers; *b)* any placenta may vary in its constitution from one stage of pregnancy to another, and most placentas do so; *c)* transfer of substances between maternal and fetal bloodstreams is not a matter of simple diffusion in which mere distance to be traveled determines rate and volume of transfer; and *d)* no account is taken in the Grosser classification of the role played in transfer by the fetal membranes and such auxiliary structures as the yolk sac, placental hematomas, and others. Grosser himself recognized the importance of these structures but purposely excluded them from consideration as having no part in the classification of the placenta, strictly defined.

Increase in the quantity and variety of material available for examination, improved techniques of conventional histological study, and above all electron microscopy have laid the foundation for the first two objections. Physicochemical studies demonstrating transfer of nondiffusible substances have raised the third objection, and electron microscopy has supported them by indicating means of mediated transfer (e.g., intracellular gaps, pinocytosis, phagocytosis) to supplement simple diffusion. Demonstration of the active participation in transfer by elements of the membrane itself has clinched the argument and has shown that the placenta can degrade elaborate chemicals presented to it and synthesize others, rather than simply admitting or mechanically preventing their passage. In addition, if the factors of uneven distribution of flow and of shunting, mentioned above, are established for primates, as well as for other animals, yet more complicating features will be introduced.

It cannot be denied that the Grosser system provides a far more sophisticated classification than any of those

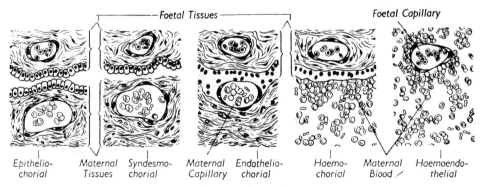

FIG. 20. A diagrammatic representation of Grosser's classification of placentas by histological type with Mossman's hemoendothelial type added. The sequential arrangement emphasizes the progressive reduction in the number of layers between maternal and fetal circulations. [From Amoroso (4).]

that preceded it. Furthermore even those who denounce it have been unable to devise a satisfactory substitute. The grouping remains of practical usefulness to anatomists and zoologists who can employ it as a general sorting tool. However, the expectation, generated by the studies of Flexner & Gellhorn (23) on water transfer, that the classification would also be valid physiologically can no longer be entertained.

REFERENCES

1. AHERNE, W., AND M. S. DUNNILL. Morphometry of the human placenta. *Brit. Med. Bull.* 22: 5–8, 1966.
2. AHERNE, W., AND M. S. DUNNILL. Quantitative aspects of placental structure. *J. Pathol. Bacteriol.* 91: 123–139, 1966.
3. ALADJEM, S. Studies in placental circulation. Vascular area of the terminal villus in normal and abnormal pregnancies. *Am. J. Obstet. Gynecol.* 107: 88–92, 1970.
4. AMOROSO, E. C. Placentation. In: *Marshall's Physiology of Reproduction*, edited by A. S. Parkes. London: Longmans, 1952, vol. II, p. 127–311.
5. ARTS, N. F. TH. Investigations on the vascular system of the placenta. *Am. J. Obstet. Gynecol.* 82: 147–158; 159–166, 1961.
6. ASSALI, N. S., P. V. DILTS, JR., A. A. PLENTL, T. H. KIRSCHBAUM, AND S. J. GROSS. Physiology of the placenta. In: *Biology of Gestation*, edited by N. S. Assali. New York: Acad. Press, 1968, p. 185–203.
7. BARCROFT, J., AND D. H. BARRON. Observations upon the form and relations of the maternal and fetal vessels in the placenta of the sheep. *Anat. Record* 94: 569–595, 1946.
8. BARTELMEZ, G. W. Premenstrual and menstrual ischemia and the myth of endometrial arteriovenous anastomoses. *Am. J. Anat.* 98: 69–96, 1956.
9. BARTELMEZ, G. W. The form and the functions of the uterine blood vessels in the rhesus monkey. *Contrib. Embryol. Carnegie Inst. Wash.* 36: 153–182, 1957.
10. BARTELS, H., W. MOLL, AND J. METCALFE. Physiology of gas exchange in the human placenta. *Am. J. Obstet. Gynecol.* 84: 1714–1730, 1962.
11. BØE, F. Studies on the vascularization of the human placenta. *Acta Obstet. Gynecol. Scand.* 32, Suppl. 5: 1–92, 1953.
12. BORELL, U., I. FERNSTRÖM, L. OHLSON, AND N. WIQVIST. Effect of uterine contractions on the human uteroplacental blood circulation. An arteriographic study. *Am. J. Obstet. Gynecol.* 89: 881–890, 1964.
13. BORELL, U., I. FERNSTRÖM, L. OHLSON, AND N. WIQVIST. Influence of uterine contractions on the uteroplacental blood flow at term. *Am. J. Obstet. Gynecol.* 93: 44–57, 1965.
14. BOYD, J. D., AND W. J. HAMILTON. *The Human Placenta*. Cambridge: Heffer, 1970.
15. CLAVERO, J. A., AND J. B. LLUSIA. Measurement of the villus surface in normal and pathologic placentas. *Am. J. Obstet. Gynecol.* 86: 234–240, 1963.
16. CRAWFORD, J. M. Vascular anatomy of the human placenta. *Am. J. Obstet. Gynecol.* 84: 1543–1567, 1962.
17. DARON, G. H. The arterial pattern of the tunica mucosa of the uterus in *Macacus rhesus*. *Am. J. Anat.* 58: 349–419, 1936.
18. DARON, G. H. The veins of the endometrium (*Macacus rhesus*) as a source of the menstrual blood. *Anat. Record* 67, Suppl. 13, 1937.
19. DEES-MATTINGLY, M. Absorptive area and volume of chorionic villi in circumvallate placenta. *Am. J. Anat.* 59: 485–507, 1936.
20. DODDS, G. S. The area of the chorionic villi in the full term placenta. *Anat. Record* 24: 287–294, 1922.
21. FARRER-BROWN, G., J. O. W. BEILBY, AND M. H. TARBIT. The blood supply of the uterus. 1. Arterial vasculature. *J. Obstet. Gynaecol. Brit. Commonwealth* 77: 673–681, 1970.
22. FARRER-BROWN, G., J. O. W. BEILBY, AND M. H. TARBIT. The blood supply of the uterus. 2. Venous pattern. *J. Obstet. Gynaecol. Brit. Commonwealth* 77: 682–689, 1970.
23. FLEXNER, L. B., AND A. GELLHORN. The comparative physiology of placental transfer. *Am. J. Obstet. Gynecol.* 43: 965–994, 1942.
24. FREESE, U. E. The fetal-maternal circulation of the placenta. I. Histomorphologic, plastoid injection and x-ray cinematographic studies on human placentas. *Am. J. Obstet. Gynecol.* 94: 354–360, 1966.
25. FREESE, U. E., K. RANNINGER, AND H. KAPLIN. The fetal-maternal circulation of the placenta. II. An x-ray cinematographic study of pregnant rhesus monkeys. *Am. J. Obstet. Gynecol.* 94: 361–366, 1966.
26. FUCHS, F., T. SPACKMAN, AND N. S. ASSALI. Complexity and nonhomogeneity of the intervillous space. *Am. J. Obstet. Gynecol.* 86: 226–233, 1963.
27. GROSSER, O. *Frühentwicklung, Eihautbildung und Placentation des Menschen und der Säugetiere*. Müchen: Bergman, 1927.
28. HARRIS, J. W. S., M. L. HOUSTON, AND E. M. RAMSEY. Intravascular trophoblast in human, baboon and monkey uteri. *Anat. Record* 169: 334, 1971.
29. HARRIS, J. W. S., AND E. M. RAMSEY. The morphology of human uteroplacental vasculature. *Contrib. Embryol. Carnegie Inst. Wash.* 38: 43–58, 1966.
30. HELLEGERS, A. E. Some developments in opinions about the placenta as a barrier to oxygen. *Yale J. Biol. Med.* 42: 180–190, 1970.
31. HENDRICKS, C. H. The hemodynamics of a uterine contraction. *Am. J. Obstet. Gynecol.* 76: 969–982, 1958.
32. HOUSTON, M. L. The villous period of placentogenesis in the baboon (*Papio* sp.). *Am. J. Anat.* 126: 1–15, 1969.
33. HOUSTON, M. L. The development of the baboon (*Papio* sp.) placenta during the fetal period of gestation. *Am. J. Anat.* 126: 17–29, 1969.
34. LONGO, L. D., G. G. POWER, AND R. E. FOSTER. Respiratory function of the placenta as determined with carbon monoxide in sheep and dogs. *J. Clin. Invest.* 46: 812–827, 1967.
35. MAKOWSKI, E. L., G. MESCHIA, W. DROEGEMUELLER, AND F. C. BATTAGLIA. Distribution of uterine blood flow in the pregnant sheep. *Am. J. Obstet. Gynecol.* 101: 409–412, 1968.
36. MARKEE, J. E. Menstruation in intraocular transplants in the rhesus monkey. *Contrib. Embryol. Carnegie Inst. Wash.* 28: 219–308, 1940.
37. MARTIN, C. B., JR., H. S. McGAUGHEY, JR., I. H. KAISER, M. W. DONNER, AND E. M. RAMSEY. Intermittent functioning of the uteroplacental arteries. *Am. J. Obstet. Gynecol.* 90: 819–823, 1964.
38. MARTIN, C. B., JR., AND E. M. RAMSEY. Gross anatomy of the placenta of rhesus monkeys. *Obstet. Gynecol.* 36: 167–177, 1970.
39. MOSSMAN, H. W. Discussion on comparative biology of the placenta and fetal membranes. In: *Fetal Homeostasis*, edited by R. M. Wynn. Baltimore: Port City Press, 1967, vol. II, p. 58–59.
40. NOER, R. A study of the effect of flow direction on the placental transmission, using artificial placentas. *Anat. Record* 96: 383–389, 1946.
41. OKKELS, H., AND E. T. ENGLE. Studies on the finer structure of the uterine blood vessels of the macacus monkey. *Acta Pathol. Microbiol. Scand.* 15: 150–168, 1938.
42. PANIGEL, M. Placental perfusion experiments. *Am. J. Obstet. Gynecol.* 84: 1664–1683, 1962.
43. RAMSEY, E. M. The vascular pattern of the endometrium of the pregnant rhesus monkey (*Macaca mulatta*). *Contrib. Embryol. Carnegie Inst. Wash.* 33: 113–147, 1949.
44. RAMSEY, E. M. Venous drainage of the placenta of the rhesus monkey (*Macaca mulatta*). *Contrib. Embryol. Carnegie Inst. Wash.* 35: 151–173, 1954.

45. RAMSEY, E. M. Circulation in the maternal placenta of the rhesus monkey and man, with observations on the marginal lakes. *Am. J. Anat.* 98: 159–190, 1956.
46. RAMSEY, E. M. Vascular anatomy of uteroplacental and fetal circulation. In: *Proceedings of the Macy Foundation—CIOMS Conference on Oxygen Supply to the Human Fetus*, edited by J. Walker and A. C. Turnbull. Oxford: Blackwell, 1959, p. 67–79.
47. RAMSEY, E. M. Uteroplacental circulation during labor. *Clin. Obstet. Gynecol.* 11: 78–95, 1968.
48. RAMSEY, E. M., G. W. CORNER, JR., AND M. W. DONNER. Serial and cineradioangiographic visualization of maternal circulation in the primate (hemochorial) placenta. *Am. J. Obstet. Gynecol.* 86: 213–225, 1963.
49. RAMSEY, E. M., G. W. CORNER, JR., M. W. DONNER, AND H. M. STRAN. Visualization of maternal circulation in the monkey placenta by radioangiography. In: *Scritti in onore del Prof. Giuseppe Tesauro nel xxv anno del Suo insegnamento*, edited by V. Danesino. Napoli: Montanino, 1962, vol. II, p. 1779–1784.
50. RAMSEY, E. M., AND J. W. S. HARRIS. Comparison of uteroplacental vasculature and circulation in the rhesus monkey and man. *Contrib. Embryol. Carnegie Inst. Wash.* 38: 59–70, 1966.
51. RAMSEY, E. M., C. B. MARTIN, JR., AND M. W. DONNER. Fetal and maternal placental circulations. *Am. J. Obstet. Gynecol.* 98: 419–423, 1967.
52. RAMSEY, E. M., C. B. MARTIN, JR., H. S. MCGAUGHEY, JR., I. H. KAISER, AND M. W. DONNER. Venous drainage of the placenta in rhesus monkeys: radiographic studies. *Am. J. Obstet. Gynecol.* 95: 948–955, 1966.
53. RECH, W. Untersuchungen über die Grösse der Zottenoberfläche der menschlichen Plazenta. *Z. Biol.* 80: 349–358, 1924.
54. REYNOLDS, S. R. M. Relation of maternal blood flow within the uterus to change in shape and size of the conceptus during pregnancy; physiological basis of uterine accommodation. *Am. J. Physiol.* 148: 77–85, 1947.
55. ROMNEY, S. L., AND D. E. REID. Observations on the fetal aspects of placental circulation. *Am. J. Obstet. Gynecol.* 61: 83–98, 1951.
56. SPANNER, R. Mütterlicher und kindlicher Kreislauf der menschlichen Placenta und seine Strombahnen. *Z. Anat. Entwicklungsgeschichte* 105: 163–242, 1935.
57. STIEVE, H. Das Zottenraumgitter der reifen menschlichen Plazenta. *Z. Geburtshilfe Gynaekol.* 122: 289–315, 1941.
58. WILKIN, P. Morphogenese. In: *Le Placenta Humain—Aspects Morphologiques et Fonctionnels*, edited by J. Snoeck. Paris: Masson, 1958, p. 23–70.
59. WILKIN, P. Changes in area of the placenta with gestational age. In: *The Placenta and Fetal Membranes*, edited by C. A. Villee. Baltimore: Williams & Wilkins, 1960, p. 225–233.
60. WULF, H. [Cited by Bartels, Moll, and Metcalfe (10).]
61. WYNN, R. M. Morphology of the placenta. In: *Biology of Gestation*, edited by N. S. Assali. New York: Acad. Press, 1968, vol. I, p. 94–184.

CHAPTER 48

Immunologic studies of the endocrine system in relation to reproduction

K. A. LAURENCE

H. HASSOUNA

*The Population Council, The Rockefeller University,
New York, New York*

CHAPTER CONTENTS

THE APPLICATION of immunologic techniques to the study of the reproductive processes had been limited in scope and direction for many years. Until recently attention was directed almost exclusively toward the most obvious and most obtainable of all immunogens of the reproductive system—the spermatozoa. The determination of the antigenicity of the male gamete and the antifertility effect of an immune response to sperm in the female were the primary concerns of those involved in early studies of immunoreproduction. Tyler (96), Katsh & Katsh (38), Behrman (5), and Shulman (88) comprehensively reviewed the early studies. Interest in this field has not waned. In fact in 1967 an entire symposium was devoted to the immunology of spermatozoa and fertilization (8).

Since the turn of the century the antigens derived from semen, sperm, and the testes and the effects of these antigens on fertility in the male and female have been discussed in more than 300 reports involving more than 350 experiments.

The advances in endocrinology that have helped elucidate the sequential events leading to reproduction have suggested, however, that there are many parameters subject to immunologic study in addition to those involving the sperm. Experience has now shown that every step of the reproductive sequence, from the hypothalamic releasing hormones to fertilization and from pregnancy maintenance to parturition and lactation, involves molecules that, simply because of their size and structure, possess at least potential antigenicity and therefore might be subject to selected immunologic control.

The recognition of this fact has caused the rather rapid maturation of the science of immunoreproduction within the last decade. It has advanced from the stage of accumulating isolated facts concerning the antigenicity of cells, tissues, organs, and protein hormones to the more important stage of observing and measuring physiological effects of specific and individual antigen-antibody reactions within an intact animal.

For several reasons, the techniques of immunology have finally contributed to furthering the knowledge of the reproductive process, after many years of frustration and misunderstanding. Of prime importance has been the development of adjuvant techniques that enhance antibody formation and potentiate the antigenicity of minute quantities of low-molecular-weight substances (25). The paraffin oil-type adjuvant has proven to be exceptionally effective in stimulating the formation of antibodies to hormones (19).

More sensitive tests whereby small quantities of most antigens and levels of circulating antibodies can be detected have finally been developed and successfully employed for the study of reproduction. The hemagglutination (7) and hemagglutination inhibition (84) tests, agar gel diffusion (12), immunoelectrophoresis (71), fluorescent (15) and peroxidase-labeled (65) antibody procedures, and the radioimmunoassay (17) have proven invaluable in the detection of hormones, either circulating or fixed in tissues. With these technical advances in immunology it is now possible to approach the as yet unsolved problems of reproduction and endocrinology from a new vantage point.

Although the techniques of immunology have been applied to all aspects of reproduction, the following is concerned only with the methods that have been utilized in a study of the endocrine system in relation to reproduction. Briefly, the discussion follows follicular development to ovulation, ovum implantation, steroidogenesis, and pregnancy maintenance and shows how immunologic techniques may affect these various steps. Because of this limitation, concentration is on the antibodies formed to only those endocrinologic mechanisms involved in the reproductive process.

GENERAL ANTIGENICITY OF GONADOTROPHINS

Since the epic studies that led to the determination of the role played by the hypophysis in reproduction, the protein hormones of the anterior pituitary have been subjected to extensive physiochemical studies and purification processes (28). As the experience in the separation and purification techniques have increased and improved, each purified hormone [follicle-stimulating hormone (FSH), luteinizing hormone (LH), prolactin (LTH)] has been subjected, as well, to immunologic study.

Interestingly, just a few decades ago, the refractoriness of experimental animals to exogenously administered gonadotrophins was not considered a truly immunologic phenomenon. It was nonetheless admitted that serum from such treated animals contained substances (antihormones) that had the capacity to neutralize the hormonal activity of the administered gonadotrophin (13, 14, 45). For example, Kupperman et al. (42) demonstrated that serum antigonadotrophic substances obtained from rabbits injected with sheep pituitary gland extracts could inhibit the hormonal action of endogenous gonadotrophins in the rat. By means of parabiosis and gonadectomy of one partner, the administration of the antihormone was found to inhibit the biological action of the gonadotrophin of the castrate partner's pituitary. Injected into either the castrate or intact partner, the antihormone was of sufficient strength to prohibit the ovarian hypertrophy and luteinization generally found in the controls. That the antihormones were probably antibodies was recognized by Parkes & Rowlands (72), and yet most investigators remained unconvinced that these antihormone substances were actually immune bodies. Unfortunately the sensitive immunologic techniques presently employed to detect antigenicity of the gonadotrophin and to measure antibody titers were not available.

Most, if not all, of the gonadotrophins made available for study to date have proven not only to be antigenic but also to possess multiple antigens. The evidence that the gonadotrophins as antigens are not immunologically pure has been based primarily on the use of four techniques: 1) the agar gel double diffusion procedure, which permits the visualization of the precipitation lines formed between antibodies and their specific antigens; 2) hemagglutination, a procedure in which dilutions of an antibody combine with tanned red blood cells modified with a specific and constant quantity of soluble protein antigens; 3) hemagglutination inhibition, a sensitive procedure in which a constant, measured quantity of antibody is reacted with dilutions of a known or unknown antigen, which may inhibit the agglutination of the red blood cells as described in (2) above; 4) the complement fixation test, based on a 50% hemolytic end point in which a specific or related antigen and an antibody combine with complement to prevent the lysis of red blood cells that are used as part of the indicator system.

With the application of these simple techniques it has been easily demonstrated that most preparations of LH or FSH contain from two to ten antigens (76). Some of the antigens are nonhormonal, antigenic contaminants—usually serum proteins or tissue proteins. Henry & van Dyke (34) reported that an antiserum (produced in rabbits) to a purified ovine interstitial cell-stimulating hormone (ICSH) contained as many as six antibodies. By selective absorption of the antiserum with sheep plasma and tissue extracts, the number of antigen-antibody reactions was reduced to one single precipitin line. Segal et al. (87) also reported that absorption of an antiserum to ovine LH with serum proteins reduced the number of reacting precipitin systems, but, despite exhaustive absorption, two distinct precipitin lines always remained. Further, these investigators revealed that ovine FSH and ovine LH had an antigen in common. The LH contaminant was removable by using an antiserum to ovine LH. Rao and Munshi (64, 77) removed the common antigen by absorbing antiovine FSH with serum from either normal or hypophysectomized sheep.

Ely & Chen (19) produced a hyperimmune antiserum to LH (NIH-LH-S2) in rabbits, which, when reacted with its homologous antigen by immunoelectrophoresis or agar gel diffusion, developed a minimum of 10 precipitin lines. At least three of these reactions were attributed to sheep tissue and serum proteins. Selective and consecutive absorption with FSH, pregnant mares' serum (PMS), human chorionic gonadotrophin (HCG), and thyroid-stimulating hormone (TSH) removed specific lines with each absorption process. There remained, however, a single precipitin line against the homologous hormone, LH.

Immunoelectrophoresis was also used by Wolfe (100, 101) and by Illei & Moritz (37) to determine the purity of human FSH that had been previously purified by starch gel electrophoresis. At least three components were present after this purification process. Talaat & Laurence (93) reported that ovine FSH (NIH-FSH), as supplied for study by the Endocrine Study Section, National Institutes of Health, contained at least two antigenic components, even after absorption of the homologous antiserum with sheep serum proteins.

Bovine and ovine prolactin (LTH) have also been

proven to possess antigenicity. S. Badawy and K. A. Laurence (personal communication), using agar gel diffusion, demonstrated that rabbit antibovine prolactin had at least one detectable precipitation band. Sundaram & Sonenberg (92) consistently found one precipitin line with rabbit antiovine prolactin. Interestingly the antiprolactin reacted with bovine growth hormone as well.

Recently, Hershman & Starnes (35) isolated and characterized human chorionic thyrotrophin. With immunoelectrophoresis, precipitin bands that corresponded to those of bovine TSH were formed. Although the human chorionic thyrotrophin shares a major immunologic determinant with the bovine TSH, these investigators believe a significant molecular difference exists between them, based on their movement in disk gel electrophoresis.

El Tomi et al. (18) were able to demonstrate that human placental lactogen was antigenic in the rat and apparently possessed no cross reactivity with human FSH, LH, or HCG.

Immunologic analysis of two other substances commonly demonstrating gonadotrophic hormone activity has shown them to have multiple antigens. Pregnant mares' serum gonadotrophin (PMSG) and HCG stimulated the formation of antiserum containing from five to six antibodies. Of five distinct reactions between the antiserum and PMSG, only two were hormone-specific responses, according to Rao et al. (78). Van Hell and associates (97) indicated that, despite extensive physiochemical purification procedures, an active HCG preparation contained at least six antigens.

Thus all these studies indicated that most, if not all, purified gonadotrophin preparations available for immunologic study are not homogenously pure antigens. The methodology required for purification of the gonadotrophin is still being developed, and the immunologic techniques will continue to be employed in the determination of the purity of each preparation. It is, however, more than possible that in the near future the molecular structure of each of the hormones will be determined, and synthetic, pure, and hormonally active hormones will become available; this will make the development of further methodology for purification of hormones from animal sources unnecessary.

SPECIES SPECIFICITY

The discovery that the pituitary gonadotrophins had antigenic properties stimulated studies of the species specificity of the gonadotrophic antigens and their antibodies. Until recently it was believed that any antibody produced would combine only with the gonadotrophin from the species from which it was obtained (26, 33).

That an antiserum to any of the gonadotrophins is not strictly species specific was established by a number of investigators in the 1960s. Moudgal & Li (63), using an antiserum to ovine ICSH, showed that cross reactions with the same trophic hormone from other species could occur, as demonstrated in vitro by a variety of immunologic procedures. Further, Munshi and Rao (64, 77) observed that ovine LH had antigens common to LH of human, bovine, and porcine origin.

In more specific tests of antigonadotrophins, antibodies labeled with fluoroscein isothiocyanate or horseradish peroxidase have been used to localize hormone-producing cells within the anterior pituitary. Although there were early reports of relative failure in localizing the gonadotrophic cells (58), the cells responsible for the synthesis in the pituitary of ACTH (47) and growth hormone (GH) (48, 59) and GH within the placenta (30, 85) have been located with these methods with some degree of success.

Midgley (60), demonstrating by agar gel double diffusion that an anti-HCG would combine with purified human pituitary LH, used the antibody labeled with fluoroscein to localize the presence of LH within the pituitary gland itself. Nakane and Pierce (65, 66) utilized an antibody labeled with peroxidase to localize those cells producing gonadotrophin within the hypophysis.

All these studies presented circumstantial evidence that the antibodies produced against the gonadotrophins reacted in a specific immunologic combination with homologous and heterologous gonadotrophin preparations during in vitro procedures.

Even though these serological reactions indicated specific combinations of antibodies to gonadotrophins and suggested a similarity of molecular structure of the hormones, irrespective of species, definitive proof of complete combination of antibody antigen awaited studies of the effectiveness of an antigonadotrophin serum to counterbalance the hormonal activity of each hormone in an in vivo situation.

NEUTRALIZATION OF BIOLOGICAL
ACTIVITY OF HORMONES

Segal et al. (87) reported that an antiovine LH (NIH-LH-S1), when combined in vitro with 40 μg of LH in the region of antibody excess, resulted in precipitation of the antigen-antibody complex. After removal of this complex, bioassay of the supernatant by the Weaver-Finch test revealed that it contained no LH activity (86). On the same occasion these investigators demonstrated that the LH contaminant in ovine FSH (NIH-FSH-S1) could be removed with the rabbit antiovine LH serum, as indicated by the same Weaver-Finch reaction.

Tamada et al. (94) prepared an antiserum to human urinary FSH that inhibited the biological activity of the human FSH in the ovarian augmentation assay.

These observations thus confirmed that the combination of an antigonadotrophin with a homologous hormone, as shown previously by in vitro procedures, is capable of neutralizing the biological activity of the hormone in bioassay procedures.

IMMUNOLOGIC DETECTION OF GONADOTROPHINS IN PLASMA AND URINE

Bioassay techniques have demonstrated changes in pituitary potency of the gonadotrophins during the reproductive cyclic phenomena of numerous animals (28). Bioassay techniques have also been available to measure levels of gonadotrophins excreted during the course of the menstrual cycle of the human being. Generally assays for LH have involved the ventral prostate assay of Greep et al. (29) or the ovarian ascorbic acid depletion test described by Parlow (73). Detection of urinary FSH has usually depended on the ovarian augmentation assay developed by Steelman & Pohley (90). These assay systems require that urinary gonadotrophin extracts be concentrated because of the low sensitivity of the procedures. The bioassays are involved, complicated, and time consuming. Obviously an improvement in techniques to measure gonadotrophins would be desirable and useful.

Two factors made possible development of sensitive immunoassays for detection of gonadotrophins in urinary extracts and circulating fluids. The major factor was the observation that HCG or pituitary LH cross-reacts with an anti-HCG serum. Using this observation, Wide & Gemzell (98) developed an immunologic method for estimating urinary LH excreted during the normal menstrual cycle. Utilizing the hemagglutination inhibition technique, these investigators found LH excretion patterns not unlike the LH levels determined by bioassay. There was generally a broad midcycle peak of LH, and occasionally high levels of LH were found at other times in the cycle. This study then opened the door to the development of gonadotrophin assays by immunologic means. Later, Sato et al. (81) and Mishell (61), employing the same basic immunologic methodology, confirmed that it was possible to measure daily LH levels during the course of a normal menstrual cycle. Although this was a step forward, this immunoassay was not overly sensitive and was subject to criticism because the specificity of the procedure was not well established.

After the development of the radioimmunoassay by Yalow & Berson (102) and Hunter & Greenwood (36) for insulin and growth hormone, respectively, the sensitive and specific immunologic assays for gonadotrophins were soon applied.

The principle of the radioimmunoassay is a simple one. It is based on the competition between a labeled and an unlabeled hormone for a specific amount of antibody. The ratio of bound to free labeled hormone is then determined and is directly related to the amount of hormone in the sample undergoing examination. Today there are a variety of radioimmunoassays for LH, FSH, and LTH (17).

Reports from various laboratories indicate that there are some similarities and some differences in the individual measurements of serum or urinary LH and FSH patterns (91, 95). The quantitative differences in gonadotrophin levels are undoubtedly associated with the lack of established standards for the reagents involved in the radioimmunoassay. The differences in values for the gonadotrophins from the laboratories are probably due to the strength of the antibodies involved, the methodology employed to label the hormones, and the other unknown and unpublished techniques developed during the individualization of the assay procedure. The Karolinska Symposium on the Immunoassay of Gonadotrophins (17) provided an excellent summary of the latest procedures developed. Radioimmunoassay has been successfully used for the measurement and quantitation of LH and FSH in the human being and other animals during the course of a menstrual or estrous cycle. Almost all investigators have indicated that in the human female, there is a sharp, significant peak of LH at midcycle. The FSH, on the other hand, is often shown to peak in the early follicular phase (9, 69, 70, 75) and later at midcycle (83). The presence of FSH and LH at midcycle in urine and plasma appears to be in harmony with the concept of the cyclic patterns of menstruation.

Prolactin levels during different reproductive states have been determined in the rat by use of the radioimmunoassay (67). Amenomori et al. (2) reported that prolactin levels were highest at estrus and lowest in diestrus. Estrogen injections increased the amount of prolactin detected in the pituitary and in the serum. Neil & Reichart (67) disagree, for with the technique developed in their laboratory, prolactin levels were highest in the evening of proestrus.

The understanding of the FSH, LH, and LTH patterns should help clarify the present knowledge of the events of follicular development, ovulation, and luteal and pregnancy maintenance. The studies confirmed the earlier observations that the rise in FSH and LH results in follicular development and ovulation.

EFFECTS OF ACTIVE IMMUNIZATION WITH FOREIGN GONADOTROPHINS ON REPRODUCTION IN THE FEMALE

The active immunization of laboratory animals with foreign, purified gonadotrophins results in the formation of antibodies that can sequester and neutralize the biological activity of the same hormones. Whether the formation of the antibodies that develop to FSH, LH, or LTH antigens have any neutralizing effect on the endogenous hormonal activity requires investigation.

Recently, reports of several studies indicate that the reproductive capacity of rabbits and rats is adversely affected by injections of the hormones in adjuvants.

Basing their experiment on studies indicating that FSH is responsible for the stimulation of follicular development, Talaat & Laurence (93) immunized rats and rabbits with ovine FSH to determine whether the antibodies that would arise could prevent the follicles from developing to the stage required for ovulation.

Results were more varied than merely preventing follicular maturation. Female rats reacted to the immunization by becoming anestrous, by presenting a nonmating behavior, or by having sterile matings. Examination of the ovarian tissue revealed, as might be expected, diminished follicular development. Occasionally follicles became filled with thick, curled granulosa tissues. In other animals, persistent corpora lutea were found in ovaries containing few follicles. Rabbits immunized with FSH in adjuvants were affected similarly. Libido was often affected, and, when mating did occur, either there were no implantations or the implants had undergone resorption. Thus the immunization with FSH not only impaired follicular maturation and ovulation, but also interfered with implantation and pregnancy maintenance.

Laurence & Ichikawa (43), in their studies of active immunization of female rats with bovine LH, found reproductive failures similar to those found with FSH immunization. Animals responded by remaining anestrous for periods up to 129 days. In addition some reacted by exhibiting nonmating behavior, sterile matings, or an extended gestation. In most cases, when pregnancy was confirmed by laparotomy, the offspring delivered were stillborn and were delivered over a period of days, rather than within a few hours, as is the general rule. Each of the females was obviously distressed during delivery.

Histologically the ovaries of the rats remaining in diestrus for periods up to 129 days gave evidence that corpora lutea diminished in number and size, with an indication that follicle development was not greatly impaired.

Therefore, on a biological basis, immunization of the rat with either FSH or LH resulted in an indistinguishable reduction in reproductive performance. Only after histological examination of the ovaries was a difference in response to the immunization with FSH and LH evident.

Badawy and Laurence (personal communication) examined female rats after immunization with LTH. The results were not as dramatic as with the gonadotrophins. Cyclic times were affected, but, if mating occurred, the pregnancies were maintained.

These results indicate that active immunization can result in the production of antibodies to the hormones that subsequently neutralize the endogenous hormones. The variation in response, however, made it difficult to interpret exactly when and where the antibodies were actually affecting the biological activity of the endogenous hormones. Clarification of these results could best be interpreted through short-term, passive immunization with preformed antibodies administered at various times in the reproductive cycle.

EFFECTS OF ANTIGONADOTROPHINS ON PUBERTY

That an antiserum to one of the gonadotrophins would combine with its homologous hormone and a heterologous hormone antigen and that the antibody could neutralize the biological activity of its homologous hormone when combined in vitro opened a new area of study and interest. In 1961 Bourdel (6) reported that the administration of an antiovine LH into immature female rats (27–35 days old) prevented the expected increase in ovarian weights as these animals approached puberty. Histologically the ovaries of the females treated with anti-LH contained a decreased amount of interstitial tissue, the cells being smaller and the nuclei irregular in shape and size. Uterine weights were also depressed by the antiserum. Apparently there was sufficient similarity in molecular configuration between the endogenous rat pituitary LH and ovine LH to enable the antibody to the ovine preparation to neutralize the LH in the experimental animals. The action of the anti-LH may have prevented the interstitial tissue and perhaps the developing follicles from secreting estrogen (41) or may have prevented the entire steroidogenic activity in the ovary, since the uterine weight was also somewhat depressed.

Active immunization of newborn female rabbits with LH and FSH has recently been reported by Monastirsky et al. (62). The injection of ovine FSH in Freund's adjuvant into rabbits 3 weeks old failed to affect the histological appearance of the ovaries when the females reached puberty. The immunization with LH, on the other hand, resulted only in a reduction in total ovarian weight and apparent follicular size. Although morphological impairment was the only apparent effect with development of the antibodies to LH, the possibility of functional disability in the LH- and FSH-immunized female can not be discounted.

EFFECTS OF ANTI-LH AND ANTIESTROGEN ON OVULATION

Kelly et al. (39) and later Laurence & Ichikawa (44) demonstrated that antibodies to ovine LH or bovine LH could prevent the continuation of the estrous cycle in the rat and thereby prevent ovulation during the treatment period. The neutralization of the endogenous LH kept the animals in a continuous state of diestrus. Animals treated for 5 days with the anti-LH remained in diestrus for as long as 8 days. After the inhibitory effects of the anti-LH serum were dissipated, the estrous cycle resumed and further ovulation was apparent.

It should be recalled that there is evidence of the release of LH in the rat on the afternoon of proestrus (22), probably through the stimulation of estrogen (21). That anti-LH suppressed the continuation of the estrous cycle and prevented ovulation implicates the antibody in the impairment of the estrogen synthesis.

Further immunologic proof of the relationship of LH release, ovulation, and estrogen production comes from studies of antibodies to the estrogen molecule itself. Lieberman et al. (50) established that steroids could be rendered antigenic by coupling these compounds to a protein carrier of known antigenic qualities. On the basis of these early studies, Ferin et al. (24) developed antibodies to estradiol-17β and progesterone by conjugating the steroid hemisuccinate to bovine serum albumin and combining the conjugate with Freund's adjuvant, and extensively immunizing ewes. Specific antibodies to the steroidal hapten are formed, and these antibodies subsequently are capable of neutralizing the biological action of the hormone itself. Antisera to estradiol prevent the uptake of exogenously administered tritiated estradiol in the uterus, pituitary, and ovaries of the rat. The antiestrogen, apparently neutralizing the steroid in the peripheral circulation (23), prevented the LH surge and consequently the process of ovulation. The expected ballooning of the uterine tissue and the cornification of the vaginal mucosa was also prevented by this antisteroidal serum (24).

These immunologic studies have thus contributed more information to the understanding of the feedback mechanisms involved in pituitary function and steroidogenesis during the critical period from ovulation to implantation. It would appear that the initiation of LH release is somehow under the influence of estrogen, and estrogen synthesis may very well be influenced by LH.

EFFECTS OF ANTI-LH ON IMPLANTATION

Evidence that the synthesis of estrogen is directly related to an interaction of the ovary with the LH molecule is exemplified by the fact that an anti-LH serum can induce a state of delayed implantation not unlike the classic delayed implantation that occurs in ovariectomized but progesterone-maintained pregnant rats (57, 68). Laurence & Ichikawa (44) administered an antibovine LH serum to rats on day 1 of pregnancy and caused delay of ovum implantation for several days. More recently, Chang and Laurence (personal communication) found that a potent antiserum to bovine LH given to female rats for a period of 9 consecutive days, beginning on day 1, delayed the nidation process for as long as 17 days. Based on the size of the implantations and on the time of parturition, spontaneous implantation occurred either on day 14 or day 17 in most of the treated animals. Implantation failed to occur in other females, with or without exogenously administered estrogen, after day 20.

Therefore one might conclude that the anti-LH serum delayed the nidation by suppressing the estrogen surge required for that process. The delay continued until the inhibitory capacity of the antiserum diminished.

While estrogen synthesis and release apparently have been affected by the anti-LH treatment, progesterone synthesis has not, as evidenced by the viability of the blastocysts that remain free within the uterine cavity. That implantation can occur spontaneously or can be induced by a single injection of estrone and that the blastocysts can be successfully transferred to the uterus of synchronized pseudopregnant animals and can undergo normal fetal development imply that pro-

gesterone production is maintained at sufficient physiological levels to maintain the viability of the blastocysts despite the anti-LH treatment (Chang and Laurence, personal communication). The mechanism by which estrogen production is suppressed remains undetermined. There is evidence that the corpus luteum, the ovarian interstitial tissue, or the Graafian follicle may be responsible for steroidogenesis in the rat ovary (82). The LH molecule can stimulate the corpus luteum to secrete estrogen in hypophysectomized rats, as demonstrated by Macdonald et al. (55). Alloiteau (1) showed that the nonluteal tissue may have some responsibility in the synthesis and production of estrogen between day 4 and day 11 of pregnancy in the rat. On the other hand, evidence that the Graafian follicles produce estrogen during the first half of pregnancy has been presented by Greenwald & Johnson (27). Irrespective of where estrogen is synthesized, its production or release is impaired in the rat by the immunologic neutralization of the luteinizing hormone, as indicated by the prevention of the nidation process.

ANTI-LH AND POSTIMPLANTATION PHENOMENA

Several groups of investigators working independently found that an anti-LH serum, prepared against either bovine or ovine LH, could not only affect ovulation or delay implantation, but could cause resorption of the fetuses already implanted. Spies & Quadri (89), using an antiovine LH prepared in male rabbits, passively immunized pregnant female rabbits at various stages between 16 hr after mating and day 18 of pregnancy. When the antiserum was administered intravenously daily between days 3 and 18, regression of corpora lutea and complete resorption of the embryos occurred. Progesterone dosages of 4 mg/day given to antiserum-treated females overcame the effects of the antibodies to LH, and the females maintained their pregnancy. The progesterone, however, did not prevent the loss of weight of the corpora lutea. Estrogen, on the other hand, prevented the luteolysis but did not prevent the resorption of the embryos.

Similar findings were made in the pregnant rat by Loewit and associates (53, 54) and Madhwa Raj & Moudgal (56). When the antiserum was given to pregnant female rats from day 7 through day 11 of pregnancy, no viable fetuses could be found at laparotomy on day 12 (54). If the treatment was delayed until day 12 and continued through day 16, resorption of the implanted fetuses was also noted. Only when the antiserum was given from day 14 onward was it ineffective in terminating pregnancy in the rat. Madhwa Raj & Moudgal (56) noted similar phenomena. These investigators indicated further that deprivation of LH for only 2–4 hr (its hormonal action being neutralized by an anti-LH) was sufficient to cause resorption of the fetuses on day 8 of pregnancy. Progesterone, however, administered concomitantly with antiserum to the LH, was reported to overcome the inhibitory effect of the anti-LH, and the pregnancies were maintained.

The general steroidogenic pathway during early pregnancy in the rat involves a rapid production of progesterone with a concomitant decrease in the amount of 20α-hydroxyprogesterone. Histochemical measurement of Δ^5-3β-hydroxysteroid dehydrogenase (Δ^5-3β-OHSDH) and 20α-hydroxysteroid dehydrogenase (20α-OHSDH), the enzymes responsible for the synthesis of the progesterone, and 20α-OH-progesterone, indicates an almost reciprocal relationship for the duration of the gestation period (4, 40, 46, 74). Although both enzymes can be detected within the luteal tissue during the preimplantation period of pregnancy, the activity of 20α-OHSDH begins to decrease by day 5, whereas that of Δ^5-3β-OHSDH begins to increase. Between days 8 and 20, 20α-OHSDH cannot be demonstrated histochemically. As parturition approaches, the activity of 20α-OHSDH rises once again. The Δ^5-3β-OHSDH is present in greatest quantity in the luteal tissue from days 9–20 but diminishes as pregnancy nears its natural end.

Loewit et al. (53) found that treatment with anti-LH immediately after implantation (days 7–9) resulted in the return of the 20α-OHSDH activity in the luteal tissue concomitant with the resorption of the fetuses. As indicated above, the 20α-OHSDH activity in the luteal tissue is generally not detectable at this time of pregnancy. This phenomenon, the return of 20α-OHSDH activity, is not unlike the results of Wiest et al. (99) who ascertained the reappearance of strong 20α-OHSDH activity after placental dislocation. The question thus arises as to whether the anti-LH directly affects the steroidogenic pathway in the ovary or whether the anti-LH adversely affects placental function, which is then reflected in an altered function of the corpus luteum.

USE OF ANTI-LH TO DISCRIMINATE BETWEEN HORMONAL ACTIVITIES OF NIDUS AND MOTHER

The process of implantation involves reactions from both the maternal and fetal sides. It is difficult to discriminate between the hormonal properties of the mother and the fetus during the early stages of the implantation process.

One way in which the maternal hormonal events necessary for pregnancy maintenance can be discriminated is by creating a pseudopregnant condition with the formation of a deciduomata within the uterine horn. Loeb (51, 52), in his classic work of the early 1900s, found a striking similarity between the trauma artificially induced and the trauma that occurs naturally as a result of a fetus beginning to nidate. De Feo (16) recently discussed the hormonal requirements necessary to induce and maintain the decidua in a variety of animals. One can state that this artificially induced trauma can serve as a useful model of the events of nidation without the association of an invading trophoblast or a growing fetus.

Utilizing the decidualization response in pseudopregnant rats, Chang et al. (11) studied the effect of anti-LH on the maternal hormone response and steroidogenic activity during the initiation of the nidation process. Administration of rabbit antibovine LH from day 1 through day 4 of pseudopregnancy resulted in reduced uterine response to traumatization. The decidual response was about one-third that expected by day 9. The response, however, was never completely inhibited. If initiation of anti-LH treatment was delayed until the day of traumatization and continued for three additional days (days 5–8), the decidual response was again about one-third that achieved in the normal serum control animals. The stimulation of a decidual response depends on a specific hormonal condition. It must be assumed therefore that the anti-LH interferes with the proper steroid balance.

The concomitant administration of either estrogen or progesterone with the anti-LH serum did not prevent the action of the antibody completely. Progesterone (4 mg) given daily with anti-LH from day 1 through day 4 resulted in a decidual response about one-half that of control animals. The use of 1.0 μg estrone for 4 days again resulted in a decidual response equivalent to one-half that of the controls. A combination of 1.0 μg estrone and 4.0 mg progesterone given for eight consecutive days induced a decidual response equal to that found in the nontreated control animals.

A decided difference was noted in a comparison of the histochemical responses of the luteal tissue in normal pregnancies with those in pseudopregnancies with deciduomata. It will be recalled that in the rat the diminution of 20α-OHSDH activity becomes apparent between days 4 and 8 of pregnancy. The Δ^5-3β-OHSDH activity, on the other hand, begins to rise. In pseudopregnancy the 20α-OHSDH activity never disappeared, with or without an induced decidual response. The passive immunization with anti-LH neither increased nor decreased the activity of either of these steroidogenic enzymes, even though the decidual response had been reduced. By inference then, the change in the steroidogenic pathway in the ovary during early pregnancy must in some way be due to the presence of an implanted fetus. As the trophoblast implants, it must stimulate the action of the ovary to synthesize the Δ^5-3β-OHSDH, and subsequently all the luteal tissue, to produce progesterone. As exemplified by the decidual response in pseudopregnancy, the maternal placenta apparently cannot by itself trigger the luteal tissue, old and new, to actively synthesize the enzymes responsible for production of progesterone.

Wiest et al. (99) found that 20α-OHSDH activity reappears in luteal tissue immediately after surgical dislocation of the placental tissues. This study and the study of the termination of a pregnancy with anti-LH tend to support a concept that a functional corpus luteum of pregnancy is in some way regulated by a placental hormone. If the fetal placenta becomes non-functional, the stimulus necessary for pregnancy maintenance is lacking and 20α-OHSDH activity returns to the luteal tissue. The luteal tissue is then a nonfunctional body, and the pregnancy is terminated. The anti-LH that terminates the pregnancy in the rat may well be affecting placental function by neutralizing a placental hormone possessing an antigenic structure similar, but not identical, to the pituitary LH molecule.

ANTI-LH AND REPEATED FETAL RESORPTION

Hassouna & Laurence (31) reported recently that a single injection of anti-LH into 10-day-pregnant rats could terminate the pregnancy within 2 days. Moreover, within 6 to 7 days after the administration of the anti-LH, the estrous cycle returned and the females mated once again when caged with a fertile male. On day 10 of pregnancy the anti-LH was administered once again. As before, the pregnancy was terminated, and the estrous cycle resumed within a 7-day period. In some animals, three pregnancies were terminated within a total time of 43 days. Other animals, after termination of two pregnancies, delivered a normal litter during the third untreated pregnancy.

Thus the anti-LH treatment does not permanently impair the reproductive capacity of the female rat. The neutralization of the gonadotrophin simply was of a temporary nature and caused only fetal resorption with no apparent significant side effects. Eventually the repeated injections of the rabbit anti-LH would be expected to cause the formation of antibodies to the rabbit serum and thus to reduce the effectiveness of the anti-LH.

EFFECTS OF ANTIPROLACTIN ON LACTOGENIC RESPONSE

The development of antibodies to ovine prolactin in rabbits has been confirmed by Li et al. (49), Emmart et al. (20), Hayashida (32), and Rumke & Ladiges (79). When the antiovine prolactin was administered intraductally just before an injection of prolactin into the same duct, the lactogenic effect of the hormone on the rabbit mammary gland was inhibited (80). As judged by the inhibition of the local lactogenic response, as little as 0.15 ml of the antiserum neutralized 50 μg or more of ovine prolactin (NIH-P-S5).

CONCLUSIONS

It is by chance that the field of immunoreproduction has developed as rapidly as it has during the last decade. Only because the antisera raised to foreign gonadotrophins in laboratory animals were able to cross-react and neutralize the biological activity of endogenous hormones in a third species was it possible for advances to be made.

The recognition of this fact by the scientific community during the last 10 years has opened an entirely new area of research. It can be predicted that immunologic procedures will not only continue to be used as a tool to study the known events of reproduction, but undoubtedly will be applied to study many of the intermediate events concerned with enzyme synthesis, other biochemical functions, and such misunderstood phenomena as capacitation of sperm, fertilization, and parturition. Perhaps the application of immunologic techniques will raise more questions concerning the entire reproduction process than it can supply answers. Only time will tell what major contribution the field of immunology will make to the physiology of reproduction.

REFERENCES

1. ALLOITEAU, J. J. Obtention de deciduomes traumatiques à tous les stodes de la gestation chez la ratte. *Compt. Rend. Soc. Biol.* 157: 1153–1157, 1963.
2. AMENOMORI, Y., C. L. CHEN, AND J. MEITES. Serum prolactin levels in rats during different reproductive states. *Endocrinology* 86: 506–510, 1970.
4. BALOGH, K. A histochemical method for the demonstration of 20α-hydroxysteroid dehydrogenase activity in rat ovaries. *J. Histochem. Cytochem.* 12: 670–673, 1964.
5. BEHRMAN, S. J. The immune response and infertility: experimental evidence. In: *Progress in Infertility*, edited by S. J. Behrman and R. W. Kistner. Boston: Little, Brown, 1968, p. 675–699.
6. BOURDEL, G. Effect of rabbit antiserum to sheep pituitary interstitial cell stimulating hormone in immature female rats. *Gen. Comp. Endocrinol.* 1: 375–385, 1961.
7. BOYDEN, S. V. The adsorption of proteins on erythrocytes treated with tannic acid and subsequent hemagglutination by antiprotein sera. *J. Exptl. Med.* 93: 107–120, 1951.
8. BRATANOV, K., V. H. VULCHANOV, V. DIKON, V. K. DOKOV, AND B. SOMLEV (editors). *Immunology of Spermatozoa and Fertilization*. Bulgaria: Bulgarian Acad. Sci. Press, 1969.

9. CARGILLE, C. M., G. T. ROSS, AND T. YOSHIMI. Daily variations in plasma follicle stimulating hormone, luteinizing hormone and progesterone in the normal menstrual cycle. *J. Clin. Endocrinol.* 29: 12–19, 1969.
11. CHANG, C. C., S. BADAWY, AND K. A. LAURENCE. Decidual cell response (DCR) and enzyme activity of the ovary in pseudopregnant rats after administration of antiluteinizing hormone (LH) serum. *Fertility Sterility* 22: 663–670, 1971.
12. CLAUSEN, J. *Immunochemical Techniques for the Identification of Macromolecules*. Amsterdam: North-Holland, 1969.
13. COLLIP, J. B., AND E. M. ANDERSON. The production of serum inhibitory to the thyrotropic hormone. *Lancet* 1: 76–78, 1934.
14. COLLIP, J. B., AND E. M. ANDERSON. Studies on the thyrotropic hormone of the anterior pituitary. *J. Am. Med. Assoc.* 104: 965–996, 1935.
15. COONS, A. H., AND M. H. KAPLAN. Localization of antigen in tissue cells. II. Improvements in a method for the detection of antigen by means of fluorescent antibody. *J. Exptl. Med.* 91: 1–13, 1950.
16. DE FEO, V. J. Decidualization. In: *Cellular Biology of the Uterus*,

edited by R. Wynn. New York: Appleton-Century-Crofts, 1967, p. 191–290.

17. Diczfalusy, E. Immunoassay of gonadotrophins. *Acta Endocrinol. Suppl.* 142, 1969.

18. El Tomi, A. E. F., L. Boots, and V. C. Stevens. Effects of immunization with human placental lactogen on reproduction in female rats. *Endocrinology* 87: 1181–1185, 1970.

19. Ely, C. A., and B. L. Chen. Immunological studies of the luteinizing hormone. I. Identification of the antigenic components of sheep luteinizing hormone and the development of a serologically specific antiserum. *Endocrinology* 79: 362–372, 1966.

20. Emmart, E. W., R. W. Bates, P. G. Condliffe, and W. A. Turner. Immunochemical studies with ovine prolactin. *Proc. Soc. Exptl. Biol. Med.* 114: 754–763, 1963.

21. Everett, J. W., and O. H. Sawyer. Estimated duration of the spontaneous activation which causes release of ovulating hormone from the rat hypophysis. *Endocrinology* 26: 121–127, 1953.

22. Everett, J. W., O. H. Sawyer, and J. E. Markee. A neurogenic timing factor in control of the ovulating discharge of lutenizing hormone in the cyclic rat. *Endocrinology* 44: 235–250, 1949.

23. Ferin, M., A. Tempone, P. E. Zimmering, and R. Vande Wiele. Effect of antibodies to 17β-estradiol and progesterone on the estrous cycle of the rat. *Endocrinology* 85: 1070–1078, 1969.

24. Ferin, M., P. E. Zimmering, S. Lieberman, and R. Vande Wiele. Inactivation of the biological effects of exogenous and endogenous estrogens by antibodies to 17β-estradiol. *Endocrinology* 83: 565–571, 1968.

25. Freund, J., M. M. Lipton, and G. E. Thompson. Aspermatogenesis in the guinea pig, induced by testicular tissue and adjuvants. *J. Exptl. Med.* 97: 711–725, 1953.

26. Geschwind, I. I. Species variation in protein and polypeptide hormones. In: *Comparative Endocrinology*, edited by A. Gorbman. New York: Wiley, 1959, p. 421.

27. Greenwald, G. S., and D. C. Johnson. Gonadotropic requirements for the maintenance of pregnancy in the hypophysectomized rat. *Endocrinology* 83: 1052–1069, 1968.

28. Greep, R. O. Physiology of the anterior hypophysis in relation to reproduction. In: *Sex and Internal Secretions I*, edited by William Young. Baltimore: Williams & Wilkins, 1961, p. 240–301.

29. Greep, R. O., H. B. van Dyke and B. F. Chow. Use of anterior lobe of prostate gland in assay of metakentrin. *Proc. Soc. Exptl. Biol. Med.* 46: 644–649, 1941.

30. Grumbach, M. M. Intracellular detection of hormones by immunochemical means. *Ciba Found. Colloq. Endocrinol.* 14: 373–374, 1962.

31. Hassouna, H., and K. A. Laurence. Repeated termination of pregnancy in the rat with antiLH sera. *Fertility Sterility.* In press.

32. Hayashida, T. Immunological studies with pituitary lactogenic hormone (prolactin). Immunoassay of hormones. *Ciba Found. Colloq. Endocrinol.* 14: 338–372, 1962.

33. Hays, E. E., and S. L. Steelman. Chemistry of the anterior pituitary hormones. In: *The Hormones*, edited by G. Pincus and K. V. Thimann. New York: Acad. Press, 1955, p. 201–234.

34. Henry, S. S., and H. B. van Dyke. A study of the antibodies produced in response to purified preparations of sheep interstitial cell stimulating hormone. *J. Endocrinol.* 16: 310–325, 1958.

35. Hershman, J. M., and W. R. Starnes. Placental content and characterization of human chorionic thyrotropin. *J. Clin. Endocrinol.* 32: 52–58, 1971.

36. Hunter, W. M., and F. C. Greenwood. A radio-immuno-electrophoretic assay for growth hormone. *Biochem. J.* 85: 39–40, 1962.

37. Illei, G., and P. M. Moritz. Further observations on the immunologic behavior of human pituitary and chorionic gonadotropin. *J. Endocrinol.* 29: 263–271, 1964.

38. Katsh, S., and G. F. Katsh. Antigenicity of spermatozoa. *Fertility Sterility* 12: 522–537, 1961.

39. Kelly, W. A., H. A. Robertson, and D. A. Stansfield. The suppression of ovulation in the rat by rabbit antiovine LH serum. *J. Endocrinol.* 27: 127–128, 1963.

40. Kidwell, W. R., K. Balogh, and W. G. Wiest. Effects of luteinizing hormones on glucose-6-phosphate and 20-α-hydroxysteroid dehydrogenase activities in superovulated rat ovaries. *Endocrinology* 79: 352–361, 1966.

41. Kracier, P. F. Secretion of the prenidation estrogen surge by the nonluteal tissues. *Endocrinology* 85: 177–178, 1969.

42. Kupperman, H. S., R. K. Meyer, and R. Hertz. The effect of antigonadotropic sera upon gonadotropic secretion in parabiotic rats. *Endocrinology* 24: 115–118, 1939.

43. Laurence, K. A., and S. Ichikawa. Effects of active immunization with bovine luteinizing hormone on reproduction in the female rat. *Endocrinology* 82: 1190–1199, 1968.

44. Laurence, K. A., and S. Ichikawa. The effects of antiserum to bovine luteinizing hormone on the estrus cycle and early pregnancy in the female rat. *Intern. J. Fertility* 14: 8–15, 1969

45. Leathem, J. H. The antihormone problem in endocrine therapy. *Recent Progr. Hormone Res.* 4: 115–152, 1949.

46. Levy, H., H. W. Deane, and B. L. Rubin. Visualization of steroid-3β-ol-dehydrogenase activity in tissues of intact and hypophysectomized rats. *Endocrinology* 65: 932–943, 1959.

47. Leznoff, A., J. Fishman, L. Goodfriend, E. McGarry, J. Beck, and B. Rose. The cytological localization of ACTH in the human pituitary. *J. Clin. Invest.* 41: 1720–1724, 1962.

48. Leznoff, A., J. Fishman, L. Goodfriend, E. M. McGarry, J. Beck, and B. Rose. Localization of fluorescent antibodies to human growth hormone in human anterior pituitary glands. *Proc. Soc. Exptl. Biol. Med.* 104: 232–235, 1960.

49. Li, C. H., N. R. Moudgal, A. Trenkle, G. Bourdel, and K. Sadri. Some aspects of immunochemical methods for the characterization of protein hormones. Immuno-assay of hormones. *Ciba Found. Colloq. Endocrinol.* 14: 20–32, 1962.

50. Lieberman, S., B. F. Erlander, S. M. Beiser, and F. G. Agate, Jr. Aspects of steroid chemistry and metabolism. Steroid-protein conjugates: their chemical, immunochemical and endocrinological properties. *Recent Progr. Hormone Res.* 15: 165–200, 1959.

51. Loeb, L. The experimental production of the maternal part of the placenta in the rabbit. *Proc. Soc. Exptl. Biol. Med.* 5: 102–105, 1908.

52. Loeb, L. The production of deciduomata and the relation between the ovaries and the formation of the decidua. *J. Am. Med. Assoc.* 50: 1897–1901, 1908.

53. Loewit, K. K., S. Badawy, and K. A. Laurence. Alteration of corpus luteum function in the pregnant rat by antiluteinizing serum. *Endocrinology* 84: 244–251, 1969.

54. Loewit, K. K., and K. A. Laurence. Termination of pregnancy in the rat with rabbit antibovine LH serum. *Fertility Sterility* 20: 679–688, 1969.

55. Macdonald, G. J., D. T. Armstrong, and R. O. Greep. Stimulation of estrogen secretion from normal rat corpora lutea by luteinizing hormone. *Endocrinology* 79: 289–293, 1966.

56. Madwa Raj, H. G., and N. R. Moudgal. Hormonal control of gestation in the intact rat. *Endocrinology* 86: 874–889, 1970.

57. Mayer, G. Delayed nidation in rats: a method of exploring the mechanisms of ovoimplantation. In: *Delayed Implantation*, edited by A. C. Enders. Chicago: Univ. of Chicago Press, 1963, p. 213–231.

58. McGarry, E. E., and J. C. Beck. Some studies with antisera to human FSH. *Fertility Sterility* 14: 558–564, 1963.

59. Meneghelli, V., and R. Scapinelli. The site and time of onset of growth hormone production in bovine adenohypophysis, determined by the fluorescent antibody method. *Acta Anat.* 51: 198–208, 1962.

60. Midgley, A. R. Immunofluorescent localization of human

pituitary luteinizing hormone. *Exptl. Cell Res.* 32: 606–609, 1963.

61. MISHELL, D. R., JR. Daily urinary assay of luteinizing hormone by an immunologic method. *Am. J. Obstet. Gynecol.* 95: 747–758, 1966.
62. MONASTIRSKY, R., K. A. LAURENCE, AND E. TOVAR. The effects of gonadotropin immunization of prepubertal rabbits on gonadal development. *Fertility Sterility* 22: 318–324, 1971.
63. MOUDGAL, N. R., AND C. H. LI. An immunochemical study of sheep pituitary interstitial cell stimulating hormone. *Arch. Biochem. Biophys.* 95: 93–98, 1961.
64. MUNSHI, S. R., AND S. S. RAO. Biological specificity of antigens present in ovine follicle-stimulating hormone. *Indian J. Exptl. Biol.* 6: 1–6, 1968.
65. NAKANE, P. K. Simultaneous localization of multiple tissue antigens using the peroxidase labeled antibody method: a study of the pituitary glands of the rat. *J. Histochem. Cytochem.* 16: 557–560, 1968.
66. NAKANE, P. K., AND G. B. PIERCE. Enzyme labelled antibodies: preparation and application for the localization of antigens. *J. Histochem. Cytochem.* 14: 929–931, 1966.
67. NEILL, J. D., AND L. E. REICHART, JR. Development of a radioimmunoassay for rat prolactin and evaluation of the NIAMD rat prolactin radioimmunoassay. *Endocrinology* 88: 548–555, 1971.
68. NUTTING, E. F., AND R. K. MEYER. Implantation delay, nidation and embryonal survival in rats treated with ovarian hormones. In: *Delayed Implantation*, edited by A. C. Enders. Chicago: Univ. of Chicago Press, 1963, p. 233–252.
69. ODELL, W. D., A. F. PARLOW, C. M. CARGILLE, AND G. T. ROSS. Radioimmunoassay for human follicle-stimulating hormone: physiological studies. *J. Clin. Invest.* 47: 2551–2562, 1968.
70. ODELL, W. D., G. T. ROSS, AND P. L. RAYFORD. Radioimmunoassay for luteinizing hormone in human plasma or serum: physiological studies. *J. Clin. Invest.* 46: 248–255, 1967.
71. OSSERMAN, E. F. A modified technique of immunoelectrophoresis facilitating the identificiation of specific precipitin areas. *J. Immunol.* 84: 93–97, 1960.
72. PARKES, A. S., AND I. W. ROWLANDS. Inhibition of ovulation in the rabbit by anti-gonadotropic serum. *J. Physiol., London* 88: 305–311, 1936.
73. PARLOW, A. F. Bioassay of pituitary luteinizing hormone by depletion of ovarian ascorbic acid. In: *Human Pituitary Gonadotropins*, edited by A. Albert. Springfield, Ill.: Thomas, 1961, p. 300–310.
74. PUPKIN, M., H. BRATT, J. WEISZ, C. W. LLOYD, AND K. BALOGH. Dehydrogenases in the rat ovary. I. Histochemical study of Δ^5-3β- and 20α-hydroxysteroid dehydrogenases and enzymes of carbohydrate oxidation during the estrous cycle. *Endocrinology* 79: 316–327, 1966.
75. RAITI, S., AND W. T. DAVIS. The principles and application of radioimmunoassay with special reference to the gonadotropins. *Obstet. Gynecol. Surv.* 24: 289–310, 1969.
76. RAO, S. S. Antibodies against reproductive hormones. In: *Immunology and Reproduction*, edited by R. G. Edwards. London: Intern. Planned Parenthood Federation, 1969, p. 63–84.
77. RAO, S. S., AND S. R. MUNSHI. The antigenicity of sheep follicle stimulating hormone. *Experientia* 19: 92–94, 1963.
78. RAO, S. S., S. K. SHAHANI, S. R. MUNSHI, AND K. N. RANGNEKAR. Selective inhibition of the follicle stimulating and luteinizing principles in the gonadotrophic hormones of different species. [Cited in (76).]
79. RUMKE, P., AND N. C. J. J. LADIGES. Comparative immunochemical studies with antisera to sheep prolactin and bovine growth hormone on anterior pituitaries of ox, sheep, rats and mice. *Z. Zellforsch. Bd.* 67: 575–583, 1965.
80. SAJI, M. A., AND D. B. CRIGHTON. A study of the antihormonal activity of an antiserum to ovine prolactin using the local lactogenic response in the rabbit. *J. Endocrinol.* 41: 555–561, 1968.
81. SATO, T., R. B. GREENBLATT, AND V. B. MAHESH. Levels of luteinizing hormone during the menstrual cycle determined by immunologic technics. *Fertility Sterility* 16: 223–228, 1965.
82. SAVARD, K. The biogenesis of steroids in the human ovary. In: *The Ovary*, edited by H. C. Mack. Springfield, Ill.: Thomas, 1968, p. 10–26.
83. SAXENA, B. B., G. LEYENDECKER, W. CHEN, H. GANDY, AND R. E. PETERSON. Radioimmunoassay of follicle stimulating (FSH) and luteinizing (LH) hormones by chromatoelectrophoresis. *Acta Endocrinol. Suppl.* 142, 1969.
84. SCHUURS, A. H. W. M. Agglutination inhibition reactions for the determination of gonadotrophins. *Acta Endocrinol. Suppl.* 142, 1969.
85. SCIARRA, J. J., S. L. KAPLAN, AND M. M. GRUMBACH. Localization of anti-human growth hormone serum within the human placenta: evidence for a human chorionic growth hormone—prolactin. *Nature* 199: 1005–1006, 1963.
86. SEGAL, S. J. Response of the Weaver Finch to chorionic gonadotrophin and hypophyseal luteinizing hormone. *Science* 13: 1242–1243, 1957.
87. SEGAL, S. J., K. A. LAURENCE, M. PERLBACHS, AND S. HAKIM. Immunologic analysis of sheep pituitary gonadotropins. *Gen. Comp. Endocrinol. Suppl.* 1: 12–21, 1962.
88. SHULMAN, S. Antigenic analysis of the male tract. In: *Immunology of Reproduction*, edited by R. G. Edwards. London: Intern. Planned Parenthood Federation, 1969, p. 111–135.
89. SPIES, H. G., AND S. K. QUADRI. Regression of corpora lutea and interruption of pregnancy in rabbits following treatment with rabbit serum to ovine LH. *Endocrinology* 80: 1127–1132, 1967.
90. STEELMAN, S. L., AND F. M. POHLEY. Assay of follicle stimulating hormone based on the augmentation with human chorionic gonadotropin. *Endocrinology* 53: 604–616, 1953.
91. STEVENS, V. C. Discrepancies and similarities of urinary FSH and LH patterns as evaluated by different assay methods. *Acta Endocrinol. Suppl.* 142, 1969.
92. SUNDARAM, K., AND M. SONENBERG. Immunochemical studies of human growth hormone, ovine prolactin, bovine growth hormone and a tryptic digest of bovine growth hormone. *J. Endocrinol.* 44: 517–522, 1969.
93. TALAAT, M., AND K. A. LAURENCE. Effects of active immunization with ovine FSH on the reproduction capacity of female rats and rabbits. *Endocrinology* 84: 185–191, 1969.
94. TAMADA, T., M. SOPER, AND M. L. TAYMOR. Immunologic studies with urinary follicle stimulating hormone. *J. Clin. Endocrinol.* 27: 379–384, 1967.
95. TAYMOR, M. L., AND J. MIYATA. Discrepancies and similarities of serum FSH and LH patterns as evaluated by different assay methods. *Acta Endocrinol. Suppl.* 142, 1969.
96. TYLER, A. Approaches to the control of fertility based on immunological phenomena. *J. Reprod. Fertility* 2: 473–506, 1961.
97. VAN HELL, H., B. C. GOVERDE, A. H. SCHUURS, E. DE JAGER, AND R. MATTHIYSEN. Purification, characterization and immunochemical properties of human chorionic gonadotropin. *Nature* 212: 261–262, 1966.
98. WIDE, L., AND C. GEMZELL. Immunological determination of pituitary luteinizing hormone in the urine of fertile and postmenopausal women and adult men. *Acta Endocrinol.* 39: 539–546, 1962.
99. WIEST, W. G., W. R. KIDWELL, AND K. BALOGH, JR. Progesterone catabolism in the rat ovary: a regulatory mechanism for progestational potency during pregnancy. *Endocrinology* 82: 844–859, 1968.
100. WOLFE, A. Antigenic components in human pituitary follicle stimulating hormone preparations of various purities. *Nature* 205: 504–505, 1965.
101. WOLFE, A. Antiserum to human pituitary follicle stimulating hormone. *Nature* 198: 1308–1309, 1968.
102. YALOW, R. S., AND S. A. BERSON. Immunoassay of endogenous plasma insulin in man. *J. Clin. Invest.* 39: 1157–1175, 1960.

CHAPTER 49

Biological effects of oral contraceptive steroids

SHELDON J. SEGAL
LINDA E. ATKINSON

*Biomedical Division, The Population Council, Rockefeller University,
New York, New York*

CHAPTER CONTENTS

THE ADDITION OF STEROIDS to the body imposes alterations not only on the reproductive system, but on nearly all the physiological processes. Since oral contraceptives (OCs) are synthetic steroids and structurally dissimilar, they will not have precisely the same activity or metabolism as do the natural steroids. Thus it may be inaccurate to assert that contraceptive steroid therapy mimics the pregnant state or the normal cycle. A large selection of orally active synthetic steroids or steroidlike drugs is available (e.g., more than 5 estrogens, about 18 C_{18} and C_{19} compounds, and a half dozen C_{21} steroids). Each may differ in its relative estrogenic or antiestrogenic, progestational or antiprogestational activities on the reproductive tract or in its induction of liver enzymes. The structures of the most commonly used compounds for contraceptive drugs are illustrated in Figure 1.

The scientific literature contains many descriptions of the biological effects of OCs. The extent to which the reports differ in their conclusions may reflect the specific steroid or combination of steroids, the dosage, the estrogen-to-progestin ratios used, the length of administration, and the physiological state of the subject. Indications are that many conditions brought about by synthetic steroids are reversible once treatment has stopped or that the body may accommodate to these disturbances and in time regain physiological balance. Whether long-term therapy (a decade or more) will produce permanent or adverse changes in the health of the individual is not known at present.

ROLE OF ORAL CONTRACEPTIVE STEROIDS IN THE CONTROL OF FERTILITY

Attempts to control human fertility through oral medicaments are as old as written history. Ancient manuscripts contain prescriptions for potions and other medication for the prevention of pregnancy. The exotic content and the application of these ancient prescriptions have little or no rationale for the modern student.

In our own times, the work done in the United States by such pioneers as John Rock and the late Gregory Pincus has brought OCs into the realm of practical reality. After intensive investigation in the laboratory and some clinical study in the early 1950s, field trials began in 1956 (44). By 1960 the first OCs were approved by the Food and Drug Administration for general distribution in the United States, and since then their use has spread rapidly throughout the world.

The OCs in general use today are prescribed according to two distinct regimens—combined and sequential. Under the combined regimen, 20 or 21 identical tablets containing one of several synthetic progestins, as well as estrogen, are taken from days 5 to 24 or 25 of the cycle. Under the sequential regimen, 15 or 16 tablets containing estrogen only are followed by five tablets containing progestin and estrogen. Under both regimens, suspension of the medication ordinarily results in withdrawal bleeding within a few days; medication is resumed on the day 5 of the new cycle. An alternative procedure is "three weeks on the pill, one week off," with inert tablets sometimes included for the "off" week to facilitate adherence to the regimen. A third regimen, which involves daily medication with small doses of progestin without estrogen, has been investigated and approved for use in the United States.

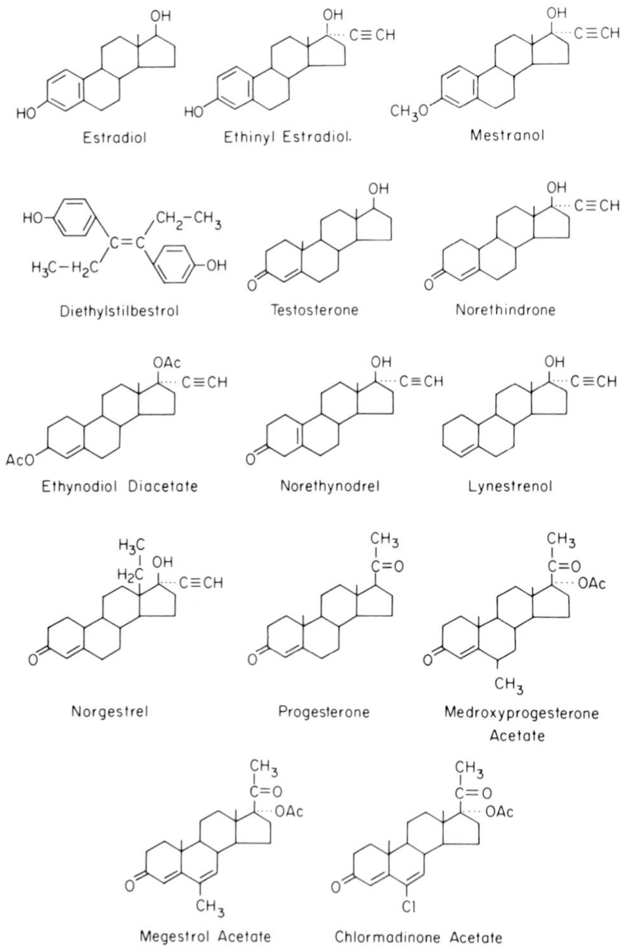

FIG. 1. The natural steroids and some of the common synthetic steroids used in antifertility drugs.

Other countries together account for a slightly larger total of users than does the United States, with the highest rates of use reported from Australia and New Zealand, Canada, and several countries in western Europe. The number of users in Latin America exceeds 2.5 million and appears to be growing rapidly (34, 54).

Although in the United States the OCs are most popular among younger women with better than average education, clinicians generally agree that most women can be taught to take them with reasonable consistency. This method of birth control has also proved acceptable to many couples who had been unwilling to try the traditional methods or were unable to use them successfully.

A major measure of the acceptability of a contraceptive method is the continuation rate, which indicates the proportion of couples still using the method at a given time after use was initiated. For the OCs, data from a national survey in the United States suggest a continuation rate of 73% after 24 months; women who discontinued use because they wanted to plan a pregnancy were excluded (73). The same survey also showed that the continuation rate was higher among younger women and those with a better education than among older and less-educated women, but the differences were not very significant. Recent attempts to introduce OCs into the family planning programs of several developing countries have been characterized by lower continuation rates than had been expected on the basis of experience in the United States (27). Because the continuation rates are so low, failure rates based on all unplanned pregnancies, including those occurring after discontinuation of contraception, tend to be disappointingly high.

Taken in the prescribed manner, OCs of the combined type are almost 100% effective in preventing pregnancy. Major reports cover an aggregate of some 325,000 cycles of medication; according to statements of the users, 17 pregnancies not associated with the omission of one or more tablets occurred. This corresponds to a pregnancy rate of less than 0.1 per 100 women per year (64). Sequential OCs are somewhat less effective; the pregnancy rate was about 0.3 per 100 women per year and was based on 116,000 cycles and 30 pregnancies, which apparently resulted from method failures.

The high acceptability of the OCs in the United States is attested by the fact that, within 5 years of the approval of the first product by the Food and Drug Administration, the number of current users reached about 3.8 million; this figure accounts for close to one-quarter of all users of contraceptives in the United States (72). By early 1969, 20 brands of OCs were distributed in the United States at a rate of about 8.5 million cycles per month (53). The Senate hearings of 1970 resulted in at least a temporary reduction in the number of users, the long-term effect of which has not been evaluated.

INTERFERENCE WITH FERTILITY BY ORAL CONTRACEPTIVE STEROIDS

From the developing egg to the delivery of an infant, the female reproductive cycle is a complex and delicately balanced interplay of events, any one of which, if distorted, may interrupt the succeeding processes. Shown in Figure 2 are the many target organs and feedback connections that may be affected by the contraceptive steroids. The antifertility effect may result from alterations in one or in several of these vulnerable areas.

The antifertility effectiveness of many contraceptive steroids has been thought to reside in their ability to suppress ovulation by interference with the normal interactions of the hypothalamus and pituitary, which results in alterations in the secretion of gonadotrophins. Most studies of urinary gonadotrophin excretion by women taking nonsequential OCs of mestranol combined with one of a variety of progestins indicate the abolition of the midcycle luteinizing hormone (LH) peak and changes in follicle-stimulating hormone (FSH) excretion different from those occurring during untreated cycles (13). These findings have been substantiated in experi-

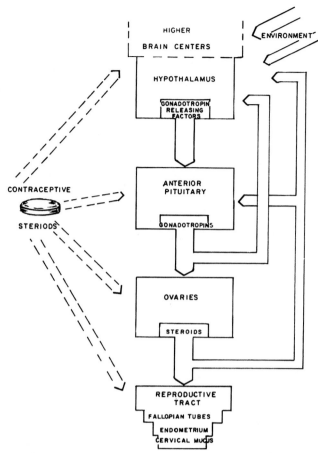

FIG. 2. Schematic representation of interrelationship and feedback mechanisms of female reproductive system and possible areas of interference by contraceptive steroids.

ments utilizing the more definitive radioimmunoassays to evaluate serum LH and FSH in subjects receiving 2.5 mg norethynodrel and 0.1 mg mestranol (61). Both LH and FSH midcycle elevations were absent, so that serum gonadotrophin concentrations were kept at a rather constant level approximating that of the luteal phase in untreated cycles. Long-term administration of OCs apparently does not differ from the first OC administration with respect to the effect on patterns of gonadotrophin release.

Administration of mestranol alone apparently did not eliminate the elevation in urinary LH excretion at midcycle as measured by bioassay (70), but suppression was observed when serum LH concentrations were examined by radioimmunoassay (61). In the latter instance, during sequential therapy, multiple and irregular LH peaks were seen; no concomitant rises in serum FSH were evident. Inclusion of 2 mg chlormadinone acetate with the mestranol produced an additional LH peak followed by a more quiescent LH pattern.

The influence of small doses of progestins on pituitary secretion of LH and FSH is variable. Chlormadinone acetate (0.5 mg/day) produced normal urinary LH excretion patterns in some treatment cycles, but in other

cycles no distinct midcycle LH elevation was evident (33). Daily administration of 0.5 mg norethindrone resulted in the immediate disappearance of the high midcycle urinary LH followed by large day-to-day variations (32). Larger doses of progestins are consistent in the suppression of the LH peak in urinary measurements of this gonadotrophin (13). Serum LH patterns were also dissimilar from control cycles in the absence of a well-defined midcycle surge and the presence of elevated levels before and after the expected time of the surge (63).

That cyclic ovulation may also be interrupted by reduced ovarian responsiveness to gonadotrophins as a result of OCs is a possibility. However, experiments by Starup & Ostergaard (58) indicate that, even after a 20-cycle regimen of mestranol (0.1 mg) and megestrol acetate (5 mg), ovulation can be induced by exogenously administered gonadotrophins, such as PMS (pregnant mares' serum) and HCG (human chorionic gonadotrophin).

Although the above contraceptive steroids have been shown to interfere with normal gonadotrophin patterns, there is evidence that ovulation may occur in women to whom they are given. Corpora lutea have been observed during treatment cycles in which megestrol acetate and/or mestranol (42) and chlormadinone acetate (38, 78) are used, even after long-term administration (38). Martinez-Manautou and co-workers (37, 38) estimate that some 60% of women receiving low doses of chlormadinone will ovulate during treatment. Pregnanediol levels over 1 mg/ml (38) and plasma progesterone concentrations typical of the luteal phase have been observed (33). Whether the fertility protection of chlormadinone is related to changes in cervical mucus that inhibit sperm transport (38, 78), to its interference with progesterone synthesis and metabolism (13), or to its allowing luteinization of the follicle without release of ovum is not understood.

Recovery of fertility after discontinuation of contraceptive steroids is generally rapid. The chance of finding a secretory endometrium during the first ovulation after withdrawal (indicating that ovulation has occurred and that the endometrial glands are under the influence of progesterone) declined in relation to the duration of therapy and the type of therapy used. The highest percentage of secretory endometria was associated with sequential pills and the lowest with injectable progestin preparations (36). Amenorrhea and infertility of 12 months were reported in some women after norethynodrel and medroxyprogesterone acetate regimens (74).

Whereas no increase has been noted in the prevalence of gross congenital malformations among children born to women taking OCs, a highly significant excess of chromosomal abnormalities has been reported in spontaneously aborted embryos from women who conceived within 6 months after the discontinuation of OCs (9). It should be noted that the abnormalities in question (polyploidy) are always lethal early in pregnancy.

EFFECTS OF ORAL CONTRACEPTIVES
ON THE REPRODUCTIVE TRACT

Changes in the histology and enzymology of the endometrium during treatment with OCs usually reflect the estrogenic or progestational action of the administered steroid. Generally, combination products produce secretory changes in the endometrium after only a few days of exposure and thus result in a shorter proliferative phase. The secretory endometrium develops rapidly, and within a few days the glands involute and the stroma may appear predecidual (16, 45). By days 22–25 of the treated cycle, the endometrium appears to be atrophic or in an early proliferative phase (16). Administration of ethinyl estradiol or mestranol during the first part of a sequential regimen induces a prolonged proliferative phase in the endometrium. Addition of the progestogen, megestrol acetate, results in a secretory response of the endometrial glands (16).

Utilization of continuous low doses of progestogen, such as chlormadinone acetate, has a varied effect on the histology and histochemistry of the endometrium in that specimens from some women indicate an ovulatory cycle, whereas those from other women are anovulatory (11).

Oral contraceptives containing progestins decrease the number of cornified cells present in vaginal epithelium when compared to the number of such cells present during untreated cycles. Norethindrone and lynestrenol are claimed to be more effective in suppressing cornification than are norethynodrel and megestrol. In sequential therapy, as expected, the cornification index remains high in response to the estrogen but falls rapidly once the progestin is included in the regimen (25).

Alterations in cervical mucus are under the influence of the steroids used in OCs. Progestational compounds produce an alkaline pH, poor ferning, shortened spinnbarkeit, and an increased viscosity. Several investigators have reported changes in cervical mucus induced by OCs that are apparently hostile to sperm or hinder their penetration (7, 28, 38, 40). Postcoital tests have shown reduced sperm count and motility when continuous low doses of progestogens are employed (38, 78). Other researchers, however, using cervical mucus collected from women taking OCs, found sperm penetration moderate to high throughout sequential therapy, and, in those women receiving low-dose combination OCs, sperm penetration in their cervical mucus did not vary from that of normally cycling, untreated women (1).

Cervical erosion, hypersecretion, and hyperplasia of the cervical glands have been found in association with continuous low-dose progestational compounds. These abnormalities were reversible with cessation of oral contraceptive medication (62).

In 1969 a survey of women attending the clinics of Planned Parenthood of New York City revealed a higher prevalence of epithelial abnormalities of the uterine cervix, diagnosed as carcinoma in situ, among women using OCs, compared with those using the diaphragm (39). The diagnosis was made in each case on the basis of a biopsy examined by two pathologists without knowledge of the contraceptive used. Women who had used OCs for one year or more were individually matched against diaphragm users with respect to five variables: age, parity, age at first pregnancy, ethnic group, and family income. The prevalence of carcinoma in situ was about twice as high among those who used OCs as among those who used the diaphragm, which was a significant difference.

For the interpretation of these findings, it would be important to know how diaphragm users differ from pill users with respect to age at first coitus, frequency of coitus, number of sexual partners, and previous medical history, all of which may contribute to the prevalence of carcinoma in situ. One would assume that such factors are highly correlated with one or more of the variables used in matching, but important residual differences may remain. In a California study, a significantly higher prevalence of dysplasia was found among women who had chosen OCs as their method of contraception but had not yet taken them compared with women who selected other methods (59). The two groups of women were quite similar with regard to such variables as age at first intercourse, age at first pregnancy, and age at clinic attendance, number of children, ethnic group, and religion.

In 1970 several types of OCs were withdrawn from the market or from clinical investigation because of the development of nodules in the mammary glands of beagle bitches after long-term administration of the products according to regimen and in the dosage per body weight used in women. The relevance of these findings to human beings is open to question. The latest available statistics on the incidence of, and mortality from, breast cancer do not show any changes in trend attributable to the increasing use of OCs. Since the effect of all known carcinogens in humans is delayed, with a latency period of about a decade, it will not be possible to make a definitive statement on this point until substantial numbers of women have used OCs for prolonged periods.

Preliminary results of a British study (M. P. Vessey, R. Doll, and P. M. Sutton, unpublished data) were interpreted to mean that OCs may protect against the occurrence of breast cancer in women of reproductive age. In this investigation of nondiseased women and women with breast malignancies who were matched by such variables as age and parity, 74 % of the women with breast cancer had never used OCs, whereas 64 % of the controls did have a history of oral contraceptive use.

Claims of increased breast size in a small percentage of women taking OCs are countered by the same number of women noting a decrease in size (46). There is an apparent reduction in lactation when norethynodrel is given in amounts greater than 2.5 mg (6). Lynestrenol, 2.5 mg, significantly reduced milk production in nursing women, whereas mestranol and ethinyl estradiol did not (6) The quality of milk or of infant growth was not hampered when mothers were taking ethylestrenol or 6 α-methyethynylestrenol (18).

CHANGES IN METABOLISM DURING ORAL CONTRACEPTIVE TREATMENT

The OCs have wide-ranging metabolic effects extending far beyond their primary target organs—the genital tract, the pituitary gland, and the hypothalamus. Laboratory studies of carbohydrate metabolism and of hepatic and thyroid function, to mention only a few, have revealed deviations from normal values in many women taking these compounds. Although they do not produce clinical symptoms, these abnormal findings are a cause for concern, since their significance for the health of women is not fully understood.

Carbohydrate Metabolism

The ability of contraceptive steroids to alter normal carbohydrate metabolism and the extent to which these steroids can affect normal carbohydrate metabolism have been studied extensively. However, the disturbances of carbohydrate metabolism have been entirely defined by the stimulus-response test of acute glucose administration. Glucose and insulin concentrations are elevated, and, although significantly different from untreated subjects, for the most part they do not fall in the abnormal range. Long-term contraceptive use has not produced a flood of cases of overt diabetes mellitus but has raised questions as to the exhaustion of pancreatic beta cells.

Waine et al. (71) in 1963 noted that the clearance of glucose from the blood after an oral glucose tolerance test was abnormal in women taking birth control pills. Since then numerous reports describing the responses to oral and intravenous glucose tolerance tests in relation to a variety of oral contraceptive steroids have appeared (56). In the majority of these studies, changes in fasting blood glucose levels during treatment periods that ranged from 3 weeks to 7 years were not found. Within one month of the initiation of oral contraceptive (OC) administration, peripheral glucose and insulin concentrations were significantly elevated after an intravenous glucose tolerance test (55). After taking a combination OC for 3 years, insulin and glucose values appeared to decline to control levels. Oral glucose tolerance tests were significantly higher with respect to glucose and insulin after 12 months of a mestranol-ethynodiol diacetate regimen in 40% of normal women. In contrast, 50% of women whose tests were borderline abnormal before taking the above OC combination improved after 12 months of treatment (57). In a study in which a sequential OC product was utilized, blood glucose and insulin levels remained significantly higher than control values for only 6 months (55).

The diabetogenic properties of oral contraceptive drugs are apparently related to the structure or dosage, or both, of the component steroids. Chlormadinone

acetate and megestrol acetate treatment did not alter the normal response to a glucose load, whereas norethynodrel (5 and 10 mg/day) combined with mestranol caused deterioration of glucose tolerance. A smaller dose (2.5 mg/day) of norethynodrel did not have this effect. Mestranol was observed to produce hyperglycemia more readily than ethinyl estradiol, a similar compound lacking the 3-methyl ether (3).

That older women with high parity who have a history of familial diabetes mellitus and who have given birth to large infants are more likely to have abnormal responses to glucose tolerance tests was reported in one study (55), although these correlations were not found in another group of women (76). Beck has shown that women who can be classified as gestational diabetics are affected by short-term treatment with mestranol to a greater extent than are nondiabetic women (3).

Growth hormone secretion is also known to be affected by OCs. Significantly higher serum growth hormone levels were attained when subjects taking contraceptive drugs were given hypoglycemic and arginine stimulation tests (55, 66). Medroxyprogesterone acetate caused a progressive elevation of fasting growth hormone concentrations in potential diabetics over a 3-month treatment period (20).

Another major participant in carbohydrate metabolism, pyruvate, has also been observed to increase after oral and intravenous glucose tests given to patients taking OCs. Serum pyruvate levels (obtained during the fasting state) were elevated in women who had just begun OC regimens (14, 76). Doar et al. (14) have also reported that fasting blood pyruvate levels are significantly higher in nonobese women taking combination OCs than in a nonobese control group. Calculation of the pyruvate levels attained by conversion from lactate in lactate infusion experiments performed in OC subjects suggests that the elevated pyruvate levels are due to increased rates of production rather than to faulty metabolism (14). Whether the increased pyruvate concentrations are the result of the estrogen and/or the progestin component of the contraceptive drug, or to elevations in other hormones affecting metabolism, such as cortisol, growth hormone, or thyroxine, is not known. Preliminary experiments, however, indicated a rise in pyruvate concentrations after short-term mestranol administration (14).

Lipid Metabolism

A consistent rise of serum triglyceride concentrations, but not of cholesterol, has been shown to follow long- or short-term administration of OCs (5, 21, 77). Investigations into the causes of this phenomenon reflect the association of epidemiological studies of increased concentrations of lipids and lipoproteins with clinical evidence of atherosclerosis. Alterations of serum lipid values resulting from OC treatment can be attributed to the estrogenic component of the OCs, since they can be duplicated by the administration of estrogen or the estrogenic component of the OC alone (5). Serum triglyceride levels fall after OC therapy is stopped, which indicates reversibility of the effect (77).

Hypertriglyceridemia during contraceptive steroid treatment may result from increased dietary intake, hepatic release and synthesis, or impaired triglyceride removal from the blood into adipose tissue. The ability of adipose tissue to remove triglycerides from the plasma can be assessed indirectly by the postheparin lipolytic activity test, which measures heparin-releasable lipoprotein-lipase activity. Lipoprotein-lipase activity is decreased under the influence of estrogen (17) and OCs (21). However, responses to a large amount of fat taken orally are normal in women taking OCs (21). More relevant perhaps to the increased concentration of plasma triglycerides is the stimulation of synthesis and release by the liver under the influence of insulin. Hyperinsulinemia has been found under certain conditions in subjects using OCs (21), and elevated triglyceride levels have been correlated to hyperinsulin secretion secondary to an oral glucose load (48).

Lipoprotein concentrations are known to be affected by steroid treatment (21). Thus administration of estrogen increases the high-density lipoproteins and decreases the amount of low-density lipoproteins (5, 19); this is consistent with an increase of plasma phospholipid, in particular, lecithin, which is associated with high-density lipoproteins (60).

Liver Function

Oral contraceptives have an anabolic effect on the liver in its production of many proteins, particularly those that bind hormones and metal ions. Thus elevated levels of thyroxin-binding globulin are reflected in higher amounts of protein-bound iodine detectable in blood. Corticosterone-binding globulin (transcortin) levels are also raised (49), which may have effects on corticoid and progestin metabolism. Serum copper levels are nearly doubled in women taking combination OCs (52); this is a result of the increase by OCs of ceruloplasmin, the copper-binding protein (10). Iron-binding protein (49) and vitamin B_{12}-binding capacity are also elevated after OC treatment (4).

Hepatic excretory function, as measured by the disappearance of sulfobromophthalein (BSP) from the peripheral circulation, was diminished in normal women taking OCs (2). Contraceptive steroids usually do not precipitate jaundice unless the subject is predisposed to that condition through hereditable liver disease or abnormal liver function. Sulfobromophthalein excretion into the bile rapidly returns to normal after cessation of OC medication. Other indices of liver function temporarily disturbed by OC treatment in some subjects include β-glucuronidase, isocitrate dehydrogenase, serum glutamic oxaloacetic transaminase (SGOT), alkaline phosphatase, and lactic dehydrogenase activities (31, 47).

An important aspect of the effect of contraceptive steroids on the liver is their ability to induce the mitochondrial enzyme, δ-amino-livulinic acid (ALA) synthetase. The result of increased ALA synthetase is a greater synthesis of heme protein and of its intermediary porphyrins. This finding may have relevance in the pathogenesis of hepatic porphyria, an inheritable disease. Indeed, elevated amounts of urinary porphyrins have been observed in healthy women taking OCs (8). It should also be noted that OCs can have an ameliorative role in women suffering from acute intermittent porphyria associated with their menstrual cycle and pregnancy (43). The availability of more heme from increased ALA synthetase activity may result in enhanced synthesis of the liver microsomal cytochrome oxidase, P-450. The primary function of the P-450 heme protein is metabolism of foreign chemicals and some endogenous substrates. Whether or not OC regimens ultimately produce abberations in this system has not been studied extensively. Morphological changes in the smooth endoplasmic reticulum of the liver, which is the location of cytochrome P-450, have been observed with OC use (30).

EFFECTS OF CONTRACEPTIVE STEROIDS ON THE VASCULAR SYSTEM AND BLOOD

Hypertension and the Renin-Angiotensin System

A number of cases of elevated blood pressure (systolic and diastolic) have been associated with the use of OCs. Results of large studies have not been published, and the overall incidence of hypertension is not predictable (35). However, in one analysis by Tyson (65), 15% of previously normotensive women had elevated blood pressures and 6% of the total group were frankly hypertensive. Blood pressure of all the women returned to normal after withdrawal of treatment.

Investigations of the causes of hypertension by OCs have focused on the renin-angiotensin system. Increasing plasma renin activity and higher renin substrate (angiotensinogen) concentrations have been observed even during the first cycle treatment with various birth control pills (21, 41, 75). These values tend to return to normal when contraceptive steroids are withheld. When medication was withheld from individuals with elevated blood pressure, declining values of renin substrate and falling blood pressure were observed simultaneously (41). It must be noted that abnormalities in renin and angiotensinogen activity may occur without increased blood pressure (29).

Crane & Harris (12) demonstrated that high doses of ethinyl estradiol caused increased plasma renin activity, which became significant during the third week of treatment. In contrast, medroxyprogesterone acetate did not induce any changes from premedication values. Thus involvement of the estrogenic component of oral contraceptive steroids is indicated in the changes in the renin-angiotensinogen activity. It may be possible that estrogenic activity stimulates liver production of angiotensinogen.

In vitro experiments indicate that the rate of production of angiotensin in the presence of a fixed amount of renin is enhanced (29). In some patients, although OCs induced higher substrate and substrate-enzyme interaction, the enzyme concentration tended to fall. The authors suggest that perhaps those subjects who are hypertensive do not compensate for the angiotensinogenemia by reduced enzyme levels.

Clotting Mechanisms

In a recent review of the effects of oral contraceptives on blood clotting, Dugdale & Masi have summarized studies on over 1,000 OC users (15). It is thought that blood platelets act as the precipitating factor in arterial clotting, and therefore changes in platelet number and function as a result of OC administration were examined. The testing procedures included bleeding time (a measure of the in vivo effectiveness of platelet adhesiveness) and aggregability (an in vitro test that assesses platelet adhesion to a foreign surface and aggregation in response to chemicals like ADP and norepinephrine).

Administration of OCs for less than 3 months has little effect on the number of platelets or any measurable function. Platelet numbers are higher in two-thirds of women using OCs for longer than 3 months. In one-third of the women examined, platelets adhered more readily to a foreign surface. Synthetic estrogens tended to increase the aggregation ability of platelets, whereas progestin administration was without effect on platelets.

The use of birth control pills is associated also with certain alterations in coagulation tests. Clotting time is decreased in 25–33% of the women tested; prothrombin consumption is increased in 25% of the subjects. Similar changes were observed in the prothrombin and partial thromboplastin time tests. Clotting time tends to become more rapid with duration of OC treatment. In the thrombin generation test, the most sensitive measure of clotting time, a decrease in this parameter in 66% of OC users is detected. An assessment of potential clotting ability is given by specific clotting factor activity measurements. Fibrinogen activity is increased in 50% of oral contraceptive users tested, Factor VIII is elevated in 25%, Factors II and IX are elevated in 75%, and Factor XII is increased in all users. These increases are apparent after short-term OC use.

The fibrinolytic system has also been examined for changes during OC therapy. Lytic activators increase in all women, and clot lysis time decreases significantly; such factors suggest that fibrinolysis is enhanced. These changes are reversible after OC treatment is terminated. A balance between elements of clot formation and clot lysis appears to occur in women using OCs. Whether the specific tests actually reflect the mechanism of thrombosis formation or the prevention thereof in vivo is not known.

THROMBOEMBOLIC DISEASE AND USE OF ORAL CONTRACEPTIVES

In a series of retrospective studies, an association has been made between idiopathic thrombosis and embolism and the use of OCs by women of childbearing age. Cases of this type among users of OCs have been reported as early as 1961 and have generated a lively and occasionally heated controversy. The first definitive statistical evidence associating the two phenomena was provided in 1967–1969 by three major investigations published in the United Kingdom and one in the United States.

The first of the investigations was sponsored by the Royal College of General Practitioners (50). A selected group of 29 doctors reported on 97 women with pulmonary embolism or other forms of thromboembolic disease of the venous system not associated with pregnancy or the puerperium. For each patient, two control cases matched for age, marital status, and parity were selected from the doctors' files. The patients and controls were interviewed by the doctors concerning their reproductive and contraceptive histories. Oral contraceptives had been used before the relevant illness by 16 of the 97 women treated for thromboembolic disorder as compared with only 13 of the 194 controls for this group. The risk of thromboembolic disorder was estimated to be about three times higher among OC users.

The starting point of another British study was a group of married women under 40 years of age who had been discharged from 19 large general hospitals in London between 1964 and 1967 with a diagnosis of deep vein thrombosis or pulmonary embolism without evidence of a predisposing cause (67). They were subsequently interviewed in their homes at which time information was obtained about their medical, obstetric, and contraceptive histories. For comparison, married control patients, who had been admitted to the same hospitals with acute surgical or medical conditions or for elective surgery, were matched with the affected patients for age, parity, date of admission, and absence of any predisposing cause of thromboembolic disease and were selected and similarly interviewed. Of 84 patients with thromboembolic disorder, 42 had been using OCs during the month preceding the onset of the illness, whereas only 23 of the corresponding 168 controls had done so. From these data, it was estimated that the risk of hospital admission for venous thromboembolism was six to seven times greater in women who use OCs than in those who do not.

The third British study concerned women of reproductive age who died in 1966 (22). Inquiries were made about the use of OCs by these women, and this information was compared with that of controls selected from the practices of the general practitioners who had cared for the deceased women. Of 36 women who died from pulmonary embolism or infarction or from cerebral thrombosis, without evidence of a predisposing condition, 21 (58.3%) had used OCs, compared with only 15.8% expected on the basis of the experience of control women of the same age and parity. The mortality from these two conditions was estimated to be about seven times higher among users than among nonusers.

In the United States an investigation of the association of thromboembolic disease with the use of OCs was completed in 1969 (51). The subjects were 175 women, 15–44 years old, discharged from 43 hospitals in five cities after initial attacks of idiopathic thrombophlebitis, pulmonary embolism, or cerebral thrombosis. They and 175 carefully matched controls, free of chronic conditions either associated with thromboembolism or constituting contraindications to pregnancy and presumably fertile, were interviewed to provide information on their use of OCs before hospitalization. Sixty-seven women with thromboembolism and 23 controls had used OCs until within one month before they were hospitalized. From these data the authors estimated that the risk of hospital admission for thromboembolism was four to five times greater for women taking OCs than for nonusers. It was found that medication that terminated over one month before hospitalization was not associated with thromboembolism.

In summary, then, the incidence of idiopathic thromboembolic disease of the venous system (pulmonary embolism or cerebral thrombosis) appears to be several times higher among women taking OCs than among women with comparable characteristics not using these compounds. Duration of use does not appear to affect the risk.

A recent retrospective study in the United Kingdom has demonstrated an association between postoperative deep vein thromboembolism and use of OCs (68). Of 30 patients with thromboembolism, 12 had taken OCs during the month preceding surgery, compared with only 9 of 60 matched controls, which suggests a three- to fourfold greater risk for users than for nonusers.

The incidence of thromboembolic disease among women taking OCs in the United Kingdom, Sweden, and Denmark was found to be directly associated with the estrogen content of the tablets, according to another study published in 1970 (24). The same study also established for the first time a statistically significant association of coronary thrombosis with OC use. On the basis of these findings, the regulatory agencies of several countries have taken steps to discourage, or even prohibit, the use of OCs containing more than 50 μg of estrogen per tablet.

According to a cooperative investigation conducted in the United States, the United Kingdom, and Sweden, the risk of thromboembolic disease among women taking OCs is almost three times higher for those with blood groups A, B, or AB than for those with blood group O (26).

The annual rate of mortality from idiopathic thromboembolic disease in the United Kingdom, in the absence of predisposing conditions, per 100,000 women of specified age, has been estimated to be 1.5 for OC users 20–34 years of age and 3.9 for OC users 35–44 years of age (22). The corresponding estimates for nonusers are 0.3 and 0.5 per 100,000 women, respectively. Differences between these two sets of rates have been interpreted widely as measuring the excess mortality due to the taking of OCs. This interpretation overlooks two factors: 1) mortality from coronary thrombosis is excluded; and 2) the use of OCs by the general population appears to have been substantially overestimated. If allowance is made for these two factors, the estimated rates of mortality among British women taking OCs rise to 3 per 100,000 in the younger group, which contains the majority of users, and to 9 per 100,000 in the older group (23). The meaning of the excess mortality from thromboembolic disease should be interpreted against a current annual death rate from all causes in the United Kingdom of about 100 per 100,000 women of reproductive age (15–44 years) and against a risk to maternal life resulting from or associated with pregnancy and delivery, exclusive of death from illegal abortion, of about 25 per 100,000 pregnancies. The comparable rates in the United States are slightly higher.

OTHER SIDE EFFECTS

Clinically, the initial use of OCs is frequently associated with symptoms similar to those occurring during early pregnancy, such as nausea, vomiting, or breast engorgement, which are primarily related to the estrogen content of the tablets. Other common complaints are breakthrough bleeding during medication, weight gain, headache, dizziness, and a brownish discoloration of the facial epidermis known as chloasma. Whereas most of these symptoms last only a few months, some users become discouraged and turn to other methods or even abandon their efforts at family planning.

In addition to the relatively minor symptoms associated with early use, a wide range of adverse experience has been observed, some of which has been attributed to the medication. The evaluation of these findings is extremely difficult because the conditions under consideration also occur among women not "on the pill" and may therefore be expected to occur among the millions of women taking OCs.

REFERENCES

1. ANSBACHER, R., AND C. CAMPBELL. Cervical mucus in women on oral contraception or with an IUD *in situ*. *Contraception* 3: 209–217, 1971.
2. ARIAS, I. M. Some effects of contraceptive steroids on hepatic function in normal women and in patients with acquired and inheritable defects in hepatic excretory function. In: *Metabolic Effects of Gonadal Hormones and Contraceptive Steroids*, edited by H. A. Salhanick, D. M. Kipnis, and R. L. Vande Wiele. New York: Plenum Press, 1969, p. 30–39.
3. BECK, P. Effects of gonadal hormones and contraceptive

steroids on glucose and insulin metabolism. In: *Metabolic Effects of Gonadal Hormones and Contraceptive Steroids*, edited by H. A. Salhanick, D. M. Kipnis, and R. L. Vande Wiele. New York: Plenum Press, 1969, p. 97–125.

4. BIANCHINE, J. R., B. BONNLANDER, P. V. J. MACARAEG, JR., R. HERSEY, J. W. BIANCHINE, AND P. A. MCINTYRE. Serum vitamin B_{12} binding capacity and oral contraceptive hormones. *J. Clin. Endocrinol.* 29: 1425–1428, 1969.

5. BIERMAN, E. L. Oral contraceptives, lipoproteins, and lipid transport. In: *Metabolic Effects of Gonadal Hormones and Contraceptive Steroids*, edited by H. A. Salhanick, D. M. Kipnis, and R. L. Vande Wiele. New York: Plenum Press, 1969, p. 207–218.

6. BORGLIN, N. E., AND L.-E. SANDHOLM. Effect of oral contraception on lactation. *Fertility Sterility* 22: 39–41, 1971.

7. BOWMAN, J. A. The effect of norethindrone-mestranol on cervical mucus. *Am. J. Obstet. Gynecol.* 102: 1039–1040, 1968.

8. BURTON, J. L., N. B. Loudon, AND A. T. WILSON. Urinary coproporphyrin excretion and hepatic function in woman taking oral contraceptives. *Lancet* 2: 1326–1327, 1967.

9. CARR, D. H. Chromosome studies in selected spontaneous abortions. I. Conceptions after oral contraceptives. *Can. Med. Assoc. J.* 103: 343–348, 1970.

10. CARRUTHERS, M. E., C. B. HOBBS, AND R. K. WARREN. Raised serum copper and caeruloplasmin levels in subjects taking oral contraceptives. *J. Clin. Pathol.* 19: 498–500, 1966.

11. CONNELL, E. B., A. SEDLIN, AND M. L. STONE. Endometrial enzyme histochemistry in oral contraceptive therapy. *Fertility Sterility* 18: 35–45, 1967.

12. CRANE, M. G., AND J. J. HARRIS. Effects of gonadal hormones on plasma renin activity and aldosterone excretion rate. In: *Metabolic Effects of Gonadal Hormones and Contraceptive Steroids*, edited by H. A. Salhanick, D. M. Kipnis, and R. L. Vande Wiele. New York: Plenum Press, 1969, p. 446–463.

13. DICZFALUSY, E. Mode of action of contraceptive drugs. *Am. J. Obstet. Gynecol.* 100: 136–163, 1968.

14. DOAR, J. W. H., V. WYNN, AND D. G. CRAMP. Studies of venous blood pyruvate and lactate levels during oral and intravenous glucose tolerance tests in women receiving oral contraceptives. In: *Metabolic Effects of Gonadal Hormones and Contraceptive Steroids*, edited by H. A. Salhanick, D. M. Kipnis, and R. L. Vande Wiele. New York: Plenum Press, 1969, p. 178–192.

15. DUGDALE, M., AND A. T. MASI. Effects of the oral contraceptives on blood clotting. In: *Second Report on the Oral Contraceptives. Advisory Committee on Obstetrics and Gynecology*. Washington, D.C.: Food and Drug Administration, 1969, p. 43–51.

16. DURKIN, J. W., T. J. LIN, AND Y. J. KIM. Endometrial effects produced by the oral administration of steroids to control the reproductive cycle. *Am. J. Obstet. Gynecol.* 91: 110–113, 1965.

17. FABIAN, E., A. STORK, J. KOBILKOVA, AND J. SPONAROVA. The activity of the lipoprotein lipase and estrogens. *Enzymol. Biol. Clin.* 8: 451–455, 1967.

18. FERIN, J., J. CHARLES, G. ROMMELART, AND A. BEUSELINCK. Ovarian inhibition during lactation. *Intern. J. Fertility* 9: 41–43, 1964.

19. FURMAN, R. H. Gonadal steroid effects on serum lipids. In: *Metabolic Effects of Gonadal Hormones and Contraceptive Steroids*, edited by H. A. Salhanick, D. M. Kipnis, and R. L. Vande Wiele. New York: Plenum Press, 1969, p. 246–264.

20. GERSHBERG, H., E. ZORRILLA, A. HERNANDEZ, AND M. HULSE. Effects of medroxyprogesterone acetate on serum insulin and growth hormone levels in diabetes and potential diabetes. *Obstet. Gynecol.* 33: 383–389, 1969.

21. HAZZARD, W. R., M. J. SPIGER, AND E. L. BIERMAN. Studies on the mechanism of hypertriglyceridemia induced by oral contraceptives. In: *Metabolic Effects of Gonadal Hormones and Contraceptive Steroids*, edited by H. A. Salhanick, D. M. Kipnis, and R. L. Vande Wiele. New York: Plenum Press, 1969, p. 232–241.

22. INMAN, W. H. W., AND M. P. VESSEY. Investigations of deaths from pulmonary, coronary, and cerebral thrombosis and embolism in women of childbearing age. *Brit. Med. J.* 2: 193–199, 1968.

23. INMAN, W. H. W. Role of drug reaction monitoring in the investigation of thrombis and "the pill." *Brit. Med. Bull.* 26: 248–256, 1970.

24. INMAN, W. H. W., M. P. VESSEY, B. WESTERHOLM, AND A. ENGELUND. Thromboembolic disease and the steroidal content of oral contraceptives: a report to the Committee on Safety of Drugs. *Brit. Med. J.* 2: 203–209, 1970.

25. JACKSON, M. C. N., AND R. LINN. Optimal dosage for estrogen-progestogen balance to inhibit ovulation. *Intern. J. Fertility* 9: 75–86, 1964.

26. JICK, H., D. SLONE, B. WESTERHOLM, W. H. W. INMAN, M. P. VESSEY, S. SHAPIRO, G. P. LEWIS, AND J. WORCESTER. Venous thromboembolic disease and ABO blood type: a cooperative study. *Lancet* 1: 539–542, 1969.

27. JONES, G. W., AND W. P. MAUDLIN. Use of oral contraceptives: with special reference to developing countries. *Studies Family Planning* 1(24): 1–13, 1967.

28. KESSERU, E., AND A. LARRANAGA. *In vitro* sperm migration in the human cervical mucus with different contraceptive methods. *Contraception* 3: 195–208, 1971.

29. LARAGH, J. H., M. A. NEWTON, J. E. SEALEY, AND J. G. G. LEDINGHAM. Oral contraceptives and high blood pressure: changes in plasma renin, renin substrate, and aldosterone excretion. In: *Metabolic Effects of Gonadal Hormones and Contraceptive Steroids*, edited by H. A. Salhanick, D. M. Kipnis, and R. L. Vande Wiele. New York: Plenum Press, 1969, p. 405–421.

30. LARSSON-COHN, U., AND U. STENRAM. Liver ultrastructure and function in icteric and non-icteric women using oral contraceptive agents. *Acta Med. Scand.* 181: 257–264, 1967.

31. LARSSON-COHN, U. The two hour sulfobromophthalein retention test and the transaminase activity during oral contraceptive therapy. *Am. J. Obstet. Gynecol.* 98: 188–193, 1967.

32. LARSSON-COHN, U., E. D. B. JOHANSSON, L. WIDE, AND C. GEMZELL. Effects of continuous daily administration of 0.5 mg of norethindrone on the plasma levels of progesterone and on the urinary excretion of luteinizing hormone, pregnandiol, and total estrogens. *Acta Endocrinol.* 63: 216–224, 1970.

33. LARSSON-COHN, U., E. D. B. JOHANSSON, L. WIDE, AND C. GEMZELL. Effects of continuous daily administration of 0.5 mg of chlormadinone acetate on the plasma levels of progesterone and on the urinary excretion of luteinizing hormone and total estrogens. *Acta Endocrinol.* 63: 705–716, 1970.

34. LEVIN, H. Making and marketing birth-control products. In: *Family Planning Programs*, edited by B. Berelson. New York: Basic Books, 1969, p. 206–214.

35. LUETSCHER, J. A., M. H. WEINBERGER, A. J. DOWDY, AND G. W. NOKES. Clinical course and laboratory data in hypertension associated with oral contraceptives. In: *Metabolic Effects of Gonadal Hormones and Contraceptive Steroids*, edited by H. A. Salhanick, D. M. Kipnis, and R. L. Vande Wiele. New York: Plenum Press, 1969, p. 476–481.

36. MAQUEO, M., E. RICE-WRAY, J. GORODOVSKY, AND J. W. GOLDZIEHER. Endometrial regeneration in patients discontinuing oral contraceptives. *Fertility Sterility* 21: 224–229, 1970.

37. MARTINEZ-MANAUTOU, J., V. CORTES, J. GINER, R. AZNAR, J. CASASSOLA, AND H. W. RUDEL. Low doses of progestogen as an approach to fertility control. *Fertility Sterility* 17: 49–57, 1966.

38. MARTINEZ-MANAUTOU, M., J. GINER-VELASQUEZ, V. CORTES-GELLEGOS, R. AZNAR, R. ROJAS, A. GUITTEREZ-NAJAR, AND H. W. RUDEL. Daily progestogen for contraception: a clinical study. *Brit. Med. J.* 2: 730–732, 1967.

39. MELAMED, M. R., L. G. KOSS, B. J. FLEHINGER, R. P. KELISKY, AND H. DUBROW. Prevalence rates of uterine cervical carcinoma in situ for women using the diaphragm or contraceptive oral steroids. *Brit. Med. J.* 3: 195–200, 1969.

40. MOGHISSI, K. S. Cyclic changes of cervical mucus in normal and progestin-treated women. *Fertility Sterility* 17: 663–675, 1966.

41. NEWTON, M. A., J. E. SEALEY, J. G. G. LEDINGHAM, AND J. H.

LARAGH. High blood pressure and oral contraceptives. *Am. J. Obstet. Gynecol.* 101: 1037–1045, 1968.

42. OSTERGAARD, E., AND J. STARUP. Occurrence and function of corpora lutea during different forms of oral contraception. *Acta Endocrinol.* 57: 386–394, 1968.

43. PERLROTH, M. G., H. S. MARVER, AND D. P. TSCHUDY. Oral contraceptive agents and the management of acute intermittent porphyria. *J. Am. Med. Assoc.* 194: 1037–1042, 1965.

44. PINCUS, G., J. ROCK, C. R. GARICA, E. RICE-WRAY, M. PINIAGUA, AND I. RODRIGUES. Fertility control with oral medication. *Am. J. Obstet. Gynecol.* 75: 1333–1346, 1958.

45. PINCUS, G. *The Control of Fertility.* New York: Acad. Press, 1965, p. 210–212.

46. PINCUS, G. *The Control of Fertility.* New York: Acad. Press, 1965, p. 261.

47. PULKINEN, M. O., AND K. WILLIAM. The effects of oral contraceptives on serum enzymes. *Acta Obstet. Gynecol. Scand.* 46: 525–536, 1967.

48. REAVEN, G. M., R. L. LERNER, M. P. STERN, AND J. W. FARQUHAR. Role of insulin in endogenous hypertriglyceridemia. *J. Clin. Invest.* 46: 1756–1767, 1967.

49. ROMAN, W., AND R. HECKER. The liver toxicity of oral contraceptives: a critical review of the literature. *Med. J. Australia* 2: 268–287, 1968.

50. Royal College of General Practitioners. Oral contraception and thromboembolic disease: a report by the Records Unit and Research Advisory Service of the Royal College of General Practitioners. *J. Coll. Gen. Pract.* 13: 267–279, 1967.

51. SARTWELL, P. E., A. L. MASI, F. G. ARTHES, G. R. GREENE, AND H. E. SMITH. Thromboembolism and oral contraceptives: an epidemiological case-control study. *Am. J. Epidemiol.* 90: 365–380, 1969.

52. SCHENKER, J. G., E. JUNGREIS, AND W. Z. POLISHUK. Oral contraceptives and serum copper concentrations. *Obstet. Gynecol.* 37: 233–237, 1971.

53. SEGAL, S. J. Report of the Task Force on utilization, effectiveness, and current investigations. In: *Second Report on the Oral Contraceptives. Advisory Committee on Obstetrics and Gynecology.* Washington, D.C.: Food and Drug Administration, 1969, p. 13–17.

54. SOLLINS, A. D., AND R. L. BELSKY. Commercial production and distribution of contraceptives. *Rept. Population Family Planning* 4: 1–23, 1970.

55. SPELLACY, W. N. The effect of ovarian steroids on glucose, insulin, and growth hormone. In: *Metabolic Effects of Gonadal Hormones and Contraceptive Steroids,* edited by H. A. Salhanick, D. M. Kipnis, and R. L. Vande Wiele. New York: Plenum Press, 1969, p. 126–143.

56. SPELLACY, W. N. A review of carbohydrate metabolism and the oral contraceptives. *Am. J. Obstet. Gynecol.* 104: 448–460, 1969.

57. SPELLACY, W. N., W. C. BUHI, S. A. BIRK, AND S. A. MC-CREARY. Studies of ethynodiol acetate and mestranol on blood glucose and plasma insulin. *Contraception* 3: 185–194, 1971.

58. STARUP, J., AND E. OSTERGAARD. The mechanism in inhibition of ovulation in oral contraception. *Acta Endocrinol.* 52: 292–304, 1967.

59. STERN, E., V. A. CLARK, AND C. F. COFFELT. Contraceptives and dysplasia: higher rate for pill choosers. *Science* 169: 497–498, 1970.

60. SVANBORG, A. Possible relationship between plasma lipids and hormonal steroids. In: *Metabolic Effects of Gonadal Hormones and Contraceptive Steroids,* edited by H. A. Salhanick, D. M. Kipnis,

and R. L. Vande Wiele. New York: Plenum Press, 1969, p. 242–246.

61. SWERDLOFF, R. S., AND W. D. ODELL. Serum luteinizing and follicle stimulating hormone levels during sequential and nonsequential contraceptive treatment of eugonadal women. *J. Clin. Endocrinol.* 29: 157–163, 1969.

62. TAYLOR, H. B., N. S. IREY, AND H. J. NORRIS. Atypical endocervical hyperplasia in women taking oral contraceptives. *J. Am. Med. Assoc.* 202: 637–639, 1967.

63. TAYMOR, M. L., AND L. A. LEVESQUE. Levels of serum follicle stimulating hormone, luteinizing hormone, and plasma progestin during microdose chlormadinone treatment. *Fertility Sterility* 22: 1–8, 1971.

64. TIETZE, C. Effectiveness of contraceptive methods. In: *Control of Human Fertility: Proceedings of the Fifteenth Nobel Symposium,* edited by E. Diczfalusy and U. Borell. New York: Wiley, 1971, p. 303–314.

65. TYSON, J. E. A. Oral contraception and elevated blood pressure. *Am. J. Obstet. Gynecol.* 100: 875–876, 1968.

66. VELA, P., AND S. S. C. YEN. Serum insulin and growth hormone responses to arginine infusion before and during treatment with contraceptive steroids. *J. Clin. Endocrinol.* 29: 1212–1216, 1969.

67. VESSEY, M. P., AND R. DOLL. Investigation of relation between use of oral contraceptives and thromboembolic disease: a further report. *Brit. Med. J.* 2: 651–657, 1969.

68. VESSEY, M. P., R. DOLL, A. S. FAIRBAIRN, AND G. GLOBER. Postoperative thromboembolism and the use of oral contraceptives. *Brit. Med. J.* 3: 123–126, 1970.

70. VORYS, N., J. ULLERY, AND V. STEVENS. The effects of sex steroids on gonadotropins. *Am. J. Obstet. Gynecol.* 93: 641–658, 1965.

71. WAINE, H., E. H. FRIEDEN, H. I. CAPLAN, AND T. COLE. Metabolic effects of Enovid in rheumatoid patients. *Arthritis Rheumat.* 6: 796, 1963.

72. WESTHOFF, C. F., AND N. B. RYDER. United States: methods of fertility control, 1955, 1960, 1965. *Studies Family Planning* 1(17): 1–5, 1967.

73. WESTHOFF, C. F., AND N. B. RYDER. Duration and use of oral contraception in the United States. 1960–1965. *Public Health Rept.* 83: 277–287, 1968.

74. WHITELAW, M. J., V. F. NOLA, AND C. F. KALMAN. Irregular menses, amenorrhea, and infertility following synthetic progestational agents. *J. Am. Med. Assoc.* 195: 780–782, 1966.

75. WOODS, J. W. Interrelationships of oral contraceptives and hypertension. In: *Metabolic Effects of Gonadal Hormones and Contraceptive Steroids,* edited by H. A. Salhanick, D. M. Kipnis, and R. L. Vande Wiele. New York: Plenum Press, 1969, p. 471–475.

76. WYNN, V., AND J. W. H. DOAR. Longitudinal studies of the effects of oral contraceptive therapy on plasma, glucose, non-esterified fatty acid, insulin, and blood pyruvate levels during oral and intravenous glucose tolerance tests. In: *Metabolic Effects of Gonadal Hormones and Contraceptive Steroids,* edited by H. A. Salhanick, D. M. Kipnis, and R. L. Vande Wiele. New York: Plenum Press, 1969, p. 157–177.

77. WYNN, V., AND J. W. H. DOAR. Fasting serum triglyceride and cholesterol levels during oral contraceptive therapy. In: *Metabolic Effects of Gonadal Hormones and Contraceptive Steroids,* edited by H. A. Salhanick, D. M. Kipnis, and R. L. Vande Wiele. New York: Plenum Press, 1969, p. 219–231.

78. ZANARTU, J., G. RODRIGUES-MOORE, M. PUPKIN, O. SALAS, AND R. GUERRERS. Antifertility effects of continuous low-dosage oral progestogen therapy. *Brit. Med. J.* 2: 263–266, 1968.

CHAPTER 50

Mechanism of contraceptive action of intrauterine foreign bodies

SHELDON J. SEGAL

LINDA E. ATKINSON

Biomedical Division, The Population Council, Rockefeller University, New York, New York

CHAPTER CONTENTS

THE INTRAUTERINE DEVICE (IUD) provides a method of conception control that combines a high degree of effectiveness and safety with advantages of economy and simplicity. The method has come into widespread use only in the last decade, with the total number of women throughout the world who have had insertions of IUDs exceeding 10 million. The countries listed in Table 1 are among those having nationwide family planning programs that emphasize the use of IUDs.

The effectiveness of several types of IUDs over the first year of use is compared in Table 2. With each successive year of use, the incidence of contraceptive failure or symptoms leading to removal or expulsion declines. Data accumulated during 6 years of use of the Lippes loop exemplifies its success (Table 3). Thus, by the third year, 86% of the women continue to use the method during that year; the pregnancy rate is near one per 100 women and continues to decline in subsequent years.

The prevention of pregnancy by insertion of a foreign body into the uteri of domestic animals or women has been known for more than 2,000 years. In 1930 Graefenberg (17a) reported successful contraception with an intrauterine silver ring and suggested that its effectiveness was related to increased functional activity of the endometrium. About this time scientists formally demonstrated that foreign bodies in the uteri of experimental animals prevented pregnancy. Research concerning the mode of action of the IUD in preventing fecundity was not stimulated until Oppenheimer (48a) and Ishihama (23a) described the use of a modified Graefenberg ring and the plastic Ota ring, respectively, in large populations of women. Several new designs for IUDs were introduced and tested in the next few years (14a) with concomitant investigations in animals.

History points to the use of silk and linen threads, gold and silver objects, pebbles, and rings containing jewels. The most commonly used materials in IUDs at present are several types of plastic and stainless steel. In small experimental animals, threads of silk, nylon, or catgut or devices made of plastic, copper, lead, nickel, and steel have been used. The effectiveness of the device in preventing pregnancy has been correlated with its size (surface area) and to some extent with its shape (60). Some of the devices in current use and of historical interest are illustrated in Figure 1.

An antifertility effect of the IUD has been observed in every species studied, although conclusions concerning that aspect of the female reproductive process influenced by the device are numerous. No systemic effect other than that on the hypothalamicohypophysial-ovarian axis is apparent. Within this area, alterations on the timing of LH release from the pituitary of rabbits and ewes have been reported (15, 26), but ovulation does not seem to be disturbed. In the Indian water buffalo, corpora lutea have failed to form in the presence of an IUD (6); however, the particular device used was found to cause uterine distention, a phenomenon that, in itself, could cause neurogenic suppression of ovulation (23). Normal ovulatory cycles have been found in all other species, including women (10).

Most of the theories and experiments concerning the biological effect of intrauterine foreign bodies have focused on local changes in the uterotubal anatomic unit. Some of these have proposed *a*) that myometrial function was altered so as to prevent fertilization or to expel the fertilized egg; *b*) that tubal transport of fertilized or unfertilized ova was accelerated or blocked; *c*) that biochemical changes in the endometrium rendered this tissue unable to decidualize and nidate a blastocyst; *d*) that endometrial sensitivity to mechanical stimuli at the time of implantation was impaired; *e*) that the response

TABLE 1. *Acceptance of Intrauterine Contraceptives in Family Planning Programs*

Country	Approximate Number of IUD Insertions		
	Sept., 1964	March, 1967	March, 1971
South Korea	50,000	700,000	1,800,000
Taiwan	25,000	400,000	800,000
Chile	6,500	100,000	400,000
Pakistan	5,000	1,000,000	2,500,000
India	2,000	1,700,000	3,500,000
Turkey		50,000	300,000

From Segal (56a).

of the uterus to endogenous hormones was altered; *f*) that the mobilization of polymorphonuclear leukocytes created a uterine environment hostile to spermatozoa or to blastocysts. Several of these theories have been abandoned in the light of subsequent data, whereas others have developed from observations in a single species that do not transfer to other species, including man. The differences in action are due in part to variations in the anatomic and physiological features of the reproductive systems among animal forms and probably also to the individuality in size, configuration, and composition of the devices used.

POSSIBLE LOCI OF ANTIFERTILITY EFFECT OF INTRAUTERINE DEVICES

Effect on Transportation of Ova Through the Fallopian Tubes

Obstruction of fertilized ova as they pass through the ipsilateral Fallopian tube of mice bearing a thread in one horn of their uteri has been reported to prevent nidation of the eggs in the uterus (13). However, the "tube-locking" effect of IUDs in the mouse and also in human beings was not substantiated in other studies (41, 57).

Acceleration of ova through the oviducts in the presence of an IUD has been suggested by ova recovery experiments in rabbits (34) and in rhesus monkeys that were superovulated with exogenous gonadotrophins (45). Ova transport was normal, however, when this parameter was investigated in naturally ovulating monkeys (36, 46). Ova movement through the Fallopian tubes of IUD-bearing rabbits has been reported to be normal in other studies (24). Although increases in tonus in human Fallopian tubes after the insertion of an IUD have been observed (38), ova transport has not been altered (31).

Effects on the Myometrium

Myometrial hypertrophy has been associated with the presence of an IUD in rats (52), rabbits (11), and man (25). Loss of sperm or expulsion of the fertilized egg resulting from changes in uterine tonus and motility have been suggested as possible antifertility mechanisms of the

IUD (4, 21). Increased sperm loss from the uterus or reduced transport of sperm to the oviducts with the placement of an intrauterine coil has been observed only in the ewe (9, 21); these phenomena may be caused by the reversal in direction of uterine contractions that appear after the insertion of a device (3). Studies of myometrial activity after placement of an IUD in the human uterus show either an increase (40), no increase (28), or an increase diminishing with adaption of the uterus to the device (3). Since sperm have been found in oviducts of women bearing IUDs, the changes in uterine motility apparently do not affect sperm transport (39). Expulsion of the fertilized ovum or prevention of its nidation was postulated from evidence of uterine distention and separation of the walls of the uterine lumen in the presence of an IUD (53). Premature expulsion of the ovum probably does not occur as a result of the IUD in rhesus monkeys, since the rate of ova recovery in IUD-bearing monkeys was similar to that in control monkeys when ova were counted 2–4 days after being placed in the uterine cavity (43).

Changes in the Ability of the Uterus to Support Implantation

Failure of the fertilized ova to implant could be explained by impaired sensitivity of the mechanically stim-

TABLE 2. *Effectiveness of Several Types of Intrauterine Devices*

Intrauterine Device[a]	Net Cumulative Event Rates[b,c]			Closure Rate[d]	Continuation Rate	Insertions	Months of Use
	Pregnancy	Expulsion	Removal				
Margulies spiral, small	4.2	38.2	23.8	32.7	67.3	448	3,797
Margulies spiral, large	1.5	25.8	27.0	26.9	73.1	2,203	18,730
Birnberg bow, small	10.8	4.3	16.6	21.3	78.7	1,476	14,899
Birnberg bow, large	4.7	2.6	16.8	19.1	80.9	2,259	24,679
Stainless steel, ring	6.7	18.0	12.5	23.4	76.6	1,706	15,085
Double coil	2.8	19.3	21.3	30.5	69.5	2,463	17,636
Lippes polyethylene loop C/3	3.0	19.1	17.0	23.5	76.5	3,489	31,032
Lippes polyethylene loop D/2	2.7	12.7	18.3	22.6	77.4	7,553	72,046
Lippes silicone loop D/2	2.2	10.8	12.9	18.5	81.5	1,520	11,346
Lippes shell loop D/2	0.5	3.8	16.2	16.9	83.1	1,241	9,696
Majzlin metal alloy spring	2.2	4.1	25.2	28.0	72.0	2,587	14,139
Dalkon polyethylene shield	1.1	2.3	2.6	6.0	94.0	640	3,549
Copper T-200[e]	0.8	6.0	5.4	21.0	79.0	785	6,727

[a] Rates expressed per 100 users over the first year of use. [b] Computed by means of multiple decrement table and designed to measure incidence of each type of event in the presence of all other types of events. [c] Based on all pregnancies, expulsions, and removals whether or not followed by a reinsertion. [d] Number of women per 100 users beyond a given time; based on events not followed by a reinsertion. [e] Data on the Copper T-200 is from Tatum (59a). [From Sobrero (58).]

TABLE 3. *Annual Event Rates for Lippes Loop D*

Events	1st Year	2nd Year	3rd Year	4th Year	5th Year	6th Year
Pregnancies	2.4	1.6	1.0	1.1	0.4	0.6
Expulsions	4.8	1.6	1.1	0.5	0.1	0.0
Removals	15.4	12.1	11.5	10.3	8.1	5.7
Annual continuation rate	77.4	84.7	86.4	88.1	91.4	93.7
Woman-months of use	72,046	49,520	32,647	19,098	7,375	2,363

Rates expressed per 100 users.   [From Tietze & Lewit (60).]

ulated endometrium to decidualize (1). In the rat, uterine threads inserted before the period of maximum sensitivity for decidua formation inhibit the ability of the endometrium to decidualize (13). However, decidua formation may be induced by trauma if the insertion of the threads is properly timed and the antifertility effect of the threads is retained (32). In other species, such as the hamster and the rhesus monkey, the decidual response is not inhibited by an IUD (37, 49). That biochemical changes of the endometrium would render this tissue unable to decidualize and support nidation of a blastocyst was also proposed (56). Many studies of endometrial tissues of rats, rabbits, monkeys, and man show no changes in levels of alkaline phosphatase, glycogen, nucleic acids, or other substances as a result of IUD insertion (10, 19, 32, 33). In rats and monkeys, oxygen uptake in uterine tissue is elevated after insertion of the IUD. Since the effect declines slowly with time, the increase may be a result of trauma (10).

Intrauterine devices may retard the increase in the nonphospholipid-to-phospholipid ratio found coincident with ovulation. This change is interpreted to represent retardation in biochemical maturation of the human endometrium (17).

UTERINE INFLAMMATORY RESPONSE AND INFERTILITY

Greenwald (18) was the first to call attention to the inflammatory reaction that occurs along the entire length of rat uterine horns containing foreign bodies. He reported that a leukocytic infiltration of the endometrium was consistently observed in uteri from which embryos were missing, whereas implantations did occur when the foreign body failed to mobilize leukocytes. The antifertility effect of a localized foreign body was enhanced by treating the animals with phenylbutazone, a compound that increases the production of leukocytes by bone marrow. In such animals, the leukocytic invasion of the endometrium was enhanced. On the other hand, the use of a more inert foreign body, stainless steel rather than silk, reduced the inflammatory response and the antifertility effect as well.

That the association of inflammation with the activity of an IUD is not specific to the rat is evident from ob-

servations of cattle (23), sheep (16), rhesus monkeys (44), and women (27, 48, 59). In each of these species, microscopic evidence of inflammation associated with intrauterine devices is reported. It should be noted that the term inflammation, although generally accepted, may be too broad to characterize the observed leukocytic infiltration of the endometrium. Another usual sign of inflammation in tissues is increased capillary permeability. Wrenn et al. (62), using a trypan blue dye technique, found no difference in dye uptake between rat uteri with a foreign body and control uteri.

The experiments of Parr et al. (51) contribute significantly toward establishing the relationship between leukocytic invasion and the antifertility effect of an IUD. In three species—the rat, mouse, and rabbit—these investigators have shown a correlation between the segment of the uterus rendered infertile by the presence of an IUD and the segment infiltrated by polymorphonuclear leukocytes. Furthermore they demonstrated that, by reducing the region of inflammation in the rat uterus caused by a foreign body with the use of germ-free animals, the segment of the uterus that becomes infertile is correspondingly reduced. It was also observed that polymorphonuclear leukocytes remained along the entire length of the rat uterine horn containing a silk suture at all stages of the estrous cycle. Under normal circumstances, leukocytes are present only for a brief postovulatory period and then recede (63). In the experimental uteri, leukocytes, 95% of which were polymorphonuclear, were present in the lumen, occasionally in the endometrial gland between the epithelial cells lining the

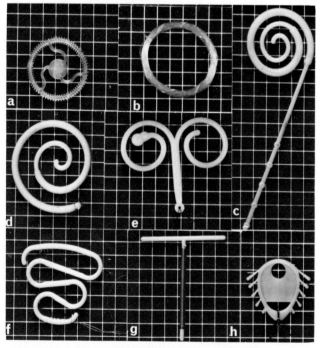

FIG. 1. Intrauterine contraceptive devices in current use. *a*, Ota ring; *b*, Zipper nylon ring; *c* and *d*, Margulies spirals; *e*, double coil (Saf-T-Coil); *f*, Lippes loop D; *g*, copper-T; *h*, Dalkon shield. Scale = 0.5 cm.

lumen, in the endometrial epithelial cells lining the lumen, and especially in the endometrial stroma. Leukocytes were observed as early as 2 days after insertion of the foreign body and remained for at least 100 days. In contrast, leukocytes were absent from the contralateral control horns, except for the normal transitory influx in the postovulatory phase of the estrous cycle. Since many studies have shown that the entire rat uterine horn containing a foreign body is infertile, whereas the contralateral horn remains fertile, this observation associates leukocyte infiltration with the infertile region.

In contrast to the rat uterus, the mouse uterus responds to a unilateral foreign body by exhibiting bilateral infertility (41). Also in contrast to those of the rat, both mouse uterine horns show leukocytic infiltration into the endometrium and uterine lumen. Several experimental results prove that this apparent difference between the mouse and the rat is based on an important anatomic difference between the bicornuate uteri of these two species and not on differing modes of action of intrauterine foreign bodies. In the rat a cervical septum separates the two uteri completely; each cornu has an independent cervix. The mouse has an incomplete cervical septum so that a contiguity exists between right and left uterine lumina. Surgical separation of the mouse uterus into two independent horns simulates the normal anatomic configuration in the rat and results in the restoration of fertility in the non-IUD-bearing horn and a parallel pattern of leukocyte distribution (i.e., only in the horn with the foreign body). Thus the response of the mouse with surgically separated uterine horns is identical to that of the intact rat with respect to fertility and leukocyte infiltration. On the other hand, surgical anastomosis of the independent horns of the rat uterus to create a common lumen results in the establishment of bilateral infertility in response to a unilateral foreign body (42, 45). When this result was first reported, the logical conclusion was that a pharmacologically active substance is produced by the uterus in response to the foreign body and that this substance passes to the contiguous horn (42). In parallel experiments (45), however, both uterine horns showed leukocytic infiltration into the endometrium. These experiments can be viewed therefore as further evidence confirming a direct relationship between the region of infertility created by an intrauterine foreign body and the region of leukocyte infiltration.

Additional evidence for this correlation comes from observations in the rabbit. In this species, in the presence of a unilateral IUD, ova are released, fertilization occurs, tubal transport is normal, implantation takes place in both horns, although not in the region of the IUD, and embryos not immediately adjacent to the device proceed to term (Fig. 2). Embryos adjacent to the IUD are sometimes resorbed at about the seventh day. A foreign body in the rabbit uterus therefore is rather ineffective in preventing pregnancy when compared to one in the rat or mouse. Similarly, leukocytic infiltration in response to an IUD is mild in this species, and the inflammation

is confined to the segment containing the IUD; this is consistent with the fertility pattern (Table 4).

El-Sahwi & Moyer (14) have utilized the rabbit's mild response to an IUD to establish quantitative correlations between the number of leukocytes per cubic millimeter of uterine flushing and several measures of fertility. In these experiments a relatively inert IUD consisting of a silicone rubber tube 2 cm long and 0.2 cm in diameter is inserted transcervically into one uterine horn. The fertility ratio of each horn is measured in terms of implantation sites per number of corpora lutea in the corresponding ovary. In the control horn, which has about two leukocytes per cubic millimeter of uterine washing, the ratio of implantations to corpora lutea is near unity. In the IUD-bearing horn, the leukocyte count is increased more than tenfold, and the fertility ratio is reduced to 50% (Fig. 3). The leukocytes in these washings are primarily polymorphonuclear leukocytes and some mononuclear cells. El-Sahwi and Moyer observed a direct relationship between the density of leukocytes in rabbit uterine horns and the fertility ratio. When there are no more than 10

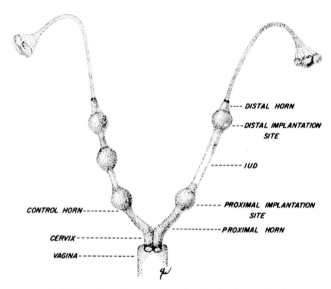

FIG. 2. Effect of an intrauterine foreign body on implantation sites in the rabbit uterus. [From El-Sahwi & Moyer (14).]

TABLE 4. *Leukocyte Infiltration and Loss of Fertility*

Species	Region of IUD		Remainder of IUD Horn		Control Horn	
	Loss of fertility	Leukocyte infiltration	Loss of fertility	Leukocyte infiltration	Loss of fertility	Leukocyte infiltration
Rat*	+	+	+	+	−	−
Mouse*	+	+	+	+	+	+
Rabbit*	+	+	−	±	−	−
Rat, germ-free*	+	+	−	±	−	−
Rat, anastomosed**	+	+	+	+	+	+
Mouse, separated**	+	+	+	+	−	−

* Data from Parr et al. (51).   ** Data from Marston & Kelly (41).

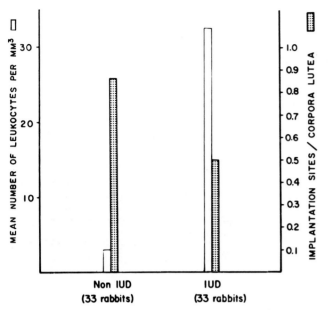

FIG. 3. Fertility rate compared to number of uterine leukocytes. [From El-Sahwi & Moyer (14).]

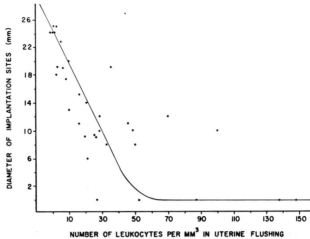

FIG. 4. Concentration of uterine leukocytes correlated with antifertility effect of an IUD (diameter of implantation sites). [From El-Sahwi & Moyer (14).]

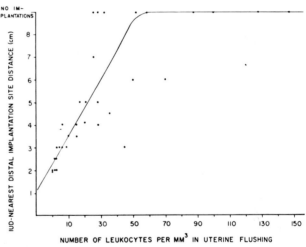

FIG. 5. Concentration of uterine leukocytes compared to the distance (cm) of the nearest distal implantation site from the IUD. [From El-Sahwi & Moyer (14).]

leukocytes per cubic millimeter, virtually all ovulated ova implant. However, if the IUD causes 50 or more leukocytes per cubic millimeter to appear in the uterine washing, the number of implantations is always below 25%, and no pregnancies are noted if 90 leukocytes per cubic millimeter are present.

The normal development of a rabbit implantation site may also be taken as a measure of fertility and can be used to evaluate the influence of an IUD. By this parameter, also, the concentration of leukocytes elicited by the foreign body correlates directly with the intensity of the antifertility effect. In the IUD-containing uteri with 10 leukocytes per cubic millimeter, the average diameter of the implantation sites at 10 days of pregnancy is the same as that in control uteri. With increasing numbers of leukocytes, the average diameter of the implantation sites is considerably decreased (Fig. 4). The antifertility effect of an IUD in the rabbit can be expressed, also, as a measure of the length of the uterine segment distal to the foreign body that will not accommodate an implantation site. As the concentration of leukocytes increases, this distance increases linearly until a concentration of 50 leukocytes per cubic millimeter is reached; at this concentration no implantations occur (Fig. 5). Thus by three different measures of the effect of an IUD on fertility, El-Sahwi and Moyer have established that the action of the device is directly correlated with the leukocytic stimulation evoked by the foreign body. The uterine fluid of a uterus with a foreign body resembles an inflammatory exudate containing polymorphonuclear leukocytes and the products released from leukocytes. For example, measurable quantities of lysozyme were found in IUD-containing uteri of rats or rabbits, but not in control uterine horns of the same animals (51).

White blood cells, β-glucuronidase, and acid phos-

phatase concentrations were found to increase significantly in luminal washings from rat uteri containing IUDs when compared with washings from control uteri. A parallel effect was not seen in endometrial tissues. These same parameters were not different when washings from IUD-bearing uteri of baboons or human beings were compared with washings from normal uteri of baboons or human beings (30).

Further studies (50) have shown a quantitative relationship between the concentration of extracts of polymorphonuclear leukocytes and the degree of inhibition of blastulation of rat ova in vitro. The toxic activity of the polymorph extracts was heat resistant at acid and alkaline pHs and was inactivated by dialysis. However, the toxic factors were not related to leukocytic lysosomes and were present in several other cell types examined, including macrophages, KB cells (human carcinoma cells of the nasal pharynx), and thyroid cells. Thus lytic enzymes from any degenerating cells in the vicinity of the blastocyst may be involved in the antifertility effect.

In vivo recovery studies in the rat have shown that blastocysts do not survive well in an IUD-influenced environment (12). But the embryo-toxic effect of uterine fluid may also relate only to particular species. Washings from the uteri of IUD-bearing rats inhibited development of mouse embryos in vitro, whereas washings from baboon uteri influenced by IUDs had no effect on blastulation (29).

Phagocytic activity by macrophages is also characteristic of the inflammatory process. Investigators working with fixed material have not singled out phagocytosis as a remarkable histological characteristic of uteri containing foreign bodies. However, by making smear preparations from IUDs freshly removed from human uteri, Sagiroglu & Sagiroglu (54) observed large numbers of macrophages surrounding the device. Smears obtained from control patients by endometrial aspiration showed few, if any, macrophages. These investigators also found that the number of macrophages in the smear increased during the first months after IUD insertion, whereas the number of leukocytes decreased within a few days after the insertion of the loop (55).

ANTIFERTILITY EFFECTS OF METAL IONS

Because of the involvement of metal ions in particular enzyme systems, the effect of various metals on intrauterine fertility has been investigated. Copper or zinc wires significantly decreased the number of implantation sites in the rabbit, whereas silver, tin, and magnesium did not (64). In rats and hamsters, copper was completely effective in preventing pregnancy; zinc, cobalt, cadmium, lead, and nickel were somewhat less effective. Silver, gold, and platinum wires were poor contraceptive agents (8). The addition of copper wire to a polyethylene

TABLE 5. *Effect of an Intrauterine Copper Wire on the Implantation of Rat Blastocysts*

Variable	Left Horn	Right Horn
Implantation of Cu-influenced* blastocysts transferred into normal uteri of 17 rats		
Condition of uteri	Normal	Normal
Number of normal blastocysts transferred	0	86
Number of Cu-influenced blastocytsts transferred	58	0
Number of implantation sites	42 (72.4)	70 (81.4)
Implantation of normal blastocysts transferred into Cu-influenced uteri of 20 recipient rats		
Condition of uteri	Cu-influenced	Normal
Number of blastocysts transferred	108	81
Number of implantation sites	0 (0)	62 (76.5)

Values in parentheses expressed as percentages.   * Cu wire in uterine horn through day 4 of pregnancy. Blastocysts transferred on day 5.   [From Chang & Tatum (7).]

IUD greatly increases its contraceptive effect in human beings. The effectiveness increases with the surface area of copper on the device (65).

In contrast to the apparent blastotoxic effect of the uterine milieu in some species, the antifertility effect of intrauterine copper is clearly due to an influence on the uterus and not on the ovum. Normal blastocysts transplanted on day 5 of pregnancy into rat uteri that had contained a copper device until the day before transfer fail to implant. Conversely, when copper-influenced blastocysts taken on day 5 from uteri containing copper through day 4 of pregnancy are transferred to normal uteri, the proportion of successful implantations equals the control values [Table 5; (7)]. It has been shown also that the copper must be in utero from days 3 to 5 of pregnancy to prevent nidation in the rat (C. C. Chang, unpublished observations).

REFERENCES

1. BARTKE, A. J. Effect of an IUD on implantation and the decidual reaction in different strains of mice. *J. Reprod. Fertility* 15: 185–190, 1968.
2. BATTA, S. K., AND R. R. CHAUDHURY. Antifertility effect of an intrauterine silk thread suture in rats with a connection between the two uterine horns. *J. Reprod. Fertility* 16: 371–379, 1968.
3. BEHRMAN, S. J., AND W. BURCHFIELD. The intrauterine contraceptive device and myometrial activity. *Am. J. Obstet. Gynecol.* 100: 194–202, 1968.
4. BENGTSSON, L. P., AND A. H. MOAWAD. The effect of the Lippes loop on human myometrial activity. *Am. J. Obstet. Gynecol.* 98: 957–965, 1967.
5. BRINSFIELD, T. H., AND H. W. HAWK. Modification of the direction of uterine contractions by intrauterine devices in the ewe. *J. Reprod. Fertility* 18: 535–537, 1969.
6. BUCH, N. C., D. O. SHUKLA, AND H. W. HAWK. Interference with ovulation of intrauterine devices in Indian water buffaloes. *Proc. Intern. Congr. Animal Reprod., 5th, Trento, Italy, 1964,* p. 242–244.

7. CHANG, C. C., AND H. J. TATUM. A study of the antifertility effect of intrauterine copper. *Contraception* 1: 265–270, 1970.
8. CHANG, C. C., H. J. TATUM, AND F. A. KINCL. The effect of intrauterine copper and other metals on implantation in rats and hamsters. *Fertility Sterility* 21: 274–278, 1970.
9. CONLEY, H. H., AND H. W. HAWK. Intensification by intrauterine devices of sperm loss from the sheep uterus. *Biol. Reprod.* 2: 401–407, 1970.
10. CORFMAN, P. A., AND S. J. SEGAL. Biological effects of intrauterine devices. *Am. J. Obstet. Gynecol.* 100: 448–459, 1968.
11. CSAPO, A., T. ERDOS, C. R. DE MATTOS, E. GRAMSS, AND C. MOSKOWITZ. Stretch-induced uterine growth, protein synthesis, and function. *Nature* 207: 1378–1379, 1965.
12. DOYLE, L. L., AND A. J. MARGOLIS. Intrauterine foreign body. 1. Effect on reproductive processes in the rat. *Fertility Sterility* 15: 597–606, 1964.
13. DOYLE, L. L., AND A. J. MARGOLIS. Intra-uterine foreign body studies in rodents. In: *Intra-uterine Contraception,* edited by S. J. Segal, A. L. Southam, and K. D. Shafer. Amsterdam: Excerpta Medica Foundation, 1965, p. 185–188.

14. EL-SAHWI, S., AND D. L. MOYER. The leukocytic response to an intrauterine foreign body in the rabbit. *Fertility Sterility* 22: 398–408, 1971.

14a. Food and Drug Administration Advisory Committee on Obstetrics and Gynecology. *Report on Intrauterine Contraceptive Devices.* Washington, D.C.: Dept. of Health, Education, and Welfare, 1968, p. 3.

15. GINTHER, O. J., H. W. HAWK, AND L. E. CASIDA. Pituitary LH activity of ewes treated with an intrauterine device. *J. Animal Sci.* 25: 1262, 1966.

16. GINTHER, O. J., A. L. POPE, AND L. E. CASIDA. Local effect of an intrauterine plastic coil on the corpus luteum of the ewe. *J. Animal Sci.* 25: 472–475, 1966.

17. GLASSER, S. Response of human endometrial lipid to the intrauterine device (IUDs). *Federation Proc.* 56: 536, 1967.

17a. GRAEFENBERG, E. Die intrauterine Methode der Konzeptionsverhutung. In: *Sexual Reform Congress*, edited by N. Haire. London: Kegan, Paul, Trench, Trubner, 1930, p. 116.

18. GREENWALD, G. S. Interruption of pregnancy in the rat by a uterine suture. *J. Reprod. Fertility* 9: 9–17, 1965.

19. HALL, H. H., A. SEDLIS, I. CHABON, AND M. L. STONE. Effect of intrauterine stainless steel ring on endometrial structure and function. *Am. J. Obstet. Gynecol.* 93: 1031–1041, 1965.

20. HAWK, H. W. Inhibition of ovum fertilization in the ewe by intra-uterine plastic spirals. *J. Reprod. Fertility* 10: 267–269, 1965.

21. HAWK, H. W. Some effects of intrauterine devices on reproductive function in the ewe. *Fertility Sterility* 20: 1–13, 1969.

22. HAWK, H. W. Rapid disruption of sperm transport mechanisms by intrauterine devices in the ewe. *J. Reprod. Fertility* 23: 139–142, 1970.

23. HAWK, H. W., H. H. CONLEY, T. H. BRINSFIELD, AND H. F. RIGHTER. Contraceptive effect of plastic devices in cattle uteri. In: *Intra-uterine Contraception*, edited by S. J. Segal, A. L. Southam, and K. D. Shafer. Amsterdam: Excerpta Medica Foundation, 1965, p. 189–193.

23a. ISHIHAMA, A. Clinical studies on intrauterine rings, especially by the present state of contraception in Japan and the experience in the use of intrauterine rings. *Yokohama Med. Bull.* 10: 89–105, 1959.

24. ISHIHAMA, A., Y. NAKAMURA, AND T. MIYAI. Pertubal, cinesalpingographical and radiotubal observations using IUD. *Yokohama Med. Bull.* 17: 45–50, 1966.

25. ISRAEL, R., AND H. J. DAVIS. Effect of intrauterine contraceptive devices on the endometrium. *J. Am. Med. Assoc.* 195: 764–768, 1966.

26. JANKIRAMAN, K., AND L. E. CASIDA. Ovulation, corpora lutea development and pituitary LH activity in rabbits with intrauterine devices. *J. Reprod. Fertility* 15: 395–399, 1968.

27. JESSEN, D. A., R. E. LANE, AND R. R. GREENE. Intrauterine foreign body: a clinical and histopathologic study on the use of the Graefenberg ring. *Am. J. Obstet. Gynecol.* 85: 1023–1032, 1963.

28. JOHNSON, W. L., T. W. EK, AND L. L. BREWER. Motility of the human uterus before and after insertion of an intrauterine device. *Obstet. Gynecol.* 28: 526–527, 1966.

29. JOSHI, S. G., AND D. C. KRAEMER. Development of mouse embryos in uterine washings of rats and baboons bearing an intrauterine foreign body. *Contraception* 2: 353–359, 1970.

30. JOSHI, S. G., D. C. KRAEMER, AND C. B. CHENAULT. Effect of an intrauterine foreign body on lysosomal enzyme activity and white blood cell numbers in uterine washings of rats, baboons, and humans. *Contraception* 2: 339–351, 1970.

31. KAR, A. B. Mechanism of action of intra-uterine contraceptive devices. *Proc. Intern. Conference Intern. Planned Parenthood Federation, 8th, Santiago, April, 1967,* p. 393–402.

32. KAR, A. B., AND V. P. KAMBOJ. Effect of an intrauterine device on gestation in rats. *Indian J. Exptl. Biol.* 2: 229, 1964.

33. KAR, A. B., AND V. P. KAMBOJ. Effect of intrauterine contraceptive devices on histological and histochemical changes in rabbit uterus. *Indian J. Exptl. Biol.* 3: 141–142, 1965.

34. KAR, A. B., AND V. P. KAMBOJ. Effect of an intra-fallopian tube suture on pregnancy in rabbits. *Indian J. Exptl. Biol.* 4: 119–120 1966.

35. KAR, A. B., V. P. KAMBOJ, A. GOSWAMI, AND S. R. CHOWDHURY. Effect of an intra-uterine contraceptive suture on the uterus and fertility of rats. *J. Reprod. Fertility* 9: 317–323, 1965.

36. KELLY, W. A., AND J. H. MARSTON. Contraceptive action of intrauterine devices in the Rhesus monkey. *Nature* 214: 735–737, 1967.

37. KELLY, W. A., J. H. MARSTON, AND P. ECKSTEIN. Effect of an intrauterine device on endometrial morphology and the deciduomal reaction in the Rhesus monkey. *J. Reprod. Fertility* 19: 331–340, 1969.

38. MAKHLOUF, A. M., AND A. F. ABDEL-SALAM. Kymographic studies of the fallopian tubes after insertion of intrauterine contraceptive devices using the Lippes loop and the nylon ring. *Am. J. Obstet. Gynecol.* 106: 759–764, 1970.

39. MALKANI, P. K., AND S. SUJAN. Sperm migration in the female reproductive tract in the presence of intrauterine devices. *Am. J. Obstet. Gynecol.* 88: 963–964, 1964.

40. MANN, E. C. Cineradiographic observations on intra-uterine contraceptive devices. In: *Intrauterine Contraceptive Devices*, edited by C. Tietze and S. Lewit. Amsterdam: Excerpta Medica Foundation, 1962, p. 91–94.

41. MARSTON, J. H., AND W. A. KELLY. The time and site of contraceptive action of an intra-uterine device in the mouse. *J. Endocrinol.* 43: 83–93, 1969.

42. MARSTON, J. H., AND W. A. KELLY. The effect of uterine anastomosis on the action of an intra-uterine device in the rat. *J. Endocrinol.* 43: 95–103, 1969.

43. MARSTON, J. H., W. A. KELLY, AND P. ECKSTEIN. Effect of an intra-uterine device on uterine motility in the Rhesus monkey. *J. Reprod. Fertility* 19: 321–330, 1969.

44. MARSTON, J. H., W. A. KELLY, AND P. ECKSTEIN. Effect of an intra-uterine device on gamete transport and fertilization in the Rhesus monkey. *J. Reprod. Fertility* 19: 149–156, 1969.

45. MASTROIANNI, L., JR., AND C. H. ROSSEAU. Influence of the intrauterine coil on ovum transport and sperm distribution in the monkey. *Am. J. Obstet. Gynecol.* 93: 416–420, 1965.

46. MASTROIANNI, L., JR., S. SUZUKI, Y. MANABE, AND F. WATSON. Further observations on the influence of the intrauterine device on ovum and sperm distribution in the monkey. *Am. J. Obstet. Gynecol.* 96: 649–661, 1967.

47. MORESE, K. N., W. F. PETERSON, AND S. T. ALLEN. Endometrial effects of an intrauterine contraceptive device. *Obstet. Gynecol.* 28: 323–328, 1966.

48. MOYER, D. L., AND D. R. MISHELL, JR. Studies of the endometrium in patients using intrauterine contraceptive devices. I. Histologic changes in the uterus. In: *Intra-uterine Contraception*, edited by S. J. Segal, A. L. Southam, and K. D. Shafer. Amsterdam: Excerpta Medica Foundation, 1965, p. 159–165.

48a. OPPENHEIMER, W. Prevention of pregnancy by the Graefenberg ring method. *Am. J. Obstet. Gynecol.* 78: 446–454, 1959.

49. ORSINI, M. W. Effect of an intrauterine foreign body on the cycle and pregnancy in the hamster (Abstract). *Anat. Record* 151: 468, 1965.

50. PARR, E. L. Intrauterine foreign bodies: a toxic effect of leucocyte extracts on rat morulae *in vitro. Biol. Reprod.* 1: 1–11, 1969.

51. PARR, E. L., R. W. SCHAEDLER, AND J. G. HIRSCH. The relationship of polymorphonuclear leucocytes to infertility in uteri containing foreign bodies. *J. Exptl. Med.* 126: 523–538, 1967.

52. PARR, E. L., AND S. J. SEGAL. The effect of an intrauterine contraceptive device on the weight of the rat uterus. *Fertility Sterility* 17: 648–653, 1966.

53. ROZIN, S., A. SCHWARTZ, AND J. G. SCHENKER. The mode of action of an intrauterine contraceptive device. *Intern. J. Fertility* 14: 174–179, 1969.

54. SAGIROGLU, N., AND E. SAGIROGLU. Biological mode of action of Lippes loop in intrauterine contraception. *Am. J. Obstet. Gynecol.* 106: 506–515, 1970.

55. SAGIROGLU, N., AND E. SAGIROGLU. Cytology of intrauterine devices. *Acta Cytol.* 14: 58–61, 1970.

56. SCOMMEGNA, A., AND S. C. CHATTERAJ. Influence of the intrauterine foreign body and estrogen administration on the diamineoxidase activity of the castrated rat uterus. *Fertility Sterility* 19: 802–809, 1968.

56a.SEGAL, S. J. Intrauterine devices and their mechanism of action. In: *Control of Human Fertility*, edited by E. Diczfalusy, and U. Borell. Stockholm: Almqvist & Wiksell, 1971, p. 181–197.

57. SIEGLER, A. M., AND L. M. HELLMANN. The effect of the intrauterine contraceptive coil on the oviduct. *Obstet. Gynecol.* 23: 173–175, 1964.

58. SOBRERO, A. J. Intrauterine devices in clinical practice. *Family Planning Perspectives* 3: 16–24, 1971.

59. TAMADA, T., AND M. MARUYAMA. Endometrial histology in woman using Ota's ring. In: *Intra-uterine Contraception*, edited by S. J. Segal, A. L. Southam, and K. D. Shafer. Amsterdam: Excerpta Medica Foundation, 1965, p. 235.

59a.Tatum, H. J. The first year of clinical experience with the Copper T intrauterine contraceptive system in the United States and Canada. *Contraception* 6: 179–189, 1972.

60. TIETZE, C., AND S. LEWIT. Evaluation of intrauterine devices: ninth progress report of the cooperative statistical program. In: *Studies in Family Planning.* New York: The Population Council, 1970, no. 55, p. 1–14.

62. WRENN, T. R., J. R. WOOD, AND J. BITMAN. IUDs and the biochemical responses of the uterus to estrogen in ovariectomized rats. *Biol. Reprod.* 1: 234–237, 1969.

63. YANAGAMACHI, R., AND M. C. CHANG. Infiltration of leucocytes into the uterine lumen of the golden hamster during the oestrous cycle and following mating. *J. Reprod. Fertility* 5: 389–396, 1963.

64. ZIPPER, J., M. MEDEL, AND R. PRAGER. Suppression of fertility by intrauterine copper and zinc in rabbits. *Am. J. Obstet. Gynecol.* 105: 529–534, 1969.

65. ZIPPER, J., H. J. TATUM, M. MEDEL, L. PASTENE, AND M. RIVERA. Human fertility control through the use of endouterine metal antagonisms of trace elements (EMATE). In: *Control of Human Fertility*, edited by E. Diczfalusy, and U. Borell. Stockholm: Almqvist & Wiksell, 1971, p. 199–213.

INDEX

Index